DATE DUE

OC 17			

DEMCO 38-297

ANNUAL REVIEW OF PHYSIOLOGY

ANNUAL REVIEW OF PHYSIOLOGY

VOLUME 46, 1984

ROBERT M. BERNE, *Editor*

University of Virginia Medical School

JOSEPH F. HOFFMAN, *Associate Editor*

Yale University School of Medicine

ANNUAL REVIEWS INC.   4139 EL CAMINO WAY   PALO ALTO, CALIFORNIA 94306 USA

ANNUAL REVIEWS INC.
Palo Alto, California, USA

International Standard Serial Number: 0066-4278
International Standard Book Number: 0-8243-0346-6
Library of Congress Catalog Card Number: 39-15404

Annual Review and publication titles are registered trademarks of Annual Reviews
Inc.

Annual Reviews Inc. and the Editors of its publications assume no responsibility
for the statements expressed by the contributors to this *Review*.

Typesetting by Kachina Typesetting Inc., Tempe, Arizona; John Olson, President
Typesetting coordinator, Janis Hoffman

PRINTED AND BOUND IN THE UNITED STATES OF AMERICA

Annual Review of Physiology
Volume 46, 1984

CONTENTS

PREFATORY CHAPTER

A Life with Several Facets, *Alexander von Muralt*   1

ENDOCRINOLOGY

Introduction, *Dorothy T. Krieger, Section Editor*   15

The Brain Renin-Angiotensin System, *William F. Ganong*   17

Variants of Growth Hormone and Prolactin and Their
Posttranslational Modifications, *Urban J. Lewis*   33

Relaxin, *Gerson Weiss*   43

Mechanism of Action of Mullerian Inhibiting Substance,
*Patricia K. Donahoe, John M. Hutson, Mary E. Fallat,
Shoichiro Kamagata, and Gerald P. Budzik*   53

Effects of Molybdate and Endogenous Inhibitors on
Steroid-Receptor Inactivation, Transformation, and
Translocation, *Mary K. Dahmer, Paul R. Housley, and
William B. Pratt*   67

Structure of Mammalian Steroid Receptors: Evolving Concepts
and Methodological Developments, *Merry R. Sherman and
John Stevens*   83

Androgen and Antiandrogen Receptor Binding, *Olli A. Jänne and
C. Wayne Bardin*   107

Regulation of β-Adrenergic Receptors by Steroid Hormones,
Albert O. Davies and Robert J. Lefkowitz   119

CARDIOVASCULAR PHYSIOLOGY

Introduction, *Harvey V. Sparks, Jr., Section Editor, and Robert
B. Stephenson, Guest Section Editor*   131

Modification of Reflex Regulation of Blood Pressure by
Behavior, *Robert B. Stephenson*   133

Interactions of Stress, Salt, and Blood Pressure, *David E.
Anderson*   143

Behavioral Stress and Cardiac Arrhythmias, *Richard L. Verrier
and Bernard Lown*   155

Cardiovascular Response to Stress in Man, *J. Alan Herd*   177

(*continued*)   v

Classical Conditioning of Cardiovascular Responses,
   D. H. Cohen and D. C. Randall   187

Operant Conditioning and the Modulation of Cardiovascular
   Function, *Bernard T. Engel and Neil Schneiderman*   199

SPECIAL TOPIC: ADVANCES IN THE PHYSIOLOGY
OF AUDITORY INFORMATION PROCESSING

Introduction, *Edwin W Rubel, Section Editor*   211

Ontogeny of Auditory System Function, *Edwin W Rubel*   213

Cochlear Mechanics, *William S. Rhode*   231

Relation of Receptor Potentials of Cochlear Hair Cells to Spike
   Discharges of Cochlear Neurons, *T. F. Weiss*   247

Neural Coding of Complex Sounds: Speech, *Murray B. Sachs*   261

Neural Mechanisms of Sound Localization, *R. Bruce Masterton
   and Thomas J. Imig*   275

RENAL PHYSIOLOGY

Introduction, *Carl W. Gottschalk, Section Editor*   289

Interaction of Signals Influencing Renin Release,
   G. H. Gibbons, V. J. Dzau, E. R. Farhi, and A. C. Barger   291

The Kallikrein-Kinin System and the Kidney,
   Harry S. Margolius   309

Renal Arachidonic Acid Metabolism, *Mark G. Currie and
   Philip Needleman*   327

Natriuretic Hormone, *Vardaman M. Buckalew, Jr. and
   Kenneth A. Gruber*   343

GASTROINTESTINAL PHYSIOLOGY

Introduction, *John G. Forte, Section Editor*   359

Regulatory Mechanisms in Pancreas and Salivary Acini, *John A.
   Williams*   361

The Mammalian Gastric Parietal Cell in Vitro, *Thomas Berglindh* 377

Cellular Control of Pepsinogen Secretion, *S. J. Hersey,
   S. H. Norris, and A. J. Gibert*   393

Primary Hepatocytes in Monolayer Culture: A Model for Studies
   on Lipoprotein Metabolism, *Trudy M. Forte*   403

Intestinal Transport of Amino Acids and Sugars: Advances Using
   Membrane Vesicles, *Bruce R. Stevens, Jonathan D. Kaunitz,
   and Ernest M. Wright*   417

A Cellular Model for Active Sodium Absorption by Mammalian
   Colon, *Stanley G. Schultz*   435

CELL AND MEMBRANE PHYSIOLOGY

Introduction, *Joseph F. Hoffman, Section Editor*   453

Patch Clamp Techniques for Studying Ionic Channels in
    Excitable Membranes, *B. Sakmann and E. Neher*   455

Ion Channels in Cardiac Cell Membranes, *Harald Reuter*   473

K^+ Channels Gated by Voltage and Ions, *Ramon Latorre,*
    Roberto Coronado, and Cecilia Vergara   485

Fluctuation Analysis of Sodium Channels in Epithelia,
    B. Lindemann   497

Voltage-Regulated Sodium Channel Molecules,
    William S. Agnew   517

Gramicidin Channels, *Olaf Sparre Andersen*   531

Ion Channels in Liposomes, *Christopher Miller*   549

COMPARATIVE PHYSIOLOGY

Introduction, *James E. Heath, Jr., Section Editor*   559

The Electric Sense of Weakly Electric Fish,
    Walter Heiligenberg and Joseph Bastian   561

Magnetic Field Sensitivity in Animals, *James L. Gould*   585

Physiological Mechanisms for Spatial Filtering and Image
    Enhancement in the Sonar of Bats,
    J. A. Simmons and S. A. Kick   599

RESPIRATORY PHYSIOLOGY

Introduction, *Robert E. Forster, III, Section Editor*   615

Fetal and Postnatal Development of the Lung, *Peter H. Burri*   617

Hypoxia and Respiratory Control in Early Life,
    Gabriel G. Haddad and Robert B. Mellins   629

Function of the Larynx in the Fetus and Newborn, *R. Harding*   645

Control of Ventilation in the Newborn, *H. Rigatto*   661

Regulation of Breathing in the Newborn During Different
    Behavioral States, *D. J. C. Read and D. J. Henderson-Smart*   675

Peripheral and Central Chemoreceptors in the Fetus and
    Newborn, *David W. Walker*   687

INDEXES

Subject Index   705

Cumulative Index of Contributing Authors, Volumes 42–46   717

Cumulative Index of Chapter Titles, Volumes 42–46   720

OTHER REVIEWS OF INTEREST TO PHYSIOLOGISTS

From the *Annual Review of Biochemistry*, Volume 52 (1983):

Adenylate Cyclase–Coupled β-Adrenergic Receptors: Structure and Mechanisms of Activation and Desensitization, Robert J. Lefkowitz, Jeffrey M. Stadel, and Marc G. Caron
Leukotrienes, Sven Hammarström
Mechanism of Free Energy Coupling in Active Transport, Charles Tanford
Gluconeogenesis and Related Aspects of Glycolysis, H. G. Hers and L. Hue
A Molecular Description of Nerve Terminal Function, Louis F. Reichardt and Regis B. Kelly

From the *Annual Review of Biochemistry*, Volume 53 (1984):

Myosin, W. F. Harrington and M. E. Rogers

From the *Annual Review of Medicine*, Volume 35 (1984):

Physiological Pacemakers, Vincent DiCola and J. Warren Harthorne
Cellular Action of Calcium Channel Blocking Drugs, Arnold Schwartz and David J. Triggle
Cardiac Adrenergic Receptors, Gary L. Stiles and Robert J. Lefkowitz
Physiology of Fibronectin, Deane F. Mosher
Renovascular Hypertension, Katherine K. Treadway and Eve E. Slater
Autonomic Regulation of the Airways, Jay A. Nadel and Peter J. Barnes
Physiological Bases for New Approaches to Mechanical Ventilation, A. F. Saari, T. H. Rossing, and J. M. Drazen

From the *Annual Review of Neuroscience*, Volume 7 (1984):

The Accessory Optic System, John I. Simpson
Central Neural Integration for the Control of Autonomic Responses Associated with Emotion, Orville A. Smith and June DeVito
New Neuronal Growth Factors, Darwin K. Berg
Endogenous Opioids: Biology and Function, Huda Akil, Stanley J. Watson, Elizabeth Young, Michael E. Lewis, Henry Khachaturian, and J. Michael Walker
Effects of Intracellular H^+ on the Electrical Properties of Excitable Cells, William Moody, Jr.
The Neural Basis of Language, Antonio R. Damasio and Norman Geschwind
Endogenous Pain Control Systems: Brainstem Spinal Pathways and Endorphin Circuitry, Allan I. Basbaum and Howard L. Fields
The Analysis of Stereopsis, Gian F. Poggio and Tomaso Poggio

Gonadal Steroid Induction of Structural Sex Differences in the Central Nervous System, Arthur P. Arnold and Roger A. Gorski

Modulation of Cell Adhesion During Induction, Histogenesis, and Perinatal Development of the Nervous System, Gerald M. Edelman

Proteolysis in Neuropeptide Processing and Other Neural Functions, Y. Peng Loh, Harold Gainer, and Michael J. Brownstein

From the *Annual Review of Pharmacology and Toxicology*, Volume 23 (1983):

β-*Receptor Blocking Agents in the Secondary Prevention of Coronary Heart Disease*, J. Anders Vedin and Claes E. Wilhelmsson

Mechanisms of Calcium Antagonist-Induced Vasodilation, Cynthia Cauvin, Rodger Loutzenhiser, and Cornelis Van Breemen

Cardiovascular Effects of Endogenous Opiate Systems, John W. Holaday

Transport of Organic Anions and Cations in Isolated Renal Plasma Membranes, C. R. Ross and P. D. Holohan

The Endorphins: A Growing Family of Pharmacologically Pertinent Peptides, Floyd E. Bloom

Insulin Receptors, Steven Jacobs and Pedro Cuatrecasas

Purinergic Neurotransmission and Neuromodulation, Che Su

ANNUAL REVIEWS INC. is a nonprofit scientific publisher established to promote the advancement of the sciences. Beginning in 1932 with the *Annual Review of Biochemistry,* the company has pursued as its principal function the publication of high quality, reasonably priced *Annual Review* volumes. The volumes are organized by Editors and Editorial Committees who invite qualified authors to contribute critical articles reviewing significant developments within each major discipline. The Editor-in-Chief invites those interested in serving as future Editorial Committee members to communicate directly with him. Annual Reviews Inc. is administered by a Board of Directors, whose members serve without compensation.

For the convenience of readers, a detachable order form/envelope is bound into the back of this volume.

Ann. Rev. Physiol. 1984. 46:1–13

A LIFE WITH SEVERAL FACETS

Alexander von Muralt

Physiological Institute, Hallerianum, University of Bern, Switzerland

GREAT LEARNING EXPERIENCES

I had the great fortune to be in the right place, when original steps in scientific research were made, three times in my early life. My good luck enabled me to share, on a modest level, the excitement and intellectual stimulation emanating from these unforgettable experiences.

The first experience was in 1926 at the University of Zurich, where I studied physics and mathematics. Erwin Schrödinger (1877–1961), our professor of theoretical physics, gave unforgettable lectures. If the weather was cold, he delivered them in the lecture theater of the Institute of Physics; when it was warm enough, we all went to a beach on Lake Zurich. This lean man with his highly intelligent face would stand in front of us in bathing trunks, demonstrating on an improvised blackboard. With his exceptional brain he would describe, in mathematical terms, events happening at an atomic and even subatomic level, way beyond the thresholds of our sensorial perception.

Schrödinger's theoretical research closed the gap that then existed between quantum physics (introduced by Max Planck and Albert Einstein) and the classical concept of radiant energy, propagating as a continuum of electromagnetic waves (J. Cl. Maxwell). With a shy smile, he sometimes told us how his own work was progressing: a genial new theory that became known as "wave mechanics" and gained him the Nobel Prize in 1933!

My second great experience came when I was fortunate enough to stay at the Harvard Medical School from 1928 to 1930. The first year I was a fellow of the Rockefeller Foundation; the second year I was advanced to a research fellow, paid by Harvard University. My luck was to find a rare combination of outstanding scientists active at the Medical School: Walter Cannon, eminent

1

professor of physiology; Edwin Cohn, the great expert on proteins; Alexander Forbes and Hallowel Davis, two distinguished neurophysiologists; Lawrence Henderson, philosopher and expert in physical chemistry of the blood; and Alfred Redfield and Cecil Drinker, in comparative and applied physiology. Lawrence Henderson, whom I visited first, suggested that I start in Edwin Cohn's department, where outstanding work in the field of proteins was going on. This excellent advice was soon a major factor in my own scientific development.

Edwin Cohn asked me to work with one of his collaborators, John T. Edsall, who was busy preparing pure solutions of muscle globulin. John obtained the muscles at a Kosher slaughterhouse: because the animals had been bled at killing, their muscles were practically free of blood. This was a great help in the preparation of pure muscle globulin, because one did not have to get rid of the hemoglobin bulk in the process of muscle-globulin purification. Muscle globulin prepared by John Edsall's technique is a viscous liquid that is golden-yellow in transmitted light but bluish in scattered daylight. If a single, isolated muscle fiber is placed at a 45° angle under a polarizing microscope, the anisotropic bands appear brilliant with light and the isotropic bands appear black. The faint chance that the dissolved protein units in John Edsall's muscle-globulin solutions might have interesting optical properties encouraged us. We mounted a polarizing microscope with its optical axis in a horizontal position and fixed a vertical glass tube in the field of vision so we could let John's muscle globulin flow through it. With the solution at rest, the field of vision was pitch dark: the nicol prisms were crossed. When we let the globulin flow through the tube, brilliant light appeared—only to disappear at once when we stopped the flow!

The particles in John's solution were birefringent, an optical property only apparent when the particles were oriented by the flow in the tube, just like logs in a flowing river. In the solution in front of our noses we had the basic birefringent elements of living muscle. To summarize from our final publication in 1930: "The evidence appears to us to favor the view that the anisotropic particles are of uniform size and shape. Stuebel's work points to the existence of oriented rod-shaped particles, small compared to the wavelength of light, which are responsible for the double refraction (birefringence) in the anisotropic discs of muscle fibre. The properties of myosin solutions suggest that they may contain these rod-shaped particles." Albert Szent-Györgyi and his research group discovered in 1944 that the two principal proteins that function as the essential building stones of the muscle machinery are myosin and F-actin, which in solution aggregate easily into actomyosin. John and I in 1930 were probably dealing with actomyosin. Joseph Needham and his group repeated our experiments on birefringence of flow and showed that a small amount of ATP, added to an actomyosin solution, produced a drastic reduction of the flow-birefringence, confirming the disaggregation into myosin and actin. John Edsall and I had contributed a small building stone in the development of knowledge of the "muscle machine." I am happy to add that a lifelong friendship was the most rewarding by-product of our work together!

The research with John Edsall was only one part of my stimulating experience at the Harvard Medical School. The other benefits were the personal contacts with outstanding men, especially with Edwin Cohn. The way he directed his remarkable research group had a strong and lasting influence on me.

Towards the end of my Harvard stay, the University offered me the post of Professor of Biophysics. This generous offer forced me to decide whether or not to return to Europe to finish my studies in clinical medicine. I would have only a vague hope of obtaining an appropriate position at a Swiss university. I am now amused that I was faced with a decision between being a professor at Harvard or student in Europe. But the question, "Why did you want to finish your medical studies?" was answered by the regulations of Swiss universities. There the chair of physiology is incorporated in the faculty of medicine, and in those days the rule was adamant that a professor of physiology had to be a medical doctor! So I went back to Europe to finish the clinical part of my studies.

My third great experience brought me into an exciting phase in the development of our knowledge about the chemical background of the muscle machinery. In 1930 the research work of two great physiologists stood out in the field of muscle physiology: A. V. Hill's careful measurements of the phases of heat production; and Otto Meyerhof's studies on the chemical sources providing the necessary energy for every muscular contraction. This prompted me to write Meyerhof to ask if he would accept me as a scientific collaborator at the brand new Kaiser Wilhelm Institut in Heidelberg, with the understanding that I would like to spend some time at hospitals to finish my clinical training for an M.D. He answered positively, offering me a position at his institute and meeting my condition. Moreover, he mentioned his great interest in the work on birefringence and suggested that I continue with similar optical methods, using whole muscles.

A "Revolution in Muscle Physiology," as A. V. Hill titled a paper, happened at just about that time (early 1930). A Danish physiologist, Einar Lundsgaard, published a sensational scientific paper: "Studies on muscle contraction without formation of lactic acid." One has to realize today, what that meant at the time! The lactic acid cycle had been considered the principal energy source for all working muscles, mainly based on Meyerhof's research work. Suddenly this whole scientific edifice seemed to break down with Lundsgaard's discovery that although iodo-acetic acid (IAA) in very small amounts blocks glycolysis completely, the poisoned muscles are able to perform a considerable amount of work before ending up in an alactacid rigor.

All the previous work on the central role of glycolysis in working muscles seemed invalidated. This was the exciting scene when I entered Meyerhof's laboratory in Heidelberg in the fall of 1930. Karl Lohmann, Meyerhof's right hand man, had discovered in 1928—simultaneously with Fiske and Subarow in the United States—first the splitting of creatine-phosphate (CrP) in active muscles and one year later the presence of adenosine-triphosphate (ATP). Both compounds were considered additional sources of energy for muscular contraction, but no one had any indication of the "timetable" by which they deliver their energy. Generously, Lundsgaard came to Heidelberg to help Meyerhof disentangle the dilemma created by his discovery. In a classic example of scientific investigation, he found that the levels of CrP in poisoned, working muscles dropped exactly in proportion to the work performed, reaching zero when the poisoned muscle went into a final rigor. This showed unmistakably that CrP is one of the primary sources of energy, preceding the glycolytic sequences. But what about ATP? All attempts at that time to demonstrate a breakdown of ATP in normal or poisoned working muscles failed. Two aspects were discussed: (a) ATP is so rapidly resynthesized after breakdown that its level seems to remain constant; and (b) ATP is the primary source of energy in muscular contraction, but new methods of research must be found to prove this point.

It was again Lundsgaard who showed, somewhat later, that by very rapid cooling of IAA-poisoned muscles in liquid air one can produce a contraction, followed by a rigor without a trace of lactic acid. He also showed that the energy for this mechanical work is furnished by the splitting of ATP into ADP, which remains "frozen." All this new knowledge was very exciting.

Contracting muscles show not only the development of tension but also a transient decrease of their birefringence. I suggested to Meyerhof that I record optically this "negative wave of birefringence" in contracting muscles, an optical change that had been described by microscopists in the last century merely by visual observation. Meyerhof found the idea intriguing because he always tried to combine his chemical work with physical measurements on live muscles. I devised a spectral-optical method, independent of simultaneous changes of light scattering and possible movements of the whole muscle during isometric contractions, and yielding good optical records of the "negative wave." At the same time I saw that there were also increasing changes in light scattering, which correlated with the increase of anaerobic work performed. I measured these changes with another optical method, independent of the changes in birefringence.

A TIME OF TRANSITIONS

I stayed for five rewarding years in Meyerhof's laboratory, during which time I completed my clinical studies with the degree of M.D. One year later I became an assistant professor at the University of Heidelberg. But I remained in Meyerhof's institute, where I had the privilege of continuing my research and meeting such interesting guests and new collaborators as Hermann Blaschko, André Lwoff, George Wald, Rodolfo Margaria, and many others. But as time went by, the disintegration of the political scene dominated by the rise of Adolf Hitler, 51 years ago, became increasingly alarming. Meyerhof and his research group were left in peace until 1936, but it was sad to watch the increasing apathy and even anxiety of the academic community in Heidelberg. Fortunately, I was elected professor of physiology at the University of Bern in 1935, so I could return to my native Switzerland.

My new duties in Bern were to start in spring of the following year, so I was free to do something else for the winter and I decided to spend a few months in England to learn more about English physiology, research, and teaching. The officers of the Rockefeller Foundation heard about my plan and came to Heidelberg to ask me whether I would do a certain job for them. They wanted to know more about promising junior members in the various physiology departments in England; Would I send them a strictly confidential report? This was just the kind of task that was dear to my heart.

In London, A. V. Hill and Lovatt Evans received me most cordially. In Cambridge, Adrian, Barcroft, and Matthews spent much of their time showing me everything, including their research and teaching methods. Driving north as far as Edinburgh, in various physiology departments I was kindly received—and I learned a lot of physiology. At the end of my journey I sent the requested report to the Rockefeller Foundation: I am happy to say that four of the junior physiologists who were on my list later became winners of the Nobel Prize!

On April 1st, 1936, I started as the new professor of physiology at the University of Bern in the Hallerianum (Physiological Institute). With Walter Wilbrandt, my new assistant who became a very close friend, we reorganized the rather obsolete equipment for teaching and research. The Rockefeller Foundation came to our aid generously, enabling us to build up a modern course in physiology. At nearly every lecture we gave a demonstration. Five hours a week were reserved for practical work in human physiology, with students required to perform experiments on themselves. To aid them I wrote a book on practical physiology, which was successful in Switzerland and Germany and was translated into Spanish and Russian. Teaching physiology gave me a great deal of satisfaction. I was invited to give guest lectures in Austria, Belgium, Denmark, France, Germany, Italy, and Sweden. The outbreak of World War II put an end to this activity; I had to meet new reponsibilities.

SWITZERLAND IN WORLD WAR II

I have often been asked, in jest, "Were you an admiral in the Swiss Navy?" It shows, sadly, how little most people know about the great military efforts of my small country, especially during World War II.

At the outbreak of the war (September 1939), 400,000 Swiss soldiers were immediately mobilized. As the situation in Europe became more menacing, their number was doubled by auxiliary services—a large figure considered in relation to a total population then of 4.5 million. My personal record of military service spans five full years. I do not regret one bit of it; on the contrary, I am proud to have rendered this service to my country. I started as commander of a field artillery battery, became commander of an artillery group with the rank of major, and when the war ended I was promoted to colonel. The central figure in our army was General Henri Guisan, who was determined to defend our small country against any foreign military invasion. He was a fine leader, in whom the entire Swiss army and the majority of the civilian population had full confidence. By hard training he created a small but powerful army, ready to fight against any invader to the last cartridge in those strong defensive positions in the Swiss mountains that had been built and perfected in the course of the war years.

It is not exactly within the scope of the *Annual Review of Physiology* to cover the last war, but it might interest readers to learn how Switzerland escaped invasion, while similarly neutral Belgium, Holland, Denmark, and Norway could not. When France collapsed under the strong German attack in 1940, our small country was suddenly surrounded by the armies of the Axis powers: Austria, Germany, and Italy. They were tempted to "liquidate" and incorporate Switzerland; in order to demoralize us, maps were smuggled into our country showing Switzerland as part of the German Reich! A new and menacing situation arose when the Italian army had to retreat towards northern Italy, under the pressure of the attacking American armies advancing from the south. It was obvious that Germany had to come to the aid of the Italians. The shortest and most efficient way to bring troops and war material to northern Italy was through Switzerland, using the railroad tunnels through the Alps. But these tunnels were guarded by our army, which was prepared for and committed to destruction of the tunnels at the first sign of an invasion. The German high command knew that. They discarded their existing plans for a military invasion of Switzerland, and we remained independent and neutral.

In 1960 General Guisan died. I received the honorable order to command the military funeral procession, which went from his home on Lake Geneva all the way up through Lausanne to the cathedral. All traffic had stopped in the town. In the strange silence, one heard only the sounds of the military music and the rhythm of the marching steps of the military escort. Silent throngs of mourning people, who had come to Lausanne from all over Switzerland, lined both sides of the streets to pay their last respects to the gallant leader who had kept our country out of war by foresight and strong will.

What happened to the Physiological Institute in Bern during my long absence for military service? Fortunately, I had three able and devoted collaborators who were not obliged to serve in the army for reasons of age or nationality: Dr. I. Abelin, Dr. N. Scheinfinkel and Dr. W. Wilbrandt. They maintained admirable standards of teaching and research during my absence. The majority of male students served in the army, but during less dangerous periods they obtained sufficient leaves of absence to study and prepare for the exams. Most of them passed at the first trial! We were kept informed about important new advances in research abroad by batches of American and British scientific journals that mysteriously arrived.

During the long years of war, the European continent had suffered badly, but after the war communications were reestablished. Substantial American aid was a great help, and is not forgotten! For a program to reestablish intellectual and teaching contacts, I was asked to give physiology lectures at various universities in Holland. All the lecture students had grown up during the dark years of war; they were now eager to learn and to freely discuss the lectures. It was a great experience for me. When later I was asked to give lectures at the University of Cologne, I lectured with an improvised blackboard among the ruins under the open sky (Cologne was practically destroyed). When rains came, we all took shelter in a dugout. It was a fine occasion to talk with the young students, who were equally eager to forget the war. Since those days Holland and Germany have recovered completely; one hardly remembers the enormous civilian suffering of those years.

SWISS SUPPORT FOR SCIENCE

In Switzerland the administrative structures of education and research on the university level are entrusted to seven cantonal universities, two technical high schools financed by the federal government, and a business high school in St. Gallen. This is a great number for a small country and is a heavy load on the finances of the smaller cantons. But each school has maintained a fine level of education and at the same time kept its own, unmistakable character.

The isolation of Switzerland during World War II, coupled with the rapid development of research in the United States and Great Britain, presented serious problems for Switzerland during and after the war. It became very important for our young scientists to spend one or two years abroad, to learn about all the new advances in their specific line of research, with the hope that most of them would come back to Switzerland and find suitable positions and funds. Then they could not only continue, but also teach new research methods to the next generation. The most compelling solution to this problem was the creation of travelling fellowships for young scientists. I tried to help by two separate approaches, aided by a great number of devoted friends.

All our great industries have efficient research departments which they wish to staff with creative young scientists. The same desire exists in university departments of science and medicine because a good scientist is also, generally speaking, a good teacher and a stimulating example. To produce strong young staffs, I prepared two projects: a foundation for fellowships in biology and medicine; and, even more important, a Swiss National Foundation for the Advancement of Scientific Research. They were accepted and realized in consecutive steps.

Even in the midst of World War II, a neutral and independent foundation for fellowships in biology and medicine was created with the generous aid of leaders of our chemical and nutritional industries. This foundation, still active today, became very important when the war came to an end: our young Swiss scientists could travel abroad with fellowships for one or two years. But this raised a problem. Our universities found it difficult to meet the growing research equipment requirements of the returning young scientists.

This led to the creation of the National Fund for Scientific Research in 1952. Funded and officially recognized by the Swiss government, it is nonetheless an independent private foundation. It supports scientific research in all branches of science, and in law, literature, philosophy, and other humanities. A research council, composed of scientists from all branches of research, decides on most requests for support; very large requests are submitted to the Foundation Council. Since I helped create this fund and served as its president during the first ten years, I should not judge its success. But the financial support by our federal government has increased considerably since its origin: a reliable sign, I feel, that the National Fund not only is necessary for the advancement of scientific research in Switzerland, but also has been a success.

THE JUNGFRAUJOCH SCIENTIFIC STATION

Not far from Bern is the well-known resort town of Interlaken, situated between two lakes *(inter lacus)* in the midst of three high mountains. These beautiful snow-covered peaks are called Jungfrau, Mönch, and Eiger. Between Jungfrau and Mönch is a saddle, called Jungfraujoch, which can be reached by a cog-wheel railroad built at the beginning of this century. Rail cars take tourists up through a long tunnel, inside Eiger and Mönch, to an altitude of 3475 m (11, 389 ft). On arrival at Jungfraujoch one can enjoy, weather permitting, a magnificent alpine panorama of glaciers and mountains.

Fifty-four years ago physiologist Walter R. Hess created an international foundation to support scientific research in a research station to be built on

Jungfraujoch. He invited the leading scientific organizations in Europe to become members. Austria, Belgium, France, Germany, Great Britain, and Switzerland were represented first, followed by Holland and Italy.

The scientific station on Jungfraujoch, built in 1930, has one unique advantage for high-altitude research: the railroad. It not only delivers strong electric currents, but also can bring heavy research instruments to the scientific station. After the inauguration festivities in 1931, which I attended, Hess asked me if I would accept the directorship of the new scientific station. It was (and still is) a modern research installation with laboratories, a workshop, a library, comfortable sleeping facilities, a dining room, a kitchen and so on. This was a tempting offer, but I had to turn it down: my own research, in Meyerhof's laboratory in Heidelberg, was in an exciting phase. Five years later, when I was a professor in Bern, Hess asked me to be his successor as president of the International Foundation and at the same time direct the scientific station on Jungfraujoch. This post, second to my duties as professor, I accepted and held 37 years. Among other pleasant duties it was a welcome occasion to meet many foreign scientists, from biologists and physicists to astronomers and astrophysicists. Their principal subjects of research were cosmic radiation, UV spectroscopy of stars, the radiation of the sun, and high-altitude physiology.

High-altitude physiology is a field Joseph Barcroft, with his studies in the Andes of South America, greatly advanced. It had also its place in the Jungfraujoch station. Alfred Fleisch (Lausanne) and I developed a program of studies on hypoxia in healthy humans at Jungfraujoch, where the barometric pressure is 500 torr., two thirds of the sea-level pressure. We had enthusiastic groups of medical students, who volunteered as human "guinea pigs" during stays of 7–14 days on Jungfraujoch. They all showed upon arrival an increased ventilation rate, hypocapnia, and sometimes giddiness. All their sensorial thresholds were lowered but returned to normal by acclimatization after about five days on Jungfraujoch. In the field of cosmic radiation we had for long periods the group of P.M.S. Blackett. After the war we had a successful collaboration with a Belgian group. They installed a large sun-spectrometer, working mainly in the infrared region. Their results gave the basis for the publication of the most accurate atlas of the sun-spectrum. Among the many astonomers who came to work in the clear but very cold night air, Chalonge from the Observatoire de Paris is recognized worldwide for the precision and completeness of his work. I am happy to say that the friendships between the scientists who came to know each other on Jungfraujoch were not broken by World War II; on the contrary, many examples of mutual aid across hostile frontiers were the fruits of this international collaboration. My successor, professor Hermann Debrunner, enlarged the activities by installing two astronomical domes on Gornergrat, near Zermatt. The astronomical work and the work on cosmic radiation are now the main activities of the two Swiss high-altitude research stations.

AN EXAMPLE OF OUR RESEARCH

One research project in which we were engaged after World War II was the work with single, myelinated nerve fibers, mainly from frogs. The technique of their preparation was first introduced by G. Kato in Japan. It was considerably improved by I. Tasaki, who in 1939 developed a special "bridge-method" for recording the nodal action potentials. ("Nodal" refers to their origin in the nodes of Ranvier, which are periodical interruptions of the myelin sheath in myelinated nerve fibers.) At that time neurophysiologists were split into two groups: those who believed that the propagation of the nervous impulse in myelinated nerve fiber is "saltatory" from one node to the neighboring one; and those who refused to accept this new insight. It is surprising how many clever experiments were necessary to convince the skeptical ones.

One of the best experiments to prove saltatory conduction was by Andrew Huxley and Robert Stämpfli in Bern in 1948. Stämpfli was at that time my close collaborator, friend, and an expert in preparing long bits of single nerve fibers. The two of them developed an entirely new approach, by "threading" a single myelinated nerve fiber of the frog through a thin hole in an insulating partition. This hole was so small that the Ringer-solution on the surface of that part of the fiber that lay in the hole had a very high electrical resistance. The protruding ends of the nerve fiber were fastened onto holders on both sides of the partition in such a way that the fiber could be moved forward and backward through the hole. Each time another node had passed it, the registered action potential of the excited nerve fiber made a jump on the time-scale. This perfect and technically convincing experiment eliminated most doubts against the notion of saltatory conduction—except one. Saltatory propagation could be the result of the "isolation" of the nerve fibers, but the same fibers in situ might conduct the nervous impulses in a continuous way.

Yngve Zotterman, who came from Stockholm to work with us in Bern for a few months, planned—together with Robert Stämpfli—another fine experiment, which eliminated this objection. They used a thin, cutaneous, single nerve fiber in situ in the skin and showed with a very clever device that this single fiber conducts all nervous impulses in its natural environment with a saltatory propagation. This ended all doubts. To our great joy I. Tasaki, who had initiated electrophysiological work with single nerve fibers in Japan, came to Bern for a month to work with us. He and Robert Stämpfli improved the preparation and recording techniques of single nerve fibers to an extremely high level.

THE OPTICAL SPIKE

At 65 I retired as professor of physiology. Silvio Weidmann, who had done excellent research work in heart-action potentials, succeeded me. Suddenly I was free to escape into my laboratory to do some quiet research. I had always cherished the idea that the changes of membrane permeability for Na and K ions, which are the basis of the action potential in nerves and muscles, must be connected with a detectable optical signal or even several optical signals. One day in 1969 I saw, to my great surprise, an announcement that a scientific paper titled "Birefringence Changes During Nerve Activity" was to be presented at the imminent meeting of the Physiological Society in Hampstead. The authors were Richard Keynes and Larry Cohen. I immediately booked a flight to London, but the first announcement I heard when I reached the airport in Kloten was that the flight was delayed. Finally the plane reached London airport, but the time was short. I hired a taxi and asked the driver to take me to Hampstead as quickly as possible. Driving up Hampstead Heath, the clutch of the taxi started smoking. We both had to jump out of the car. Luckily, a kind gentleman picked me up and took me to the meeting.

When I entered the auditorium it was dark, except for the illuminated screen on which Richard Keynes was showing a slide. The transient change of birefringence in a nerve, synchronous with the action potential, was brightly revealed. I was not at all disappointed; I was fascinated that my wishful thinking had a real basis. At the end of the meeting I congratulated Richard for his great success. We agreed that I would visit Plymouth during the next "squid season" (The Atlantic squid appears in large numbers in the waters off Plymouth only from November until the new year). This was the start of a very happy six-year collaboration, during which I learned new electronic techniques and gained a close friend in Richard.

From talks I had with Herbert Gasser when I was a visiting professor at the Rockefeller Institute (University) I knew that the pike *(Esox)* has a unique olfactory nerve. It has four million unmyelinated nerve fibers on each side of the nose—more channels of communication than the entire Swiss telephone network! The isolation of this nerve is easy. Examination with a polarizing microscope shows its strong negative birefringence with regard to the fiber–axis. The average fiber diameter is two microns, with a very narrow range of diameters, so that conducted nervous impulses remain almost synchronized in all fibers over quite a distance. First experiments showed that the birefringence of the nerve changes during excitation! I built equipment that registered this optical change synchronous with the action potential at low temperatures close to $0°$ C. I invited Richard Keynes, Victor Howarth, and Murdoch Ritchie to come to Bern to exploit with me this new possibility to register a transient optical change, synchronous with the action potential. In the meantime Ewald Weibel, the anatomist in Bern, had made a careful analysis of the size distribution in these four million single fibers. He found that they are close to 2 μm, with only a small spread in diameter. When my friends arrived we immediately started the experiments, obtaining really fine records of the synchronized electrical and optical (birefringence) spikes at low temperature. In the Hallerianum the younger team called us "the four old foxes." Our records clearly showed that there is an appreciable, fully reversible transient change of the macromolecular structure in the excitable membrane, synchronous with the action potential. Its optical equivalent is the reversible change of birefringence, which occurs in radially oriented structural elements of the excitable membrane.

Victor Howarth had brought one of his extremely sensitive thermopiles of his own construction with him to register the heat changes, which occur synchronous with the electrical and optical spike. There is a small heat production in the rising phase of the action potential and a reabsorption of this heat in the falling phase. The optical and thermal signals can be interpreted in the following, simplified way. The excitable membrane is a highly ordered structure on the macromolecular level. In the rising phase this order increases and produces two external signals: (a) heat is given off to the environment; and (b) the birefringence increases. In the falling phase the heat is re-absorbed and the birefringence decreases. Both "signals" are extremely small: the heat changes in the order of 10^{-6} centigrades while the birefringence changes in the order of 10^{-5} µm.

We often asked ourselves how these eight million separate nerve fibers perform from the point of view of signal transmission. In any case, the pike has a remarkable sense organ. Recently I heard of an unexpected practical application of this extremely sensitive faculty of pikes to smell minute impurities in water. In Göppingen, Germany, the director of the water works keeps Nile pikes *(Gnothonemus petersi)* in an aquarium. They take turns swimming in a special pool through which small samples of the incoming drinking water for the town are deviated. The moment the slightest impurity appears, the pike "on watch" emits electrical impulses, which release an alarm system. This is a true story!

VON MURALTS PAST AND PRESENT

In 1978 Richard Keynes invited me to give a review on the transient optical changes that occur in synchrony with the action potential in excited nerves. They are changes in light scattering, in birefringence, and in artificially induced fluorescence. It was at a symposium in the lecture theater of the Royal Society in London. I gave this talk in memory of my ancestor, the well-known anatomist Johannes von Muralt, from Zürich, who in 1669 presented a paper to the Royal Society, "Concerning the Icy and Christallin Mountains of Helvetia Call'd the Gletscher." With a twinkle in the eye I would now like to remind the reader: ice is also birefringent!

The Muralt family has its origin in Italy, where they lived as the "Capitanei of Locarno" from the Twelfth century until 1550. In that year they changed from Catholic to the new Protestant faith, and were forced to leave Catholic Italy.

They emigrated to the Protestant town of Zürich, Switzerland, at that time an important center for all those who adhered to the new Protestant faith. In Zürich they found a kind reception by the reformator Heinrich Bullinger. All the members of the family became citizens of Zürich, where most of my relatives live today.

My father, Doctor Ludwig von Muralt, was a well-known specialist in tuberculosis. My mother, Doctor Florence Watson, was an American, born in Philadelphia. She worked as a physician until her marriage. My American great-grandfather, Doctor John Watson, had been one of the early presidents of the New York Academy of Medicine. The ties with New York are happily renewed by the marriage of our second daughter Regula with Doctor William T. Foley of New York.

My wife Alice and I spent our first year of married life in Munich, while I studied clinical medicine. We were two years in Boston, where our eldest daughter Charlotte was born, five years in Heidelberg, where Regula was born, and we have lived in Bern, where our third daughter Elisabeth was born, since 1936. We have seven grandchildren and live now out in the country on our farm, called Arniberg.

It was an honor and a pleasure to write this prefatory chapter. I wish to thank the editors for inviting me to undertake such an interesting task.

ENDOCRINOLOGY AND METABOLISM

Introduction, Dorothy T. Krieger, *Section Editor*

Inclusion of topics for an Annual Review usually seems to represent both an appraisal of their scientific significance and the personal biases and interests of the editor. At the conclusion of my editorship of this section, a perusal of previous volumes indicates a predominance of certain themes. These include advances in the elucidation of hormone action and metabolism (both peptide and steroid), description of new hormones and new sites of their production and delineation of their physiological roles, and the interrelationship of the body's two major homeostatic systems, the nervous and endocrine systems. I hope the advances presented in this subsection have indicated some of the major currents in this rapidly advancing area, and that those topics unable to be presented because of space limitations or previous commitments by acknowledged experts will be forthcoming in subsequent volumes.

This section continues such emphasis. Dr. Ganong has critically reviewed the evidence for the presence of a brain renin-angiotensin system apart from that present in the periphery, its relationship with the peripheral system, and its possible functional role not only in fluid homeostasis and blood pressure but with regard to regulation of pituitary hormonal secretion. This represents yet another instance in which hormones previously described as being present in other tissues are demonstrated to be present and to be synthesized in the central nervous system, providing new insights into central nervous system function and juxtaposition and interrelations with previously well-described CNS neurotransmitters. The question of heterogeneous forms of peptide hormones arising from genomic and posttranslational modifications has arisen with regard to a number of hormones; the discussion by Dr. Lewis regarding growth hormone presents a panorama of the potential richness of products derived from this single precursor and the variations in biological activity that ensue from such modifications. Utilizing structure-function analysis, the basis of such biological variation can be elucidated. Recognition of the physiological signifiance of relaxin, as noted by Dr. Weiss, was hampered by lack of suitably sensitive, reproducible assay methodology, which has recently become available, as well as by the lack of purified synthetic material, which is now becoming available as knowledge of its chemical structure in several species, including the human, has accumulated. Mullerian inhibitory substance is representative of a "newly described" hormone, whose presence and function have been elucidated chiefly by Dr. Donahoe et al, with insights not only into reproductive tract development but with possible clinical applications in reproductive tract–derived neoplasms.

Newer methodologies for receptor stabilization have allowed for considerable progress in receptor characterization and isolation that are fundamental in elucidating their physiological role(s). This is evident in the chapters contributed by Drs. Dahmer, Housley & Pratt, Sherman & Stevens, and Jänne & Bardin, which consider the advances with regard to glucocorticoid and androgen receptors. It is also becoming increasingly apparent that steroid hormones influence other types of receptors—i.e. those for neurotransmitters—and that neurotransmitters can influence expression of steroid receptors. The studies of Drs. Davies & Lefkowitz on the interrelationships of glucocorticoids and β-adrenergic receptors provide the basis for understanding the previously known physiological interactions of these systems in both health and disease.

Ann. Rev. Physiol. 1984. 46:17–31

THE BRAIN RENIN-ANGIOTENSIN SYSTEM

William F. Ganong

Department of Physiology, University of California, San Francisco, San Francisco, California 94143

INTRODUCTION

The components of the renin-angiotensin system that produce angiotensin II (AII) in the circulation are summarized in Figure 1. There appear to be additional, separate renin-angiotensin systems in the uterus, salivary glands, blood vessels, adrenal glands, anterior pituitary gland, and pineal gland (34), and all the components of the system have been reported to exist in the brain (36). This review is a summary of current knowledge about the nature of the components in the brain and their possible interactions and functions. The brain renin-angiotensin system has been discussed elsewhere (31, 36), but it has not been the subject of a recent short review.

RELATION TO THE COMPONENTS OF THE RENIN-ANGIOTENSIN SYSTEM IN THE CIRCULATION

The Blood-Brain Barrier

Although it is difficult to prove that the components of the renin-angiotensin system found in the brain are not of peripheral origin, most of the available data suggest they are not. There is no renin in cerebrospinal fluid (CSF), and the distribution of renin in brain tissue does not parallel the vascularity of the tissue. The chemical composition of brain and plasma renin differ (43), and the concentration of brain renin does not decline after bilateral nephrectomy (20, 35). The renin substrate in CSF is a glycoprotein that resembles the substrate in plasma, but there are immunological and other differences which probably relate primarily to the carbohydrate portions (52, 64, 80). Nephrectomy,

17

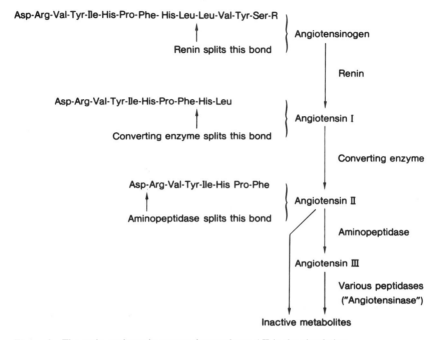

Figure 1   The renin-angiotensin system that produces AII in the circulation.

adrenalectomy, and treatment with dexamethasone produce prompt changes in the plasma concentration of substrate with little if any change in the concentration in CSF (77, 85). Converting enzyme in the brain cross-reacts with antibodies to pulmonary and renal converting enzyme (70), but there is no evidence that converting enzyme crosses the blood-brain barrier. In general, angiotensin I (AI) and AII also fail to cross the blood-brain barrier; systemically administered ^{125}I AII is taken up in the circumventricular organs but does not enter the rest of the brain (103) or the CSF (1, 68). The only exception is when transient disruption of the blood-brain barrier produced by rapid, marked increases in blood pressure permit small amounts of AII to enter the brain (68). However, the blood pressure rise must be rapid and large, and increments of this magnitude are unusual. Various conditions that change plasma AII fail to affect the concentration of AII in the central nervous system (1, 33, 86).

The Circumventricular Organs

Although angiotensins do not cross the blood-brain barrier, they cross the fenestrated capillaries of circumventricular organs (103, 104), and act on these small areas of brain tissue that are outside the blood-brain barrier to increase water intake, blood pressure, and the secretion of vasopressin. There are several reviews on the actions of AII on the circumventricular organs (68, 74).

Most of the angiotensin-like immunoreactivity in the brain is in nerve endings, rather than cell bodies, but staining in cell bodies can be enhanced by inhibiting axoplasmic flow with colchicine. The staining is largely in the cell bodies of supraoptic and paraventricular neurons, and appears to be in the neurons that secrete vasopressin (24, 53). Thus, renin-like immunoreactivity appears to be in oxytocin-secreting neurons, and angiotensin-like immunoreactivity in vasopressin-secreting neurons. The reason for this puzzling arrangement is unknown. In endings, the staining is most intense in the median eminence, the posterior lobe of the pituitary, the central nucleus of the amygdala, the spinal nucleus of the trigeminal nerve, the substantia gelatinosa, and the intermediolateral column of the spinal cord. It is uncertain whether all these endings also contain vasopressin. A pathway can be followed from the paraventricular nucleus to the median eminence. Obviously, additional research is needed on the localization of AII and the possible coexistence within neurons of components of the renin-angiotensin system and other peptides.

Interactions   How do the components of the renin-angiotensin system in the brain interact to form AII? There is no renin in CSF, and the AII content is low. However, AI, AII, and related peptides are formed when renin is added to CSF in vivo and in vitro (46, 79). This suggests that brain renin is normally not in contact with cerebrospinal fluid. Intraventricular injection of TDP produces prompt increases in drinking, presumably because AII is generated in CSF. Some investigators report that the response to TDP is blocked by renin inhibitors (22, 102), but others (75, 91) failed to observe any blockade and argued that the AII was generated by serial removal of three dipeptide residues from the C-terminal of TDP by converting enzyme (75, 91). These latter investigators also reported that intraventricular injection of naturally occurring substrate failed to increase AII in CSF, but others have reported that it does (44). In view of these discrepancies, additional research in needed. It seems unlikely, however, that brain renin is normally located outside cells.

AII could be formed in the brain by a totally intracellular renin-angiotensin system. The difference in the distribution of AII immunoreactivity and converting enzyme immunoreactivity argue against this, but low levels of converting enzyme could have been missed. Alternatively, brain renin could form AII directly from substrate without prior formation of AI and conversion. Two renin-like enzymes, tonin (55) and cathepsin G (108), have been reported to be capable of catalyzing the direct formation of AII. A third possibility is that AI is formed in cells, secreted into CSF, and converted to AII in the choroid plexus, with the AII being transported back to neurons and internalized. All these possibilities merit additional study.

POSSIBLE FUNCTIONS

Relation to Effects Also Produced by the Action of Systemic AII on Circumventricular Organs

One way to study the possible functions of AII in the brain is to catalog the responses produced when the peptide is injected into the cerebral ventricles. These include an increase in blood pressure, increased water intake, and increased secretion of vasopressin. The same three effects are also produced by circulating AII acting on the circumventricular organs. Is it necessary to postulate the existence of additional intracerebral receptors to explain the production of the responses by intraventricular AII, or could they simply be due to AII penetrating the circumventricular organs from the CSF? There are two obvious ways to approach this problem: one is to determine whether lesions of the circumventricular organs abolish the responses to intraventricular as well as systemically administered AII; the other is to determine whether intraventricular saralasin blocks the response to intravenous AII. The available data from these two types of experiments, which are reviewed elsewhere (31), are somewhat conflicting, but intraventicular saralasin in systemically ineffective doses generally reduces or abolishes the drinking, blood pressure and vasopressin responses to circulating AII. We have found that intraventricular saralasin abolishes the uptake of circulating ^{125}I-AII by the median eminence and organum vasculosum of the lamina terminalis and reduces binding to the subfornical organ and area postrema (Van Houten, Mangiapane, Reid and Ganong, unpublished data). Thus the bulk of the evidence indicates that the increase in blood pressure and water intake and the increased secretion of vasopressin produced by intraventricular AII are due to penetration of the AII into the circumventricular organs.

Intraventricular and intravenous AII also increase ACTH secretion. The effect of intraventricular AII is reduced but still present in Brattleboro rats, so it is independent of vasopressin (32). However, AII also increases ACTH secretion by a direct action on the anterior pituitary (96), and the effect of intraventricular AII could be due to transport of the peptide to the anterior pituitary via the portal hypophyseal vessels. Intraventricular and intravenous AII inhibit renin secretion, but the circulating AII acts directly on the juxtaglomerular cells in the kidneys, whereas the central action appears to be due in part to increased vasopressin secretion (32) and in part to a selective decrease in renal nerve discharge (23).

Of course, penetration of AII into the circumventricular organs from the CSF can only be invoked to explain effects that are produced by intraventricular and systemic administration of AII. Effects of intraventricular AII that cannot be produced by systemic administration are presumably due to activation of AII receptors located inside the blood-brain barrier. These effects include selective alterations in the turnover of brain catecholamines, increased secretion of LH, and decreased secretion of prolactin.

Relation to Brain Amines

AII facilitates noradrenergic transmission in the autonomic nervous system by increasing the release of norepinephrine (57). The extensive systems of noradrenergic, dopaminergic, adrenergic and serotonergic neurons in the brain have widespread effects on neural function (16, 30), so AII-induced alterations in the release of amine transmitters in the brain could affect many different functions. Evidence is now accumulating that centrally produced AII can cause selective changes in cathecholamine turnover in the central nervous system (3, 4, 15, 24, 37, 100). In the hypothalamus, the changes include increased dopamine turnover in the median eminence and increased norepinephrine turnover in the supraoptic nuclei and the preoptic area (3). An effect on serotonin turnover is also a possibility, since AII has been reported to stimulate the release of serotonin from synaptosomes, and to have a complex, biphasic effect on serotonin synthesis (65).

Relation to Regulation of Blood Pressure

Because circulating renin and AII are involved in the regulation of blood pressure and salt and water metabolism, it has been popular to search for similar functions for the renin and angiotensin in the brain (7, 11, 59, 101). Intraventricular saralasin and converting enzyme inhibitors have been reported to have no effect on blood pressure in normal animals but to lower blood pressure in spontaneously hypertensive rats (17, 33). However, these results need to be confirmed. If a role for brain AII in the regulation of blood pressure is eventually established, it could well be exerted by way of the central noradrenergic and adrenergic neurons that among other things participate in the regulation of cardiovascular function (82).

Relation to the Pituitary Gland

POSTERIOR LOBE   The relation of renin and angiotensin to the posterior pituitary may be complex. Not only does AII act on circumventricular organs to increase vasopressin secretion (see above), but there is angiotensin-like immunoreactivity in the cell bodies of vasopressin-secreting supraoptic neurons inside the blood-brain barrier (12, 24). There is evidence that AII acts directly on supraoptic neurons to increase their activity (66), and that it affects the release of vasopressin from the hypothalamus in organ culture (84, 94). AII also increases oxytocin secretion (56). The physiologic significance of these observations is still unknown.

ANTERIOR LOBE   Intraventricular AII increases LH secretion in estrogen-treated ovariectomized rats and normally cycling proestrus rats (97, 98). This effect is probably due to an action of AII in the brain, since systemically administered AII does not have a comparable effect, and AII added to pituitary cells in vitro does not increase LH secretion. Intraventricular administration of saralasin and the converting enzyme inhibitor enalapril diacid prevent the midcycle LH surge and block ovulation in rats (97; Steele, Gallo, and Ganong, unpublished data). These alterations in anterior pituitary secretion could well be due to catecholamine-mediated changes in the secretion of LHRH. Norepinephrine is know to act in the preoptic area to stimulate LH secretion, presumably via LHRH (106), and as noted above, this is one of the regions in which intraventricular AII increases norepinephrine turnover. Intraventricular AII also inhibits prolactin secretion (3, 98), whereas it either has no effect or stimulates prolactin secretion when added to isolated pituitary cells in vitro (2). Dopamine secreted into the portal vessels inhibits prolactin secretion, and intraventricular AII increases dopamine turnover in the median eminence (3, 4). In addition, the effect of intraventricular AII on prolactin secretion is abolished when dopamine receptors are blocked (99). Intraventricular AII also increases ACTH secretion (see above) and inhibits growth hormone secretion (98).

Other Actions

AII has been reported to alter the electrical activity of neurons in the spinal cord, hippocampus, and cerebral cortex (21, 67) as well as the supraoptic nucleus. AII also increases the electrical activity of hypothalamic neurons in culture (28, 69).

The effect on hippocampal neurons may be related to postulated effects of AII on memory. It has been reported that the concentration of AII in the hippocampus is high, and that increased CSF AII is associated with disruption of conditioned avoidance responses (54). In addition, injection of AII into the neostriatum has been reported to produce amnesia (61).

Another speculative possibility is that AII plays a role in regulating the permeability of capillaries within the brain (39).

CONCLUSIONS

The data reviewed above make it clear that much remains to be done if we are to understand the nature and function of the components of the renin-angiotensin system found in the brain. However, certain tentative conclusions can at least be presented as working hypotheses.

1. All the components of the renin-angiotensin system, or at least substances that closely resemble them, are present in the central nervous system. Under normal conditions, these components are not of peripheral origin and are presumably synthesized in the brain.

2. Renin-like immunoreactivity and angiotensin-like immunoreactivity are located in neurons, but converting enzyme has a different distribution than renin and AII. It is possible that AII is produced directly from substrate by an intraneuronal renin-angiotensin system without AI as an intermediate.

3. The effects of intraventricular AII that are also produced by intravenous AII, i.e. increased drinking, increased blood pressure, and increased secretion of vasopressin, are probably due to AII in CSF penetrating the circumventricular organs.

4. A major function of the brain renin-angiotensin system may be selective adjustment of the output of monoamines from the endings of the noradrenergic, dopaminergic, and possibly serotenergic neurons in the brain, thus playing a role in the multiple, widespread functions of these systems.

5. Effects of brain AII that may be mediated via catecholamines in the central nervous system include stimulation of LH secretion and inhibition of prolactin secretion. Reported effects on blood pressure in hypertensive animals could also be exerted via the central noradrenergic and adrenergic system.

ACKNOWLEDGMENT

This review includes previously unpublished data obtained in experiments in the author's laboratory supported by USPHS Grant AMO6704 and the Kroc Foundation.

Literature Cited

1. Abraham, S. F., Coghlan, J. P., Denton, D. A., Fei, D. T. W., McKinley, M. J., Scoggins, B. A. 1980. Correlation of cerebrospinal fluid and blood angiotensin II in sheep. *6th Int. Cong. Endocrin., Melbourne, Australia.* 725 pp. (Program and Abstr.)

2. Aguilera, G., Hyde, C. L., Catt, K. J. 1982. Angiotensin II receptors and prolactin release in pituitary lactotrophs. *Endocrinology* 111:1045–50

3. Alper, R. H., Steele, M. K., Ganong, W. F. 1982. Angiotensin II increases catecholamine synthesis in selected hypothalamic nuclei. *Neurosci. Abstr.* 8:421

4. Andersson, K., Fuxe, K., Agnati, L. F., Ganten, D., Zim, I., et al. 1982. Intraventricular injections of renin increase amine turnover in the tuberoinfundibular dopamine neurons and reduce the secretion of prolactin in male rats. *Acta Physiol. Scand.* 116:317–20

5. Arregui, A., Bennett, J. P. Jr., Bird, E. D., Yamamura, H. I., Iversen, L. L., et al. 1977. Huntington's chorea: selective depletion of activity of angiotensin converting enzyme in the corpus striatum. *Ann. Neurol.* 2:294–98

6. Arregui, A., Emson, P. C., Spokes, E. G. 1978. Angiotensin converting enzyme in substantia nigra: reduction of activity in Huntington's disease and after intrastriatal kainic acid in rats. *Eur. J. Pharmacol.* 52:121–24

7. Basso, N., Ruiz, P., Mangiarua, E., Taquini, A. C. 1981. Renin-like activity in the rat brain during the development for DOC-salt hypertension. *Hypertension* 3:II14–17

8. Baxter, C. R., Horvarth, J. S., Duggin, C. G., Tiller, D. J. 1980. Effect of age on specific angiotensin II binding sites in rat brain. *Endocrinology* 106:995–99

9. Bennett, J. P. Jr., Snyder, S. H. 1976. Angiotensin II binding to brain membranes. *J. Biol. Chem.* 251:7423–30

10. Bennett, J. P. Jr., Snyder, S. H. 1980. Receptor binding interactions of the angiotensin II antagonist, [125]I [sarcosine[1], leucine[8]] angiotensin II with mammalian brain and peripheral tissues. *Eur. J. Pharmacol.* 67:11–25

11. Brosnihan, K. B., Smeby, R. R., Ferrario, C. M. 1982. Effects of chronic sodium depletion on canine brain renin and cathepsin D activities. *Hypertension* 4:604–8

12. Brownfield, M. S., Reid, I. A., Ganten, D., Ganong, W. F. 1982. Differential distribution of immunoreactive angiotensin and converting enzyme in rat brain. *Neuroscience* 7:1759–69

13. Calza, L., Fuxe, K., Agnati, L. F., Zini, I., Ganten, D., et al. 1982. Presence of renin-like immunoreactivity in oxytocin immunoreactive nerve cells of the paraventricular and supraoptic nuclei in rat hypothalamus. *Acta Physiol. Scand.* 116:313–16

14. Changaris, D. G., Keil, L. C., Severs, W. B. 1978. Angiotensin II immunohistochemistry of the rat brain. *Neuroendocrinology* 25:257–74

15. Chevillard, C., Duchene, N., Pasquier, R., Alexandre, J-M. 1979. Relation of the centrally evoked pressor effect of angiotensin II to central noradrenaline in the rabbit. *Eur. J. Pharmacol.* 58:203–6

16. Cooper, J. R., Bloom, F. E., Roth, R. H. 1978. *The Biochemical Basis of Neuropharmacology*, 327 pp. New York: Oxford Univ. Press. 3rd ed.

17. Crofton, J. T., Rockhold, R. W., Share, L., Wang, B. C., Horovitz, Z. P., et al. 1981. Effect of intracerebroventricular captopril on vasopressin and blood pressure in spontaneously hypertensive rats. *Hypertension* 3:II71–74

18. Day, R. P., Reid, I. A. 1976. Renin activity in dog brain. Enzymological similarity to cathepsin D. *Endocrinology* 99:93–100

19. Defendini, R., Zimmerman, E. A., Weare, J. A., Alhenc-Gelas, F., Erdös, E. G. 1983. Angiotensin converting enzyme in epithelial and neuroepithelial cells. *Neuroendocrinology* 37:32–40

20. Dzau, V. J., Brenner, A., Emmett, N., Haber, E. 1980. Identification of renin and renin-like enzymes in rat brain by a renin-specific antibody. *Clin. Sci.* 59(Suppl. 6):45s–48s

21. Felix, D., Schelling, P., Haas, H. L. 1982. Angiotensin and single neurons. See Ref. 36, pp. 255–69

22. Fitzsimons, J. T., Epstein, A. N., Johnson, A. K. 1978. Peptide antagonists of the renin-angiotensin system in the characterization of receptors for angiotensin-induced drinking. *Brain Res.* 153:319–31

23. Fukiyama, K. 1972. Central action of angiotensin and hypertension-increased central vasomotor outflow by angiotensin. *Jpn. Circ. J.* 36:599–602

24. Fuxe, K., Ganten, D., Andersson, K., Calza, L., Agnati, L. F., et al. 1982. Immunocytochemical demonstration of angiotensin II and renin-like immunoreactive nerve cells in the hypothal-amus. Angiotensin peptides as comodulators in vasopressin and oxytocin neurons and their regulation of various types of central catecholamine nerve terminal systems. See Ref. 36, pp. 192–207

25. Fuxe, K., Ganten, D., Hökfelt, T., Bolme, P. 1976. Immunohistochemical evidence for the existence of angiotensin II containing nerve terminals in the brain and spinal cord of the rat. *Neurosci. Lett.* 2:229–34

26. Fuxe, F., Ganten, D., Hökfelt, T., Locatelli, V., Poulsen, K., et al. 1980. Renin-like immunocytochemical activity in the rat and mouse brain. *Neurosci. Lett.* 18:245–50

27. Fuxe, F., Ganten, D., Köhler, C., Schüll, B., Speck, G. 1980. Evidence for differential localization of angiotensin I–converting enzyme and renin in the corpus striatum of the rat. *Acta Physiol. Scand.* 110:321–23

28. Gahwiler, B. H., Dreifuss, J. J. 1980. Transition from random to phasic firing induced in neurons cultured from the hypothalamic supraoptic area. *Brain Res.* 193:415–25

29. Ganong, W. F. 1981. The brain and the renin angiotensin system. In *Central Nervous System Mechanisms in Hypertension*, ed. J. D. Buckley, C. M. Ferrario, pp. 283–92. New York: Raven

30. Ganong, W. F. 1983. *Review of Medical Physiology*. Los Altos, CA: Lange Med. Publ. 11th ed.

31. Ganong, W. F. 1983. The brain renin-angiotensin system. In *Brain Peptides*, ed. D. T. Kreiger, M. Brownstein, J. Martin. New York: Wiley. In press

32. Ganong, W. F., Shinsako, J., Reid, I. A., Keil, L. C., Hoffman, D. L., et al. 1982. Role of vasopressin in the renin and ACTH responses to intraventricular angiotensin II. *Ann. NY Acad. Sci.* 394:619–24

33. Ganten, D., Fuxe, K., Phillips, M. I., Mann, J. F. E., Ganten, U. 1978. The brain isorenin-angiotensin system: biochemistry, localization, and possible role in drinking and blood pressure regulation. In *Frontiers in Neuroendocrinology*, ed. W. F. Ganong, L. Martini, 5:61–100. New York: Raven

34. Ganten, D., Hutchinson, J. S., Schelling, P., Ganten, U., Fischer, H. 1976. The isorenin angiotensin systems in extrarenal tissue. *Clin. Exp. Pharmacol. Physiol.* 3:103–26

35. Ganten, D., Marquez-Julio, A., Granger, P., Hayduk, K., Karsunky, K. P., et al. 1971. Renin in dog brain. *Am. J. Physiol.* 221:1733–37

36. Ganten, D., Printz, M., Phillips, M. I., Schölkens, B. A., eds. 1982. *The Renin Angiotensin System in the Brain*. Berlin: Springer Verlag
37. Garcia-Sevilla, A. J., Dubocovich, M. L., Langer, S. Z. 1979. Angiotensin II facilitates the potassium-evoked release of ³H-noradrenaline from the rabbit hypothalamus. *Eur. J. Pharmacol.* 56: 173–76
38. Gregory, T. J., Wallis, C. J., Printz, M. P. 1982. Regional changes in rat brain angiotensinogen following bilateral nephrectomy. *Hypertension* 4:827–38
39. Grubb, R. L. Jr., Raichle, M. E. 1981. Intraventricular angiotensin II increases brain vascular permeability. *Brain Res.* 210:426–30
40. Harding, J. W., Stone, L. P., Wright, J. W. 1981. The distribution of angiotensin II binding sites in rodent brain. *Brain Res.* 205:265–74
41. Hermann, K., Ganten, D., Bayer, C., Unger, T., Lang, R. E., et al. 1982. Definite evidence for the presence of (Ile⁵)-angiotensin I and (Ile⁵)-angiotensin II in the brain of rats. See Ref. 36, pp. 192–207
42. Hirata, Y., Orth, D. N. 1979. Epidermal growth factor, nerve growth factor, and renin relationships in mouse submandibular gland. *Endocrinology* 104:244A (Abstr.)
43. Hirose, S., Yokosawa, A., Inagami, T., Workman, R. S. 1980. Renin and prorenin in the hog brain: ubiquitous distribution and high concentration in the pituitary and pineal. *Brain Res.* 191:489–99
44. Hoffman, W. E., Schelling, P., Phillips, M. I., Ganten, D. 1976. Evidence for local angiotensin formation in brain of nephrectomized rats. *Neurosci. Lett.* 3:299–303
45. Horvarth, J. S., Baxter, C., Furby, F., Tiller, D. J. 1977. Endogenous antiotensin in brain. *Prog. Brain Res.* 47:161–69
46. Husain, A., Bumpus, F. M., Smeby, R. R., Brosnihan, K. B., Khosla, M. C., et al. 1983. Evidence for the existence of a family of biologically active angiotensin I-like peptides in the dog central nervous system. *Circ. Res.* 52:460–64
47. Hutchinson, J. S., Csicsmann, J., Korner, P. I., Johnston, C. I. 1978. Characterization of immunoreactive angiotensin in canine cerebrospinal fluid as Des-Asp¹-angiotensin II. *Clin. Sci. Mol. Med.* 54:147–51
48. Igic, R. P., Robinson, C. J. G., Erdös, E. G. 1977. Angiotensin I converting enzyme activity in the choroid plexus and in the retina. In *Central Actions of Angiotensin and Related Hormones*, ed.

J. P. Buckley, C. M. Ferrario, pp. 23–27. New York: Pergamon
49. Inagami, T., Celio, M. R., Clemens, D. L., Lau, D., Takii, Y., et al. 1980. Renin in rat and mouse brain: immunohistochemical identification and localization. *Clin. Sci.* 59:495–515
50. Inagami, T., Okamoto, H., Ohtsuki, K., Shimamoto, K., Chao, J., et al. 1982. Human plasma inactive renin: purification and activation by proteases: *J. Clin. Endocrinol. Metab.* 55:619–27
51. Inagami, T., Okamura, T., Hirose, S., Clemens, D. L., Celio, M. R., et al. 1982. Identification, characterization, and evidence for intraneuronal function of renin in the brain and neuroblastoma cells. See Ref. 36, pp. 64–75
52. Ito, T., Eggena, P., Barrett, J. D., Katz, D., Metter, J., et al. 1980. Studies on angiotensinogen in plasma and cerebrospinal fluid in normal and hypertensive human subjects. *Hypertension* 2: 432–36
53. Kilcoyne, M. M., Hoffman, D. L., Zimmerman, E. A. 1980. Immunocytochemical localization of angiotensin II and vasopressin in rat hypothalamus: evidence for production in the same neuron. *Clin. Sci.* 59:57s–60s
54. Köller, M., Krause, H. P., Hoffmeister, F., Ganten, D. 1979. Brain angiotensin II (ang II) disrupts avoidance learning. *Neurosci. Lett. Suppl.* 3:S327 (Abstr.)
55. Kondo, K., Garcia, R., Boucher, R., Genest, J. 1980. Effects of intracerebroventricular administration of tonin on water intake and blood pressure in the rat. *Brain Res.* 200:437–41
56. Lang, R. E., Rascher, W., Heil, J., Unger, T., Wiedemann, G., et al. 1981. Angiotensin stimulates oxytocin release. *Life Sci.* 29:1425–28
57. Langer, S. Z. 1981. Presynaptic regulation of the release of catecholamines. *Pharmacol. Rev.* 32:337–62
58. Lewicki, J. A., Fallon, J. H., Printz, M. P. 1978. Regional distribution of angiotensinogen in rat brain. *Brain Res.* 158:359–71
59. Mendelsohn, F. A. O., Csicsmann, J., Hutchinson, J. S., DiNicolantonio, R., Takata, Y. 1982. Modification of brain angiotensin-converting enzyme by dietary sodium and chronic intravenous and intracerebroventricular infusion of angiotensin II. *Hypertension* 4:590–96
60. Meyer, D. K., Phillips, M. I., Eiden, L. 1982. Studies on the presence of angiotensin II in rat brain. *J. Neurochem.* 38:816–20
61. Morgan, J. M., Routtenberg, A. 1977. Angiotensin injected into the neostriatum

after learning disrupts retention performance. *Science* 196:87–89

62. Morris, B. J., Catanzaro, D. F., De-Zwart, R. T. 1981. Evidence that the arginine esteropeptidase (gamma) subunit of nerve growth factor can activate inactive renin. *Neurosci. Lett.* 24:87–93

63. Morris, B. J., Reid, I. A. 1978. The distribution of angiotensinogen in dog brain studied by cell fractionation. *Endocrinology* 103:492–500

64. Morris, B. J., Reid, I. A. 1979. Difference in immunochemical properties of dog angiotensinogens in plasma and cerebrospinal fluid. *IRCS Med. Sci.* 7:194

65. Nahmod, V. E., Finkielman, S., Benarroch, E. E., Pirola, C. J. 1978. Angiotensin regulates release and synthesis of serotonin in brain. *Science* 202:1091–93

66. Nicoll, R. A., Barker, J. L. 1971. Angiotensin II: Excitation of supraoptic neurosecretory cells. *Nature* 233:172–73

67. Nicolov, N. A., Sudakov, K. V., Deleva, J. I., Badikov, V. I., Sherstnev, V. I., et al. 1982. Effects of angiotensin and bradykinin on neurons of the sensomotor cortex. See Ref. 36, pp. 270–83

68. Phillips, M. I. 1978. Angiotensin in the brain. *Neuroendocrinology* 25:354–77

69. Phillips, M. I., Nelson, P. G., Neal, E., Quinlan, J. 1980. Angiotensin induced phasic firing of spinal cord neurons in culture. *Soc. Neurosci. Abstr.* 6:619

70. Polsky-Cynkin, R., Fanburg, B. 1979. Immunochemical comparison of angiotensin I converting enzyme from different rat organs. *Int. J. Biochem.* 10:669–74

71. Printz, M. P., Ganten, D., Unger, T., Phillips, M. I. 1982. Miniview. The brain renin angiotensin system. See Ref. 36, pp. 3–52

72. Quinlan, J. T., Phillips, M. I. 1981. Immunoreactivity for an angiotensin-like peptide in the human brain. *Brain Res.* 205:212–18

73. Raizada, M. K., Phillips, M. I., Gerndt, J. S. 1983. Primary cultures from total rat brain incorporate [^{3}H]-isoleucine and [^{3}H]-valine into immunoprecipitable angiotensin II. *Neuroendocrinology* 36:64–67

74. Ramsay, D. J. 1982. Effects of circulating angiotensin II on the brain. In *Frontiers in Neuroendocrinology*, ed. W. F. Ganong, L. Martini, 7:263–86. New York: Raven

75. Ramsay, D. J., Reid, I. A., Brown, C. 1979. Mechanism of the dipsogenic action of tetradecapeptide renin substrate in dogs. *Endocrinology* 105:947–51

76. Reid, I. A., Brownfield, M. S. 1982. The brain renin-angiotensin system. Some unresolved problems. See Ref. 36, pp. 284–94

77. Reid, I. A., Day, R. P. 1977. Interactions and properties of some components of the renin-angiotensin system. See Ref. 48, pp. 267–82

78. Reid, I. A., Day, R. P., Moffat, B., Hughes, H. G. 1977. Apparent angiotensin immunoreactivity in dog brain resulting from angiotensinase. *J. Neurochem.* 28:435–38

79. Reid, I. A., Moffat, B. 1978. Angiotensin II concentration in cerebrospinal fluid after intraventricular injection of angiotensinogen or renin. *Endocrinology* 103:1494–98

80. Reid, I. A., Moffat, B., Morris, B. J. 1978. Two forms of angiotensinogen in dog cerebrospinal fluid. *IRCS Med. Sci.* 6:383

81. Reid, I. A., Ramsay, D. J. 1975. The effect of intracerebroventricular administration of renin on drinking and blood pressure. *Endocrinology* 97:536–42

82. Reis, D. J., Doba, N. 1974. The central nervous system and neurogenic hypertension. *Prog. Cardiovasc. Dis.* 17:51–71

83. Rix, F., Ganten, D., Schüll, B., Ungerth, T., Taugner, R. 1981. Converting enzyme in the choroid plexus brain and kidney: immunocytochemical and biochemical studies in rats. *Neurosci. Lett.* 22:125–30

84. Sakai, K. K., Marks, B. H., George, J., Koestner, A. 1974. Specific angiotensin II receptors in organ-cultured canine supraoptic nucleus cells. *Life Sci.* 14:1337–44

85. Schelling, P., Felix, D., Liard, J. F. 1982. Regulation of angiotensinogen in cerebrospinal fluid. See Ref. 36, pp. 178–91

86. Schelling, P., Ganten, U., Sponer, G., Unger, T., Ganten, D. 1980. Components of the renin-angiotensin system in the cerebrospinal fluid of rats and dogs with special consideration of the origin and the fate of angiotensin II. *Neuroendocrinology* 31:297–308

87. Schelling, P., Meyer, D., Loos, H-E., Speck, G., Johnson, A. K., et al. 1981. Renin activity in different brain regions of spontaneously hypertensive rats. See Ref. 29. pp. 397–406

88. Semple, P. F., Macrae, W. A., Norton, J. J. 1980. Angiotensin II in human cerebrospinal fluid may be an immunoassay artifact. *Clin. Sci.* 59:61s–64s

89. Sernia, C., Reid, I. A. 1980. Release of angiotensinogen by rat brain *in vivo*. *Brain Res.* 192:217–25

90. Severs, W. B., Changaris, D. G., Kapsha, J. M., Keil, L. C., Petro, D. J., et al.

1977. Presence and significance of angiotensin in cerebrospinal fluid. See Ref. 48, pp. 225–32

91. Simpson, J. B., Reid, I. A., Ramsay, D. J., Kipen, H. 1978. Mechanism of the dipsogenic action of tetradecapeptide renin substrate. *Brain Res.* 157:63–72

92. Sirett, N. E., Bray, J. J., Hubbard, J. I. 1981. Localization of immunoreactive angiotensin II in the hippocampus and striatum of rat brain. *Brain Res.* 217:405–11

93. Sirett, N. E., McLean, A. S., Bray, J. J., Hubbard, J. R. 1977. Distribution of angiotensin II receptors in rat brain. *Brain Res.* 122:299–312

94. Sladek, C. D., Blair, M. L., Ramsay, D. J. 1982. Further studies on the role of angiotensin in the osmotic control of vasopressin release by the organ-cultured rat hypothalamo-neurohypophyseal system. *Endocrinology* 111:599–607

95. Slater, E. E., Defendini, R., Zimmerman, E. 1982. Wide distribution of immunoreactive renin in nerve cells of human brain. *Proc. Natl. Acad. Sci. USA* 77:5458–60

96. Sobel, D. O. 1983. Characterization of angiotensin-mediated ACTH release. *Neuroendocrinology* 36:249–53

97. Steele, M. K., Brownfield, M. S., Reid, I. A., Ganong, W. F. 1982. A possible role for the renin-angiotensin system in the regulation of LH secretion. *Endocrinology* 110:387A (Abstr.)

98. Steele, M. K., Negro-Vilar, A., McCann, S. M. 1981. Effect of angiotensin II on *in vivo* and *in vitro* release of anterior pituitary hormones in the female rat. *Endocrinology* 109:893–99

99. Steele, M. K., Negro-Vilar, A., McCann, S. M. 1982. Modulation by dopamine and estradiol of central effects of angiotensin II on anterior pituitary hormone release. *Endocrinology* 111:722–29

100. Sumners, C., Phillips, M. I. 1983. Central injection of angiotensin II alters catecholamine activity in rat brain. *Am. J. Physiol.* 244:R257–63

101. Suzuki, H., Ferrario, C. M., Speth, R. C., Brosnihan, K. B., Smeby, R. R. 1983. Effect of renal hypertension on plasma and cerebrospinal norepinephrine and angiotensin II in conscious dogs. *Hypertension* 5(1):139–48

102. Tonnaer, J. A. D. M., Wiegant, V. M., de Jong, W. 1981. Angiotensin generation in the brain and drinking: indications for the involvement of endopeptidase activity distinct from cathepsin D. *Brain Res.* 223:343–53

103. Van Houten, M., Schiffrin, E. L., Mann, J. F. E., Posner, B. I., Boucher, R. 1980. Radioautographic localization of specific binding sites for blood-borne angiotensin II in the rat brain. *Brain Res.* 186:480–85

104. Weindl, A. 1973. Neuroendocrine aspects of circumventricular organs. In *Frontiers in Neuroendocrinology 1973*, ed. W. F. Ganong, L. Martini, pp. 3–32. New York: Oxford Univ. Press

105. Weindl, A., Schweisfurth, H., Sofroniew, M. V., Dahlheim, H. 1977. Distribution of converting enzyme in the rat brain: high activities in subfornical organ, area postrema, and choroid plexus. *Acta Endocrinol.* 85(Suppl. 212):158 (Abstr.)

106. Weiner, R. I., Ganong, W. F. 1978. The role of brain monoamines and histamine in the regulation of anterior pituitary secretion. *Physiol. Rev.* 58:905–76

107. Weyhenmeyer, J. A., Phillips, M. I. 1982. Angiotensin-like immunoreactivity in the brain of the spontaneously hypertensive rat. *Hypertension* 4:514–23

108. Wintroub, B. U., Klickstein, L. B., Kaempfer, C. E., Austen, K. F. 1981. A human neutrophil-dependent pathway for generation of angiotensin II: purification and physiochemical characterization of the plasma protein substrate. *Proc. Natl. Acad. Sci. USA* 78:1204–08

109. Yang, H-Y. T., Neff, N. H. 1972. Distribution and properties of angiotensin converting enzyme of rat brain. *J. Neurochem.* 19:2443–50

Ann. Rev. Physiol. 1984. 46:33–42

VARIANTS OF GROWTH HORMONE AND PROLACTIN AND THEIR POSTTRANSLATIONAL MODIFICATIONS

Urban J. Lewis

The Whittier Institute for Diabetes and Endocrinology, La Jolla, California 92037

INTRODUCTION

The multicomponent nature of growth hormone, known since the introduction of gel electrophoresis to the study of pituitary hormones, has been attributed to contamination by such posttranslational modifications as aggregates, an interchain disulfide dimer, desamido, and proteolytically altered forms (26). With the identification of the 20,000-dalton variant of human GH (6, 22), another source of heterogeneity was established: alternate routes of synthesis to produce forms with different structures (9, 47). Expression of multiple genes for the hormone is also likely (33), introducing further heterogeneity. There is mounting evidence that not only are there variants of the GH structure but that this is also true for that of prolactin (PRL). The variants may have individual properties that, when combined, express the many known actions of the hormones; or, they may provide a diversity of structures that serve as prohormones in the production of smaller peptides, each with a specific, restricted metabolic action. This review discusses these possibilities.

This review focuses on recent articles and, in many instances, the latest paper in a series, in order to provide key references rather than an exhaustive bibliography. Two recent reviews on human growth hormone (hGH) (7, 27) are noteworthy.

33

0066-4278/84/0315-0033$02.00

VARIANTS

The 20,000-Dalton Variant (hGH$_{20K}$)

The term isohormone would be appropriate for what is referred to as a variant in this review. This would be consistent with the recommendation made by the Commission on Biochemical Nomenclature that suggests that "isoenzyme" be reserved for forms arising from genetically determined factors and not be used for posttranslational modification. However, because "isohormone" has been employed in the past to designate proteolytic cleavage products of GH, the term "variant" is used here. Avoidance of "isohormone" to denote posttranslational forms would help standardize nomenclature. Additional comments on this subject have been made (24).

The hGH$_{20K}$ variant is identical to the major form of hGH except for a deletion of a 15–amino acid segment, residues 32–46 of hGH (22). Wallis (47) suggested a mechanism for removal of the 15 residues from an inner portion of the molecule. Because an intervening sequence in the hGH gene begins after the codon for residue 31, which is the starting point for the deletion, he reasoned that hGH$_{20K}$ could be formed if part of the translated sequence of hGH (corresponding to residues 32–46) was treated as part of the intervening sequence during processing of the mRNA precursor. Direct evidence for this came from the work of DeNoto et al (9). The presence of alternate pathways of synthesis for hGH and hGH$_{20K}$ raises the question of the signal to the pituitary gland to process the hGH-mRNA in one of two different ways. Is it the demand of metabolic status for specific endocrine needs that affects the transcriptional process, and is this demand mediated by a particular releasing factor? The variant accounts for about 10% of the GH in the pituitary gland; two isolation procedures have appeared (6, 41).

The hGH$_{20K}$ variant stimulates growth and has other properties of a GH (24). However, several characteristic activities of hGH are greatly diminished in hGH$_{20K}$. The variant lacks the early (1 hr) insulin-like action of hGH; it fails to produce an in vivo lowering both of blood glucose and of free fatty acids in fasted, hypophysectomized rats (14). The ability to stimulate glucose uptake and utilization in vitro in rat adipose tissue, a property of hGH, cannot be demonstrated for hGH$_{20K}$. The variant also fails to stimulate a late (5 hr) rise in serum-free fatty acids in hypophysectomized rats, a well known action of hGH. The diabetogenic activity of hGH also is significantly less in hGH$_{20K}$. The variant does not produce glucose intolerance in dogs when given at a dosage of 0.25 mg kg^{-1}, nor can this activity be enhanced by limited proteolysis with substilisin as is found for hGH (25). To be answered then is whether hGH$_{20K}$ fulfills a special endocrine need. Are there processes that require a GH with both insulin-like and anti-insulin properties, and others that demand a hormone lacking these actions? A hypothesis is that regulation of their proteolytic processing, not control of secretion of the two forms, is important. This implies that modified forms and fragments are the actual functional agents in cellular processes.

The hGH_{20K} variant is about 20–40% as effective as hGH in displacing ^{125}I-hGH from its antibody (19, 26). This cross-reactivity has made it difficult to produce a specific antibody to hGH_{20K} and has prevented direct measurement of the variant in blood (24). That hGH_{20K} is secreted is indicated by the studies of Baumann et al (2), who by a combination of immunological and electrophoretic techniques detected a component of serum with properties of hGH_{20K}. The hGH_{20K} variant is 30–50% as reactive as hGH in displacing labeled hGH from rabbit liver receptors (19, 40, 48). Altered binding of hGH_{20K} to cultured human lymphocytes (IM-9 cells) also has been noted (19). With liver membranes the displacment curves of ^{125}I-hGH for the two variants are nonparallel, whereas both forms displace ^{125}I-hGH_{20K} in a parallel manner (24). It is not known whether this is a result of different receptor sites for the variants, or whether the forms bind differently to a single receptor. Also to be learned is whether hGH_{20K} can react with hGH tissue receptors and block a subsequent insulin-like action of hGH, thereby participating in a receptor regulation.

Alkaline Forms of Human Growth Hormone

There is evidence that the pituitary gland makes two additional biologically active variants of hGH (26). Because urea has to be incorporated into the electrophoresis gel for the components to be resolved from hGH, the question arose as to whether the forms are artifacts. A result that spoke against this is that the components are undetectable in some preparations of hGH, indicating that treatment of hGH with urea does not promote their formation. Additionally, when the two components are separated from hGH by preparative electrophoresis and then rerun, they migrate with hGH in absence of urea but with their characteristic slower mobilities when analyzed with urea. It has been suggested that the more alkaline properties of these forms result from buried basic amino acids that are exposed when the proteins are subjected to denaturants (26). The less alkaline of the two forms stimulated the crop sac to a greater degree than did hGH, although the dose response was not parallel to the prolactin control. By RIA the alkaline forms are essentially equipotent to hGH.

SV-hGH-2

An hGH gene from which a form with 13 amino acid substitutions can be produced was reported by Seeburg (39). The gene was expressed in monkey kidney cells by cloning in a simian virus, but as yet it is not known whether this DNA sequence is expressed in the human pituitary gland (19). From its amino acid composition, it was predicted that the variant has an alkaline isoelectric point (39). Of importance then will be electrophoretic comparison of this substance with the alkaline forms of hGH detected in the pituitary gland. Because of its ease of aggregation, Hizuka et al (19) suggested that if the SV-hGH-2 variant is found in blood, it may account for some of the big forms of hGH and may also be the substance with a ratio of receptor binding activity to immunoactivity greater than one.

Prolactin (PRL)

Forms of PRL for which the ratio of biological to immunological activities is greater than that for the major PRL form present ($M_r = 23K$) were noted for rat prolactin (1). Sinha (44) reported substances with similar characteristics in both rat and mouse pituitary extracts. More recently a 26K form of murine prolactin was found in pituitary extracts (45). The structures of these rodent PRLs have not been determined, but since only a single PRL gene has been found in the rat (8), the newly recognized forms may be products of alternative splicing of mRNA precursor. Prediction of such a process for rat PRL has been made (8). A possible 25K mRNA splicing variant of ovine PRL has been isolated (author's laboratory; unpublished results.) The tryptic peptide containing residues 22–43 of ovine PRL could not be found in the newly recognized form when examined by peptide mapping. It is in this region that the PRL gene has an intron (8). An unusual form of bovine PRL, lacking the cystine bridge at Cys_{58}–Cys_{173}, was isolated from preparations of bovine PRL (43). A separate gene that could account for the formation of the substance has not been reported. Three additional forms of human PRL (M_r 29K, 45K, and 16K) were found in pituitary homogenates (29). The structural relationships of these substances to the major form of PRL are not known.

POSTTRANSLATIONAL MODIFICATIONS

Interchain Disulfide Dimer

Both GH and PRL form disulfide dimers, but only the dimer of hGH has been isolated and studied in detail (26). Evidence for a human PRL dimer comes from RIA analysis of serum fractions obtained by gel filtration (3). To be stressed is that in formation of the hGH dimer, the growth promoting properties of hGH are greatly diminished while lactogenic characteristics are preserved. Since hGH binds to both GH and lactogen membrane receptors (48), a study of receptor binding properties of this form of hGH could be important. If the dimer did bind and was competitively displaced by hGH, the dimer could be thought of as participating in regulation of receptor binding. Similarly, competitive inhibition of in vitro hGH-stimulated glucose uptake would suggest that the dimer functions as a modulator of hGH actions. Still another function for the dimer could be serving as a substrate for the production of specific peptide fragments (see below). Because of its poor reactivity to antibodies to hGH (26), the hGH dimer has never been accurately measured in blood, nor are the factors influencing its secretion known. A dimer of bovine GH, crosslinked through lysines, was inactive in growth promotion (12).

Proteolytically Cleaved Forms (Two-Chain Modifications)

The region of the hGH molecule between positions 134 and 150 is extremely sensitive to proteolytic attack. The enzymes used and the cleavage products generated have been reviewed (7, 24, 27). Removal of as many as 12 residues from the susceptible region does not diminish lactogenic and growth-promoting activities. In some instances an enhancement is noted. The points of cleavage required for the enhancement are not known precisely (24). Cleavage of bovine and ovine growth hormones to form two-chain modifications does not alter the growth promoting activity (17, 18). A recent report (20) indicates that a large portion of the GH bound to plasmalemma undergoes a proteolytic cleavage similar to that noted in forms isolated from pituitary extracts.

Cleavage of ovine PRL by trypsin produced a two-chain structure with the peptide chain opened between residues 125 and 126 (16); biological activity was not reported. A cleaved form of PRL was detected in the rat pituitary gland, and electrophoretic evidence indicated that the peptide chain has been opened in the large disulfide loop of the hormone (32). Of even greater interest was that the largest fragment produced after reduction of this two-chain form has mitogenic effects on mammary tissue that were not produced by intact PRL. Y. N. Sinha and T. A. Gilligan (unpublished observations) found a cleaved form of mouse prolactin in pituitary extracts, and even greater amounts were detected in the medium in which pituitary glands had been incubated. Possibly related to these cleaved forms are the 14K modifications of GH and PRL that were found in rat pituitary glands (28, 38).

Noncovalently Linked Two-Chain Forms

An unusual property of hGH is that the disulfide bridges can be reduced and S-carbamidomethylated, with retention of about 60% of growth promoting activity (27) and essentially all lactogenic properties (4, 30). If S-carboxymethylation is used, there is loss of growth activity but not of lactogenic activity (4, 31). In contrast, porcine GH loses all activity when either S-alkylating reagent is used (31). Treatment of hGH with sulfite, where there is evidence that only the COOH-disulfide is opened, causes a significant loss of growth activity but not lactogenic activity (31). The growth activity of bovine GH, on the other hand, is not altered by sulfite treatment (31). Cleavage of all three disulfides of ovine PRL abolishes biological activity, whereas if only the NH_2- or COOH-bridge is opened, activity is retained (10). The ability of

S-carbamidomethyl hGH to retain activity has permitted experimentation on recombination of major fragments to produce biologically active, noncovalently linked complexes. When a two-chain form of hGH is reduced and S-alkylated, the hormone can be separated into two fragments. Thrombin has been most used to produce the two-chain hGH because the enzyme cleaves a single bond (Arg_{134}-Leu_{135}) in the large disulfide loop. The NH_2 fragment (residues 1–134) exhibits a low order of growth activity (5% or less of the intact hormone), whereas the COOH-segment (residues 135–191) is inactive (30). However, when the two S-alkylated fragments are permitted to recombine in solution (presumably by a hydrophobic bonding process), biological activities are restored in varying degrees; the extent of this restoration differs depending on the assay used. Although the growth-promoting activity is decreased to 35% of the intact hormone, the diabetogenic activity is completely restored and the insulin-like property is 20% of unaltered hGH (36). Receptor binding is equivalent to that of S-alkylated hGH (18). Recombination of various COOH-fragments with the 1–134 segment restores full growth promoting activity (27), an indication that the COOH-segment can dictate an acceptable folding pattern for the complex. Recombination of fragments of ovine GH has been unsuccessful, as has production of a human-ovine hybrid. The recombination reaction has been reviewed by Li (27).

FRAGMENTS

Insulin-Potentiating Peptides

Because hGH_{20K} lacks some of the insulin-like actions of hGH, a question to ask is whether the 15–amino acid segment that is absent from hGH_{20K} (hGH_{32-46}), denoted here as deletion peptide, would have insulin-like properties. Such properties were not detected, but the peptide did potentiate the action of insulin in vitro by enhancing glucose uptake by rat adipose tissue. It also improved glucose tolerance of diabetic mice (13). The insulin-potentiating activity of hGH_{32-46} has also been found by Dryburgh et al (11). Using an RIA for deletion peptide (46), an immunoreactive substance was detected in serum. This suggests that the peptide may be a proteolytic cleaved product of hGH. This would be definite evidence that a physiologically active fragment of GH does circulate. It is puzzling that Ng & Bornstein (34) found that hGH_{4-15} had insulin-potentiating effects. That a longer segment comprising both regions may actually be a more important peptide is indicated by the isolation of hGH_{1-43} from pituitary extracts (author's laboratories, unpublished observations). The significance of this finding is enhanced by the observation that hGH_{1-43} has potent insulin-potentiating actions (L. G. Frigeri et al, unpublished observations).

Hyperglycemic Peptide

There is no agreement on the portion of the GH structure that is responsible for its hyperglycemic effects, nor is it certain that such a segment is cleaved from the hormone and then acts as a diabetogenic factor. These topics have been reviewed (24, 26). It is clear that hGH will produce glucose intolerance in man when given (37) in enormous dosages (about 32 mg day^{-1} for four days) and that large amounts have similar effects in dogs (25). There is a low molecular weight substance (M_r near 5,000) in the pituitary gland that is active in μg amounts (15, 42). That the low-molecular-weight substance is a proteolytic cleavage product of GH is indicated by enhancement of hyperglycemic properties following limited proteolysis of GH by subtilisin (25).

Prolactin Fragments

That this hormone also undergoes proteolytic processing was discussed above in the section on two-chain forms of PRL. Nolin (35) noted that fragments of PRL are produced in the ovary, suggesting that these may have physiologic importance.

SUMMARY: GROWTH HORMONE AS A PROHORMONE (A HYPOTHESIS)

To explain the variety of actions of growth hormone in carbohydrate metabolism, Bornstein et al (5) proposed that the intact hormone acts as a prohormone for smaller active peptides. Levine & Luft (21) offered another explanation for the multiple actions, suggesting that GH was not a single substance but two, one catabolic and the other anabolic. Mills et al (30) interpreted the multiple effects as possibly expressing the actions of a variety of receptors reacting with different regions of the GH structure. Identification of variants and their posttranslational modifications could support all three explanations. There could be fragments with limited activities and variant forms with specific actions, each with its own receptor. An overall hypothesis is that proteolytic processing of a variety of forms of GH, each acting as a specific substrate, could produce numerous fragments with affinities for specific receptors.

If GH and PRL serve as prohormones, a mechanism that permits specific cleavages must be found. A double basic amino acid sequence is the structure involved in the proteolytic processing of numerous proteins, yet hGH has only one double basic sequence (Arg_{167}-Lys_{168}). It has been proposed (23) that deamidation of GH might direct points of attack by proteinases. Acylation of the NH_2 terminus, a process for which there is evidence (26), could alter folding of the peptide chain and expose new areas to proteolytic attack. Amino acid substitutions in the two alkaline forms of hGH (26) could not only alter the tertiary structures but might also provide double basic sequences as loci for proteolytic cleavage. The 15–amino acid deletion in hGH_{20K} alters folding of the peptide chain (6). This would expose new areas to proteolytic attack. Because hGH_{20K} is more resistant to proteolysis than hGH (25), its lower hyperglycemic activity might be due to the inability to cleave an active hyperglycemic fragment from the hormone. The interchain disulfide dimer may also alter the folding characteristics of the monomer and expose a different region of the surface. Posttranslational alterations could therefore provide a variety of fragments from a small number of structures. In certain instances altered folding might be detrimental to production of specific fragments. Lack of growth activity for hGH_{1-134}, S-carboxymethyl-hGH, and S-alkylated bovine GH could be explained by inability of proteinases to cleave certain linkages in these substances. Bewley et al (4) found different proteolytic digestion rates for S-alkylated forms of hGH. Regeneration of biological activity upon recombination of fragments would then result from reestablishment of folding characteristics in the reconstituted molecule which then permits correct proteolysis. Similarly, enhanced activities of two-chain hGH could be attributed to a more favorable substrate configuration for proteolytic processing. Bovine GH is more extensively degraded by plasmin than is hGH (T. K. Surowy, M. Wallis, in preparation), an indication that its somewhat different structure alters the points of proteolytic attack. Whether this can explain the inability of bovine GH to promote growth in man is yet to be investigated.

No peptide has been found that is equipotent on a molar basis to intact GH in causing a growth response. This may be because somatic growth is a result of the action of a group of fragments. When such an assembly of actions is not needed, however, the individual peptides could act in well-defined minute-to-minute cellular reactions. A study of the variants and their proteolytic cleavage products will permit experimental examination of these ideas.

Literature Cited

1. Asawaroengchai, H., Russell, S. M., Nicoll, C. S. 1978. Electrophoretically separable forms of rat prolactin with different bioassay and radioimmunoassay activities. *Endocrinology* 102:407–14
2. Baumann, G., MacCart, J. G., Amburn, K. 1983. The molecular nature of circulating growth hormone in normal and acromegalic man: Evidence for a principal and minor monomeric forms. *J. Clin. Endocrinol. Metab.* 56:946–51
3. Benveniste, R., Helman, J. D., Orth, D. N., McKenna, T. J., Nicholson, W. E., Rabinowitz, D. 1979. Circulating big human prolactin: Conversion to small human prolactin by reduction of disulfide bonds. *J. Clin. Endocrinol.* 48:883–86

4. Bewley, T. A., Brovetto-Cruz, J., Li, C. H. 1969. Human pituitary growth hormone. Physicochemical investigations of the native and reduced-alkylated protein. *Biochemistry* 8:4701–8
5. Bornstein, J., Armstrong, J. McD., Taft, H. P., Ng, F. M. Gould, M. K. 1973. The mechanism of the diabetogenic effects of pituitary growth hormone. *Postgrad. Med. J.* 49(Suppl.):1/219–24/242
6. Chapman, G. E., Rogers, K. M., Brittain, T., Bradshaw, R. A., Bates, O. J., Turner, C., Cary, P. D., Crane-Robinson, C. 1981. The 20,000 molecular weight variant of human growth hormone. Preparation and some physical and chemical properties. *J. Biol. Chem.* 256:2395–401

7. Chawla, R. K., Parks, J. S., Rudman, D. 1983. Structural variants of human growth hormone: Biochemical, genetic and clinical aspects. *Ann. Rev. Med.* 34:519–47

8. Cooke, N. E., Baxter, J. D. 1982. Structural analysis of the prolactin gene suggests a separate origin for its 5' end. *Nature* 297:603–6

9. DeNoto, F. M., Moore, D. D., Goodman, H. M. 1981. Human growth hormone DNA sequence and mRNA structure: Possible alternative splicing. *Nucleic Acids Res.* 9:3719–30

10. Doneen, B., A., Bewley, T. A., Li, C. H. 1979. Studies on prolactin. Selective reduction of the disulfide bonds of the ovine hormone. *Biochemistry* 18:4851–60

11. Dryburgh, J. R., Rudman, C. G., Stebbing, N. 1983. The effect of a fragment of human growth hormone on induced hyperglycemia in normal and glucose-intolerant animals. *Endocrinology* 112 (Suppl.):379 (Abstr.)

12. Fernandez, H. N., Delfino, J. M. 1983. Covalent cross-linking of bovine somatotropin dimer. *Biochem. J.* 209:107–15

13. Frigeri, L. G., Ling, N. 1982. Biological activities of the synthetic fragment 32–46 of the human growth hormone sequence. *Endocrinology* 110 (Suppl.):101 (Abstr.)

14. Frigeri, L. G., Peterson, S. M., Lewis, U. J. 1979. The 20,000-dalton structural variant of human growth hormone: Lack of some early insulin-like effects. *Biochem. Biophys. Res. Commun.* 91:778–82

15. Frigeri, L. G., Wolff, G. L., Robel, G. 1983. Impairment of glucose tolerance in yellow (A^{vy}/A) (BALB/c x VY) F-1 hybrid by hyperglycemic peptide(s) from human pituitary glands. *Endocrinology.* In press

16. Graf, L. 1982. Studies on prolactin. *Int. J. Peptide Protein Res.* 19:212–14

17. Graf, L., Barat, E., Borvendeg, J., Hermann, I., Patthy, A. 1976. Action of thrombin on ovine, bovine and human pituitary growth hormones. *Eur. J. Biochem.* 64:333–40

18. Graf, L., Li, C. H., Cheng, C. H. K., Jibson, M. D. 1981. Two contiguous thrombin fragments of human somatotropin form a functionally active recombinant, but the two homologous fragments from sheep hormones do not. *Biochemistry* 20:7251–58

19. Hizuka, N., Hendricks, C. M., Pavlakis, G. N., Hamer, D. H., Gorden, P. 1982. Properties of human growth hormone polypeptides: Purified from pituitary extracts and synthesized in monkey kidney cells and bacteria. *J. Clin. Endocrinol. Metab.* 55:545–50

20. Hughes, J. P., Hughes, E. F. 1983. Cleavage of growth hormone by rabbit liver plasmalemma. *Endocrinology* 112 (Suppl.):217 (Abstr.)

21. Levine, R., Luft, R. 1964. The relation between the growth and diabetogenic effects of the so-called growth hormone of the anterior pituitary. *Diabetes* 13:651–55

22. Lewis, U. J., Bonewald, L. F., Lewis, L. J. 1980. The 20,000-dalton variant of human growth hormone: Location of the amino acid deletion. *Biochem. Biophys. Res. Commun.* 92:511–16

23. Lewis, U. J., Singh, R. N. P., Bonewald, L. F., Seavey, B. K. 1981. Altered proteolytic cleavage of human growth hormone as a result of deamidation. *J. Biol. Chem.* 256:11645–50

24. Lewis, U. J., Singh, R. N. P., Sigel, M. B., Frigeri, L. G., Sinha, Y. N., VanderLaan, W. P. 1983. Variants, posttranslational modifications and fragments of growth hormone and prolactin. In *Hormone Receptors in Growth and Reproduction,* ed. B. B. Saxena. New York: Raven Press. In press

25. Lewis, U. J., Singh, R. N. P., Tutwiler, G. F. 1981. Hyperglycemic activity of the 20,000-dalton variant of human growth hormone. *Endocrinol. Res. Commun.* 8:155–64

26. Lewis, U. J., Singh, R. N. P., Tutwiler, G. F., Sigel, M. B., VanderLaan, E. F., VanderLaan, W. P. 1980. Human growth hormone: A complex of proteins. *Recent Prog. Horm. Res.* 36:477–504

27. Li, C. H. 1982. Human growth hormone: 1974–1981. *Mol. Cell. Biochem.* 46:31–41

28. Mayer, G. L., Russell, S. M. 1983. Identification of a low molecular weight (14K) form of bioactive rat PRL that lacks immunoactivity. *Endocrinology* 112(Suppl.):223 (Abstr.)

29. Meuris, S., Svoboda, M., Vilamala, M., Christophe, J., Robyn, C. 1983. Monomeric pituitary growth hormone and prolactin variants in man characterized by immunoperoxidase electrophoresis. *FEBS Lett.* 154:111–15

30. Mills, J. B., Kostyo, J. L., Reagan, C. R., Wagner, S. A., Moseley, M. H., Wilhelmi, A. E. 1980. Fragments of human growth hormone produced by digestion with thrombin: Chemistry and biological properties. *Endocrinology* 107:391–98

31. Mills, J. B., Wilhelmi A. E. 1968. Effects of treatment of bovine, porcine

and human growth hormones with sulfite. *Ann. NY Acad. Sci.* 148:343–51

32. Mittra, I. 1980. A novel "cleaved prolactin" in the rat pituitary: Part II *In vivo* mammary mitogenic activity of its N-terminal 16K moiety. *Biochem. Biophys. Res. Commun.* 95:1760–67

33. Moore, D. D., Walker, M. D., Diamond, D. J., Conkling, M. A., Goodman, H. M. 1982. Structure, expression and evolution of growth hormone genes. *Recent Prog. Horm. Res.* 38:197–222

34. Ng, F. M., Bornstein, J. 1982. Comparison of hypoglycaemic responses to human growth hormone and the synthetic 4–15 fragment between 16–18-day-old and 45–50-day-old rats. *Diabetologia* 23:534–38

35. Nolin, J. M. 1982. Molecular homology between prolactin and ovarian peptides: Evidence for physiologic modification of the parent molecule by the target. *Peptides* 3:823–31

36. Reagan, C. R., Kostyo, J. L., Mills, J. B., Gennick, S. E., Messina, J. L., Wagner, S. A., Wilhelmi, A. E. 1981. Recombination of fragments of human growth hormone: Altered activity profile of the recombinant molecule. *Endocrinology* 109:1663–71

37. Rosenfeld, R. G., Wilson, D. M., Dollar, L. A., Bennett, A., Hintz, R. L. 1982. Both human pituitary growth hormone and recombinant DNA-derived human growth hormone cause insulin resistance at a post-receptor site. *J. Clin. Endocrinol. Metab.* 54:1033–38

38. Russell, S. M., Mayer, G. L., 1983. Rat anterior pituitaries contain and secrete a low molecular weight (14–15K) protein with growth activity. *Endocrinology* 112(Suppl.): 310 (Abstr.)

39. Seeburg, P. H. 1982. The human growth hormone gene family: Nucleotide sequences show recent divergence and predict a new polypeptide hormone. *DNA* 1: 239–49

40. Sigel, M. B., Thorpe, N. A., Kobrin, M. S., Lewis, U. J., VanderLaan, W. P. 1981. Binding characteristics of a biologically active variant of human growth hormone (20K) to growth hormone and lactogen receptors. *Endocrinology* 108: 1600–3

41. Singh, R. N. P., Lewis, U. J. 1981. Procedure for isolation of the 20,000-dalton variant of human growth hormone. *Prep. Biochem.* 11:559–70

42. Singh, R. N. P., Lewis, L. J., O'Brien, R., Lewis, U. J., Tutwiler, G. F., 1982. Characterization of the pituitary hyperglycemic factor as a low molecular weight peptide. *Endocrinology* 110 (Suppl.):102 (Abstr.)

43. Singh, R. N. P., Lewis, L. J., Seavey, B. K., Lewis, U. J. 1983. An open loop variant of prolactin. *Endocrinology* 112 (Suppl.):166 (Abstr.)

44. Sinha, Y. N. 1981. Plasma prolactin analysis as a potential predictor of murine mammary tumorigenesis. In *Hormones and Breast Cancer*, Banbury Rep. 8, pp. 377–91. Cold Spring Harbor: Cold Spring Harbor Lab.

45. Sinha, Y. N., Gilligan, T. A. 1983. A high molecular weight variant of prolactin in the murine pituitary gland. *Endocrinology* 112(Suppl.):384 (Abstr.)

46. VanderLaan, W. P., VanderLaan, E. F., Sigel, M. B., Caravaca-Trujillo, J. 1982. Studies with a synthetic hGH fragment. *Endocrinology* 110(Suppl.):101 (Abstr.)

47. Wallis, M. 1980. Deletions in the proteins and introns in the gene. *Nature* 284:512

48. Wohnlich, L., Moore, W. V. 1982. Binding of a variant of human growth hormone to liver plasma membranes. *Horm. Metab. Res.* 14:138–41

Ann. Rev. Physiol. 1984. 46:43–52
Copyright © 1984 by Annual Reviews Inc. All rights reserved

RELAXIN

Gerson Weiss

Department of Obstetrics and Gynecology, New York University School of Medicine,
550 First Avenue, New York, New York 10016

INTRODUCTION

Hisaw (16) showed, more than 55 years ago, that an aqueous extract of corpora
lutea from pregnant sows caused intrapubic ligament formation in estrogen-
primed guinea pigs. The hormone contained in this extract, which is responsible for "relaxing" the pubic symphysis, was named relaxin.

The major source of relaxin is the ovary of the pregnant sow, which contains
much more relaxin than reproductive tissues of other species. Measurement of
porcine relaxin by radioimmunoassay (RIA) is hampered by the absence of
iodinatable amino acids in the molecule. In 1975, Sherwood et al (43) developed a specific RIA for porcine relaxin using ^{125}I-labeled polytyrosylrelax-
in. The structure of porcine relaxin was determined by two groups of investigators placing relaxin studies on a firm scientific base (39, 18).

STRUCTURE OF RELAXIN

Relaxin is a peptide hormone with an approximate molecular weight of 6,000
daltons. The amino acid sequences of pig, rat, and shark relaxin have been
published (2). These relaxins consist of two dissimilar peptide chains linked by
disulfide bridges. There is significant structural homology to insulin and the
somatomedins. Relaxin and insulin have almost identical three-dimensional
structures. However, there is less than 25% homology of amino acids between
relaxin and insulin. Unlike insulin, the amino acid sequence of relaxin is poorly
conserved across species lines. Pig, rat, and shark relaxin have less than 50%
amino acid homology.

Relaxin is derived from a larger precursor in which the two chains, A and B,
are connected by a C peptide. In the rat, this C peptide is twice the size of the
native molecule (24). Hudson et al (17) determined the structure of the entire

43

coding region of a human preprorelaxin gene as identified from a library of human DNA. The tertiary structure is similar to that of other known relaxins, and the C peptide is similar in length to that identified in rat and pig. There is also relatively little amino acid homology to the other known relaxins. An exciting finding is what appears to be an accessible tyrosine in human relaxin. This would suggest that human relaxin can be directly iodinated.

Preliminary data from Green et al (13) suggests that there are two distinct human relaxin in vitro translation products, a major 19,000- and a minor 17,000-dalton preprorelaxin species; this in turn suggests that there are two expressed human relaxin genes.

ASSAY METHODS

The classical bioassay methods for relaxin depend on the ability of relaxin to inhibit myometrial activity or to induce an interpubic ligament in either the guinea pig or mouse. They also require estrogen pretreatment for effectiveness. In the absence of either endogenous or exogenous estrogen, relaxin is inactive in both the uterine muscle and the pubic symphysis assays (45).

Practically, pubic symphysis assays require approximately 1 μg of relaxin per animal. These methods are qualitative. Precise quantitation requires a large number of animals and the use of different dose levels of standard and unknown. This is not done today because of the scarcity of relaxin from most species. Results from different bioassays may not be parallel. For instance, shark relaxin is active in the guinea pig but not in the mouse pubic sympyhis assays.

No uterine motility inhibition assay has been uniformly accepted. Each laboratory seems to have developed its own method. Relaxin is active on myometrium of many species, both in vivo and in vitro, but most laboratories are now using in vitro systems. The most sensitive assays utilize isometric electrically stimulated contractions. Sarosi et al have recently shown that progesterone increases the sensitivity of estrogen-treated rat uterine horn segments to relaxin, thus increasing sensitivity of the assay even further (36). The myometrial inhibition assays are far more sensitive than public symphysis assays. As little as 20 ng can elicit a positive response. These uterine activity assays are not specific. They are best used for monitoring the activity of relaxin preparations during purification.

After Sherwood's iodination of polytyrosyl relaxin (43), several radioimmunoassays (RIAs) have been developed against porcine relaxin. Sherwood's group also developed a specific antirat relaxin antiserum and a rat relaxin RIA (41).

The RIA currently used to measure human relaxin in most recent reports utilizes antibody R6, developed by O'Byrne & Steinetz (27). This antibody, raised in a rabbit against porcine relaxin, detects relaxin immunoactivity in many species. Because of differences in amino acid sequence in different relaxin molecules, most antiporcine relaxin antisera do not cross-react with relaxin from other species. Extracts of pig pregnancy corpora lutea have been assayed in both the guinea pig public symphsis palpation assays and by RIA using R6, with the ratio of bioactivity to immunoactivity set at one. A similar evaluation for extracts of human pregnancy corpora lutea shows bioactivity: immunoactivity ratios of 1.3–4.4 to 1, suggesting that most human relaxin is detected by this antibody (26).

SPECIES SPECIFICITY OF RELAXIN

It is important to recognize that not only is there poor conservation of relaxin primary structure and biopotency across species lines, but that relaxin serves multiple functions and may have different sources in various animals. Extrapolation across species lines is perilous. Relaxin is detectable in the circulation during pregnancy in all mammals (that have been examined). However, the secretory patterns, and perhaps the function, of circulating relaxin differs in various species. Relaxin can be found in peripheral blood of the nonpregnant state as well. It is occasionally detected in the luteal phase of nonpregnant women. The major source of circulating relaxin in pregnant women, baboons, monkeys, rats, pigs, and cows is the corpus luteum, but the endometrium produces relaxin in the guinea pig (29), and the placenta is the main source of relaxin in the pregnant mare (46). Interpubic ligament formation, important in the parturition process of mice and guinea pigs, is not demonstrable in rats and women. The dramatic obligatory action of relaxin on cervical ripening, softening, and dilation seen in pigs and rats has no clear analogy in women (44).

RELAXIN IN THE NONPREGNANT STATE

Most studies of relaxin secretion in the nonpregnant state have been performed in female subjects. Relaxin can occasionally be detected in the serum of nonpregnant luteal-phase women. Relaxin is found in corpora lutea of nonpregnant women at concentrations 100-fold less than in the corpora lutea of pregnant women. Bigazzi (3) found relaxin in breast cyst fluid from nonpregnant women. The relaxin may be produced there, or the cyst may concentrate relaxin from other sources.

Loeken et al (20) observed that cultured granulosa cells from preovulatory porcine follicles secrete relaxin. Luteinizing hormone, which stimulates ovulation, enhances relaxin secretion by cells from large preovulatory follicles.

Relaxin may stimulate plasminogen activator secretion by rat granulosa cells in vitro (52). These results suggest that relaxin may have a local ovarian effect, perhaps facilitating ovulation.

Thomas et al (51) demonstrated the presence of relaxin in peritoneal fluid obtained from women in the mid-to-late luteal phase, as well as at the time of cesarean section ending pregnancy. They postulate that this relaxin is a luteal product since it is only found in the presence of an active corpus luteum. The relaxin in peritoneal fluid may have uterine activity even prior to the time circulating relaxin is detectable in early pregnancy. Ovarian products can be transmitted directly into the uterine cavity via the follopian tubes. Relaxin present in peritoneal fluid may also reach the endometrium through the tube and may also be involved in the connective tissue alterations involved in implantation should pregnancy ensue. Thomas et al (51) have shown that acute treatment with GnRh can increase levels of circulating relaxin in nonpregnant luteal-phase women. Quagliarello et al have shown that hCG given on day 8–10 of the luteal phase is capable of inducing relaxin secretion (31). Although this treatment produces an abrupt rise in serum progesterone concentrations, relaxin does not become detectable for 2–6 days. Levels of serum progesterone fall while relaxin levels rise, suggesting different control mechanisms of the hormones even though their secretion is stimulated by the same exogenous stimulus.

The timing of the hCG injections is critical to relaxin secretion. When the hCG injections were given on day 2–3 of the luteal phase, no relaxin secretion was detectable. In studies in which hCG was used to induce ovulation after human menopausal gonadotropin was given to mature a follicle, relaxin was not detected in the luteal phase (54). However, if these women conceived during the treatment cycle, then relaxin was detected at the time of the missed menses. This is presumably due to endogenous luteal stimulation from the blastocyst. Since hCG stimulus was given in all these experiments but the response was variable, it appears that appropriate ovarian conditions are necessary for relaxin secretion. Constant doses of hCG were not capable of maintaining relaxin secretion in the nonpregnant state for more than two weeks (31).

Goldsmith et al (11) stimulated relaxin secretion in vitro using long-term monolayer cultures of luteal cells from nonpregnant rats. In this sytem, while progesterone secretion was stimulated by, in order of increasing effectiveness, estradiol, epinephrine, hCG, human placental lactogen (hPL), or dibutyrl cAMP, none of these agents stimulated relaxin secretions. However, when luteal cells were incubated with a combination of progesterone, hCG, and either bPRL or hPL, relaxin was detectable in the media from day 6 through day 16 of culture. Relaxin secretion has not been induced from human luteal cells of the menstrual cycle in vitro (19).

RELAXIN AND PREGNANCY

In the rat, circulating relaxin is a hormone of the second half of pregnancy. It is first detected in sera on day 10, its levels rise rapidly, and it is then present in serum in constant concentration until a prelabor surge occurs. Levels fall rapidly in the postpartum period (41). Pituitary LH may be involved in the production of the prelabor surge of serum relaxin concentration (12). Goldsmith et al have shown that a placental luteotropin is necessary for the maintenance of relaxin secretion in day 16 pregnant rats (10). One candidate for this luteotropic effect is placental testosterone, which is effectively aromatized to estradiol by the corpus luteum. Testosterone and estradiol, but not dihydrotestosterone, a nonaromatizable androgen, are capable of attenuating the fall of relaxin in day 15 pregnant, hysterectomized rats (8).

In sows, serum relaxin levels rise on about day 110. Approximately one day before delivery there is a marked surge of relaxin (42). This is associated with luteolysis and the release of storage granule contents from the corpus luteum. Prostaglandin F2α is apparently responsible for this event (23).

In the human female, relaxin is detectable in serum by postconception day 14 (34). Relaxin concentrations in both sera and corpora lutea are highest in the first trimester of pregnancy. By the end of the first trimester, serum levels have fallen by approximately 20%. Concentrations then remain stable throughout pregnancy (48). There appears to be no diurnal variation in serum relaxin concentrations. There is no prelabor elevation in relaxin secretion in women (32).

Since circulating relaxin appears to be luteal in origin in women, relaxin can be used as a luteal marker to allow study of the effects of various agents on the corpus luteum.

After delivery, circulating relaxin levels fall gradually to below assay detectability in approximately three days. There is no signficant difference in the serum relaxin pattern in nursing and nonnursing women, suggesting that the prolactin levels seen in nursing postpartum women are not luteotropic Administration of hCG prolongs the puerperal secretion of relaxin (49). Relaxin is undetectable in human cord blood at term. This finding is consistent with relaxin's role as a modulator of the maternal reproductive system in pregnancy.

ACTIONS OF RELAXIN IN PREGNANCY

One may generalize that the actions of relaxin involve changing the reproductive tract to accomodate pregnancy and facilitate delivery. The exact actions of relaxin in a given species as well as the mechanisms of action are not yet well worked out.

Relaxin Effect on the Interpubic Ligament

Relaxin was discovered because of its action on the public symphysis. The mechanism of this action is unknown, however. Estrogen, which is necessary for this effect, causes a loss of proteoglycans. Relaxin produces a breakdown of fibrous material and ground substance. Collagen fibers are dissociated, but total collagen is increased. The changes noted seem to be changes in aggregation of collagen. Also, growth hormone is necessary for the effects of relaxin and estrogen on interpublic ligament formation in mice (40). Relaxin increases the amount of cAMP in the public symphysis (4).

Relaxin Effect on the Uterus

Relaxin causes an increase in uterine weight, glycogen content, water content, and nitrogen content (53). Relaxin increases the collagen framework of the uterus in ovariectomized rats, with the greatest effect noted in the prescence of estradiol and progesterone. Uterine distensibility is also increased. Since collagen is not distensible, this latter finding suggests that elastin is also increased. The effect of relaxin on the endometrium has been summarized in an earlier report (40, pp. 163–68).

Effect of Relaxin on the Myometrium

Since the initial observation 30 years ago of in vitro inhibition of rat uterine contractions by relaxin (38), inhibition of uterine activity has been noted in guinea pigs, sheep, and hamsters. Human relaxin decreases the amplitude of spontaneous human myometrial contractions in vitro (47). Progesterone, which alone has little effect on this system, synergizes with relaxin in this action. Doses of relaxin and progesterone, which are ineffective independently, together inhibit myometrial contraction amplitude (1). Since relaxin and progesterone are both luteal products, and the corpus luteum is necessary for the maintenance of early pregnancy, it is likely that these hormones act in concert physiologically in the maintenance of human pregnancy. In fact, the secretion pattern of relaxin, its human myometrial action, and the necessity of the corpus luteum in the maintenance of early human pregnancy suggest that the major actions of relaxin in women occur in the beginning of pregnancy.

Progesterone synergizes with relaxin in the inhibition of amplitude of contractions of electrically driven rat uterine segments, when it is given in vitro, with 45 minutes needed for the effect to be observed (36), or when given in vivo.

Relaxin may improve myometrial coordination (5). Porter has shown that during relaxin inhibition of spontaneous myometrial activity, the uterus is still responsive to oxytocin (30). Relaxin inhibits the stimulatory effect of Pg F2α on the rat uterus but has no effect on oxytocin-stimulated activity, suggesting that oxytocin and relaxin affect the uterus through different mechanisms. Relaxin inhibits basal and oxytocin-stimulated prostacyclin release from myometrium of pregnant rats. Relaxin does not inhibit prostacyclin release after incubation with arachidonic acid, suggesting that relaxin inhibits phospholipase A2 (55).

Relaxin elevates rat uterine cAMP, but this has not been related to its myometrial inhibitory properties (35). A mechanism of action of relaxin on rat myometrial activity has been suggested by Nishikori et al (25). They showed that myosin light-chain kinase activity, myosin light-chain phosphorylation, and calcium activated ATPase activity were decreased by relaxin.

Effect of Relaxin on the Cervix

The effect of relaxin on the uterine cervix has been recently reviewed (44). Relaxin seems to be responsible for cervical softening in several subprimate species, including rat and pigs. Relaxin stimulates cervical fibroblasts to release proteases whose actions allow collagen fibers to move freely. Relaxin also changes the cervical proteoglycans. There appears to be an interaction between relaxin and prostaglandin in this effect.

Porcine relaxin, in late-pregnancy luteectomized pigs, induced premature cervical dilatation, decreased the time from the surgery to delivery, and reduced the duration of the delivery time (19).

MacLennan et al (22) have demonstrated that porcine relaxin can cause cervical ripening in pregnant women at term. This suggests an exciting pharmacological use for human relaxin when it becomes available. There is as yet no evidence, however, that relaxin is physiologically involved in human cervical ripening.

Other Effects of Relaxin

Several reports suggest effects of relaxin on vaginal cornification in rats and mice and vaginal opening in guinea pigs (40).

The mammary gland is a target organ for relaxin (40). Relaxin has been reported to reduce milk yield and decrease mammary RNA in lactating rats (14). Relaxin lengthens the mammary gland ducts in rats and causes growth of ducts and alveola in synergy with other mammotropic substances (15). Segaloff (3) has shown that relaxin stimulates the growth of mammary gland malignancies in vitro in rats.

Olefsky showed that relaxin increases the binding of insulin to its receptor and increases glucose uptake in adipocytes from mature female rats (28). This suggests a role for relaxin in making cells more sensitive to the biological effects of insulin, possibly countering the diabetogenic effects of pregnancy.

RELAXIN IN THE MALE

While relaxin has not been detected in male serum from any species, it is found in rooster and boar testes, and armadillo prostate gland.

Loumaye et al (21) demonstrated relaxin immunoactivity in human seminal plasma with concentrations 1–2 orders of magnitude higher than contained in pregnancy serum. We have found relaxin immunoactivity in semen plasma of baboons, monkeys, rats, bulls, and boars. Essig and associates have characterized human semen plasma immunoactive relaxin as being bioactive (7). The likely source of seminal relaxin is the prostate gland, since semen samples that exclude testicular and seminal vesicle components still have undiminished relaxin concentrations. Relaxin affects sperm motility and attenuates the loss of activity seen over time in washed human sperm (6). Preliminary data suggest that relaxin augments the penetration of sperm into cervical mucus. Sarosi et al (37) have shown that relaxin antiserum promptly immobilizes human sperm. This action can be blocked by pretreatment with excess relaxin. These data suggest that relaxin may play an important role in sperm motility and penetration of sperm into the female reproductive tract. Relaxin, an exocrine male secretion, and an endocrine female hormone may thus facilitate fertility.

SUMMARY

The past decade has seen major advances in understanding the chemistry of relaxin. Sensitive radioimmunoassays have allowed description of the secretion patterns of relaxin in several species. It is likely that technical advances in the near future will provide significant quantities of human relaxin as well as monoclonal antibodies to various relaxins. These tools should clarify the physiological roles of relaxin, elucidate its mechanisms of action, and enable testing of human relaxin as a potentially useful pharmacological agent.

Literature Cited

1. Beck, P., Adler, P., Szlachter N., Goldsmith, L. T., Steinetz, B. G., Weiss, G. 1982. Synergistic effect of human relaxin and progesterone on human myometrial contractions. *Int. J. Gynecol. Obstet.* 20:141–44
2. Bedarker, S., Blundell, T., Gowan, L., K., McDonald, J. K., Schwabe, C. 1982. On the three-dimensional structure of relaxin. *Ann. NY Acad. Sci.* 380:22–33
3. Bigazzi, M., Greenwood, F. C. 1983. Biology of relaxin and its role in the human. *Proc. 1st Conf. Human Relaxin.* Excerpta Medica. In press
4. Braddon, S. A. 1978. Relaxin-dependent adenosine 3',5'-monophosphate concentration changes in the mouse pubic symphysis. *Endocrinology* 102:1292–99
5. Downing, S. J., Bradshaw, J. M. C., Porter, D. G. 1980. Relaxin improves the coordination of rat myometrial activity *in vivo. Biol. Reprod.* 23:899–903
6. Essig, M., Schoenfeld, C., Amelar, R. D., Dubin, L., Weiss, G. 1982. Stimulation of human sperm motility by relaxin. *Fertil. Steril.* 38:339–43
7. Essig, M., Schoenfeld, C., D'Eletto, R., Amelar, R., Dubin, L., Steinetz, B. G., O'Byrne, E. M., Weiss, G. 1982.

Relaxin in human seminal plasma. *Ann. NY Acad. Sci.* 380:224–30

8. Goldsmith, L. T., de la Cruz, J. L., Weiss, G., Castracane, V. D. 1982. Steroid effects on relaxin secretion in the rat. *Biol. Reprod.* 27:886–90

9. Goldsmith, L. T., Essig, M., Sarosi, P., Beck, P., Weiss, G. 1981. Hormone secretion by monolayer cultures of human luteal cells. *J. Clin. Endocrinol. Metab.* 53:90–92

10. Goldsmith, L. T., Grob, H. S., Scherer, K. J., Surve, A., Steinetz, B. G., Weiss, G. 1981. Placental control of ovarian immunoreactive relaxin secretion in the pregnant rat. *Endocrinol.* 109:548–52

11. Goldsmith, L. T., Grob, H. S., Weiss, G. 1982. *In vitro* induction of relaxin secretion in corpora lutea from nonpregnant rats. *Ann. NY Acad. Sci.* 380:60–74

12. Gordon, W. L., Sherwood, O. D. 1982. Evidence that luteinizing hormone from the maternal pituitary gland may promote antepartum release of relaxin, luteolysis and birth in rats. *Endocrinology* 111:1299–1310

13. Green, R., Weiss, G., Goldsmith, L. T., Shields, D. 1983. Human preprorelaxins in *in vitro* translation of mRNA from corpus luteum and other reproductive tissues. See Ref. 3. In press

14. Harness, J., Anderson, R. 1975. Effect of relaxin in mammary gland growth and lactation in the rat. *Proc. Soc. Exp. Biol. Med.* 148:933–36

15. Harness, J., Anderson, R., 1977. Effect of relaxin and somatotropin in combination with ovarian steroids on mammary glands in rats. *Biol. Reprod.* 17:599–603

16. Hisaw, F. L. 1926. Experimental relaxation of the pubic ligament of the guinea pig. *Proc. Soc. Exp. Biol. Med.* 23:661–63

17. Hudson, P., Haley, J., John, M., Cronk, M., Crawford, R., Haralanbidis, J., Tregear, G., Shine, J., Niall, H. 1983. Structure of a genomic clone encoding biologically active human relaxin. *Nature* 301:628–31

18. James, R., Niall, H., Kwok, S., Bryant-Greenwood, G. 1977. Primary structure of porcine relaxin: homology with insulin and related growth factors. *Nature* 267:544–46

19. Kertiles, L. P., Anderson, L. L. 1979. Effect of relaxin on cervical dilatation, parturition and lactation in the pig. *Biol. Reprod.* 21:57–68

20. Loeken, M. R., Channing, C. P., D'Eletto, R., Weiss, G. 1983. Stimulatory effect of luteinizing hormone upon relax-in secretion by cultured porcine preovulatory granulosa cells. *Endocrinology* 112:769–71

21. Loumaye, E., De Cooman, S., Thomas, K. 1980. Immunoreactive relaxin-like substance in human seminal plasma. *J. Clin. Endocrinol. Metab.* 50:1142–43

22. Mac Lennan, A. H., Green, R. C., Bryant-Greenwood, G. C., Greenwood, F. C., Seamark, R. F. 1980. Ripening of the human cervix and induction of labor with purified porcine relaxin. *Lancet* 1:220–23

23. Nara, B. S., Ball, G. D., Rutherford, J. E., Sherwood, O. D., First, N. L. 1982. Release of relaxin by a nonluteolytic dose of prostaglandin F2α in pregnant swine. *Biol. Reprod.* 27:1190–95

24. Niall, H., Hudson, P., Haley, J., Cronk, M., Shine, J. 1982. Rat preprorelaxin: complete amino acid sequence derived from cDNA analysis. *Ann. NY Acad. Sci.* 380:13–21

25. Nishikori, K., Weisbrodt, N. W., Sherwood, O. D., Sanborn, B. M. 1982. Relaxin alters rat uterine myosin light chain phosphorylation and related enzymatic activities. *Endocrinology* 111:1743–45

26. O'Byrne, E. M., Flitcraft, J. F., Sawyer, W. I., Hochman, J., Weiss, G., Steinetz, B. G. 1978. Relaxin bioactivity and immunoactivity in the human corpus luteum. *Endocrinology* 102:1641–44

27. O'Byrne, E. M., Steinetz, B. G. 1976. RIA of relaxin in sera of various species using an antiserum to porcine relaxin. *Proc. Soc. Exp. Biol. Med.* 152:272–76

28. Olefsky, J. M., Saekow, M., Kroc, R. L. 1982. Potentiation of insulin binding and insulin action by purified porcine relaxin. *Ann. NY Acad. Sci.* 380:200–16

29. Pardo, R., Larkin, L. H., Fields, P. A. 1980. Immunocytochemical localization of relaxin in endometrial glands of the pregnant guinea pig. *Endocrinology* 107:2110–12

30. Porter, D. G., Downing, S. J. Bradshaw, J. M. C. 1979. Relaxin inhibits spontaneous and prostaglandin-driven myometrial activity in anesthetized rats. *J. Endocrinol.* 83:183–92

31. Quagliarello, J., Goldsmith, L., Steinetz, B., Lustig, D. S., Weiss, G. 1980. Induction of relaxin secretion in non-pregnant women by human chorionic gonadotropin. *J. Clin. Endocrinol. Metab.* 51:74–77

32. Quagliarello, J., Lustig, D. S., Steinetz, B. G., Weiss, G. 1980. Absence of a pre-labor relaxin surge in women. *Biol. Reprod.* 22:202–4

33. Quagliarello, J., Nachtigall, R., Goldsmith, L. T., Hochman, J., Steinetz,

B. G., O'Bryne, E. M., Weiss, G. 1979. Serum immuno-reactive relaxin concentrations in human pregnancy, labor and the puerperium. In *Ovarian Follicular and Corpus Luteum Function,* ed. C. P. Channing, J. M. Marsh, W. A. Sadler, pp. 743–74. New York: Plenum

34. Quagliarello, J., Steinetz, B. G., Weiss, G. 1979. Relaxin secretion in early pregnancy. *Obstet. Gynecol.* 53:62–63

35. Sanborn, B. M., Kuo, H. S., Weisbrodt, N. W., Sherwood, O. D. 1980. The interaction of relaxin with the rat uterus. I. Effect on cyclic nucleotide levels and spontaneous contractile activity. *Endocrinology* 106:1210–15

36. Sarosi, P., Schmidt, C. L., Essig, M., Steinetz, B. G., Weiss, G. 1983. The effect of relaxin and progesterone on rat uterine contractions. *Am. J. Obstet. Gynecol.* 145:402–05

37. Sarosi, P., Schoenfeld, C., Berman, J., Basch, R., Randolph, G., Amelar, R., Dubin, L., Steinetz, B. G., Weiss, G. 1983. Effect of anti-relaxin antiserum on sperm motility *in vitro. Endocrinology* 112:1860–61

38. Sawyer, W. H., Frieden, E. H. Martin, A. C. 1953. *In vitro* inhibition of spontaneous contractions of the rat uterus by relaxin containing extracts of sow ovaries. *Am. J. Physiol.* 172:547–52

39. Schwabe, C., McDonald, J. K., Steinetz, B. G. 1977. Primary structure of the B-chain of porcine relaxin. *Biochem. Biophys. Res. Commun.* 75: 503–10

40. Schwabe, C., Steinetz, B. G., Weiss, G., Segaloff, A., McDonald, J. K., O'Byrne, E., Hochman, J., Carriere, B., Goldsmith, L. 1978. Relaxin. *Recent Prog. Horm. Res.* 34:123–211

41. Sherwood, O. D., Crnekovic, V. E., Gordon, W. L., Rutherford, J. E. 1980. Radioimmunoassay of relaxin throughout pregnancy and during parturition in the rat. *Endocrinology* 107:691–98

42. Sherwood, O. D., Nara, B.S., Welk, F. A., First, N. L., Rutherford, J. E. 1981. Relaxin levels in the maternal plasma of pigs before, during, and after parturition, and before, during, and after suckling. *Biol. Reprod.* 25:65–71

43. Sherwood, O. D., Rosentreter, K. R., Birkhimer, M. L. 1975. Development of a radioimmunoassay for porcine relaxin using ^{125}I labeled polytyrosyl-relaxin. *Endocrinology* 96:1106–13

44. Steinetz, B. G., O'Byrne, E. M., Kroc, R. L. 1980. The role of relaxin in cervical softening during pregnancy in mammals. In *Dilatation of the Uterine Cervix,* ed. F. Naftolin, P. G. Stubblefield, pp. 157–77. New York: Raven

45. Steinetz, B. G., O'Byrne, E. M., Weiss, G., Schwabe, C. 1982. Bioassay methods for relaxin: uses and pitfalls. In *Relaxin, Proc. 15th Midwest Conf. Endocrinol. Metabol.* pp. 79–113. New York: Plenum

46. Stewart, D. R., Stabenfeldt, G. H., Hughes, J. P., Meagher, D. M. 1982. Determination of the source of equine relaxin. *Biol. Reprod.* 27:17–24

47. Szlachter, N., O'Byrne, E. M., Goldsmith, L., Steinetz, B. G., Weiss, G. 1980. Myometrial-inhibiting activity of relaxin containing extracts of human corpora lutea of pregnancy. *Am. J. Obstet. Gynecol.* 136:584–86

48. Szlachter, B. N., Quagliarello, J., Jewelewicz, R., Osathanondh, R., Spellacy, W. N., Weiss, G. 1982. Relaxin in normal and pathogenic pregnancies. *Obstet. Gynecol.* 59:167–70

49. Thomas, K. 1982. Release of relaxin. *Ann. NY Acad. Sci.* 380:219–22

50. Thomas, K., Loumaye, E., Donnez, J. 1982. Immunoreactive relaxin in the peritoneal fluid during spontaneous menstrual cycle in women. *Ann. NY Acad. Sci.* 380:126–30

51. Thomas, K., Loumaye, E., Ferin, J. 1980. Relaxin in non-pregnant women during ovarian stimulation. *Gynecol. Obstet. Invest.* 11:75–80

52. Too, C. K. L., Weiss, T. J., Bryant-Greenwood, G. D. 1982. Relaxin stimulates plasminogen activator secretion by rat granulosa cells *in vitro. Endocrinology* 111:1424–26

53. Vasilenko, P., Adams, W. C., Frieden, E. H. 1981. Uterine size and glycogen content in cycling and pregnant rats: influence of relaxin. *Biol. Reprod.* 25: 162–69

54. Weiss, G., Goldsmith, L. T., 1981. Dissociation of luteal progesterone and relaxin secretion: Modulation by ovarian factors. *Bioregulators of Reproduction,* ed. Jagiello & Vogel, pp. 403–7. New York: Academic

55. Williams., K. I., El Tahir, K. E. H. 1982. Relaxin inhibits prostacyclin release by the rat pregnant myometrium prostaglandins. *Biol. Reprod.* 24:129–36

Ann. Rev. Physiol. 1984. 46:53–65

MECHANISM OF ACTION OF MULLERIAN INHIBITING SUBSTANCE

Patricia K. Donahoe, John M. Hutson, Mary E. Fallat, Shoirchiro Kamagata, and Gerald P. Budzik

Pediatric Surgical Research Laboratories, Division of Pediatric Surgery, Department of Surgery, Massachusetts General Hospital and Harvard Medical School, Boston, Massachusetts 02114

INTRODUCTION

Recent studies have begun to elucidate the mechanism of action of Mullerian Inhibiting Substance (MIS). These have paralleled attempts both to purify MIS (5, 5a, 11, 14, 24, 39, 43) and to develop a monoclonal antibody (36, 37, 48) to the glycoprotein, a testicular substance which Jost first proposed (25–27) was responsible for regression of the Mullerian duct in the male mammalian embryo.

Two lines of investigation into the mechanism of action of MIS have been pursued in this laboratory. One has focused on the long-term morphologic changes in the epithelial–basement membrane–mesenchymal complex and their extracellular constituents (16, 40, 41, 46; Schwartz et al, Ref. 42a). The other had dealt with more short-term divalent cation–dependent phosphorylation changes. Both are probably part of a cascade of biochemical and morphological events that are important to Mullerian duct regression. It is the latter, MIS-induced membrane phosphorylation events, however, that will be the subject of this review.

ANALYSIS OF PHOSPHORYLATION EVENTS

Serendipity guided our initial analysis of phosphorylation during Mullerian duct regression. Semi-purified fractions with MIS biological activity, as detected by a semi-quantitative organ culture assay (13), were stabilized with

53

0066-4278/84/0315-0053$02.00

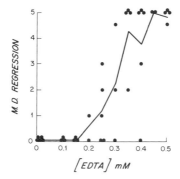

Figure 1 Regression of the Mullerian duct in vitro with increasing concentrations of EDTA, graded on a semiquantitative scale from 0 to 5. The line represents the mean of the individual assay results at each dose tested [Reproduced with permission from Budzik et al (4).]

EDTA, although the chelating agent itself was dialyzed out and the larger molecular weight moieties preserved for assay in the retentate. The organ culture assay, although meticulous and somewhat insensitive, is noted for its specificity, with very few substances causing false-positive regression of the Mullerian duct. Therefore, when we subsequently noted that EDTA alone caused Mullerian duct regression, we felt intuitively that some clues were being provided regarding the mechanism of action of MIS (Figure 1).

We attempted to block the action of EDTA (4) with a number of divalent cations, succeeding with Zn^{2+}, which also singularly inhibited MIS-induced regression (Figure 2). The analogy of these events to those involved with a membrane-associated, phosphotyrosyl-protein phosphatase, which cleaves phosphotyrosine bonds previously formed by an EGF-stimulated protein kinase

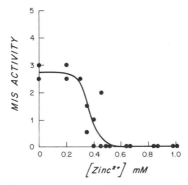

Figure 2 Effect of increasing concentrations of Zn^{2+} on Mullerian duct regression induced by semipurified MIS (wheat germ lectin–fraction 2). This MIS preparation has a biological activity of 2–3+ regression, and a protein concentration of 0.25 mg ml^{-1} (= 1000-fold purification) [Reproduced with permission from Budzik et al (4).]

(3), was intriguing. This phosphatase uniquely was stimulated by EDTA as well as fluoride. It was inhibited by zinc, as opposed to other phosphatases such as acid phosphatase and alkaline phosphatase, which are inhibited by EDTA and fluoride. Fluoride was examined for its ability to stimulate Mullerian duct regression (Figure 3), which it did at about twice (1 mM F⁻) the concentration required for EDTA-induced regression (0.5 mM EDTA; Hutson et al, submitted). These findings led to the hypothesis that MIS might act by causing dephosphorylation of membrane proteins, perhaps at tyrosine residues which had been previously phosphorylated by an EGF-stimulated, cAMP-independent protein kinase (6, 47). This view was supported by the finding that sodium vanadate, which is known to inhibit a phosphotyrosyl protein phosphatase (44), progressively inhibited MIS-induced regression (Figure 4).

Factors which stimulate the phosphotyrosyl protein phosphatase (EDTA or F⁻) mimic Mullerian duct regression. The morphologic changes, however, are somewhat different from that observed with MIS, and are characterized by breakdown of the basement membrane and disorientation of the cells within the contained epithelial compartment (Schwartz et al, Ref. 42a). The additional hallmarks of MIS-induced Mullerian duct regression, i.e. condensation of mesenchyme, which forms a cuff around the basement membrane, and migration of epithelial cells into the mesenchyme, are not observed. A disruption of

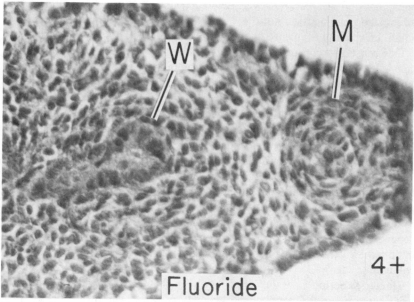

Figure 3   Urogenital ridge of 14 1/2-day-old female fetal rat after 3-day incubation with 1.0 mM sodium fluoride, showing 4+ regression in the absence of MIS. M, Mullerian duct; W, Wolffian duct (X340).

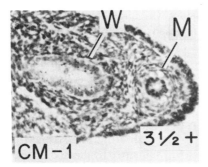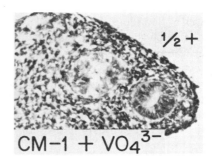

Figure 4 Effect of sodium vanadate on the action of MIS (CM-1: carboxymethyl cellulose–fraction 1). Left panel shows a urogenital ridge (female rat fetus) after 3 days of incubation with CM-1 (3 1/2+ regression). Right panel demonstrates a similar ridge incubated with CM-1 and 50 μM sodium vanadate (1/2+ regression) (X150).

the extracellular scaffolding characterizes the EDTA-F$^-$-induced event, rather than the combination of basement membrane breakdown and cell movement that is observed with MIS. Although circumstantial evidence points to an important role for a phosphotyrosyl protein phosphatase in Mullerian duct regression, it is still not clear whether MIS exerts its effect primarily on the phosphatase. It is clear, however, that regression is inhibited by factors which inhibit the phosphatase, i.e. Zn^{2+} and vanadate, and stimulated by factors which enhance phosphatase activity, i.e. EDTA and F$^-$.

One must also consider the phosphorylation side of the equation, namely, that MIS also might act to inhibit a protein kinase. We investigated this hypothesis by determining if agents that stimulate phosphorylation of tyrosine residues might inhibit Mullerian duct regression. The role of EGF in Mullerian duct regression was investigated, since this growth factor is known to act via a cAMP-independent protein kinase to phosphorylate tyrosine (Hutson et al, submitted). Initially, EGF was added to the organ culture in the presence of MIS, to determine whether by promoting phosphorylation, EGF might inhibit regression caused by MIS. Regression, however, proceeded normally. When repeated in the presence of 1 mM Mn^{2+}, which is known to serve as an obligatory cofactor in EGF-stimulated phosphorylation of tyrosine in human epidermoid (A431) cells, EGF caused suppression of MIS activity in a dose-dependent manner (Figure 5). Neither EGF nor Mn^{2+} alone significantly inhibited MIS induced Mullerian duct regression. Mg^{2+} was ineffective as a cofactor.

Hunter & Sefton's parallel discovery (22), that the transforming protein of Rous sarcoma virus (src) phosphorylates tyrosines of certain membrane proteins, added an element of increased interest to EGF-induced phosphorylation.

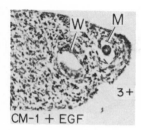
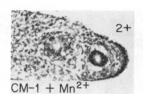
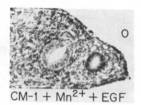

Figure 5 Effect of epidermal growth factor (EGF) and manganese ions on the action of MIS (CM-1). Left panel shows a urogenital ridge (female rat fetus) after 3 days of incubation with CM-1 and 1 μg ml⁻¹ EGF (3+ regression). Middle panel shows a similar ridge incubated with CM-1 and 1.0 mM MnCl² (2+ regression). Right panel shows a ridge incubated with CM-1, MnCl² 1.0 mM together with 1 μg ml EGF (0 regression) (X145).

Subsequently, many different mRNA tumor viruses such as Abelson murine leukemia virus (49), Fujinama sarcoma virus (20), PRC II virus (38), Snyder-Theilin feline sarcoma virus (1), and Y73 virus (29) have been found to produce transforming proteins that phosphorylate tyrosine (34). In addition to EGF, Kasuga et al (28) have reported that when insulin binds to its receptor, the receptor in turn phosphorylates tyrosine. Similar findings have been reported by Ek & Heldin (17) regarding platelet-derived growth factor (PDGF); binding of this growth factor to its receptor is followed by phosphorylation of tyrosine.

Thus tumor viruses, which cause undisciplined growth, and growth factors, which stimulate controlled growth, both phosphorylate tyrosines (30). The EGF protein kinase has been found to be both structurally and antigenically related to the Rous sarcoma virus transforming proteins (7, 8). The fact that both EGF and viral transforming proteins phosphorylate tyrosine, which represents only a small percentage of the membrane phosphorylation events when compared to serine and threonine, indicates that the unique phosphorylation of tyrosine may play an important role in influencing growth regulatory signals.

DEPHOSPHORYLATION HYPOTHESIS

We have constructed a hypothesis, based on indirect evidence, that the fetal regressor, MIS, antagonizes growth-promoting or transforming substances either by dephosphorylating or by preventing phosphorylation of proteins (Figure 6). To prove this hypothesis we studied another aspect of the "substrate" side of the equation, reasoning that an extracellular nucleotide might serve either as a substrate for a membrane-bound protein kinase or as a competitive inhibitor of dephosphorylation. A wide variety of nucleotides were tested in the MIS bioassay by incubating them with MIS and observing changes in Mullerian duct regression from that caused by MIS alone. Many nucleotides were found to cause either complete or partial inhibition of Mullerian duct

Table 1 Nucleotides and analogues that affect the biological activity of Mullerian Inhibiting Substance.

Complete inhibition of MIS with Mn^{2+} (1 mM)	Partial inhibition of MIS with MN^{2+} (1 mM)
ATP	UTP
GTP	CTP
AMP	GMP
AMP–PNP	ADP
AMP–CPP	NADP
AMP–PSP	cAMP
NAD	UDP–N.Ac.Glc.–NH^2
	UDP–Gal.
	GDP–Mann.
	GDP–Glc.
	adenosine
	p–NO^2–0–PO^4

regression but each, as with EGF, was manganese-dependent (Hutson et al, submitted) (Table 1).

The polar nature of these nucleotides suggested that they would remain in the extracellular compartment, and that the inhibition of regression might be an extracellular event (10, 32). How then might this diverse group of extracellular nucleotides be involved in altering the level of membrane phosphorylation? The duct cells may contain an "exokinase" which can use ATP (or GTP)

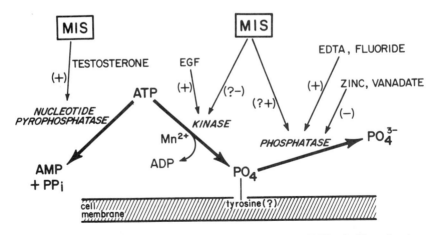

Figure 6 Current working hypothesis for the mechanism of action of MIS as it affects phosphorylation of membrane proteins (? on tyrosine residues) in the cells of the Mullerian duct. MIS (on the right) may act to either stimulate a phosphatase or inhibit a kinase and thus result in diminished phosphorylation. Conceivably MIS may act to deplete the extracellular nucleotide pool by stimulating nucleotide pyrophosphatase (as on the left).

translocated from the cytosol (Hutson et al, submitted; see also 10, 32, 45), or exogenously added, as provided in these in vitro studies. Extracellular nucleotides may be needed to maintain a basal level of phosphorylation in order to preserve Mullerian duct integrity. Growth factors such as EGF or insulin may be required to initiate early Mullerian duct growth and development.

There are a variety of hydrolytic enzymes known to act at the extracellular level, presumably to prevent excessive extracellular accumulation of triphosphates that might have deleterious effects on cell physiology (Hutson et al, submitted). These hydrolytic enzymes include membrane-bound protein kinase (32, 35), phosphoprotein phosphatase (33), and nucleotide pyrophosphatase (2, 18–19, 31). Only the membrane-bound enzyme nucleotide pyrophosphatase (NPPase), however, has a sufficiently broad hydrolytic activity to accept all of the nucleotide species which inhibit MIS-initiated duct regression (19a).

We attempted to demonstrate histochemical localization of this enzyme, assuming that if extracellular nucleotides were important in Mullerian duct maintenance, NPPase might be found in or around the regressing duct. NPPase, a membrane-bound phosphodiesterase with dual specificity toward nucleotide pyrophosphate and phosphodiester bonds, is a sialic acid–containing glycoprotein located on the external plasma membrane and in the endoplasmic reticulum of hepatocytes. The enzyme causes rapid degradation of many sugar nucleotides and trinucleotides to their respective nucleoside-5'-monophosphates and pyrophosphate (2, 18, 19). NPPase activity is recognized by a-naphthyl-thymidine-5'-monophosphate (naphthyl-TMP) hydrolysis (9). NPPase hydrolyzes the substrate naphthyl-TMP, causing release of naphthol, which then reacts with the diazonium salt, Fast Red TR, resulting in color formation and thus localization at the enzyme site. Urogenital ridges from 14- to 17-day male and female rat embryos were studied, as were cultured ridges of 14-day females incubated with MIS for 72 hours. NPPase activity was present in the fetal urogenital ridge and specifically was enhanced in and around the regressing Mullerian duct of the male, while it was absent in the female Mullerian duct (Figure 7; 19a). Nucleotide hydrolysis was detected over regressing Mullerian ducts in vitro only if they were incubated in the presence of both a semipurified fraction of MIS and testosterone. In this case, cell-surface NPPase may be necessary for the rapid turnover of extracellular nucleotide pools in the way that cAMP phosphodiesterase carefully modulates the concentration of this important regulatory nucleotide inside the cell.

Thus a model (Figure 6) for the mechanism of action of MIS may be proposed, the central theme of which is that MIS may function to diminish the level of phosphorylation of membrane protein, a basal level of which may be required for continued growth of the Mullerian duct. MIS may act in one of several ways to selectively diminish this phosphorylation of membrane protein. For example, it may activate or act as an exophosphatase (EDTA effect), it may

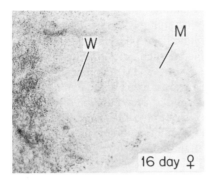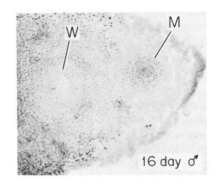

Figure 7   In vivo histochemical localization of NPPase in the urogenital ridge of 16 1/2-day-old male and female fetal rats. Left panel shows little NPPase activity around the female Mullerian duct. The intense staining to the left of the Wolffian duct does not vary with MIS modulation. The right panel shows intense NPPase activity around the partially regressed male Mullerian duct. (M, Mullerian duct; W, Wolffian duct; X183).

inhibit an exokinase (inhibit EGF), or it may activate or act as a pyrophosphatase (remove ATP as substrate for exokinase).

In order to more directly test the effect of MIS on the level of phosphorylation in the Mullerian duct (Hutson et al, submitted), fetal rat agonadal urogenital ridges were incubated with ^{32}P-ATP, Mn^{2+}, and EGF, with or without a highly purified MIS fraction prepared after dye-ligand affinity chromatography (5a). After labeling, the ridges were solubolized in SDS, and the ^{32}P-proteins were separated by gel electrophoresis and autoradiographed.

^{32}P-labeling of the agonadal urogenital ridge in the presence of MIS yielded a decrease in phosphorylation in a broad band of high molecular weight moieties. The loss of ^{32}P incorporation in the MIS-incubated ridges does not appear to be affected by EGF; however, labeling of the urogenital ridge is enhanced in the presence of EGF. Although the tissue phosphorylation data alone cannot differentiate between a stimulation of dephosphorylation or an inhibition of phosphorylation as the direct effect of MIS, coupled with the indirect organ culture and histochemical data previously described, this evidence suggests that MIS may actually promote dephosphorylation of the heterogeneous urogenital ridge.

We demonstrated that dibutyryl cAMP (DBcAMP) inhibits Mullerian duct regression when incubated in vitro in the presence of exogenous MIS (23). Phosphodiesterase inhibitors have the same inhibitory effect on MIS fractions. Extracellular cAMP caused no inhibition (Figure 8). Since DBcAMP was not divalent-cation dependent, its mechanism of MIS inhibition was different from that caused by the large number of extracellular, Mn^{2+}-dependent nucleotides shown to influence Mullerian duct regression. The interplay between the extracellular cAMP-independent, probable tyrosine phosphorylation event re-

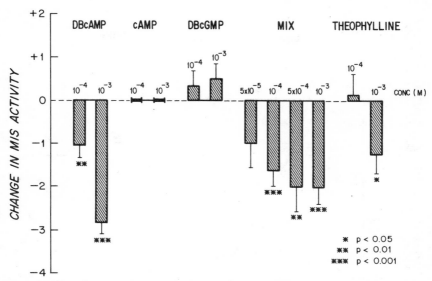

Figure 8   The effect of cyclic nucleotides and phosphodiesterase inhibitors on the action of MIS (CM-1) on the Mullerian duct of a female embryo. Dibutyryl cyclic AMP (DBcAMP) caused significant inhibition of MIS at 0.1 and 1.0 mM, while cyclic AMP and DBcGMP were ineffective. Methyl-isobutyl-xanthine (MIX) and theophylline also caused suppression of MIS activity at the concentrations shown. Each bar represents the mean + SE of at least 4 observations.

quired to inhibit MIS and the intracellular cAMP-dependent serine, threonine phosphorylation event is, as yet, not understood. One could speculate that the phosphorylations may be mutually inhibitory or may cascade to interact upon some final common mechanism that is necessary to maintain Mullerian duct integrity. The results of the diverse experiments presented support the hypothesis that events which prevent or delay phosphorylation or accelerate dephosphorylation may tend to accelerate or permit Mullerian duct regression.

CHEMOTHERAPEUTIC EFFECT RELATED TO DEPHOSPHORYLATION

MIS was studied in our laboratory as a potential chemotherapeutic agent against tumors of Mullerian duct origin. The underlying hypothesis of these studies was that a substance causing regression of an embryonic organ system may cause regression of tumors derived from the homologous adult organs, since tumors share many characteristics of embryonic tissues, often reexpres-

CM-1
(Biologically Active)

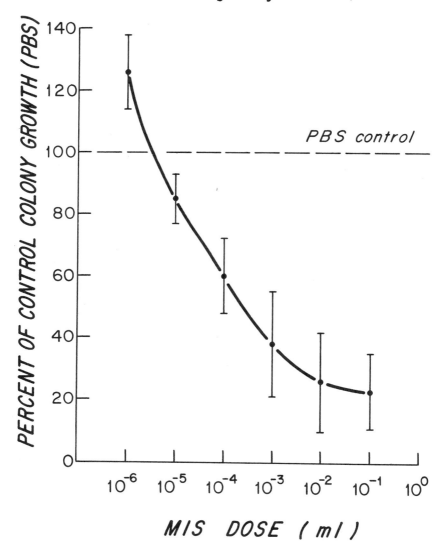

Figure 9   Colony inhibition by MIS (CM-1) was expressed as a percentage of colony growth of control cultures treated with phosphate buffered saline (PBS). The vertical lines indicate the SD at each dose. Colony growth at doses of 10^{-1} to 10^{-4} ml were significantly different from that observed in PBS controls. [Reproduced with permission from Fuller et al (21).]

sing fetal antigens, receptors or hormones. Encouraging preliminary studies with HeLa, demonstrating monolayer cytotoxicity (unpublished data), led to further investigations, but fear of this ubiquitous cell line prompted choice of another Mullerian tumor. We instead elected to test MIS against human ovarian carcinoma, since this epithelial carcinoma originates from the coelomic epithelium that invaginates in the embryo to form the Mullerian duct (12). Practicality also directed our choice of this tumor, since it was the most available Mullerian-like tumor in tissue culture when we began our antitumor studies early in 1975, and it grew well in a microtitre system using small Terasaki plates, thereby allowing the miniscule amounts of available semipurified material to be tested in a reproducible in vitro system. MIS was shown to delay or inhibit growth of the HOC-21 ovarian carcinoma line in monolayer (15). As more purified material became available, we demonstrated (Figure 9) that MIS was effective against the HOC-21 line in colony inhibition (21), using soft agar technique (42). This same cell line (12), as well as an endometrial carcinoma cell line (Fuller & Donahoe, Reference 21a), were heterotransplanted into nude mice. Preincubation of the tumor cells with purified fractions with MIS activity resulted in a prolonged tumor-free interval that compared well to that produced by adriamycin, cis-platinin or hexamethamelamine.

Growth factors like EGF, insulin, and PDGF initiate, after receptor binding, phosphorylation of membrane tyrosyl proteins, while many RNA tumor viruses code for proteins responsible for transformation. One of these transforming proteins, Rous sarcoma virus protein, which produces uncontrolled growth, is antigenically similar to an EGF stimulated protein kinase (7, 8) and also phosphorylates tyrosine. It seems tempting to classify MIS, which dephosphorylates urogenital ridge proteins and inhibits Mullerian-derived tumors, into a special category of "anti-transforming" agents that may act by reversing transformation, at least as measured by the function of protein phosphorylation or dephosphorylation. Whether the concept of an "antitransforming" agent can be translated into effective, specific cancer chemotherapy remains to be determined. However, it seems reasonable to speculate that if membrane phosphorylation is important in transformation, dephosphorylation or inhibition of phosphorylation may be important to prevent or reverse transformation.

ACKNOWLEDGMENT

This work was supported in part by National Institutes of Health/National Cancer Institute CA17393; American Cancer Society PDT-221; National Health and Medical Research Council (Australia) Fellowship in Applied Health Sciences (JMH); American Cancer Society Junior Faculty Award (MEF); Charles A. King Trust Fellowship (GPB).

Literature Cited

1. Barbacid, M., Beemon, K., Devare, S. G. 1980. Origin and functional properties of the major gene product of the Snyder-Theilin strain of feline sarcoma virus. *Proc. Natl. Acad. Sci. USA* 77:5158–62
2. Bischoff, E., Tran-Thi, T. A., Decker, K. F. A. 1975. Nucleotide pyrophosphatase of rat liver. *Eur. J. Biochem.* 51:353–61
3. Brautigan, D. L., Bornstein, P., Gollis, B. 1981. Phosphotyrosyl-protein phosphatase. Specific inhibition by Zn^{2+}. *J. Biol. Chem.* 256:6519–22
4. Budzik, G. P., Hutson, J. M., Ikawa, H., Donahoe, P. K. 1982. The role of zinc in Mullerian duct regression. *Endocrinology* 110:1521–25
5. Budzik, G. P., Swann, D. A., Hayashi, A., Donahoe, P. K. 1980. Enhanced purification of Mullerian inhibiting substance by lectin affinity chromatography. *Cell* 21:909–15
5a. Budzik, G. P., Powell, S. M., Kamagata, S., Donahoe, P. K. 1983. Mullerian inhibiting substance fractionation by dye affinity chromatography. *Cell.* 34:307–14
6. Carpenter, G., King, L. Jr., Cohen, S. 1979. Rapid enhancement of protein phosphorylation in A-431 cell membrane preparations by epidermal growth factor. *J. Biol. Chem.* 254:4884–91
7. Cohen, S., Chinkers, M., Ushiro, H. 1981. EGF-receptor-protein kinase phosphorylates tyrosine and may be related to the transforming kinase of Rous sarcoma virus. *Cold Spring Harbor Conf. Cell Prolif.* 8:801–8
8. Collett, M. S., Erikson, R. L. 1978. Protein kinase activity associated with the avian sarcoma virus src gene product. *Proc. Natl. Acad. Sci. USA* 75:2021–24
9. Decker, K., Bischoff, E. 1972. Purification and properties of nucleotide pyrophosphatase from rat liver. *FEBS Lett.* 21:95–98
10. DePierre, J. W., Karnovsky, M. L. 1973. Plasma membranes of mammalian cells. A review of methods for their characterization and isolation. *J. Cell Biol.* 56:275–303
11. Donahoe, P. K., Budzik, G. P., Trelstad, R., Mudgett-Hunter, M., Fuller, A. Jr. et al 1982. Mullerian inhibiting substance. An update. *Recent Prog. Horm. Res.* 38:279–330
12. Donahoe, P. K., Fuller, A. F. Jr., Scully, R. E., Guy, S. R., Budzik, G. P. 1981. Mullerian inhibiting substance inhibits growth of a human ovarian cancer in nude mice. *Ann. Surg.* 194:472–80
13. Donahoe, P. K., Ito, Y., Hendren, W. H. 1977. A graded organ culture assay for the detection of Mullerian inhibiting substance. *J. Surg. Res.* 23:141–48
14. Donahoe, P. K., Ito, Y., Price, J. M., Hendren, W. H. 1977. Mullerian inhibiting substance activity in bovine fetal, newborn and prepubertal testes. *Biol. Reprod.* 16:238–43
15. Donahoe, P. K., Swann, D. A., Hayashi, A., Sullivan, M. D. 1979. Mullerian duct regression in the embryo correlated with cytotoxic activity against a human ovarian cancer. *Science* 205:913–15
16. Dyche, W. J. 1979. A comparative study of the differentiation and involution of the Mullerian duct and Wolffian duct in the male and female fetal mouse. *J. Morphol.* 163:175–210
17. Ek, B., Heldin, C.-H. 1982. Characterization of a tyrosine-specific kinase activity in human fibroblast membranes stimulated by platelet-derived growth factor. *J. Biol. Chem.* 257:10486–92
18. Evans, W. H. 1974. Nucleotide pyrophosphatase, a sialoglycoprotein located on the hepatocyte surface. *Nature* 250:391–94
19. Evans, W. H., Hood, D. O., Gurd, J. W. 1973. Purification and properties of a mouse liver plasma–membrane glycoprotein hydrolysing nucleotide pyrophosphate and phosphodiester bonds. *Biochem. J.* 135:819–28
19a. Fallat, M. E., Hutson, J. M., Budzik, G. P., Donahoe, P. K. 1983. The role of nucleotide pyrophosphatase in Mullerian duct regression. *Devel. Biol.* In press.
20. Feldman, R. A., Hanafusa, T., Hanafusa, H. 1980. Characterization of protein kinase activity associated with the transforming gene product of Fujinama sarcoma virus. *Cell* 22:757–66
21. Fuller, A. F., Guy, S., Budzik, G. P., Donahoe, P. K. 1982. Mullerian inhibiting substance inhibits colony growth of a human ovarian carcinoma cell line. *J. Clin. Endocrinol. Metab.* 54:1051–55
21a. Fuller, A. R. Jr., Budzik, G. P., Krane, I. M., Donahoe, P. K. 1983. Mullerian Inhibiting Substance inhibition of a human endometrial carcinoma cell line xenografted in nude mice. *Gynecol. Oncol.* In press
22. Hunter, T., Sefton, B. M. 1980. Transforming gene product of Rous sarcoma virus phosphorylates tyrosine. *Proc. Natl. Acad. Sci. USA* 77:1311–15
23. Ikawa, H., Hutson, J. M., Budzik, G. P., Donahoe, P. K. 1983. Cyclic AMP mod-

ulation of Mullerian duct regression. *Endocrinology.* In press.

24. Josso, N., Picard, J. Y., Tran, D. 1977. The anti-Mullerian hormone. *Recent Prog. Horm. Res.* 33:117–67

25. Jost, A. 1946. Sur la differenciation sexuelle de l'embryon de lapin remarques au sujet de certaines operations chirurgical. *C. R. Soc. Biol.* 140:460–62

26. Jost, A. 1946. Sur la differenciation sexuelle de l'embryon de lapin experiences de paraboise. *C. R. Soc. Biol.* 140:463–64

27. Jost, A. 1947. Sur les derives mulleriens d'embryons de lapin des deus sexes castres a 21 jours. *C. R. Soc. Biol.* 141:135–36

28. Kasuga, M., Karlson, F. A., Kahn, C. R. 1982. Insulin stimulates the phosphorylation of the 95,000-dalton subunit of its own receptor. *Science* 215:185–87

29. Kawai, S., Yoshida, M., Segawa, K., Sugiyama, H., Ishizaki, R., et al 1980. Characterization of Y73, an avian sarcoma virus. A unique transforming gene and its product, a phosphopolyprotein with protein kinase activity. *Proc. Natl. Acad. Sci. USA* 77:6199–203

30. Kolata, G. 1983. Is tyrosine the key to growth control? *Science* 219:377–78

31. Kubler, D., Pyerin, W., Kinzel, V. 1980. Generation of pyrophosphatase from extracellular ATP at the surface of HeLa cells. *J. Cell Biol.* 21:231–33

32. Kubler, D., Pyerin, W., Kinzel, V. 1982. Protein kinase activity and substrates at the surface of intact HeLa cells. *J. Biol. Chem.* 257:322–29

33. Makan, N. R. 1979. Phosphoprotein phosphatase activity at the outer surface of intact normal and transformed 3T3 fibroblasts. *Biochim. Biophys. Acta* 585:360–73

34. Marx, J. L. 1981. Tumor viruses and the kinase connection. *Science* 211:1336–38

35. Mastro, A. M., Rozengurt, E. 1976. Endogenous protein kinase in outer plasma membrane of cultured 3T3 cells. *J. Biol. Chem.* 251:7899–906

36. Mudgett-Hunter, M., Budzik, G. P., Sullivan, M. D., Donahoe, P. K. 1981. *Fed. Proc.* 40(1):995 (Abstr.)

37. Mudgett-Hunter, M., Budzik, G. P., Sullivan, M., Donahoe, P. K. 1982. Monoclonal antibody to Mullerian inhibiting substance. *J. Immunol.* 128:1327–33

38. Neil, J. C., Ghysdael, J., Vogt, P. K. 1981. Tyrosine-specific kinase activity associated with p105 of avian sarcoma virus PRC 11. *Virology* 109:223–28

39. Picard, J. Y., Tran, D., Josso, N. 1978. Biosynthesis of labeled anti-Mullerian hormone by fetal testes. Evidence for the glycoprotein nature of the hormone and for its disulfide-bonded structure. *Mol. Cell. Endocrinol.* 12:17–30

40. Price, J. M., Donahoe, P. K., Ito, Y. 1979. Involution of the female Mullerian duct of the fetal rat in the organ culture assay for the detection of Mullerian inhibiting substance. *Am. J. Anat.* 156:265–84

41. Price, J. M., Donahoe, P. K., Ito, Y., Hendren, W. H. III. 1977. Programmed cell death in the Mullerian duct induced by Mullerian inhibiting substance. *Am. J. Anat.* 149:353–76

42. Salmon, S. E., Hamburger, A. W., Soehnlen, B., Durie, B. G. M., Alberts, D. S., et al 1978. Quantitation of differential sensitivity of human-tumor stem cells to anticancer drugs. *New Engl. J. Med.* 298:1321–27

42a. Schwartz, B. R., Trelstad, R. L., Hutson, J. M., Ikawa, H., Donahoe, P. K. 1983. Zinc chelation and Mullerian duct regression. *J. Exper. Pathol.* In press

43. Swann, D. A., Donahoe, P. K., Ito, Y., Morikawa, Y., Hendren, W. H. 1979. Extraction of Mullerian inhibiting substance from newborn calf testis. *Dev. Biol.* 69:73–84

44. Swarup, G., Speeg, K. V. Jr., Cohen, S., Garbers, D. L. 1982. Phosphotyrosyl-protein phosphatase of TCRC-2 cells. *J. Biol. Chem.* 257:7298–301

45. Trams, E. G. 1974. Evidence of ATP action on the cell surface. *Nature* 252:480–82

46. Trelstad, R. L., Hayashi, A., Hayashi, K., Donahoe, P. K. 1982. The epithelial-mesenchymal interface of the male rat Mullerian duct. Loss of basement membrane integrity and ductal regression. *Dev. Biol.* 92:27–40

47. Ushiro, H., Cohen, S. 1980. Identification of phosphotyrosine as a product of epidermal growth factor–activated protein kinase in A-431 cell membranes. *J. Biol. Chem.* 255:8363–65

48. Vigier, B., Picard, J.-Y., Josso, N. 1982. A monoclonal antibody against bovine anti-Mullerian hormone. *Endocrinology* 110:131–37

49. Witte, O. N., Dasgupta, A., Baltimore, D. 1980. The Abelson murine leukemia virus protein is phosphorylated *in vitro* to form phosphotyrosine. *Nature* 283:826–31

Ann. Rev. Physiol. 1984. 46:67–81

EFFECTS OF MOLYBDATE AND ENDOGENOUS INHIBITORS ON STEROID-RECEPTOR INACTIVATION, TRANSFORMATION, AND TRANSLOCATION

Mary K. Dahmer, Paul R. Housley, and William B. Pratt

Department of Pharmacology, University of Michigan Medical School, Ann Arbor, Michigan 48109

INTRODUCTION

To exert their specific effects on the regulation of gene expression, steroid hormones must first bind to cytoplasmic receptors that are subsequently translocated to specific acceptor sites in the cell nucleus. Prior to this translocation, the steroid-receptor complex is transformed by a temperature-dependent process to a state that can bind to nuclear components. This general model of binding, followed by receptor transformation and translocation to the nucleus, was originally proposed in 1968 on the basis of studies in intact cells (25, 37).

The initial events in this pathway, hormone binding and receptor transformation, can be readily studied under cell-free conditions. Although clearly valid cell-free models of nuclear translocation have not been developed, binding of transformed receptors to nuclei or to DNA-cellulose can be assayed in a quantitative manner and is employed as an operational method of assaying translocation of receptors that have been transformed under cell-free conditions. Both group VI-A transition-metal oxyanions (42, 66, 92) and a small, heat-stable endogenous factor (7, 9, 24, 43, 77, 79, 80) have been found to

67

stabilize unoccupied steroid receptors and to inhibit the transformation of receptors to the DNA-binding state in cell-free assay systems. Macromolecular, heat-labile factors that inhibit translocation of transformed receptors have been identified in cytosols prepared from a variety of tissues (12, 19, 55, 87). We review here the actions, under cell-free conditions, of transition metal oxyanions and the two endogenous inhibitors on steroid receptor stability, transformation, and translocation.

REGULATION OF RECEPTORS BY PHOSPHATE AND SULFHYDRYL MOIETIES

In order to understand the rationale behind some of the experiments described here, it is important to understand the potential role of receptor phosphate and the clear role of receptor sulfhydryl moieties in determining the ability of steroid receptors to bind hormone.

It has recently been demonstrated that the murine glucocorticoid receptor in L929 cells (34) and the avian progesterone receptor in hen oviduct (20) are phosphorylated in vivo. In both cases the major phosphorylated species isolated by affinity chromatography is a protein of $M_r = 90,000-92,000$ (90–92K) that is phosphorylated on a serine moiety (or perhaps moieties). In the case of the glucocorticoid receptor, a minor species at 100K is also phosphorylated. In the case of the progesterone receptor, a second phosphorylated receptor species that migrates at about 109K in sodium dodecyl sulfate–polyacrylamide gels has been identified.

Several observations in cell-free systems suggest that phosphorylation of steroid receptors may be important for determining their ability to bind the hormone. It has been shown, for example, that the specific glucocorticoid binding capacity of mouse L-cell or rat liver cytosol is inactivated by purified calf intestine alkaline phosphatase or rabbit muscle phosphoprotein phosphatase (32, 63). We have recently shown that inactivation of binding capacity in L-cell cytosol by the calf intestine phosphatase is accompanied by loss of ^{32}p from the 92K receptor (P. R. Housley & W. B. Pratt, work in progress). Estrogen binding capacity of rat uterine cytosol is also inactivated by purified alkaline phosphatase (1). The glucocorticoid binding capacity of cytosol prepared from L cells or rat liver is inactivated by an endogenous process in a temperature-dependent manner. This inactivation is slowed by several phosphatase inhibitors, such as fluoride, and by some low-molecular-weight phosphorylated compounds, such as glucose-1-phosphate (42, 64, 65). Fluoride also inhibits inactivation of progesterone receptors in chick oviduct cytosol (27). A glucocorticoid receptor–inactivating enzyme has been demonstrated in membrane preparations from rat thymocytes and rat liver (64, 65), and an estrogen receptor–inactivating enzyme has been demonstrated in mouse uterine nuclei (1, 4, 5). In both cases receptor inactivation by the enzyme is inhibited by several phosphatase inhibitors. Finally, ATP-dependent reactivation of steroid-binding capacity has been demonstrated for glucocorticoid-binding capacity in L-cell cytosol (80) and for estrogen-binding capacity in rat and mouse uterine cytosols (1, 6). These observations suggest that the steroid-binding capacity of cytosol preparations is affected by a phosphorylation-dephosphorylation process. Two steroid receptors have now been shown to be phosphoproteins, so it is possible that phosphorylation of the receptor itself is required to maintain the active binding state.

One functional group that is clearly required for glucocorticoid binding is a receptor sulfhydryl moiety(ies). The sulfhydryl requirement was demonstrated by Rees & Bell (75), who reactivated the glucocorticoid-binding capacity of partially inactivated rat thymocyte cytosol with dithiothreitol (DTT). Activation of glucocorticoid-binding capacity by DTT was subsequently demonstrated by Granberg & Ballard (26) in cytosols prepared from several rat tissues that had low endogenous reducing capacity. As the steroid-binding capacity of cytosol preparations in general is eliminated by sulfhydryl-reactive reagents such as N-ethylmaleimide, a sulfhydryl requirement has been inferred for the binding of most steroids. Glucocorticoid-binding systems, however, appear to be particularly sensitive to inactivation by oxidation and reactivation by reduction. As glucocorticoid receptors can be covalently labeled with dexamethasone 21–mesylate, a site-specific affinity label containing a methanesulfonyl group that reacts with sulfhydryl moieties (21), there is probably a sulfhydryl moiety(ies) in or near the steroid-binding site. It is not known whether sulfhydryl moieties in the binding site or elsewhere on the receptor are the labile moieties responsible for receptor inactivation.

EFFECTS OF MOLYBDATE ON STEROID RECEPTORS

Effects of Molybdate on the Stability of Unbound Receptors

The profound effect of molybdate in stabilizing unbound receptors was first discovered during experiments performed to determine whether phosphatase inhibitors could inhibit temperature-mediated inactivation of the unbound receptor (64, 65). As mentioned above, inactivation of glucocorticoid receptors in cell-free preparations is inhibited by a variety of phosphatase inhibitors; molybdate, however, is much more effective than the rest, producing almost complete stabilization of glucocorticoid-binding capacity in cytosols incubated at 25°C (42, 64, 65). At pH 7.35, a concentration of 10 mM sodium molybdate is required for maximal stabilization, and the effect is reversible (42). Glucocorticoid receptors are also inactivated at 0°C by incubation with salt or by ammonium sulfate precipitation, and molybdate inhibits the loss of binding capacity caused by these procedures (42, 53). It is now clear that molybdate stabilizes receptors for androgens (23, 68, 93, 102), estrogens (2, 41, 73), progestins (8, 13, 27, 92), mineralocorticoids (50), and dihydroxycholecalciferol (22, 89). Two other group VI-A transition-metal oxyanions, vanadate and tungstate, also inhibit steroid receptor inactivation (98).

An important characteristic of molybdate action is that the metal oxyanion interacts with glucocorticoid receptors that are inactivated by oxidation, stabilizing them such that they can be subsequently reactivated to the steroid-binding state by addition of dithiothreitol (DTT). This observation was first made in rat thymocyte cytosol, where glucocorticoid receptors are rapidly inactivated even when molybdate is present (79). If 10 mM molybdate is present in this system while receptors are being inactivated by incubation at 25°C, they can be completely reactivated at any time by adding DTT. Molybdate must be present during the inactivation for reactivation to occur, and addition of DTT in the absence of molybdate does not prevent receptor inactivation.

The observation that molybdate stabilizes receptors even when they cannot bind steroid has been exploited in a second series of experiments that may eventually permit some insight into the mechanism of molybdate action. The experiments were suggested by the finding that 10 mM molybdate does not inhibit calf intestine alkaline phosphatase activity assayed with p-nitrophenyl phosphate as substrate, and it does not prevent alkaline phosphatase–mediated inactivation of the glucocorticoid receptor (44). We reasoned that although molybdate might not be inhibiting inactivation of the receptor by dephosphorylation, it might nevertheless stabilize the dephosphoreceptor such that it could be reactivated. Accordingly, we carried out the experiment shown in Figure 1 (32). Rat liver cytosol was first filtered and washed free of low M_r compounds that might inhibit phosphatase activity. Receptors were then inactivated in the presence of 10 mM molybdate by incubation with calf intestine alkaline phosphatase that had been purified to homogeneity. We found that the phosphatase-inactivated receptor can be restored to a steroid-binding state by the addition of DTT. Again, the presence of molybdate is required for reactivation with DTT to occur, and DTT alone does not prevent receptor inactivation. The binding capacity can also be inactivated by highly purified rabbit muscle phosphoprotein phosphatase in the presence of molybdate, and subsequently reactivated in a similar manner (32).

Three potential binding states exist in this experiment; Figure 2 presents them in the form of a model. There is the untreated, active binding form, which is represented in the model by the phosphorylated and reduced receptor in state 1. Incubating cytosol in the presence of molybdate and phosphatase produces a nonbinding form of the receptor (state 3) that can be returned to a steroid-binding form (state 2) by addition of the reducing agent. As this reactivation occurs in the absence of ATP at 0°C, phosphorylation is not involved, and some

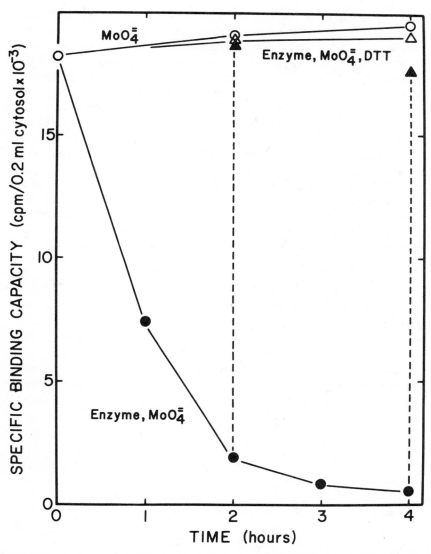

Figure 1 Reactivation of phosphatase-treated receptors by dithiothreitol. Filtered cytosol-containing molybdate was incubated alone (○), with purified calf intestine alkaline phosphatase at 20 μg ml^{-1} (●), or with alkaline phosphatase at 20 μg ml^{-1} plus 10 mM dithiothreitol (△). At the indicated times, 0.2 ml aliquots were removed and assayed for specific glucocorticoid-binding capacity. At 2 and 4 h, 0.2 ml aliquots were removed from the incubation mixture containing alkaline phosphatase alone, dithiothreitol was added to a final concentration of 10 mM, and the specific binding capacity assayed. The dithiothreitol-reactivated samples (▲) are connected to their corresponding phosphatase-inactivated samples by dashed lines. From (32)

kind of reduction must be occurring. If molybdate is not present, incubation with protein phosphatases results in a nonbinding state (state 4) that is not reactivated by reduction. As the binding capacity of cytosol is clearly being inactivated by dephosphorylation and reactivated by reduction, we infer that dephosphorylation in some way promotes oxidation of sulfhydryl groups that are essential for steroid binding. It is reasonable to propose that a phosphate moiety(ies) on the receptor may be stabilizing vicinal thiol residues to maintain the active steroid-binding form. Molybdate clearly prevents some change that produces a form of the receptor that cannot be reactivated by dithiothreitol. As the molybdate-stabilized, phosphatase-inactivated receptor can be reactivated, it would seem that the phosphate moiety(ies) itself is not required for steroid binding. Rather, it would seem that phosphorylation of the receptor may ensure a conformation such that sulfhydryl oxidation does not readily occur. The model provides a conceptual framework for consideration of different binding states that appear to be determined by phosphate and sulfhydryl moieties on the receptor and for considering potential mechanisms of molybdate action.

Effects of Molybdate on the Transformation and Physical Behavior of Bound Receptors

In addition to inhibiting inactivation of steroid receptors, molybdate reversibly blocks transformation of the bound steroid-receptor complex to the DNA-binding state. Inhibition of temperature-dependent transformation was first reported for the avian progesterone receptor by Toft & Nishigori (92). Later studies have shown that molybdate reversibly inhibits temperature-mediated transformation of glucocorticoid (35, 42, 54), estrogen (57, 84), and androgen (68) receptors. Vanadate and tungstate also inhibit receptor transformation (42,

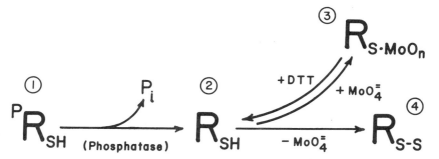

Figure 2   Hypothetical model describing the different binding states of the receptor that exist in the experiment of Figure 1. Receptor in States 1 and 2 binds steroid; in State 3 is nonbinding, but reversible by reduction; and in State 4 is nonbinding and not reversible by reduction. Molybdate is designated MoO_n when it is interacting with the receptor, because the valence state is unknown under these conditions. The rationale for the model is described in the text.

66). Inhibition by molybdate is pH-dependent with half-maximal inhibition achieved with 1 mM molybdate at pH 8.0 and 0.1 mM at pH 7.0 (66). Transformation of the glucocorticoid-receptor complex caused by salt or by precipitation with ammonium sulfate also is inhibited by molybdate (42, 95), as is salt-mediated transformation of progesterone receptor and estrogen receptor (66, 74).

In addition to inhibiting transformation of glucocorticoid- and estrogen-bound receptors, molybdate prevents the shift of these complexes to a less negatively charged state that occurs during DEAE-cellulose chromatography (17, 74, 95). The shift of the steroid-receptor complex to a less negatively charged state is characteristic of the steroid-receptor complex transformed either under cell-free conditions (17, 77) or in intact cells (51, 58). Molybdate also affects the size of the steroid-binding complex. In the presence of 10 mM sodium molybdate, steroid receptors remain in a very large complex with a sedimentation value of 8–10S. This stabilization of an 8–10S form of the binding complex has been demonstrated with glucocorticoid (15, 45, 54), estrogen (56, 83, 91), and progesterone (27, 67, 72, 101) receptors. The effects of molybdate on size and other physicochemical parameters are discussed in greater detail in the review by Sherman et al in this volume (83). It is important to note that recent studies by Holbrook et al (30) show that untransformed glucocorticoid receptor from intact cells has a sedimentation coefficient of 9.2S while the transformed receptor from intact cells sediments at 4.8S, suggesting that molybdate may be stabilizing a physiologically relevant state of the receptor.

The molecular mechanism by which molybdate stabilizes steroid receptors is not known. Although molybdate and some of the other group VI-A transition-metal oxyanions inhibit a variety of phosphatases (48, 69–71, 76, 94) and some phosphohydrolases [e.g. (Na^+, K^+)-ATPases (11, 40, 88)], this action does not account for their ability to stabilize steroid receptors and inhibit receptor transformation. Rather, it seems clear that molybdate is directly interacting with the receptor.

Nishigori & Toft (66) have examined the effect of a number of compounds on both progesterone-receptor transformation and endogenous phosphatase activity (assayed with p-nitrophenyl phosphate as substrate) in chick oviduct cytosol, and found that some compounds, like chromate and arsenate, inhibited phosphatase activity but not transformation. Although molybdate, vanadate, and tungstate inhibited both phosphatase activity and receptor transformation, the results obtained with the other inhibitors suggested that these two activities might not be related. Leach et al (42) found that molybdate inhibited inactivation and transformation of glucocorticoid receptors caused by salt or ammonium sulfate precipitation at 0°–4°C. As these are physical methods of receptor inactivation and transformation that are unlikely to involve phosphatase action, it does not seem likely that phosphatase inhibition plays any role in molybdate effects on steroid receptors.

Molybdate has a profound affect on the physical behavior of glucocorticoid and estrogen receptors submitted to ammonium sulfate precipitation. In the absence of molybdate, the receptor is precipitated at 30% of ammonium sulfate saturation and is transformed, while in the presence of molybdate the receptor is precipitated at 40–55% ammonium sulfate saturation and is not transformed (17, 52). Grody et al (27) have shown that the ability of molybdate to stabilize the progesterone-receptor complex in cytosol to thermal inactivation is lost if the receptor is precipitated with ammonium sulfate prior to incubating it at 30°C. These observations suggest that molybdate interacts directly with the receptor and possible exclusively with the untransformed form. The strongest evidence of a direct interaction between molybdate and the receptor protein itself is from work of Puri et al (72) on the progesterone receptor. They have extensively purified the progesterone receptor and found that in high salt gradients run in the presence of molybdate the receptor still sediments at 8S, indicating that molybdate is still capable of interacting with the purified, untransformed progesterone receptor to maintain it in the 8S form.

The observations made to date strongly suggest that molybdate interacts directly with the receptor or perhaps with another component of a large M_r receptor complex. The interaction is weak: a concentration of 0.5–1 mM molybdate or 0.2 mM vanadate is required to produce a half-maximal stabilization of receptors at pH 7.35 (98). It is unlikely that the interaction between steroid receptors and group VI-A transition-metal oxyanions is the same as the interaction between vanadate and (Na^+, K^+)-ATPases; these enzymes are inhibited at several orders of magnitude lower vanadate concentration (11, 96). The transition-metal oxyanions inhibit phosphatase enzymes by binding quite specifically at the phosphate-binding site on the enzyme (48, 94). In the case of acid phosphatases, there is evidence that molybdate complexes with a histidyl residue in the active site of the enzyme, functioning as an analog of the transition state (94). Again, the concentration of metal ion required for inhibition of these enzymes is in the order of 10^{-8}–10^{-6} M, and this effect is probably quite different from the weak interaction occuring with steroid receptors.

The type of functional group(s) required for the proposed molybdate-receptor interaction is not known. Molybdate, vanadate, and tungstate can form chelates with a variety of functional groups, including oxygen, nitrogen, and sulfur ligands (94). We have previously proposed that phosphate and sulfur moieties on the receptor protein (or on some other component of a receptor complex) are two sites of interaction that should be considered for molybdate (42). The data of Housley et al (32) strongly suggest that molybdate does not interact with phosphate moieties, because it maintains receptors that have been inactivated by protein phosphatase in a form that is capable of being reactivated. It is possible that, as defined for some other molybdate-protein interactions (97), the transition-metal oxyanion complexes with sulfur groups on the receptor. It is also possible that molybdate interacts elsewhere with the receptor to prevent conformational changes that lead to irreversible inactivation after oxidation of a sulfhydryl moiety(ies) that is required for steroid binding. It is important to note that sulfhydryl groups are required for receptor transformation as well as for steroid binding (39, 49), and molybdate-sulfur interactions might account for all of the molybdate effects on steroid receptors.

THE ENDOGENOUS INHIBITOR OF INACTIVATION AND TRANSFORMATION

The existence of an endogenous steroid-receptor stabilizing component was first proposed by Cake et al in 1976 (9). They found that removal of low M_r components from rat liver cytosol by gel filtration promoted both inactivation of the unbound glucocorticoid receptor and transformation of the bound receptor. Litwack and his coworkers (9, 24) have suggested that this low M_r component(s) maintains the glucocorticoid receptor in a conformational state that allows the binding of glucocorticoid and that it must be removed from the steroid-receptor complex before binding to DNA can occur. Subsequently it was suggested that this endogenous "modulator" of the glucocorticoid receptor might be pyridoxal phosphate (10, 18). It is now clear, however, that the endogenous factor inhibits receptor transformation, whereas pyridoxal phosphate interacts with the transformed receptor and blocks binding to DNA (82). Bailly et al (7) have also described a low-M_r heat-stable inhibitor of glucocorticoid-receptor transformation in rat liver cytosol, and Sakaue & Thompson (77) have shown that the heat-stable fraction of cytosol inhibits glucocorticoid-receptor transformation as defined by a shift to the low-salt-eluting form on DEAE-cellulose chromatography.

These observations were recently expanded by Leach et al (43), who showed that rat liver cytosol contains two heat-stable activities that affect glucocorticoid binding. One is a reducing activity that increases steroid-binding capacity when added to cytosol preparations that have a low endogenous reducing capacity (26, 78, 79). This heat-stable reducing activity has a M_r of about 12K and has now been identified as thioredoxin (Grippo et al, submitted manuscript), a polypeptide that catalyzes the reduction of protein disulfides in an NADPH-dependent manner (99). The second heat-stable factor has a M_r of less than 700, and it inhibits both inactivation of unbound glucocorticoid receptors and transformation of bound receptors (43). We would suggest that inhibition of receptor inactivation and inhibition of receptor transformation may be due to the same heat-stable component, because both activities coelute from Sephadex

G-10 and Dowex 1 columns and have been copurified more than 200-fold with respect to Lowry-reactive material (43). It seems likely that we are studying the same low-M_r heat-stable activity that was reported earlier by these other laboratories. We have noted only one discrepancy: Bailly et al (7) found that the transformation-inhibiting activity is removed by a cation-exchange resin and have suggested that it may be positively charged, whereas we have found (43) that it behaves as an anion at pH 7.35.

The endogenous inhibitor affects receptors somewhat as molybdate does in that it reversibly inhibits both receptor inactivation and transformation, it stabilizes glucocorticoid receptors that are inactivated by oxidation, and it does not inhibit the binding of already transformed receptors to DNA (43). This heat-stable activity is found in a wide variety of tissues in higher organisms and is present in primitive eukaryotes, like lobster and yeast, which are lower on the evolutionary scale than the point at which glucocorticoid receptors emerged (43). Sato et al (81) have reported that transformation of both androgen and estrogen receptors is also inhibited by a small M_r (dialyzable) endogenous factor, suggesting that the inhibitor may have a general ability to stabilize steroid receptors. The mechanism of action of this endogenous inhibitor(s) is not known. We have found that the 200-fold purified inhibitor preparation inhibits purified rat liver phosphorylase phosphatase activity over the same range of concentrations that is required for inhibition of glucocorticoid-receptor inactivation and transformation in rat liver cytosol (33), but a causal relationship between these two observations has not been established.

ENDOGENOUS TRANSLOCATION INHIBITORS

Interest in endogenous inhibitors of translocation developed because several laboratories reported a limited number of nuclear binding sites for transformed steroid-receptor complexes (28, 29, 38), whereas others had found a larger number of sites with lower affinity (12,100). On further investigation, it became clear that the binding of glucocorticoid-receptor complexes to nuclei or DNA reaches an apparent saturation when concentrated rat liver cytosol preparations are employed, because the cytosol contains an inhibitor that appears to interact with the transformed steroid-receptor complex and limits DNA binding (55, 87). The initial studies with rat liver systems showed that the inhibitor is a heat-labile activity that is macromolecular and is precipitated by ammonium sulfate (55, 87). Subsequently, several laboratories have demonstrated the existence of a macromolecular inhibitor of glucocorticoid-receptor translocation in both normal and neoplastic rat liver cells (3, 31, 36, 47, 86, 90).

Interest in this endogenous translocation inhibitor has focused on its role in explaining the apparent saturability of nuclear acceptor sites in cell-free experiments, but a reversible inhibitor of translocation could prove to be a useful experimental tool for studying the receptor requirements for DNA or nuclear binding in more detail. We have recently purified this activity almost 700-fold from rat liver cytosol (16; M. K. Dahmer, W. B. Pratt, manuscript in preparation). The translocation-inhibitor activity behaves as a single species during purification, and it copurifies with a cationic (adsorbs to phosphocellulose at pH 7.4) protein doublet that migrates with a M_r of about 37K on sodium dodecyl sulfate–polyacrylamide gel electrophoresis. Under low-salt conditions the inhibitor aggregates with itself to form a large complex.

The existence of translocation inhibitors has also been proposed for both estrogen-receptor (12) and progesterone-receptor (19, 49) complexes. In this regard, it is interesting that reconstitution experiments with progesterone and estrogen receptors with cytosol components suggest the existence of entities that can bind to the 4S progesterone receptor to yield an 8S form (62) and with the 4S estrogen receptor to yield a 5S, 6S, or 8S form, depending on the cytosol fraction that is added (59–61). Rat ventral prostate produces a major glycoprotein, called the prostate α-protein, that inhibits binding of the androgen-receptor complex to nuclei and promotes release of complex that is already bound to nuclei (14, 85). The α-protein can be separated into three different polypeptide components with sodium dodecyl sulfate. One of the three (Component I, $M_r = 10K$) is responsible for inhibition of nuclear binding by transformed androgen receptor. The prostate α-protein exists in vast stoichiometric excess with respect to the androgen receptor. Its physiological role is unknown. Component I has been purified and sequenced (46) and it should prove to be a useful model for studying potential interactions between transformed steroid receptors and endogenous inhibitors of receptor translocation.

ACKNOWLEDGMENT

The author's work reported herein was supported by NIH grants CA-28010 and AM31573.

Literature Cited

1. Abou-Issa, H., Foecking, M. K., Minton, J. P. 1982. Regulation of estrogen-receptor binding by phosphorylation-dephosphorylation. Fed. Proc. 41:1164
2. Anderson, K. M., Bonomi, P., Marogil, M., Hendrickson, C., Economou, S. 1980. Comparison of dextran-coated charcoal and sucrose density gradient analyses of estrogen and progesterone receptors in human breast cancer. Cancer Res. 40:4127–32
3. Atger, M., Milgrom, E. 1978. Interaction of glucocorticoid-receptor com-

plexes with rat liver nuclei. Biochim. Biophys. Acta 539:41–53
4. Auricchio, F., Migliaccio, A. 1980. In vitro inactivation of oestrogen receptor by nuclei. FEBS Lett. 117:224–26
5. Auricchio, F., Migliaccio, A., Rotondi, A. 1981. Inactivation of oestrogen receptor in vitro by nuclear dephosphorylation. Biochem. J. 194:569–74
6. Auricchio, F., Migliaccio, A., Castoria, G., Lastoria, S., Schiavone, E. 1981. ATP-dependent enzyme activating hormone binding of estradiol receptor.

Biochem. Biophys. Res. Commun. 101: 1171–78

7. Bailly, A., Sallas, N., Milgrom, E. 1977. A low molecular weight inhibitor of steroid-receptor activation. *J. Biol. Chem.* 252:858–63

8. Bevins, C. L., Bashirelahi, N. 1980. Stabilization of 8S progesterone receptor from human prostate in the presence of molybdate ion. *Cancer Res.* 40:2234–39

9. Cake, M. H., Goidl, J. A., Parchman, L. G., Litwack, G. 1976. Involvement of a low molecular weight component(s) in the mechanism of action of the glucocorticoid receptor. *Biochem. Biophys. Res. Commun.* 71:45–52

10. Cake, M. H., DiSorbo, D. M., Litwack, G. 1978. Effect of pyridoxal phosphate on the binding site of the activated hepatic glucocortocoid receptor. *J. Biol. Chem.* 253:4886–91

11. Cantley, L. C., Cantley, L. G., Josephson, L. J. 1978. A characterization of vanadate interactions with the (Na$^+$, K$^+$)-ATPase. *J. Biol. Chem.* 253:7361–68

12. Chamness, G. C., Jennings, A. W., McGuire, W. L. 1974. Estrogen-receptor binding to isolated nuclei. A nonsaturable process. *Biochemistry* 13:327–31

13. Chen, T. J., MacDonald, R. G., Leavitt, W. W. 1981. Uterine progesterone receptor: stabilization and physicochemical alterations produced by sodium molybdate. *Biochemistry* 20:3405–11

14. Chen, C., Schilling, K., Hiipakka, R. A., Huang, I-Y., Liao, S. 1982. Prostate α-protein. *J. Biol. Chem.* 257:116–21

15. Cidlowski, J. A., Currie, R. A. 1982. Pyridoxal phosphate blocks aggregation of molybdate-treated glucocorticoid receptors in HeLa S$_3$ cells. *J. Steroid Biochem.* 17:277–80

16. Dahmer, M. K. 1983. Inhibition of glucocorticoid-receptor transformation and translocation. PhD thesis. Univ. Mich.

17. Dahmer, M. K., Quasney, M. W., Bissen, S. T., Pratt, W. B. 1981. Molybdate permits resolution of untransformed glucocorticoid receptors from the transformed state. *J. Biol. Chem.* 256:9401–5

18. DiSorbo, D. M., Phelps, D. S., Ohl, V. S., Litwack, G. 1980. Pyridoxine deficiency influences the behavior of the glucocorticoid receptor. *J. Biol. Chem.* 255:3866–70

19. Dougherty, J. J., Toft, D. O. 1980. A macromolecular inhibitor of progesterone-receptor activation in the chick oviduct. *Abst. 62nd Ann. Meet. Endocrine Soc.*, p. 132

20. Dougherty, J. J., Puri, R. K., Toft, D. O. 1982. Phosphorylation *in vivo* of chicken oviduct progesterone receptor. *J. Biol. Chem.* 257:14226–30

21. Eisen, J. H., Schleenbaker, R. E., Simons, S. S. Jr. 1981. Affinity labeling of the rat liver glucocorticoid receptor with dexamethasone 21-mesylate. *J. Biol. Chem.* 256:12920–25

22. Feldman, D., McCain, T. A., Hirst, M. A., Chen, T. L., Colston, K. W. 1979. Characterization of a cytoplasmic receptor-like binder for 1α, 25-dihydroxycholecalciferol in rat intestinal mucosa. *J. Biol. Chem.* 254:10378–84

23. Gaubert, C. M., Tremblay, R. R., Dube, J. Y. 1980. Effect of sodium molybdate on cytosolic androgen receptors in rat prostate. *J. Steroid Biochem.* 13:931–37

24. Goidl, J. A., Cake, M. H., Dolan, K. P., Parchman, L. G., Litwack, G. 1977. Activation of the rat liver glucocorticoid-receptor complex. *Biochemistry* 16:2125–30

25. Gorski, J., Toft, D. O., Shyamala, G., Smith, D., Notides, A. 1968. Hormone receptors: Studies on the interaction of estrogen with the uterus. *Rec. Prog. Horm. Res.* 24:45–80

26. Granberg, J. P., Ballard, P. L. 1977. The role of sulfhydryl groups in the binding of glucocorticoids by cytoplasmic receptors of lung and other mammalian tissues. *Endocrinology* 100:1160–68

27. Grody, W. W., Compton, J. G., Schrader, W. T., O'Malley, B. W. 1980. Inactivation of chick oviduct progesterone receptors. *J. Steroid Biochem.* 12:115–20

28. Higgins, S. J., Rousseau, G. G., Baxter, J. D., Tomkins, G. M. 1973. Early events in glucocorticoid action: Activation of the steroid receptor and its subsequent specific nuclear binding, studied in a cell-free system. *J. Biol. Chem.* 248:5866–72

29. Higgins, S. J., Rousseau, G. G., Baxter, J. D., Tomkins, G. M. 1973. Nature of nuclear acceptor sites for glucocorticoid- and estrogen-receptor complexes. *J. Biol. Chem.* 248:5873–79

30. Holbrook, N. J., Bodwell, J. E., Jeffries, M., Munck, A. 1983. Characterization of nonactivated and activated glucocorticoid-receptor complexes from intact rat thymus cells. *J. Biol. Chem.* 258:6477–85

31. Horiuchi, M., Isohashi, F., Terada, M., Okamoto, K., Sakamoto, Y. 1981. Interaction of ATP with a macromolecular translocation inhibitor of the nuclear binding of "activated" receptor-glucocorticoid complex. *Biochem. Biophys. Res. Commun.* 98:88–94

32. Housley, P. R., Dahmer, M. K., Pratt, W. B. 1982. Inactivation of glucocorticoid-binding capacity by protein phosphatases in the presence of molybdate and complete reactivation by dithiothreitol. *J. Biol. Chem.* 257:8615–18

33. Housley, P. R., Grippo, J. F., Dahmer, M. K., Pratt, W. B. 1983. Inactivation, activation and stabilization of glucocorticoid receptors. In *Biochemical Actions of Hormones,* ed. G. Litwack, Vol. 11. New York: Academic. In press

34. Housley, P. R., Pratt, W. B. 1983. Direct demonstration of glucocorticoid-receptor phosphorylation by intact L cells. *J. Biol. Chem.* 258:4630–35

35. Hubbard, J., Kalimi, M. 1982. Synergistic effect of molybdate plus dithiothreitol on stabilization, reactivation, and partial purification of the kidney glucocorticoid receptor. *J. Biol. Chem.* 257:14263–70

36. Isohashi, F., Terada, M., Tsukanaka, K., Nakanishi, Y., Sakamoto, Y. 1980. A low-molecular-weight translocation modulator and its interaction with a macromolecular translocation inhibitor of the activated receptor-glucocorticoid complex. *J. Biochem.* 88:775–81

37. Jensen, E. V., Suzuki, T., Kawashima, T., Stumpf, W. E., Jungblut, P. W., DeSombre, E. R. 1968. A two-step mechanism for the interaction of estradiol with rat uterus. *Proc. Natl. Acad. Sci. USA* 59:632–38

38. Kalimi, M., Beato, M., Feigelson, P. 1973. Interaction of glucocorticoids with rat liver nuclei. I. Role of the cytosol proteins. *Biochemistry* 12:3365–71

39. Kalimi, M., Love, K. 1980. Role of chemical reagents in the activation of rat hepatic glucocorticoid-receptor complex. *J. Biol. Chem.* 255:4687–90

40. Karlish, S. J. D., Beauge, L. A., Glynn, I. M. 1979. Vanadate inhibits (Na⁺, K⁺)-ATPase by blocking a conformational change of the unphosphorylated form. *Nature* 282:333–35

41. Krozowski, Z. S., Murphy, L. C. 1981. Stabilization of the cytoplasmic estrogen receptor by molybdate. *J. Steroid Biochem.* 14:363–66

42. Leach, K. L., Dahmer, M. K., Hammond, N. D., Sando, J. J., Pratt, W. B. 1979. Molybdate inhibition of glucocorticoid-receptor inactivation and transformation. *J. Biol. Chem.* 254:11884–90

43. Leach, K. L., Grippo, J. F., Housley, P. R., Dahmer, M. K., Salive, M. E., Pratt, W. B. 1982. Characteristics of an endogenous glucocorticoid-receptor stabilizing factor. *J. Biol. Chem.* 257:381–88

44. Leach, K. L., Dahmer, M. K., Pratt, W. B. 1983. Glucocorticoid-receptor stabilization: relative effects of molybdate ion on inactivation by alkaline phosphatase and phospholipase A₂. *J. Steroid Biochem.* 18:105–7

45. Lee, H. J., Bradlow, H. L., Moran, M. C., Sherman, M. R. 1981. Binding of glucocorticoid 21-oic acids and esters to molybdate-stabilized hepatic receptors. *J. Steroid Biochem.* 14:1325–35

46. Liao, S., Chen, C., Huang, I-Y. 1982. Prostate α-protein. *J. Biol. Chem.* 257:122–25

47. Liu, S-L., Webb, T. E. 1977. Elevated concentration of a dexamethasone-receptor translocation inhibitor in Novikoff hepatoma cells. *Cancer Res.* 37:1763–67

48. Lopez, V., Stevens, T., Lindquist, R. N. 1976. Vanadium ion inhibition of alkaline phosphatase-catalyzed phosphate ester hydrolysis. *Arch. Biochem. Biophys.* 175:31–38

49. MacDonald, R. G., Leavitt, W. W. 1982. Reduced sulfhydryl groups are required for activation of uterine progesterone receptor. *J. Biol. Chem.* 257:311–15

50. Marver, D. 1980. Aldosterone receptors in rabbit renal cortex and red medulla. *Endocrinology* 106:611–18

51. Markovic, R. D., Litwack, G. 1980. Activation of liver and kidney glucocorticoid-receptor complexes occurs *in vivo.* *Arch. Biochem. Biophys.* 202:374–79

52. Mauck, L. A., Day, R. N., Notides, A. C. 1982. Molybdate interaction with the estrogen receptor: Effects on estradiol binding and receptor activation. *Biochemistry* 21:1788–93

53. McBlain, W. A., Shyamala, G. 1980. Inactivation of mammary cytoplasmic glucocorticoid receptors under cell-free conditions. *J. Biol. Chem.* 255:3884–91

54. McBlain, W. A., Toft, D. O., Shyamala, G. 1981. Transformation of mammary cytoplasmic glucocorticoid receptor under cell-free conditions. *Biochemistry* 20:6790–98

55. Milgrom, E., Atger, M. 1975. Receptor translocation inhibitor and apparent saturability of the nuclear acceptor. *J. Steroid Biochem.* 6:487–92

56. Miller, L. K., Tuazon, F. B., Niu, E. M., Sherman, M. R. 1981. Human breast tumor estrogen receptor: Effects of molybdate and electrophoretic analyses. *Endocrinology* 108:1369–78

57. Muller, R. E., Abdulmaged, M. T., Beebe, D. A., Wotiz, H. H. 1982. Reversible inhibition of estrogen-receptor activation by molybdate. *J. Biol. Chem.* 257:1295–1300

58. Munck, A., Foley, R. 1979. Activation

of steroid hormone-receptor complexes in intact target cells in physiological conditions *Nature* 278:752–754

59. Murayama, A., Fukai, F., Hazato, T., Yamamoto, T. 1980. Estrogen receptor of cow uterus. I. Characterization of native and proteolyzed "4S" estrogen receptors. *J. Biochem.* 88:955–61

60. Murayama, A., Fukai, F., Hazato, T., Yamamoto, T. 1980. Estrogen receptor of cow uterus. II. Characterization of a cytoplasmic factor which binds with native "4S" estrogen receptor to give "8S" estrogen receptor. *J. Biochem.* 88:963–68

61. Murayama, A., Fukai, F., Yamamoto, T. 1980. Estrogen receptor of cow uterus. III. Molecular constitution of estrogen receptor-binding factors. *J. Biochem.* 88:969–76

62. Murayama, A., Fukai, F., Yamamoto, T. 1980. Progesterone receptor system of hen oviduct. *J. Biochem.* 88:1305–15

63. Nielsen, C. J., Sando, J. J., Pratt, W. B. 1977. Evidence that dephosphorylation inactivates glucocorticoid receptors. *Proc. Natl. Acad. Sci. USA* 74:1398–1402

64. Nielsen, C. J., Sando, J. J., Vogel, W. M., Pratt, W. B. 1977. Glucocorticoid-receptor inactivation under cell-free conditions. *J. Biol. Chem.* 252:7568–78

65. Nielsen, C. J., Vogel, W. M., Pratt, W. B. 1977. Inactivation of glucocorticoid receptors in cell-free preparations of rat liver. *Cancer Res.* 37:3420–26

66. Nishigori, H., Toft, D. 1980. Inhibition of progesterone-receptor activation by sodium molybdate. *Biochemistry* 19:77–83

67. Niu, E. -M., Neal, R. M., Pierce, V. K., Sherman, M. R. 1981. Structural similarity of molybdate-stabilized steroid receptors in human breast tumors, uteri and leukocytes. *J. Steroid Biochem.* 15:1–10

68. Noma, K., Nakao, K., Sato, B., Nishizawa, Y., Matsumoto, K., Yamamura, Y. 1980. Effect of molybdate on activation and stabilization of steroid receptors. *Endocrinology* 107:1205–11

69. Nordlie, R. C., Arion, W. J. 1964. Evidence for the common identity of glucose 6-phosphatase, inorganic pyrophosphatase, and pyrophosphate-glucose phosphotransferase. *J. Biol. Chem.* 239:1680–85

70. Paietta, E., Sands, H. 1978. Phosphoprotein phosphatase in bovine tracheal smooth muscle. *Biochim. Biophys. Acta* 282:121–32

71. Paigen, K. 1958. The properties of particulate phosphoprotein phosphatase. *J. Biol. Chem.* 233:388–94

72. Puri, R. K., Grandics, P., Dougherty, J. J., Toft, D. O. 1982. Purification of "nontransformed" avian progesterone receptor and preliminary characterization. *J. Biol. Chem.* 257:10831–37

73. Ratajczak, T., Samec, A. M., Hahnel, R. 1982. Requirement for a reduced sulphydryl entity in the protection of molybdate-stabilized estrogen receptor. *FEBS Lett.* 149:80–84

74. Redeuilh, G., Secco, C., Baulieu, E., Richard-Foy, H. 1981. Calf uterine estradiol receptor. Effects of molybdate on salt-induced transformation process and characterization of a nontransformed state. *J. Biol. Chem.* 256:11496–502

75. Rees, A. M., Bell, P. A. 1975. The involvement of receptor sulfhydryl groups in the binding of steroids to the cytoplasmic glucocorticoid receptor from rat thymus. *Biochim. Biophys. Acta* 411:121–32

76. Roberts, R. M., Brazer, F. W. 1976. Phosphoprotein phosphatase activity of the progesterone-induced purple glycoprotein of the porcine uterus. *Biochem. Biophys. Res. Commun.* 68:450–55

77. Sakaue, Y., Thompson, E. B. 1977. Characterization of two forms of glucocorticoid hormone-receptor complex separated by DEAE-cellulose column chromatography. *Biochem. Biophys. Res. Commun.* 77:533–41

78. Sando, J. J., Nielsen, C. J., Pratt, W. B. 1977. Reactivation of thymocyte glucocorticoid receptors in a cell-free system. *J. Biol. Chem.* 252:7579–82

79. Sando, J. J., Hammond, N. D., Stratford, C. A., Pratt, W. B. 1979. Activation of thymocyte glucocorticoid receptors to the steroid-binding form. *J. Biol. Chem.* 254:4779–89

80. Sando, J. J., LaForest, A. C., Pratt, W. B. 1979. ATP-dependent activation of L-cell glucocorticoid receptors to the steroid-binding form. *J. Biol. Chem.* 254:4772–78

81. Sato, B., Noma, K., Nishizawa, Y., Nakao, K., Matsumoto, K., Yamamura, Y. 1980. Mechanism of activation of steroid receptors: Involvement of low molecular weight inhibitor in activation of androgen, glucocorticoid, and estrogen receptor systems. *Endocrinology* 106:1142–48

82. Sekula, B. C., Schmidt, T. J., Litwack, G. 1981. Redefinition of modulator as an inhibitor of glucocorticoid-receptor activation. *J. Steroid Biochem.* 14:161–66

83. Sherman, M. R., Stevens, Y-W., Stevens, J. 1984. *Ann. Rev. Physiol.* 46:83–105

84. Shyamala, G., Leonard, L. 1980. Inhibition of uterine estrogen-receptor transformation by molybdate. *J. Biol. Chem.* 255:6028–31

85. Shyr, C-I., Liao, S. 1978. Protein factor that inhibits binding and promotes release of androgen-receptor complex from nuclear chromatin. *Proc. Natl. Acad. Sci. USA* 75:5969–73

86. Simons, S. S. Jr. 1977. Evidence for nuclear and DNA binding forms of the receptor-glucocorticoid complex from hepatoma tissue culture cells. *Biochim. Biophys. Acta* 496:339–48

87. Simons, S. S., Jr., Martinez, H. M., Garcea, R. L., Baxter, J. D., Tomkins, G. M. 1976. Interactions of glucocorticoid receptor-steroid complexes with acceptor sites. *J. Biol. Chem.* 251:334–43

88. Simons, T. J. B. 1979. Vanadate: A new tool for biologists. *Nature* 281:337–8

89. Simpson, R. U., DeLuca, H. F. 1980. Characterization of a receptor-like protein for 1, 25-dihydroxyvitamin D₃ in rat skin. *Proc. Natl. Acad. Sci. USA* 77: 5822–26

90. Taira, M., Terayama, H. 1978. Comparison of corticoid receptor and other cytoplasmic factors among liver and hepatoma cell lines with different sensitivities to corticoid inhibition of cell growth. *Biochim. Biophys. Acta* 541: 45–58

91. Tilzer, L. L., McFarland, R. T., Plapp, F. V., Evans, J. P., Chiga, M. 1981. Different ionic forms of estrogen receptor in rat uterus and human breast carcinoma. *Cancer Res.* 41:1058–63

92. Toft, D., Nishigori, H. 1979. Stabilization of the avian progesterone receptor by inhibitors. *J. Steroid Biochem.* 11: 413–16

93. Traish, A., Muller, R. E., Wotiz, H. H. 1981. A new procedure for the quantitation of nuclear and cytoplasmic androgen receptors. *J. Biol. Chem.* 256:12028–33

94. VanEtten, R. L., Waymack, P. P., Rehkop, D. M. J. 1974. Transition-metal ion inhibition of enzyme-catalyzed phosphate ester displacement reactions. *J. Am. Chem. Soc.* 96:6782–85

95. Vedeckis, W. V. 1981. Activation and chromatographic properties of the AtT-20 mouse pituitary tumor cell line glucocorticoid receptor. *Biochemistry* 20: 7237–45

96. Wallick, E. T., Lane, L. K., Schwartz, A. 1979. Regulation by vanadate of ouabain binding to (Na⁺, K⁺)-ATPase. *J. Biol. Chem.* 254:8107–9

97. Weathers, B. J., Grate, J. H., Schrauzer, G. N. 1979. The chemical evolution of a nitrogenase model. 17. Simulation of steric and of inhibitory effects at the enzymic active site with acetylenes and nitriles as the substrates, and "molybdoinsulin" catalysts. *J. Am. Chem. Soc.* 101: 917–24

98. Wheeler, R. H., Leach, K. L., LaForest, A. C., O'Toole, T. E., Wagner, R., Pratt, W. B. 1981. Glucocorticoid-receptor activation and inactivation in cultured human lymphocytes. *J. Biol. Chem.* 256:434–41

99. Williams, C. H. Jr. 1976. Flavin-containing dehydrogenases. *Enzymes, 3rd Ed.,* 13:89–173

100. Williams, D., Gorski, J. 1972. Kinetic and equilibrium analysis of estradiol in uterus: A model of binding-site distribution in uterine cells. *Proc. Natl. Acad. Sci. USA* 69:3464–68

101. Wolfson, A., Mester, J., Chang-Ren, Y., Baulieu, E. E. 1980. "Nonactivated" form of the progesterone receptor from chick oviduct: Characterization. *Biochem. Biophys. Res. Commun.* 95: 1577–84

102. Wright, W. W., Chan, K. C., Bardin, C. W. 1981. Characterization of stabilizing effect of sodium molybdate on the androgen receptor present in mouse kidney. *Endocrinology* 108:2210–16

Ann. Rev. Physiol. 1984. 46:83–105

STRUCTURE OF MAMMALIAN STEROID RECEPTORS: Evolving Concepts and Methodological Developments

Merry R. Sherman[1]

Endocrine Biochemistry Laboratory, Memorial Sloan-Kettering Cancer Center, New York, New York 10021

John Stevens

Research Department, American Cancer Society, Inc., New York, New York 10017

INTRODUCTION

Despite much work and significant progress on the stabilization, purification, and structural analysis of steroid receptors extracted from mammalian tissues, the native state still remains largely unknown. Receptors for a single class of steroids from the same tissue have been detected in various molecular forms and at least three functional states. In this review, these states are referred to as the untransformed, transformed, and inactive states. They are distinguished by differences in the affinity of the receptor for steroids and in the affinity of the steroid-receptor complex for nuclei, DNA, and ionic resins.

The *untransformed* steroid-receptor complexes are detected in cytoplasmic extracts (cytosols) of cells or tissues that were incubated with steroid in the cold, or in cytosols incubated with steroid at low temperature and low ionic strength. These complexes are characterized by low affinity for nuclei, chromatin, DNA, or anionic resins, such as DNA-cellulose or ATP-agarose, and high affinity for cationic resins, such as DEAE-cellulose or DEAE-agarose [reviewed in (15, 31, 63, 92)]. *Transformation,* defined as the acquisition of high affinity for nuclei, DNA, and anionic resins, is effected by warming cells that were incubated in the cold with steroid (68, 69, 123a) or by various manipulations of steroid-containing cytosols, such as prolonged storage, dilution, gel

[1]To whom correspondence should be addressed.

83

0066-4278/84/0315-0083$02.00

filtration, warming, exposure to salt, or precipitation by ammonium sulfate (31, 40, 59, 63, 92). In some systems, receptors that are *inactive* with respect to steroid binding can be converted to a steroid-binding state in the absence of new protein synthesis. The energy-dependent process by which this occurs is referred to as *activation* (15, 89, 122).

In addition to the fundamental question of the relationship of the untransformed complex detected in vitro to the native state in the cytoplasm of intact cells, numerous issues remain unresolved. They include the number of steroid-binding sites, the number and identity of polypeptide chains comprising the receptor, the number of genes coding for these polypeptides, and the presence and role of phosphate groups (15, 38) or other constituents such as metals (104) or RNA (11, 13, 39, 51, 64, 114). Other questions concern the possible existence of proreceptors, the structural relationships among the unliganded receptor and the complexes with agonists and antagonists (18, 43, 66, 105), the identity or dissimilarity of receptors for the same steroid in different healthy tissues (3, 26, 47, 55, 56, 58, 99, 126), and the structural as well as quantitative factors that may account for the diminished responsiveness to steroids of certain benign (24) and malignant tissues (34, 60, 93, 112).

A similar degree of uncertainty surrounds the transformed state and the molecular events by which a receptor acquires high affinity for nuclei and polyanions. Diverse mechanisms of transformation have been proposed. These include: a conformational change without a change in mass (1, 2); dimerization of the receptor or association with a nonsteroid-binding protein (77, 78); the dissociation of an oligomeric receptor (35, 85, 100, 115, 116, 128); the dissociation of macromolecular or low-molecular-weight inhibitors (63, 73, 76, 95); proteolysis (84); or dephosphorylation (15, 71). The mechanisms of nuclear uptake and retention, and the structural identity of the transformed cytoplasmic complex and its nuclear counterpart also remain to be established (18, 46, 55, 57). Finally, the mechanisms by which steroidal actions are terminated and reinitiated are presently shrouded in uncertainty. The cycle of molecular events presumably includes the dissociation of the steroid-receptor complex, release of the receptor from nuclear binding sites, recycling of the receptor to the cytoplasm, reformation of the untransformed complex, and degradation of the receptor, but the underlying mechanisms have not been elucidated (37, 41, 62, 65, 85).

The majority of studies of receptor structure, including our own, have used radioactive steroids of high specific activity to detect the steroid-receptor complexes in crude extracts of fresh or frozen tissues. Such extracts also contain nucleic acids, ribonucleoproteins, proteases, nucleases, phosphatases, and other enzymes, which may interact with or degrade the receptors during prolonged fractionation procedures. These effects may have contributed to the discrepancies among the molecular parameters reported and to the differences among the resultant concepts of receptor structure.

With these problems in mind, we have attempted to summarize the available data with reference to a simple schematic model of receptor structure (100) and to review several methodological developments which may facilitate the definitive characterization of receptors in various functional states. In the interest of brevity, methods that have been applied to receptors for several classes of steroids will be illustrated primarily by studies of glucocorticoid receptors (GR).

AN EVOLVING MODEL OF STEROID RECEPTOR FORMS

A discussion of the diverse concepts of receptor structure is facilitated by the schematic model shown in Figure 1. This model integrates the available data for the various forms of mammalian receptors that have been characterized by hydrodynamic techniques. It does not encompass the conversion of inactive receptors to a steroid-binding state, which is not thought to be accompanied by a change in size or shape (15). The various receptor forms are discussed in

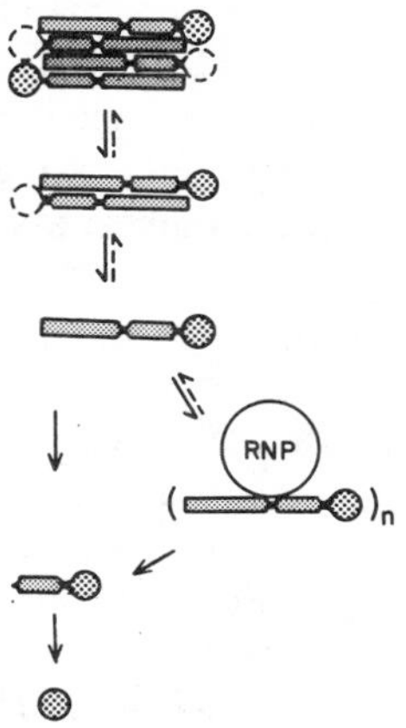

Receptor Form	Schematic Model	$s_{20,w}$ S	R_S nm	M_r $\times 10^{-3}$	a/b prolate
Tetramer		9–10	8.0–8.5	320–350	12–13
Dimer		5–7			
Monomer		4–5	5.3–6.0	90–110	12–14
Aggregate	RNP $(\quad)_n$	>20	>10	>900	
Intermediate Fragment(s)		3–4	2.5–4.0	40–70	3–7
Mero-receptor		2–3	1.9–2.4	20–25	1–3

Figure 1   An evolving model of steroid receptor forms in mammalian tissue cytosols. In the schematic drawings, the *stippled circles* represent the globular steroid-binding sites, the *dashed circles* denote the presence or absence of additional steroid-binding sites, the *rectangular segments* denote the asymmetric portions of the molecule, and the *narrow connections* denote regions of high protease sensitivity. *RNP* represents a ribonucleoprotein or ribosomal fragment, with which an unspecified number (n) of monomeric receptors or fragments may form an aggregate. Ranges of values of the sedimentation coefficient ($s_{20,w}$), Stokes radius (R_S), molecular weight (M_r), and axial ratio (a/b) of a hydrodynamically equivalent prolate ellipsoid are indicated. The ranges shown for M_r and a/b of each form represent our best current estimates, rather than combinations of the lowest or highest values of R_S and $s_{20,w}$ [Adapted from 100].

terms of their Stokes radii (R_S), sedimentation coefficients ($s_{20,w}$), molecular weights (M_r), and axial ratios (a/b).

Stokes radii and $s_{20,w}$ were evaluated by gel filtration and ultracentrifugation, respectively. Values of M_r were determined electrophoretically or were calculated from the product of R_S (in nm) and $s_{20,w}$ (in Svedberg units) and a factor of 4224. The frictional ratio due to shape, $(f/f_o)_{shape}$, was calculated from 13.93 ($R_S/M_r^{1/3}$). These factors were based on assumed values of 0.732 cm^3 g^{-1} for the partial specific volume ($\bar{v}$) (9, 14, 61) and 0.2 g g^{-1} of protein for the hydration (96). The axial ratios (a/b) of hydrodynamically equivalent prolate ellipsoids were determined from (f/f_o) $_{shape}$ and a published table (90).

Molybdate-Stabilized Receptor Forms

Discrete, relatively stable complexes, characterized by the parameters shown in the top line of Figure 1, have been detected in analyses of cytosol receptors for glucocorticoids, estrogens, and progestins in hypotonic buffers containing 10 or 20 mM Na_2MoO_4 (+Mo buffers) (35, 49, 72, 75, 85, 100, 112, 116). Molybdate and related oxyanions have been shown to inhibit the transformation of receptors (10, 35, 48, 59, 70, 85, 86, 112, 116). Hence, the complexes with R_S of 8.0-8.5 nm and $s_{20,w}$ of 9–10 S can be identified as untransformed receptors. The molecular weight of the molybdate-stabilized complex is approximately four times that of the product of its dissociation in hypertonic molybdate-free buffer (-Mo buffer) (75, 85, 100, 116), or that determined by electrophoresis of the reduced and denatured affinity-labeled receptor (12, 20, 38, 74, 105, 106). As the latter complex is apparently a single polypeptide chain, the untransformed receptor is probably a tetramer, assuming that it is composed exclusively of these monomeric units.

While there is growing experimental support for the proposal that the untransformed receptors are oligomeric proteins in vitro, the existence of the oligomers in vivo has not been established. Moreover, the number of steroid-binding sites and the structural relationships among the subunits require further research. The putative tetramer could contain between one and four steroid-binding sites; these sites could be located on identical or dissimilar polypeptide chains; and the tetramer could, in principle, contain subunits of receptors for more than one class of steroids. This uncertainty is indicated in Figure 1, where two of the subunits of the tetramer are drawn with stippled circles, which represent the steroid-binding sites, and two are drawn with dashed circles, which denote either the presence or absence of additional steroid-binding sites or other differences between the subunits.

Despite the use of hypotonic +Mo buffers for all analyses, receptors in certain cytosols, particularly those prepared from frozen tissues, appear to have somewhat lower values of R_S and M_r than those shown for the tetramer in Figure 1. In the case of the rat liver GR, freezing the tissue resulted in a statistically significant decrease in R_S, from 8.4 to 7.4 nm, and a decrease in the calculated value of M_r from ~330,000 to ~300,000 (99, 100). Similarly, in cytosols prepared from frozen human breast tumors and uterine specimens, values of R_S for the estrogen and progestin receptors were between 7.0 and 8.0 nm (64, 72, 86). Our recent results support the notion that in protease-rich cytosols, such as those prepared from various frozen tissues or fresh kidney, the receptors may be partially degraded by endogenous enzymes, despite the use of +Mo buffers for all analyses (100; Y.-W. Stevens & M. R. Sherman, unpublished observations).

In reports from several laboratories, steroid-receptor complexes with $s_{20,w}$ exceeding 8 S or M_r exceeding 300,000 have been described as "aggregates" or molybdate-induced artifacts (6, 25, 31). This interpretation is refuted by several observations: (a) The peaks of bound radioactivity detected after ultracentrifugation and gel filtration of steroid-labeled cytosols in hypotonic +Mo buffers are generally sharp and symmetrical (49, 72, 99, 103). Such patterns are characteristic of discrete complexes, rather than nonspecific aggregates. (b) Complexes of similar size are detected in +Mo buffers containing 0.12-0.15 M KCl, suggesting that they are not maintained primarily by nonspecific electrostatic interactions (64, 72, 99). (c) Some complexes with R_S of at least 7 nm are detected by filtration in hypotonic −Mo buffers of cytosols that have low activities of specific proteases (49, 99). Thus, molybdate stabilizes the large steroid-receptor complexes, but is not required for their formation. (d) Complexes of similar size to those obtained with molybdate are detected in protease-rich cytosols treated with leupeptin, a bacterial protease inhibitor containing N-acetyl- and N-propionyl-L-leucyl-L-leucyl-DL-arginine aldehydes (101–103).

Dimeric Receptor Forms

A 6 S dimer, composed of dissimilar steroid-binding subunits, has been proposed as the native form of the chick oviduct progestin receptor [reviewed in (31)]. Our analyses of mammalian receptors for several classes of steroids under various conditions have revealed forms with a continuous range of hydrodynamic parameters, including values of $s_{20,w}$ of 5–7 S. These observations are consistent with the existence of dimers as intermediates between the monomers and tetramers discussed above. From studies of GR in cytosols from mouse liver and pituitary tumor cells, Vedeckis (116) inferred that the transformed receptor states include a homologous dimer, characterized by R_S of 8.3 nm and $s_{20,w}$ of 5.0 S, in addition to a 3.2 S monomer. Confirmation of this proposal will require demonstrations of the integrity of the monomer and of the stability of the dimer during fractionation. Our studies of various receptor forms in rat liver cytosol suggest that complexes with $s_{20,w}$ of ~3 S include partially degraded monomers, and that those with $s_{20,w}$ of 5–7 S are unstable during repeated analyses (99, 100). Because of this instability, we have not reported values for R_S, M_r or the axial ratio of the putative dimer in Figure 1.

Identical or Dissimilar Subunits

The assumption that two types of steroid-binding subunits are present in mammalian steroid receptors has been based largely on analogies with the chick oviduct progestin receptor. In that system, two steroid-binding components were revealed by agarose filtration in hypertonic -Mo buffer (98) and were subsequently resolved by ion exchange chromatography (94). Although their steroid-binding domains are similar, the smaller component does not appear to be a proteolytic fragment of the larger one (4). Studies of affinity-labeled receptors in extracts of a human breast cancer cell line appear to support a similar model for mammalian progestin receptors (50). This interpretation would be strengthened, however, by additional data concerning the correspondence among the receptor forms detected by various techniques and by documentation of the effectiveness of the protease inhibitors used.

On the other hand, the concept of a single class of steroid-binding subunits in mammalian receptors is supported by data from studies of both estrogen and glucocorticoid receptors (77, 85, 100, 116). An example is the report of Raaka and Samuels (85), in which the rates of GR synthesis and degradation in rat pituitary tumor cells were evaluated by the density labeling technique. The cells were grown for various intervals in media containing amino acids that were enriched in the dense isotopes ^2H, ^{13}C, and ^{15}N. Resolution of the receptors containing dense amino acids from those containing normal (light) amino acids was enhanced by centrifugation through sucrose gradients prepared in 95% D_2O, 5% H_2O. This approach revealed a single biosynthetic rate constant for the untransformed steroid-receptor complexes. The results are consistent with the proposal that the untransformed ($\sim$10 S) receptor is composed of four homologous steroid-binding subunits (3.5 S).

Raaka & Samuels (85) also inferred that the untransformed (tetrameric) and transformed (monomeric) forms of the receptor are in equilibrium in the intact cell. Research on other systems by other techniques, however, has suggested that the regeneration of active cytoplasmic receptors following their release from the nucleus may involve enzymatic reactions, such as phosphorylation (15, 62). Thus, the equilibrium model of Raaka & Samuels (85), which is based on studies of receptors in intact cells, does not imply that the transitions among the tetramer, the monomer, and the presumed dimeric intermediate are also reversible in vitro. This uncertainty regarding the nature of the transitions is indicated in Figure 1 by showing the reverse reactions between these receptor forms as dashed arrows.

Monomeric Receptor Forms and Fragments

A relatively wide range of values is shown for M_r of the intact monomer in Figure 1. Many analyses of transformed GR from rodent liver and pituitary tumor cells have indicated values of $\sim$90,000. For example, the values of

$s_{20,w}$ (3.4 S) and R_S (6.0 nm) for the receptor purified from rat liver and characterized in isotonic buffers correspond to M_r of ~85,000 (for an assumed $\bar{v}$ of 0.725 cm³ g⁻¹) (125). Approximately the same value (90,000) was obtained for the covalently labeled rat liver receptor by polyacrylamide gel electrophoresis in the presence of sodium dodecyl sulfate (SDS–PAGE) (20). A slightly higher estimate (100,000) was obtained when receptors were transformed by warming intact rat thymocytes in the presence of steroid and the complexes were characterized in hypotonic +Mo buffers (35). A similar value (98,000) was obtained by electrophoresis of covalently labeled receptors from murine lymphoma and thymoma cells (16; see section on Affinity Labeling). The upper estimate of M_r indicated in Figure 1 (110,000) corresponds to R_S of 6.0 nm and $s_{20,w}$ of 4.3 S. These values are within the range reported for transformed receptors in several systems (34, 35, 55, 59, 66, 99).

In the schematic drawings in Figure 1, the steroid-binding site was arbitrarily placed at one end of the monomeric subunit. It should be noted, however, that the location of this domain at either the amino- or carboxyl-terminal of the polypeptide chain has not been established. On the other hand, various products of receptor cleavage by both endogenous and exogenous enzymes have been detected by means of their immunoactivity and/or their retention of bound steroid, and have been characterized extensively (5–7, 16, 33, 100, 111, 112, 117) (see section on Immunologic Techniques). These studies have revealed and confirmed the presence of several segments that are particularly vulnerable to proteolysis and of intervening domains that are relatively resistant to cleavage. Two of the protease-sensitive segments are designated in Figure 1 by the constricted regions proximal and distal to the steroid-binding site.

Cleavage close to the steroid-binding site (as drawn) releases that part of the monomer as a compact, globular structure. This fragment, called the *mero-receptor* (101), has M_r of 20,000–25,000 and appears to be the smallest form of the receptor still capable of retaining noncovalently bound steroid. These fragments have negligible affinity for nuclei, DNA, or DEAE-cellulose under the usual conditions of analysis (35, 112, 117). Similar fragments of receptors for five classes of steroids have been detected when cytosols from a wide range of healthy and malignant tissues were analyzed under conditions that favor proteolysis (31, 47, 64, 97, 101–103, 123). Mero-receptors have also been produced by treatment of cytosols with lysosomal extracts, papain, or trypsin [reviewed in (7)], or by treatment of molybdate-stabilized receptors with high concentrations of α-chymotrypsin or trypsin (100, 112). These results demonstrate the remarkable stability of the steroid-binding domain.

Cleavage of the monomer at points more distal to the binding site produces receptor forms of intermediate size. These were designated Form IV in our earlier model (101). Intermediate fragments can be formed either by the action of endogenous cytosolic enzymes or by the addition to cytosol of lysosomal extracts, chymotrypsin or moderate doses of trypsin (5–7, 31, 97, 100–102,

112, 117). In several mammalian systems, complexes of this size were found to have higher affinity for nuclei and DNA than the larger monomeric forms (6, 7, 111, 112, 117, 127).

The wide range of values shown for the parameters of the intermediate fragments in Figure 1 reflects our inclusion in this category of all receptor forms that are larger than the mero-receptor and smaller than the intact monomer. More precise characterization of these fragments is also impeded by their instability, particularly during repeated analyses. For example, values of 3.2 and 2.7 nm, respectively, were obtained for R_S of such fragments in rat liver cytosol in the first and second analyses by agarose filtration in hypertonic $-Mo$ buffer (100). Estimates of R_S of the products of chymotryptic digestion of rat liver GR analyzed in hypertonic buffers have also varied significantly. The use of different gel filtration matrices, buffers, and standards for column calibration in these studies may have contributed to the variation among the reported values, including 2.8–2.9 nm (112), 3.3 nm (6, 80), and 3.6 nm (5).

A complex with properties resembling those of intermediate fragments has been detected following transformation of receptors in rat liver and kidney cortex cytosols, and has been identified by Litwack and coworkers as a separate, physiologically active entity, called Corticosteroid Binder IB (53, 56, 92). In kidney cortex cytosol, Binder IB is the major component, while in liver cytosol it is a minor component. From experiments involving mixtures of liver and kidney cytosols (3, 56) and the use of protease inhibitors of various specificities (58), it was inferred that Binder IB is not a proteolytic fragment of the 6 nm receptor form.

Several types of evidence favor reconsideration of the possibility that Binder IB may be an intermediate fragment: (a) Apparent differences between the steroid-binding specificities of Binder IB and the larger receptor form were not based on studies of these components under comparable conditions (53). (b) The failure of Binder IB to cross-react with antibodies prepared against the larger receptor form may be explained by assuming that the antigenic sites were removed during formation of the fragment (6, 7; see section on Immunologic Techniques). (c) Binder IB was not detected when gel filtration was performed in hypotonic $+Mo$ buffer (58, 99, 103), in which the oligomeric receptor form is stabilized. Under these conditions, however, the kidney receptor was still somewhat smaller than the liver receptor [R_S of 7.1 ± 0.3 nm (n=21) vs 8.4 ± 0.2 nm (n=20), p<0.001] (99, 100). Reanalysis of the $\sim$7 nm complex from kidney cytosol in hypertonic $-Mo$ buffer revealed a complex with R_S of $\sim$3 nm. We infer that this complex (i.e. Binder IB) is a product of the dissociation (transformation) and/or cleavage of the molybdate-stabilized $\sim$7 nm complex. (d) Experiments in which a small amount of kidney cortex plus medulla (10–20% w/w) was mixed with a larger amount of liver prior to homogenization resulted in "kidney-type" receptor patterns when the cytosols were analyzed in either hypotonic +Mo buffer or hypertonic −Mo buffer (Ref. 103a; also, unpublished observations). (e) Chromatographic patterns of the kidney cytosol receptor in both buffer systems (0.4 M KCl −Mo; −KCl +Mo) were similar to those of the liver receptor following mild chymotryptic digestion (100; Tuazon & Sherman, unpublished observations).

Finally, we include in the category of intermediate fragments the components with M_r of ~70,000 that have been detected following SDS gel electrophoresis of receptors from protease-rich tissues (44, 50, 62, 66). It is known that certain proteases are relatively resistant to denaturation by heat and/or detergents, compared with other proteins (119). Therefore, the receptors may have been cleaved by such enzymes during the preparation of samples for electrophoresis.

Aggregated Receptors; Interactions with RNA

Receptors have also been found to form large aggregates, particularly when cytosols from rapidly proliferating tissues, such as mammary tumors and uterine endometrium, are analyzed in the absence of molybdate. These aggregates are sufficiently large to be excluded from the usual gel filtration columns and to sediment to the bottom of the tubes during centrifugation under the usual conditions (13, 64, 72, 102). Formation of aggregates is inhibited by the inclusion of molybdate or moderate concentrations of salt in the buffers, or by treatment of the cytosol with high concentrations of ribonucleases. From this, it was inferred that the large complexes consist of receptors bound by electrostatic interactions to ribonucleoproteins (possibly ribosomal fragments). This interpretation was supported by the concomitant destruction by ribonuclease of the receptor aggregates, of material in the void volume of the columns with high optical density at 260 nm, and of cytoplasmic particles with $s_{20,w}$ of ~34 and 50 S (13). The inhibition by RNA of receptor binding to DNA, and the direct interactions of receptors with ribonucleoproteins, homologous and heterologous RNA, and synthetic polyribonucleotides, have been documented in a variety of steroid-receptor systems (11, 22, 39, 51, 114). Some of the essential questions to be answered by future research are: (a) Do interactions of receptors with RNA or ribonucleoproteins occur in vivo? (b) If so, what is their functional significance? (c) Are specific RNAs integral constituents of the untransformed cytoplasmic receptors and/or components of the nuclear binding sites of the transformed steroid-receptor complexes?

ALTERED RECEPTORS IN MALIGNANCY

Tumor cells that are resistant to the catabolic effects of steroids and contain receptors with altered physical-chemical properties are valuable sources of material for studies of the relationship between receptor structure and function.

Glucocorticoid receptors in two model systems have been investigated in considerable detail: P1798 lymphoma, a transplantable tumor in mice (80, 111, 112), and S49 murine lymphoma tissue culture cells (16, 32, 74, 127). More recent studies of corticosteroid-sensitive (CS) and corticosteroid resistant (CR) lines of hamster melanoma cells (34) are summarized below.

Analyses in hypotonic +Mo buffer of untransformed cytosolic GR complexes from CS P1798 tumor lymphocytes revealed R_S of 8.1 nm, $s_{20,w}$ of 9.2 S, and an apparent M_r of ~325,000 (for an assumed $\bar{v}$ of 0.74 cm^3 g^{-1}). Transformed GR complexes from the same tumors had R_S of 6.0 nm and $s_{20,w}$ of 3.7 S in hypertonic −Mo buffers, corresponding to M_r of ~90,000 (112). Similarly, transformed complexes from the CS S49 cells had M_r of ~90,000 (127), but the hydrodynamic parameters of untransformed CS S49 receptors have not been reported. The physical-chemical properties of GR from corticosteroid-resistant P1798 tumors and from S49 variants with increased nuclear transfer of receptors, S49 (nt^i), were strikingly different from those of the CS tumors and cells. Thus, transformed GR complexes from CR P1798 lymphocytes had R_S of only 2.8–2.9 nm, $s_{20,w}$ of 3.3 S, and an apparent M_r of ~40,000 (112). Corticosteroid-resistant S49 (nt^i) cells contained similarly altered GR complexes, with M_r of ~40,000 (127). Elution of these complexes from nuclei or from nonspecific DNA required higher concentrations of salt than elution of the wild-type complexes (112, 127).

Despite the susceptibility of steroid receptors to proteolytic cleavage, as discussed above, it has been considered unlikely that the ~40,000 M_r complex was formed by the cleavage of a putative CS-like ~90,000 M_r precursor (74, 112). No conversion of the larger CS receptor to the smaller form was observed in extracts of mixtures of CS and CR tumors (112). Moreover, somatic cell hybrids between the wild-type S49 and S49 (nt^i) cells synthesized a mixture of the ~90,000 and ~40,000 M_r receptor forms characteristic of the parental lines (127).

The hydrodynamic parameters of untransformed complexes from CR P1798 (R_S of 7.0 nm, $s_{20,w}$ of 9.9 S) also differed significantly from those of untransformed CS P1798 receptors determined under the same conditions (R_S of 8.1 nm, $s_{20,w}$ of 9.2 S). The calculated value of M_r of untransformed CR P1798 complexes was ~300,000, compared with ~325,000 for the CS P1798 complexes. After incubation of cytosol from CS P1798 with α-chymotrypsin, R_S of the untransformed complexes was decreased from 8.1 to 7.0 nm. Similar treatment had no effect on R_S of the CR P1798 receptors. In contrast, trypsin treatment converted the untransformed GR complexes from both CS and CR tumors to the mero-receptor (R_S of ~2.2 nm) (112). A prominent difference between the transformed receptors in both CR P1798 and S49 (nt^i) tumor lymphocytes and the normal CS complexes is the apparent absence of a domain with M_r of ~50,000. Hence, Stevens et al (112) inferred that this portion of the receptor is essential for the molecular events that trigger the phenotypic responses to glucocorticoids.

Differences between the properties of GR in corticosteroid-sensitive and -resistant lines of transplantable hamster melanomas have been reported by Hawkins et al (34). Growth of the sensitive tumors was retarded significantly by daily administration of dexamethasone (9α-fluoro-11β,17,21-trihydroxy-16α-methyl-pregna-1,4-diene-3,20-dione) to tumor-bearing animals, while growth of resistant tumors was unaffected. It was shown that cytosol from sensitive tumors contained two forms of [^{3}H]dexamethasone-receptor complexes, with $s_{20,w}$ in -Mo buffer of 7 and 13 S, respectively, while only the 7 S form was detected in cytosol from resistant tumors. No further physical-chemical analyses were performed on the 7 or 13 S complexes. Transformed complexes from CS tumors appeared to contain more than one component, as reflected in a heterodisperse elution pattern from DEAE-cellulose. Those from CR tumors were eluted as a single, sharp peak from DEAE-cellulose, and had slightly higher affinity for DNA-cellulose than the CS receptors. Transformed complexes from CR and CS tumors were indistinguishable by centrifugation in −Mo buffer; both had $s_{20,w}$ of 4–5 S.

To the best of our knowledge, there has been no definitive demonstration of structurally altered receptors in steroid-resistant tumor cells of human origin. Schmidt et al (91) studied a CR leukemic cell line of human origin in which resistance is associated with a defect in the stability of the transformed receptor. The structural modification responsible for this "activation labile" phenotype, however, has not been identified. McCaffrey et al (60) detected apparent changes in GR structure in peripheral blood cells from some leukemia patients. Untransformed and transformed receptors from those patients were eluted anomalously from DEAE-cellulose, generally as a single, low-salt peak, in which the complexes were characterized by $s_{20,w}$ of only 2–2.5 S. In contrast, the elution profile from DEAE-cellulose of untransformed receptors in normal specimens had both low- and high-salt peaks, in which the complexes had $s_{20,w}$ of 3.5 and 8.5 S, repectively. All of these analyses were performed in −Mo buffers. Even after transformation by heat, the "abnormal" receptors displayed minimal affinity for DNA-cellulose. These results could not be correlated with the steroid-responsiveness of the disease, since all of the patients had received multiple agent chemotherapy. Furthermore, as noted by the investigators, all of the samples that contained "abnormal" receptors were obtained from cells that had been frozen. As discussed above and elsewhere (100), freezing of cells may result in spurious changes in the physical-chemical properties of the receptors. Stevens et al (112) have also emphasized the importance of distinguishing between intrinsic and artifactual alterations in receptor structure. Further characterization of receptors in corticosteroid-sensitive and -resistant cells by means of affinity labeling and immunologic techniques is discussed below in the section on Immunologic Techniques.

SELECTED METHODOLOGICAL DEVELOPMENTS AND RESULTS

A comprehensive survey of recent developments in the methodology of receptor analysis is beyond the scope of this review. Much effort has been invested in the application to receptors of techniques for the rapid fractionation and characterization of proteins. These methods include density gradient centrifugation in vertical rotors (8, 114), ion exchange and DNA-cellulose chromatography on "minicolumns" (35), chromatofocusing (8, 108–110), and high performance liquid chromatography (42, 82, 87, 124). A method that may permit the evaluation of the size of the steroid-binding unit of receptors in intact cells, and is thus of great potential utility, is radiation inactivation (32). This involves the calculation of the size of a functional unit in a protein from the target volume for destruction by ionizing radiation (45). We have chosen to discuss in some detail only two experimental approaches and their results. These are the immunologic and affinity labeling techniques, which have already contributed significantly to our understanding of receptor structure.

Affinity Labeling

Formation of covalent complexes of labeled steroids with receptors permits studies of receptor structure and function under conditions that might cause dissociation of noncovalent complexes. Affinity labeling also facilitates the purification of receptors and their subunits. Among the possible chemical mechanisms of affinity labeling, two have been used in most studies of glucocorticoid receptors: electrophilic affinity labeling (20, 105) and photoaffinity labeling (16, 74, 120). A third approach, chemoaffinity labeling (107), has not been widely applied to GR and will not be discussed further. Affinity labeling has also been used in research on progestin (4, 17, 36, 50, 120) and estrogen receptors (44). In keeping with the emphasis of this review, however, this discussion will be restricted to GR.

ELECTROPHILIC AFFINITY LABELING   In search of suitable reagents for affinity labeling, Simons & Thompson (106) synthesized both radioinert and tritiated dexamethasone 21-methanesulfonate (dexamethasone mesylate; DM) and examined their interactions with hepatoma tissue culture (HTC) cells. Radioinert DM inhibited the induction by dexamethasone of tyrosine aminotransferase in intact HTC cells and blocked the binding of [^{3}H]dexamethasone to cell-free extracts. Simons & Thompson (106) suggested that the covalent binding of DM to the receptor might involve displacement of the methanesulfonic acid anion from C-21 and the formation of an irreversible thioether between C-21 and a cysteine residue in the steroid-binding site.

Combinations of biochemical and immunochemical techniques have been used to identify the products obtained by labeling intact cells and cytosols with [3H]DM (19, 20). The results of these studies have supported the identification of a covalently labeled ~90,000 M_r complex as a fundamental structural unit of the receptor, in reduced and denatured form.

[3H]Dexamethasone 21-mesylate has also been used to label GR in HeLa cells (12), mouse fibroblasts (38), rat thymocytes, and human malignant lymphoid cells (23). As in rat liver and HTC cells, the major specifically labeled covalent complex in HeLa cells, thymocytes, and fibroblasts was the ~90,000 M_r complex. In the neoplastic lymphocytes, however, several smaller components, with M_r of 31,000 to 75,000, were also specifically labeled.

Simons et al (105) recently demonstrated that covalent [3H]DM-receptor complexes could undergo in vitro transformation to the DNA- and nuclear-binding state. They found that the covalent complexes were transformed by gel filtration or warming to the same extent as noncovalent complexes with dexamethasone. In whole HTC cells at 37°C, however, receptors labeled with [3H]DM were translocated to the nuclei much less efficiently than those labeled with [3H]dexamethasone.

PHOTOAFFINITY LABELING   An alternative approach to the formation of covalently labeled steroid-protein complexes is photoaffinity labeling with ketosteroids containing multiple conjugated double bonds (113). This method was applied to the chick oviduct progestin receptor by Dure et al (17), who used the synthetic progestin, R5020 (17α, 21-dimethyl-19-nor-pregna-4, 9-diene-3, 20-dione) as the ligand. This compound is available in tritiated form of high specific activity and can be photoactivated by ultraviolet light at wavelengths above 300 nm, thus minimizing damage to the proteins.

As R5020 also binds specifically to glucocorticoid receptors (52), Baxter and coworkers (74) used it to label GR in HTC cell cytosol. Under the conditions used, however, the receptors were covalently labeled with only ~2–5% efficiency. Analysis of the labeled complexes by SDS-PAGE revealed three major bands, with M_r of ~87,000, ~48,000, and 30,000–40,000. Excess radioinert R5020 or dexamethasone suppressed the labeling of the ~87,000 M_r component, supporting its identification as the receptor. A small amount of specifically labeled material with M_r of ~75,000 was presumably a fragment of the larger complex.

Glucocorticoid receptors in corticosteroid-sensitive and -resistant lines of mouse lymphoma cells have also been studied by photoaffinity labeling with [3H]R5020 (74) or [3H]triamcinolone acetonide (9α-fluoro-11β,16α,17,

21-tetrahydroxy-pregna-1,4-diene-3,20-dione 16,17-acetonide; TA) (16) (see section on Altered Receptors in Malignancy). Triamcinolone acetonide has the advantages of being a potent, high affinity glucocorticoid, and of having a higher efficiency of covalent attachment than R5020 (16). When characterized by SDS-PAGE, the photoaffinity-labeled complexes from CS cells and from the nuclear transfer deficient variant, CR S49(nt⁻), had an apparent M_r of ~90,000, while the covalent complexes from S49(nt^i) lymphoma cells had M_r of ~40,000 (16, 74). These results are in agreement with previous analyses of noncovalent complexes from these cells (127).

Limited chymotryptic digestion of photoaffinity-labeled receptors in wild-type S49 or S49(nt⁻) lymphoma cells resulted in the apparent conversion of the ~90,000 M_r form to a 39,000 M_r species. No shift in size was detected after similar treatment of CR S49(nt^i) cell cytosol (16). Analogous results were obtained previously by Stevens et al (112), who used noncovalent GR complexes from CS and CR strains of murine lymphoma P1798. Exhaustive digestion with trypsin or α-chymotrypsin of a partially purified, covalently labeled ~40,000 M_r complex from rat liver cytosol gave rise to a single band on SDS-PAGE in the presence of urea (120). The molecular weight of the resultant covalently labeled fragment (~8,000) was considerably less than that of the mero-receptor (~23,000), which is the smallest form of the receptor capable of retaining noncovalently bound steroid (101).

Immunologic Techniques

ANTIBODIES AGAINST STEROID RECEPTORS

Polyclonal antisera Greene, Jensen, and coworkers were the first to raise antibodies against steroid-receptor complexes [reviewed in (30)]. Subsequently, antibodies have been raised against receptors for glucocorticoids (19, 28, 29, 79, 121), progestins (21, 54, 88), and 1,25-dihydroxyvitamin D₃ (83). Only the work on glucocorticoid receptors will be discussed in detail.

The antigens used for developing polyclonal anti-GR antisera were highly purified preparations of transformed receptors from rat liver cytosol (6, 19, 28, 79). All of these antisera recognized the ~90,000 M_r form of the rat liver receptor. The antiserum prepared by Govindan (28) also cross-reacted with a ~45,000 M_r complex, which is probably a proteolytic fragment. Furthermore, Govindan showed that antiserum raised against the ~45,000 M_r component cross-reacted with the ~90,000 M_r complex. In contrast, the antisera described by Okret et al (79) and by Eisen (19) did not recognize the fragment generated by treatment of rat liver cytosol with α-chymotrypsin (R_S of 2.8–3.6 nm, M_r of 40,000–45,000). Specificity was demonstrated by the inability of the anti-GR antisera to cross-react appreciably with rat serum corticosteroid-binding globulin (transcortin) (19, 79), rat liver estrogen-binding protein (19), rat prostate androgen receptor, or rat uterine estrogen or progestin receptors (79).

Monoclonal antibodies   The first monoclonal antibodies against a steroid-receptor complex were obtained by Greene, Jensen and coworkers [reviewed in (30)]. Subsequently, monoclonal antibodies were generated against ER isolated from MCF-7 human breast cancer cells. Moncharmont et al (67) have also raised monoclonal antibodies against ER from calf uterus.

Westphal et al (121) succeeded in generating several monoclonal antibodies to rat liver GR. Eight out of 102 hybridomas produced anti-receptor antibodies. Seven of these were of the IgM isotype, and the eighth one had the heavy chain isotype IgG_1. The apparent dissociation constants of the antibody-GR complexes varied from 0.5 to 77 nM at 4°C, but the values did not appear to be correlated with the heavy chain isotype. The IgG_1 monoclonal antibody bound the ~90,000 M_r form of GR quantitatively, while three different antibodies of the IgM class bound only 45–65% of the GR complexes in rat liver cytosol. This lack of quantitative recognition was probably not due to the immunologic heterogeneity of the receptor preparation, since a mixture of all three IgM antibodies did not increase the degree of antibody-receptor complex formation.

While the IgG_1 monoclonal antibody cross-reacted appreciably with liver receptors from mouse and hen, and to some extent with those from rabbit and guinea pig, the three IgM antibodies recognized only the rat liver GR (121). In all cases, liver cytosol was prepared in the presence of Na_2MoO_4, and it was shown by gel filtration that the receptors had not been degraded. A monoclonal antibody to rat liver GR described by Gametchu and Harrison (27) also recognized mouse liver GR.

As was found previously with most polyclonal antisera, none of the monoclonal antibodies prepared by Westphal et al (121) recognized the ~40,000 M_r receptor fragment containing the DNA- and steroid-binding sites. Therefore, the antigenic determinants recognized by the monoclonal antibodies appear to be located in a domain of the receptor which lacks steroid-binding or DNA-binding capability (6, 7, 112). Since none of the monoclonal antibodies prevented adsorption of the GR complexes to DNA-cellulose, the immunoactive domains were apparently not close to the amino acid sequence(s) involved in these interactions.

Another immunologic approach to the study of receptor structure consists of attaching a hapten that interacts with specific groups on the receptor, and using antibodies against the hapten to examine the derivatized receptor. This has been done recently, using 5'-phosphopyridoxylated GR and monoclonal antibodies to the 5'-phosphopyridoxyl group (118).

STRUCTURAL AND FUNCTIONAL ANALYSES OF RECEPTORS WITH IMMUNO-LOGIC PROBES   As discussed above, in some murine tumor lymphocytes that are resistant to the lethal effects of glucocorticoids, the transformed receptors have R_S of only 2.8–2.9 nm, M_r of only ~40,000, and apparently lack the third (nonsteroid-binding, nonDNA-binding) domain (16, 74, 112). The development of methods for the detection and characterization of this domain was essential to understanding its role in the functional complex. The enzyme-linked immunoadsorbent assay (ELISA) described by Okret et al (79) has proven extremely useful in this regard. This assay is based on the use of a polyclonal anti-GR immunoglobin that interacts with the third domain of the rat liver GR (6) and with the receptor in corticosteroid-sensitive murine P1798 tumors, but not with the smaller receptor form in corticosteroid-resistant tumors (112).

The GR complex from rat liver cytosol and the products of its cleavage by α-chymotrypsin were fractionated by gel filtration and DNA-cellulose chromatography and the eluates were analyzed with the ELISA. The results showed clear resolution between a 3.3 nm steroid-binding, nonimmunoactive fragment and a 2.6 nm immunoactive, nonsteroid-binding fragment. Both of these fragments were adsorbed to DNA-cellulose, but the fragment containing bound steroid was adsorbed more tightly than the immunoactive fragment (6). In another study of fragments of the rat liver GR, employing immunochemical and other techniques, Harrison et al (33 and unpublished results) detected at least seven trypsin-sensitive sites. All of the fragments with M_r of at least 45,000 were both immunoactive and labeled covalently with steroid, while the smaller fragments were detectable by only one or the other technique.

There are several plausible explanations for the origin of the ~40,000 M_r receptor form detected in extracts of corticosteroid-resistant tumor lymphocytes. It could be the result of (*a*) the failure of separately synthesized receptor domains to be joined into the wild-type polypeptide; (*b*) a mutational event or alteration in gene transcription or post-transcriptional processing resulting in the synthesis of either a truncated polypeptide or a larger precursor with increased sensitivity to proteolysis; or (*c*) the cleavage of a wild-type ~90,000 M_r precursor by unusually active endogenous enzymes.

Studies of extracts of mixtures of CR and CS tumors appeared to rule out the third explanation (112). An immunologic approach was used in exploring the other possibilities. Okret et al (80) confirmed that the ELISA was capable of detecting the immunoactive fragment produced by chymotryptic cleavage of the CS P1798 murine receptor, as observed in earlier studies of the rat liver receptor (6). In contrast, no immunoactive fragment was detected in cytosol from CR P1798 tumors. These results are consistent with the synthesis in CR P1798 tumors of either truncated receptor monomers, lacking the immunoactive domain, or receptors with increased susceptibility to cleavage. It is clear that extensive degradation of the immunoactive domain could have precluded its detection by the ELISA. An alternative explanation is that the missing fragment of the CR P1798 receptor may have been sequestered in another compartment of the tumor cells, since only the cytosol was analyzed (80).

Future investigations of this possibility and of other questions concerning the intracellular distribution of various receptor forms may be facilitated by immunocytochemical techniques, such as those described by Sekeris and coworkers (81).

CONCLUSIONS

Our concept of mammalian steroid receptors as oligomeric proteins with multiple functional domains has been strengthened considerably by recent research. Nevertheless, significant gaps remain in our knowledge of their chemical composition, quaternary structure, and metabolism. The discovery that the noncovalently labeled, untransformed steroid-receptor complexes can be stabilized by molybdate and related oxyanions has permitted the confirmation of their oligomeric nature in vitro and the demonstration of remarkable parallels among the structures of receptors for estrogens, progestins, androgens, mineralocorticoids and glucocorticoids in a wide variety of tissues. The recognition of this similarity has greatly reduced the complexity of the problems to be solved.

Characterization of the transformed receptors and their proteolytic products under denaturing conditions was made possible by the development of radioactively labeled steroid analogs that bind with high affinity and selectivity and can be attached covalently to the receptors. The presence of separate structural and functional domains within the monomeric units was revealed by limited digestion of the receptors by endogenous or exogenous enzymes, and analyses of the products by physical-chemical and immunologic techniques. Structural analyses of altered receptors in steroid-resistant tumor cells have also been facilitated by these methods. Finally, the first definitive information about the rates of biosynthesis and degradation of receptors in intact cells has emerged from the application of the density labeling technique. Further insights into the structure and metabolism of receptors will be provided by the introduction of covalent cross-links between the receptor subunits and by the use of recombinant DNA technology. This will permit the determination of the sequences of the structural genes, nuclear RNA precursors, and mRNAs of the receptors, and studies of the regulation of their transcription, processing, and translation, respectively.

ACKNOWLEDGMENTS

We are grateful to Fe B. Tuazon, Yee-Wan Stevens, Mary C. Moran, En-Mei Niu and numerous other collaborators for their essential contributions to the research performed in our laboratories at Sloan-Kettering Institute (M. R. S.) and at the Research Institute of the Hospital for Joint Diseases and Medical Center, Mount Sinai School of Medicine of the City University of New York

(J. S.). We also acknowledge with appreciation the many colleagues who provided preprints of their forthcoming publications. The research at Sloan-Kettering Institute was generously supported by grants CA 28392, CA 32178, CA 29564, and CA 08748 from the National Cancer Institute, grants AM 20505 and AM 07313 from the National Institutes of Health, grant GA-PS-8118 from the Rockefeller Foundation, and by contributions from the Margolish Fund, Sinatra Fund, and Borden Cancer Research Fund. Research at the Hospital for Joint Diseases was supported by grant CA 14987 from the National Cancer Institute, grant BC 327 from the American Cancer Society, a Special Fellowship (1974–1976), and a Scholar Award (1976–1981) to J. S. from the Leukemia Society of America, Inc.

Literature Cited

1. Atger, M., Milgrom, E. 1976. Mechanism and kinetics of the thermal activation of glucocorticoid hormone·receptor complex. *J. Biol. Chem.* 251:4758–62
2. Bailly, A., Le Fevre, B., Savouret, J.-F., Milgrom, E. 1980. Activation and changes in sedimentation properties of steroid receptors. *J. Biol. Chem.* 255:2729–34
3. Barnett, C. A., Litwack, G. 1982. Additional evidence that Corticosteroid Binder IB is not derived from Binder II by limited proteolysis. *Biochem. Biophys. Res. Commun.* 108:1670–75
4. Birnbaumer, M., Schrader, W. T., O'Malley, B. W. 1983. Assessment of structural similarities in chick oviduct progesterone receptor subunits by partial proteolysis of photoaffinity-labeled proteins. *J. Biol. Chem.* 258:7331–37
5. Carlstedt-Duke, J., Gustafsson, J.-Å., Wrange, Ö. 1977. Formation and characteristics of hepatic dexamethasone-receptor complexes of different molecular weight. *Biochim. Biophys. Acta* 497:507–24
6. Carlstedt-Duke, J., Okret, S., Wrange, Ö., Gustafsson, J.-Å. 1982. Immunochemical analysis of the glucocorticoid receptor: Identification of a third domain separate from the steroid-binding and DNA-binding domains. *Proc. Natl. Acad. Sci. USA* 79:4260–64
7. Carlstedt-Duke, J., Wrange, Ö., Okret, S., Stevens, J., Stevens, Y.-W., Gustafsson, J.-Å. 1983. Functional analysis of the glucocorticoid receptor by limited proteolysis. In *Gene Regulation by Steroid Hormones*, Vol. 2, ed. A. K. Roy, J. H. Clark, pp. 151–80. New York: Springer.
8. Chang, C. H., Rowley, D. R., Lobl, T. J., Tindall, D. J. 1982. Purification and characterization of androgen receptor from steer seminal vesicle. *Biochemistry* 21:4102–9
9. Charlwood, P. A. 1957. Partial specific volumes of proteins in relation to composition and environment. *J. Am. Chem. Soc.* 79:776–81
10. Chong, M. T., Lippman, M. E. 1981–82. Effects of temperature, nucleotides and sodium molybdate on activation and DNA binding of estrogen, glucocorticoid, progesterone and androgen receptors in MCF-7 human cancer cells. *J. Receptor Res.* 2:575–600
11. Chong, M. T., Lippman, M. E. 1982. Effects of RNA and ribonuclease on the binding of estrogen and glucocorticoid receptors from MCF-7 cells to DNA-cellulose. *J. Biol. Chem.* 257:2996–3002
12. Cidlowski, J. A., Richon, V. 1983. Physical characterization and purification of affinity labeled human glucocorticoid receptors. *Abstr. 65th Ann. Meet. Endocrine Soc.*, San Antonio, Tex. p. 227
13. Costello, M. A., Sherman, M. R. 1980. Modification of mouse mammary tumor glucocorticoid receptor form by ribonuclease treatment. *Abstr. 62nd Ann. Meet. Endocrine Soc.*, Washington DC, p. 174
14. Currie, R. A., Cidlowski, J. A. 1982. Physicochemical properties of the cytoplasmic glucocorticoid receptor complex in HeLa S$_3$ cells. *J. Steroid Biochem.* 16:419–28
15. Dahmer, M. K., Housley, P. R., Pratt, W. B. 1984. Effects of molybdate and endogenous inhibitors on steroid receptor inactivation, transformation, and translocation. *Ann. Rev. Physiol.* 46:67–81
16. Dellweg, H.-G., Hotz, A., Mugele, K.,

Gehring, U. 1982. Active domains in wild-type and mutant glucocorticoid receptors. *EMBO Journ.* 1:285–89

17. Dure, L. S., IV, Schrader, W. T., O'Malley, B. W. 1980. Covalent attachment of a progestational steroid to the chick oviduct progesterone receptor by photoaffinity labeling. *Nature* 283:784–86

18. Eckert, R. L., Katzenellenbogen, B. S. 1982. Physical properties of estrogen receptor complexes in MCF-7 human breast cancer cells. Differences with antiestrogen and estrogen. *J. Biol. Chem.* 257:8840–46

19. Eisen, H. J. 1982. Immunochemical approaches to the study of glucocorticoid receptors. In *Biochemical Actions of Hormones,* ed. G. Litwack, New York: Academic 9:255–70.

20. Eisen, H. J., Schleenbaker, R. E., Simons, S. S., Jr. 1981. Affinity labeling of the rat liver glucocorticoid receptor with dexamethasone 21-mesylate. Identification of covalently labeled receptor by immunochemical methods. *J. Biol. Chem.* 256:12920–25

21. Feil, P. D. 1983. Characterization of guinea pig anti-progestin receptor antiserum. *Endocrinology* 112:396–98

22. Feldman, M., Kallos, J., Hollander, V. P. 1981. RNA inhibits estrogen receptor binding to DNA. *J. Biol. Chem.* 256:1145–48

23. Foster, C. M., Eisen, H. J., Bloomfield, C. D. 1983. Covalent of rat thymocyte and human lymphoid glucocorticoid receptors. *Cancer Res.* 43: In press

24. Fox, T. O., Wieland, S. J. 1981. Isoelectric focusing of androgen receptors from wild-type and *Tfm* mouse kidneys. *Endocrinology* 109:790–97

25. Franceschi, R. T., DeLuca, H. F. 1979. Aggregation properties of the 1,25-dihydroxyvitamin D_3 receptor from chick intestinal cytosol. *J. Biol. Chem.* 254:11629–35

26. Funder, J. W., Barlow, J. W. 1980. Heterogeneity of glucocorticoid receptors. *Circ. Res.* 46:I 83–87

27. Gametchu, B., Harrison, R. W. 1984. Characterization of a monoclonal antibody to the rat liver glucocorticoid receptor. *Endocrinology* 114: In press

28. Govindan, M. V. 1979. Purification of glucocorticoid receptors from rat liver cytosol. Preparation of antibodies against the major receptor proteins and application of immunological techniques to study activation and translocation. *J. Steroid Biochem.* 11:323–32

29. Grandics, P., Gasser, D. L., Litwack, G.

1982. Monoclonal antibodies to the glucocorticoid receptor. *Endocrinology* 111:1731–33

30. Greene, G. L. 1983. Application of immunochemical techniques to the analysis of estrogen receptor structure and function. In *Biochemical Actions of Hormones,* ed. G. Litwack, Vol. 11. New York: Academic. In press

31. Grody, W. W., Schrader, W. T., O'Malley, B. W. 1982. Activation, transformation, and subunit structure of steroid hormone receptors. *Endocr. Rev.* 3:141–63

32. Gruol, D. J., Kempner, E. S., Bourgeois, S. 1983. Measurements of the size of glucocorticoid receptors using radiation inactivation. *Biophys. J.* 41:199a (Abstr.)

33. Harrison, R. W., Fairfield, S. J., Eisen, H. J., Reichman, M. 1982. Immunologic localization of the rat glucocorticoid receptor on "Western blots" of sodium dodecyl sulfate polyacrylamide gels. *Abstr. 64th Ann. Meet. Endocrine Soc.,* San Francisco, p. 192

34. Hawkins, E. F., Hutchens, T. W., Fligiel, S., Horn, D., Markland, F. S. 1982. Glucocorticoids and melanoma: Receptor properties of dexamethasone sensitve and resistant tumors. *J. Steroid Biochem.* 16:673–81

35. Holbrook, N. J., Bodwell, J. E., Jeffries, M., Munck, A. 1983. Characterization of nonactivated and activated glucocorticoid-receptor complexes from intact rat thymus cells. *J. Biol. Chem.* 258:6477–85

36. Holmes, S. D., Smith, R. G. 1983. Identification of histidine and methionine residues in the active site of the human uterine progesterone receptor with the affinity labels 11α- and 16α-(bromoacetoxy)progesterone. *Biochemistry* 22:1729–34

37. Horwitz, K. B., McGuire, W. L. 1980. Nuclear estrogen receptors. Effects of inhibitors on processing and steady state levels. *J. Biol. Chem.* 255:9699–705

38. Housley, P. R., Pratt, W. B. 1983. Direct demonstration of glucocorticoid receptor phosphorylation by intact L-cells. *J. Biol. Chem.* 258:4630–35

39. Hutchens, T. W., Markland, F. S., Hawkins, E. F. 1982. RNA induced reversal of glucocorticoid receptor activation. *Biochem. Biophys. Res. Commun.* 105:20–27

40. Jensen, E. V., Suzuki, T., Kawashima, T., Stumpf, W. E., Jungblut, P. W., DeSombre, E. R. 1968. A two-step mechanism for the interaction of estradiol

with rat uterus. *Proc. Natl. Acad. Sci. USA* 59:632–38

41. Kassis, J. A., Gorski, J. 1981. Estrogen receptor replenishment. Evidence for receptor recycling. *J. Biol. Chem.* 256:7378–82

42. Kato, Y., Komiya, K., Sasaki, H., Hashimoto, T. 1980. Separation range and separation efficiency in high-speed gel filtration on TSK-GEL SW columns. *J. Chromatogr.* 190:297–303

43. Katzenellenbogen, B. S., Pavlik, E. J., Robertson, D. W., Katzenellenbogen, J. A. 1981. Interaction of a high affinity anti-estrogen (α-[4-pyrrolidinoethoxy] phenyl-4-hydroxy-α'-nitrostilbene, CI628M) with uterine estrogen receptors. *J. Biol. Chem.* 256:2908–15

44. Katzenellenbogen, J. A., Carlson,, K. E., Heiman, D. F., Robertson, D. W., Wei, L. L., Katzenellenbogen, B. S. 1983. Efficient and highly selective covalent labeling of the estrogen receptor with [³H]tamoxifen aziridine. *J. Biol. Chem.* 258:3487–95

45. Kempner, E. S., Schlegel, W. 1979. Size determination of enzymes by radiation inactivation. *Anal. Biochem.* 92:2–10

46. Krieger, N. S., Middlebrook, J. L., Aronow, L. 1976. Effect of salt on reversibility of glucocorticoid receptor binding. *J. Steroid Biochem.* 7:395–99

47. Lea, O. A., Wilson, E. M., French, F. S. 1979. Characterization of different forms of the androgen receptor. *Endocrinology* 105:1350–60

48. Leach, K. L., Dahmer, M. K., Hammond, N. D., Sando, J. J., Pratt, W. B. 1979. Molybdate inhibition of glucocorticoid receptor inactivation and transformation. *J. Biol. Chem.* 254:11884–90

49. Lee, H. J., Bradlow, H. L., Moran, M. C., Sherman, M. R. 1981. Binding of glucocorticoid 21-oic acids and esters to molybdate-stabilized hepatic receptors. *J. Steroid Biochem.* 14:1325–35

50. Lessey, B. A., Alexander, P. S., Horwitz, K. B. 1983. The subunit structure of human breast cancer progesterone receptors: Characterization by chromatography and photoaffinity labeling. *Endocrinology* 112:1267–74

51. Liao, S., Smythe, S., Tymoczko, J. L., Rossini, G. P., Chen, C., Hiipakka, R. A. 1980. RNA-dependent release of androgen· and other steroid·receptor complexes from DNA. *J. Biol. Chem.* 255:5545–51

52. Lippman, M., Huff, K., Bolan, G., Neifeld, J. P. 1977. Interactions of R5020 with progesterone and glucocorticoid receptors in human breast cancer and peripheral blood lymphocytes *in vitro*. In

Progress in Cancer Research and Therapy, ed. W. L. McGuire, J.-P. Raynaud, E.-E. Baulieu, 4:193–210. New York: Raven

53. Litwack, G., Mayer, M., Ohl, V., Sekula, B. 1983. Corticosteroid Binder IB, a potential second glucocorticoid receptor. See Ref. 7, pp. 135–49

54. Logeat, F., Hai, M. T. V., Milgrom, E. 1981. Antibodies to rabbit progesterone receptor: Crossreaction with human receptor. *Proc. Natl. Acad. Sci. USA* 78:1426–30

55. Mainwaring, W.I.P., Irving, R. 1973. The use of deoxyribonucleic acid-cellulose chromatography and isoelectric focusing for the characterization and partial purification of steroid-receptor complexes. *Biochem. J.* 134:113–27

56. Marković, R. D., Eisen, H. J., Parchman, L. G., Barnett, C. A., Litwack, G. 1980. Evidence for a physiological role of Corticosteroid Binder IB. *Biochemistry* 19:4556–64

57. Marver, D., Goodman, D., Edelman, I. S. 1972. Relationships between renal cytoplasmic and nuclear aldosterone-receptors. *Kidney Int.* 1:210–23

58. Mayer, M., Schmidt, T. J., Barnett, C. A., Miller, A., Litwack, G. 1983. *In vitro* production of Corticosteroid Binder IB in the presence of proteolytic inhibitors. *J. Steroid Biochem.* 18:111–20

59. McBlain, W. A., Toft, D. O., Shyamala, G. 1981. Transformation of mammary cytoplasmic glucocorticoid receptor under cell-free conditions. *Biochemistry* 20:6790–98

60. McCaffrey, R., Lillquist, A., Bell, R. 1982. Abnormal glucocorticoid receptors in acute leukemia cells. *Blood* 59:393–400

61. Middlebrook, J. L., Aronow, L. 1977. Physicochemical properties of glucocorticoid receptors from mouse fibroblasts. *Endocrinology* 100:271–82

62. Migliaccio, A., Lastoria, S., Moncharmont, B., Rotondi, A., Auricchio, F. 1982. Phosphorylation of calf uterus 17β-estradiol receptor by endogenous Ca^{2+}-stimulated kinase activating the hormone binding of the receptor. *Biochem. Biophys. Res. Commun.* 109:1002–10

63. Milgrom, E. 1981. Activation of steroid-receptor complexes. In *Biochemical Actions of Hormones,* ed. G. Litwack, 8:465–92. New York: Academic

64. Miller, L. K., Tuazon, F. B., Niu, E.-M., Sherman, M. R. 1981. Human breast tumor estrogen receptor: Effects of molybdate and electrophoretic analyses. *Endocrinology* 108:1369–78

65. Mockus, M. B., Horwitz, K. B. 1983.

Progesterone receptors in human breast cancer. Stoichiometric translocation and nuclear receptor processing. *J. Biol. Chem.* 258:4778–83

66. Molinari, A. M., Medici, N., Moncharmont, B., Puca, G. A. 1977. Estradiol receptor of calf uterus: Interaction with heparin-agarose and purification. *Proc. Natl. Acad. Sci. USA* 74:4886–90

67. Moncharmont, B., Su, J.-L., Parikh, I. 1982. Monoclonal antibodies against estrogen receptor: Interaction with different molecular forms and functions of the receptor. *Biochemistry* 21:6916–21

68. Munck, A., Foley, R. 1979. Activation of steroid hormone-receptor complexes in intact target cells in physiological conditions. *Nature* 278:752–54

69. Munck, A., Foley, R. 1980. Activated and non-activated glucocorticoid-receptor complexes in rat thymus cells: Kinetics of formation and relation to steroid structure. *J Steroid Biochem.* 12:225–30

70. Murakami, N., Quattrociocchi, T. M., Healy, S. P., Moudgil, V. K. 1982. Effects of sodium tungstate on the nuclear uptake of glucocorticoid-receptor complex from rat liver. *Arch. Biochem. Biophys.* 214:326–34

71. Nielsen, C. J., Sando, J. J., Vogel, W. M., Pratt, W. B. 1977. Glucocorticoid receptor inactivation under cell-free conditions. *J. Biol. Chem.* 252:7568–78

72. Niu, E.-M., Neal, R. M., Pierce, V. K., Sherman, M. R. 1981. Structural similarity of molybdate-stabilized steroid receptors in human breast tumors, uteri and leukocytes. *J. Steroid Biochem.* 15:1–10

73. Noma, K., Nakao, K., Sato, B., Nishizawa, Y., Matsumoto, K., Yamamura, Y. 1980. Mechanism of activation of steroid receptors: Involvement of low molecular weight inhibitor in activation of androgen, glucocorticoid and estrogen receptor systems. *Endocrinology* 106:1142–48

74. Nordeen, S. K., Lan, N. C., Showers, M. O., Baxter, J. D. 1981. Photoaffinity labeling of glucocorticoid receptors. *J. Biol. Chem.* 256:10503–8

75. Norris, J. S., Kohler, P. O. 1983. Syrian hamster glucocorticoid receptors. Characteristics of binding of partially purified receptor to DNA. *J. Biol. Chem.* 258:2350–56

76. Notides, A. C. 1978. Conformational forms of the estrogen receptor. In *Receptors and Hormone Action*, ed. B. W. O'Malley, L. Birnbaumer, 2:33–61. New York: Academic

77. Notides, A. C., Lerner, N., Hamilton,

D. E. 1981. Positive cooperativity of the estrogen receptor. *Proc. Natl. Acad. Sci. USA* 78:4926–30

78. Notides, A. C., Nielsen, S. 1974. The molecular mechanism of the in vitro 4 S to 5 S transformation of the uterine estrogen receptor. *J. Biol. Chem.* 249:1866–73

79. Okret, S., Carlstedt-Duke, J., Wrange, Ö., Carlström, K., Gustafsson, J.-Å. 1981. Characterization of an antiserum against the glucocorticoid receptor. *Biochim, Biophys. Acta* 677:205–19

80. Okret, S., Stevens, Y.-W., Carlstedt-Duke, J., Wrange, Ö., Gustafsson, J.-Å., Stevens, J. 1983. Absence in glucocorticoid-resistant mouse lymphoma P1798 of a glucocorticoid receptor domain responsible for biological effects. *Cancer Res.* 43:3127–31

81. Papamichail, M., Ioannidis, C., Tsawdaroglou, N., Sekeris, C. E. 1981. Translocation of glucocorticoid receptor from the cytoplasm into the nucleus of phytohemagglutinin-stimulated human lymphocytes in the absence of the hormone. *Exp. Cell Res.* 133:461–65

82. Pavlik, E. J., van Nagell, J. R., Jr., Muncey, M., Donaldson, E. S., Hanson, M., Kenady, D., Rees, E. D., Talwalker, V. R. 1982. Rapid analysis of estrogen and progesterone receptors using gel-exclusion high-performance liquid chromatography. *Biochemistry* 21:139–45

83. Pike, J. W., Marion, S. L., Donaldson, C. A., Haussler, M. R. 1983. Serum and monoclonal antibodies againt the chick intestinal receptor for 1,25-dihydroxyvitamin D_3. Generation by a preparation enriched in a 64,000-dalton protein. *J. Biol. Chem.* 258:1289–96

84. Puca, G. A., Nola, E., Sica, V., Bresciani, F. 1977. Estrogen-binding proteins of calf uterus. Molecular and functional characterization of the receptor transforming factor: a Ca^{2+}-activated protease. *J. Biol. Chem.* 252:1358–66

85. Raaka, B. M., Samuels, H. H. 1983. The glucocorticoid receptor in GH_1 cells. Evidence from dense amino acid labeling and whole cell studies for an equilibrium model explaining the influence of hormone on the intracellular distribution of receptor. *J. Biol. Chem.* 258:417–25

86. Redeuilh, G., Secco, C., Baulieu, E.-E., Richard-Foy, H. 1981. Calf uterine estradiol receptor. Effects of molybdate on salt-induced transformation process and characterization of a nontransformed receptor state. *J. Biol. Chem.* 256:11496–502

87. Regnier, F. E., Gooding, K. M. 1980. High-performance liquid chromatogra-

SHERMAN & STEVENS

phy of proteins. *Anal. Biochem.* 103:1–25

88. Renoir, J.-M., Radanyi, C., Yang, C.-R., Baulieu, E.-E. 1982. Antibodies against progesterone receptor from chick oviduct. Cross-reactivity with mammalian progesterone receptors. *Eur. J. Biochem.* 127:81–86

89. Sando, J. J., Hammond, N. D., Stratford, C. A., Pratt, W. B. 1979. Activation of thymocyte glucocorticoid receptors to the steroid binding form. The roles of reducing agents, ATP, and heat-stable factors. *J. Biol. Chem.* 254:4779–89

90. Schachman, H. K. 1959. *Ultracentrifugation in Biochemistry*, p. 239. New York: Academic

91. Schmidt, T. J., Harmon, J. M., Thompson, E. B. 1980. 'Activation-labile' glucocorticoid-receptor complexes of a steroid-resistant variant of CEM-C7 human lymphoid cells. *Nature* 286:507–10

92. Schmidt, T. J., Litwack, G. 1982. Activation of the glucocorticoid-receptor complex. *Physiol. Rev.* 62:1131–92

93. Schmidt, T. J., Thompson, E. B. 1978. Glucocorticoid receptor function in leukemic cells. In *Endocrine Control in Neoplasia*, ed. R. K. Sharma, W. E. Criss, pp. 263–90. New York: Raven

94. Schrader, W. T., O'Malley, B. W. 1972. Progesterone-binding components of chick oviduct. IV. Characterization of purified subunits. *J. Biol. Chem.* 247:51–59

95. Sekula, B. C., Schmidt, T. J., Litwack, G. 1981. Redefinition of modulator as an inhibitor of glucocorticoid receptor activation. *J. Steroid Biochem.* 14:161–66

96. Sherman, M. R. 1975. Physical-chemical analysis of steroid hormone receptors. *Methods Enzymol.* 36:211–34

97. Sherman, M. R., Barzilai, D., Pine, P. R., Tuazon, F. B. 1979. Glucocorticoid receptor cleavage by leupeptin-sensitive enzymes in rat kidney cytosol. In *Steroid Hormone Receptor Systems*, ed. W. W. Leavitt, J. H. Clark, pp. 357–75. New York: Plenum

98. Sherman, M. R., Corvol, P. L., O'Malley, B. W. 1970. Progesterone-binding components of chick oviduct. I. Preliminary characterization of cytoplasmic components. *J. Biol. Chem.* 245:6085–96

99. Sherman, M. R., Moran, M. C., Neal, R. M., Niu, E.-M., Tuazon, F. B. 1982. Characterization of molybdate-stabilized glucocorticoid receptors in healthy and malignant tissues. In *Progress in Research and Clinical Applications of Corticosteroids*, ed. H. J. Lee, T. J.

Fitzgerald, pp. 45–66. Philadelphia: Heyden

100. Sherman, M. R., Moran, M. C., Tuazon, F. B., Stevens, Y.-W. 1983. Structure, dissociation, and proteolysis of mammalian steroid receptors. Multiplicity of glucocorticoid receptor forms and proteolytic enzymes in rat liver and kidney cytosols. *J. Biol. Chem.* 258:10366–77

101. Sherman, M. R., Pickering, L. A., Rollwagen, F. M., Miller, L. K. 1978. Meroreceptors: proteolytic fragments of receptors containing the steroid-binding site. *Fed. Proc.* 37:167–73

102. Sherman, M. R., Tuazon, F. B., Miller, L. K. 1980. Estrogen receptor cleavage and plasminogen activation by enzymes in human breast tumor cytosol. *Endocrinology* 106:1715–27

103. Sherman, M. R., Tuazon, F. B., Sömjen, G. J. 1981. Stabilization and cleavage of steroid receptors: Effects of leupeptin and molybdate on rat kidney glucocorticoid receptors. In *Physiopathology of Endocrine Diseases and Mechanisms of Hormone Action*. ed. R. J. Soto, A. De Nicola, J. Blaquier, pp. 321–37. New York: Liss

103a. Sherman, M. R., Tuazon, F. B., Stevens, Y.-W., Niu, E.-M. 1984. Oligomeric steroid receptor forms and the products of their dissociation and proteolysis. In *Steroid Hormone Receptors: Structure and Function*, ed. J.-Å. Gustafsson, H. Eriksson. Amsterdam; Elsevier. In press.

104. Shyamala, G. 1975. Is the estrogen receptor of mammary glands a metalloprotein? *Biochem. Biophys. Res. Commun.* 64:408–15

105. Simons, S. S. Jr., Schleenbaker, R. E., Eisen, H. J. 1983. Activation of covalent affinity labeled glucocorticoid receptor-steroid complexes. *J. Biol. Chem.* 258: 2229–38

106. Simons, S. S. Jr., Thompson, E. B. 1981. Dexamethasone 21-mesylate: An affinity label of glucocorticoid receptors from rat hepatoma tissue culture cells. *Proc. Natl. Acad. Sci. USA* 78:3541–45

107. Simons, S. S. Jr., Thompson, E. B. 1982. Affinity labeling of glucocorticoid receptors: New methods in affinity labeling. In *Biochemical Actions of Hormones*, ed. G. Litwack, 9:221–54. New York: Academic

108. Simpson, R. U., DeLuca, H. F. 1982. Purification of chicken intestinal receptor for 1α,25-dihydroxyvitamin D₃ to apparent homogeneity. *Proc. Natl. Acad. Sci. USA* 79:16–20

109. Sluyterman, L. A. A., Elgersma, O. 1978. Chromatofocusing: isoelectric

focusing on ion-exchange columns. I. General principles. *J. Chromatogr.* 150:17–30

110. Sluyterman, L. A. A., Wijdenes, J. 1978. Chromatofocusing: isoelectric focusing on ion-exchange columns. II. Experimental verification. *J. Chromatogr.* 150:31–44

111. Stevens, J., Stevens, Y.-W. 1981. Influence of limited proteolysis on the physicochemical and DNA-binding properties of glucocorticoid receptors from corticoid-sensitive and -resistant mouse lymphoma P1798. *Cancer Res.* 41:125–33

112. Stevens, J., Stevens, Y. -W., Haubenstock, H. 1983. Molecular basis of glucocorticoid resistance in experimental and human leukemia. In *Biochemical Actions of Hormones*, ed. G. Litwack, 10:383–446. New York: Academic

113. Taylor, C. A., Jr., Smith, H. E., Danzo, B. J. 1980. Photoaffinity labeling of rat androgen binding protein. *Proc. Natl. Acad. Sci. USA* 77:234–38

114. Tymoczko, J. L., Phillips, M. M. 1983. The effects of ribonuclease on rat liver dexamethasone receptor: Increased affinity for deoxyribonucleic acid and altered sedimentation profile. *Endocrinology* 112:142–49

115. Vedeckis, W. V. 1981. Activation and chromatographic properties of AtT-20 mouse pituitary tumor cell line glucocorticoid receptor. *Biochemistry* 20:7237–45

116. Vedeckis, W. V. 1983. Subunit dissociation as a possible mechanism of glucocorticoid receptor activation. *Biochemistry* 22:1983–89

117. Vedeckis, W. V. 1983. Limited proteolysis of the mouse liver glucocorticoid receptor. *Biochemistry* 22:1975–83

118. Viceps-Madore, D., Cidlowski, J. A., Kittler, J. M., Thanassi, J. W. 1983. Preparation, characterization, and use of monoclonal antibodies to vitamin B_6. *J. Biol. Chem.* 258:2689–96

119. Weber, K., Pringle, J. R., Osborn, M. 1972. Measurement of molecular weights by electrophoresis on SDS-acrylamide gel. *Methods Enzymol.* 26:3–27

120. Westphal, H. M., Fleischmann, G., Beato, M. 1981. Photoaffinity labeling of steroid binding proteins with unmodified ligands. *Eur. J. Biochem.* 119:101–6

121. Westphal, H. M., Moldenhauer, G., Beato, M. 1982. Monoclonal antibodies to the rat liver glucocorticoid receptor. *EMBO. Journ.* 1:1467–71

122. Wheeler, R. H., Leach, K. L., La Forest, A. C., O'Toole, T. E., Wagner, R., Pratt, W. B. 1981. Glucocorticoid receptor activation and inactivation in cultured human lymphocytes. *J. Biol. Chem.* 256:434–41

123. Wilson, E. M., French, F. S. 1979. Effects of proteases and protease inhibitors on the 4.5 S and 8 S androgen receptor. *J. Biol. Chem.* 254:6310–19

123a. Wira, C. R., Munck, A. 1974. Glucocorticoid-receptor complexes in rat thymus cells. "Cytoplasmic"-nuclear transformations. *J. Biol. Chem.* 249:5328–36

124. Wittliff, J. L., Feldhoff, P. W., Fuchs, A., Wiehle, R. D. 1981. Polymorphism of estrogen receptors in human breast cancer. See Ref. 103, pp. 375–96

125. Wrange, Ö., Carlstedt-Duke, J., Gustafsson, J.-Å. 1979. Purification of the glucocorticoid receptor from rat liver cytosol. *J. Biol. Chem.* 254:9284–90

126. Wrange, Ö., Norstedt, G., Gustafsson, J.-Å. 1980. The estrogen receptor in rat liver: Quantitative and qualitative analysis by isoelectric focusing in polyacrylamide gel. *Endocrinology* 106:1455–62

127. Yamamoto, K. R., Gehring, U., Stampfer, M. R., Sibley, C. H. 1976. Genetic approaches to steroid hormone action. *Rec. Prog. Horm. Res.* 32:3–32

128. Yang, C.-R., Mešter, J., Wolfson, A., Renoir, J.-M., Baulieu, E.-E. 1982. Activation of the chick oviduct progesterone receptor by heparin in the presence or absence of hormone. *Biochem. J.* 208:399–406

Ann. Rev. Physiol. 1984. 46:107–18

ANDROGEN AND ANTIANDROGEN RECEPTOR BINDING

Olli A. Jänne and C. Wayne Bardin

The Population Council and The Rockefeller University, New York, New York 10021

INTRODUCTION

Even though the ultimate effects of androgens on cellular constituents are tissue specific, the initial steps of androgen action are common to many organs and similar to those of other steroid hormones (2, 14, 15, 46). The events leading to increased RNA and protein synthesis and altered target cell function include: (*a*) the entrance of androgens to cells, and the binding of testosterone or its metabolite, 5α-dihydrotestosterone, to specific cytoplasmic receptor proteins that are transferred to nuclei; (*b*) an interaction of the receptor-steroid complexes with chromatin that is accompanied by facilitated synthesis of precursors of different RNAs; and (*c*) the translation of steroid-specific RNAs on the polyribosomes, resulting in formation of hormone-specific proteins along with other cellular components needed for altered target cell function. In some androgen responsive tissues, but not all, an enhanced DNA replication also takes place during hormone action (1, 2). Which mRNAs and proteins are stimulated and which cells undergo division in response to androgens are functions of each individual tissue. For example, in the mouse, androgens increase the synthesis of β-glucuronidase and ornithine decarboxylase in the kidney (53, 60) and of epidermal growth factor in the submaxillary gland (3), but do not facilitate the production of the same proteins in other tissues where they are constitutively synthesized. These and other observations suggest that there are two major factors regulating androgenic responses in individual tissues: (*a*) the steroid recognition machinery that includes the concentration and steroid-binding specificity of the androgen receptors; and (*b*) the structure of chromatin, which is determined during differentiation so that the androgen receptor complexes will activate selective tissue responses. In this chapter we will review recent studies on the first of these topics. We will first present some

107

of the characteristics of these receptors, then describe how androgen receptor dynamics regulate biological responses. Finally, mechanisms by which anti-androgens interfere with androgen receptor function will be considered.

CHARACTERISTICS OF ANDROGEN RECEPTORS

As a rule, all the tissues that respond to androgen administration contain measurable cytosol androgen receptor protein (2, 14, 15, 38, 46). Similarly, nuclear translocation of this receptor has been reported in many studies where radioactive androgens have been administered to experimental animals. Owing to the great lability of the androgen receptor, variable estimates for the physical-chemical characteristics of cytoplasmic and nuclear androgen receptors have been presented (11, 20, 36, 38, 40, 42, 45, 52, 59, 67, 68). In most studies, cytosol androgen receptors have been found to sediment at 8–10S on sucrose density gradient centrifugation in low ionic strength and to exhibit molecular weights (M_r) of 280,000–360,000 (11, 38, 40, 45, 52). Upon exposure to 0.4 M KCl, conversion of the receptor to a faster sedimenting form (4–4.5S) with a M_r of about 100,000 has been observed (20, 36, 38, 45, 52). These two forms of the cytosol receptor seem to be in equilibrium (68), but whether the larger entities derive from self-association of the smaller components, or from a mixed aggregation of receptor and non-receptor proteins, is currently unknown. Even though the nuclear androgen receptor seems to originate from the cytoplasmic receptor, the physical chemical characteristics of these two proteins have been reported to be dissimilar in many studies (38, 59, 68). For example, cytosol androgen receptor sediments somewhat faster (4–4.5S) than the nuclear receptor protein (3–3.5S) in the presence of 0.4 M KCl. This difference may have resulted from in vitro proteolytic cleavage of the latter protein, because a larger receptor was observed in the presence of the protease inhibitor, di-isopropylfluorophosphate (68). In addition to the nuclear receptor, the cytosol androgen receptor is also subject to extensive proteolytic degradation in a variety of tissues, if analyzed in vitro without any protective agents.

The fact that androgen receptor structure is currently so poorly understood originates from difficulties encountered in its extensive purification. Few studies on the purification of androgen receptors have been reported (8, 16, 21, 26, 28, 42, 59). Only a modest purification was achieved in all but one of these attempts (16). In that study, cytoplasmic androgen receptor was purified 540,000-fold from steer seminal vesicle and was shown to migrate as a single protein band with a M_r of 60,000 on sodium dodecylsulfate polyacrylamide gel electrophoresis. It is not known, however, whether this molecule represents an intact oligomer or a proteolytic fragment of the native androgen receptor.

ANDROGEN RECEPTORS AS REGULATORS OF ANDROGEN ACTION

The best evidence for the importance of cytoplasmic androgen receptor in the expression of biological androgen action originates from studies of testicular feminized (Tfm) animals which are androgen resistant (2, 23). A reduced amount of cytosol androgen receptor has been demonstrated in both rats and mice with the Tfm locus (9, 48, 66), although these two animals differ in their degree of androgen resistance (2). Many of the cellular components of the preputial gland, kidney, and pituitary in Tfm rats exhibit a dose-dependent response to very large doses of testosterone. By contrast, Tfm mice are more resistant: most gene products are not at all affected by androgens, while a few show a minimal or fractional response (2). In accordance with their dissimilar androgenic responses, the residual androgen receptor concentrations in rats and mice are different: Tfm rats have approximately 10% of the cytosol receptor concentration found in normal littermates, and its properties seem to be normal (48). By contrast, the DNA-binding characteristics of the residual receptor in Tfm mice appear to differ from those of the receptor in wild type animals (66). It should be emphasized, however, that most of the above studies were performed under conditions that did not maximally stabilize androgen receptors (i.e. without protease inhibitors or molybdate) and, hence, these data may represent relative rather than absolute differences due to receptor breakdown. In this regard, some humans with androgen insensitivity have residual androgen receptors which cannot be stabilized (22). Before detailed comparisons of defective and normal androgen receptors in experimental animals and in man (2, 23, 34) are possible, isolation of stable preparations and/or studies of covalently labeled androgen receptors will be required.

As mentioned above, receptor-steroid complexes bind to target cell nuclei, where they presumably activate genes for steroid-specific proteins. Binding of androgen receptors to nuclear constituents has been shown in a number of studies; this interaction in vivo or in vitro renders chromatin a better template for transcription by RNA polymerase enzymes (19, 31, 39, 43, 64). Little is known, however, about the details of this process, such as where in the genes androgen receptor binds and what is the ultimate mechanism of gene activation by the receptor protein. Another important question is the role of nuclear receptor concentrations and nuclear receptor occupancy for activation of specific androgen-responsive genes in vivo. In the case of female sex steroids, an interesting but rather complex relationship seems to exist in this respect. Some of the genes responding rapidly to female sex steroids (e.g. estrogen-induced uterine protein) are activated in a direct proportion to the amount of the nuclear receptors accumulated (33), while others require either a low or a very high occupancy of the nuclear receptors for a half-maximal induction (17, 47, 54). By contrast, long-term responses to estradiol, such as uterine growth, are not directly related to the initial nuclear receptor content; rather, the residence time of a limited population of estrogen receptors is a more important determinant for the long-term biological responses in the rat uterus (18, 32). Another intriguing feature in steroid receptor dynamics has emerged in the studies of female sex steroids: In the case of both estrogens (24, 25) and progestins (29), nuclear receptors are "consumed" (i.e. steroid binding site is lost or masked) during the biologic hormone action. This event has been postulated to be a prerequisite for certain biochemical responses such as induction of progesterone receptor synthesis by estradiol (24, 25).

Studies on the temporal events which follow a single dose of testosterone suggest that nuclear receptor residence time rather than the quantity of initially accumulated nuclear androgen receptors is a major regulatory factor for induction of both early (ornithine decarboxylase) and late (β-glucuronidase) androgenic responses in the mouse kidney (53). In this context, an early response may be defined as one occurring within a few hours after hormone administration, while a late response is one that occurs more than 24 hr following treatment. These experiments correlated nuclear androgen receptor concentrations with the increased synthesis of androgen-specific proteins in groups of castrated male mice that received various amounts of testosterone as a single dose (0.3, 1, 3, and 10 mg). All treatments produced a comparable increase in nuclear androgen receptors at 30–60 min (from about 100 to 650–800 receptors per renal nucleus) with a concomitant loss in the cytoplasmic receptor concentration (30, 53). After the first hour, the residence time of the androgen receptor in the nucleus was related to the dose of testosterone: the smaller the steroid dose, the faster the receptor concentration declined to the level of vehicle-treated animals. For example, in mice that received 0.3–3 mg testosterone, the nuclear androgen receptor concentration returned to control levels within 6–12 hrs, while after administration of 10 mg of the steroid, the receptor concentration remained increased for at least 120 hrs (53).

In addition to the dissimilar nuclear receptor residence times, the above dose of testosterone elicited changes in renal ornithine decarboxylase and β-glucuronidase enzyme activities which had markedly different temporal profiles: ornithine decarboxylase activity rose only a few hours after steroid administration, while 2–4 days were required before an increased β-glucuronidase activity was detected (53). Two interesting correlations between the nuclear receptor concentrations and biological androgenic response emerged in these studies. First, a long-lasting residence of the androgen receptors in renal cell nuclei was accompanied by a pronounced and sustained stimulation of androgen-responsive gene products. This is illustrated (Figure 1) by the facts that the nuclear androgen receptor residence time was shorter than 6

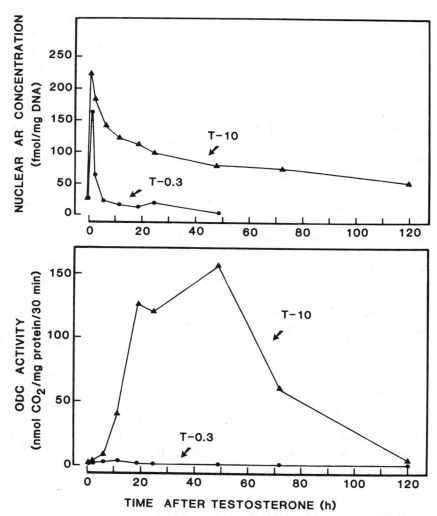

Figure 1 Renal nuclear androgen receptor (AR) concentration and ornithine decarboxylase (ODC) activity in castrated male mice treated with a single dose of 0.3 mg testosterone (T-0.3) or 10 mg testosterone (T-10). Adapted from Pajunen et al (53).

hr after 0.3 mg of testosterone and was accompanied by only a 4-fold increase in the ornithine decarboxylase activity, which returned to the control level by 24 hr. By contrast, 10 mg of testosterone elicited nuclear androgen receptor accumulation for over 120 hr, which was associated with a 150-fold increased ornithine decarboxylase activity that remained elevated for at least 120 hr. Second, a sustained nuclear accumulation of the androgen receptors resulted in a shorter lag period required to detect increased ornithine decarboxylase (Figure 1) and β-glucuronidase activities in the mouse kidney. These data seem to provide the first direct evidence for the hypothesis (65) that both the duration of the lag period in β-glucuronidase induction and the subsequent rate of synthesis of this enzyme are regulated by the number of androgen receptors associated with "β-glucuronidase chromatin."

Androgen receptor concentration is highly variable in different androgen responsive tissues, but whether or not the receptor quantity is directly related to the number of genes regulated by androgens is not known. Some of the cytosol and nuclear receptors may represent "spare" hormone binding sites similar to those reported for peptide hormones (13). In support of this notion, androgenic regulation of RNA polymerase II enzyme in Sertoli cells has been reported to require occupancy of only a small fraction of the nuclear androgen receptors for the maximal enzyme activation (35). Similarly, a relatively small nuclear androgen receptor content was capable of maintaining a defined sexual dimorphism in mouse kidney, as evidenced by the physiological nuclear receptor concentrations in female and male mice: about 300 androgen receptors per nucleus in the males were accompanied by 12-fold higher renal ornithine decarboxylase activity than in the female mice, whose renal cells possessed about 100 receptors per nucleus (30, 53). Although this sex difference might suggest that it is the nuclear receptor content per se that regulates the magnitude of the androgenic response, the results of the experiments on acute adrogen action referred to above suggest that there is a more complex relationship between the nuclear receptors and biological response. Moreover, the basal ornithine decarboxylase activity in the kidney of female mice was similar to that in androgen-insensitive Tfm/Y animals, suggesting that it represented a constitutive rather than androgen-regulated enzyme concentration (53). On the basis of these and other findings we hypothesize that, at least in the mouse kidney, a certain threshold nuclear androgen receptor concentration (more than 100 receptors per cell) must be exceeded and should be present for an extended period of time before a stimulation of androgen-responsive genes occurs.

INTERFERENCE OF ANTIANDROGENS WITH ANDROGEN RECEPTOR FUNCTION

A wide variety of molecules will antagonize biological actions of androgens and can, therefore, be termed antiandrogens. Examples of these compounds are steroids such as estrogens (27), progestins (10), and derivatives of androgens (44, 62); non-steroidal antiandrogens such as flutamide (49) and RU 23,908 (56); certain drugs (4, 69); and analogues of luteinizing hormone-releasing hormone (37, 58). The mechanisms by which these antiandrogenic compounds elicit their actions are variable and include interference with androgen action in the target cells, inhibition of androgen biosynthesis, and inhibition of uptake or metabolism of androgens by the responding cells. Several review articles have covered properties and mechanisms of action of antiandrogenic compounds (10, 38, 41, 50, 51, 55); in this review we will concentrate on those molecules whose actions seem to involve interaction with androgen receptor.

One of the mechanisms by which antiandrogens could oppose androgen action is the direct interference with steroid binding by the cytosol receptor. The antagonist-receptor complex formed during the interaction should be structurally incapable of eliciting hormonal effects, e.g. due to its rapid dissociation, defective nuclear translocation, or inability to associate with correct nuclear acceptor sites. Steroidal antiandrogens, e.g. cyproterone acetate (5, 10), BOMT (44), SKF 7690 (62), spironolactone (4), and RU 2956 (56), are indeed capable of competing for the cytosol receptor binding sites and subsequently inhibit nuclear retention of 5α-dihydrotestosterone in the rat prostate and seminal vesicle in vivo and in vitro. However, it has been impossible to identify antiandrogens in receptor binding assays because these procedures do not differentiate between hormone agonists and antagonists. This pitfall is perhaps best illustrated by studies on the binding properties of different progestins to mouse renal androgen receptors: Despite the fact that progestins are capable of evoking androgenic, antiandrogenic, and synandrogenic actions in this organ (10), their binding affinity to the androgen receptors (cytosol or nuclear) correlated only with the androgenic potency of these compounds (5).

One postulated way of distinguishing an androgen from an antiandrogen is the relatively short biological half-life (rapid rate of dissociation) of the cytosol receptor–antagonist complex (56, 57). One the basis of this consideration, it was proposed that steroid agonists and antagonists could be discriminated by using two different conditions for measuring the relative binding of compounds for androgen receptor: a short-term incubation to achieve estimates for the relative rates of association and a long-term incubation to determine the rate of dissociation of the complex. Steroid antagonists typically associate with kinetics similar to those of the agonists, but dissociate at faster rates. As a consequence, the antiandrogens should have a higher relative binding affinity during the short-term than the long-term incubation, while androgens should exhibit roughly identical binding affinities under the two conditions (56, 57). By using the above approach, Raynaud et al (56) concluded that both steroidal and non-steroidal antiandrogens elicit their action through forming a rapidly-dissociating complex with the cytosol androgen receptor. By contrast, Wakeling et al (63), using a similar assay principle, found that although the relative binding affinities of various antiandrogens were, as expected, markedly lower in long-term than short-term incubations, there was no obvious correlation between antiandrogenic potency in vivo and relative receptor binding activity in vitro. Furthermore, these investigators were also unable to distinguish unequivocally between androgen agonists and antagonists on the basis of the above mentioned receptor binding studies.

The fate of the cytosol receptor–antiandrogen complex is poorly understood. Most importantly, very little is known about the nuclear translocation of these complexes. The findings that many of the antiandrogens do not show any agonistic activity in vivo suggest (*a*) that the compounds are not translocated at all to target cell nuclei or, (*b*) that the nuclear androgen receptor–antiandrogen complexes are biologically inactive, i.e. the antagonists hold the receptors in a state that is different from that of the receptor–androgen complex. Some recent findings are pertinent in this respect. First, the experiments we have performed with steroidal and nonsteroidal antiandrogens, some of which were completely devoid of agonistic actions, have indicated that these compounds are capable of translocating mouse renal cytosol androgen receptors to nuclei in vivo (30; unpublished observations). Studies on androgen receptor dynamics with exchange assays have also shown that, when given concomitantly with or prior to testosterone or 5α-dihydrotestosterone, non-steroidal antiandrogens can prevent androgen-elicited translocation of cytosol androgen receptors to nuclei in mouse kidney (unpublished observations), as well as rat prostate and epididymis (12, 61). Even more interestingly, a single dose of a non-steroidal antiandrogen, flutamide, is capable of depleting nuclear androgen receptors in mouse kidney in animals implanted with testosterone-releasing rods, despite the continuous presence of the implants during the experiment. The depletion was not, however, complete; rather, a level reached by the antiandrogen alone was achieved (unpublished observations). Second, some very potent new non-steroidal antiandrogens have also been shown to possess partial agonistic activity (63) similar to that of non-steroidal antiestrogens (33). It thus appears that some antiandrogens seem to be capable of initiating androgen action in a manner similar to that of the androgens; the mechanisms leading to a complete or partial abortion of the action in the subsequent steps remain to be elucidated.

Finally, part of the action of antiandrogens may be mediated via binding proteins other than the androgen receptor. This is suggested by the studies on 6α-methylprogesterone, a progestin that potentiates and inhibits androgen action in low and high doses, respectively (6). In addition to the androgen receptor, nuclear uptake of 6α-methylprogesterone and its 20α-hydroxylated metabolite seems to occur by way of another receptor or steroid–binding protein in the mouse kidney (7). 6α-Methylprogesterone given alone is able to translocate androgen receptors to mouse renal nuclei in vivo (30), thus explaining its androgenic properties (6). On the basis of these findings, it is tempting to suggest that nuclear accumulation of this progestin through the additional binding-protein mechanism would be responsible for the inhibition of the action of concurrently administered testosterone.

SUMMARY AND CONCLUSIONS

Recent studies have demonstrated that androgenic stimulation of early and late responding genes depends on the nuclear uptake of the receptor-steroid complex. The longer the complex is retained in the nucleus, the shorter the lag period and the greater the magnitude of the response. Most antiandrogens or their metabolites bind to the cytosolic androgen receptor, but the relative receptor binding affinities do not strictly relate to their biological activities, since the former assay does not differentiate antagonists from weak agonists. Alternatively, androgen antagonists are believed to abrogate the action of androgenic steroids by interfering with the receptor function. However, the exact mechanisms by which antiandrogens bring about their actions remain to be established.

ACKNOWLEDGMENT

The work performed in the authors' laboratories was supported by NIH Grants HD-13541 and RR-05860.

Literature Cited

1. Bardin, C. W., Brown, T. R., Mills, N. C., Gupta, C., Bullock, L. P. 1978. The regulation of the β-glucuronidase gene by androgens and progestins. *Biol. Reprod.* 18:74–83
2. Bardin, C. W., Catterall, J. F. 1981. Testosterone: a major determinant of extragenital sexual dimorphism. *Science* 211:1285–94
3. Barthe, P. L., Bullock, L. P., Mowszowicz, I., Bardin, C. W. 1974. Submaxillary gland epidermal growth factor: A sensitive index of biologic androgen action. *Endocrinology* 95:1019–25
4. Bonne, C., Raynaud, J.-P. 1974. Mode of spironolactone anti-androgen action: inhibition of androstanolone binding to rat prostate androgen receptor. *Mol. Cell. Endocrinol.* 2:59–67
5. Brown, T. R., Bullock, L., Bardin, C. W. 1979. *In vitro* and *in vivo* binding of progestins to the androgen receptor of mouse kidney: Correlation with biological activities. *Endocrinology* 105:1281–87
6. Brown, T. R., Bullock, L. P., Bardin, C. W. 1981. The biological actions and metabolism of 6α-methylprogesterone: A progestin that mimics and modifies the effects of testosterone. *Endocrinology* 109:1814–20
7. Brown, T. R., Bullock, L. P., Bardin, C. W. 1981. The nuclear uptake of 6α-[³H]methylprogesterone and its 20α-hydroxy metabolite: The requirement for multiple receptors. *Endocrinology* 109:1821–29
8. Bruchovsky, N., Rennie, P. S., Comeau, T. 1981. Partial purification of nuclear androgen receptor by micrococcal nuclease digestion of chromatin and hydrophobic interaction chromatography. *Eur. J. Biochem.* 120:399–405
9. Bullock, L. P., Bardin, C. W. 1974. Androgen receptors in mouse kidney: a study of male, female and androgen-insensitive (Tfm/y) mice. *Endocrinology* 94:746–56
10. Bullock, L. P., Bardin, C. W., 1977. Androgenic, synandrogenic and antiandrogenic actions of progestins. *Ann. NY Acad. Sci.* 286:321–30
11. Bullock, L. P., Mainwaring, W. I. P., Bardin, C. W. 1975. The physicochemical properties of the cytoplasmic androgen receptor in the kidneys of normal, carrier female (Tfm/+) and androgen-insensitive (Tfm/y) mice. *Endocr. Res. Commun.* 2:25–45
12. Callaway, T. W., Bruchovsky, N., Rennie, P. S., Comeau, T. 1982. Mechanism of action of androgens and antiandrogens: Effects of antiandrogens on translocation of cytoplasmic androgen re-

ceptor and nuclear abundance of dihydrotestosterone. *The Prostate* 3:599–610

13. Catt, K. T., Harwood, J. P., Aquilera, G., Dufau, M. L. 1979. Hormonal regulation of peptide receptors and target cell response. *Nature* 280:109–16

14. Chan, L., O'Malley, B. W. 1976. Mechanism of action of the sex steroid hormones. *N. Engl. J. Med.* 294:1322–28; 1372–81; 1430–37

15. Chan, L., O'Malley, B. W. 1978. Steroid hormone action: Recent advances. *Ann. Int. Med.* 89:694–701

16. Chang, C. H., Rowley, D. R., Lobl, T. J., Tindall, D. J. 1982. Purification and characterization of androgen receptor from steer seminal vesicle. *Biochemistry* 21:4102–9

17. Clark, J. H., Anderson, J. N., Peck, E. J. Jr. 1973. Nuclear receptor estrogen complexes of rat uteri: concentration-time-response parameters. *Adv. Expt. Med. Biol.* 36:15–59

18. Clark, J. H., Peck, E. J. Jr. 1976. Nuclear retention of receptor-oestrogen complex and nuclear acceptor sites. *Nature* 260:635–37

19. Davies, P., Griffiths, K. 1974. Further studies on the stimulation of prostatic ribonucleic acid polymerase by 5α-dihydrotestosterone receptor complex. *J. Endocrinol.* 62:385–400

20. Fang, S., Liao, S. 1971. Androgen receptors. Steroid- and tissue-specific retention of a 17β-hydroxy-5α-androstan-3-one protein complex by cell nuclei of ventral prostate. *J. Biol. Chem.* 246:16–24

21. Foekens, J. A., Mulder, E., Vrij, L., van der Molen, H. J. 1982. Purification of the androgen receptor of sheep seminal vesicle. *Biochem. Biophys. Res. Commun.* 104:1279–86

22. Griffin, J. E., Durrant, J. L. 1982. Qualitative receptor defects in families with androgen resistance: Failure of stabilization of the fibroblast cytosol androgen receptor. *J. Clin. Endocrinol. Metab.* 55:465–74

23. Griffin, J. E., Wilson, J. D. 1980. The syndromes of androgen resistance. *N. Engl. J. Med.* 302:198–209

24. Horwitz, K. B., McGuire, W. L. 1978. Estrogen control of progesterone receptor in human breast cancer. Correlation with nuclear processing of estrogen receptors. *J. Biol. Chem.* 253:2223–28

25. Horwitz, K. B., McGuire, W. L. 1978. Nuclear mechanism of estrogen action: effects of estradiol and antiestrogens on estrogen receptors and nuclear receptor processing. *J. Biol. Chem.* 253:8185–91

26. Hu, A.-L., Loor, R. M., Wang, T. Y. 1975. Purification of a 3S cytosol androgen receptor from rat prostate that stimulates DNA-dependent RNA synthesis *in vitro*. *Biochem. Biophys. Res. Commun.* 65:1327–33

27. Huggins, C., Hodges, C. V. 1941. Studies on prostatic cancer. I. The effect of castration, of estrogen, and of androgen injection on serum phosphatases in metastatic carcinoma of the prostate. *Cancer Res.* 1:293–97

28. Ichii, S. 1975. 5α-Dihydrotestosterone binding protein in rat ventral prostate; purification, nuclear incorporation, and subnuclear localization. *Endocrinol. Jpn.* 22:433–37

29. Isomaa, V., Isotalo, H., Orava, M., Torkkeli, T., Jänne, O. 1979. Changes in cytosol and nuclear progesterone receptor concentrations in the rabbit uterus and their relation to induction of progesterone-regulated uteroglobin. *Biochem. Biophys. Res. Commun.* 88:1237–43

30. Isomaa, V., Pajunen, A. E. I., Bardin, C. W., Jänne, O. A. 1982. Nuclear androgen receptors in the mouse kidney: validation of a new assay. *Endocrinology* 111:833–43

31. Jänne, O., Bullock, L. P., Bardin, C. W., Jacob, S. T. 1976. Early androgen action in kidney of normal and androgen insensitive (Tfm/y) mice. Changes in RNA polymerase and chromatin template activities. *Biochim. Biophys. Acta* 418:330–43

32. Katzenellenbogen, B. S. 1980. Dynamics of steroid hormone receptor action. *Ann. Rev. Physiol.* 42:17–35

33. Katzenellenbogen, B. S., Bhakoo, H. S., Ferguson, E. R., Lan, N. C., Tatee, T., Tsai, T. L., Katzenellenbogen, J. A. 1979. Estrogen and antiestrogen action in reproductive tissues and tumors. *Recent Prog. Horm. Res.* 35:259–300

34. Kaufman, M., Pinsky, L., Simard, L., Wong, S. C. 1982. Defective activation of androgen-receptor complexes: A marker of androgen insensitivity. *Mol. Cell. Endocrinol.* 25:151–62

35. Lamb, D. J., Steinberger, A., Sanborn, B. M. 1981. Temporal and quantitative correlations between nuclear androgen binding and stimulation of RNA polymerase II activity in Sertoli cells. *Endocr. Res. Commun.* 8:263–72

36. Lea, O. A., Wilson, E. M., French, F. S. 1979. Characterization of different forms of the androgen receptor. *Endocrinology* 105:1350–60

37. Lecomte, P., Wang, N. G., Sundaram, K., Rivier, J., Vale, W., Bardin, C. W. 1982. The antiandrogenic action of gona-

dotropin-releasing hormone and its agonists on the mouse kidney. *Endocrinology* 110:1–6

38. Liao, S. 1977. Molecular action of androgens. In *Biochemical Actions of Hormones*, ed. G. Litwack, 4:351–406. New York: Academic

39. Lin, Y.-C., Bullock, L. P., Bardin, C. W., Jacob, S. T. 1978. Effects of medroxyprogesterone acetate and testosterone on solubilized RNA polymerases, and chromatin template activity in kidney from normal and androgen-insensitive (Tfm/y) mice. *Biochemistry* 17:4833–38

40. Mainwaring, W. I. P. 1969. A soluble androgen receptor in the cytoplasm of rat prostate. *J. Endocrinol.* 45:531–41

41. Mainwaring, W. I. P. 1977. Modes of action of antiandrogens: a survey. In *Androgens and Antiandrogens*, ed. L. Martini, M. Motta, pp. 151–61. New York: Raven

42. Mainwaring, W. I. P., Irving, R. 1973. The use of deoxyribonucleic acid–cellulose chromatography and isoelectric focusing for the characterization and partial purification of steroid-receptor complexes. *Biochem. J.* 134:113–27

43. Mainwaring, W. I. P., Mangan, F. R., Peterken, B. M. 1971. Studies on the solubilized ribonucleic acid polymerase from rat ventral prostate gland. *Biochem. J.* 123:619–28

44. Mangan, F. R., Mainwaring, W. I. P. 1972. An explanation of the antiandrogenic properties of 6α-bromo-17β-hydroxy-17α-methyl-4-oxa-5α-androstane-3-one. *Steroids* 20:331–43

45. McLean, W. S., Smith, A. A., Hansson, V., Naess, O., Nayfeh, S. N., French, F. S. 1976. Further characterization of the androgen receptor in rat testis. *Mol. Cell. Endocrinol.* 4:239–55

46. Muldoon, T. G. 1980. Regulation of steroid hormone receptor activity. *Endocr. Reviews* 1:339–64

47. Mulvihill, E. R., Palmiter, R. D. 1977. Relationship of nuclear estrogen receptor levels to induction of ovalbumin and conalbumin mRNA in chick oviduct. *J. Biol. Chem.* 252:2060–68

48. Naess, O., Haug, E., Attramadal, A., Aakvaag, A., Hansson, V., French, F. 1976. Androgen receptors in the anterior pituitary and central nervous system of androgen insensitive (Tfm) rat. Correlation between receptor binding and effects of androgens on gonadotropin secretion. *Endocrinology* 99:1295–303

49. Neri, R., Florance, K., Koziol, P., van Cleave, S. 1972. A biological profile of a nonsteroidal antiandrogen SCH 13521 (4,-nitro-3,-trifluoromethylisobutyranil-

ide). *Endocrinology* 91:427–37

50. Neri, R., Kassem, N. 1982. Pharmacological and clinical effects of antiandrogens. In *Hormone Antagonists*, ed. M. K. Agarwal, pp. 247–68. Berlin & New York: Walter de Gruyter

51. Neumann, F., von Berswordt-Wallrabe, R., Elger, W., Steinbeck, H., Hahn, J. D., Kramer, M. 1970. Aspects of androgen-dependent events as studied by antiandrogens. *Recent Prog. Horm. Res.* 26:337–410

52. Norris, J. S., Kohler, P. O. 1978. Comparison of steroid receptors from the androgen responsive DDT_1 cell line and the nonresponsive HVP cell line. *Endocr. Res. Commun.* 5:219–28

53. Pajunen, A. E. I., Isomaa, V. V., Jänne, O. A., Bardin, C. W. 1982. Androgenic regulation of ornithine decarboxylase activity in mouse kidney and its relationship to changes in cytosol and nuclear androgen receptor concentrations. *J. Biol. Chem.* 257:8190–98

54. Palmiter, R. D., Mulvihill, E. R., Shepherd, J. H., McKnight, G. S. 1981. Steroid hormone regulation of ovalbumin and conalbumin gene transcription. A model based upon multiple regulatory sites and intermediary proteins. *J. Biol. Chem.* 256:7910–16

55. Raynaud, J.-P. 1978. Mechanism of action of antihormones. In *Advances in Pharmacology and Therapeutics*, ed. J. Jacob, 1:259–78. Oxford: Pergamon

56. Raynaud, J.-P., Bonne, C., Bouton, M.-M., Lagace, L., Labrie, F. 1979. Action of a non-steriodal antiandrogen, RU 23908, in peripheral and central tissues. *J. Steroid Biochem.* 11:93–99

57. Raynaud, J.-P., Bouton, M. M., Moguilewsky, M., Ojasoo, T., Philibert, D., et al. 1980. Steroid hormone receptors and pharmacology. *J. Steroid Biochem.* 12:143–57

58. Redding, T. W., Schally, A. V. 1981. Inhibition of prostate tumor growth in two rat models by chronic administration of D-Trp[6] analogue of luteinizing hormone–releasing hormone. *Proc. Natl. Acad. Sci. USA* 78:6509-12

59. Rennie, P. S., van Doorn, E., Bruchovsky, N. 1977. Methods for estimating the concentration of different forms of androgen receptor in rat ventral prostate. *Mol. Cell. Endocrinol.* 9:145–57

60. Swank, R. T., Paigen, K., Davey, R., Chapman, V., Labarca, C., et al. 1978. Genetic regulation of mammalian glucuronidase. *Recent Prog. Horm. Res.* 34:401–36

61. Tezon, J. G., Vazquez, M. H., Blaquier, J. A. 1982. Androgen-controlled sub-

cellular distribution of its receptor in the rat epididymis: 5α-Dihydrotestosterone-induced translocation is blocked by anti-androgens. *Endocrinology* 111:2039–45

62. Tveter, K. J. 1971. Effect of 17α-methyl-β-nortestosterone (SK & F 7690) on the binding *in vitro* of 5α-dihydrotestosterone to macromolecular components from the rat ventral prostate. *Acta Endocrinol.* 66:352–56

63. Wakeling, A. E., Furr, B. J. A., Glen, A. T., Hughes, L. R. 1981. Receptor binding and biological activity of steroidal and nonsteroidal antiandrogens. *J. Steroid Biochem.* 15:355–59

64. Wang, T. Y., Loor, R. M. 1979. Testosterone-activated RNA synthesis in isolated prostate nuclei. *J. Steroid Biochem.* 10:299–304

65. Watson, G., Davey, R. A., Labarca, C.,

Paigen, K. 1981. Genetic determination of kinetic parameters in β-glucuronidase induction by androgen. *J. Biol. Chem.* 256:3005–11

66. Wieland, S. J., Fox, T. O. 1979. Putative androgen receptors distinguished in wild-type and testicular-feminized (Tfm) mice. *Cell* 17:781–87

67. Wilson, E. M., French, F. S. 1976. Binding properties of androgen receptors. Evidence for identical receptors in rat testis, epididymis and prostate. *J. Biol. Chem.* 251:5620–29

68. Wilson, E. M,. French, F. S. 1979. Effects of proteases and protease inhibitors on the 4.5S and 8S androgen receptor. *J. Biol. Chem.* 254:6310–19

69. Winters, S. J., Banks, J. L., Loriaux, D. L. 1979. Cimetidine is an antiandrogen in the rat. *Gastroenterology* 76:504–8

Ann. Rev. Physiol. 1984. 46:119–30

REGULATION OF β-ADRENERGIC RECEPTORS BY STEROID HORMONES

Albert O. Davies

Division of Allergy, Critical Care, and Respiratory Medicine, Department of Medicine, Duke University Medical Center, Durham, North Carolina 27710

Robert J. Lefkowitz

Howard Hughes Medical Institute, Division of Cardiology, Department of Medicine, Department of Biochemistry, Duke University Medical Center, Durham, North Carolina 27710

INTRODUCTION

Adrenal steroid hormones and catecholamines play central roles both in maintaining survival in times of stress and in regulating normal physiologic responsiveness. The interplay between these two hormonal systems is of great physiological importance. Whereas catecholamines exert highly specific effects on specific tissues, steroid hormones have rather broad effects upon many physiologic functions in many tissues. The general pattern observed is one of steroid hormone-induced refinement or regulation of catecholamine-mediated processes. In this chapter we review what is known about the mechanisms by which adrenal steroid hormones regulate the action of the β-adrenergic receptor–adenylate cyclase system. Effects on the α-adrenergic receptors and the effects of gonadal steroids are not addressed (13, 29).

PHYSIOLOGIC MANIFESTATIONS OF STEROID-INDUCED β-ADRENERGIC RECEPTOR REGULATION

Steroid hormones enhance several β-adrenergic actions at the tissue level. Myocardial β_1-adrenergic responses such as positive inotropism (3, 25), posi-

119

0066-4278/84/0315-0119$02.00

tive chronotropism (20), and increased arrhythmogenicity (20) are enhanced by steroid hormones (29). Steroid hormones facilitate catecholamine stimulation of both hepatic glucose production (17) and glucose uptake by muscle (42). Vasodilation mediated by β_2-adrenergic action is also enhanced by steroid hormones (1, 4).

Steroid enhancement of β_2-adrenergic receptor action in the lung is of particular interest in view of the simultaneous use of steroids and catecholamines in asthma and related pulmonary disorders. Chronic administration of catecholamines results in a fall in the bronchodilatory response to catecholamines (9, 13). This phenomenon of diminished responsiveness is referred to as tachyphylaxis, desensitization, or refractoriness. In intact, tachyphylactic human lung, as well as in isolated tachyphylactic human bronchial muscle, hydrocortisone restores responsiveness to subsequent catecholamine challenge (9, 23). Similarly in dogs, methylprednisolone reverses the state of bronchial tachyphylaxis (48).

MECHANISMS OF β-ADRENERGIC RECEPTOR REGULATION

Research over the past decade has documented two major modes of β-adrenergic receptor regulation that appear to contribute to the regulation of tissue sensitivity to catecholamine action. Steroid hormones participate in both forms of regulation. The first form of β-adrenergic receptor regulation is regulation of the number of receptors in plasma membranes. A wide variety of factors regulate the concentration of these receptors (13, 30). The concentration of receptors can be regulated by translocation of receptors from the plasma membrane to intracellular compartments (46) or by altering rates of synthesis or degradation. Steroid hormones regulate the number of β-adrenergic receptors on cells (see below; 12). Direct demonstration of steroid effects on the rate of transcription of receptor genes has not yet been demonstrated.

The second major mechanism for regulation of β-adrenergic receptor function concerns the regulation of the "coupling" of the receptors to their effectors, the adenylate cyclase system. Steroid hormones have been found to regulate these coupling processes (see below; 14). In order to understand this form of receptor regulation, it is necessary to understand something about the mechanisms by which the receptors are normally coupled to the adenylate cyclase system. It is thought that hormone receptors first interact with a special class of guanine nucleotide regulatory proteins variably referred to as N_s or G/F (because they appear to mediate the stimulatory effects of both guanine nucleotides and fluoride ion on the enzyme) (12, 29, 39). Interaction of the receptors with the nucleotide regulatory protein is promoted by the prior interaction of agonists with the receptors (16). R-N_s interaction leads to conformational changes in N_s, accompanied by the dissociation of GDP, which is ordinarily tightly bound to this protein. GTP binds to this altered form of the nucleotide regulatory protein, thereby promoting its interaction in turn with the catalytic moiety of adenylate cyclase (C). $N_s \cdot GTP \cdot C$ is thought to be the physiologically active form of the enzyme. GTP is cleaved by a GTPase activity resident on the N_s protein (6). This appears to lead to the dissociation of N_s from C, thus terminating the activation of the enzyme and converting the N_s protein to its physiologically inactive state liganded with GDP. The role of the hormone receptor is to facilitate activation of the enzyme by guanine nucleotides acting through the nucleotide regulatory protein (45).

A major clue to the mechanism of adenylate cyclase activation by β-adrenergic receptors was provided by ligand binding data. This came from a careful study of differences between agonist and antagonist binding receptors are revealed by competition binding experiments. Figure 1A shows a typical antagonist competition curve for occupancy of β-adrenergic receptors. Such binding curves can be analyzed by computerized methods based on the law of mass action. Antagonist curves such as that shown in Figure 1A are found to be uniphasic and "steep" (hill slopes ≈ 1) and model best to a single affinity state. Such curves are unaffected by added guanine nucleotides. In contrast, agonist curves such as that for isoproterenol, shown in Figure 1B, model best to two affinity states with the dissociation constants (K_H for higher-affinity and K_L for lower-affinity) being about 100-fold apart. The higher-affinity state accounts for about three quarters of the receptors. When or hypothyroeotides are added, all the high-affinity receptors appear to be converted into low-affinity state receptors which have affinity identical to that of the lower-affinity state seen in the absence of guanine nucleotides (26).

A series of biochemical experiments has indicated that the high-affinity state of the receptor appears to represent a ternary complex of the agonist, the receptor, and the nucleotide regulatory protein (HRN), whereas the low-affinity state appears to represent the binary complex H-R (32, 44, 45). Agonists stabilize formation of the ternary complex and thus promote the activation of the cyclase.

Since the high-affinity form of the receptor appears to be a reflection of formation of the ternary complex HRN, computer modeling of agonist competition curves can be used to assess the extent of formation of this complex in membranes. Any influence that interferes with the coupling of the receptors with the nucleotide regulatory protein decreases the formation or stability of this complex and shifts the agonist competition curve to the right. This is because there is less of the high-affinity form of the receptor formed. This observation has provided a basis for experimentally assessing the efficiency of coupling of receptors with N proteins under the influence of agonists (26, 32, 44, 45). A variety of circumstances—for example desensitization (26, 30, 46)

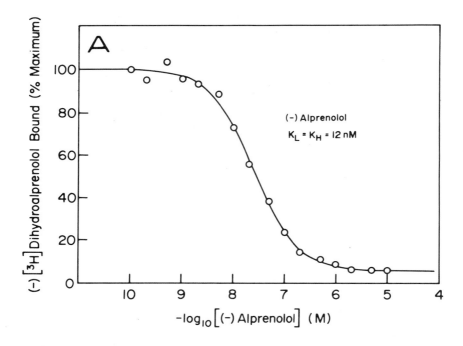

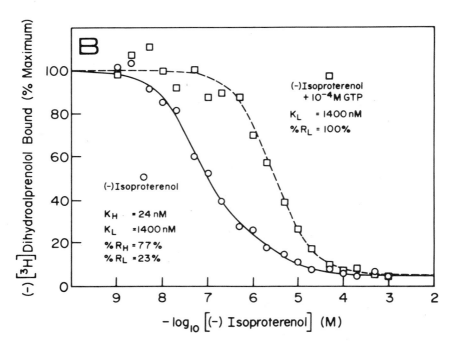

or hypothyroidism (47)—have previously been shown to be associated with impaired coupling of the receptors with the N_s protein. As discussed below, steroid hormones appear to modulate the coupling of receptors with N_s proteins and hence alter the properties of agonist competition curves. In summary, therefore, the steroid hormones regulate both the number and the coupling of the β-adrenergic receptors.

BIOCHEMICAL MANIFESTATIONS OF STEROID-INDUCED β-ADRENERGIC RECEPTOR REGULATION

This section highlights steroid-induced changes in various components of the β-adrenergic receptor–adenylate cyclase system. We address steroid-induced regulation, which applies to most tissues, and note the circumstances in which tissue-specific effects are present.

In Normal Tissues

Most studies involving adrenal steroid hormone regulation of β-adrenergic receptors have been performed with human leukocytes. The initial approach used to was to assess how much cAMP accumulated in response to stimulation by isoproterenol in vitro (27, 33, 37). There was a reproducible "direct" effect (i.e. without added catecholamine) of hydrocortisone to increase cAMP accumulation that was not adequately explained by an alteration of phosphodiesterase activity (33, 35, 37). In addition to this "direct" effect, hydrocortisone increases isoproterenol-stimulated cAMP accumulation (27, 33, 35). Similar hydrocortisone enhancement of isoproterenol-stimulated cAMP accumulation is observed in mast cells (49). When examined directly, isoproterenol-stimulated adenylate cyclase activity is increased 93% in neutrophils exposed in vivo to glucocorticoids (12).

The steroid-induced changes in adenylate cyclase activity are associated with increased receptor binding sites. Oral adminstration of cortisone acetate results in a 39% rise in neutrophil β-adrenergic receptor density (12). Similarly, after two days of oral prednisone therapy, receptor density appears to be elevated in both lymphocytes and granulocytes (41). Glucocorticoids also increase β-adrenergic receptor density in rat lung (34), cultured human lung cells (19),

---

Figure 1   Competition curves derived from frog erythrocyte β-adrenergic receptors. A: Antagonist binding. Frog erythrocyte membranes were incubated with [³H]-dihydroalprenolol in competition with increasing concentrations of the β-adrenergic antagonist (−) alprenolol and then assayed for [³H]-DHA binding. Maximum binding represents the binding of [³H]-DHA in the absence of competing (−) alprenolol. The solid line is the computer-generated curve best fitting the observed data points.

   B. Agonist binding. Frog erythrocyte membranes were incubated with [³H]-DHA in competition with increasing concentrations of the strong β-adrenergic agonist (−) isoproterenol, in both the absence and presence of $10^{-4}M$ GTP. Taken from (26).

cultured human astrocytoma cells (18), and in rabbit fetal lung tissues (2, 8). Thus, steroid exposure results in both supersensitization (increased β-agonist stimulation of adenylate cyclase activity) and "up-regulation" of β-adrenergic receptors (increased receptor density).

Once supersensitization and "up-regulation" were demonstrated, attention was directed to potential changes in "coupling" induced by steroid hormones. Receptor "coupling" and high-affinity-state formation were assessed by constructing isoproterenol competition curves as noted above in the section on Mechanisms of β-Adrenergic Receptor Regulation. The ratio of dissociation constants, K_L/K_H, correlates with both the percentage of receptors in the high-affinity state and the intrinsic activity (the maximum ability to stimulate adenylate cyclase relative to isoproterenol) of the competing agent. Thus, the value K_L/K_H can be used as a measure or index of the formation of HRN (i.e. of the "coupling" of receptor occupation to enzyme activation) (14).

After oral cortisone administration to normal human volunteers, the measured K_L/K_H rises from 44 to 130 and the estimated proportion of receptors in the high-affinity state rises from 54% to 80% (14). Moreover, exposure of human neutrophils to hydrocortisone in vitro yields very similar results (14). Thus, glucocorticoids regulate β-adrenergic receptor function by facilitating the formation of the high-affinity "coupled" form of the receptor.

In Desensitized Tissues

Prolonged exposure to endogenous or exogenous catecholamines reduces physiologic responsiveness to subsequent catecholamine stimulation. This phenomenon is known as desensitization (13, 30). Prolonged exposure of β-adrenergic receptors to catecholamine agonists results in three defects: down-regulation (fall in receptor density or number), desensitization (fall in catecholamine-stimulated adenylate cyclase activity), and uncoupling (destabilization of the high-affinity state of the receptor). There may be different time courses for the appearance of each defect, with uncoupling preceding down-regulation at least in some circumstances (22). Further, the relative magnitude of these defects may differ. Thus physiologic desensitization is associated with several biochemical defects in the β-adrenergic receptor–adenylate cyclase system (30).

Since human asthma is a state in which adrenergic receptors are exposed to high concentrations of catecholamines from endogenous or exogenous sources, asthma has been a prime condition under study. Leukocytes from asthmatics appear to have diminished isoproterenol-stimulated cAMP accumulation (10, 28). After exposure to adrenal steroid hormones either in vivo or in vitro, there is a complete or near complete return of responsiveness in isoproterenol-stimulated cAMP accumulation in leukocytes from asthmatics (28, 33). Moreover, prednisone increases β-adrenergic receptor density in lymphocytes and granulocytes obtained from asthmatics (41).

The effects of steroid hormones upon desensitized tissues have been examined in a model of in vitro desensitization of human neutrophil β-adrenergic receptors. The typical pattern of desensitization occurred with reduced cAMP accumulation, decreased receptor density, and uncoupling. The uncoupling is apparent in Figure 2 (15). The curve derived from desensitized cells was shifted to the right of the control curve. This shift to the right was quantitated as an 8-fold increase in the EC_{50} for isoproterenol and was associated with a reduction in K_L/K_H from 120 to 39 (15). Thus exposure of human neutrophils to isoproterenol in vitro results in diminished ability of agonists to stabilize the high-affinity state of β-adrenergic receptors. The effect of steroid hormones was examined in neutrophils simultaneously exposed to isoproterenol and hydrocortisone. The post-exposure (isoproterenol + hydrocortisone) cAMP accumulation was statistically significantly greater than that of cells exposed to isoproterenol alone (15). The β-adrenergic receptor density in the isoproterenol + hydrocortisone treatment group was not different from that of the isoproterenol treatment group. Thus the presence of hydrocortisone attenuates the iso-

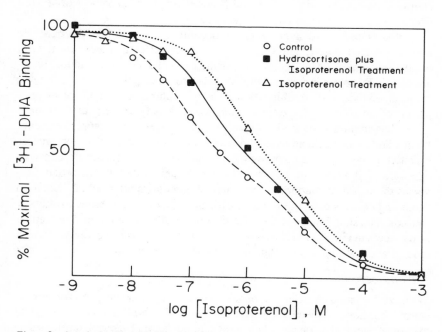

Figure 2 Agonist binding to human β-adrenergic receptors exposed to isoproterenol and hydrocortisone. The abscissa represents the concentration of isoproterenol competing for [³H]-DHA binding to β-adrenergic receptors. The ordinate represents bound [³H]-DHA expressed as a percentage of maximal [³H]-DHA binding. The computer drawn lines represent the best fits to the data. Reproduced from *The Journal of Clinical Investigation*, 1983, 71(3), pp. 565–71 by copyright permission of the American Society for Clincal Investigation.

proterenol-induced desensitization of the β-adrenergic receptor without altering isoproterenol-induced down-regulation (15).

Altered "coupling" could explain the steroid effect on desensitization while leaving down-regulation unaltered. "Coupling" was again examined by constructing isoproterenol competition curves for receptors derived from neutrophils simultaneously exposed to isoproterenol and hydrocortisone. This resulted in isoproterenol competition curves that were shallow and complex, lying between the control and the desensitized curves (Figure 2). The resultant EC_{50} for the isoproterenol + hydrocortisone treatment curve is intermediate between EC_{50} values for the control and for the desensitized curves (15). The K_L/K_H determined for the combined treatment curve is also intermediate between the control and the desensitized values. The effect of hydrocortisone in combined treatment could be reproduced by prednisolone (15). Thus isoproterenol-induced desensitization reduces stability of the agonist-induced high-affinity state, while the presence of glucocorticoids attenuates this reduction. These regulatory processes, induced by prolonged catecholamine and steroid exposure, could allow overall β-adrenergic responsiveness to be very finely tuned according to physiologic need (15).

In vivo studies also indicate that glucocorticoids modulate β-adrenergic agonist-induced desensitization but by a rather different mechanism. Oral terbutaline was used to induce desensitization and down-regulation of β-adrenergic receptors in lymphocytes derived from normal or mildly asthmatic subjects. Subsequent administration of a single intravenous dose of methylprednisolone 10 mg kg^{-1} restored the receptor density to pretreatment values (24). Thus simultaneous in vivo exposure of β-adrenergic receptors to catecholamine and glucocorticoid results in attenuation of the desensitization process by altering the impaired coupling of the receptors, while consecutive in vivo exposure of β-adrenergic receptors to catecholamine then glucocorticoid reverses the down-regulation. As yet there is no confirmation that a change in "coupling" occurs after in vivo desensitization followed by resensitization by steroids. The significance of the different effects of steroids on the desensitization process in vitro and in vivo is not yet clear. In both cases, however, steroids tend to attenuate the catecholamine-induced refractoriness.

Adrenalectomy

We have discussed the effects of exposure to elevated concentrations of adrenal steroid hormones. Specific changes in the β-adrenergic receptor–adenylate cyclase system also occur when exposure to adrenal steroid hormones is reduced through adrenalectomy. These changes may vary from system to system, however. In the rat myocardium, adrenalectomy results in a reduction in adenylate cyclase sensitivity to catecholamines and uncoupling without a reduction in β-adrenergic receptor density (11). Similarly, rat myocardial cAMP accumulation is reduced after adrenalectomy (38). Adrenalectomy leads to decreased numbers of adipocyte β-adrenergic receptors and reduced isoproterenol-induced cAMP accumulation (43). Similarly, adrenalectomy results in decreased β-adrenergic receptor density in rat lung membranes (34). The situation in rat liver and brain is somewhat less clear. In contrast to the changes described above, adrenalectomy appears to increase catecholamine-stimulated cAMP accumulation (7, 17), adenylate cyclase activity (5, 31, 50), and β-adrenergic receptor density in rat liver (21, 50). This effect can be abolished by administration of cortisone. A similar adrenalectomy-induced increase in isoproterenol-stimulated cAMP accumulation occurs in the rat brain (36, 40). The reason for these apparently disparate results is not presently known, as no single study has carefully compared changes in rat liver, heart, lung, and brain.

Mineralocorticoids

Relatively few studies have directly examined isolated mineralocorticoid (as opposed to glucocorticoid) effects on the β-adrenergic receptor. However, using the desoxycorticosterone-salt hypertensive rat model, it appears that mineralocorticoid-induced increases in blood pressure are associated with a reduction in β-adrenergic receptor density (51). Information is not available as to whether mineralocorticoids also alter "coupling" or adenylate cyclase activity.

SUMMARY AND PERSPECTIVES FOR THE FUTURE

Exposure to steroid hormones may result in increases in receptor density, enhanced coupling, and enhanced adenylate cyclase activity. At least in rat heart and lung, adrenalectomy appears to result in the converse changes. Further, if reductions in receptor density, coupling, and adenylate cyclase activity are induced through desensitization, steroid hormones may act to return the receptor-cyclase system to a more normal state of sensitivity. This general model seems to apply to several tissues in several species and thus may be quite useful in understanding the biochemical basis for the observed physiologic effects of steroids upon catecholamine action.

There remain, however, many questions concerning steroid hormone effects upon β-adrenergic receptors. The three major unresolved issues are: (a) the mechanisms of the steroid regulatory effects, (b) tissue and species differences, and (c) differences in effects among different types of steroid hormones.

The studies available thus far do not address the question of whether changes in protein synthesis are necessary for the steroid-induced changes in the β-adrenergic receptor–adenylate cyclase system. Moreover, although direct effects upon the N-site seem to occur, it is unclear whether there is a change in the amount of N-site or whether N-site activity is altered. Since steroid hormones alter pre- and post-receptor events as well as receptor events, it is unknown which effects are relatively most important in normal and abnormal states. Resolving these issues should refine our understanding of receptor biochemistry as well as provide potential new therapeutic approaches.

Literature Cited

1. Altura, B. M., Altura, B. T. 1974. Peripheral vascular actions of glucocorticoids and their relationship to protection in circulatory shock. *J. Pharmacol. Exp. Therap.* 190:300–15
2. Barnes, P., Jacobs, M., Roberts, J. 1983. Glucocorticoids preferentially increase fetal alveolar β-adrenoceptors: autoradiographic evidence. *Clin. Res.* 31:70A
3. Bassett, J. R., Strand, F. L., Cairncross, K. D. 1978. Glucocorticoids, adrenocorticotropic hormone and related polypeptides on myocardial sensitivity to noradrenaline. *Eur. J. Pharmacol.* 49:243–49
4. Besse, J. C., Bass, A. D. 1966. Potentiation by hydrocortisone of responses to catecholamines in vascular smooth muscle. *J. Pharmacol. Exp. Therap.* 154:224–38
5. Bitensky, M. W., Russell, V., Blanco, M. 1970. Independent variation of glucagon and epinephrine responsive components of hepatic adenyl cyclase as a function of age, sex and steroid hormones. *Endocrinology* 86:154–59
6. Cassel, D., Selinger, Z. 1978. Mechanism of adenylate cyclase activation through the β-adrenergic receptor: Catecholamine-induced displacement of bound GDP by GTP. *Proc. Natl. Acad. Sci. USA* 75:4155–59
7. Chan, T. M., Blackmore, P. F., Steiner, K. E., Exton, J. H. 1979. Effects of adrenalectomy on hormone action on hepatic glucose metabolism. *J. Biol. Chem.* 254:2428–33
8. Cheng, J. B., Goldfien, A., Ballard, P. L., Roberts, J. M. 1980. Glucocorticoids increase pulmonary β-adrenergic receptors in fetal rabbit. *Endocrinology* 86:154–59
9. Conolly, M. E. 1980. Cyclic nucleotides, β receptors, and bronchial asthma. *Adv. Cyclic Nucl. Res.* 12:151–59
10. Conolly, M. E., Greenacre, J. K. 1976. The lymphocyte β-adrenoceptor in normal subjects and patients with bronchial asthma. *J. Clin. Invest.* 58:1307–16
11. Davies, A. O., DeLean, A., Lefkowitz, R. J. 1981. Myocardial β-adrenergic receptors from adrenalectomized rats: impaired formation of high-affinity agonist-receptor complexes. *Endocrinology* 108:720–22
12. Davies, A. O., Lefkowitz, R. J. 1980. Corticosteroid-induced differential regulation of β-adrenergic receptors in circulating human polymorphonuclear leukocytes and mononuclear leukocytes. *J. Clin. Endocrinol. Metab.* 51:599–605
13. Davies, A. O., Lefkowitz, R. J. 1981. Regulation of adrenergic receptors. In *Receptors and Recognition*, ed. R. Lefkowitz, 13:83–121. London: Chapman and Hall
14. Davies, A. O., Lefkowitz, R. J. 1980. Agonist-promoted high affinity state of the β-adrenergic receptor in human neutrophils: modulation by corticosteroids. *J. Clin. Endocrinol. Metab.* 51:703–38
15. Davies, A. O., Lefkowitz, R. J. 1983. In vitro desensitization of β-adrenergic receptors in human neutrophils: attenuation by corticosteroids. *J. Clin. Invest.* 71:565–71
16. DeLean, A., Stadel, J. M., Lefkowitz, R. J. 1980. A ternary complex model explains the agonist-specific binding properties of the adenylate cyclase coupled β-adrenergic receptor. *J. Biol. Chem.* 255:7108–17
17. Exton, J. H., Friedmann, N., Wong, E. H-A., Brineau, J. P., Corbin, J. D., Park, C. R. 1972. Interaction of glucocorticoids with glucagon and epinephrine in the control of gluconeogenesis and glycogenolysis in liver and of lipolysis in adipose tissue. *J. Biol. Chem.* 11:3579–88
18. Foster, S. J., Harden, T. K. 1980. Dexamethasone increases β-adrenoceptor density in human astrocytoma cells. *Biochem. Parmacol.* 29:2151–53
19. Fraser, C. M., Venter, J. C. 1980. The synthesis of β-adrenergic receptors in

cultured human lung cells: induction by glucocorticoids. *Biochem. Biophys. Res. Commun.* 94:390–97

20. Guideri, G., Green, M., Lehr, D. 1978. Potentiation of isoproterenol carditoxicity by corticoids. *Res. Commun. Chem Pathol.* Pharmacol. 21:197–212

21. Guellaen, G., Yates-Aggerbeck, M., Vauquelin, G., Strosberg, D., Hanoune, J. 1978. Characterization with [^{3}H]dihydroergocryptine of the α-adrenergic receptor of the hepatic plasma membrane. *J. Biol. Chem.* 253:1114–20

22. Harden, T. K., Su, Y. F., Perkins, J. P. 1979. Catecholamine-induced desensitization involves an uncoupling of β-adrenergic receptors and adenylate cyclase. *J. Cyclic Nucl. Res.* 5:99–106

23. Holgate, S. T., Baldwin, C. J., Tattersfield, A. E. 1977. β-adrenergic agonist resistance in normal human airways. *Lancet* 2:375–77

24. Hui, K. K., Conolly, M. E., Tashkin, D. P. 1982. Reversal of human lymphocyte β-adrenoceptor desensitization by glucocorticoids. *Clin. Pharmacol. Ther.* 32:566–71

25. Kaumann, A. J. 1972. Potentiation of the effects of isoprenaline and noradrenaline by hydrocortisone in cat heart muscle. *Naunyn-Schmiedeberg's Arch. Pharmacol.* 273:134–53

26. Kent, R., DeLean A., Lefkowitz, R. J. 1980. Quantitative analysis of β-adrenergic receptor interactions: resolution of high and low affinity states of the receptor by computer modeling of ligand binding data. *Mol. Pharmacol.* 17:14–23

27. Lee, T. P., Reed, C. E. 1977. Effects of steroids on the regulation of the levels of cyclic AMP in human lymphocytes. *Biochem. Biophys. Res. Commun.* 78:998–1004

28. Lee, T. P., Busse, W. W., Reed, C. E. 1977. Effect of β-adrenergic agonist, prostaglandins, and cortisol on lymphocyte levels of cyclic adenosine monophosphate and glycogen: abnormal lymphocytic metabolism in asthma. *J. Allergy Clin. Immunol.* 59:408–18

29. Lefer, A. M. 1975. Corticosteroids and circulatory function. *Handbook of Physiology.* 6:191–207. Washington, D. C.: Amer. Physiol. Soc.

30. Lefkowitz, R. J. 1982. Clinical physiology of adrenergic receptor regulation. *Am. J. Physiol.* 243:E43–47

31. Leray, F., Chambaut, A-M., Perrenoud, M-L., Hanoune, J. 1973. Adenylate-cyclase activity of rat-liver plasma membranes: hormonal stimulations and effect of adrenalectomy. *Eur. J. Biochem.* 38:185–92

32. Limbird, L. E., Gill, D. M., Stadel, J. M., Hickey, A. R. 1980. Loss of β-adrenergic receptor–guanine nucleotide regulatory protein interactions accompanies decline in catecholamine responsiveness of adenylate cyclase in maturing rat erythrocytes. *J. Biol. Chem.* 255:1854–61

33. Logsdon, P. J., Middleton, E. Jr., Coffey, R. G. 1972. Stimulation of leukocyte adenyl cyclase by hydrocortisone and isoproterenol in asthmatic and non-asthmatic subjects. *J. Allergy Clin. Immunol.* 50:45–56

34. Mano, K., Akbarzadeh, A., Townley, R. G. 1979. Effect of hydrocortisone on β-adrenergic receptors in lung membranes. *Life Sci.* 25:1925–30

35. Marone, G., Lichtenstein, L. M., Plaut, M. 1980. Hydrocortisone and human lymphocytes: increases in cyclic adenosine 3':5'-monophosphate and potentiation of adenylate cyclase-activating agents. *J. Pharmacol. Exp. Therap.* 215:469–78

36. Mobley, P. L., Sulser, F. 1980. Adrenal corticoids regulate sensitivity of noradrenaline receptor–coupled adenylate cyclase in brain. *Nature* 286:608–9

37. Parker, C. W., Smith, J. W. 1973. Alterations in cyclic adenosine monophosphate metabolism in human bronchial asthma. *J. Clin. Invest.* 52:48–59

38. Phornchirasilp, S., Matangkasombut, O. P. 1982. Role of adrenal steroids on the cardiac c-AMP response to isoprenaline in the rat. *Horm. Metab. Res.* 14:207–9

39. Ross, E. M., Gilman, A. G. 1980. Biochemical properties of hormone-sensitive adenylate cyclase. *Ann. Rev. Biochem.* 49:533–64

40. Roberts, D. C. S., Bloom, F. E. 1981. Adrenal steroid-induced changes in β-adrenergic receptor binding in rat hippocampus. *Eur. J. Pharmacol.* 74:37–41

41. Sano, U., Ford, L., Begley, M., Watt, G., Townley, R., Tsai, H., Bewtra, A. 1980. Effect of in vivo anti-asthma drugs on human leukocyte β-adrenergic receptors. *Clin. Res.* 28:431A

42. Schonberg, M., Smith, T. J., Krichevsky, A., Bilezikian, J. P. 1981. Glucocorticoids enhance glucose uptake and affect differentiation and β-adrenergic responsiveness in muscle cell cultures. *Cell Differ.* 10:101–7

43. Schonhoferr, P. S., Skidmore, I. F., Paul, M. I., Ditzion, B. R., Pauk, G. L., Krishna, G. 1972. Effects of glucocorticoids on adenyl cyclase and phosphodiesterase activity in fat cell homogenates and the accumulation of cyclic AMP in intact

fat cells. *Naunyn-Schmiedeberg's Arch. Pharmacol.* 273:267–82

44. Stadel, J. M., DeLean, A., Lefkowitz, R. J. 1980. A high affinity agonist β-adrenergic receptor complex is an intermediate for catecholamine stimulation of adenylate cyclase in turkey and frog erythrocyte membranes. *J. Biol. Chem.* 255:1436–41

45. Stadel, J. M., DeLean, A., Lefkowitz, R. J. 1982. Molecular mechanisms of coupling in hormone receptor adenylate cyclase systems. *Adv. Enzymol.* 53:1–43

46. Stadel, J. M., Strulovici, B., Nambi, P., Lavin, T. N., Briggs, M. M., Caron, M. G., Lefkowitz, R. J. 1983. Desensitization of the β-adrenergic receptor of frog erythrocytes: recovery and characterization of the down-regulated receptors in sequestered vesicles. *J. Biol. Chem.* 258:3032–38

47. Stiles, G. L., Stadel, J. M., DeLean, A., Lefkowitz, R. J. 1981. Hypothyroidism modulates β-adrenergic receptor–adenylate cyclase interactions in rat reticulocytes. *J. Clin. Invest.* 68:1450–55

48. Stephan, W. C., Chick, T. W., Avner, B. P., Jenne, J. W. 1980. Tachyphylaxis to inhaled isoproterenol and the effect of methylprednisolone in dogs. *J. Allergy Clin. Immunol.* 65:105–9

49. Tolone, G., Bonasera, L., Sajeva, R. 1979. Hydrocortisone increases the responsiveness of mast cells to β-adrenergic agonists by an action distal to the β-adrenoreceptors. *Br. J. Exp. Pathol.* 60:269–75

50. Wolfe, B. B., Harden, T. K., Molinoff, P. B. 1976. β-adrenergic receptors in rat liver: effects of adrenalectomy. *Proc. Natl. Acad. Sci. USA* 73:1343–47

51. Woodcock, E. A., Funder, J. W., Johnston, C. I. 1979. Decreased cardiac β-adrenergic receptors in deoxycorticosterone-salt and renal hypertensive rats. *Circ. Res.* 45:560–65

CARDIOVASCULAR PHYSIOLOGY

Introduction, Harvey V. Sparks, Jr., *Section Editor,* and Robert B. Stephenson, *Guest Section Editor*

"Cardiovascular Correlates of Behavior" is a very old topic, yet decidedly contemporary. That cardiovascular manifestations of behavior can sometimes be pathogenic is also an old idea. Despite a long history and intense popular interest, the cardiovascular correlates of behavior have been little studied by physiologists. This is not to imply that they have been unknown. John Hunter, the great 18th century anatomist and physiologist who suffered from angina pectoris, said his "life was in the hands of any rascal who chose to annoy and tease" him. He died following a meeting of the Board of Governors of St. George's Hospital (1); anyone who deals with a medical center bureaucracy knows this was no coincidence.

Nevertheless, behavioral studies have not been prominent in the history of cardiovascular physiology. Certainly one reason is that formidable experimental complexities and ambiguities arise when behavior is included as an independent variable. Much cardiovascular research has been directed to understanding the mechanisms that stabilize the internal environment, making use of anesthetized subjects in which constant or steady state conditions prevail until the experimenter institutes a perturbation.

In the last several years ever increasing experiments have been directed at the interrelated ideas that behavior profoundly influences the cardiovascular system and that these cardiovascular responses may have pathological consequences (2).

Two factors in particular have speeded progress in understanding cardiovascular consequences of behavior. First, technical advances have made it easier to monitor and/or control a variety of cardiovascular parameters in unanesthetized animals and humans. Second, our knowledge of the central neural mechanisms of cardiovascular control has increased tremendously in recent years (e.g. 60 abstracts on "Neural Control of the Circulation" were submitted at the spring 1983 FASEB meetings, up from 24 in 1975.)

The influence of each of these developments is evident in the following pages. Dr. Stephenson describes experiments done on awake dogs with isolated carotid sinuses. This preparation allows a more precise description of baroreflex characteristics and provides convincing evidence for maintained baroreflex function during exercise in behaving animals. Dr. Anderson summarizes studies that show that behavioral stress influences renal regulation sodium balance, and that this coupled with increased dietary sodium can produce hypertension in animals without a genetic predisposition for the disease. Drs. Verrier & Lown show that the combination of coronary artery obstruction and behavioral stress can result in fatal cardiac arrhythmia. They also provide provocative suggestions as to central mechanisms for the interaction. Dr. Herd reviews the work demonstrating a relationship between the development of hypertension and exaggerated cardiovascular responses to physiological and psychological stimuli. He discusses the great difficulty in understanding the causal relationship between these two complex phenomena. Drs. Cohen & Randall describe the development of effective conditioning methods that can be used to investigate the neural pathways responsible for the cardiovascular correlates of behavior. Development of these methods is essential for further developments in this field. Finally, Drs. Engel & Schneidermann discuss the use of operant conditioning to study behaviorally induced cardiovascular disease. They point to the success of investigators who have combined operant conditioning with a genetic or environmental substratum favoring pathological changes.

Each of the articles raises more questions than it answers, as is appropriate in a field beginning a period of rapid growth. The many unanswered questions point to the need for new ideas and approaches from investigators in both the neural and cardiovascular communities.

Literature Cited

1. Willius, F. A., Keys, T. E. 1961. *Classics of Cardiology*, 1:265–67. New York: Dover. 400 pp.

2. Smith, O. A., Galosy, R. A., Weiss, S. M., eds. 1982. *Circulation, Neurobiology and Behavior*. New York: Elsevier. 346 pp.

Ann. Rev. Physiol. 1984. 46:133–42
Copyright © 1984 by Annual Reviews Inc. All rights reserved

MODIFICATION OF REFLEX REGULATION OF BLOOD PRESSURE BY BEHAVIOR

Robert B. Stephenson

Department of Physiology, Michigan State University, East Lansing, Michigan 48824

INTRODUCTION

The arterial baroreceptor reflex has been the subject of hundreds of experimental studies over more than 50 years. However, there have been relatively few studies concerning the role of the baroreflex in the regulation of blood pressure during changes in behavioral state. Nonbehavioral studies have revealed the basic characteristics of the baroreflex and have identified certain limitations of the reflex as a regulator of blood pressure. For example, the baroreflex has limited importance in setting the long-term, average level of blood pressure (15, 33). The salient abnormality that accompanies chronic denervation of baroreceptors is increased lability of blood pressure (14, 28, 31), indicating that the baroreflex plays a critical role in stabilizing blood pressure against acute fluctuations. However, some behavioral studies have indicated that the role of the baroreflex in moment-to-moment regulation of blood pressure is more complex than that of a simple buffer system (4, 42). This review focuses on evidence relevant to the hypothesis that the central nervous system modifies the baroreflex as part of its adjustment of the cardiovascular system for particular behaviors.

POTENTIAL MECHANISMS OF BAROREFLEX MODULATION

The ability of the baroreflex to control blood pressure is affected by activity in chemoreceptor, cardiopulmonary, and somatic afferent neurons (11, 32, 38, 47, 57). In addition, the central nervous system may act by "central command"

133

to modify the functional characteristics of the baroreflex. Electrical stimulation of specific supramedullary structures can facilitate or inhibit the reflex (12, 30). In some cases these same structures are known to be important in organizing the cardiovascular responses to behavioral states such as exercise or emotion (27, 51).

The central nervous system can act via the sympathetic innervation of the carotid sinuses to alter the transduction characteristics of the carotid baroreceptors, themselves. In anesthetized animals, baroreflex function can be altered by cutting or stimulating the cervical sympathetic trunk (6, 56, 59). Sympathetic nerves and circulating catecholamines can affect the baroreceptors directly or indirectly via alterations in the tone of the carotid sinus vascular smooth muscle (58). However, little is known about the functional significance of the sympathetic innervation of the sinuses during various behaviors.

Behavioral state may also affect the baroreflex by altering the responsiveness of cardiac and vascular tissues. During exercise, for example, metabolic vasodilation in working skeletal muscle may counter the ability of the baroreflex to change peripheral resistance (4, 48). For this reason it can be difficult to determine, in a given behavioral situation, whether or not an observed alteration in the baroreflex is due to central or peripheral modulaton. Whereas skeletal muscle vasculature is strongly affected by intrinsic factors, heart rate is predominantly under neural control. Therefore, the responses of heart rate to baroreceptor stimulation may provide quite direct evidence for central neural modulation of the baroreflex (19, 40, 46, 55). Nevertheless, since heart rate is only one determinant of blood pressure, a change in the cardiac component of the baroreflex does not necessarily mean that the ability of the baroreflex to regulate blood pressure has been altered (10, 37).

BAROREFLEX IN EXERCISE

Both controlled stimulation of the baroreceptors and interruption of afferent activity from the baroreceptors have been employed to study the role of the baroreflex in exercise. Most studies based on altering the stimulus to the baroreceptors have indicated that the ability of the baroreflex to control blood pressure is largely preserved during the transition from rest to exercise.

Bilateral carotid occlusion caused equivalent reflex increases in blood pressure in dogs at rest and during treadmill exercise (23, 42). The depressor responses to electrical stimulation of the carotid sinus nerves were not affected by dynamic exercise in dogs (60) or humans (20). An airtight chamber encasing the neck has been used to alter carotid sinus transmural pressure in humans. Pressurization of the chamber decreases baroreceptor stimulation and partial evacuation of the chamber increases baroreceptor stimulation. This technique has shown that the baroreflex in humans retains the ability to raise and lower pressure relative to the prevailing level during dynamic treadmill exercise and during isometric handgrip exercise (5, 36, 40).

The classical method for characterizing the baroreflex of anesthetized animals has been to isolate the carotid sinuses and to derive complete stimulus-response relations for the effect of carotid sinus pressure on arterial blood pressure, heart rate, cardiac output, or peripheral resistance. Shifts in stimulus-response curves or changes in their slopes have been taken to indicate resetting or altered sensitivity of the baroreflex (10, 30). Recently techniques have been developed for deriving complete stimulus-response relations for the carotid baroreflex in conscious animals (21, 23, 53, 54). Mild and moderately severe treadmill exercise caused significant, graded, upward displacements of the sigmoidal curves relating blood pressure (response) to carotid sinus pressure (stimulus) (42). The prevailing level of blood pressure (sinuses not isolated) also increased during exercise. Since the stimulus-response curve and the prevailing blood pressure were both shifted upward by equivalent amounts during exercise, the ability of the baroreflex to increase or decrease blood pressure relative to its prevailing value was unchanged. The data imply that (*a*) exercise was accompanied by pressor influences that were independent of the baroreflex, and (*b*) the potential of the baroreflex to regulate blood pressure (i.e. reflex gain as indicated by the slope of the curves) was unaltered by exercise (30). Results of a similar study by another research group were corroborative except that a diminution of baroreflex gain was evident during exercise (23). Potential reasons for this discrepancy include differences in the preparation (e.g. aortic depressor nerves were cut; 23) or differences in the experimental setting (e.g. degree of thermal stress or emotion involved in the exercise).

If the baroreflex continues to operate during exercise, then the increase in blood pressure that accompanies exercise cannot be attributed to a turning off of the baroreflex, as had been suggested earlier (41). Indeed, an operating baroreflex should oppose the increase in blood pressure during exercise, because the baroreceptors are presented with increases in both mean and pulse pressure. That is, blood pressure would be expected to increase more during exercise in an animal deprived of its normal baroreflexes than in an intact animal (5, 31).

In dogs that had had an intrathoracic denervation of aortic baroreceptors and had also been prepared for reversible vascular isolation of the carotid sinuses, the responses of blood pressure to treadmill exercise were qualitatively similar when the carotid sinuses were exposed to natural blood pressure and when carotid sinus pressure was fixed at a constant level (61). However, when the sinuses were isolated at a fixed pressure, the initial, momentary decline in blood pressure at the onset of exercise and the subsequent, sustained increase in blood pressure were both significantly exaggerated. The exaggerated elevation of blood pressure resulted from subnormal decreases in total peripheral resistance rather than excessive increases in heart rate or cardiac output. This finding suggests that the baroreflex buffers increases in blood pressure during exercise by limiting sympathetic vasoconstriction, and this finding illustrates the risk of making inferences about the effect of the baroreflex on blood pressure simply from measurements of heart rate. In an earlier study by the same research group, dogs without aortic denervation did not have a greater increase in blood pressure during exercise when carotid sinus pressure was fixed at a constant value than when the sinuses were exposed to the pulsatile, prevailing blood pressure (42). Taken together, the studies indicate that either the carotid or aortic baroreceptors can act to buffer both the fall in blood pressure at the beginning of exercise and also the subsequent increase in pressure as exercise continues or work load increases.

The preceeding statement is not supported by results of studies on dogs whose baroreflexes were disabled by surgical denervation of both the carotid and aortic baroreceptor afferents. In chronically denervated dogs, blood pressure transiently decreased with the onset of exercise (31, 61). If the exercise was strenuous and prolonged, blood pressure tended eventually to reach equivalent levels in the denervated and innervated animals, but pressure was not higher in the denervated animals (31, 41, 61). The tendency for the blood pressure of denervated dogs to fall during exercise was especially pronounced when interruption of the aortic baroreflex was achieved by complete block of the cervical vagi (2, 42). These results suggest that aortic baroreceptor afferents or other afferent pathways in the vagi must be intact in order for normal increases in blood pressure to occur during exercise. Superficially, this suggestion is reminiscent of the idea that metabolic vasodilation tends to cause blood pressure to fall at the onset of exercise, and the baroreceptors detect this tendency and initiate a pressor response. However, this idea has been rejected because, if the baroreflex brought about a pressor response, it would thereby eliminate the error signal necessary to sustain that response (3). The failure of blood pressure to rise abnormally high during exercise in baroreceptor denervated dogs might instead be attributed to (a) the surgical interruption of nonbaroreceptor neurons and (b) secondary effects of the adaptation to chronic baroreceptor denervation.

Recent efforts to achieve complete aortic baroreceptor denervation have involved drastic cervical and thoracic neural ablations. Such procedures necessarily interrupt cardiac efferent neurons and cardiac and pulmonary afferent neurons as well as aortic afferent neurons (13, 28). Even the denervation of the carotid sinus baroreceptors is complicated by the inadvertent damage to carotid body afferent neurons (25). Thus, it is imprudent to attribute the effects of "baroreceptor denervation" exclusively to the loss of the baroreceptors.

If conscious, resting dogs with aortic denervation are acutely deprived of carotid baroreceptor afferent activity, blood pressure rises to 210 mm Hg (61). In the chronic phase of sinoaortic denervation, blood pressure is much less elevated (2, 4, 14, 22, 28, 41, 61). Sinoaortic denervated cats and dogs tend to have abnormally low cardiac output and high peripheral resistance at rest (2, 4, 31). Blood pressure tends to be more stable in chronically sinoaortic denervated dogs than in aortic denervated dogs with temporarily fixed carotid sinus pressure. Such adaptations to chronic sinoaortic denervation secondarily affect the cardiovascular responses to exercise (61). It is therefore invalid to assume that the precise role of the baroreflex in the regulation of blood pressure during exercise can be inferred from the presence or absence of deficits in that regulation after chronic sinoaortic denervation.

Cardiac Component of the Baroreflex

As mentioned above, many studies indicate that exercise does not diminish the overall gain of the baroreflex. However, this does not preclude the possibility of central modulation of the baroreflex in exercise. A centrally mediated diminution of one component of the baroreflex could be offset by enhanced responsiveness of another component (10, 37). A popular (but disputed) hypothesis is that the cardiac component of the baroreflex is inhibited during exercise (7, 39). Support for this hypothesis has been derived primarily from examination of the reflex cardiac slowing during the rising phase of a pressor transient caused by injection of an α-adrenergic agonist (7). Baroreflex sensitivity, calculated as "milliseconds change in heart interval per millimeter Hg change in systolic pressure," was decreased during dynamic exercise in dogs (41) and during dynamic and static exercise in humans (7, 16). When the neck chamber technique was used to transiently distend the carotid sinuses of human subjects, the reflex prolongation in heart interval was less during handgrip exercise than during rest (39). All these cardiac responses represented predominantly parasympathetic effects, because they occurred rapidly (50) and because atropine reduced reflex sensitivity essentially to zero during both rest and dynamic exercise, whereas propranolol had little effect (46). Thus, the data provide evidence for a central inhibition of the parasympathetic component of the baroreflex during exercise.

In contrast, other studies showed no diminution of the cardiac component of the baroreflex during exercise (5, 36, 49, 60). Three factors appear to account for this discrepancy. First, the formerly mentioned studies were based on analysis of the immediate responses to baroreceptor stimulation; in the latter studies, the stimulus to the baroreceptors was sustained long enough to allow development of steady-state cardiac responses (including sympathetic components). Studies utilizing the neck chamber technique have clearly shown the importance of stimulus duration (18, 36, 39). Second, the former studies were based on increasing the stimulus to the baroreceptors. Cardiac responses to an increase in baroreceptor stimulation are more affected by exercise than are the responses to a decrease in baroreceptor stimulation (36). Third, the cardiac responses were measured in terms of heart interval in the former studies, whereas heart rate was used in the latter. Heart rate and heart interval are reciprocals, so the relation between them is hyperbolic rather than linear. As a result, even if reflex changes in heart rate are of equal magnitude in rest and exercise, the corresponding changes in interval will be smaller during exercise (42, 52, 55). Since there are no compeling reasons to select rate or interval as the "correct" measure, the interpretation of many studies remains moot (29).

BAROREFLEX IN EMOTIONAL STRESS

There have been relatively few studies of the role of the baroreflex in behaviors that involve psychological as opposed to physical stress. Yet, there is reason to suspect that the baroreflex is inhibited during such "emotional" behaviors (26, 30). Although the cardiovascular responses during exercise and during emotional behavior are superficially similar, important differences exist. In contrast to dynamic exercise, shock avoidance behavior was characterized by an increase in cardiac output in excess of that needed to meet the metabolic demands of the situation (34). Exercise led to natriuresis and diuresis, whereas avoidance had the opposite effects (24). Inasmuch as overperfusion of tissues, sodium retention, and emotional stress have been implicated in the genesis of hypertension (1, 24), the role of the baroreflex in emotional responses becomes a matter of practical interest.

There is some evidence for an inhibition of the cardiac component of the baroreflex during emotional stress in man (8), monkeys (19), and baboons (55). To stimulate the baroreflex of conscious baboons, blood pressure was altered in a sinusoidal pattern by cyclic constriction of the descending aorta (55). For equivalent amplitudes of alteration of blood pressure, the reflex responses of heart rate were significantly smaller during a shock avoidance task that involved mild, dynamic leg exercise than during operantly conditioned lever pressing for food reinforcement. The reduction in baroreflex sensitivity during the avoidance task was found whether the cardiac responses were measured in terms of heart rate or heart interval. Baroreflex sensitivity was reduced during the avoidance behavior because the parasympathetic contribution to the baroreflex responses was withdrawn and was not replaced by a significantly increased sympathetic contribution. The results implicate a central inhibition of the parasympathetic component of the baroreflex.

The sensitivity of the cardiac component of the baroreflex was decreased in monkeys that were operantly conditioned to raise or lower their heart rate to avoid shock (19). The cardiac responses to a pressor stimulus (phenylephrine) and a depressor stimulus (nitroglycerine) were found to be significantly smaller when the expected reflex response would have increased the likelihood of getting a shock. The data indicate that the sensitivity of the cardiac component of the baroreflex is not fixed and is subject to modification by operant conditioning.

Surgical denervation of baroreceptors has been used to infer the role of the baroreflex in emotional stress. Several researchers have noted that the blood pressure of baroreceptor denervated animals fluctuates widely in response to novel environmental stimuli (14, 22). Naturally elicited fighting behavior was associated with significantly smaller increases in heart rate, cardiac output, and mesenteric resistence in baroreceptor-denervated cats than in intact cats (4). Blood pressure increased during fighting in intact cats but fell during fighting in denervated cats. The denervation apparently interrupted neural pathways that were necessary to achieve the increase in pressure during fighting. It was hypothesized that the neurally mediated cardiovascular excitation that accompanied fighting was reinforced by a central inhibition of the tonic depressor influence exerted by the baroreceptor afferents. Such a reinforcement could not occur in baroreceptor-denervated animals because the tonic depressor influence was already absent. In intact cats bilateral carotid occlusion caused a smaller increase in pressure during fighting than during rest, which supports the hypothesis that the baroreflex is inhibited during fighting.

Baroreflexes have been abolished in cats, dogs, and rats by bilateral lesions of the nucleus tractus solitarii (9, 17, 35, 45). Blood pressure in lesioned cats was significantly elevated both during daytime (143% of intact control) and at night (125% of control) (45). The lability of blood pressure was significantly greater in the lesioned cats during the day, but this difference disappeared at night. Grooming and orienting behaviors were associated with substantially greater increases in blood pressure in the lesioned cats. Classically conditioned increases in blood pressure (electric shock for unconditioned stimulus) were five times larger in the lesioned cats (44). These results suggest that the baroreflex effectively buffers both spontaneous and classically conditioned increases in blood pressure. However, in view of the multiple functions of the nucleus of the tractus solitarius, it may be invalid to attribute the effects of lesions of the nucleus solely to the loss of the baroreflex. The hypothesis that the baroreflex buffers conditioned pressor responses is also supported by the finding that the magnitude of the conditioned pressor response in intact cats was inversely correlated with the sensitivity of the cardiac component of the baroreflex (43).

CONCLUSION

The central nervous system clearly has the capability to facilitate, inhibit, or reset the baroreflex. Nevertheless, firm conclusions about central modulation of the baroreflex in various behaviors have been elusive because: (a) studies based on baroreceptor denervation are complicated by inadvertent damage to other neurons and by secondary effects of adaptation to the loss of activity in baroreceptor afferent nerves; (*b*) studies of the cardiac component of the baroreflex are confounded by the difficulty of obtaining controlled, sustained stimuli to the baroreceptors and by the heart rate vs heart interval enigma; and (*c*) it is difficult to distinguish experimentally between central and peripheral influences on baroreflex characteristics. These technical limitations must be dealt with if investigators are successfully to explore the relationship between the regulation of blood pressure and behavior. Techniques to control the baroreceptor stimulus independently of arterial pressure (so that complete stimulus-response curves can be derived) have recently been developed and have provided convincing evidence for continued working of the baroreflex during dynamic exercise in dogs. Further studies are needed in order to characterize the ability of the baroreflex to control blood pressure during behavioral states other than rest and dynamic exercise. A powerful impetus for such studies is the growing interest in the role of behavior and central neural mechanisms in the genesis of hypertension.

Literature Cited

1. Anderson, D. E. 1982. Behavioral hypertension mediated by salt intake. In *Circulation, Neurobiology, and Behavior*, ed. O. A. Smith, R. A. Galosy, S. M. Weiss, pp. 247–57. New York: Elsevier. 346 pp.
2. Ardell, J. L., Scher, A. M., Rowell, L. B. 1980. Effects of baroreceptor denervation on the cardiovascular response to dynamic exercise. In *Arterial Baroreceptors and Hypertension*, ed. P. Sleight, pp. 311–17. Oxford: Oxford Univ. 540 pp.
3. Asmussen, E., Nielsen, M. 1955. Cardiac output during muscular work and its regulation. *Physiol. Rev.* 35:778–800
4. Baccelli, G., Albertini, R., Del Bo, A., Mancia, G., Zanchetti, A. 1981. Role of sinoaortic reflexes in hemodynamic patterns of natural defense behaviors in the cat. *Am. J. Physiol.* 240:H421–29
5. Bevegard, B. S., Shepherd, J. T. 1966. Circulatory effects of stimulating the carotid arterial stretch receptors in man at rest and during exercise. *J. Clin. Invest.* 45:132–42
6. Bolter, C. P., Ledsome, J. R. 1976. Effect of cervical sympathetic nerve stimulation on canine carotid sinus reflex. *Am. J. Physiol.* 230:1026–30
7. Bristow, J. D., Brown, E. B. Jr., Cunningham, D. J. C., Howson, M. G., Petersen, E. S., et al. 1971. Effect of bicycling on the baroreflex regulation of pulse interval. *Circ. Res.* 28:582–92

8. Brooks, D., Fox, P., Lopez, R., Sleight, P. 1978. The effect of mental arithmetic on blood pressure variability and baroreflex sensitivity in man. *J. Physiol.* 280:75P-76P
9. Carey, R. M., Dacey, R. G., Jane, J. A., Winn, H. R., Ayers, C. R., et al. 1979. Production of sustained hypertension by lesions in the nucleus tractus solitarii of the American Foxhound. *Hypertension* 1:246–54
10. Combs, C. A. 1982. Behavioral modulation of arterial baroreflexes. See Ref. 1, pp. 185–99
11. Coote, J. H., Dodds, W. N. 1976. The baroreceptor reflex and the cardiovascular changes associated with sustained muscular contraction in the cat. *Pfluegers Arch.* 363:167–73
12. Coote, J. H., Hilton, S. M., Perez-Gonzalez, J. F. 1979. Inhibition of the baroreceptor reflex on stimulation in the brain stem defence centre. *J. Physiol.* 288:549–60
13. Cowley, A. W. Jr., Quillen, E. W., Barber, B. J. 1980. Further evidence for lack of baroreceptor control of long-term level of arterial pressure. See Ref. 2, pp. 391–99
14. Cowley, A. W. Jr., Liard, J. F., Guyton, A. C. 1973. Role of the baroreceptor reflex in daily control of arterial blood pressure and other variables in dogs. *Circ. Res.* 32:564–76
15. Cowley, A. W. Jr., DeClue, J. W. 1976. Quantification of baroreceptor influence

on arterial pressure changes seen in primary angiotensin-induced hypertension in dogs. *Circ. Res.* 39:779–87

16. Cunningham, D. J., Peterson, E. S., Peto, R., Sleight, P. 1972. Comparison of the effect of different types of exercise on the baroreflex regulation of heart rate. *Acta Physiol. Scand.* 86:444–55

17. Doba, N., Reis, D. J. 1973. Acute fulminating neurogenic hypertension produced by brainstem lesions in the rat. *Circ. Res.* 32:584–93

18. Eckberg, D. L., Eckberg, M. J. 1982. Human sinus node responses to repetitive, ramped carotid baroreceptor stimuli. *Am. J. Physiol.* 242:H638–44

19. Engel, B. T., Joseph, J. A. 1982. Attenuation of baroreflexes during operant cardiac conditioning. *Psychophysiology* 19:609–14

20. Epstein, S. E., Beiser, G. D., Goldstein, R. E., Stampfer, M., Wechsler, A. S., et al. 1969. Circulatory effects of electrical stimulation of the carotid sinus nerves in man. *Circulation* 40:269–76

21. Faris, I. B., Iannos, J., Jamieson, G. G., Ludbrook, J. 1980. The carotid sinus baroreceptor reflex in conscious rabbits. *J. Physiol.* 298:321–31

22. Ferrario, C. M., McCubbin, J. W., Page, I. H. 1969. Hemodynamic characteristics of chronic experimental neurogenic hypertension in unanesthetized dogs. *Circ. Res.* 24:911–22

23. Geis, G. S., Wurster, R. D. 1980. Baroreceptor reflexes during exercise. See Ref. 2, pp. 305–10

24. Grignolo, A., Koepke, J. P., Obrist, P. A. 1981. Renal function, heart rate, and blood pressure during exercise and avoidance in dogs. *Am. J. Physiol.* 242:R482–90

25. Guazzi, M., Baccelli, G., Zanchetti, A. 1968. Reflex chemoceptive regulation of arterial pressure during natural sleep in the cat. *Am. J. Physiol.* 214:969–78

26. Hilton, S. M. 1980. Inhibition of the baroreceptor reflex by the brainstem defence centre. See Ref. 2, pp. 318–23

27. Hobbs, S. F. 1982. Central command during exercise: parallel activation of the cardiovascular and motor systems by descending command signals. See Ref. 1, pp. 217–31

28. Ito, C. S., Scher, A. M. 1981. Hypertension following arterial baroreceptor denervation in the unanesthetized dog. *Circ. Res.* 48:576–91

29. Jennings, J. R., Berg, W. K., Hutcheson, J. S., Obrist, P., Porges, S. 1981. Publication guidelines for heart rate studies in man. *Psychophysiology* 18:226–31

30. Korner, P. I. 1979. Central nervous control of autonomic cardiovascular function. In *Handbook of Physiology*, Sect. 2, Vol. 1, ed. R. M. Berne, pp. 691–739. Bethesda, MD: Am. Physiol. Soc. 970 pp.

31. Krasney, J. A., Levitzky, M. G., Koehler, R. C. 1974. Sinoaortic contribution to the adjustment of systemic resistance in exercising dogs. *J. Appl. Physiol.* 36:679–85

32. Kumada, M., Nogami, K., Sagawa, K. 1975. Modulation of carotid sinus baroreceptor reflex by sciatic nerve stimulation. *Am. J. Physiol.* 228:1535–41

33. Kunze, D. L. 1981. Rapid resetting of the carotid baroreceptor reflex in the cat. *Am. J. Physiol.* 241:H802–6

34. Langer, A. W., Obrist, P. A., McCubbin, J. A. 1979. Hemodynamic and metabolic adjustments during exercise and shock avoidance in dogs. *Am. J. Physiol.* 236:H225–30

35. Laubie, M., Schmitt, H. 1979. Destruction of the nucleus tractus solitarii in the dog: comparison with sinoaortic denervation. *Am. J. Physiol.* 236:H736–43

36. Ludbrook, J., Faris, I. B., Iannos, J., Jamieson, G. G., Russell, W. J. 1978. Lack of effect of isometric handgrip exercise on the responses of the carotid sinus baroreceptor reflex in man. *Clin. Sci. Mol. Med.* 55:189–94

37. Ludbrook, J., Mancia, G., Zanchetti, A. 1980. Does the baroreceptor–heart rate reflex indicate the capacity of the arterial baroreceptors to control blood pressure? *Clin. Exp. Pharm. Physiol.* 7:499–503

38. Mancia, G., Shepherd, J. T., Donald, D. E. 1976. Interplay among carotid sinus, cardiopulmonary, and carotid body reflexes in dogs. *Am. J. Physiol.* 230:19–24

39. Mancia, G., Iannos, J., Jamieson, G. G., Lawrence, R. H., Sharman, P. R., et al. 1978. Effect of isometric hand-grip exercise on the carotid sinus baroreceptor reflex in man. *Clin. Sci. Mol. Med.* 54:33–37

40. Mancia, G., Ferrari, A., Gregorini, L., Parati, G., Pomidossi, G. 1982. Effects of isometric exercise on the carotid baroreflex in hypertensive subjects. *Hypertension* 4:245–50

41. McRitchie, R. J., Vatner, S. F., Boettcher, D., Heyndrickx, G. R., Patrick, T. A., et al. 1976. Role of arterial baroreceptors in mediating cardiovascular response to exercise. *Am. J. Physiol.* 230:85–89

42. Melcher, A., Donald, D. E. 1981. Maintained ability of carotid baroreflex to regulate arterial pressure during exercise. *Am. J. Physiol.* 241:H838–49

43. Nathan, M. A., Buchholz, R. A. 1982. Effect of ambient and conditioned stimuli on arterial pressure after central disruption of the baroreflexes. See Ref. 1, pp. 157–70

44. Nathan, M. A., Tucker, L. W., Severini, W. H., Reis, D. J. 1978. Enhancement of conditioned arterial pressure responses in cats after brainstem lesions. *Science* 201:71–73

45. Nathan, M. A., Reis, D. J. 1977. Chronic labile hypertension produced by lesions of the nucleus tractus solitarii in the cat. *Circ. Res.* 40:72–81

46. Pickering, T. G., Gribbin, B., Peterson, E. S., Cunningham, D. J. C., Sleight, P. 1972. Effects of autonomic blockade on the baroreflex in man at rest and during exercise. *Circ. Res.* 30:177–85

47. Quest, J. A., Gebber, G. L. 1972. Modulation of baroreceptor reflexes by somatic afferent nerve stimulation. *Am. J. Physiol.* 222:1251–59

48. Remensnyder, J. P., Mitchell, J. H., Sarnoff, S. J. 1962. Functional sympatholysis during muscular activity. *Circ. Res.* 11:370–380

49. Robinson, B. F., Epstein, S. E., Beiser, G. D., Braunwald, E. 1966. Control of heart rate by the autonomic nervous system: studies in man on the interrelation between baroreceptor mechanisms and exercise. *Circ. Res.* 19:400–11

50. Scher, A. M., Young, A. C. 1970. Reflex control of heart rate in the unanesthetized dog. *Am. J. Physiol.* 218:780–89

51. Smith, O. A., Astley, C. A., DeVito, J. L., Stein, J. M., Walsh, K. E. 1980. Functional analysis of hypothalamic control of the cardiovascular responses accompanying emotional behavior. *Fed. Proc.* 39:2487–94

52. Stephenson, R. B. 1982. Behavioral modulation of the baroreceptor reflex. See Ref. 1, pp. 171–83

53. Stephenson, R. B., Donald, D. E. 1980. Reflexes from isolated carotid sinuses of intact and vagotomized conscious dogs. *Am. J. Physiol.* 238:H815–22

54. Stephenson, R. B., Donald, D. E. 1980. Reversible vascular isolation of carotid sinuses in conscious dogs. *Am. J. Physiol.* 238:H809–14

55. Stephenson, R. B., Smith, O. A., Scher, A. M. 1981. Baroreceptor regulation of heart rate in baboons during different behavioral states. *Am. J. Physiol.* 241: R277–85

56. Stinnett, H. O., Sepe, F. J., Magnusson, M. R. 1981. Rabbit carotid baroreflexes after carotid sympathectomy, vagotomy, and β blockade. *Am. J. Physiol.* 241: H600–5

57. Streatfeild, K. A., Davidson, N. S., McCloskey, D. I. 1977. Muscular reflex and baroreflex influences on heart rate during isometric contractions. *Cardiovasc. Res.* 11:87–93

58. Tomomatsu, E., Nishi, K. 1981. Increased activity of carotid sinus baroreceptors by sympathetic stimulation and norepinephrine. *Am. J. Physiol.* 240:H650–58

59. Tuttle, R. S., McCleary, M. 1981. Carotid sinus distension and superior cervical ganglion transmission. *Am. J. Physiol.* 240:H716–20

60. Vatner, S. F., Franklin, D., Van Citters, R. L., Braunwald, E. 1970. Effects of carotid sinus nerve stimulation on blood-flow distribution in conscious dogs at rest and during exercise. *Circ. Res.* 27:495–503

61. Walgenbach, S. C., Donald, D. E. 1983. Inhibition by carotid baroreflex of exercise-induced increases in arterial pressure. *Circ. Res.* 52:253–62

Ann. Rev. Physiol. 1984. 46:143–53

INTERACTIONS OF STRESS, SALT, AND BLOOD PRESSURE

David E. Anderson

University of South Florida College of Medicine and J. A. Haley Veterans Administration Hospital, Tampa, Florida

INTRODUCTION

Behavioral stress and/or increased dietary intake of sodium may participate in the pathogenesis of primary hypertension (19, 53, 73). Laboratory studies relevant to this hypothesis have shown that experimental hypertension can be potentiated or exacerbated in genetically susceptible animals by behavioral stress (e.g. 23, 48) or increases in sodium intake (e.g. 64, 72). Efforts to produce hypertension in genetically normotensive animals via prolonged exposure to either behavioral stress (22, 25) or salt loading (21) have produced equivocal results, however. Thus, understanding of the role of these environmental-behavioral variables in long-term blood pressure control has remained elusive. In this review, evidence is summarized that suggests that the cardiovascular effects of stress and salt are synergistic, and that experimental hypertension can be produced in intact animals by a combination of sustained behavioral stress and increased sodium intake.

BEHAVIORAL STRESS, SYMPATHETIC AROUSAL, AND RENAL FUNCTION

Cardiovascular responses to behavioral demands occur in coordinated patterns, integrated by the central nervous system. These responses subserve, but need not be accompanied by, adaptive behavioral interactions (12). For example, the "fight or flight" reaction is a sympathetically mediated response to acute aversive stimulation that is characterized by increases in heart rate, cardiac output, and arterial pressure. Total peripheral resistance is typically not in-

143

0066-4278/84/0315-0143$02.00

creased under these conditions, however, because vasodilation in skeletal muscle offsets vasoconstriction in other regions. When this response pattern is evoked by classical (66) or avoidance (20) conditioning procedures, renal blood flow usually decreases while plasma renin activity increases (9). Acute inhibition of urinary excretion of sodium and fluid can occur, however, in saline-loaded dogs during avoidance training sessions without accompanying renal hemodynamic changes (29, 45), due to direct α-adrenergic effects on sodium reabsorption in the proximal tubules (14). The inhibitory response can be prevented by section of the sympathetic nerves (45). If α-adrenergic receptors are blocked by administration of phenoxybenzamine (POB), renal hemodynamic changes occurring during avoidance sessions are prevented. Inhibition of sodium and fluid excretion continues to be observed, however, due to an increase in circulating vasopressin levels produced by POB injection (46). Blockade of β-adrenergic receptors does not prevent the inhibition of sodium and fluid excretion during avoidance, unless the β-blocker (e.g. propranolol) crosses the blood-brain barrier (44). By contrast, renal excretion of fluid and sodium increased in response to treadmill exercise that increased heart rate levels of saline-loaded dogs proportionally (29).

Another hemodynamic response pattern evoked by environmental stimuli is associated with inhibition of behavioral activity, apparently in the service of vigilant attention to the environment. This cardiovascular pattern is characterized by an increase in skeletal muscle vasoconstriction and total peripheral resistance, which maintains or elevates arterial pressure while heart rate and cardiac output decrease. This response pattern has been observed in cats during immobile confrontations with other animals, and includes a decrease in renal blood flow that can be prevented by section of the sympathetic nerves (78). One recent study reported that the magnitude of peripheral vasoconstriction and bradycardia observed when birds dive underwater is larger when the dive is forced than when the subject dives spontaneously, indicating an emotional component to the diving reflex (36). Virtual cessation of renal flow, glomerular filtration, and urine flow have been observed during diving, and these effects can be prevented by infusion of a cholinergic antagonist (58). Increases in total peripheral resistance and arterial pressure accompanied by decreases in heart rate and cardiac output have also been observed in dogs over periods of hours immediately preceding performance on free-operant avoidance tasks (2). These preavoidance cardiovascular changes were not prevented by blockade of either α- (7) or β- (3) adrenergic activity that, however, did alter patterns of cardiovascular arousal during the avoidance sessions. The persistence of the blood pressure elevation during preavoidance following α-adrenergic blockade could have resulted from a compensatory rise in circulating vasopressin levels evoked by adminstration of phenoxybenzamine.

The potential significance of such behavioral stress procedures is indicated by the fact that renal sympathetic activity is critical to the development of several forms of experimental hypertension (75). Experiments have shown that continuous intrarenal infusion of norepinephrine produces a sustained hypertension in genetically normotensive but uninephrectomized dogs, accompanied by increases in renal vascular resistance and total peripheral resistance, with a positive sodium balance (37). Efferent renal sympathetic activity in the Okamoto & Aoki spontaneously hypertensive rat (SHR) has been found to be twice that of normotensive Wistar Kyoto controls (WKY) (71), and the density of renal α-adrenergic receptors is greater in SHR than in WKY (61). Young SHR have been found to retain more sodium than WKY rats, while plasma volume and blood volume are not expanded, however, but reduced (15). Section of the renal sympathetic nerves of young SHR has been shown to increase fractional excretion of sodium (74) and to retard the development of hypertension (15). Subsequent reinnervation in these subjects (as assessed by renal norepinephrine levels) was associated with a rise in blood pressure. Repeated renal denervation at three-week intervals resulted in a sustained prevention of hypertension in SHR (60).

Sympathetic activity is also important in the development of several forms of sodium-dependent hypertension. Section of the sympathetic nerves (68) and anteroventral third-ventricle lesion (27) have been associated with significant prevention or attenuation of the hypertensive response in Dahl S rats on a high-salt diet. Renal denervation of young, uninephrectomized rats prior to DOCA-salt treatment has been shown to increase the fractional excretion of sodium and retard the development of hypertension in this model (38). Similar effects have been observed in one-kidney (40) and two-kidney (39) Goldblatt hypertensive rats.

Thus, the development of hypertension could be facilitated by sustained decreases in sodium excretion occurring in association with either (a) α-adrenergically mediated increases in total peripheral resistance but not cardiac output, facilitating vigilant attention, or (b) β-adrenergically mediated increases in cardiac output but not total peripheral resistance, facilitating emergency behavioral response.

ADRENERGIC AND CHOLINERGIC HYPERREACTIVITY IN HYPERTENSION

It is well documented that the magnitude of cardiovascular response to environmental stimulation and to central adminstration of pressor substances tends to be greater in hypertensive than in normotensive subjects (24, 31, 35). This response characteristic is associated with changes in central nervous system catecholamine levels observed in experimental hypertension (10). However, alterations in central cholinergic activity may also be involved. Studies have found that central cholinergic enzymatic activity is greater in SHR than in WKY controls (77), and that there is an increased concentration of cholinergic receptor sites and increased cholinergic enzymatic activity in cortex, hypothalamus, and medulla of normotensive, as well as hypertensive, Dahl S rats in comparison with Dahl R rats (56). That this altered central nervous system activity may mediate an increased total peripheral resistance in resting normotensive Dahl S rats is suggested by the observation that the resting heart rates of Dahl S rats are lower than those of Dahl R rats (24). That altered central cholinergic activity may also be involved in hyperreactive cardiovascular responses to stimulation is suggested by the observation that administration of a cholinergic agonist, physostigmine, produces a pressor response in SHR (77) and Dahl S rats (11) greater than that observed in WKY and Dahl R rats, respectively.

The extent to which genetic or environmental influences are responsible for cardiovascular hyperreactivity remains to be determined. The significance of a genetic component is suggested, though not proven, by the observation that the magnitude of pressor response to a mental arithmetic task observed in normotensive adolescents was related to the presence of a family history of hypertension (17). That nongenetic influences could be involved in cardiovascular hyperreactivity is illustrated by the finding that sympathoadrenal responses to unavoidable electric shocks are exaggerated in one-kidney Goldblatt hypertensive rats (41).

Renal hyperreactivity to behavioral stress has also been observed in genetically hypertensive animals. Aversive stimulation (blast from an air jet) decreases renal excretion of sodium and water, and the magnitude of this response is greater in SHR than in WKY controls (54). It can be prevented by renal denervation. Similar effects have been reported in human hypertension. In one study (34), administration of a nonverbal IQ test was found to increase blood pressure and heart rate to a significantly greater extent in hypertensive than in normotensive control human subjects. In addition, the hypertensive subjects consistently showed decreases in renal blood flow and increases in plasma renin activity, while the normotensive subjects typically showed increases in renal blood flow and decreases in plasma renin activity. A group of normotensive subjects with a family history of hypertension showed an intermediate response. In another study (49), participation in a competitive perceptual-motor task was found to result in decreases in urinary fluid and sodium excretion in saline-loaded young adults with hypertension or with a family history of hypertension, but not in normotensive subjects with no family history of hypertension. The magnitude of inhibition of diuresis was directly correlated with the magnitude of change in blood pressure and heart rate occurring under these conditions.

The cardiovascular hyperreactivity of hypertension may be symptomatic of a chronic central nervous system state that mediates the pathogenesis of hypertension, and this state may involve both genetic and experiential influences. This central nervous system state may exert sustained effects upon renal regulation of sodium.

EFFECTS OF SALT INTAKE IN BLOOD PRESSURE REGULATION

Increased intake of sodium reliably elevates blood pressure of laboratory animals and man with impaired renal functions. One series of experiments showed that intravenous infusion of hypertonic saline for two hours significantly increased blood pressure of bilaterally nephrectomized, but conscious and semirestrained rats (32). The elevation in pressure was attenuated by administration of an arginine-vasopressin (AVP) antagonist. Saline infusion of these anephric rats following α- and β-adrenergic blockade resulted in a comparable magnitude rise in arterial pressure, which, however, could then be completely prevented by the AVP antagonist. These observations suggest a significant sympathetic nervous system influence on the circulation under these conditions that contributed to the salt-induced hypertension, and a complex interaction between the sympathetic nervous system and vasopressin, with the blockade of the former resulting in compensatory increases in the latter (33). In other experiments, it was shown that infusion of hypertonic saline into anephric rats previously treated for two weeks with DOCA-salt resulted in an increase in blood pressure whose magnitude was directly correlated with concurrent increases in plasma norepinephrine and decreases in plasma volume (26). A recent study with human subjects with renal insufficiency showed that blood pressure levels were increased by two weeks on a high salt diet, and that the magnitude of increase was a function of the extent of renal insufficiency that characterized this group (47).

Effects of increased salt intake on blood pressure are more variable in subjects with intact renal functions. That salt feeding for periods of months can generate chronic hypertension in some genetically normotensive rats was first reported three decades ago (57), and it was subsequently shown that the hypertension could be attenuated by concurrent feeding of potassium (8). Less success has been reported in attempts to produce sodium hypertension in larger animals, perhaps because of the inherent autoregulatory capacity of the healthy kidney (30). Increases in blood pressure and forearm vascular resistance have been produced in men with borderline hypertension by 10 days on a 400 mEq sodium/day diet (55). An 800–1500 mEq daily sodium intake was required to increase blood pressure in normotensive men. Increases were also oberved in extracellular fluid volume, and decreases in circulating catecholamines, renal, and adrenal hormones (51, 52, 59). This hypertension was also prevented by concurrent increases in potassium intake (51). Volume expansion by infusion of isotonic saline was associated with lower rates of sodium excretion in those at risk for hypertension, including blacks, those over 40 years of age, and relatives of hypertensive patients, than were observed in other subjects (50).

Changes in dietary sodium intake can also affect central nervous system activity. High salt intake by SHR that increased blood pressure was also found to increase hypothalamic levels of norepinephrine (76). Moreover, high salt intake that did not increase blood pressure levels of rabbits did decrease norepinephrine turnover in areas of the central nervous system (70). High salt intake by Dahl S rats has been shown to increase hypertension and increase concentrations of muscarinic receptor sites (16). In addition, high salt intake has been shown to increase the density of renal α-adrenergic receptors in both genetically normotensive and hypertensive rats (65), and renal vascular reactivity of SHR (68, 69). Research has also shown that the magnitude of pressor response to mental arithmetic performance was increased by a high-salt diet in normotensive subjects with a family history of hypertension, but not in a control group with no family history of hypertension (18). By contrast, when Dahl S rats were maintained on a low-salt, high-potassium diet, blood pressure increases to central administration of pressor substances were decreased (28). Similarly, borderline hypertensive subjects showed smaller pressor responses to mental arithmetic after four weeks on a low-sodium, high-potassium diet (1). These effects occurred in proportion to concurrently observed decreases in intralymphocytic sodium levels.

The levels of salt intake of genetically normotensive animals have also been shown to determine the magnitude of cardiovascular response to adrenergic stimulation. Sodium feeding in combination with DOCA administration is associated with an increased cardiovascular response to β adrenergic stimulation (42). The magnitude of hypertension induced in dogs by intrarenal infusion of norepinephrine is directly correlated with magnitude of concurrent salt intake (13). The blood pressure response is accompanied by decreases in effective renal plasma flow and glomerular filtration rate that are also proportional to salt intake. Similarly, it was shown that five days of an 800 mEq sodium diet significantly lowered the threshold of pressor response of normotensive human subjects to intravenous norepinephrine infusion (63) and resulted in a significant decrease in fractional excretion of sodium, though not in renal blood flow or glomerular filtration rate (62). When normotensive subjects were maintained for four weeks on a low-sodium, high-potassium diet, the magnitude of cardiovascular response to mental arithmetic and to norepinephrine infusion was decreased (67). Taken together, these studies are consistent with the view that increased sodium intake may alter the responsiveness of the cardiovascular system to adrenergic stimulation, and participate in the development of hypertension and the cardiovascular hyperreactivity of hypertension via central, arterial, or renal mechanisms.

EXPERIMENTAL HYPERTENSION VIA BEHAVIORAL STRESS AND SALINE INFUSION

It has recently been found that sustained hypertension can be produced in intact, genetically normotensive dogs by exposure to a combination of avoidance schedules and saline infusion. In one series of experiments (4), instrumented dogs were trained on a 30-minute free-operant avoidance task that recurred every 7.5 hours in a residential environment in which blood pressure and heart rate were monitored 24 hours per day (43). During avoidance sessions, blood pressure and heart rate remained elevated. Between avoidance sessions, heart rate levels decreased progressively as the onset of the next session approached, while blood pressure levels remained stable or increased. After stabilization of behavioral and cardiovascular patterns, isotonic saline was continuously infused intra-arterially 24 hours per day at a rate of 50 ml/hr (185 mEq sodium/day). Over the next 14 days, 24-hour mean levels of arterial pressure increased progressively (22/14 mmHg) with no consistent changes in 24-hour mean heart rate levels. Substantial individual differences were observed in magnitude of cardiovascular response to the procedures. Termination of the avoidance schedules and saline infusion resulted in a return of blood pressure to pre-experimental levels, sometimes within 24–48 hours.

By contrast, blood pressure levels remained unchanged in dogs who received saline infusion but no avoidance sessions, or avoidance schedules without salt loading, for 14 days. In addition, it was observed that saline infusion during avoidance training also did not produce significant hypertension. This observation indicates that the progressive hemodynamic response (i.e. increases in total peripheral resistance and decreases in cardiac output) preceding the brief avoidance sessions emerges as a result of experience with the consistent schedule and is an essential aspect of the pathogenetic process.

In another study (5), dogs were maintained on the avoidance schedule and saline infusion procedure for 36 days. During the first 14 days on this schedule, 24-hour mean levels of arterial pressure increased progressively (22/12 mmHg), with no consistent heart rate changes. Concurrent infusion of potassium chloride during days 15–28 resulted in a progressive decrease in arterial pressure. Discontinuation of potassium infusion during days 29–36 resulted in a resumption of the upward trend in blood pressure. In addition, the magnitude of acute increases in blood pressure and heart rate during avoidance sessions were smaller during periods of potassium infusion than during other periods. 24-Hour levels of urinary volume and electrolytes were also measured in dogs made hypertensive by exposure to avoidance schedules and saline infusion (6). It was observed that urine volume was greater during 14-day periods of avoidance sessions and saline infusion than during 14-day periods of saline infusion but no avoidance sessions. By contrast, urinary sodium concentrations were significantly lower during avoidance-saline periods than during baseline periods of saline infusion only, indicating sodium retention. The data are consistent with the hypothesis that avoidance-saline hypertension does not involve expansion of extracellular fluid volume, and that these experimental procedures produce an increased sodium/water concentration in arteriolar smooth muscle cells.

In summary, recent studies have shown that (a) behavioral stress can affect renal regulation of sodium within the context of at least two sustainable hemodynamic response patterns; (b) changing intake of sodium (and potassium) can affect the magnitude of cardiovascular response to behavioral stress; and (c) behavioral stress can potentiate sodium hypertension in intact and genetically normotensive animals, apparently in the absence of expansion of extracellular fluid volume. It remains for future research to clarify the relationship of these complex findings to the pathogenesis of primary hypertension in man.

ACKNOWLEDGMENTS

This review was supported in part by NIH Grant No. 28462. The author is grateful to Sandra L. Anderson for her assistance in the preparation of the manuscript and to Dr. Ray A. Olsson and Dr. Celso Gomez-Sanchez of the University of South Florida College of Medicine for their critique of the manuscript.

Literature Cited

1. Ambrosioni, E., Costa, F. V., Borghi, C., Montebugnoli, L., Giordani, M. F., et al. 1982. Effects of moderate salt restriction on intralymphocytic sodium and pressor response to stress in borderline hypertension. *Hypertension* 4:789–94
2. Anderson, D. E. 1981. Inhibitory behavioral stress effects upon blood pressure regulation. In *Perspectives on Behavioral Medicine,* ed. S. M. Weiss, J. A. Herd, B. Fox, pp. 307–19. New York: Academic
3. Anderson, D. E., Brady, J. V. 1976. Cardiovascular responses to avoidance conditioning: effects of β-adrenergic blockade. *Psychosom. Med.* 38:4–12
4. Anderson, D. E., Kearns, W. D., Better,

W. E. 1983. Progressive hypertension in dogs by avoidance conditioning and saline infusion. *Hypertension* 5:286–91
5. Anderson, D. E., Kearns, W. D., Worden, T. J. 1983. Potassium infusion attenuates avoidance-saline hypertension in dogs. *Hypertension* 5:415–20
6. Anderson, D. E., Sharinus, M. W., Kearns, W. D. 1983. Urinary sodium concentration decreases in avoidance-saline hypertension. *Pav. J. Biol. Sci.* In press
7. Anderson, D. E., Yingling, J. E., Brady, J. V. 1976. Cardiovascular responses to avoidance conditioning: effects of α-adrenergic blockade. *Pav. J. Biol. Sc.* 11:150–61

8. Battarbee, H. D., Funch, D. P., Dailey, J. W. 1979. The effect of dietary sodium and potassium upon blood pressure and catecholamine excretion in the rat. *Proc. Soc. Exp. Biol. Med.* 161:32–37

9. Blair, M. F., Feigl, E. O., Smith, O. A. 1976. Elevations of plasma renin activity during avoidance performances in baboons. *Am. J. Physiol.* 231:772–76

10. Brody, M. J., Haywood, J. R., Touw, K. B. 1980. Neural mechanisms in hypertension. *Ann. Rev. Physiol.* 42:441–53

11. Buccafusco, J. J., Spector, S. 1980. Role of central cholinergic neurons in experimental hypertension. *J. Cardiovasc. Pharmacol.* 2:347–55

12. Cohen, D., Obrist, P. A. 1975. Interactions between behavior and the cardiovascular system. *Circ. Res.* 37:693–706

13. Cowley, A. W., Lohmeier, T. E. 1979. Changes in renal vascular sensitivity and arterial pressure associated with sodium intake during long-term intrarenal norepinephrine infusion in dogs. *Hypertension* 1:549–58

14. DiBona, G. F., Zambraski, E. J., Aguilera, A. J., Kaloyanides, G. J. 1977. Neurogenic control of renal tubular sodium reabsorption in the dog: a brief review and preliminary report concerning possible humoral mediation. *Circ. Res.* 40:Suppl. I, pp. I127–34

15. Dietz, R., Schomig, A., Haebara, H., Mann, J. F. E., Rascher, W., et al. 1978. Studies on the pathogenesis of spontaneous hypertension of rats. *Circ. Res.* 43:Suppl. I, pp. I98–106

16. Edwards, E., McCaughran, J. A., Friedman, R., McNally, W., Schechter, N. 1983. Cholinergic receptor site binding in the Dahl model of hypertension. *Clin. Exp. Hypertension.* In press

17. Falkner, B., Onesti, G., Angelakos, E., Fernandes, M., Langman, C. 1979. Cardiovascular response to mental stress in normal adolescents with hypertensive parents. *Hypertension* 1:23–30

18. Falkner, B., Onesti, G., Angelakos, E. 1981. Effect of salt loading on the cardiovascular response to stress in adolescents. *Hypertension* 3:Suppl. II, pp. II195–99

19. Folkow, B. 1982. Physiological aspects of primary hypertension. *Physiol. Rev.* 62:347–504

20. Forsyth, R. P. 1971. Regional blood flow changes during 72-hour avoidance schedules in the monkey. *Science* 173:546–48

21. Fregly, M. J., Kare, M. R., eds. 1982. *The Role of Salt in Cardiovascular Hypertension.* New York: Academic

22. Friedman, R. 1981. Experimental psychogenic hypertension. In *Stress and the Heart*, ed. D. Wheatley. pp. 209–28. New York: Raven

23. Friedman, R., Dahl, L. K. 1975. The effect of chronic conflict on the blood pressure of rats with a genetic susceptibility to experimental hypertension. *Psychosom. Med.* 37:402–16

24. Friedman, R., McCann, M., Leder, R., Iwai, J. 1982. Genetic predisposition to hypertension and stress-induced alterations in heart rate. *Behav. Neur. Biol.* 35:426–31

25. Galosy, R. A., Gaebelein, C. J. 1977. Cardiovascular adaptation to environmental stress: Its role in the development of hypertension, responsible mechanisms, and hypotheses. *Biobehav. Rev.* 1:165–75

26. Gavras, H. 1982. Possible mechanisms of sodium-dependent hypertension: volume expansion or vasoconstriction? *Clin. Exp. Hyperten.* A4:737–49

27. Goto, A., Ganguli, M., Tobian, L., Johnson, M. A., Iwai, J. 1982. Effect of an anteroventral third-ventricle lesion on sodium chloride hypertension in the rat. *Clin. Sci.* 63:Suppl., pp. 319–22

28. Goto, A., Tobian, L., Iwai, J. 1981. Potassium feeding reduces hyperactive central nervous system pressor responses in Dahl salt-sensitive rats. *Hypertension* 3:Suppl. I, pp. I128–34

29. Grignolo, A., Koepke, J. P., Obrist, P. A. 1982. Renal function, heart rate, and blood pressure during exercise and avoidance in dogs. *Am. J. Physiol.* 242:R482–90

30. Guyton, A. C. 1977. Personal views on mechanisms of hypertension. In *Hypertension*, ed. J. Genest, E. Koiw, O. Kuchel, pp. 566–75. New York: McGraw Hill

31. Hallback, M., Folkow, B. 1974. Cardiovascular response to acute mental "stress" in spontaneously hypertensive rats. *Acta Physiol. Scand.* 90:684–98

32. Hatzinikolaou, P., Gavras, H., Brunner, H. R., Gavras, I. 1980. Sodium-induced elevation of blood pressure in the anephric state. *Science* 209:935–36

33. Hatzinikolaou, P., Gavras, H., Brunner, H. R., Gavras, I. 1981. Role of vasopressin, catecholamines, and plasma volume in hypertonic saline-induced hypertension. *Am. J. Physiol.* 240 (*Heart Circ. Physiol.* 9):H827–31

34. Hollenberg, N. K., Williams, G. H., Adams, D. F. 1981. Essential hypertension: abnormal renal vascular and endocrine responses to a mild psychological stimulus. *Hypertension* 3:11–17

35. Ikeda, T., Tobain, L., Iwai, J., Goossen, P. 1978. Central nervous system pressor responses in rats susceptible and resistant to sodium chloride hypertension. *Clin. Sci. Mol. Med.* 55:Suppl., pp. 225–27

36. Kanwisher, J. W., Gabrielson, G., Kanwisher, N. 1981. Free and forced diving in birds. *Science* 211:717–19

37. Katholi, R. E., Carey, R. M., Ayers, C. R., Vaughan, E. D. Jr., Yancey, M. R., et al. 1977. Production of sustained hypertension by chronic intrarenal norepinephrine infusion in conscious dogs. *Circ. Res. (Suppl. I)* 40:I118–25

38. Katholi, R. E., Naftilan, A. J., Oparil, S. 1980. Importance of renal sympathetic tone in the development of DOCA-salt hypertension in the rat. *Hypertension* 2:266–73

39. Katholi, R. E., Whitlow, P. L., Winternitz, S. R., Oparil, S. 1982. Importance of the renal nerves in established two-kidney, one-clip Goldblatt hypertension. *Hypertension* 4:Suppl. II, pp. II166–74

40. Katholi, R. E., Winternitz, S. R., Oparil, S. 1981. Role of the renal nerves in the pathogenesis of one-kidney renal hypertension in the rat. *Hypertension* 3:404–9

41. Katholi, R. E., Winternitz, S. R., Oparil, S. 1982. Decrease in sympathetic nervous system activity and attenuation in response to stress following renal denervation in the one-kidney one-clip Goldblatt hypertensive rat. *Clin. Exp. Hyperten.* A4:707–16

42. Katovich, M. J., Fregly, M. J. 1982. β-adrenergic responsiveness in deoxycorticosterone-salt-induced hypertension in rats. In *The Role of Salt in Cardiovascular Hypertension,* ed. M. J. Fregly, M. R. Kare, pp. 293–312. New York: Academic

43. Kearns, W. D., Better, W. E., Anderson, D. E. 1981. A tether system for cardiovascular studies in the behaving dog. *Behav. Res. Instr. Meth.* 13:323–27

44. Koepke, J. P., Grignolo, A., Light, K. C., Obrist, P. A. 1983. Central β-andrenoceptor mediation of the antinatriuretic responses to behavioral stress in conscious dogs. *J. Pharm. Exp. Therap.* In press

45. Koepke, J. P., Light, K. C., Grignolo, A., Obrist, P. A. 1983. Neural control of renal excretory function during behavioral stress in dogs. *Amer. J. Physiol.* 245:R251–58

46. Koepke, J. P., Light, K. C., Obrist, P. A. 1982. α-adrenoceptors in the renal excretory response to avoidance in conscious dogs. *Fed. Proc.* 41:1105

47. Koomans, H. A., Ropos, J. C., Boer, P., Geyskes, G. G., Mees, E. J. D. 1982. Salt sensitivity of blood pressure in chronic renal failure. *Hypertension* 4: 190–97

48. Lawler, J. E., Barker, G. F., Hubbard, J. W., Schaub, R. G. 1981. Effects of stress on blood pressure and cardiac pathology in rats with borderline hypertension. *Hypertension* 3:496–505

49. Light, K. C., Koepke, J. P., Obrist, P. A., Grignolo, A., Willis, P. W. 1983. Psychological stress induces sodium and fluid retention in men at high risk for hypertension. *Science.* 220:429–31

50. Luft, F. C., Fineberg, N. S., Miller, J. Z., Rankin, L. I., Grim, C. E., et al. 1980. The effects of age, race, and heredity on glomerular filtration rate following volume expansion and contraction in normal man. *Am. J. Med. Sc.* 279:15–24

51. Luft, F. C., Rankin, L. I., Bloch, R., Weyman, A. E., Willis, L. R., et al. 1979. Cardiovascular and humoral responses to extremes of sodium intake in normal black and white men. *Circulation* 60:697–706

52. Luft, F. C., Rankin, L. I., Henry, D. P., Bloch, R., Grim, C. E., et al. 1979. Plasma and urinary norepinephrine values at extremes of sodium intake in normal man. *Hypertension* 1:261–66

53. Luft, F. C., Weinberger, M. N. 1982. Sodium intake and essential hypertension. *Hypertension* 4:III14–19

54. Lundin, S., Thoren, P. 1982. Renal function and sympathetic activity during mental stress in normotensive and spontaneously hypertensive rats. *Acta Physiol. Scand.* 115:115–24

55. Mark, A. L., Lawton, W. J., Abboud, F. M., Fitz, A. E., Connor, W. E., et al. 1975. Effects of high and low sodium intake on arterial pressure and forearm vascular resistance in borderline hypertension. *Circ. Res.* 36 & 37:Suppl. I, pp. I194–98

56. McCaughran, J. A., Murphy, D., Schechter, N., Friedman, R. 1983. Participation of the central cholinergic system in blood pressure in the Dahl model of essential hypertension. *J. Cardiovas. Pharmacol.* In press

57. Meneeley, G. R., Tucker, R. G., Darby, W. J., Auerbach, S. H. 1953. Chronic sodium chloride toxicity in albino rat. II. Occurrence of hypertension and syndrome of edema and renal failure. *J. Exp. Med.* 98:71

58. Murdaugh, H. V., Schmidt-Nielsen, J. W., Wood, J. W., Mitchell, W. L. 1961. Cessation of renal function during diving in the trained seal. *J. Cellular Comp. Physiol.* 58:261–65

59. Murray, R. H., Luft, F. C., Bloch, R.,

Weyman, A. E. 1978. Blood pressure responses to extremes of sodium intake in normal man. *Proc. Soc. Exp. Biol. Med.* 159:432–36

60. Norman, R. A., Cage, C., Dzielak, D. J., Klein, R. L. 1981. Role of renal nerves in maintenance of spontaneous hypertension. *Fed. Proc.* 40:391

61. Pettinger, W. A., Sanchez, A., Mulvihill-Wilson, J., Saavedra, J., Haywood, J. R., et al. 1982. Renal and platelet α-adrenergic receptors in hypertensive rats and man. *Hypertension (Suppl. II)* 4:II188

62. Rankin, L. I., Henry, D. P., Weinberger, M. H., Gibbs, P. S., Luft, F. C. 1981. Sodium intake alters the effects of norepinephrine on the renin system and the kidney. *Am. J. Kidn. Dis.* 1:177–84

63. Rankin, L. I., Luft, F. C., Henry, D. P., Gibbs, P. S., Weinberger, M. H. 1981. Sodium intake alters the effects of norepinephrine on blood pressure. *Hypertension* 3:650–56

64. Rapp, J. P. 1982. Dahl salt-susceptible and salt-resistant rats: a review. *Hypertension* 4:753–63

65. Sanchez, A., Pettinger, W. A. 1981. Dietary sodium regulation of blood pressure and renal α one- and α two-receptors in WKY and SH rats. *Life Sci.* 29:2795–802

66. Schramm, L. P., Anderson, D. E., Randall, R. C. 1975. Effects of aversive Pavlovian conditioning upon renal blood flow in the dog. *Experientia* 31:71–73

67. Skrabal, F., Aubock, J., Hortnagl, H., Brausteiner, H. 1980. Effect of moderate salt restriction and high potassium intake on pressor hormones, response to noradrenaline, and baroreceptor function in man. *Clin. Sci.* 59:Suppl., pp. 157–60

68. Takeshita, A., Mark, A. L. 1978. Neurogenic contribution to hindquarters vasoconstriction during high sodium intake in Dahl strain of genetically hypertensive rat. *Circ. Res.* 43:Suppl., pp. 86–91

69. Takeshita, A., Tsutomu, I., Toshiaki, A. Nakamura, M. 1982. Adrenergic mechanisms do not contribute to salt-induced vasoconstriction in stroke-prone spontaneously hypertensive rat. *Hypertension* 4:288–93

70. Tanaka, T., Seki, A., Fuji, J. 1982. Effect of high and low sodium intake on norepinephrine turnover in the cardiovascular tissues and brain stem of the rabbit. *Hypertension* 4:294–98

71. Thoren, P., Rickstein, S. E. 1979. Recordings of renal and splanchnic sympathetic nervous system activity in normotensive and spontaneously hypertensive rats. *Clin. Sci.* 57:197–99 (Suppl.)

72. Tobian, L. 1978. Salt and hypertension. *Annals NY Acad. Sci.* 304:178–97

73. Weiner, H. 1977. *Psychobiology and Human Disease,* pp. 107–217. New York: Elsevier

74. Winternitz, S. R., Katholi, R. E., Oparil, S. 1980. Role of the renal sympathetic nerves in the development and maintenance of hypertension in the spontaneously hypertensive rat. *J. Clin. Invest.* 66:971–78

75. Winternitz, S. R., Oparil, S. 1982. Importance of the renal nerves in the pathogenesis of experimental hypertension. *Hypertension* 4:III108–14

76. Winternitz, S. R., Wyss, J. M., Meadows, J. R., Oparil S. 1982. Increased noradrenaline content of hypothalamic nuclei in association with worsening of hypertension after high sodium intake in the young spontaneously hypertensive rat. *Clin. Sci.* 63:Suppl., pp. 339–42

77. Yamori, Y. 1975. Neurogenic mechanisms of spontaneous hypertension. In *Regulation of Blood Pressure by the Nervous System,* ed. G. Onesti, M. Fernandez, K. E. Kim, pp. 65–77. New York: Grune & Stratton

78. Zanchetti, A., Stella, A., Baccelli, G., Mancia, G. 1979. Neural influences on kidney function in the pathogenesis of arterial hypertension. In *Hypertension: Determinants, Complications, and Intervention,* 5th Hahnemann Symp. Hyperten., ed. G. Onesti, C. R Klimt, p. 99. New York: Grune & Stratton.

Ann. Rev. Physiol. 1984. 46:155–76
Copyright © 1984 by Annual Reviews Inc. All rights reserved

BEHAVIORAL STRESS AND CARDIAC ARRHYTHMIAS

Richard L. Verrier and Bernard Lown

Cardiovascular Division, Department of Medicine, Brigham and Women's Hospital, Harvard Medical School, and Department of Nutrition, Harvard School of Public Health, Boston, Massachusetts 02115

INTRODUCTION

The main objective of this review is to present an overview of contemporary issues related to the role of behavioral factors in the genesis of cardiac arrhythmias. Particular emphasis will be placed on the effects of stress on vulnerability to ventricular fibrillation (VF), because this arrhythmia is the primary mechanism responsible for sudden cardiac death, the leading cause of fatality in the industrially developed world (53). We begin by discussing some historical aspects and then proceed to review the contemporary literature. Finally, we discuss the new avenues of research that, in our opinion, provide novel directions for future work.

HISTORICAL CONSIDERATIONS

Early evidence of a link between higher nervous activity and cardiac arrhythmias derives from experiments on anesthetized animals. Levy (47) demonstrated more than 60 years ago that injection of drugs such as nicotine, barium chloride, or epinephrine into certain areas of the brain in chloroform-anesthetized cats provoked major ventricular arrhythmias. In these animals the coronary circulation was intact. The neural pathways involved in arrhythmogenesis were subsequently defined by electrical stimulation of various central nervous system structures by means of stereotaxically positioned electrodes (36, 37). But experiments on anesthetized animals could not address the pressing issue of determining the effects of psychological and biobehavioral factors on heart rhythm.

0066-4278/84/0315-0155$02.00

The classic studies of Cannon (16) suggested that the biologically active amine adrenaline was secreted in response to stimuli that produced fear and rage reactions in animals. He considered this biogenic amine to play a role in Voodoo death (Table 1). The later experiments of Richter (88) shifted the attention of psychological investigators from the sympatho-adrenal system to the vagus as a precipitating element in sudden death. Richter demonstrated that rats forced to swim in water tanks died in bradycardia and asystole rather than from VF, presumably as a result of intense vagal discharge. While the simple faint in man is caused by this means, it is unlikely to be the mechanism for sudden cardiac death in man for two main reasons. First, whereas enhanced vagal activity is capable of permanently arresting the small rat heart, it is incapable of doing so in the large mammalian hearts of the dog or man (60). Secondly, VF, not asystole, has been shown by means of extensive clinical observation to be the primary mechanism for sudden cardiac death (18, 53).

A number of studies exposed normal animals to severe behavioral stress until either death or induction of extensive cardiac damage ensued. These stresses involved interference with the animals' access to food (80, 81), exposing rats to tape recordings of noisy rat-cat fights (80, 81), "yoked chair" aversive avoidance experiments in monkeys (22), and animal crowding (81). Subjecting normal pigs paralyzed by muscle relaxants to unavoidable electric shocks was reported to induce cardiac myofibrillar damage within 24 hours (39).

Until recently studies exploring the role of neural activity on the heart were largely oriented toward the induction of myocardial injury or asystole in normal animals. This was an unfortunate trend, because the biologic model was remote from the clinical syndrome in man as gleaned from coronary care unit experience in the 1960s (55). For example, stress-induced arrhythmias usually occur in the presence of underlying coronary disease, not in normal individuals. The fatal event is usually abrupt in onset (symptoms lasting seconds to minutes) and is due primarily to VF and not to asystole. And finally, acute myocardial

Table 1   Historical perspective of experimental modeling of biobehavioral factors in sudden cardiac death

Investigator (Ref.)	Year	Biological model	Proposed mechanism of death
Cannon (16)	1942	"Voodoo death"	Sympatho-adrenal activation
Richter (88)	1957	Swimming rats	Vagally induced asystole
Raab (80)	1964	Sensory and emotional stress in rats	Cardiac myofibrillar damage
Corley (22)	1974	Shock avoidance in squirrel monkeys	Myocardial degeneration leading to asystole
Johansson (39)	1974	Restraint stress in pigs	Myocardial necrosis

damage is rarely present, suggesting that sudden death is due to a derangement in cardiac electrical function rather than to a discrete anatomical lesion.

It is our view that animal modeling needs to be focused on the effect of psychological factors on ventricular electrical stability. This, however, presents difficult methodological problems. Specifically, how can vulnerability to VF be assessed in the free-moving conscious animal? Such assessment requires the use of painful test stimuli, induction of VF, and use of traumatic resuscitation procedures that preclude meaningful investigation of psychological variables.

The use of the repetitive extrasystole threshold as an indicator of vulnerability to VF afforded a possible solution to this problem (58, 59, 68, 121). Customarily, the threshold for ventricular fibrillation is assessed by delivering small electric currents to the heart during the narrow zone of the so-called vulnerable period of the ventricle, coinciding with the apex of the T-wave in the surface electrocardiogram. By stepwise increases of current intensity, ventricular fibrillation can be provoked and the electrical threshold for this event measured. Since ventricular fibrillation is preceded by single or multiple extrasystoles (a response that is not perceived by the animals), the threshold for the latter endpoint can be utilized, obviating the induction of VF and the resort to cardiac resuscitation.

PSYCHOLOGICAL INFLUENCES ON VENTRICULAR VULNERABILITY

In our initial studies, a simple classical aversive conditioning protocol was employed (21, 58). Dogs were exposed to two different environments: a cage in which the animal was left largely undisturbed, and a Pavlovian sling in which the animal received a single 5-joule transthoracic shock at the end of each experimental period for three successive days. The two environments were compared on days 4 and 5. At these times, the dogs in the sling were restless, salivated excessively, exhibited somatic tremor, sinus tachycardia, and increased mean arterial blood pressure. In the cage, as evidenced by behavioral signs and hemodynamic variables, the animals appeared relaxed. Transferring the animals from the nonaversive to the aversive environment resulted in a substantial [41%] reduction in vulnerable period threshold (27, 51). These findings indicate that psychological stress profoundly lowers the cardiac threshold for ventricular fibrillation (Figure 1).

It was pertinent to examine whether the type of stress was crucial to the changes in ventricular vulnerability. We therefore utilized a different psychological stress model in which dogs were subjected to programmed signalled shock avoidance (67). Exposure to such an aversive conditioning program resulted in a 50% reduction in the repetitive extrasystole threshold, a

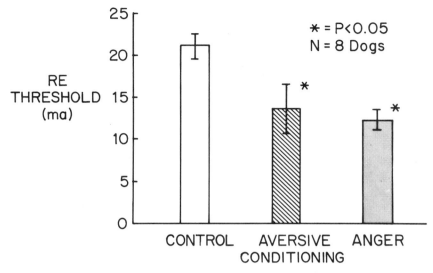

Figure 1 Effects of behavioral stress on the repetitive extrasystole (RE) threshold in normal dogs. Both passive aversive conditioning using a mild electric shock and induction of an anger-like state by food-access-denial produced significant reductions in the vulnerable-period threshold. Heart rate was maintained constant during cardiac electrical testing by ventricular pacing (115).

change comparable to that observed in the cage-sling environments. Recently, we have found that inducing an anger-like state in dogs by food-access-denial is also capable of lowering the vulnerable-period threshold by 30–40% (117, 119).

BEHAVIORAL STRESS AND VULNERABILITY DURING MYOCARDIAL ISCHEMIA AND REPERFUSION

An unresolved issue was whether these moderate aversive psychological states were of sufficient magnitude to provoke ventricular arrhythmias in the predisposed animal without the need to subject the heart to external electrical stimulation.

To shed light on this question, animals were subjected to psychological stress during the very inception of acute cardiac ischemia, a time when there is extreme electrical instability of the myocardium. Our experimental model involved a 10-minute period of left anterior descending coronary artery occlusion followed by abrupt release. This model was chosen because it exhibits a highly reproducible time course of changes in ventricular vulnerability. Specifically, within 1–2 minutes after onset of coronary occlusion, the vulnerable period threshold recedes to extremely low levels. The period of enhanced vulnerability persists for 6–7 minutes; thereafter the vulnerable period threshold recovers despite continued occlusion. Upon release of the occlusion after an ischemic period of 10 minutes, a brief period of enhanced vulnerability reappears within 20–30 seconds and lasts for less than one minute (59).

A major reason for choosing an occlusion-release model relates to the possibility that provocation of ventricular fibrillation in man may result from acute myocardial ischemia caused by transient infringement of arterial flow or from the release of obstruction with ensuing reperfusion, such as might follow coronary artery spasm. The effects of the cage and sling environments were therefore evaluated by means of the occlusion-release model (59). When acute myocardial ischemia was induced in the aversive sling setting, the incidence of ventricular fibrillation was more than three times greater [46% vs 14%, p<0.01] than that observed in the nonaversive environment (117, 119). The episode of ventricular fibrillation occurred within 3–5 minutes of coronary artery occlusion or within 20–30 seconds following release and reperfusion. These intervals correspond closely with the periods of maximum myocardial electrical instability as exposed by electrical testing of the heart.

Skinner and coworkers (103) have reported that psychologic stimuli affect susceptibility to ventricular fibrillation during acute coronary artery occlusion in pigs. Myocardial ischemia was induced in either a familiar or unfamiliar environment. In the unfamiliar setting, following coronary artery occlusion, fibrillation occurred within a few minutes; however, onset of fibrillation was greatly delayed and even entirely prevented in some animals in an environment to which the pigs had been previously adapted.

The precise pathways that mediate psychophysiologic activity to the heart affecting vulnerability to ventricular fibrillation in the conscious animal remain undefined. Recently, Skinner & Reed (105) shed some light on this question by means of cryogenic techniques. They adapted farm pigs to a laboratory environment during a 4 to 8–day period and noted significant retardation or even prevention in the onset of ventricular fibrillation associated with coronary occlusion. These effects of stress on susceptibility to fibrillation appeared to be mediated via the thalamic gating mechanism. This conclusion was based on the findings that cryogenic blockade of this system or its output from the frontal cortex to the brainstem delayed or prevented the occurrence of ventricular fibrillation.

These results indicate that diverse biobehavioral stresses are capable of lowering the vulnerable period threshold in the normal heart and predisposing the acutely ischemic heart to ventricular fibrillation during both occlusion and reperfusion. It is worth examining the more immediate neural mechanism by which biobehavioral factors alter cardiac susceptibility to VF.

ADRENERGIC FACTORS AND VULNERABILITY DURING PSYCHOLOGIC STRESS

Normal Hearts

Adrenergic factors play a substantial role in mediating ventricular vulnerability during biobehavioral stress in conscious animals. A number of observations support this conclusion in the type of aversive psychologic conditioning we have so far employed. First, the levels of circulating catecholamines vary directly with the changes in ventricular vulnerability during psychologic stress. When dogs were transferred from a nonaversive cage to an aversive sling environment, or when an anger-like state was evoked, there was a substantial rise in blood epinephrine and norepinephrine concentrations indicative of enhanced sympathetic neural activity as well as adrenal medullary discharge. The observed reductions in vulnerable-period threshold corresponded with the concomitant elevations in circulating catecholamine levels (51).

An essential involvement of adrenergic mechanisms is also suggested by the effects of pharmacologic (67, 116) and surgical sympathectomy (116) on stress-induced changes in ventricular vulnerability. Indeed, it has been shown that β-adrenergic blockade with propranolol (116) or the cardioselective agents tolamolol (67) or metoprolol (115) completely prevents the effects of aversive conditioning on the vulnerable-period threshold. This is the case whether the conditioning is classical or instrumental. It is noteworthy that stellectomy, whether of the left or right ganglion, did not prevent the reduction in repetitive extrasystole threshold associated with aversive conditioning. Only partial protection was conferred by bilateral stellectomy (116) (Figure 2). Thus, adrenergic inputs in addition to those derived from stellate ganglia affect the myocardium during psychologic stress to alter ventricular vulnerability. Most probably these additional inputs derive from other thoracic ganglia and from adrenal medullary catecholamines.

Ischemic Hearts

The precise neural mechanisms involved in the biobehavioral provocation of ventricular arrhythmias during myocardial ischemia and infarction are only partially understood (84, 91, 103). For example, whereas farm pigs adapted to a laboratory environment have a reduced and delayed onset of ventricular fibrillation during coronary artery obstruction, surprisingly, β-adrenergic blockade with propranolol did not afford any protection against the development of ventricular fibrillation in unadapted animals (103). It remains to be determined whether the failure of propranolol to protect against ventricular fibrillation resulted from inadequate blockade of adrenergic inputs to the heart or from the involvement of extra-adrenergic factors in the antifibrillatory effect of psychologic adaptation.

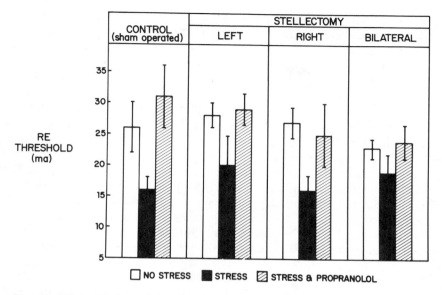

Figure 2 Effect of β-adrenergic blockade with propranolol (0.25 mg kg^{-1}) and stellectomy on ventricular vulnerability during psychological stress. Stress induced a significant decrease in vulnerable-period threshold, which was prevented by propranolol. Unilateral stellectomy did not prevent the decrease in threshold and only partial protection was afforded by bilateral stellectomy (116, 117).

By contrast, Rosenfeld, Rosen & Hoffman (91) reported that β-adrenergic blockade protected against malignant ventricular arrhythmias associated with acute coronary artery occlusion in dogs exposed to behavioral stresses. The animals were chronically instrumented to record electrocardiograms and electrograms from ischemic and nonischemic coronary artery occlusion. The dogs were exposed to several forms of behavioral stress. These included presentation in an unfamiliar environment of stressful stimuli: a light followed by a sudden noise or a noise followed by subcutaneous electrical shock. Shock significantly decreased the latency and increased the severity of ventricular arrhythmias. β-adrenergic blockade with the cardioselective agent tolamolol substantially reduced the adverse effects of stress on cardiac rhythm. Moreover, they found that the quaternary analog of propranolol, UM 272, which lacks β-adrenergic blocking properties but exerts direct local anesthetic effects on the heart, did not confer a protective action. Thus, the beneficial effect of tolamolol appears to result from its antiadrenergic action rather than from a nonspecific effect on myocardial tissue. These workers also demonstrated an antiarrhythmic effect of the antianxiety drug diazepam.

The involvement of α-adrenergic receptors in stress-induced arrhythmias is as yet uncertain. This relates to the complexity of their influences, including both direct actions on myocardial excitable properties (89) and indirect effects on insulin secretion (61), platelet aggregability (75), and coronary hemodynamic function (30, 69, 98, 114). The latter consideration may be of particular import in view of increasing evidence implicating neural factors in the provocation of coronary vasospasm (66). Indeed, Mudge and coworkers (71) have demonstrated in patients with coronary disease that the cold pressor test evokes intense coronary vasoconstriction often with ST segment elevation and chest pain. These effects are prevented by administration of phenoxybenzamine, indicating that the coronary vasoconstrictor response is mediated through reflex activation of α-adrenergic receptors. There is also evidence that excitation of certain brain centers may also provoke significant coronary vasoconstriction (33, 74, 101, 102). In particular, Pasyk et al (74) have shown that injection of opioids into the lateral cerebral ventricles of conscious dogs produces profound and sustained coronary vasoconstriction that is abolished by α-adrenergic blockade (74). These investigators have also obtained preliminary evidence that opiate-induced endogenous vasopressin may be associated with coronary artery spasm in man (78). They found that arginine vasopressin is increased in both spontaneous and ergonovine-induced coronary artery spasm. Their current view is that endogenous arginine vasopressin in conjunction with local vascular hypersensitivity may play a role in the pathogenesis of coronary artery spasm.

Central nervous system GABAergic receptors may also be involved in the regulation of coronary vascular tone and cardiac rhythm (33, 101, 102). Gillis and coworkers (33) have found that administration of the GABAergic antagonist picrotoxin into the lateral cerebral ventricle of chloralose-anesthetized cats produces coronary constriction, ST segment elevation, and ventricular arrhythmias. These effects are blocked by pretreatment with the GABA receptor agonist muscimol. Peripheral sympathetic-nervous-system ablation by surgical means or by injection of α-adrenoreceptor drugs also prevents the alterations in coronary vascular tone and cardiac rhythm.

Thus, there is ample evidence to suggest that α-receptor–mediated changes in coronary vasomotor tone can play a significant role in the genesis of cardiac arrhythmias.

CORONARY HEMODYNAMIC FUNCTION AND STRESS-INDUCED VULNERABILITY TO FIBRILLATION

Does coronary vasoconstriction play a role in provoking cardiac arrhythmias during behavioral stress? Surprisingly, this important question remains largely unanswered. Rayford et al (85) first described the effects of excitatory stimuli on coronary hemodynamic function in conscious animals. Loud noises or sudden squirts of ice water to a dog's face immediately and substantially increased mean coronary blood flow and myocardial oxygen consumption. Subsequently, other investigators (8, 10, 113) also reported significant increases in coronary blood flow in response to diverse behavioral stresses. In unrestrained conscious baboons, Vatner et al (113) demonstrated remarkable fluctuations in coronary blood flow that varied by as much as five-fold over the course of a day. The lowest flow occurred at night when the animals were motionless and apparently asleep. The highest coronary blood flow values were observed when the animals were judged to be emotionally aroused. These results suggest that during behavioral stress coronary blood flow adapts appropriately to the enhanced metabolic requirements of the myocardium.

Recent studies indicate, however, that certain types of behavioral stress are capable of inducing transient coronary vasoconstriction (10, 28). In particular, Billman & Randall (10), using classical aversive conditioning in dogs, observed α-adrenergically mediated vasoconstriction that persisted for less than one minute. This response was followed by a longer lasting vasodilation that was presumed to be mediated by metabolites released by enhanced metabolic activity of the heart.

Our investigations examined the particular question of whether or not behaviorally induced changes in vulnerability to fibrillation are mediated by alterations in coronary vasomotor tone (115, 122). Whereas diverse stress states elicited by passive aversive conditioning or induction of anger by food-access-denial significantly augmented myocardial blood flow, there was a concomitant increase in myocardial oxygen extraction (115) suggesting possible inadequacy in myocardial perfusion. The effects of coronary dilation using the calcium antagonist nifedipine (10 μg kg^{-1} intravenous bolus) were therefore explored. Whereas this agent prevented the stress-induced increase in myocardial oxygen extraction, it did not affect the vulnerable period threshold. In contrast, induction of β-adrenergic blockade with metoprolol (1 mg kg^{-1} intravenous bolus) did not influence the changes in oxygen extraction, whereas it did protect against the fall in vulnerable-period threshold. We concluded that vulnerability to ventricular fibrillation in the normal heart during behavioral stress is not due to alterations in myocardial perfusion but rather to the direct effects of catecholamines on myocardial β-adrenergic receptors (115, 122).

These observations in animals with intact coronary circulation leave unanswered the question of whether the response of the ischemic heart to behavioral stress is not in part mediated through changes in myocardial perfusion. Mudge and coworkers (71) and others (34, 65) have noted that a cold pressor test elicits inappropriate coronary vasoconstriction, ST segment elevation, and chest pain in patients with coronary disease but not in normal subjects. Mild-to-moderate behavioral stress, however, does not appear to induce coronary constriction in human subjects with coronary artery disease (4). It remains uncertain whether the difference in coronary vascular response between the cold pressor test and behavioral stress is due to differences in the nature of the neurogenic stimuli or to other factors yet to be defined.

CHOLINERGIC INFLUENCES AND VULNERABILITY DURING STRESS

Do cholinergic factors also modulate ventricular electrical properties in response to environmental stimuli? Two sets of observations suggest an affirmative answer. First, it has been shown that administration of morphine sulfate to dogs in the aversive sling environment described earlier increased the vulnerable-period threshold to the value observed in the nonaversive cage setting (27). When vagal efferent activity was blocked by atropine, a major component of morphine's protective effect was annulled. When morphine was given in the nonaversive environment, where adrenergic activation was absent or decreased as indicated by low circulating catecholamine levels (27, 51), drug-induced vagotonia did not affect the vulnerable-period threshold. Thus, the beneficial effect of morphine during psychologic stress appeared to result partly from vagal antagonism of the fibrillatory influence of enhanced adrenergic input to the heart and partly from the drug's sedative action.

It remained unknown, however, whether intrinsic vagal tone in the stressed animal was sufficient to affect ventricular vulnerability. To study this question, relatively small doses of atropine (0.05 mg kg^{-1}) were given to block selectively vagal efferent activity to the heart. In the aversive sling setting, vagal efferent blockade resulted in a substantial 50% reduction in the vulnerable-period threshold. The implication is that in the stressed animal a considerable level of vagal tone is present that partly offsets the profibrillatory influence of aversive psychophysiologic stimuli. In the cage, where adrenergic input was low, vagal blockade was without effect on the threshold (120) (Figure 3).

SYMPATHETIC-PARASYMPATHETIC INTERACTIONS

What is the basis for the protective effect of the vagus on ventricular vulnerability? The effects of the vagus on ventricular vulnerability appear to be contingent on the level of pre-existing cardiac sympathetic tone (118). At a low level of sympathetic tone, vagal stimulation is without effect (45). By contrast, when sympathetic tone to the heart is augmented by thoracotomy (45), sympathetic nerve stimulation (45), or catecholamine infusion (83), simultaneous vagal activation exerts a protective effect on ventricular vulnerability. Vagus nerve stimulation is without effect on vulnerability when adrenergic input to the heart is ablated by β-adrenergic blockade (45, 83) (Figure 3).

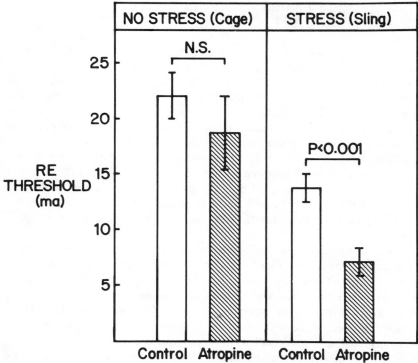

Figure 3 Influence of atropine (0.05 mg kg^{-1}) on repetitive extrasystole (RE) threshold in conscious dogs exposed to nonaversive and aversive environments. In the aversive setting, blockade of vagal efferent activity with atropine substantially reduced the vulnerable-period threshold, indicating an enhanced propensity for ventricular fibrillation. In the nonstressful setting, where adrenergic activity was low, no effect of the drug was evident. Heart rate was maintained constant during cardiac electrical testing by ventricular pacing (120).

The influence of the vagus on ventricular vulnerability appears to result from activation of muscarinic receptors, because these changes in vulnerability are prevented by atropine administration (118). The diminution of adrenergic effects by muscarinic activation has a physiologic as well as cellular basis. Muscarinic agents inhibit the release of norepinephrine from sympathetic nerve endings (48, 49, 50) and attenuate the response to norepinephrine at receptor sites by cyclic nucleotide interactions (124, 125).

Thus, results from both anesthetized- and conscious-animal experiments indicate that enhanced cardiac vagal tone, whether occurring spontaneously or induced pharmacologically, decreases susceptibility to ventricular fibrillation. This beneficial action is primarily caused by antagonism of adrenergic inputs to the heart.

VAGAL INFLUENCES IN THE ISCHEMIC AND INFARCTED HEART

The role of vagus nerve activity in altering predisposition to VF during acute coronary artery occlusion is a subject of current reappraisal (64, 79). Kent et al (41) found that vagus nerve stimulation significantly increased the VF threshold and decreased susceptibility to fibrillation in the ischemic canine heart. Subsequently, Corr, Gillis, and coworkers (23, 24) observed that the presence of intact vagi protected against VF in chloralose-anesthetized cats during left anterior descending but not right coronary artery ligation. Yoon et al (128) and James et al (38) were unable to demonstrate any effect of vagus nerve stimulation on VF threshold during left anterior descending coronary artery occlusion in the canine heart. Corr & Gillis (23) have found that cholinergic stimulation may actually exacerbate rather than ameliorate the arrhythmias that ensue upon release of occlusion, with attendant reperfusion of the ischemic myocardium.

Our investigations indicate that intense cholinergic stimulation by electrical stimulation of the decentralized vagi or by direct muscarinic enhancement with methacholine affords only partial protection during myocardial ischemia in dogs in which heart rate was maintained constant by pacing. No salutary influence of cholinergic stimulation was noted during reperfusion (117). Vagal stimulation does not, however, completely suppress the arrhythmias that result from myocardial infarction (42). In fact, it has been demonstrated that enhanced vagus activity or acetylcholine infusion consistently elicited ventricular tachycardia during the quiescent arrhythmia-free phase of myocardial infarction in dogs. This effect was rate-dependent, because obviating the vagally induced bradycardia prevented the arrhythmias. Thus, the antiarrhythmic effects of the vagus may be augmented or reversed by its profound influence on heart rate in the setting of acute myocardial infarction.

EFFECT OF SLEEP ON VENTRICULAR ARRHYTHMIAS

Kleitman's (43) pioneering work made evident that prolonged sleep deprivation in animals led to disorganized aggressive behavior and, eventually, sudden death. Postmortem examination demonstrated no anatomic lesions or chemical imbalance to account for death. A reasonable surmise is that cardiac arrhythmia was the underlying mechanism. Sleep, as a neural event, probably affects cardiac function through the autonomic nervous sytem. Much evidence suggests that diencephalic areas in the central nervous system serve as focal points of cardiac control (94, 107) and that this control is transmitted through peripheral autonomic pathways (13, 20). The same catecholamine neurotransmitters that subserve myocardial function are also associated with specific sleep stages (40, 44, 87). Baust and coworkers (6, 7) have shown that denervation of the heart prevents the usual heart rate responses to various sleep states.

Barring a single report by Skinner, Mohr & Kellaway (104), there is a paucity of experimental studies relating sleep stages to cardiac arrhythmias. They explored the influences of sleep stage on the occurrence of ventricular arrhythmias during left anterior descending coronary artery occlusion in un-anesthetized pigs. They found that the period during the early sleep cycle wherein transitional and slow-wave sleep alternate was accompanied by an increase in arrhythmias compared to the awake stage. This was true both in the acutely infarcted (two hours) as well as the recently infarcted (two days) pig heart. The maximum increase in ventricular arrhythmias was observed during sustained periods of slow-wave sleep. Later when rapid-eye-movement (REM) sleep predominated, the overall arrhythmia incidence abruptly diminished. Acute coronary artery occlusion performed after the inception of slow-wave sleep reduced the latency in onset of ventricular fibrillation compared with that observed during the awake state. Coronary occlusion during REM sleep was associated with the very opposite, namely, a delay in the development of ventricular fibrillation.

These investigators reached some unexpected conclusions: (a) slow-wave sleep, but not REM sleep, has a deleterious influence on the ischemic heart; (b) REM sleep may be beneficial, because it delays the development of ventricular fibrillation during coronary artery occlusion; and (c), the heart-rate changes during sleep do not correlate with the effects of slow-wave or REM sleep on cardiac rhythm.

The explanation for the above changes remains unclear. It is curious that in the pigs with coronary artery occlusion, arrhythmia was reduced not only during REM sleep but also during wakefulness. These investigators cite Baust & Bohnert (6), who found in cats that reduction in sympathetic tone accounts for the slow tonic heart rates during REM sleep, whereas during slow-wave sleep, bradycardia was due to increased parasympathetic tone. However, increased sympathetic tone is certainly an attribute of the awake state. Snyder, Hobson & Goldfrank (109) and others (3, 19) have demonstrated that heart rate and arterial blood pressure are higher during wakefulness than during sleep. There may indeed be hemodynamic concomitants, as well as coronary artery flow changes, linked to neural alterations during sleep stages that influence the electrically unstable ischemic heart.

In human studies the results generally indicate that sleep suppresses ventricular arrhythmia (14, 26, 57, 70, 76, 77, 90, 108, 126). Lown et al (57) found that in 54 subjects undergoing Holter monitoring in their homes, 45 exhibited significant reduction in ventricular ectopic activity during sleep. In a subsequent investigation utilizing electroencephalography in hospital, it was found that suppression of ventricular premature beats occurred during all sleep stages except REM (26). Slow-wave sleep (stages 3 and 4) was most effective in reducing the incidence of arrhythmias. These effects were not dependent on changes in heart rate, because this variable was not significantly altered during the various sleep stages. The frequency of ventricular premature beats during the awake and REM periods was similar. Pickering et al (76, 77) and others (14, 126) have reported results that are comparable to those of Lown and coworkers (26, 57). A beneficial effect of sleep on ventricular electrical stability is also suggested by the observation that sudden cardiac death is unusual during the nocturnal period (31, 72). However, ventricular tachycardia and fibrillation have been noted to occur in association with violent or frightening dreams (56, 86). It nevertheless remains highly inferential that sudden death in sleep occurs mainly during the REM period. Clearly this field of endeavor merits further investigation.

NEUROPHARMACOLOGICAL INVESTIGATIONS

Current evidence indicates that susceptibility to ventricular fibrillation is reduced by decreasing cardiac sympathetic activity and by increasing vagal tone. Various pharmacological agents that favor such a pattern of autonomic outflow protect the heart against ventricular fibrillation; these include clonidine (92), morphine sulfate (27), the digitalis drugs acetylstrophanthidin and ouabain (15), the phenothiazine-like drug ethmozin (62, 93), and bromocriptine (29).

An intriguing new approach involves changing the serum concentration of amino acid precursors of the central neurotransmitters that modulate autonomic nerve traffic. The mammalian brain employs at least four primary monoamine neurotransmitters: dopamine, noradrenaline, adrenaline, and serotonin (17). These are synthesized from tyrosine and tryptophan. Wurtman & Fernstrom (127) have shown that effects of these central neurotransmitters are determined by concentration of their amino acid precursors in the blood, which are in turn related to their dietary intake. Thus, a rationale is provided for modulating cardiac excitability by means of "precursor therapy."

NEUROTRANSMITTER PRECURSORS AND VENTRICULAR VULNERABILITY

There is considerable evidence indicating that accumulation of serotonin in the brain reduces sympathetic neural activity (1, 5, 32). One approach that has been employed to reduce cardiac sympathetic drive involves the administration of tryptophan, an essential dietary amino acid, which regulates serotoninergic neurotransmission in the brain (2). In particular, when tryptophan alone is administered, it is hydroxylated and then decarboxylated to form serotonin throughout the body. Serotonin is then rapidly degraded by monoamine oxidase to 5-hydroxyindole acetic acid. To increase the concentration of central but not peripheral serotonin requires the administration of phenelzine and carbidopa (Figure 4). Phenelzine, by inhibiting monoamine oxidase, favors the accumulation of serotonin wherever it forms. Carbidopa, an L-aromatic amino acid decarboxylase inhibitor, circulates in the periphery but does not cross the blood-brain barrier. In the presence of carbidopa, the decarboxylation of serotonin precursor is selectively diminished peripherally, and therefore serotonin accumulation is largely restricted to the central nervous system.

Rabinowitz & Lown (82) studied the effect of precursor-induced changes in central serotonin on cardiac susceptibility to repetitive extrasystoles, as a measure of vulnerability to ventricular fibrillation. When tryptophan, phenelzine, and carbidopa were given separately, the ventricular threshold for repetitive responses remained unchanged. However, when they were given together, the repetitive extrasystole threshold increased by 50%. When 5-hydroxytryptophan was administered instead of its parent compound tryptophan, thereby bypassing the rate-limiting step of hydroxylation, the threshold increase was accelerated to 1 hr, compared to 2.5 hr after administering the parent compound. The effect of altered brain serotonin on vulnerability appears to be mediated through sympathetic neural activity, because stellectomy but not vagotomy prevents these cardiac electrophysiologic changes (63).

It was also pertinent to examine whether the drug regimen could alter vulnerability to fibrillation during myocardial ischemia by suppressing cardio-cardiac sympathetic reflexes that are activated by acute coronary artery occlusion (52, 63). Indeed, Lehnert et al (46) and Marais et al (63) have demon-

NEUROCHEMICAL MANIPULATION OF PATHWAYS INVOLVED IN
BRAIN SEROTONIN PRODUCTION

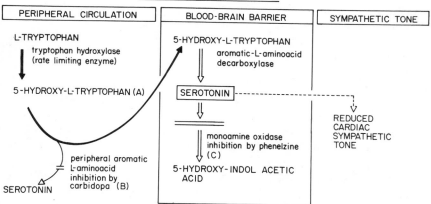

Figure 4 Mechanisms whereby pharmacologic augmentation of brain serotonin levels may result in reduced cardiac sympathetic tone.

strated in separate studies that the drug regimen does significantly reduce the surge in cardiac sympathetic firing rate and the fall in ventricular fibrillation threshold associated with left anterior descending coronary artery occlusion. It is of interest that vulnerability to fibrillation during reperfusion was unaffected, because adrenergic factors do not appear to be involved in the release-reperfusion phenomenon.

Increase in serotoninergic activity can be accomplished without the use of enzyme inhibitors, by administering agents such as melatonin, 5-methoxytryptophol, and 6-chloro-2(1-piperazinyl)-pyrazine(MK-212). Each produced significant increases in vulnerable-period threshold for repetitive electrical activity (12). The antifibrillatory action was unaffected by bilateral vagotomy, but was blocked by the specific serotonin antagonist, metergoline.

FINAL COMMENTS

Many questions remain unanswered regarding the role of behavioral factors in the provocation of cardiac arrhythmias and sudden death. Animal research has increased our understanding of this important health problem. However, limitations in biologic modeling must be acknowledged. First, the unique psychologic repertoire of man is not readily replicable. Important preconditions for sudden death in many victims are psychologic depression, a sense of abandonment, and feelings of alienation. How can these human emotions be simulated in the laboratory? Second, the anatomic substrate for sudden death consists of severe, multivessel coronary artery disease that has evolved over many years. Acute obstruction of a single coronary artery in an experimental animal does not replicate this condition. An additional difficulty is that in animal models, biobehavioral influences on vulnerability are manifest mainly through increased sympathetic neural traffic to the heart. In man, arrhythmias provoked by psychologic stress are not uncommonly impervious to interdiction of sympathetic neural activity. Evidently other pathways or neurotransmitters are involved.

While experimentalists can never hope to replicate the entire spectrum of human emotions, some guidelines from clinical investigations are available. For example, in patients with identifiable psychologic disturbances preceding malignant ventricular arrhythmias, a common affective state observed has been anger (54, 86). Thus it would seem logical in animal studies to focus on aversive paradigms designed to stimulate comparable arousal states.

Sleep is another pertinent behavioral state that has not been adequately studied. Both sleep and sleep deprivation are amenable to modeling in the research laboratory and no doubt would provide significant insights.

In light of growing clinical evidence implicating coronary spasm in the genesis of cardiac arrhythmias (34, 65), the possibility that behavioral stress may result in inappropriate coronary vasoconstriction should be explored. Indeed, the coronary vessels are richly innervated and intense coronary artery vasoconstriction can be induced by adrenergic stimulation in animals (30, 69, 114) and humans (71). If inappropriate coronary vasoconstriction were implicated in the provocation of cardiac arrhythmias during behavioral stress, an extensive armamentarium of coronary vasodilators are already available.

From the vantage point of clinical prophylaxis of sudden cardiac death, a number of approaches are becoming available (Table 2). These derive largely from animal investigations. A promising new avenue for exploring the role of higher nervous activity in the genesis of cardiac arrhythmias draws upon contemporary advances in neurochemistry and psychopharmacology. A particularly intriguing and potentially clinically relevant approach is based on the principle that neural traffic to the heart can be altered by modifying brain neurochemistry through dietary precursor intervention. As we stated in another context: "It may be that pharmacologic treatment for prevention of sudden death should be focused on restraining the neurophysiologic trigger rather than protecting the cardiac target" (59).

ACKNOWLEDGMENT

This study was supported in part by Grants HL-28387 and HL-07776 from the National Heart, Lung, and Blood Institute, National Institutes of Health, US Public Health Service, Bethesda, Maryland, and by the Rappaport Institute of Cardiology.

Table 2   Current approaches for containment of neural triggers for malignant ventricular arrhythmias

Central

    Decreasing cardiac sympathetic tone
      – Neurochemical agents (29, 33, 82, 106, 127)
      – Dietary "precursor therapy" (127)
    Increasing vagal tone
      – Digitalis drugs (15)
      – Exercise conditioning (11, 110)

Peripheral

      – Adrenergic receptor blockade (9, 25, 35, 73, 106)
      – Stellectomy (95–97, 99, 100)
      – Calcium channel blockade (111, 112, 123, 129)

Literature Cited

1. Antonaccio, M. J., Robson, R. D. 1973. Cardiovascular effects of 5-hydroxy-tryptophan in anaesthetized dogs. *J. Pharm. Pharmacol.* 25:495–97
2. Antonaccio, M. J., Robson, R. D. 1975. Centrally-mediated cardiovascular effects of 5-hydroxytryptophan in MAO-inhibited dogs: modification by autonomic antagonists. *Arch. Int. Pharmacodyn.* 213:200–10
3. Baccelli, G., Guazzi, M., Mancia, G., Zanchetti, A. 1969. Neural and non-neural mechanisms influencing circulation during sleep. *Nature* 223:184–85
4. Bassan, M. M., Marcus, H. S., Ganz, W. 1980. The effects of mild-to-moderate mental stress on coronary hemodynamics in patients with coronary artery disease. *Circulation* 62:933–35
5. Baum, T., Shropshire, A. T. 1975. Inhibition of efferent sympathetic nerve activity by 5-hydroxytryptophan and centrally administered 5-hydroxytrypta-mine. *Neuropharmacology* 14:227–33
6. Baust, W., and Bohnert, B. 1969. The regulation of heart rate during sleep. *Exp. Brain Res.* 7:169–80
7. Baust, W., Bohnert, B., Riemann, O. 1969. The regulation of the heart rate during sleep. *Electroencephalogr. Clin. Neurophysiol.* 27:626
8. Bergamaschi, M., Longoni, A. M. 1973. Cardiovascular events in anxiety: Experimental studies in the conscious dog. *Am. Heart J.* 86:385–94
9. Beta-blocker Heart Attack Study Group. 1981. The Beta-blocker heart attack trial. *J. Am. Med. Assoc.* 246:2073–74
10. Billman, G. E., Randall, D. C. 1981. Mechanisms mediating the coronary vascular response to behavioral stress in the dog. *Circ. Res.* 48:214–23
11. Billman, G. E., Schwartz, P. J., Stone, H. L. 1983. The effects of daily exercise on susceptibility to sudden cardiac death: Protection from ventricular fibrillation. *Fed. Proc.* 42:586
12. Blatt, C. M., Rabinowitz, S. H., Lown, B. 1979. Central serotonergic agents raise the repetitive extrasystole threshold of the vulnerable period of the canine ventricular myocardium. *Circ. Res.* 44:723–30
13. Bond, D. D. 1942. Sympathetic and vagal interaction in emotional responses of the heart rate. *Am. J. Physiol.* 138:468–78
14. Brodsky, M., Wu, D., Denes, P., Kanakis, A., Rosen, K. M. 1977. Arrhythmias documented by 24-hour continuous electrocardiographic monitoring in 50 male medical students without apparent heart disease. *Am. J. Cardiol.* 39:390–95
15. Brooks, W. W., Verrier, R. L., Lown, B. 1979. Digitalis drugs and vulnerability to ventricular fibrillation. *Eur. J. Pharmacol.* 57:69–78
16. Cannon, W. B. 1942. Voodoo death. *Am. Anthropologist* 44:169
17. Chalmers, J. P. 1975. Brain amines and models of experimental hypertension. *Circ. Res.* 36:469–80
18. Cobbs, L. A., Baum, R. S., Alvarez, H. III, Schaffer, W. A. 1975. Resuscitation from out-of-hospital ventricular fibrillation: 4 years follow-up. *Circulation* 51/52:III223–35
19. Coccagna, G., Mantovani, M., Brignani, F., Manzini, A., Lugaresi, E. 1971. Arterial pressure changes during spontaneous sleep in man. *Electroencephalogr. Clin. Neurophysiol.* 31:277–81
20. Cohen, D. H., Pitts, L. H. 1968. Vagal and sympathetic components of conditioned cardioacceleration in the pigeon. *Brain Res.* 9:15–31
21. Corbalan, R., Verrier, R., Lown, B. 1974. Psychological stress and ventricular arrhythmias during myocardial infarction in the conscious dog. *Am. J. Cardiol.* 34:692–96
22. Corley, K. C., Mauck, H. P., Shiel, F. O'M. 1975. Cardiac responses associated with "yoked-chair" shock avoidance in squirrel monkeys. *Psychophysiology* 12:439–44
23. Corr, P. B., Gillis, R. A. 1974. Role of the vagus nerves in the cardiovascular changes induced by coronary occlusion. *Circulation* 49:86–97
24. Corr, P. B., Pearle, D. L., Gillis, R. A. 1976. Coronary occlusion site as a determinant of the cardiac rhythm effects of atropine and vagotomy. *Am. Heart J.* 92:741–49
25. Corr, P. B., Sharma, A. D. 1982. Alpha-versus beta-adrenergic influences on dys-rhythmias induced by myocardial ischaemia and reperfusion. In *Advances in Beta-blocker Therapy II*, ed. A. Zanchetti, pp. 163–80. Amsterdam: Excerpta Medica
26. DeSilva, R. A. 1982. Central nervous system risk factors for sudden cardiac death. *Ann. NY Acad. Sci.* 382:143–61
27. DeSilva, R. A., Verrier, R. L., Lown, B. 1978. The effects of psychological stress and vagal stimulation with morphine on vulnerability to ventricular fibrillation (VF) in the conscious dog. *Am. Heart J.* 95:197–203
28. Ernst, F. A., Kordenat, R. K., Sandman,

C. A. 1979. Learned control of coronary blood flow. *Psychosom. Med.* 41:79–85

29. Falk, R. H., DeSilva, R. A., Lown, B. 1981. Reduction in vulnerability to ventricular fibrillation by bromocriptine, a dopamine agonist. *Cardiovasc. Res.* 15:175–80
30. Feigl, E. O. 1983. Coronary physiology. *Physiol. Rev.* 63:1–205
31. Friedman, M., Manwaring, J. H., Rosenman, R. H., Donlon, G., Ortega, P., Grube, S. M. 1973. Instantaneous and sudden deaths. Clinical and pathological differentiation in coronary artery disease. *J. Am. Med. Assoc.* 225:1319–28
32. Galosy, R. A., Clarke, L. K., Vasko. M. R., Crawford, I. L. 1981. Neurophysiology and neuropharmacology of cardiovascular regulation and stress. *Neurosci. Biobehav. Rev.* 5:137–75
33. Gillis, R. A. 1982. Neurotransmitters involved in the central nervous system control of cardiovascular function. In *Circulation, Neurobiology, and Behavior,* ed. O. A. Smith, R. A. Galosy, S. M. Weiss, pp. 41–53. New York: Elsevier
34. Hillis, L. D., Braunwald, E. 1978. Coronary-artery spasm. *N. Engl. J. Med.* 299:695–702
35. Hjalmarson, Å., Elmfeldt, D., Herlitz, J., Holmberg, S., Malék, I., et al. 1981. Effect on mortality of metoprolol in acute myocardial infarction. *Lancet* 2:823–27
36. Hockman, C. H., Mauck, H. P. Jr., Hoff, E. C. 1966. ECG changes resulting from cerebral stimulation: II. A spectrum of ventricular arrhythmias of sympathetic origin. *Am. Heart J.* 71:695–700
37. Hoff, E. C., Kell, J. F. Jr., Carroll, M. N. Jr. 1963. Effects of cortical stimulation and lesions on cardiovascular function. *Physiol. Rev.* 43:68–114
38. James, R. G. G., Arnold, J. M. O., Allen, J. D., Pantridge, J. F., Shanks, R. G. 1977. The effects of heart rate, myocardial ischemia, and vagal stimulation on the threshold for ventricular fibrillation. *Circulation* 55:311–17
39. Johansson, G., Jonsson, L., Lannek, N., Blomgren, L., Linberg, P., Poupa, O. 1974. Severe stress-cardiopathy in pigs. *Am. Heart J.* 87:451–57
40. Jouvet, M. 1969. Biogenic amines and the states of sleep. *Science* 163:32–41
41. Kent, K. M., Smith, E. R., Redwood, D. R., Epstein, S. E. 1973. Electrical stability of acutely ischemic myocardium. Influences of heart rate and vagal stimulation. *Circulation* 47:291–98

42. Kerzner, J., Wolf, M., Kosowsky, B. D., Lown, B. 1973. Ventricular ectopic rhythms following vagal stimulation in dogs with acute myocardial infarction. *Circulation* 47:44–50
43. Kleitman, N. 1963. *Sleep and Wakefulness.* Chicago: Univ. Chicago.
44. Koella, W. P., Feldstein A., Czicman, J. S. 1968. The effect of parachlorophenylalanine on the sleep of cats. *Electroencephalogr. Clin. Neurophysiol.* 25:481–90
45. Kolman, B. S., Verrier, R. L., Lown, B. 1975. The effect of vagus nerve stimulation upon vulnerability of the canine ventricle: Role of sympathetic-parasympathetic interactions. *Circulation* 52:578–85.
46. Lehnert, H., Lombardi, F., Verrier, R. L., Lown, B., Wurtman, R. J. 1983. Suppression of cardio-cardiac sympathetic reflexes during myocardial ischemia by increasing central serotoninergic neuro-transmission. *J. Am. Coll. Cardiol.* 1:696
47. Levy, A. G. 1914. The genesis of ventricular extrasystoles under chloroform: with special reference to consecutive ventricular fibrillation. *Heart* 5:299–334
48. Levy, M. N. 1971. Sympathetic-parasympathetic interactions in the heart. *Circ. Res.* 29:437–45
49. Levy, M. N., Blattberg, B. 1976. Effect of vagal stimulation on the overflow of norepinephrine into the coronary sinus during cardiac sympathetic nerve stimulation in the dog. *Circ. Res.* 38:81–85
50. Levy, M. N., Martin, P. J., Stuesse, S. L. 1981. Neural regulation of the heart beat. *Ann. Rev. Physiol.* 43:443–53
51. Liang, B., Verrier, R. L., Melman, J., Lown, B. 1979. Correlation between circulating catecholamine levels and ventricular vulnerability during psychological stress in conscious dogs. *Proc. Soc. Exp. Biol. Med.* 161:266–69
52. Lombardi, F., Verrier, R. L., Lown, B. 1983. Relationship between sympathetic neural activity, coronary dynamics, and vulnerability to ventricular fibrillation during myocardial ischemia and reperfusion. *Am. Heart J.* 105:958–65
53. Lown, B. 1979. Sudden cardiac death: The major challenge confronting contemporary cardiology. *Am. J. Cardiol.* 43:313–28
54. Lown, B., DeSilva, R. A., Reich, P., Murawski, B. J. 1980. Psychophysiologic factors in sudden cardiac death. *Am. J. Psychiatry* 137:1325–35
55. Lown, B., Kosowsky, B. D., Klein, M. D. 1969. Pathogenesis, prevention, and

treatment of arrhythmias in myocardial infarction. *Circulation* 39/40:IV261–70

56. Lown, B., Temte, J. V., Reich, P., Gaughan, C., Regestein, Q., Hai, H. 1976. Basis for recurring ventricular fibrillation in the absence of coronary heart disease and its management. *N. Engl. J. Med.* 294:623–29

57. Lown, B., Tykocinski, M., Garfein, A., Brooks, P. 1973. Sleep and ventricular premature beats. *Circulation* 48:691–701

58. Lown, B., Verrier, R., Corbalan, R. 1973. Psychologic stress and threshold for repetitive ventricular response. *Science* 182:834–36

59. Lown, B., Verrier, R. L. 1976. Neural activity and ventricular fibrillation. *N. Engl. J. Med.* 294:1165–70

60. McWilliam, J. A. 1887. Fibrillar contraction of the heart. *J. Physiol.* 8:296–310

61. Majid, P. A., Saxton, C., Dykes, J. R. W., Galvin, M. C., Taylor, S. H. 1970. Autonomic control of insulin secretion and the treatment of heart failure. *Br. Med. J.* 4:328–34

62. Mann, D. 1981. Personal communication. This clinical study is currently in progress in the Methodist Hospital, Houston, Texas. *Houston Electrophysiol. Soc. Newsl.*

63. Marais, G. E., Verrier, R. L., Lown, B. 1981. Mechanisms mediating the protective effects of central serotonergic agonists on vulnerability to ventricular fibrillation in the normal and ischemic heart. *Circulation* 64:IV320

64. Martins, J. B., Zipes, D. P. 1980. Epicardial phenol interrupts refractory period responses to sympathetic but not vagal stimulation in canine left ventricular epicardium and endocardium. *Circ. Res.* 47:33–40

65. Maseri, A., Chierchia, S., L'Abbate, A. 1980. Pathogenetic mechanisms underlying the clinical events associated with atherosclerotic heart disease. *Circulation* 62:V3–18

66. Maseri, A., L'Abbate, A., Chierchia, S., Parodi, O., Severi, S., et al. 1979. Significance of spasm in the pathogenesis of ischemic heart disease. *Am. J. Cardiol.* 44:788–92

67. Matta, R. J., Lawler, J. E., Lown, B. 1976. Ventricular electrical instability in the conscious dog. Effects of psychologic stress and beta-adrenergic blockade. *Am. J. Cardiol.* 38:594–98

68. Matta, R. J., Verrier, R. L., Lown, B. 1976. Repetitive extrasystole as an index of vulnerability to ventricular fibrillation. *Am. J. Physiol.* 230:1469–73

69. Mohrman, D. E., Feigl, E. O. 1978.

Competition between sympathetic vasoconstriction and metabolic vasodilation in the canine coronary circulation. *Circ. Res.* 42:79–86

70. Monti, J. M., Folle, L. E., Peluffo, C., Artucio. R., Ortiz, A., et al. 1975. The incidence of premature contractions in coronary patients during the sleep-awake cycle. *Cardiology* 60:257–64

71. Mudge, G. H. Jr., Grossman, W., Mills, R. M., Jr., Lesch, M., Braunwald, E. 1976. Reflex increase in coronary vascular resistance in patients with ischemic heart disease. *N. Engl. J. Med.* 295:1333–37

72. Myers, A., Dewar, H. A. 1975. Circumstances attending 100 sudden deaths from coronary artery disease with coroners' necropsies. *Br. Heart J.* 37:1133–43

73. Norwegian Multicenter Study Group, The. 1981. The timolol-induced reduction in mortality and reinfarction in patients surviving acute myocardial infarction. *N. Engl. J. Med.* 304:801–7

74. Pasyk, S., Walton, J., Pitt, B. 1981. Central opioid mediated coronary and systemic vasoconstriction in the conscious dog. *Circulation* 64:IV41

75. Pfister, B., Imhof, P. R. 1977. Inhibition of adrenaline-induced platelet aggregation by the orally administered alpha-adrenergic receptor blocker phentolamine (Regitine®). *Eur. J. Clin. Pharmacol.* 11:7–10

76. Pickering, T. G., Goulding, L., Cobern, B. A. 1977. Diurnal variations in ventricular ectopic beats and heart rate. *Cardiovasc. Med.* 2:1013–22

77. Pickering, T. G., Johnston, J., Honour, A. J. 1978. Comparison of the effects of sleep, exercise, and autonomic drugs on ventricular extrasystoles, using ambulatory monitoring of electrocardiogram and electroencephalogram. *Am. J. Med.* 65:575–83

78. Pitt, B., Pasyk, S., Walton, J., Grekin, R. 1982. Endogenous arginine vasopressin release in patients with coronary artery spasm. *Circulation* 66:II88

79. Prystowsky, E. N., Jackman, W. M., Rinkenberger, R. L., Heger, J. J., Zipes, D. P. 1981. Effect of autonomic blockade on ventricular refractoriness and atrioventricular nodal conduction in humans. Evidence supporting a direct cholinergic action on ventricular muscle refractoriness. *Circ. Res.* 49:511–18

80. Raab, W. 1966. Emotional and sensory stress factors in myocardial pathology. *Am. Heart J.* 72:538–64

81. Raab, W., Chaplin, J. P., Bajusz, E. 1964. Myocardial necrosis produced in

domesticated rats and in wild rats by sensory and emotional stresses. *Proc. Soc. Exp. Biol. Med.* 116:665–69

82. Rabinowitz, S. H., Lown, B. 1978. Central neurochemical factors related to serotonin metabolism and cardiac ventricular vulnerability for repetitive electrical activity. *Am. J. Cardiol.* 41:516–22

83. Rabinowitz, S. H., Verrier, R. L., Lown, B. 1976. Muscarinic effects of vagosympathetic trunk stimulation on the repetitive extrasystole (RE) threshold. *Circulation* 53:622–27

84. Randall, D. C., Hasson, D. M. 1981. Cardiac arrhythmias in the monkey during classically conditioned fear and excitement. *Pavlov. J. Biol. Sci.* 16:97–107

85. Rayford, C. R., Khouri, E. M., Gregg, D. E. 1965. Effect of excitement on coronary and systemic energetics in unanesthetized dogs. *Am. J. Physiol.* 209: 680–88

86. Reich, P., DeSilva, R. A., Lown, B., Murawski, B. J. 1981. Acute psychological disturbances preceding life-threatening ventricular arrhythmias. *J. Am. Med. Assoc.* 246:233–35

87. Reite, M., Pegram, G. V., Stephens, L. M., Bixler, E. C., Lewis, O. L. 1969. The effect of reserpine and monoamine oxidase inhibitors on paradoxical sleep in the monkey. *Psychopharmacologia* 14: 12–17

88. Richter, C. P. 1957. On the phenomenon of sudden death in animals and man. *Psychosom. Med.* 19:191–98

89. Rosen, M. R., Gelband, H., Hoffman, B. F. 1971. Effects of phentolamine on electrophysiologic properties of isolated canine Purkinje fibers. *J. Pharmacol. Exp. Ther.* 179:586–93

90. Rosenblatt, G., Zwilling, G., Hartmann, E. 1969. Electrocardiographic changes during sleep in patients with cardiac abnormalities. *Psychophysiology* 6:233

91. Rosenfeld, J., Rosen, M. R., Hoffman, B. F. 1978. Pharmacologic and behavioral effects on arrhythmias that immediately follow abrupt coronary occlusion: A canine model of sudden coronary death. *Am. J. Cardiol.* 41:1075–82

92. Rotenberg, F. A., Verrier, R. L., Lown, B., Sole, M. J. 1978. Effects of clonidine on vulnerability to fibrillation in the normal and ischemic canine ventricle. *Eur. J. Pharmacol.* 47:71–79

93. Rozenshtraukh, L. V., Verrier, R. L., Lown, B. 1978. Effect of ethmozine on ventricular arrhythmias during the early and late phases of myocardial infarction. *Newsl. Acad. Med. Sci. Sov. Union* 10:52–57

94. Rushmer, R. F., Smith, O. A. Jr.,

Lasher, E. P. 1960. Neural mechanisms of cardiac control during exertion. *Physiol. Rev.* 40:27–34

95. Schwartz, P. J. 1978. Unilateral stellectomy and dysrhythmias. *Circ. Res.* 43: 939–40

96. Schwartz, P. J. 1980. The long QT syndrome. In *Sudden Death*, ed. H. E. Kulbertus, H. J. J. Wellens, pp. 358–78. The Hague: Martinus Nijhoff

97. Schwartz, P. J., Snebold, N. G., Brown, A. M. 1976. Effects of unilateral cardiac sympathetic denervation on the ventricular fibrillation threshold. *Am. J. Cardiol.* 37:1034–40

98. Schwartz, P. J., Stone, H. L. 1977. Tonic influence of the sympathetic nervous system on myocardial reactive hyperemia and on coronary blood flow distribution in dogs. *Circ. Res.* 41:51–58

99. Schwartz, P. J., Stone, H. L., Brown, A. M. 1976. Effects of unilateral stellate ganglion blockade on the arrhythmias associated with coronary occlusion. *Am. Heart J.* 92:589–99

100. Schwartz, P. J., Verrier, R. L., Lown, B. 1977. Effect of stellectomy and vagotomy on ventricular refractoriness in dogs. *Circ. Res.* 40:536–40

101. Segal, S. A., Gillis, R. A. 1983. Blockade of CNS GABAergic tone causes sympathetic-mediated coronary constriction in cats. *Fed. Proc.* 42:1122

102. Segal, S. A., Pearle, D. L., Gillis, R. A. 1981. Coronary spasm produced by picrotoxin in cats. *Eur. J. Pharmacol.* 76:447–51

103. Skinner, J. E., Lie, J. T., Entman, M. L. 1975. Modification of ventricular fibrillation latency following coronary artery occlusion in the conscious pig. The effects of psychological stress and beta-adrenergic blockade. *Circulation* 51: 656–67

104. Skinner, J. E., Mohr, D. N., Kellaway, P. 1975. Sleep-stage regulation of ventricular arrhythmias in the unanesthetized pig. *Circ. Res.* 37:342–49

105. Skinner, J. E., Reed, J. C. 1981. Blockade of frontocortical-brain stem pathway prevents ventricular fibrillation of ischemic heart. *Am. J. Physiol.* 240:H156–63

106. Skinner, J. E., Verrier, R. L. 1982. Task force report on sudden cardiac death and arrhythmias. See Ref. 33, pp. 309–16

107. Smith, O. A. Jr., Jabbur, S. J., Rushmer, R. F., Lasher, E. P. 1960. Role of hypothalamic structures in cardiac control. *Physiol. Rev.* 40:136–41

108. Smith, R., Johnson, L., Rothfeld, D., Zir, L., Tharp, B. 1972. Sleep and cardiac arrhythmias. *Arch Intern. Med.* 130:751–53

109. Snyder, F., Hobson, J. A., Goldfrank, F. 1963. Blood pressure changes during human sleep. *Science* 142:1313–14
110. Stone, H. L., Billman, G. E., Schwartz, P. J. 1983. Exercise and sudden death. In *The First Year after a Myocardial Infarction*, ed. H. E. Kulbertus, H. J. J. Wellens. New York: Futura
111. Stone, P., Antman, E. 1983. *Calcium Channel Blocking Agents in the Treatment of Cardiovascular Disorders*. New York: Futura
112. Stone, P. H., Antman, E. M., Muller, J. E., Braunwald, E. 1980. Calcium channel blocking agents in the treatment of cardiovascular disorders. Part 2: Hemodynamic effects and clinical applications. *Ann. Intern. Med.* 93:886–904
113. Vatner, S. F., Franklin, D., Higgins, C. B., Patrick, T., White, S., Van Citters, R. L. 1971. Coronary dynamics in unrestrained conscious baboons. *Am. J. Physiol.* 221:1396–1401
114. Vatner, S. F., Higgins, C. B. Braunwald, E. 1974. Effects of norepinephrine on coronary circulation and left ventricular dynamics in the conscious dog. *Circ. Res.* 34:812–23
115. Verrier, R. L., Lombardi, F., Lown, B. 1982. Restraint of myocardial blood flow during behavioral stress. *Circulation* 66: II258
116. Verrier, R. L., Lown, B. 1977. Effects of left stellectomy on enhanced cardiac vulnerability induced by psychologic stress. *Circulation* 55/56:III80
117. Verrier, R. L., Lown, B. 1978. Influence of neural activity on ventricular electrical stability during acute myocardial ischemia and infarction. In *Management of Ventricular Tachycardia: Role of Mexiletine*, ed. E. Sandøe, D. G. Julian, J. W. Bell, pp. 133–50. Amsterdam: Excerpta Medica. Int. Cong. Ser. 458
118. Verrier, R. L., Lown, B. 1978. Sympathetic-parasympathetic interactions and ventricular electrical stability. In *Neural Mechanisms in Cardiac Arrhythmias*, ed. P. J. Schwartz, A. M. Brown, A. Malliani, A. Zanchetti, pp. 75–85. New York: Raven
119. Verrier, R. L., Lown, B. 1979. Influence of psychologic stress on susceptibility to spontaneous ventricular fibrillation during acute myocardial ischemia and reperfusion. *Clin. Res.* 27:570A
120. Verrier, R. L., Lown, B. 1980. Vagal tone and ventricular vulnerability during psychological stress. *Circulation* 62: III176
121. Verrier, R. L., Lown, B. 1981. Autonomic nervous system and malignant cardiac arrhythmias. In *Brain, Behavior, and Bodily Disease, Assoc. Res. Nerv. Ment. Dis.* ed. H. Weiner, M. A. Hofer, A. J. Stunkard, 59:273–91. New York: Raven
122. Verrier, R. L., Lown, B. 1984. Myocardial perfusion and neurally induced cardiac arrhythmias. *Ann. NY Acad. Sci.* In press
123. Verrier, R. L., Raeder, E., Lown, B. 1983. Use of calcium channel blockers after myocardial infarction: Potential cardioprotective mechanisms. In *The First Year After a Myocardial Infarction* ed. H. E. Kulbertus, H. J. J. Wellens. New York: Futura
124. Watanabe, A. M. Besch, H. R. Jr. 1975. Interaction between cyclic adenosine monophosphate and cyclic guanosine monophosphate in guinea pig ventricular myocardium. *Circ. Res.* 37:309–17
125. Watanabe, A. M., McConnaughey, M. M., Strawbridge, R. A., Fleming, J. W., Jones, L. R., Besch, H. R. Jr. 1978. Muscarinic cholinergic receptor modulation of beta-adrenergic receptor affinity for catecholamines. *J. Biol. Chem.* 253:4833–36
126. Winkle, R. A., Lopes, M. G., Fitzgerald, J. W., Goodman, D. J., Schroeder, J. S., Harrison, D. C. 1975. Arrhythmias in patients with mitral valve prolapse. *Circulation* 52:73–81
127. Wurtman, R. J., Fernstrom, J. D. 1975. Control of brain monoamine synthesis by diet and plasma amino acids. *Am. J. Clin. Nutr.* 28:638–47
128. Yoon, M. S., Han, J., Tse, W. W., Rogers, R. 1977. Effects of vagal stimulation, atropine, and propranolol on fibrillation threshold of normal and ischemic ventricles. *Am. Heart J.* 93:60–65
129. Zipes, D. P., Gilmour, R. J. Jr. 1982. Calcium antagonists and their potential role in the prevention of sudden coronary death. *Ann. NY Acad. Sci.* 382:258–88

Ann Rev. Physiol. 1984. 46:177–85

CARDIOVASCULAR RESPONSE TO STRESS IN MAN

J. Alan Herd

Department of Medicine, Baylor College of Medicine and Medical Director, Institute for Preventive Medicine of The Methodist Hospital, Houston, Texas 77030

INTRODUCTION

It is a common observation that arterial blood pressure rises as part of the behavioral response to stressful situations. This observation has drawn many to the conclusion that psychological factors contribute to arterial hypertension. However, the hypothesis that psychological factors contribute to arterial hypertension is not very useful so long as the terms "stress" and "stressful situations" are not well defined. Inevitably, then, any discussion of the cardiovascular response to stress is likely to draw us into defining "stress." By common usage, "stress" implies a psychological effect of some influence that is usually considered undesirable or even harmful in some way. In addition, notions of perception, meaning, and previous experience intrude on anyone's personal use of the term. Although the idiomatic use of the term "stress" is woefully inadequate as a scientific definition, we are unlikely to agree upon a more precise statement of what we mean by "stress." Therefore, I have chosen to focus attention on the physiological and behavioral mechanisms whereby psychological factors might contribute to arterial hypertension.

CARDIOVASCULAR AND RENAL RESPONSES TO PHYSIOLOGICAL AND PSYCHOLOGICAL FACTORS

A form of physical stress that can be well defined is exercise. Both dynamic and static exercise have consistent effects on heart rate, blood pressure, and renal excretion of sodium and potassium. Dynamic exercise has marked effects on cardiovascular function (35), renal blood flow (4), and excretion of water and electrolytes (1) in normotensive human subjects. Prolonged isometric exercise

177

0066-4278/84/0315-0177$02.00

also causes elevations in blood pressure, and subjects with normal blood pressure had an increase in rate of sodium and potassium excretion after prolonged isometric exercise (33). In patients with mild essential hypertension, the changes in heart rate, systolic blood pressure, and diastolic blood pressure were not significantly different from values observed in normotensive subjects, but the rate of sodium and potassium excretion was decreased after isometric exercise. Because patients with early essential hypertension have features suggesting hyperactive sympathetic nervous system activity (12, 13), it is possible that protracted sodium and potassium retention after isometric exercise could be caused by increased renal sympathetic nerve activity in mild essential hypertension.

The first detailed studies of cardiovascular and renal function during psychological testing were performed by Brod and his colleagues (3). They used mental arithmetic as a psychological stimulus administered in both normotensive and hypertensive subjects. During the stimulus of mental arithmetic, the systolic, diastolic, and mean blood pressures rose in association with an increase in cardiac output and a reduction in total peripheral vascular resistance. Renal clearance of para-aminohippurate decreased, indicating an increase in renal vascular resistance; forearm skin temperature fell, indicating skin vasoconstriction; and blood flow through skeletal muscle in the forearm rose to more than six-fold its original value. Cardiovascular and renal function returned to original values within a few minutes after stopping mental arithmetic. Subsequent studies by other investigators (2) also have focused attention on skeletal muscle blood flow, while effects of behavioral stimuli in renal function have been less thoroughly studied.

The influence of psychological stimuli on heart rate and contractility in human subjects has been studied by Obrist and his colleagues (30–32). In one set of experiments, a reaction-time task was imposed in which a visual preparatory signal was followed by an auditory respond signal. A correct and rapid response produced a monetary reward, and a slow or incorrect response occasionally caused delivery of an electrical shock to the leg. During the preparatory phase, heart rate and blood pressure rose, then returned towards baseline until the time of responding occurred. Then heart rate rose approximately 6 bpm until the time that electrical shock might be delivered, while systolic and diastolic blood pressures returned to baseline values. Other investigators (28) reported that human subjects varied markedly in reactivity to psychological stimuli. However, magnitude of individual responses for heart rate, systolic blood pressure, and diastolic blood pressure showed consistency over two experimental sessions separated by an interval of one week.

Individual variability in renal responses to psychological stimuli has been demonstrated in relation to patients with essential hypertension and normal subjects with a family history of hypertension. Hollenberg et al (16) used a nonverbal IQ test to demonstrate the influence of a mild psychological stimulus on arterial blood pressure, heart rate, renal blood flow, plasma renin activity, and plasma aldosterone concentration in normal subjects with no family history of hypertension, in normal subjects who had a parent with hypertension, and in patients with essential hypertension. Transient moderate increases in heart rate and blood pressure were more common in patients with hypertension. Renal blood flow fell in each of the patients with essential hypertension and rose in the majority of subjects with normal blood pressure. Plasma renin activity rose in most patients with essential hypertension and fell in a majority of normal subjects with a negative family history. Both the renal vascular response and the change in plasma renin activity were intermediate in normal subjects in whom family history was positive for hypertension. Results of these studies indicate an abnormality in the control of both the renal circulation and renin release in patients with essential hypertension, and in some normotensive subjects whose parents have hypertension.

Exposure to psychological stimuli also has been shown to reduce urinary excretion of sodium and water. Light et al (24) used a water-loading procedure in young men with normal levels of blood pressure with and without a family history of hypertension and men with borderine levels of systolic hypertension. A reaction-time task with monetary incentives was effective in evoking increases in heart rate and blood pressure. None of the men with normotensive parents reduced their excretion of sodium while performing the task, while those with borderline hypertension or hypertensive parents retained sodium and water. The greatest reductions in excretion were seen in those with the greatest increases in heart rate. Thus, psychological stimuli induced sodium retention in subjects with evidence of increased sympathetic nervous system activity.

PHYSIOLOGICAL AND BEHAVIORAL MECHANISMS INFLUENCING CARDIOVASCULAR FUNCTION

Many comparative studies of sympathetic nervous system activity have been carried out in human subjects with essential hypertension and those with average levels of blood pressure. Although many indicators have been used to estimate relative sympathetic nervous system activity, plasma norepinephrine levels are the physiological variable accepted by most investigators as the most valid measure available in human subjects. Many comparative studies have reported higher levels of norepinephrine in hypertensive groups than in normotensive controls, but the differences have been small when blood has been sampled under resting conditions. However, results of several studies suggest that patients with essential hypertension show exaggerated norepinephrine responses to physiological stimuli associated with orthostasis, isotonic and isometric exercise, exposure to cold, hypoglycemia, hypoxia or pain, and to psychological stimuli eliciting emotional responses such as anxiety or anger (12, 13).

The central nervous system control of sympathetic nervous system activity is complex (21). Catecholamine-containing neurons are located principally in the medullary region of the brain stem and send axons to numerous other regions. Dopamine-containing neurons are located principally in the mid-brain and diencephalon and send fibers to the spinal cord. Most antihypertensive drugs that affect the central nervous system influence synthesis, release, or reuptake of catecholamines. However, results of recent studies have indicated a role for dopaminergic and serotonergic input in the regulation of sympathetic nervous system activity (17, 20, 22, 36, 37, 40). The relation of dopaminergic activity and control of blood pressure has been uncovered by treatment of patients with Bromocriptine, a central and peripheral dopamine agonist (18, 38). This drug has been administered to reduce pituitary secretion of prolactin. It also has been observed to reduce arterial blood pressure in some normotensive subjects (19) and in patients with essential hypertension (18, 39). Bromocriptine reduced arterial blood pressure at rest and during isometric exercise in normotensive subjects and in patients with arterial hypertension (18). Treatment of patients with essential hypertension using Guanfacine, an α-adrenoceptor stimulant drug that acts both centrally and peripherally, produced a marked reduction in blood pressure levels, heart rate, and serum prolactin levels (15). These results obtained using a dopamine agonist and an α-adrenoceptor agonist suggest that both dopamine and norepinephrine may reduce central sympathetic outflow and plasma norepinephrine concentration. Prolactin, itself, is not known to have any central or peripheral effects on cardiovascular function.

Psychological mechanisms influencing cardiovascular responses to stimuli depend upon degree of active coping responses during behavioral challenges (11, 23, 25, 30). Intensity of efforts to cope have been shown to be influenced by the role of perceived controllability (25, 31). Thus, greater changes in heart rate and blood pressure occurred in patients with control over aversive stimuli where they continued their efforts to control them than in subjects without control. However, reduced cardiovascular responses occurred when attempts to control were easy to execute and a favorable outcome was guaranteed (7). Intense efforts to cope are postulated to facilitate sympathetic nervous system activity and to enhance cardiovascular responses to stimuli. Contrada et al (5) reported that subjects provided with an opportunity to avoid aversive stimulation displayed shorter response time latencies than subjects for whom aversive stimulation was unrelated to their performance. Greater reactivity in blood pressure and plasma levels of epinephrine occurred when aversive stimulation was contingent upon reaction-time speed. These investigators also reported that subjects with a Type A behavior pattern who displayed high levels of competitiveness, time urgency, and hostility had higher systolic blood pressure and heart rate responses than subjects displaying a Type B behavior pattern, having less competitiveness, time urgency, and hostility. The results of these experiments indicate that behavior patterns, perception of controllability, and effortful coping all influence the magnitude of cardiovascular responses to behavioral challenge. As a general indication of responsiveness, Light (23) has proposed that subjects with the greatest sympathetic nervous system response to behavioral challenge display greater than average increases in heart rate during effortful coping with behavioral challenge.

Further studies of interactions between task incentives and behavior pattern have been conducted by Blumenthal et al (2). Behavior of subjects was categorized as Type A or B by using a Structured Interview Technique. Results indicated that the presence or absence of explicit incentives affected task performance for subjects with Type A behavior, but not for those with Type B patterns. In particular, those with Type A behavior patterns gave more responses more quickly when offered monetary reward. In contrast, the effects of incentive on cardiovascular responses were observed in subjects with the Type B behavior patterns but not in those with the Type A patterns. Those with the Type A behavior patterns showed increased systolic blood pressure, heart rate, and skeletal muscle vasodilation in both conditions, while those with Type B patterns showed increased heart rate and systolic blood pressure only when incentives were offered. Thus, it would appear that subjects with Type A behavior patterns had increased cardiovascular response under all conditions, whereas those with Type B behavior patterns showed enhanced cardiovascular responses only when the opportunity for reward was made explicit. These results suggest that cardiovascular responses may be dissociated from psychomotor behavior in some individuals more than others.

Evidence that central neurochemical changes may occur in response to psychological factors has been presented in studies of serum prolactin levels. Subjects anticipating anesthesia and surgery have been shown to have increased serum prolactin levels (6). The elevation in serum prolactin levels in anticipation of the surgical procedure was enhanced by administration of a dopaminergic antagonist, Pimozide. Studies of medical students undertaking written examination showed a rise of plasma prolactin levels that continued throughout the examination (29). Results of all these studies are consistent with the observations in spontaneously hypertensive rats in which the dopamine agonist, Bromocriptine, reduced plasma catecholamine levels and plasma renin activity as well as blood pressure following stress of immobilization. These results suggest that cardiovascular, behavioral, and psychological mechanisms may be influenced by central dopaminergic and noradrenergic activity.

GENETIC INFLUENCES ON CARDIOVASCULAR AND RENAL RESPONSES TO PSYCHOLOGICAL FACTORS

An approach to the study of genetic factors is the study of twins. This strategy involves a statistical comparison of the similarities between identical and fraternal twins. Investigations using college-age twins involving a sodium-loading and -depletion protocol produced evidence for a genetic influence on physiological factors that help regulate blood pressure (14).

Additional evidence for a genetic influence on physiological factors has been presented in studies of cardiovascular responses to physiological and psychological stimuli, Manuck et al (26, 27) reported that college-aged males with a parental history of hypertension exhibited higher levels of systolic blood pressure during performance of a frustrating cognitive task than did sons of reportedly normotensive parents. A study by Falkner et al (10) showed that adolescents whose parents were hypertensive had greater heart rate and blood pressure increases during mental arithmetic than normotensive adolescents with a negative family history of hypertension. These adolescents were examined again after a period of several years. Those who had developed sustained essential hypertension had different characteristics at the time of initial evaluation than those whose pressures were closer to the normal range (9). Those with sustained essential hypertension were those with a strong family history of hypertension and a greater cardiovascular response to mental arithmetic compared to the normotensive adolescents with a negative family history. These results suggest that cardiovascular responses to psychological stimuli may have an inherited component. Alternatively, familial influences through environmental factors or learned cardiovascular responses may cause hyperactivity.

Other cardiovascular response characteristics also may have an inherited component or at least a familial component. Subjects with a family history of hypertension have been shown to have a potentiated vascular response to pharmacological stimuli (8). Hollenberg et al (16) demonstrated decreases in renal blood flow and increases in plasma renin activity in patients with essential hypertension during performance of a cognitive task. Both the renal vascular response and the change in plasma renin activity observed in normotensive subjects with a positive family history of hypertension were more like the responses observed in patients with essential hypertension than those observed in normal subjects without a family history of hypertension. In contrast, studies by Parfrey et al (34) showed no differences in cardiovascular responses to prolonged isometric exercise in medical students with and without a family history of hypertension. No differences in blood pressure, heart rate, or rate of sodium and potassium excretion following exercise were observed when sons of normotensive parents were compared to the sons of hypertensive parents. Although results of these experiments were interpreted as a lack of influence by genetic factors, it also is possible that responses to psychological stimuli are influenced by genetic factors, even though renal responses to physiological stimuli such as isometric exercise may not be influenced by heredity.

Family history of hypertension also has been reported to influence relationships between blood pressure, plasma renin activity, and plasma concentration of prolactin. Wessels et al (39) studied the relationship between family history of hypertension and blood pressure, relative body weight, 24-hour urinary sodium, plasma renin activity, and plasma concentration of prolactin and parathormone in 102 healthy male subjects. By dividing the subjects into two groups according to the family history of hypertension, those with a family history had a highly significant positive correlation between mean blood pressure and 24-hour urinary sodium, a significant negative correlation between plasma renin activity and 24-hour urinary sodium, and a significant positive correlation between systolic blood pressure and plasma concentration of prolactin. Thus, a correlation between levels of blood pressure and plasma concentrations of prolactin in subjects with a positive family history of hypertension may indicate some central dopaminergic or noradrenergic mechanism that has an inherited component. It is these central aminergic mechanisms that may confer increased susceptibility to effects of psychological stimuli on cardiovascular responses.

RELATION OF PSYCHOLOGICAL FACTORS TO ARTERIAL HYPERTENSION

Results of studies by many investigators have shown that some patients with arterial hypertension apparently have increased sympathetic nervous system activity. Those patients are more likely to be young people with labile hypertension who have a family history of essential hypertension. They are also more likely to have exaggerated cardiovascular responses to both physiological and psychological stimuli. However, it is not possible at the present time to state whether cardiovascular responsiveness is a cause of hypertension or merely an associated characteristic. Thus, we remain uncertain whether psychological factors increase the risk for developing sustained levels of arterial hypertension.

Prospective studies carried out over several decades could show whether normotensive young adults with exaggerated cardiovascular responses to psychological stimuli have an increased risk of developing sustained arterial hypertension. Ultimately, the demonstration that psychological stimuli increase the risk for sustained arterial hypertension in susceptible individuals would require a clinical trial in which some subjects with exaggerated cardiovascular responses were treated in a way that reduced their exposure to psychological stimuli, their perception of those stimuli, or their cardiovascular response to psychological stimuli. Such a clinical trial is not likely ever to be conducted, and we may be forever uncertain of the consequences that follow the cardiovascular response to stress in man.

Literature Cited

1. Aurell, M. M., Carlsson, G., Grimby, G., Hood, B. 1967. Plasma concentrations and urinary excretion of certain electrolytes during supine work. *J. Appl. Physiol.* 22:633–38

2. Blumenthal, J. A., Lane, J. D., Williams, R. B., McKee, D. C., Haney, T., et al. 1983. Effects of task incentive on cardiovascular response in Type A and Type B individuals. *Psychophysiology* 20:63–70

3. Brod, J., Fencl, V., Hejl, Z., Jirka, J. 1959. Circulatory changes underlying blood pressure elevation during acute emotional stress (mental arithmetic) in normotensive and hypertensive subjects. *Clin. Sci.* 18:269–79

4. Castenfors, J. 1967. Renal function during exercise. *Acta Physiol. Scand.* 70 (Suppl. 293):1–44

5. Contrada, R. J., Glass, D. C., Krakoff, L. R., Krantz, D. S., Kehoe, K., et al. 1982. Effects of control over aversive stimulation and Type A behavior on cardiovascular and plasma catecholamine responses. *Psychophysiology* 19:408–19

6. Corenblum, B., Taylor, P. 1981. Mechanisms of control of prolactin release in response to apprehension stress and anesthesia-surgery stress. *Fert. Steril.* 36: 712–15

7. DeGood, D. E. 1975. Cognitive control factors and vascular stress response. *Psychophysiology* 12:399–401

8. Doyle, A. E., Fraser, R. E. 1961. Vascular reactivity in hypertension. *Circ. Res.* 9:755–58

9. Falkner, B., Kushner, H., Onesti, G., Angelakos, E. T. 1981. Cardiovascular characteristics in adolescents who develop essential hypertension. *Hypertension* 3:521–27

10. Falkner, B., Onesti, G., Angelakos, E. T., Fernandes, M., Langman, C. 1979. Cardiovascular response to mental stress in normal adolescents with hypertensive parents. *Hypertension* 1:23–30

11. Frankenhaeuser, M., Rissler, A. 1970. Effects of punishment on catecholamine release and efficiency of performance. *Psychopharmacologia* 17:378–90

12. Goldstein, D. S. 1981. Plasma norepinephrine during stress in essential hypertension. *Hypertension* 3:551–56

13. Goldstein, D. S. 1983. Plasma catecholamines and essential hypertension: An analytical review. *Hypertension* 5:86–99

14. Grim, C. E., Luft, F. C., Miller, J. Z., Rose, J. R., Christian, J. C. 1980. An approach to the evaluation of genetic influences on factors that regulate arterial blood pressure in man. *Hypertension* 2(Suppl. I):1–34

15. Hauger-Klevene, J. H., Pinkas, M. B., Gerber, S. 1981. Blood pressure and prolactin: Effects of Guanfacine. Three year follow-up study. *Hypertension* 3(Suppl. II):II222–25

16. Hollenberg, N. K., Williams, G. H., Adams, D. F. 1981. Essential hypertension: Abnormal renal vascular and endocrine responses to a mild psychological stimulus. *Hypertension* 3:11–17

17. Janowsky, A., Okada, F., Manier, D. H., Applegate, C. D., Sulser, F. 1982. Role of serotonergic input in the regulation of the β-adrenergic receptor-coupled adenylate cyclase system. *Science* 218: 900–01

18. Kaye, S. B., Shaw, K. M., Ross, E. J. 1976. Bromocriptine and hypertension (letter to the editor). *Lancet* 1:1176–77

19. Kolloch, R., Kobayaski, K., DeQuattro, V. 1980. Dopaminergic control of sympathetic tone and blood pressure: Evidence in primary hypertension. *Hypertension* 2:390–94

20. Kolloch, R. E., Stumpe, K. O., Ismer, U., Kletzky, O., DeQuattro, V. 1981. *Clin. Sci.* 61(Suppl.):231s–34

21. Korner, P. I., Angus, J. A. 1981. Central nervous control of blood pressure in relation to antihypertensive drug treatment. *Pharm. Ther.* 13:321–56

22. Kuhn, D. M., Wolf, W. A., Lovenberg, W. 1980. Review of the role of central serotonergic neuronal system in blood pressure regulation. *Hypertension* 2:243–55

23. Light, K. C. 1981. Cardiovascular responses to effortful active coping: Implications for the role of stress in hypertension development. *Psychophysiology* 18:216–25

24. Light, K. C., Koepke, J. P., Obrist, P. A., Willis, P. W. 1983. Psychological stress induces sodium and fluid retention in men at high risk for hypertension. *Science* 220:429–31

25. Light, K. C., Obrist, P. A. 1980. Cardiovascular response to stress: Effects of opportunity to avoid shock, shock experience, and performance feedback. *Psychophysiology* 17:243–52

26. Manuck, S. B., Giordani, B., McQuaid, K. J., Garrity, S. J. 1981. Behaviorally induced cardiovascular reactivity among sons of reported hypertensive and normotensive parents. *J. Psychosom. Res.* 25:261–69

27. Manuck, S. B., Proietti, J. M. 1982. Parental hypertension and cardiovascular

response to cognitive and isometric challenge. *Psychophysiology*. 19:481–89

28. Manuck, S. B., Schaefer, D. C. 1978. Brief Communication. Stability of individual differences in cardiovascular reactivity. *Physiol. Behav*. 21:675–78

29. Nguyen, N. U., Dumoulin, G., Henriet, M. T., Wolf, J. P., Berthelay, S. 1982. Influence d'une activite intellectuelle associee ou non a une charge emotionnelle sur la prolactinemie chez l'homme. *C. R. Soc. Biol*. 176:314–18

30. Obrist, P. A. 1976. The cardiovascular-behavioral interaction—as it appears today. *Psychophysiology* 13:95–107

31. Obrist, P. A., Gaebelein, C. J., Teller, E. S., Langer, A. W., Grignolo, A., et al. 1978. The relationship among heart rate, carotid dP/dt, and blood pressure in humans as a function in the type of stress. *Psychophysiology* 15:102–15

32. Obrist, P. A., Lawler, J. E., Howard, J. L., Smithson, K. W., Martin, P. L., et al. 1974. Sympathetic influences on cardiac rate and contractility during acute stress in humans. *Psychophysiology* 11:405–27

33. Parfrey, P. S., Wright, P., Ledingham, J. M. 1981. Prolonged isometric exercise. Part I: Effect on circulation and on renal excretion of sodium and potassium in mild essential hypertension. *Hypertension* 3:182–87

34. Parfrey, P. S., Wright, P., Ledingham, J. M. 1981. Prolonged isometric exercise. Part II: Effect on circulation and on renal excretion of sodium and potassium in young males genetically predisposed

to hypertension. *Hypertension* 3:188–91

35. Smith, E. E., Guyton, A. C., Manning, R. D., White, R. J. 1976. Integrated mechanisms of cardiovascular response and control during exercise in the normal human. *Prog. Cardiovasc. Dis*. 18:423–43

36. Sowers, J. R., Golub, M. S., Berger, M. E., Whitfield, L. A. 1982. Dopaminergic modulation of pressor and hormonal responses in essential hypertension. *Hypertension* 4:424–30

37. Sowers, J. R., Nyby, M., Jasberg, K. 1982. Dopaminergic control of prolactin and blood pressure. Altered control in essential hypertension. *Hypertension* 4:431–37

38. Stumpe, K. O., Higuchi, M., Kulloch, R., Kruck, F., Vetter, H. 1977. Hyperprolactinemia and antihypertensive effect of Bromocriptine in essential hypertension: Identification of abnormal central dopamine control. *Lancet* 2:211–14

39. Wessels, F., Hoffman, D., Wagner, H., Zumkley, H. 1981. Influence of family history of hypertension on the relationships between blood pressure, body weight, electrolyte metabolism, renin, prolactin, and parathormone. *Clin. Sci*. 61:Suppl., pp. 359–62

40. Whitfield, L., Sowers, J. R., Tuck, M. L., Golub, M. S. 1980. Dopaminergic control of plasma catecholamine and aldosterone responses to acute stimuli in normal man. *J. Clin. Endocrin. Metab*. 51:724–29

Ann. Rev. Physiol. 1984. 46:187–97

CLASSICAL CONDITIONING OF CARDIOVASCULAR RESPONSES

D. H. Cohen

Department of Neurobiology and Behavior, State University of New York at Stony Brook, Stony Brook, New York 11794

D. C. Randall

Department of Physiology and Biophysics, University of Kentucky, Lexington, Kentucky 40536

INTRODUCTION

Our appreciation of interactions between behavior and the cardiovascular system has increased remarkably in recent years (13, 19, 42). This includes the accumulation of evidence that specific patterns of cardiovascular adjustment accompany specific behaviors and that such adjustments are generally appropriate to the metabolic demands of those behaviors (19, 27). Moreover, cardiovascular adjustments can be learned, allowing them to occur in anticipation of behavior, as in exercise (5). Paralleling this literature on behavioral-cardiovascular interactions have been significant advances in our knowledge of the neural pathways that regulate cardiovascular activity (16, 25), and the convergence of these two directions of research has established a firm foundation for investigating environmental influences on the cardiovascular system.

As in many areas of biology, advances in understanding complex phenomena frequently follow the development of simpler model systems. A particularly effective experimental model for studying the relationship between behavior and cardiovascular activity is classical (Pavlovian) conditioning. The advantages of this paradigm are numerous and include: (*a*) precise stimulus control; (*b*) stimulus-locked cardiovascular responses; (*c*) rapid establishment of reliable cardiovascular responses; (*d*) the capability of using instrumented,

0066-4278/84/0315-0187$02.00

awake animals; and (*e*) a large body of literature on the relevant behavioral variables. In this brief review we focus upon the peripheral and central autonomic control of classically conditioned changes in cardiac chronotropism, dromotropism, and inotropism, as well as upon the vascular dynamics in the renal and coronary beds. The emphasis is upon studies published since the extensive review of Galosy et al (25). This review is highly selective, and we offer a prefatory apology to the investigators whose research is not cited.

NATURE OF CONDITIONED CARDIOVASCULAR RESPONSES

In cardiovascular conditioning one systematically pairs a "neutral" stimulus (conditioned stimulus—CS) that elicits either no cardiovascular response or a minimal one with another stimulus (unconditioned stimulus—US) that evokes a vigorous cardiovascular response (unconditioned response—UR). After a sufficient number of such CS-US pairings the CS acquires the capability of reliably eliciting a cardiovascular response (conditioned response—CR) that is not necessarily identical to that elicited by the US. Simply stated, a temporal contingency between the CS and US has been learned, such that the previously neutral CS now evokes cardiovascular changes in anticipation of the US.

For some years it has been known that changes in heart rate and arterial blood pressure can be classically conditioned (e.g. 20, 22). Moreover, such responses can be established in a wide range of phylogenetic classes, including fish, birds, and mammals. The rules that govern cardiovascular conditioning are the same as those that have been extensively described in the general literature on classical conditioning (e.g. 17).

It is important to appreciate that in any conditioning situation the CS will evoke an ensemble of responses that generally can be viewed as goal-directed. For example, if an innocuous CS such as light or sound is paired with a nociceptive stimulus such as shock (aversive or defensive conditioning), the CS elicits a set of responses that collectively can be designated as escape or avoidance behavior, even though the experimental situation may not permit achievement of that goal. The conditioned cardiovascular response pattern in this situation is appropriate to escape or avoidance behavior—including increases in cardiac output, arterial blood pressure, and blood flow in the active muscle beds. Since the cardiovascular response is appropriate to the somatomotor behavior, it is generally predictable. For instance, rabbits characteristically freeze in defensive conditioning, and thus the conditioned heart-rate change is bradycardia. In contrast, many animals such as dogs and pigeons show vigorous escape behavior, and, appropriately, the conditioned heart-rate change is tachycardia. This relationship of the cardiovascular response pattern to the somatomotor behavior is nicely demonstrated in the rat, where the direction of the heart-rate change can be manipulated experimentally (32). If the rat is unrestrained, permitting escape behavior, conditioned tachycardia occurs. In contrast, the restrained rat shows bradycardia as a CR. Another example in this context involves conditioning of leg flexion in the cat established by systematically pairing a neutral stimulus with shock to the feet (6). Early in training cats tend to freeze in response to the CS, and this is accompanied by bradycardia. However, as conditioned leg flexion develops the conditioned bradycardia converts to a tachycardia. Thus, there is mounting evidence to support the hypothesis that conditioned cardiovascular responses are appropriate to and can, in fact, anticipate conditioned somatomotor responses (19).

CONDITIONING OF CARDIAC CHRONOTROPISM, DROMOTROPISM, INOTROPISM, AND OF SELECTED ORGAN VASCULAR RESISTANCES: PERIPHERAL AUTONOMIC CONTROL

Control of Chronotropism (Heart Rate)

Cohen (11) reviewed the literature through 1974 concerning the relative vagal and sympathetic contributions to conditioned heart-rate change, and Galosy et al (25) reviewed this literature through 1980. Both reviews conclude that conditioned chronotropic changes usually involve the synergistic action of sympathetic and parasympathetic cardiac innervations. Vagal influences may be more prominent in conditioned bradycardia, while changes in sympathetic outflow may prevail during conditioned tachycardia. However, regardless of the direction of heart-rate change, the shortest latency change appears to be mediated by the vagal innervation. Furthermore, early in training the changes in sympathetic outflow seem more prominent, while later in training either source of cardiac innervation seems capable of mediating a vigorous heart-rate CR.

The more recent contributions to this literature have largely derived from studies utilizing chronically instrumented dogs and monkeys. Billman & Randall (4) found that aversively conditioned tachycardia in dogs is almost eliminated by β_1-adrenergic blockade with metoprolol, with almost no change in baseline heart rate. In similar studies, Schoenfeld and his colleagues (28, 40) varied dose levels and combinations of propranolol, atropine, and phentolamine in rhesus monkeys. Atropine and propranolol each produced dose-dependent reductions in conditioned tachycardia. Using the conditioned emotional response (CER) paradigm, Smith et al (44) reported that propranolol blocked CS-evoked tachycardia in the baboon.

These findings certainly support earlier conclusions that a major contribution to aversively conditioned tachycardia is increased sympathetic outflow, and this has now been directly demonstrated with recordings from single sympathetic cardiac postganglionic neurons during conditioning (14). The more recent studies are also generally consistent with the previous conclusion of a synergistic decrease in vagal inhibition of the heart. However, recent results from the monkey (37, 40) and perhaps dog (4) suggest that, while vagal activity decreases early in the CS period, it may increase toward the end of the CS. In the pigeon, direct recording of the activity of vagal cardiac neurons during conditioned tachycardia indeed shows an initial decrease in discharge at CS onset, followed by a return toward baseline discharge levels later in the CS period (26).

In contrast to the pigeon, dog, and monkey, rabbits show a conditioned bradycardia at CS onset. Administration of 6-hydroxydopamine hydrobromide attenuates the overall conditioned bradycardia, although it does not markedly alter the immediate heart-rate decrease (1). In contrast, administration of methylatropine significantly attenuates the bradycardia, leading to the conclusion that both vagal and sympathetic inputs contribute to the conditioned bradycardia.

Appetitive conditioning in the dog, accomplished by delivering food during the last 30 seconds of a 1-minute CS, produces a modest tachycardia (41). Administration of propranolol eliminates this CR, suggesting that, in contrast to aversive conditioning, the vagal innervation plays no demonstrable role. It should be noted, however, that the UR, also tachycardia, remained relatively intact following β-adrenergic blockade.

Control of Dromotropism (A-V Nodal Conduction)

The canine appetitive conditioning experiments cited above (41) also examined the neural control of atrio-ventricular (A-V) transmission. This was accomplished by electrically pacing the right atrium. The discrepancy between the paced atrial rate and the associated ventricular rate ("mean differences") served as an index of the fidelity of A-V transmission; the smaller the difference, the closer a 1:1 ratio of atrial vs ventricular beats. A relatively large difference score for the control period indicated that the paced atrial impulse was not faithfully conducted to the ventricles. This atrio-ventricular block may be attributed to the large negative dromotropic effect exerted by the vagus nerve in resting dog. The CR consisted of a significant decrease in the mean difference, followed by a further decrease during the US (food delivery). Propranolol administration did not alter the control mean difference, eliminated the CR, and sharply attenuated the UR. The authors conclude that conditioned increases in sympathetic outflow during the CS enhance the fidelity of A-V transmission.

Control of Ventricular Inotropism (Contractility)

Insofar as the maximal rate of rise of left ventricular pressure $[d(LVP)/dt_{max}]$ is a reliable index of myocardial inotropic state, recent experiments have confirmed that classically conditioned increases in sympathetic outflow augment contractility. β-blockade with metoprolol virtually eliminates conditioned increases in $d(LVP)/dt_{max}$ during aversive conditioning in the dog (4). Similarly, propranolol eliminates appetitively conditioned increases in this same variable (41). The remaining unconditioned increases in $d(LVP)/dt_{max}$ were a fraction of those prior to β-blockade. Other related experiments in the dog (35) demonstrate that conditioned changes in the maximal rate of fall of left ventricular pressure are also directly and/or indirectly linked to increased sympathetic outflow. Although more difficult to interpret in terms of ionotropic state, recent experiments using ultrasound segment-length measurements during appetitive conditioning in the baboon (38) report modest changes in end-diastolic segment length and shortening. Infusion of phenylephrine as a control for the increase in arterial blood pressure during conditioning supported the hypothesis that the CS evoked a conditioned augmentation in myocardial contractility mediated by increased sympathetic outflow.

Control of Coronary and Renal Vascular Beds

Recent experiments in dogs and nonhuman primates have examined flow in the coronary and renal vascular beds during conditioning. The CS was a 30 sec. tone followed by a 1 sec. electric shock as a US. In dogs, changes in left circumflex coronary blood flow were measured with Doppler flow transducers, and a CR occurred that consisted of a decrease in flow 5–10 sec after CS onset, followed by increased flow later in the CS period (4). Late diastolic coronary vascular resistance first increased and then decreased, although one dog showed a monotonic increase (3). The conditioned increases in coronary vascular resistance were converted to decreases after α-adrenergic blockade with phentolamine. These data indicate that aversive conditioning induces a neurally mediated coronary vasoconstriction that, though normally transient, may endure longer in behaviorally susceptible individuals.

Smith et al (44) used the CER paradigm to study the renal circulation in the baboon; in this behavioral situation the subject was pressing a lever for food when the CS was presented. They observed a decrease in renal blood flow within seconds of CS onset, a CR that did not occur with denervated kidneys. There was a second decrease in flow later in the CS period, and this response survived denervation and is thus tentatively ascribed to increased levels of circulating epinephrine. Conditioned changes in blood flow in these and other vascular beds have also been examined in rhesus monkeys (36), and the results raise the possibility of active, sympathetic adrenergic vasodilation in skeletal muscle during aversive conditioning.

As reviewed elsewhere (39), studies of conditioned changes in coronary and renal flow may have important implications for the etiology of certain cardiovascular diseases.

NEURAL CONTROL IN CARDIOVASCULAR CONDITIONING

To achieve an understanding of the neural control of conditioned cardiovascular responses, it is first necessary to delineate the neural pathways mediating such responses (12, 19). At present, systematic information in this regard is largely restricted to conditioned heart rate change in the pigeon, with only scattered reports on the neural structures involved in other species and for other conditioned cardiovascular responses. Consequently, neurophysiological data are available primarily for the pigeon (14, 15).

Relevant Neural Pathways

The final common path for conditioned cardiovascular responses consists of the preganglionic and postganglionic sympathetic and parasympathetic neurons that influence the heart and vasculature (11). Much of the literature in this regard is based upon experiments involving pharmacological blockade and/or peripheral denervation, and this has been reviewed in an earlier section.

Given characterization of the final common path for a conditioned cardiovascular response, the subsequent task in delineating the relevant neural circuitry is to identify the descending pathways that ultimately influence the involved preganglionic neurons. This has been accomplished most comprehensively for conditioned heart rate change in the pigeon (12). In that system a descending pathway has been described that must be intact for expression of the heart rate CR. This pathway begins in a region of the avian amygdalar homologue that gives rise to a well-defined tract terminating in the posteromedial hypothalamus. From the hypothalamus the pathway maintains a ventromedial course through the rostral pons, shifting to a ventrolateral position in the medulla. As the pathway traverses the ventrolateral medulla, fibers (possibly collaterals) course dorsomedially to access (not necessarily monosynaptically) the cells of origin of the vagal cardiac preganglionics. The main descending pathway continues caudally through ventrolateral medulla to the spinal cord, where it is located in the lateral funiculus. From the lateral funiculus fibers enter the spinal gray to synapse either directly upon sympathetic preganglionic neurons or to influence them via spinal interneurons. The above describes the trajectory of the pathway from the amygdala to the preganglionic neurons. For some segments of the pathway the precise connectivity is established, whereas for others only the trajectory is specified.

This pathway can be used as a template for summarizing the literature on central pathways involved in cardiovascular conditioning in mammals. Analogous to the pigeon, conditioned heart-rate change in the rabbit (bradycardia) also involves the amygdala. Kapp et al (29, 30) reported that lesions of the central nucleus of the amygdala attenuate the conditioned bradycardia and modify its topography. To pursue the amygdalar involvement further, β-adrenergic agonists and antagonists were injected into the central nucleus (23). Propranolol significantly impaired the development of the CR, while combined injection of propranlol and isoproterenol did not. The authors thus hypothesize that β-adrenergic receptors within the central nucleus participate in CR development. In a related series of experiments (24) it was reported that opiate receptors in the central nucleus are also involved in mediating conditioned bradycardia in the rabbit.

Beyond the amygdala, no consistent story has yet emerged on possible involvement in cardiovascular conditioning of other hemispheric structures. Septal lesions have been described as having various effects on conditioned bradycardia in the rabbit (34), but they do not affect conditioned tachycardia in the pigeon (18). Extensive hippocampal lesions are reported to attenuate conditioned bradycardia in the rabbit (7), but a subsequent study (9) suggested that damage to the overlying neocortex might account for this effect. The CR might in fact be enhanced, rather than attenuated, if damage is restricted to the hippocampus (9). In rats, hippocampal lesions are reported to affect only the topography of the heart-rate CR (33), whereas in pigeons such lesions have no effect on heart-rate conditioning (10). Possible involvement of the cingulate cortex in heart-rate conditioning in the rabbit has also been reported (8). Thus, the amygdala has clearly been implicated in heart-rate conditioning in both the pigeon and the rabbit. Involvement of other limbic structures is a possibility, but further investigation is necessary to clarify this issue.

Other mammalian studies of the descending pathways primarily involve the hypothalamus. In baboons, bilateral hypothalamic lesions just rostral to the columns of the fornix abolish the cardiovascular components of the CER (43). Results from the rabbit (21) are consistent with this finding, since lateral hypothalamic lesions decreased the magnitude of conditioned bradycardia. However, in this study, compromise of the heart-rate CR is hypothesized to result from interruption of ascending, rather than descending, pathways.

In brief, considerable investigation is yet required on the descending pathways that mediate conditioned cardiovascular responses, particularly in mammals. At present, the pathway described for conditioned heart-rate change in the pigeon can serve as a working hypothesis, since the limited mammalian literature is largely consistent with it. However, a description of the descending pathways is but a start, because it is also necessary to delineate the pathways transmitting the CS and US information if one is to undertake rigorous neurophysiological analyses of the relevant circuitry (12). Less attention has been directed toward these segments of the neural circuitry, because they are probably not unique to conditioned cardiovascular responses. In contrast, the descending pathways may well be, because there are frequent reports of lesions that compromise conditioned cardiovascular responses without affecting conditioned somatomotor responses (e.g. 21, 42).

Neurophysiological Analysis

Neurophysiological studies of structures involved in cardiovascular conditioning have been undertaken only recently. The amygdala and hypothalamus have received the most attention in mammalian investigations. In the rabbit, multiple-unit activity has been recorded during conditioning in the central nucleus of the amygdala (2), and short latency increases in unit activity at CS onset were found at some electrode placements. In a single-unit analysis of the ventromedial and perifornical hypothalamic nuclei of the rabbit (31), it was found that somewhat over 40% of the neurons in these structures showed modification of their CS-evoked discharge over conditioning. Moreover, many of these neurons responded to both the CS and US.

In the pigeon model system, cellular neurophysiological studies have been directed toward the sensory and motor peripheries of the identified pathways, based on the rationale that it is difficult to interpret changes in more central structures without first characterizing training-induced modification of their inputs (15). Single-unit recordings of the activity of vagal preganglionic (14, 26) and sympathetic postganglionic (14) cardiac neurons have demonstrated the following. (a) These "cardiac motoneurons" are initially responsive to the CS, and conditioning increases the probability of occurrence and magnitude of the CS-evoked response. (b) The vagal and sympathetic cardiac innervations act synergistically, since over conditioning the CS-evoked sympathetic discharge increases and the CS-evoked decrease in vagal activity is enhanced. (c) The increase in the sympathetic outflow is the primary contributor to the conditioned heart-rate change. (d) The latencies of these CS-evoked responses are surprisingly short, approximately 60–80 msec for the vagal response and 100 msec for the sympathetic response. (e) The motoneuronal responses consist most prominently of a phasic component of restricted duration.

Given these data for the motoneurons, a description of the response characteristics of the retinal ganglion cells (the CS in this system is visual) allows estimation of the central processing time for the heart-rate CR. The retinal output consists primarily of a phasic burst at CS onset with a minimum latency of 18 msec and a duration of 80 msec (14). Thus, one can infer a minimal central processing time of approximately 60 msec for the vagal component of the CR and 80 msec for the sympathetic component (14). This processing time is surprisingly short and suggests that the entire pathway mediating the CR may be more analyzable than might have been anticipated.

The most recent focus of investigation of the pigeon model system has been on the visual pathways that transmit the CS information (15). These studies have shown that the CS pathways are not merely input lines, but show training-induced modification of CS-evoked discharge during heart-rate conditioning. Although the retinal output does not change, robust modification is seen as peripherally as the avian lateral geniculate nucleus. These modifiable neurons all receive convergent US information, and the nature of the US input appears more important in determining whether modification occurs than the nature of the CS input. Most recently it has been shown that the US input associated with cellular changes during conditioning arises in the locus coeruleus (15).

These findings have numerous implications. The most important for the present review is that the pathways mediating conditioned cardiovascular changes may show training-induced modification at most, if not all, of their central relays. Consequently a rigorous understanding of the information processing in the relevant circuitry during cardiovascular conditioning requires a description beginning at the sensory periphery and proceeding systematically centrally. Without this, changes during conditioning in central structures are not easily interpreted.

CONCLUDING COMMENTS

The field of "cardiovascular neurobiology" (16) is in an exciting developmental stage. Behavioral studies are rapidly expanding our perspective on the extent to which learning can indeed influence cardiovascular activity through rather specific response patterns. Furthermore, classical conditioning methods applied to the study of learned cardiovascular changes are allowing the development of highly effective models for investigating the neural mediation of such changes. It is important at this time that many such models be developed, beginning with a delineation or mapping of the relevant neural pathways from the sensory to the motor peripheries. With an adequate repertoire of such models, we can look forward to answering many fundamental questions concerning the influence of various environmental factors on the cardiovascular system.

Literature Cited

1. Albiniak, B. A., Powell, D. A. 1980. Peripheral autonomic mechanisms and Pavlovian conditioning in the rabbit (*Oryctolagus cuniculus*). *J. Comp. Physiol. Psychol.* 94:1101–13
2. Applegate, C. C., Frysinger, R. C., Kapp, B. S., Gallagher, M. A. 1982. Multiple unit activity recorded from amygdala central nucleus during Pavlovian heart rate conditioning in rabbit. *Brain Res.* 238:457–62
3. Billman, G. E., Randall, D. C. 1980. Classical aversive conditioning of coronary blood flow in mongrel dogs. *Pavlovian J. Biol. Sci.* 15:93–101
4. Billman, G. E., Randall, D. C. 1981. Mechanisms mediating the coronary vascular response to behavioral stress in the dog. *Circ. Res.* 48:214–23
5. Bolme, P., Novotny, J. 1969. Conditional reflex activation of the sympathetic cholinergic vasodilator nerves in the dog. *Acta Physiol. Scand.* 77:58–67
6. Bruner, A. 1969. Reinforcement strength in classical conditioning of leg flexion, freezing, and heart rate in cats. *Cond. Reflex.* 4:61–80
7. Buchanan, S. L., Powell, D. A. 1980. Divergencies in Pavlovian conditioned heart rate and eyeblink responses produced by hippocampectomy in the rabbit (*Oryctolagus cuniculus*). *Behav. Neur. Biol.* 30:20–38
8. Buchanan, S. L., Powell, D. A. 1982. Cingulate cortex: Its role.in Pavlovian conditioning. *J. Comp. Physiol. Psychol.* 96:755–74
9. Buchanan, S. L., Powell, D. A. 1982. Hippocampal lesions and Pavlovian cardiovascular conditioning. *Pavlovian J. Biol. Sci.* 17:158–64
10. Cohen, D. H. 1967. The hyperstriatal region of the avian forebrain: A lesion study of possible functions, including its role in cardiac and respiratory conditioning. *J. Comp. Neurol.* 131:559–70
11. Cohen, D. H. 1974. Analysis of the final common path for heart rate conditioning. In *Cardiovascular Psychophysiology*, ed. P. A. Obrist, A. H. Black, J. Brener, L. V. DiCara, 7:117–35. Chicago: Aldine. 662 pp.
12. Cohen, D. H. 1980. The functional neuroanatomy of a conditioned response. In *Neural Mechanisms of Goal-Directed Behavior and Learning*, ed. R. F. Thompson, L. H. Hicks, V. B. Shvyrkov, 19:283–302. New York: Academic. 639 pp.
13. Cohen, D. H. 1981. Cardiovascular neurobiology: The substrate for biobehavioral approaches to hypertension. In *Hypertension: Biobehavioral and Epidemiological Aspects*, pp. 93–103. Bethesda, MD: NIH Pub. 82–2015. 220 pp.
14. Cohen, D. H. 1982. Central processing time for a conditioned response in a vertebrate model system. In *Conditioning: Representation of Involved Neural Functions*, ed. C. D. Woody, 26:517–34. New York: Plenum. 748 pp.
15. Cohen, D. H. 1983. Sites of modification during conditioning in a vertebrate model system: Plasticity of (visual) sensory pathways. In *Primary Neural Substrates of Learning and Behavioral Change*, ed. D. L. Alkon, J. Farley. Cambridge: Cambridge Univ. In press
16. Cohen, D. H., Cabot, J. B. 1979. Toward a cardiovascular neurobiology. *Trends in Neurosci.* 2:273–76
17. Cohen, D. H., Goff, D. M. 1978. Conditioned heart rate change in the pigeon: Analysis and prediction of acquisition patterns. *Physiol. Psychol.* 6:127–41
18. Cohen, D. H., Goff, D. G. 1978. Effect of avian basal forebrain lesions, including septum, on heart rate conditioning. *Brain Res. Bull.* 3:311–18
19. Cohen, D. H., Obrist, P. A. 1975. Interactions between behavior and the cardiovascular system. *Circ. Res.* 37:693–706
20. Dykman, R. A., Gantt, W. H. 1956. Relation of experimental tachycardia to amplitude of motor activity and intensity of the motivating stimulus. *Am. J. Physiol.* 185:495–98
21. Francis, J., Hernandez, L. L., Powell, D. A. 1981. Lateral hypothalamic lesions: Effects on Pavlovian cardiac and eyeblink conditioning in the rabbit. *Brain Res. Bull.* 6:155–63
22. Fronkova, K., Ehrlich, W., Slegr, L. 1957. Die Kreislauganderung beim Hunde wahrend des bedingten und unbedingten Nahrung-reflexes und seiner Hemmung. *Pflügers Arch.* 263:704–12
23. Gallagher, M., Kapp, B. S., Frysinger, R. C., Rapp, P. R. 1980. β-adrenergic manipulation in amygdala central N. alters rabbit heart rate conditioning. *Pharmacol. Biochem. Behav.* 12:419–26
24. Gallagher, M., Kapp, B. S., McNall, C. L., Pascoe, J. P. 1981. Opiate effects in the amygdala central nucleus on heart rate conditioning in rabbits. *Pharmacol. Biochem. Behav.* 14:497–505
25. Galosy, R. A., Clarke, L. K., Vasko, M. R., Crawford, I. L. 1981. Neurophysiology and neuropharmacology of cardiovascular regulation and stress. *Neurosci. Biobehav. Rev.* 5:137–75

26. Gold, M. R., Cohen, D. H. 1981. Modification of the discharge of vagal cardiac neurons during learned heart rate change. *Science* 214:345–47
27. Hilton, S. M. 1970. Critique of current ideas of the nervous system control of circulation. In *Cardiovascular Regulation in Health and Disease,* ed. C. Bartorelli, A. Zanchetti, pp. 57–62. Milano: Inst. Rech. Cardiovasc. 339 pp.
28. Kadden, R. M., Schoenfeld, W. N., McCullough, M. R., Steele, W. A., Tremont, P. J. 1980. Classical conditioning of heart rate and blood pressure in *Macaca mulatta. J. Autonomic Nervous System* 2:131–42
29. Kapp, B. S., Frysinger, R. C., Gallagher, M., Haselton, J. R. 1979. Amygdala central nucleus lesions: Effect on heart rate conditioning in the rabbit. *Physiol. Behav.* 23:1109–17
30. Kapp, B. S., Gallagher, M., Frysinger, R. C., Applegate, C. D. 1981. The amygdala, emotion, and cardiovascular conditioning. In *The Amygdaloid Complex,* ed. Y. Ben-Ari, pp. 355–66. Elsevier: North-Holland Biomed. 516 pp.
31. Kopytova, F. V. 1980. Hypothalamic unit activity during defensive conditioning. *Neurosci. Behav. Physiol.* 10:452–59
32. Martin, G. K., Fitzgerald, R. D. 1980. Heart rate and somatomotor activity in rats during signalled escape and yoked classical conditioning. *Physiol. Behav.* 25:519–26
33. Plunkett, R. P. 1979. Effect of hippocampal lesions on heart-rate during classical fear conditioning. *Physiol. Behav.* 23:433–37
34. Powell, D. A., Milligan, W. L., Mull, P. 1982. Lateral septal lesions enhance conditioned bradycardia in rabbit. *J. Comp. Physiol. Psychol.* 96:742–54
35. Randall, D. C., Billman, G. E., Skinner, T. L. 1982. Sympathetically mediated increases in the maximal rate of fall of ventricular pressure in awake dog. *The Physiologist* 25:263
36. Randall, D. C., Cottrill, C. M., Todd, E. P., Price, M. A., Wachtel, C. C. 1982.

Cardiac output and blood flow distribution during rest and classical aversive conditioning in monkey. *Psychophysiol.* 19:490–97
37. Randall, D. C., Kaye, M. P., Randall, W. C., Brady, J. V., Martin, K. H. 1976. Response of primate heart to emotional stress before and after cardiac denervation. *Am. J. Physiol.* 230:988–95
38. Randall, D. C., Skinner, T. L., Park, K. L. 1982. Comparison of myocardial response to behaviorally conditioned vs drug-induced increases in blood pressure in the baboon. *Pavlovian J. Biol. Sci.* 17:105
39. Randall, D. C., Smith, O. A. 1983. Neural control of the heart in the intact conscious animal with implications concerning the etiology of cardiovascular disease. In *Nervous Control of Cardiovascular Function,* ed. W. C. Randall. New York: Oxford Univ.
40. Schoenfeld, W. N., Kadden, R. M., Tremont, P. J., McCullough, M. R., Steele, W. A. 1980. Effects of pharmacological autonomic blockade upon cardiac rate and blood pressure conditioned and unconditioned responses in *Macaca mulatta. J. Auton. Nerv. Syst.* 2:365–75
41. Skinner, T. L., Randall, D. C. 1981. Effects of behaviorally conditioned changes in autonomic tone on A-V transmission in dog. *The Physiologist* 24:22
42. Smith, O. A., Astley, C. A., DeVito, J. L., Stein, J. M., Walsh, K. E. 1980. Functional analysis of hypothalamic control of the cardiovascular responses accompanying emotional behavior. *Fed. Proc.* 39:2478–94
43. Smith, O. A., DeVito, J. L., Astley, C. A. 1982. Cardiovascular control centers in the brain: One more look. In *Circulation Neurobiology & Behavior,* ed. O. A. Smith, R. A. Galosy, S. M. Weiss, 233–46. Amsterdam: Elsevier. 346 pp.
44. Smith, O. A., Hohimer, A. R., Astley, C. A., Taylor, J. D. 1979. Renal and hindlimb vascular control during acute emotion in the baboon. *Am. J. Physiol.* 236:R198–205

Ann. Rev. Physiol. 1984. 46:199–210

OPERANT CONDITIONING AND THE MODULATION OF CARDIOVASCULAR FUNCTION

Bernard T. Engel and Neil Schneiderman

Gerontology Research Center, National Institute on Aging, National Institutes of Health, PHS, U.S. Department of Health and Human Services, Bethesda, Baltimore City Hospitals, Baltimore, Maryland 21224, and University of Miami, Florida

INTRODUCTION

Operant conditioning refers to procedures in which the occurrence of a specific stimulus (i.e. reinforcer or punisher) is made contingent upon the rate or magnitude of a specified response. Reinforcers (i.e. rewards such as food; avoidance or escape from noxious stimulation such as shock) increase, whereas punishers (i.e. administration of noxious stimuli) decrease, the rate or magnitude of the specified response. Thus, operant conditioning refers to those procedures used to train organisms to emit or withhold responses, termed operants, in order to obtain reinforcement. This contrasts with the classical conditioning procedure in which reinforcement is not contingent upon the organism's making a specified response. However, in either case the inferred underlying process by which the rate or magnitude of a response comes to be influenced by reinforcement is referred to as learning.

Studies of operant conditioning in relation to the circulation can be classified into two categories. In one of these, somatomotor acts such as bar-presses are the operants, and the cardiovascular concomitants of these acts are measured. In the other category, cardiovascular responses specified by the experimenter (e.g. blood pressure increases) are the operants. In this review we will call the first class of responses cardiovascular concomitants (or concomitants) and the second class of responses cardiovascular operants (or operants). Because a large number of reviews of behavioral/cardiovascular interactions have appeared in the last decade (e.g., 7, 23, 31, 53, 55, 60), this review will focus

199

0066-4278/84/0315-0199$02.00

primarily upon studies of operant conditioning published since 1977 that offer insight into the physiological mechanisms mediating the adjustments made by the circulation with regard to behavior.

CARDIOVASCULAR CONCOMITANTS OF OPERANT CONDITIONING

Most studies of concomitants have been designed such that the subject is required to emit a somatomotor response in order to prevent (avoid) or to discontinue (escape) punishment. In some of these experiments (e.g. signaled avoidance) an antecedent signal, called a discriminative stimulus (S^D), was used to indicate that reinforcement was imminent. In other experiments (e.g. unsignaled avoidance), an S^D was not employed, and appropriate responding depended upon the organism developing a temporal discrimination. Almost all of these avoidance studies used shock as the noxious stimulus, and many of the experiments can be subsumed under the rubric, "stress." In these "stress" experiments, often the goal was to demonstrate that specific kinds of aversive contingencies can induce particular pathologies.

Corley and his colleagues (10–13) attempted to correlate signs of cardiac pathology in the squirrel monkey with various operant learning procedures, especially unsignaled avoidance. Typically, they compared experimental "avoid" versus "yoked" control animals in experiments in which the experimental animal was required to press a lever at least once every 40 sec to avoid shock, or once every 5 sec to escape shock. The experimental animal controlled the shock for both it and its yoked control partner. Although the investigators found considerable evidence of diffuse myocardial damage in their studies, the specific mediating mechanisms and controlling behavioral variables were unclear, because in some experiments the experimental animals had more lesions than the controls while in other studies the outcome was reversed. There was some evidence that cervical vagotomy increased the likelihood of diffuse myocardial damage while propranolol preserved the myocardium. However, the great variability among animals combined with the relatively small sample sizes precluded definitive conclusions.

Lawler and his associates (42–44) have used a variant of the signaled avoidance procedure to study the development of hypertension in the F_1 offspring of a cross between Wistar-Kyoto (WKY) and spontaneous hypertensive rats (SHR). A conflict paradigm (i.e. pitting a reinforcer against a punisher) was used in which experimental animals were shocked five times for failing to make a "wheel turn" response and once for making it. Animals subjected to conflict ultimately developed tonic levels of systolic blood pressure of about 185 mmHg, compared to maturation and cage-restraint controls that had systolic pressures of 150 and 165 mmHg, respectively. These results are potentially interesting, but their significance in terms of controlling variables is obscured by a lack of control procedures separating the effects of conflict from physical (i.e. repeated shocks) and other behavioral (e.g. shock unpredictability) variables. Previous research has shown that the development of hypertension in SHR is influenced by environmental conditions such as noncontingent, aversive stimulation (64) that exacerbates the hypertension, or social isolation (29) that attenuates the hypertensive process. Only further research using rigorous behavioral and genetic controls will clarify whether the SHR × WKY cross has any advantage over the SHR in studies of the interaction between acquired and innate adjustments to the environment.

Operant conditioning has also been used as a "stressor" in conjunction with the Dahl hypertension-sensitive strain of rats that develops severe hypertension in response to excess dietary salt ingestion. In one experiment rats were required to press a lever to sustain themselves with food, but by so doing they also exposed themselves periodically to electric shock (20). Rats exposed for a half year to this approach-avoidance conflict while being fed a diet containing 2% NaCl developed elevations of blood pressure greater than those previously observed in conflict-exposed rats fed a very low-sodium diet (21), and greater than those observed in unstressed rats fed 2% NaCl ad libitum. However, the elevations in blood pressure were much less severe than those usually exhibited by genetically similar rats that are unstressed and fed a diet of 4% or 8% NaCl. Although the results are suggestive, the possible extent of synergism between behaviorally induced conflict and modest sodium ingestion in hypertension-sensitive rats was confounded by the use of an operant conditioning procedure that resulted in severe food deprivation and weight loss.

More recently, Anderson and colleagues infused isotonic saline (185 mEg NaCl per 24 hrs) into an arterial catheter in dogs while subjecting the animals to multiple daily sessions of unsignaled avoidance (5). After two weeks of exposure to this dual challenge, average 24-hr increases in blood pressure over the pre-exposure baselines were 23 mmHg in systolic and 11 mmHg in diastolic pressure. In contrast, control animals given two weeks of exposure to either saline infusion alone or avoidance conditioning alone showed negligible changes in blood pressure. Termination of the saline infusion and avoidance sessions in the experimental animals resulted in a decrease of blood pressure toward the pre-exposure baseline. The experimental results confirm the view that intermittent, behaviorally induced stress can act synergistically with sodium ingestion to increase blood pressure on a round-the-clock basis, but as yet the mechanisms involved have not been elucidated.

Grignolo et al (28) compared the cardiovascular and renal responses during signaled avoidance to the responses elicited during treadmill exercise in dogs that received concomitant, intravenous infusions of isotonic sali. Both exercise and avoidance conditioning led to acute increases in heart rate and blood pressure. Exercise also led to increased urine flow, sodium excretion, and glomerular filtration rate, with no change in free water clearance. In contrast, avoidance conditioning induced decreases in urine flow and sodium excretion, with no change in either glomerular filtration rate or free water clearance. The natriuretic effect of exercise was due to an increase filtered load; whereas, the antinatriuretic effect of shock avoidance was apparently due to an increased rate of tubular reabsorption of filtrate. In the experiment by Anderson et al (5), blood pressure remained elevated between, as well as during, sessions. Anderson and colleagues (2, 4) previously found that heart rate, blood pressure, and cardiac output increased during avoidance sessions; whereas, during the time period before these sessions, blood pressure and total peripheral resistance became elevated while heart rate decreased. In view of the findings of Anderson and colleagues (2, 4) and Grignolo et al (28), it would be interesting to study renal adjustments during pre-avoidance to determine whether sodium is retained. If so, then a reduction in renal function between as well as during avoidance sessions could be contributing to the tonic increases in blood pressure reported by Anderson et al (5).

Exercise has considerable biological significance because exercise capacity is an important determinant of natural selection. Thus it is not surprising that operant conditioning also has been used to study the cardiovascular concomitants of exercise (22, 26). In one study, cats were trained over a period of several months to hold a bar with the right forelimb against increasing resistance (26). Administration of selective autonomic blocking agents indicated that the increased heart rate in response to exercise was primarily mediated by the parasympathetic nervous system, whereas increases in left ventricular dp/dt_{max} were mediated by the sympathetic nervous system, Another study used operant conditioning to examine the cardiovascular concomitants of combined isometric and isotonic exercise such as occurs in rowing or lifting weights (22). Rhesus monkeys were trained to pull a T-bar during sessions in which load and total pulls were varied after injection of saline or ganglionic blocking agent. Heart-rate increases were primarily influenced by isotonic exercise duration, whereas both isometric and isotonic exercise components contributed to the systolic and diastolic blood pressure increases. After ganglionic blockade, heart rate and diastolic pressure changes were abolished; the rise in systolic pressure was attenuated but did show some increase as a function of isometric exercise.

Typically, operant conditioning studies of exercise use reinforcers that reward the animal for behaving but have minimal direct cardiovascular effects. However, it is also possible to use operant procedures that elicit strong concomitant effects. For example, the study by Grignolo et al (28) found interesting differences in the ways dogs adjusted their urine flows and sodium excretions during aversive conditioning and exercise. Langer et al (41), working in the same group with similar experimental procedures—treadmill exercise and aversive conditioning—noted that although both conditions led to significant increases in cardiac output, considerably more O_2 was extracted from the blood during exercise. This finding led them to speculate that the differential O_2 extraction meant that the vascular beds were overperfused during aversive conditioning and that if this effect persisted, it could lead to long-term increases in peripheral resistance, presumably via autoregulatory mechanisms. We have already noted that during chronic aversive conditioning, cardiovascular concomitants typically habituate. However, the findings from this group do suggest a related line of investigation. Since exercise and aversive conditioning elicit similar as well as different cardiovascular concomitants, it would be very interesting to combine the two conditions. Would animals that were exercising and at the same time responding to aversive conditional signals respond like exercising animals, like conditioned animals, or would they respond uniquely? Later in this paper we will describe studies of operant conditioning where the findings indicate a consistent tendency for responses to reflect the conditional contingencies.

Several experiments have examined relationships between cardiovascular neurobiology and aversive conditioning. Dworkin and associates (15), for instance, trained rats to avoid or escape electrical stimulation of the trigeminal nucleus by running on a treadmill. The investigators then elicited the baroreceptor reflex with bolus injections of phenylephrine, and found that animals with intact sinus nerves ran on the treadwheel less than did denervated animals. Thus, the experiment demonstrated that cardiovascular afferents can modulate the reinforcement characteristics of stimuli. However, it is not yet known whether barosensory stimulation influenced central perceptual or command processes, or whether the behavioral effects were due to feedback from the reflexive bradycardia (see 1, 14, 63 for experiments in which heart rate slowing was reinforcing).

Smith and his coworkers (56–59) used conditioning procedures specifically to investigate the role of the central nervous system (CNS) in the modulation of cardiovascular activity. Among the tasks they used with baboons were exercise and lever-pressing for food reward and a conditioned emotional response (CER) procedure. In the CER procedure a signal previously paired with subsequent shock was presented while the animals were lever-pressing for food. The resulting suppression of lever-press response rates and concomitant cardiovascular responses during the signal presentation were measured. Major findings of the studies were: (*a*) Gain of the baroreceptor reflex was largest during rest or sleep, but attenuated during shock avoidance or exercise; (*b*) Renal blood flow was not determined solely by autoregulation, because it was greatest during rest or sleep but significantly reduced during CER; (*c*) Discrete, bilateral lesions in the hypothalamus abolished the cardiovascular component of the CER without affecting either the cardiovascular concomitants of other behaviors (e.g. exercise) or other behavioral concomitants (i.e. lever-press suppression) of the CER.

The papers reviewed in this section were based upon experiments in which cardiovascular responses were measured concomitantly with other behaviors. Although operant conditioning studies have proven useful in the study of cardiovascular adjustments to somatomotor acts, it is becoming increasingly clear that the cardiovascular concomitants of behavior do not always reflect only reflexive adjustments secondary to somatomotor activity, because often the cardiovascular responses precede the somatomotor responses (e.g. 2, 4, 6, 49) or differ markedly under conditions where somatomotor differences are small but where reinforcement conditions are different (e.g. 28, 41, 59). Thus the variations in baroreflex sensitivity or renal function reviewed in this section appear to be, at least in part, sensitive to neurally mediated influences, including those involved in learning and memory. In the next section we will consider experiments in which the cardiovascular responses themselves are the operants.

CARDIOVASCULAR OPERANT LEARNING

Most studies utilizing cardiovascular operants use people as subjects and are subsumed under the rubric, "biofeedback." The majority of these studies are designed to address either behavioral or clinical issues. Therefore, they lie outside of the purview of this review (e.g. 8, 40, 54). However, many of these are germane here because they do address physiologically relevant questions. In fact, it is a major thesis of this review that cardiovascular, operant learning is a major mechanism underlying such physiological processes as: adaptation—the tendency for a response to attenuate in the presence of a sustained stimulus; habituation—the tendency for a response to attenuate to repeated presentations of the same stimulus; and central command—the concept that has been invoked to characterize the findings that the cardiovascular adjustments to exercise can be organized and emitted from the brain as well as be elicited as reflex responses to the humoral byproducts of muscle metabolism. We have already discussed adaptation and habituation in the previous section in noting that so-called stresses often become less stressful upon repeated presentation. It is clear that this process must be an active one, because it depends upon the capacity of the subject to learn from previous exposures to the situation and to remember its strategy. In this section we will review the evidence that indicates that cardiovascular responses themselves can be learned.

Most studies of operant conditioning have used either heart rate or blood pressure as the operant, although we are aware of at least one study in which dogs were trained to constrict their coronary vessels, thereby decreasing their coronary artery blood flow reliably (19). Among the cardiac conditioning studies of relevance to physiologists have been those in which monkeys were trained to slow or to speed heart rate in the face of challenges either via baroreflex stimulation (18) or via direct electrical stimulation of the brain in areas known to elicit a tachycardia and pressor response (37). In both models it was shown that the learned cardiac response occurred in the face of the imperative stimuli. Thus, the monkeys were able to: (a) attenuate the gain of the baroreflex elicited by phenylephrine injection during periods when the animals were speeding their hearts to avoid tail shock; (b) attenuate the gain of the baroreflex elicited by bolus injections of nitroglycerin during periods when the animals were slowing their hearts to avoid tail shock; and (c) maintain a relative bradycardia despite the brain stimulation, although this effect was site-specific. Other experiments from this laboratory (27) have shown that neither propranolol nor methyl-atropine abolished the capacity of the animals to slow or to speed heart rate, indicating that the learned response was an integrated skill involving coordinated autonomic effects rather than an effector-specific act such as "sympathetic-arousal" or "vagal-release." Finally, the investigators have reported evidence that somatomotor responses are not sufficient to account for the observed cardiac effects. They analyzed changes in rhythmic slow activity in the hippocampus (an index of somatomotor action) during control conditions and during operant heart rate slowing or speeding conditions (38). When they selected data from trials where there were equivalent heart rate changes (i.e. slowing vs control or speeding vs control), they reported reliable differences in rhythmic slow activity, indicating that central neural representations of somatomotor action can be dissociated from peripheral cardiovascular effects that normally accompany somatomotor adjustments.

Harris and his co-workers (24, 30, 32–35, 61, 62) have reported a series of studies in the baboon in which diastolic blood pressure was the operant. The results indicated that: (a) Baboons could be shaped to achieve and maintain 30–40 mmHg elevations in blood pressure during daily 12-hr conditioning-on sessions; (b) Pressure fell to normotensive levels during the 12-hr conditioning-off period, even after many months of training; (c) There was a strong negative correlation (−0.8) between baroreflex sensitivity and diastolic blood pressure, with sensitivity increasing beyond original baseline levels during the daily 12-hr conditioning-off period; and (d) Plasma norepinephrine was correlated with blood pressure as a function of conditioning, while plasma renin was not. Anderson & Yingling (3), working in the same group as Harris, were able to train dogs to elevate peripheral resistance (mean arterial pressure/blood flow in the ascending aorta). They found that the increase in resistance was attributable to an increase in vasomotor tone, because blood pressure rose while cardiac output fell. These investigators had shown previously that when peripheral resistance is measured as a concomitant of aversive conditioning, it falls (4).

Thus, the observed operant rise in peripheral resistance (3) cannot be explained as a concomitant of aversive conditioning but rather is attributable to the association of the reinforcement (avoidance of electric shock) to the cardiovascular response per se.

In 1974, Ainslie et al (1) showed that monkeys could be trained to modify concomitant cardiovascular responses. In their study, the animals were classically conditioned by presenting them 2-min periods of clicks at one rate, always followed by an electric shock, and periods of clicks at another, easily discriminated rate, never followed by shock. Under these conditions, the animals reliably had a faster heart rate during the clicks followed by shock than during the control clicks. Animals were then trained to slow or speed heart rate. The findings were that when the clicks were superimposed on the operant schedule, the heart-rate responses during the clicks followed the operant cardiac conditions. Thus, animals trained to raise their heart rate speeded during "aversive" clicks, whereas animals trained to slow their heart rate did so during the aversive clicks relative to the control clicks. In sum, they reversed their cardiac responses.

Several studies using human subjects have shown similar effects. Goldstein et al (25), using a treadmill, and Perski et al (47), using a bicycle ergometer, have shown that subjects can be trained operantly to attenuate the tachycardia of exercise. Magnusson (45) trained subjects to enhance the tachycardia elicited by isometric muscle tension (handgrip), and Clemens et al (9) showed that subjects could be trained to decrease as well as increase the tachycardia to handgrip. DeGood et al (14) showed that subjects could be trained to modify the increase in heart rate elicited by electric shock. Shapiro and his co-workers (51, 52, 63) have shown that the tachycardia associated with the cold pressor test can be attenuated by training subjects to slow heart rate while their hands are immersed in iced water. The use of operant training to modify elicited cardiovascular responses is a subject of considerable interest because it not only has biological significance (viz. the possible role of visceral learning in physiological regulation) but also has clinical significance, because it may be possible to train patients to attenuate pathognomonic responses (e.g. 48, 50).

A number of investigators have studied the extent to which it is possible to dissociate cardiovascular responses that normally covary. Since the vertebrate cardiovascular system is closed, there are obvious physical limitations on the extent to which dissociation is possible. However, the data are interesting because they offer some insight into the organization of the neural control of the circulation. If Hilton is correct in his notion that "the central nervous system is organized not to produced single, isolated variables but organized patterns of [cardiovascular] response" (36, p. 214), then one should expect that these organized patterns should be adaptive—i.e. conditional on the environmental contingencies—and modifiable operantly. Monkeys trained to slow or speed heart rate will emit large cardiac responses to tail shocks given for failing to perform correctly; however, these cardiac responses are not accompanied by any changes in blood pressure (16). Likewise, animals that learn to slow their hearts in the face of electrical stimulation of the brain that normally elicit a tachycardia and a pressor response, often decrease their heart rate while continuing to show the pressor effect (37). In the Ainslie et al (1) study cited above, the clicks that were followed by tail shock elicited both a tachycardia and a pressor response. Following operant training to slow heart rate, the animals slowed their hearts during the clicks but continued to increase their blood pressures. Perski et al (47) reported that their subjects attenuated the tachycardia of exercise but did not change their blood pressures, whereas Goldstein et al (25) reported a fall in both heart rate and blood pressure. Kristt et al (39) reported that hypertensive patients who were trained to raise and lower their blood pressures did so without changing their heart rates. This last finding is clinically interesting, because it is possible that the patients might have been lowering their peripheral resistance while lowering their blood pressure and maintaining their heart rate. In addition to studies of the dissociation of cardiovascular responses, some investigators have looked at the relationship between cardiovascular and somatomotor responses. Joseph et al (38) reported that monkeys that are operantly increasing and decreasing their heart rates usually also increase and decrease their somatomotor activity concomitantly. However, this covariation of cardiovascular and somatomotor activity can be dissociated in experiments where phencyclidine, given in cataleptic doses, abolishes the differences in somatomotor activity but not the differences in heart rate (17). Finally, Miller et al (46) has reported that patients with completely transected spinal cords could learn to raise blood pressure sufficiently to permit them to sit upright in wheel chairs, whereas prior to training this was not possible because they would experience syncopy secondary to severe postural hypotension.

SUMMARY

Operant learning appears to be one of the primary mechanisms underlying what cardiovascular and pulmonary physiologists have called adaptation, habituation, and central command. In general, studies that have attempted to use operant conditioning alone to create experimental models of behaviorally induced disease have been unsuccessful because the cardiovascular responses adapted or habituated over time. Thus, these studies have provided implicit demonstrations of the roles played by CNS and conditioning processes in achieving and preserving homeostasis. During the past few years those interested in behavioral contributions to cardiovascular pathology have therefore begun to look at interactions between behavior and other variables that might predispose organisms towards pathology (e.g. genetic background; excessive sodium intake). Perhaps even more promising has been the growth in the number of technically competent, well-controlled studies designed to investigate: (*a*) broad scientific questions of how behaviorally important processes such as learning and reinforcement interact with physiologically important variables such as blood flow redistribution and cardio-pulmonary integration; and (*b*) the role of behavioral variables in CNS control of the circulation. Based upon our survey of the recent literature, we believe that the time is ripe for those interested in cardiovascular neurobiology increasingly to include behavioral variables in their studies, because the *raison d'etre* of the CNS is to optimize the organism's ability to interact with its environment. Only when these organismic-environmental interactions are studied both behaviorally and physiologically, in a broad biological context, will it be possible to develop rational models of neuro-circulatory regulation.

Literature Cited

1. Ainslie, G. W., Engel, B. T. 1974. Alteration of classically conditioned heart rate by operant reinforcement in monkeys. *J. Comp. Physiol. Psychol.* 87: 373–82
2. Anderson, D. E., Brady, J. V. 1971. Preavoidance blood pressure elevations accompanied by heart rate decreases in the dog. *Science* 172:595–97
3. Anderson, D. E., Yingling, J. E. 1979. Aversive conditioning of elevations in total peripheral resistance in dogs. *Am. J. Physiol.* 236(6):H880–87
4. Anderson, D. E., Yingling, J. E. 1978. Total peripheral resistance changes in dogs during aversive classical conditioning. *Pavlovian J.* 13:241–45
5. Anderson, D. E., Kearns, W. D., Better, W. E. 1983. Progressive hypertension in dogs by avoidance conditioning and saline infusion. *Hypertension.* 5:286–91
6. Borst, C., Hollander, A. P., Bouman, L. N. 1972. Cardiac acceleration elicited by voluntary muscle contractions of minimal duration. *J. Appl. Physiol.* 32(1):70–77
7. Brady, J. V., Harris, A. H. 1976. The experimental production of altered physiological states. In *Handbook of Operant Behavior*, ed. W. K. Honig, J. E. R. Staddon, pp. 596–618. New Jersey: Prentice Hall
8. Brener, J. 1974. A general model of voluntary control applied to the phenomena of learned cardiovascular change. In *Cardiovascular Psychophysiology*, ed. P. A. Obrist, A. H. Black, J. Brener, L. V. DiCara, pp. 365–92. Chicago: Aldine

9. Clemens, W. J., Shattock, R. J. 1979. Voluntary heart rate control during static muscular effort. *Psychophysiology* 16: 327–32
10. Corley, K. C. 1982. Stress and cardiomyopathy. In *Circulation Neurobiology and Behavior, Vol. 15*, ed. O. A. Smith, R. A. Galosy, S. M. Weiss. New York: Elsevier
11. Corley, K. C., Mauck, H. P., Shiel, F. O., Barber, J. H., Clark, L. S., et al. 1979. Myocardial dysfunction and pathology associated with environmental stress in squirrel monkey: Effect of vagotomy and propranolol. *Psychophysiology* 16:554–60
12. Corley, K. C., Shiel, F. O., Mauck, H. P. 1980. Stress-induced cardiomyopathy in squirrel monkey. In *The Use of Nonhuman Primates in Cardiovascular Diseases*, ed. S. S. Kalter. Austin: Austin Univ. Press
13. Corley, K. C., Shiel, F. O., Mauck, H. P., Clark, L. S., Barber, J. H. 1977. Myocardial degeneration and cardiac arrest in squirrel monkey: Physiological and psychological correlates. *Psychophysiology* 14:322–28
14. DeGood, D. E., Adams. A. S. 1976. Control of cardiac responses under aversive stimulation. *Biofeedback Self-Regul.* 1:373–85
15. Dworkin, B. R., Filewich, R. J., Miller, N. E., Craigmyle, N., Pickering, T. G. 1979. Baroreceptor activation reduces reactivity to noxious stimulation: Implications for hypertension. *Science* 205:1299–301
16. Engel, B. T. 1974. Electroencephalo-

graphic and blood pressure correlates of operantly conditioned heart rate in the restrained monkey. *Pavlov. J. Biol. Sci.* 9:222–32

17. Engel, B. T. 1979. Somatic mediation of heart rate: A physiological analysis. In *Biofeedback and Self-regulation*, ed. N. Birbaumer, H. D. Kimmel. Hillsdale, N.J.: Erlbaum

18. Engel, B. T., Joseph, J. A. 1982. Attenuation of baroreflexes during operant cardiac conditioning. *Psychophysiology* 19: 609–14

19. Ernst, F. A., Kordenat, R. K., Sandman, M. S., Sandman, C. A. 1979. Learned control of coronary blood flow. *Psychosom. Med.* 41:79–85

20. Friedman, R., Iwai, J. 1977. Dietary sodium, psychic stress, and genetic predisposition to experimental hypertension. *Proc. Soc. Exp. Biol. Med.* 155: 449–52

21. Friedman, R., Iwai, J. 1976. Genetic predisposition and stress-induced hypertension. *Science* 193:161–62

22. Gaide, M. S, Klose, K. J., Gavin, W. J., Schneiderman, N., Robertson, T. W., et al. 1980. Hexamethonium modification of cardiovascular adjustments during combined static-dynamic arm exercise in monkeys. *Pharmac. Biochem. Behav.* 13:851–57

23. Galosy, R. A., Clarke, L. K., Vasko, M. R., Crawford, I. L. 1980. Neurophysiology and neuropharmacology of cardiovascular regulation and stress. *Neurosci. Biobehav. Rev.* 5:137–75

24. Goldstein, D. S., Harris, A. H., Izzo, J. L. Jr., Turkkan, J. S., Keiser, H. R. 1981. Plasma catecholamines and renin during operant blood pressure conditioning in baboons. *Physiol. Behav.* 26: 33–37

25. Goldstein, D. S., Ross, R. S., Brady, J. V. 1977. Biofeedback heart rate training during exercise. *Biofeedback Self-Regul.* 2:107–26

26. Gonyea, W. J., Diepstra, G., Muntz, K. H., Mitchell, J. H. 1981. Cardiovascular response to static exercise in the conscious cat. *Circ. Res.* 48:163–69

27. Gottlieb, S. H., Engel, B. T. 1979. Autonomic interactions in the control of heart rate in the monkey. *Psychophysiology* 16:528–36

28. Grignolo, A., Koepke, J. P., Obrist, P. A. 1982. Renal function, heart rate, and blood pressure during exercise and avoidance in dogs. *Am. J. Physiol.* 242: R482–90

29. Hallback, M. 1975. Consequences of social isolation on blood pressure, cardiovascular reactivity, and design in

spontaneously hypertensive rat. *Acta Physiol. Scand.* 93:455–65

30. Harris, A. H. 1980. Conditioned blood pressure elevations in the baboon. In *Advances in Physiological Science, Vol. 17, Brain and Behaviour*, ed. G. Adam, I. Meszaros, E. I. Banyai. Budapest: Akademiai, Kaido.

31. Harris, A. H., Brady, J. V. 1974. Animal learning—visceral and autonomic conditioning. *Ann. Rev. Psychol.* 25:107–33

32. Harris, A. H., Gilliam, W. J., Findley, J. D., Brady, J. V. 1973. Instrumental conditioning in large-magnitude, daily 12-hour blood pressure elevations in the baboon. *Science* 182:175–77

33. Harris, A. H., Turkkan, J. S. 1981. Generalization of conditioned blood pressure elevation: Schedule and stimulus control effects. *Physiol. Behav.* 26: 935–40

34. Harris, A. H., Turkkan, J. S. 1981. Performance characteristics of conditioned blood pressure elevations in the baboon. *Biofeedback Self-Regul* 6:11–24

35. Harris, A. H., Turkkan, J. S. 1982. Plasma lactate levels during baseline and blood pressure conditioning in the baboon. *Physiol. Behav.* 29:657–63

36. Hilton, S. M. 1975. Ways of viewing the central nervous control of the circulation—old and new. *Brain Res.* 87: 213–19

37. Joseph, J. A., Engel, B. T. 1981. Instrumental control of cardio-acceleration induced by central electrical stimulation. *Science* 214:341–43

38. Joseph, J. A., Quilter, R. E., Engel, B. T. 1982. Changes in hippocampal rhythmic slow activity during instrumental cardiovascular conditioning. *Physiol Behav.* 28:653–59

39. Kristt, D. A., Engel, B. T. 1975. Learned control of blood pressure in patients with high blood pressure. *Circulation* 51:370–78

40. Lacroix, J. M. 1981. The acquisition of autonomic control through biofeedback: The case against an afferent process and a two process alternative. *Psychophysiology* 18:573–87

41. Langer, A. W., Obrist, P. A., McCubbin, J. A. 1979. Hemodynamic and metabolic adjustments during exercise and shock avoidance in dogs. *Am. J. Physiol.* 236:H225–30

42. Lawler, J. E., Barker, G. F., Hubbard, J. W., Allen, M. T. 1980. The effects of conflict on tonic levels of blood pressure in the genetically borderline hypertensive rat. *Psychophysiology* 17:363–70

43. Lawler, J. E., Barker, G. F., Hubbard, J. W., Schaub, R. G. 1981. Effects of stress

on blood pressure and cardiac pathology in rats with borderline hypertension. *Hypertension* 3:496–505

44. Lawler, J. E., Barker, G. F., Hubbard, J. W., Schaub, R. G. 1980. Pathophysiological changes associated with stress-induced hypertension in borderline hypertensive rat. *Clin. Sci.* 59:Suppl., pp. 307–10

45. Magnusson, E. 1976. The effect of controlled muscle tension on performance and learning of heart-rate control. *Biol. Psychol.* 4:81–92

46. Miller, N. E., Brucker, B. S. 1979. A learned visceral response apparently independent of skeletal ones in patients paralyzed by spinal lesions. See Ref. 17

47. Perski, A., Engel, B. T. 1980. The role of behavioral conditioning in the cardiovascular adjustment to exercise. *Biofeedback Self-Regul.* 5:91–104

48. Perski, A., Engel, B. T., McCroskery, J. H. 1982. The modification of elicited cardiovascular responses by operant conditioning of heart rate. In *Perspectives in Cardiovascular Psychophysiology*, ed. J. T. Cacioppo, R. E. Petty. New York: Guilford

49. Petro, J. K., Hollander, A. P., Bouman, L. N. 1970. Instantaneous cardiac acceleration in man induced by a voluntary muscle contraction. *J. Appl. Physiol.* 29:794–98

50. Pickering, T., Gorham, G. 1975. Learned heart-rate control by a patient with a ventricular parasystolic rhythm. *Lancet* 1(7901):252–53

51. Reeves, J. L., Shapiro, D. 1982. Heart rate biofeedback and cold pressor pain. *Psychophysiology* 19:393–403

52. Reeves, J. L., Shapiro, D., Cobb, L. F. 1979. Relative influences of heart rate biofeedback and instructional set in the perception of cold pressor pain. See Ref. 17

53. Schneiderman, N. 1983. Behavior, autonomic function, and animal models of cardiovascular pathology. In *Biological Basis of Coronary-Prone Behavior: Behavioral Approaches to a 20th Century Epidemic*, ed. T. M. Dembroski, T. H. Schmidt, G. Blumchen. Basel: Karger

54. Schneiderman, N., Weiss, T., Engel, B. T. 1979. Modification of psychosomatic

behaviors. In *Modification of Pathological Behavior*, ed. R. S. Davidson. New York: Gardner

55. Smith, O. E. 1974. Reflex and central mechanisms involved in the control of the heart and circulation. *Ann. Rev. Physiol.* 36:93–123

56. Smith, O. A., Astley, C. A., DeVito, J. L., Stein, J. M., Walsh, K. E. 1980. Functional analysis of hypothalamic control of the cardiovascular responses accompanying emotional behavior. *Fed. Proc.* 39:2487–94

57. Smith, O. A., Astley, C. A., Hohimer, A. R., Stephenson, R. B. 1980. Behavioral and cerebral control of cardiovascular function. In *Neural Control of Circulation*, ed. M. J. Hughes, C. D. Barnes. New York: Academic

58. Smith, O. A., Hohimer, A. R., Astley, C. A., Taylor, D. J. 1979. Renal and hindlimb vascular control during acute emotion in the baboon. *Am. J. Physiol.* 236(3):R198–205

59. Stephenson, R. B., Smith, O. A., Scher, A. M. 1981. Baroreceptor regulation of heart rate in baboons during different behavorial states. *Am. J. Physiol.* 241:R277–85

60. Turkkan, J. S., Brady, J. V., Harris, A. H. 1982. Animal studies of stressful interactions: A behavioral-physiological overview. In *Handbook of Stress*, ed. L. Goldberger, L. Breznitz. New York: Macmillan

61. Turkkan, J. S., Harris, A. H. 1981. Shaping blood pressure elevations: An examination of acquisition. *Behav. Anal. Let.* 1:97–106

62. Turkkan, J. S., Lukas, S. E., Harris, A. H. 1982. Hemodynamic effects of intravenous clonidine in the conscious, normotensive baboon. *J. Cardiovasc. Pharmacol.* 4:863–69

63. Victor, R., Mainardi, J. A., Shapiro, D. 1978. Effects of biofeedback and voluntary control procedures on heart rate and perception of pain during the cold pressor test. *Psychosom. Med.* 40:216–25

64. Yamori, Y., Matsumoto, M., Yamabe, H., Okamoto, K. 1969. Augmentation of spontaneous hypertension by chronic stress in rats. *Jpn. Circul. J.* 33:399–409

SPECIAL TOPIC: ADVANCES IN THE PHYSIOLOGY OF AUDITORY INFORMATION PROCESSING

Introduction, Edwin W Rubel, *Section Editor*

The purpose of this section is to bring interested readers up to date on a few topics related to auditory information processing. Two criteria were used in choosing the subjects for presentation. First, the topics had to be among those generating substantial current interest and producing fundamental physiological advances. Second, the list of topics should include several "levels" of processing, from peripheral transformations of sound to central integration of acoustic information. Perusal of the five chapters will indicate that both criteria have been admirably met. Important recent advances are apparent, whether examining the mechanical transformation of a signal at the basilar membrane (Rhode), the combination of structures responsible for tuning at the level of transduction (Weiss), the possible mechanisms whereby the most important human attribute, speech, is encoded by the auditory nerve (Sachs), or the integration of information to decode the energy differences reaching the two ears (Masterton & Imig). Finally, in many areas of current interest we are beginning to understand much about the developmental time course, if not the ontogenetic principles.

We are now equipped with an amazing armamentarium of technology in electronics, engineering, biochemistry, and anatomy. It should be evident from these chapters that modern tools of electronics and engineering have played a critical role in our ever increasing understanding of sensory information proces-

211

sing. Similarly, if these reviews were oriented toward the biochemistry or pharmacology of the auditory system, the importance of technological advances such as HPLC or methods for synthesizing biologically active compounds would be apparent. Finally, if the plasticity of sensory systems had been stressed, the emergence of compounds to stimulate growth of nerve fibers might be emphasized, as would the great progress that is being made toward transplantation of neural tissue.

Given this level of technology, why can't we cure, prevent, or correct most sensory disorders? Why do a large proportion of children under six years of age suffer a recurrent 15–20 decibel hearing loss from otitis media? Why do *most* Americans over the age of 65 suffer a hearing loss that we are unable to fully correct with amplification devices? Why can't we rebuild a middle ear system that reliably provides restoration of function to within normal levels? Why can't we prevent language disturbances in the hearing disabled, and why can't we provide prosthetic devices that provide "perceptual" function in severely deaf individuals?

I'd like to suggest that the reasons for these shortcomings in the application of our science to clinical problems does not lie in the technology available to medical science. In fact, I'd contend that technology is available, could be easily developed, or soon will be available to electrically or mechanically stimulate the cochlea in any way desired, to amplify sound in any way desired, to stimulate nerves to grow, to replace missing or diseased tissues, or to provide adequate stimulation. If the rate-limiting step toward clinical progress is not technology, what is it? Knowledge! Knowledge of how the normal system works, so that it can be mimicked and assayed during treatment, and thorough knowledge of the pathophysiology of sensory disorders. If this is the case, advancement toward a national and international goal of improved medical effectiveness will dovetail with the goals of natural science. As we come to understand normal function we will be able to utilize available technology in medical practice. Thus, a continuing commitment of appropriate resources toward increasing our understanding of the biological principles underlying normal function and the fundamentals of pathophysiology may be the most effective and efficient way to improve medical treatment.

Ann. Rev. Physiol. 1984. 46:213–29

ONTOGENY OF AUDITORY SYSTEM FUNCTION

Edwin W Rubel

Department of Otolaryngology and Physiology, University of Virginia School of Medicine, Charlottesville, Virginia 22908

INTRODUCTION

Knowledge evolves much faster than nature. It is, however, by definition an inaccurate abstraction (31). Any attempt to describe the ontogeny of mature function is limited by the accuracy of our current abstraction. This review, with the exception of the final section, is therefore biased toward ontogenetic analyses of those physiological processes that we best understand. Space limitations kept many important areas and contributors from being treated.

Why study the ontogeny of auditory information processing? One reason is to understand the development of audition, per se, including such phenomena as the endocochlear potential (9) or the ontogeny of the frequency/place principle (74, 110). Another reason is to use unique qualities of the auditory system to approach more general issues of developmental neurobiology (106). Such issues include the demonstration that afferents influence cell death (73) or the ontogenetic elimination of supernumerary inputs in the central nervous system (60). Development can also be used as a tool to further understand the principles underlying adult function. Pujol and his colleagues, for example, have used the fact that inner hair cell differentiation precedes that of outer hair cells to investigate functional differences between these two cell types (18).

DEVELOPMENT OF CONDUCTIVE ELEMENTS: EXTERNAL EAR AND MIDDLE EAR

Maturation of the elements that collect, focus, and transmit mechanical motion to the cochlea sets physical limits on the capacities of the maturing inner ear and central processing network. Recent reviews cover functional development

213

0066-4278/84/0315-0213$02.00

(120), the embryology (81, 144), and the maturational pattern observed in humans (2).

External Ear

The shape of the pinna and size of the ear canal influence sound reaching the tympanic membrane differentially as a function of frequency (123). Therefore, as the pinna and ear canal grow, a process which is largely postnatal, we might expect to see major changes in the pattern of spectral sensitivity. Saunders et al (120) point out that the relatively small ear canal and pinna of the newborn will tend to resonate at higher frequencies, where the newborn is relatively less sensitive, than that of adults. In addition, the immature ear canal is more compliant than that of the adult, so the maximum gain due to resonance will be less in the neonate. These factors probably result in an overall loss of sensitivity in the upper half of the frequency range due to external ear immaturity.

Decreased high frequency sensitivity, along with the reduced head size of neonates, also has implications for binaural sound localization. Smaller head size will mean that the maximum interaural intensity differences (123) will occur at higher frequencies in neonates than in adults; as the head approaches adult size, progressively lower frequencies produce an interaural intensity difference (78). Therefore, sound localization using binaural cues should be more difficult for the newborn, especially in the middle frequencies where interaural intensity cues can play less of a role. Furthermore, maturation of the temporal microstructure of receptor and neural responses, usually thought to be important for the processing of interaural time differences, is prolonged. In summary, we might expect young animals and humans to show difficulties with sound localization. While it has been shown that young animals and humans can localize sounds (19, 20, 80), neither the extent to which binaural cues are used nor the accuracy of localization ability have been thoroughly studied as a function of development.

Middle Ear

Middle ear structures, tympanic membrane and ossicular chain, provide a 35–40 dB pressure gain; their development, therefore, can impose strict boundary conditions on the ontogeny of auditory sensitivity. Saunders and colleagues (121) provide a detailed and lucid review of this material; only the most important points will be mentioned here.

Most early studies, using tympanometry to measure developmental changes in tympanic membrane immittance, found a precipitous drop in the magnitude of compliance 40–80 days after birth in human neonates (11, 63, 66, 67, 133). It now appears that when the component quantities of admittance (conductance and susceptance) are considered, there is instead a net increase in admittance during the first three months after birth (55). The latter results are in accord with recent developmental studies using hamsters and chicks (98, 121). Using a capacitive probe, Relkin & Saunders (97) were able to measure developmental changes in displacement of the tympanic membrane at frequencies up to 35 kHz. Displacement increased up to 75 days of age in the hamster. Below 10 kHz the developmental change was flat across frequency. Above 10 kHz, however, displacement appeared to have a sharper roll-off, with increasing frequency in young animals than in the adults.

From these results there can be little doubt that at the youngest ages middle ear function is an important factor limiting hearing sensitivity. In both the chick and the hamster, however, it appears that adult thresholds mature *prior* to final maturation of middle ear function, at least for low frequencies (7, 46, 68, 96, 119). In addition, middle ear function in the young animals cannot account for ontogenetic changes in sensitivity across frequency (98). Therefore, developmental changes in middle ear contribute to, but do not appear to account for, maturation of adult hearing sensitivity.

In order to understand the development of hearing we must document changes in the efficiency and spectral purity of information transfer from the acoustic environment to the inner ear. Future studies simultaneously measuring input-output functions of the middle ear and the cochlea across age will be important. This gap in our knowledge is particularly apparent when we consider differences that must exist between animals which develop hearing prenatally (humans, most ungulates, and precocial birds) and those which begin hearing after birth (such as most rodents and carnivores). In animals that hear prenatally, the external and middle ear spaces are fluid-filled. Therefore, the role of the tympanic membrane and ossicular chain must be very different. Presumably the conduction of sound to the inner ear in an aquatic embryo will follow principles similar to bone conduction (136). Empirical studies of the transfer function under these conditions, however, are not available.

DIFFERENTIATION OF THE INNER EAR

Normal inner ear development has been reviewed from several perspectives (106, 143, 145, 158). The tissue interactions important for the determination and early differentiation of inner ear tissues are being intensely investigated in vivo (40, 56) and in vitro (84, 142). Of the most interest here are the final stages of differentiation which immediately precede or overlap with the maturation of auditory function.

Some of the best descriptions of the final stages of inner ear differentiation are those of Retzius (99). Over the past century his observations have been confirmed and elaborated using modern methods and on a variety of animals (18, 38, 72, 89, 91, 92, 106, 125, 130). While some generalizations are possible, such as the differentiation of inner hair cells prior to outer hair cells and the establishment of afferent synapses before efferent connections, the major point to emphasize is that no single event triggers the onset of cochlear function. As suggested by Wada (147), the events leading up to the onset of function include the simultaneous and synchronous maturation of many mechanical and neural properties, including thinning of the basilar membrane, formation of the inner spiral sulcus, maturation of the pilar cells, freeing of the inferior margin of the tectorial membrane, development of tissue spaces in the organ of Corti, differentiation of the hair cells, establishment of mature cilia structure, and the maturation of synapses.

The final stages of maturation do not occur simultaneously throughout the length of the cochlea. Retzius (99) showed a clear gradient of differentiation extending from the basal turn. This gradient may not be present in the early stages of differentiation (27, 112), but substantial evidence supports its existence during the final stages of maturation (e.g. 1, 3, 10, 26, 37, 57, 93, 95, 99, 147). In species ranging from chicken to man, differentiation occurs first in the mid-basal region and spreads in both directions, with the apex maturing last. A corresponding pattern of differentiation has been described at more central locations, including myelination of kitten spiral ganglion cells (104), axon growth into the hamster dorsal cochlear nucleus (134), and a variety of morphological and physiological events in the chick brain stem auditory nuclei (59, 108, 128). Functional implications of this developmental gradient are discussed in the next section. It is important to note that essentially nothing is known about how this gradient arises, what factors regulate it, or why it occurs. Studies aimed at these questions are needed.

The pattern of synaptic development at the base of inner and outer hair cells has been studied in detail by Pujol and his colleagues (72, 90, 91, 95, 124). Synapse formation on inner hair cells occurs early and undergoes only minor modifications. Outer hair cells are initially surrounded by afferent terminals, which are gradually replaced by numerous efferents. Then the large calyciform efferent terminal, typical of the mature cochlea, forms. Pujol speculates that the development of efferent terminals and the concurrent reduction of afferent terminals on the outer hair cells is responsible for changes in frequency selectivity.

The relationships of stereocilia structure to the tuning properties of the mature cochlea are only beginning to be appreciated (137, 138, 139). At present there is little information on the development of these structures. In the chick, stereocilia first arise near the apex and their orientation specificity emerges gradually at about the time function begins (27). The stereocilia, kinocilium, and an associated bulbous structure have been described in five- and seven-month-old human fetuses (39). In view of recent findings, indicating that the tuning properties of the cochlea may shift during ontogeny (see below), it is of obvious importance to rigorously examine the developmental relationship between cilia structure and frequency selectivity.

DEVELOPMENT OF THE PLACE PRINCIPLE

The most fundamental principle of auditory science is the place principle (4). Simply stated, there is a progression of positions along the basilar membrane that are most sensitive to (i.e. "tuned to") successively higher frequencies. Apical positions (distal in birds) are most sensitive to low frequencies; progressively more basal regions (proximal in birds) are selectively responsive to successively higher frequencies. This relationship is thought to be due to the mechanical properties of basilar membrane motion and the characteristics of the stereocilia (see reviews by Rhode and T. Weiss, this volume). Most animals do not simultaneously begin hearing all frequencies that are included in their adult dynamic range. Behavioral and physiological responses are first elicited by low or mid-low frequencies, and responsiveness to the highest frequencies develops last (44, 105, 106). Other measures of auditory system function show a corresponding developmental pattern, e.g. attainment of adult thresholds (79), phase locking by neurons in the cochlear nucleus (13), and most sensitive frequency (35, 96). While there may be exceptions (155), the pattern is remarkably universal across both avian and mammalian species.

Since responsiveness to relatively low frequencies develops early, and high frequency responsiveness matures last, the place principle predicts that apical or mid-apical regions of the cochlea are the first to mature and that basal regions mature last. As noted above, just the opposite result is consistently found: cochlear differentiation occurs first in the basal or mid-basal region, and the *last* part of the cochlea to undergo differentiation is the apex.

Developmental changes in the external and middle ear cannot account for this paradox (97). An alternative explanation, that the values of the place code along the cochlea are changing during development (106, 108), has recently been tested (74, 110). Its implications are shown in Figure 1. The upper diagram in each part schematically shows the cochlea, from base to apex, and the relative positions of the traveling waves produced by several different pure tones. In the bottom section of this diagram the orderly, "tonotopic" representation of input to the central nervous system is shown. The CNS neurons are selectively tuned to the frequencies indicated (in kHz). Our hypothesis, shown in the left and middle diagrams, was that during the early stages of hearing the base or mid-basal region of the cochlea and the basal representation areas of the central nervous system are the first to respond to sound. But these areas are initially most sensitive to relatively low frequencies. With maturation of both mechanical and neural properties, the values of the place code gradually shift toward the apex until the mature organization is achieved.

Two testable predictions emerged from this hypothesis. The first (upper part of Figure 1) was that there would be a systematic ontogenetic shift in the position of hair cell damage produced by pure tone high intensity sound exposure. Low or midrange frequencies should produce maximum damage at

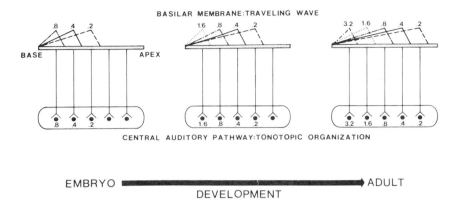

Figure 1 Model of inner ear functional development. The sequence of development is shown from left to right. The basilar membrane, from base to apex, is depicted at the top of each section; the positions of the traveling waves produced by pure tones of several frequencies (in kHz) are indicated. A region of the central auditory pathways that is tonotopically organized is shown connected to each basilar membrane. The numbers indicate the "best frequency" (in kHz) of neurons at each location. At the beginning of auditory function (left diagrams) the basal half of the cochlea is responsive to relatively low frequencies and the central nervous system areas receiving projections from the base respond to low frequencies. With maturation, middle and right sections, the apex of the cochlea begins responding to low frequencies and the base becomes more and more sensitive to high frequencies. The resulting shift in neuronal best frequencies is indicated at the bottom of each diagram.

progressively more apical locations as the animals mature. When tested by Rubel & Ryals (110) using three different frequencies on three age groups of young chickens, the position of maximum damage shifted systematically as predicted. This experiment was carried out during the very late stages of hearing development, after nearly all thresholds had already reached adult values, probably corresponding to the perinatal or immediate postnatal period in humans.

The second prediction was that in each tonotopically organized auditory region of the brain stem, the position at which neurons are responsive to a particular frequency will shift during development. Stated differently, the neurons at any given location within an auditory area of the central nervous system should respond to successively higher frequencies during development. In collaboration with William Lippe, electrophysiological "mapping" was used to determine the relationship between the location of neurons and the frequency to which they were most sensitive (75). In each area of the brain stem investigated, embryonic neurons were most sensitive to tones 1–1.5 octaves below the frequencies that activate the same neurons a few weeks after hatching.

Taken together, these two experiments strongly support the model of a shifting place code during development. In all likelihood, the underlying mechanisms in this process include both mechanical and neural changes. An exciting possibility is that the changing tuning properties are also reflected by changes in the structure of stereocilia (139).

The generality of this process across species is also supported by data available on mammals: (a) As noted above, the paradoxical relationship between cochlea development and functional ontogeny is nearly universal across species; (b) Ryan & Woolf (113) have shown an ontogenetic shift in the position of neurons in the gerbil dorsal cochlear nucleus that increases glucose uptake in response to a 3 kHz tone; (c) Pujol & Marty (94) noted that only relatively low frequency tones produced recognizable evoked potentials in the cerebral cortex of very young kittens, but the potentials were found in the "high frequency" region (157); and (d) Harris & Dallos (53) have recently reported a systematic developmental increase in the cut-off frequency of cochlear microphonic potentials recorded from the basal turn of the gerbil cochlea.

The functional implications of this model are that at some point during development each part of the cochlea, and thereby each tonotopic region of the central nervous system, will be maximally responsive to relatively low frequency tones. With maturation, each area will be responsive to successively higher frequencies until adult values are reached. It is perhaps not coincidental that low frequencies are present in the environment of young organisms, whether in a burrow, in an egg, or in utero (5, 48, 146). If the development of normal function is dependent on external stimulation, then the developmental pattern we have proposed will provide a mechanism to insure that each neuronal region receives adequate stimulation from the environment.

DEVELOPMENT OF NEURAL RESPONSE PROPERTIES

Over the past ten years many investigators have examined the ontogeny of responses to sound by neurons at several levels of the auditory pathways. There are two purposes of such studies.

First, we would like to understand the ontogeny of auditory "coding." Certain acoustic parameters are represented in the pattern of neuronal activity. This information allows the organism to "perceive" sound and to differentially act as a function of its temporal and spectral properties. By studying the development of neuronal responses, investigators hope to understand the neural events underlying the ontogeny of sensation and perception. The implicit assumption is that the neural response parameters that we have chosen to study in adult organisms, and therefore developmentally, are the ones that code relevant acoustic dimensions. To the extent that this assumption is correct, current studies will be useful for understanding the development of perception. It is important to note that as our understanding of the coding of acoustic information by the mature auditory system evolves (see Sachs, this volume), the methods and approaches for studying developmental information processing must also change.

The second reason for studying the coding properties of developing neurons is to assess structure-function relationships. Thus, development can be used to assess the structural properties necessary for a particular pattern of responsiveness to sound or to assess the relative maturity of more peripheral parts of the auditory system. The implicit assumptions are: (*a*) that the same structural features underlie a particular pattern of activity in young and adult organism; and (*b*) that causal relationships can eventually be experimentally detected among the myriad of temporal correlations.

We know remarkably little about the ontogeny of auditory perception. Threshold changes during development have been examined in a few species (e.g. 33, 35, 46, 106, 122), but psychophysical studies attempting to evaluate the spectral, temporal, or spatial resolving power of the developing auditory system are rare (34, 44a, 46, 68, 83). In order to relate the development of neurophysiological response properties to the ontogeny of perception, a great deal more emphasis must be placed on evaluating the ontogeny of behavioral abilities.

The common strategy of applying the same techniques to neurophysiological studies of young animals as to adults can lead to invalid conclusions. Young animals respond differently to anesthetics, blood loss, changes in body temperature, and the host of other physiological conditions that influence auditory responsivity. In addition, differences in responsivity along "standardized" dimensions (e.g. repetition rate) (58, 76, 107) may be influencing responses to the dimensions under investigation (e.g. thresholds or tuning).

There have now been a large number of neurophysiological studies examining developmental changes in thresholds and tuning properties of neurons in the mammalian auditory system. Reviews of this work are available (12, 103, 106, 152). At the level of the eighth nerve, cochlear nucleus, and inferior colliculus, thresholds improve and tuning curves of individual neurons become sharper (e.g. 14, 79, 101, 153). The recent methodological advance of using tone-on-tone masking paradigms for physiological studies of frequency selectivity (29, 30, 51, 52) in developing animals (16, 120, 125) has also demonstrated ontogenetic "sharpening" of frequency selectivity. Although use of the evoked potential tuning curve method makes some assumptions that have yet to be verified in developing animals, its application to developmental questions can be of great value. For example, using these techniques it will be relatively easy to simultaneously record from several regions of the auditory system, to quantitatively assess their relative developmental rates. In addition, chronic preparations are feasible.

Physiological response latencies decrease as a function of both peripheral and central changes (12, 106). The dynamic range of neurons increases, probably primarily due to changes in threshold and in the ability of synapses to follow high rates of activation (13, 59, 77). In general, the response changes that have been examined in the human fetus or neonate follow parallel developmental trends (c.f. 115, 116, 132).

Recent emphasis on the temporal microstructure of neuronal responses (see Sachs, this volume) makes developmental analysis particularly interesting. The lone published study (13) indicates that the development of phase-locking, particularly to high frequencies, is quite prolonged. This is especially interesting because maximum firing rates mature early.

Other properties of the spike train responses, peculiar to certain subsets of CNS neurons, are also receiving increasing attention by developmental neurophysiologists (e.g. 15, 77, 102, 126, 154). At present, most investigators are content with cataloging the developmental history of these properties and correlating their time-course to the myriad of morphological events that are occurring over the same time period (64, 75, 100, 114, 128, 134).

EXTRINSIC INFLUENCES ON AUDITORY SYSTEM ONTOGENY

Hypersensitive Period

Saunders & Bock (118) summarized the literature on age-dependent differential susceptibility to aminoglycosides and noise exposure. Exposure of young rodents to drugs or noise at levels that do not produce damage in adults can cause severe hearing loss and histological damage to the cochlea (6, 17, 70, 71, 88). Pujol and coworkers have proposed that the period of hypersensitivity corresponds to the final stages of anatomical and functional development of the cochlea. They hypothesized that the development of efferent endings is involved. However, the biological mechanisms underlying differential susceptability of young animals is not known. When and if hypersensitivity occurs in human infants, and if it occurs during other periods of life (e.g. aging) (54), are also still undetermined. A fruitful approach toward understanding hypersensitivity may be provided by examining age-related differences in temporary threshold shift (7).

Afferent Influences on Central Auditory Pathways

Another class of "extrinisic influences" are afferents from the inner ear to the central nervous system. In a series of studies since 1975, we have been examining how the integrity of the basilar papilla influences the development of neurons in the chick brain stem auditory system. After 11 days of incubation, when function normally begins and the second-order neurons are innervated, the presence of an intact receptor exerts a profound influence on the postsynaptic neurons (8, 32, 62, 73, 85, 111). In embryos, newly hatched chicks, or 6-week-old chickens receptor removal resulted in the loss of 25–40% of the cells in n. magnocellularis and a marked reduction in the size of the remaining cells. In the postnatal animals, cell loss and cell atrophy were evident by two days and metabolic changes in the neurons were evident within six hours. Strikingly different results were found in 66-week-old chickens: cell loss was less than 10%, and the reduction in cell size was negligible. Yet, the auditory system of the chick is quite mature at hatching and adultlike in every way we've observed even before one month posthatch (45, 46, 61, 109, 110, 119, 128). The period of susceptibility, therefore, may be determined by general maturational factors (e.g. pituitary or adrenal function) not specific to the auditory system.

The results of peripheral destruction appear to be similar in mammals. Trune (140, 141) recently reported marked changes in cell number, cell size, and dendritic size in the mouse cochlear nucleus following neonatal cochlear destruction. In newborn gerbils, cochlear removal results in similar changes accompanied by alterations of the projections of the intact cochlear nucelus to the inferior colliculus (82). Cell loss following adult cochlear removal has not been reported in mammals (65, 87, 150). Studies on other sensory systems have also reported that deafferentation in young animals results in profound cell loss or atrophy, whereas similar manipulations in adults have much less effect (28, 41, 49, 86, 156).

Monaural or binaural occlusion also influences neuronal structure or function in the brain stem auditory nuclei of birds and mammals, a number of studies have shown. Webster & Webster first reported that ear occlusion and quiet rearing result in significant reductions of perikaryon area in many areas of the cochlear nucleus and superior olivary complex (149, 151); conductive hearing deficits in adult mice did not produce reliable differences. Anatomical changes produced by presumed conductive hearing losses during development have also been shown in the rat and chick (23, 24, 25, 36, 47, 129). One serious shortcoming of all these studies is that the normalcy of inner ear function has not been verified. Clinically, the existance of normal bone conduction thresholds is required to rule out combined conductive and sensorineural deficits. These same criteria should be applied to experimental investigations.

What do these studies tell us about the relationship between the acoustic environment, neuronal activity, and development of neurons in the auditory system? Laying aside the caveat mentioned above, they imply that cellular morphology can be altered by chronically abnormal activity. Little more can be concluded at this time. Only a few studies have sought to determine whether the abnormal condition was disrupting a normal developmental trend or producing an abnormal condition following normal ontogeny (43, 131). In some cases abnormal development has been found (47) or implicated (36); in others it appears that the effects of altered hearing are superimposed on normal development (24, 148). Moreover, it is by no means certain that a conductive hearing loss will cause a simple proportional reduction in ongoing activity in the eighth nerve, much less in the cochlear nuclei or other auditory nuclei in the brain. For example, a flat 40-decibel hearing loss can produce different effects in different frequency regions that may be due to alterations in bone conduction and/or internally generated activity superimposed on the conductive loss (129). Finally, we don't even know at which stage of development activity from the ear can begin to influence the central nervous system. Webster & Webster (148) and Brugge & O'Connor (15) indicate that the ontogeny of major anatomical and physiological processes are independent of "environmental events." However, it is important to consider activity along eighth nerve fibers, whether or not influenced by sound in the external environment, as part of the "environment" of the cells in the cochlear nuclei. Thus, in order to understand how activity from the ear influences development of central auditory system structures we need to know when a functional synaptic network is established, the ontogenetic activity pattern in the eighth nerve, and how sound influences that activity pattern throughout ontogeny.

Behavioral studies on animals subjected to altered acoustic environments (42, 68, 135), examinations of language development in children suffering chronic conductive hearing loss (50), and observations of clinicians all concur that normal function can be disrupted by an abnormal acoustic environment. Yet, to date there are only scattered results indicating altered physiological function following deprivation or altered stimulation (21, 22, 117, 127). Over the next few years it is certain that considerable effort will be expended in this area and a "battery" of changes will be demonstrated. Of paramount importance is a theoretical structure by which to interpret such changes in relation to the environment of the developing organism, activity in the neuronal network, and behavioral abilities.

ACKNOWLEDGMENTS

I thank S. Davis for assistance in preparing this manuscript, my colleagues D. Born, J. Deitch, D. Durham, and S. Young for their constructive comments on the manuscript, and W. Lippe for preparing Figure 1. Support for the author's research reported here was provided by NIH grants NS 15478–04 and NS 15395–04 and the Lions of Virginia Hearing Foundation.

Literature Cited

1. Änggard, L. 1965. An electrophysiological study of the development of cochlear function in the rabbit. *Acta Oto-Laryngol. Suppl.* 203:1–64
2. Anson, B. J., Donaldson, J. A. 1981. *Surgical Anatomy of the Temporal Bone.* Philadelphia: Saunders. 734 pp.
3. Bast, T. H., Anson, B. J. 1949. *The Temporal Bone and the Ear.* Springfield, IL: Thomas. 475 pp.
4. Békésy, G. von 1960. *Experiments in Hearing.* New York: McGraw-Hill

5. Bench, J. 1968. Sound transmission to the human fetus through the maternal abdominal wall. *J. Genet. Psychol.* 113:85–87
6. Bock, G. R., Saunders, J. C. 1977. A critical period for acoustic trauma in the hamster and its relation to cochlear development. *Science* 197:396–98
7. Bock, G. R., Seifter, E. J. 1978. Developmental changes of susceptibility to auditory fatigue in young hamsters. *Audiology* 17:193–203

8. Born, D. E., Rubel, E. W 1983. Differential effects of age on transneuronal cell loss following cochlea removal in chickens. *Proc. Midwinter Meet. Assoc. Res. Otolaryngol.*, St. Petersburg, Fla. p. 5

9. Bosher, S. K., Warren, R. L. 1971. A study of the electrochemistry and osmotic relationships of the cochlear fluids in the neonatal rat at the time of the development of the endocochlear potential. *J. Physiol.* 212:739–61

10. Bredburg, G. 1968. Cellular pattern and nerve supply of the human organ of Corti. *Acta Oto-Laryngol. Suppl.* 236:1–135

11. Brooks, D. 1971. Electroacoustic impedance bridge studies on normal ears of children. *J. Speech Hear. Res.* 14:247–53

12. Brugge, J. F. 1983. Development of the lower brain stem auditory nuclei. In *Development of Auditory and Vestibular Systems*, ed. R. Romand, R. Marty. pp. 89–120 New York: Academic

13. Brugge, J. F., Javel, E., Kitzes, L. M. 1978. Signs of functional maturation of peripheral auditory system in discharge patterns of neurons in anteroventral cochlear nucleus of kittens. *J. Neurophysiol.* 41:1557–79

14. Brugge, J. F., Kitzes, L. M., Javel, E. 1981. Postnatal development of frequency and intensity sensitivity of neurons in the anteroventral cochlear nucleus of kittens. *Hearing Res.* 5:217–29

15. Brugge, J. F., O'Connor, T. A. 1983. Postnatal functional development of the dorsal and posteroventral cochlear nuclei of the cat. *J. Acoust. Soc. Am.* In press

16. Carlier, E., Lenoir, M., Pujol, R. 1979. Development of cochlear frequency selectivity tested by compound action potential tuning curves. *Hearing Res.* 1:197–201

17. Carlier, E., Pujol, R. 1980. Supranormal sensitivity to ototoxic antibiotic of the developing rat cochlea. *Arch. Otorhinolaryngol.* 226:129–33

18. Carlier, E., Pujol, R. 1978. Role of inner and outer hair cells in coding sound intensity: an ontogenetic approach. *Brain Res.* 147:174–76

19. Clements, M., Kelly, J. B. 1978. Auditory spatial responses of young guinea pigs *(Cavia porcellus)* during and after ear blocking. *J. Comp. Physiol. Psychol.* 92:34–44

20. Clements, M., Kelly, J. B. 1978. Directional responses by kittens to an auditory stimulus. *Dev. Psychobiol.* 11:505–11

21. Clopton, B. M., Silverman, M. S. 1977. Plasticity of binaural interaction. II. Critical period and changes in midline response. *J. Neurophysiol.* 40:1275–80

22. Clopton, B. M., Silverman, M. S. 1978. Changes in latency and duration of neural responding following developmental auditory deprivation. *Exp. Brain Res.* 32:39–47

23. Coleman, J. R., O'Connor, P. 1979. Effects of monaural and binaural sound deprivation on cell development in the anteroventral cochlear nucleus of rat. *Exp. Neurol.* 64:553–66

24. Conlee, J. W., Parks, T. N. 1981. Age- and position-dependent effects of monaural acoustic deprivation in nucleus magnocellularis of the chicken. *J. Comp. Neurol.* 202:373–84

25. Conlee, J. W., Parks, T. N. 1983. Late appearance and deprivation-sensitive growth of permanent dendrites in the avian cochlear nucleus (nuc. magnocellularis). *J. Comp. Neurol.* 217:216–26

26. Cotanche, D. A., Sulik, K. K. 1982. Scanning electron microscopic analyses of the developing tegmentum vasculosum. *Proc. Midwinter Meet. Assoc. Res. Otolaryngol.* St. Petersberg, Fla. p. 32

27. Cotanche, D. A., Sulik, K. K. 1983. Morphogenesis of the avian basilar papilla with special emphasis on the differentiation of stereociliary bundles. See Ref. 8, p. 13

28. Cowan, W. M. 1970. Anterograde and retrograde transneuronal degeneration in the central and peripheral nervous system. In *Contemporary Research Methods in Neuroanatomy,* ed. W. J. H. Nauta, S. O. E. Ebbesson, pp. 217–51. New York: Springer

29. Dallos, P., Cheatham, M. A. 1976. Compound action potential tuning curves. *J. Acoust. Soc. Am.* 59:591–97

30. Dallos, P., Harris, D. 1978. Properties of auditory nerve responses in absence of outer hair cells. *J. Neurophysiol.* 41:365–83

31. DuPraw, E. J. 1968. *Cell and Molecular Biology.* New York: Academic. 739 pp.

32. Durham, D., Rubel, E. W 1983. Effects of cochlea removal on metabolic activity in the avian brain stem auditory nuclei: A succinic dehydrogenase study. See Ref. 8, p. 6

33. Ehret, G. 1976. Development of absolute auditory thresholds in the house mouse (Mus musculus). *J. Am. Audiol. Soc.* 1:173–84

34. Ehret, G. 1977. Postnatal development in the acoustic system of the house mouse in the light of developing masked thresholds. *J. Acoust. Soc. Am.* 62:143–48

35. Ehret, G., Romand, R. 1981. Postnatal development of absolute auditory

thresholds in kittens. *J. Comp. Physiol. Psychol.* 95:304–11

36. Feng, A. S., Rogowski, B. A. 1980. Effects of monaural and binaural occlusion on the morphology of neurons in the medial superior olivary nucleus of the rat. *Brain Res.* 189:530–34

37. Fermin, C. F., Cohen, G. M. 1983. Developmental gradients in the embryonic chicks basilar papilla. See Ref. 8, pp. 72–73

38. Friedmann, I. 1969. The innervation of the developing fowl embryo otocyst *in vivo* and *in vitro. Acta Oto-Laryngol.* 67:224–38

39. Fujimoto, S., Yamamoto, K., Hayabuchi, I., Yoshizuka, M. 1981. Scanning and transmission electron microscope studies on the organ of Corti and Stria vascularis in human fetal cochlear ducts. *Arch. Hist. Jpn.* 44:223–35

40. Ginzberg, R. D., Gilula, N. B. 1979. Modulation of cell junctions during differentiation of the chicken otocyst sensory epithelium. *Dev. Biol.* 68:110–29

41. Globus, A. 1975. Brain morphology as a function of presynaptic morphology and activity. In *The Developmental Neuropsychology of Sensory Deprivation,* ed. A. H. Riesen, pp. 9–91. New York: Academic

42. Gottlieb, G. 1978. Development of species identification in ducklings: IV. Change in species-specific perception caused by auditory deprivation. *J. Comp. Physiol. Psychol.* 92:375–87

43. Gottlieb, G. 1976. The roles of experience in development of behavior and the nervous system. In *Studies on the Development of Behavior and the Nervous System: Neural and Behavioral Specificity,* ed. G. Gottlieb, 3:25–54 New York: Academic

44. Gottlieb, G. 1971. Ontogenesis of sensory function in birds and mammals. In *The Biopsychology of Development,* ed. E. Tobach, L. A. Aronson, E. Shaw, pp. 67–128. New York: Academic

44a. Gottlieb, G., Krasnegor, N. A., eds. 1984. *Measurement of Audition and Vision in the First Year of Life: A Methodological Overview.* Norwood, NJ: Ablex Pub. Co. In press

45. Gray, L., Rubel, E. W 1981. Development of responsiveness to suprathreshold acoustic stimulation in chickens. *J. Comp. Physiol. Psychol.* 95:188–98

46. Gray, L., Rubel, E. W 1984. Development of auditory thresholds and frequency difference limens in chickens. See Ref. 44a, in press

47. Gray, L., Smith, Z. D. J., Rubel, E. W 1982. Developmental and experiential changes in dendritic symmetry. *Brain Res.* 244:360–64

48. Grimwade, J. C., Walker, D. W., Bartlett, M., Gordon, S., Wood, C. 1971. Human fetal heart rate change and movement in response to sound and vibration. *Am. J. Obstet. Gynecol.* 109:86–90

49. Guillery, R. W. 1973. Quantitative studies of transneuronal atrophy in the dorsal lateral geniculate nucleus of cats and kittens. *J. Comp. Neurol.* 149:423–37

50. Hanson, D. G., Ulvstad, R. F., eds. 1979. Otitis media and child development: Speech language and education. *Ann. Otol. Rhinol. Laryngol.* 88:(Suppl. 60) 1–111

51. Harrris, D. M. 1979. Action potential suppression, tuning curves and thresholds: comparison with single fiber data. *Hearing Res.* 1:133–54

52. Harris, D. M., Dallos, P. 1979. Forward masking of auditory nerve fiber responses. *J. Neurophysiol.* 42:1083–1107

53. Harris, D. M., Dallos, P. 1983. CM measurements of the place/frequency code in developing gerbils. See Ref. 8, p. 96

54. Henry, K. R., Chole, R. A., McGinn, M. D., Frush, D. P. 1981. Increased ototoxicity in both young and old mice. *Arch. Otolaryngol.* 107:92–95

55. Himelfarb, M. Z., Popelka, G. R., Shanon, E. 1979. Tympanometry in normal neonates. *J. Speech Hear. Res.* 22:179–91

56. Hirokawa, N. 1978. The ultrastructure of the basilar papilla of the chick. *J. Comp. Neurol.* 181:361–74

57. Hirokawa, N. 1977. Disappearance of afferent and efferent nerve terminals in the inner ear of the chick embryo after chronic treatment with β-Bungarotoxin. *J. Cell. Biol.* 73:27–46

58. Huttenlocher, P. R. 1967. Development of cortical neuronal activity in the neonatal cat. *Exp. Neurol.* 17:247–62

59. Jackson, H., Hackett, J. T., Rubel, E. W 1982. Organization and development of brain stem auditory nuclei in the chick: ontogeny of postsynaptic responses. *J. Comp. Neurol.* 210:80–86

60. Jackson, H., Parks, T. N. 1982. Functional synapse elimination in the developing avian cochlear nucleus with simultaneous reduction in cochlear nerve axon branching. *J. Neurosci.* 2:1736–43

61. Jackson, H., Rubel, E. W 1978. Ontogeny of behavioral responsiveness to sound in the chick embryo as indicated by electrical recordings of motility. *J. Comp. Physiol. Psychol.* 92:682–96

62. Jackson, J. R. H., Rubel, E. W 1976. Rapid transneuronal degeneration fol-

lowing cochlea removal in chickens. *Anat. Rec.* 184:434–35

63. Jerger, S., Jerger, J., Mauldin, L., Segal, P. 1974. Studies in impedance audiometry. II. Children less than six years old. *Arch. Otolaryngol.* 99:1–9

64. Jhaveri, S., Morest, D. K. 1982. Sequential alterations of neuronal architecture in nucleus magnocellularis of the developing chicken: A Golgi study. *Neuroscience* 7:837–53

65. Kane, E. C. 1974. Patterns of degeneration in the caudal cochlear nucleus of the cat after cochlear ablation. *Anat. Rec.* 179:67–92

66. Keith, R. W. 1975. Middle ear function of neonates. *Arch. Otolaryngol.* 101:376–79

67. Keith, R. W. 1973. Impedance audiometry with neonates. *Arch. Otolaryngol.* 97:465–67

68. Kerr, L. M., Ostapoff, E. M., Rubel, E. W 1979. The influence of acoustic experience on the ontogeny of frequency generalization gradients in the chicken. *J. Exp. Psychol.: Anim. Behav. Proc.* 5:97–115

69. Deleted in proof

70. Lenoir, M., Bock, G., Pujol, R. 1979. Supra-normal susceptibility to acoustic trauma in the rat pup cochlea. *J. Physiol.* 75:521–24

71. Lenoir, M., Pujol, R. 1980. Sensitive period to acoustic trauma in the rat pup cochlea: Histological findings. *Acta Oto-Laryngol.* 89:317–22

72. Lenoir, M., Shnerson, A., Pujol, R. 1980. Cochlear receptor development in the rat with emphasis on synaptogenesis. *Anat. Embryol.* 160:253–62

73. Levi-Montalcini, R. 1949. The development of the acousticovestibular centers in the chick embryo in the absence of the afferent root fibers and of descending fiber tracts. *J. Comp. Neurol.* 91:209–41

74. Lippe, W., Rubel, E. W 1983. Development of the place principle: Tonotopic organization. *Science* 219:514–16

75. Martin, M. R., Rickets, C. 1981. Histogenesis of the cochlear nucleus of the mouse. *J. Comp. Neurol.* 197:169–84

76. Marty, R. 1962. Développement postnatal des réponses sensorielles du cortex cérébral chez le chat et le lapin. *Arch. Anat. Microsc. Morphol. Exp.* 51:129–264

77. Moore, D. R., Irvine, D. R. F. 1980. Development of binaural input, response patterns, and discharge rate in single units of the cat inferior colliculus. *Exp. Brain Res.* 38:103–8

78. Moore, D. R., Irvine, D. R. F. 1979. A developmental study of the sound pressure transformation by the head of the cat. *Acta Oto-Laryngol.* 87:434–40

79. Moore, D. R., Irvine, D. R. F. 1979. The development of some peripheral and central auditory responses in the neonatal cat. *Brain Res.* 163:49–59

80. Muir, D. Clifton, R. K. 1984. Infants' orientation to the location of sound sources. See Ref. 44a, in press

81. Noden, D. M. 1980. The migration and cytodifferentiation of cranial neural crest cells. In *Current Research Trends in Prenatal Craniofacial Development*, ed. R. M. Pratt, R. L. Christiansen, pp. 3–25. New York: Elsevier

82. Nordeen, K. W., Killackey, H. P., Kitzes, L. M. 1983. Ascending projections to the inferior colliculus following unilateral cochlear ablations in the neonatal gerbil, Meriones unguiculatus. *J. Comp. Neurol.* 214:144–153

83. Olsho, L. W. 1983. Infant frequency discrimination. *Infant Behav. Dev.* In press

84. Orr, M. F. 1968. Histogenesis of sensory epithelium in reaggregate of dissociated embryonic chick otocysts. *Dev. Biol.* 17:39–54

85. Parks, T. N. 1979. Afferent influences on the development of the brain stem auditory nuclei of the chicken: otocyst ablation. *J. Comp. Neurol.* 183:665–78

86. Peduzzi, J. D., Crossland, W. J. 1983. Anterograde transneuronal degeneration in the ectomamillary nucleus and ventral lateral geniculate nucleus of the chick. *J. Comp. Neurol.* 213:287–300

87. Powell, T. P. S., Erulkar, S. D. 1962. Transneuronal cell degeneration in the auditory relay nuclei of the cat. *J. Anat.* 96:249–68

88. Price, G. R. 1976. Age as a factor in susceptibility to hearing loss: young versus adult ears. *J. Acoust. Soc. Am.* 60:886–92

89. Pujol, R., Hilding, D. 1973. Anatomy and physiology of the onset of auditory function. *Acta Oto-Laryngol.* 76:1–10

90. Pujol, R., Carlier, E., Devigne, C. 1979. Significance of presynaptic formations in the very early stages of cochlear synaptogenesis. *Neurosci. Lett.* 15:97–102

91. Pujol, R., Carlier, E., Devigne, C. 1978. Different patterns of cochlear innervation during the development of the kitten. *J. Comp. Neurol.* 177:529–36

92. Pujol, R., Carlier, E., Lenoir, M. 1980. Ontogenetic approach to inner and outer hair cell function. *Hearing Res.* 2:423–30

93. Pujol, R., Marty, R. 1970. Postnatal

maturation of the cochlea of the cat. *J. Comp. Neurol.* 139:115–25

94. Pujol, R., Marty, R. 1968. Structural and physiological relationships of the maturing auditory system. In *Ontogenesis of the Brain*, ed. L. Jilek, S. Trojan, pp. 337–85. Prague: Charles Univ. Press.

95. Rebillard, M., Pujol, R. 1983. Innervation of the chicken basilar papilla during its development. *Acta Oto-Laryngol.* In press

96. Rebillard, G., Rubel, E. W 1981. Electrophysiological study of the maturation of auditory responses from the inner ear of the chick. *Brain Res.* 229:15–23

97. Relkin, E. M., Saunders, J. C. 1980. Displacement of the malleus in neonatal golden hamster. *Acta Oto-Laryngol.* 90: 6–15

98. Relkin, E. M., Saunders, J. C., Konkle, D. F. 1979. The development of middle-ear admittance in the hamster. *J. Acoust. Soc. Am.* 66:133–39

99. Retzius, G. 1884. *Das Gehörorgan der Wirbeltiere. II. Das Gehörorgan der Reptilien, der Vögel und Säugetiere.* Stockholm: Samson & Wallin. 368 pp.

100. Rogowski, B. A., Feng, A. S. 1981. Normal postnatal development of medial superior olivary neurons in the albino rat: a Golgi and Nissl study. *J. Comp. Neurol.* 196:85–97

101. Romand, R. 1979. Development of auditory nerve activity in kittens. *Brain Res.* 173:554–56

102. Romand, R., Marty, R. 1975. Postnatal maturation of the cochlear nuclei in the cat: a neurophysiological study. *Brain Res.* 83:225–33

103. Romand, R., Marty, R., eds. 1983. *Development of Auditory and Vestibular Systems,* 576 pp. New York: Academic. In press

104. Romand, R., Romand, M.-R. 1982. Myelination kinetics of spiral ganglion cells in kittens. *J. Comp. Neurol.* 204: 1–5

105. Rubel, E. W 1983. Auditory system development. See Ref. 44a, in press

106. Rubel, E. W 1978. Ontogeny of structure and function in the vertebrate auditory system. In *Handbook of Sensory Physiology, Development of Sensory Systems*, ed. M. Jacobson, 9:135–237. New York: Springer

107. Rubel, E. W 1971. A comparison of somatotopic organization in sensory neocortex in newborn kittens and adult cats. *J. Comp. Neurol* 143:447–80

108. Rubel, E. W, Smith, D. J., Miller, L. C. 1976. Organization and development of brain stem auditory nuclei of the chicken: Ontogeny of n. magnocellularis and n. laminaris. *J. Comp. Neurol.* 166: 469–90

109. Rubel, E. W, Rosenthal, M. H. 1975. The ontogeny of auditory frequency generalization in the chicken. *J. Exp. Psychol: Anim. Behav. Proc.* 1:287–97

110. Rubel, E. W, Ryals, B. M. 1983. Development of the place principle: Acoustic trauma. *Science* 219:512–14

111. Rubel, E. W, Smith, Z. D. J., Steward, O. 1981. Sprouting in the avian brain stem auditory pathway: Dependence on dendritic integrity. *J. Comp. Neurol.* 202:397–414

112. Ruben, R. J. 1967. Development of the inner ear of the mouse: A radioautographic study of terminal mitoses. *Acta Oto-Laryngol. Suppl.* 220:1–44

113. Ryan, A. F., Woolf, N. K., Sharp, F. R. 1982. Functional ontogeny in the central auditory pathway of the mongolian gerbil: sequential development and supranormal responsiveness indicated by 2-deoxyglucose uptake. See Ref. 26, pp. 19–20

114. Ryugo, D. K., Fekete, D. M. 1982. Morphology of primary axosomatic endings in the anteroventral cochlear nucleus of the cat: A study of the endbulbs of Held. *J. Comp. Neurol.* 210:239–57

115. Salamy, A., Birtley-Fenn, C., Bronshvag, M. 1979. Ontogenesis of human brainstem evoked potential amplitude. *Dev. Psychobiol.* 12:519–26

116. Salamy, A., McKean, C. 1976. Postnatal development of human brainstem potentials during the first year of life. *EEG Clin. Neurophysiol.* 40:418–26

117. Sanes, D. H., Constantine-Paton, M. 1982. The role of temporal activity during auditory maturation. *Soc. Neurosci. Abstr.* 8:669

118. Saunders, J. C., Bock, G. R. 1978. Influences of early auditory trauma on auditory development. In *Studies on the Development of Behavior and the Nervous System, Early Influences*, ed. G. Gottlieb, 4:249–87. New York: Academic

119. Saunders, J. C., Coles, R. B., Gates, G. R. 1973. The development of auditory evoked responses on the cochlea and cochlear nuclei of the chick. *Brain Res.* 63:59–74

120. Saunders, J. C., Doglin, K. G., Lowry, L. D. 1980. The maturation of frequency selectivity in C57BL/6J mice studied with auditory evoked response tuning curves. *Brain Res.* 187:69–79

121. Saunders, J. C., Kaltenbach, J. A., Relkin, E. M. 1983. The structural and functional development of the outer and middle ear. See Ref. 103, pp. 3–25

122. Schneider, B., Trehub, S. E., Bull, D.

1980. High-frequency sensitivity in infants. *Science* 207:1003–4

123. Shaw, E. A. G. 1974. The external ear. In *Handbook of Sensory Physiology, Auditory System*, ed. W. D. Keidel, W. D. Neff, 1:455–90. New York: Springer

124. Shnerson, A., Devigne, C., Pujol, R. 1982. Age-related changes in the C57BL/6J mouse cochlea. II. Ultrastructural findings. *Dev. Brain Res.* 2:77–88

125. Shnerson, A., Pujol, R. 1982. Age-related changes in the C57B1/6J mouse cochlea. I. Physiological findings. *Dev. Brain Res.* 2:65–75

126. Shnerson, A., Willott, J. F. 1979. Development of inferior colliculus response properties in C57BL/6J mouse pups. *Exp. Brain Res.* 37:373–85

127. Silverman, M. S., Clopton, B. M. 1977. Plasticity of binaural interaction. I. Effect of early auditory deprivation. *J. Neurophysiol.* 40:1266–74

128. Smith, Z. D. J. 1981. Organization and development of brain stem auditory nuclei of the chicken: Dendritic development of n. laminaris. *J. Comp. Neurol.* 203:309–33

129. Smith, Z. D. J., Gray, L., Rubel, E. W 1983. Afferent influences on brain stem auditory nuclei of the chicken: n. laminaris dendritic length following monaural acoustic deprivation. *J. Comp. Neurol.* In press

130. Sobkowicz, H. M., Rose, J. E., Scott, G. E., Slapnick, S. M. 1982. Ribbon synapses in the developing intact and cultured organ of Corti in the mouse. *J. Neurosci.* 2:942–57

131. Solomon, R. L., Lessac, M. S. 1968. A control group design for experimental studies of developmental processes. *Psychol. Bull.* 70:145–209

132. Starr, A., Amlie, R. N., Martin, W. H., Sanders, S. 1977. Development of auditory function in newborn infants revealed by auditory brainstem potentials. *Pediatrics* 60:831–39

133. Stream, R. W., Stream, K. S., Walker, J. R., Breningstall, G. 1978. Emerging characteristics of the acoustic reflex in infants. *Trans. Am. Acad. Opthal. Otolaryngol.* 86:628–36

134. Schweitzer, L., Cant, N. B. 1983. Development of the cochlear innervation of the dorsal cochlear nucleus of the hamster. *J. Comp. Neurol.* In press

135. Tees, R. C. 1967. Effects of early auditory restriction in the rat on adult pattern discrimination. *J. Comp. Physiol. Psychol.* 63:389–92

136. Tonndorf, J., Duvall, A. J. III. 1966. Loading of the tympanic membrane: its effect upon bone conduction in experimental animals. *Acta Otolaryngol. Suppl.* 213:39–54

137. Tilney, L. G., DeRosier, D. J., Mulroy, M. J. 1980. The organization of actin filaments in the stereocilia of cochlear hair cells. *J. Cell Biol.* 86:244–59

138. Tilney, L. G., Egelman, E. H., DeRosier, D. J., Saunders, J. C. 1983. Actin filaments, stereocilia, and hair cells of the bird cochlea. II. Packing of actin filaments in the stereocilia and in the cuticular plate and what happens to the organization when the stereocilia are bent. *J. Cell Biol.* 96:822–34

139. Tilney, L. G., Suanders, J. C. 1983. Actin filaments, stereocilia, and hair cells of the brid cochlea. l. Length, number, width, and distribution of stereocilia of each hair cell are related to the position of the hair cell on the cochlea. *J. Cell Biol.* 96:807–21

140. Trune, D. R. 1982. Influence of neonatal cochlear removal on the development of mouse cochlear nucleus. I. Number, size, and density of its neurons. *J. Comp. Neurol.* 209:409–24

141. Trune, D. R. 1982. Influence of neonatal cochlear removal on the development of mouse cochlear nucleus. II. Dendritic morphometry of its neurons. *J. Comp. Neurol.* 209:425–34

142. Van de Water, T. R. 1967. Effects of removal of the statoacoustic ganglion complex upon the growing ototocyst. *Ann. Otol. Rhinol. Laryngol.* 85(Suppl. 33):1–32

143. Van de Water, T. R., Li, C. W., Ruben, R. J., Shea, C. A., 1980. Ontogenetic aspects of mammalian inner ear development. In *Morphogenesis and Malformation of the Ear*, ed. R. J. Gorlin pp. 5–45. New York: Liss

144. Van de Water, T. R., Maderson, P. F. A., Jaskoll, T. F. 1980. The morphogenesis of the middle and external ear. See Ref. 143, pp. 147–80

145. Van de Water, T. R., Ruben, R. J. 1976. Organogenesis of the ear. In *Scientific Foundation of Otolaryngology*, ed. R. Hinchcliffe, D. Harrison, pp. 173–84. London: W. Heineman Med. Books

146. Vince, M. A., Armitage, S. E., Baldwin, B. A., Toner, J., Moore, B. C. J. 1982. The sound environment of the foetal sheep. *Behaviour* 81:296–315

147. Wada, T. 1923. Anatomical and physiological studies on the growth of the inner ear of the albino rat. *Am. Anat. Mem.* 10:1–74

148. Webster, D. B., Webster, M. 1980. Mouse brainstem auditory nuclei development. *Ann. Otol. Rhinol. Laryngol.* 89(Suppl. 68):254–56

149. Webster, D. B., Webster, M. 1979. Effects of neontal conductive hearing loss on brainstem auditory nuclei. *Ann. Otol. Rhinol. Laryngol.* 88:684–88

150. Webster, D. B., Webster, M. 1978. Long-term effects of cochlear nerve destruction on the cochlear nuclei. *Anat. Rec.* 190:578–79 (Abstr.)

151. Webster, D. B., Webster, M. 1977. Neonatal sound deprivation affects brainstem auditory nuclei. *Arch. Otolaryngol.* 103:392–96

152. Willott, J. F., ed. 1983. *Auditory Psychobiology of the Mouse.* Springfield, IL.: Thomas. 507 pp.

153. Willott, J. F., Shnerson, A. 1978. Rapid development of tuning characteristics of inferior colliculus neurons of mouse pups. *Brain Res.* 148:230–33

154. Willott, J. F., Urban, G. P. 1978. Response properties of neurons in nuclei of

the mouse inferior colliculus. *J. Comp. Physiol.* 127:175–84

155. Woolf, N. K., Ryan, A. F. 1983. Functional ontogeny of neural discharge patterns in the ventral cochlear nucleus of the mongolian gerbil. *Exp. Brain Res.* In press

156. Woolsey, T. A., Wann, J. R. 1976. Areal changes in mouse cortical barrels following vibrissal damage at different postnatal ages. *J. Comp. Neurol.* 170: 53–66

157. Woolsey, C. N., Walzl, E. M. 1942. Topical projection of nerve fibers from local regions of the cochlea in the cerebral cortex of the cat. *Bull. Johns Hopkins Hosp.* 71:315–44

158. Yntema, C. L. 1950. An analysis of induction of the ear from foreign ectoderm in the salamander embryo. *J. Exp. Zool.* 113:211–44

Ann. Rev. Physiol. 1984. 46:231–46
Copyright © 1984 by Annual Reviews Inc. All rights reserved

COCHLEAR MECHANICS

William S. Rhode

Department of Neurophysiology, University of Wisconsin, Madison, Wisconsin 53706

INTRODUCTION

Recent discoveries have contributed to a revolutionary atmosphere in cochlear mechanics. Previously held views of the process of transducing acoustic energy in the inner ear have undergone significant changes, due to both direct and indirect measurements of cochlear mechanics. Cochlear partition mechanics appear to provide a more complete determination of neural behavior than previously thought.

Beside direct observations of cochlear mechanics, investigative techniques have included the use of cochlear microphonics, intracellular hair-cell recording, auditory-nerve fiber responses, psychoacoustic responses, and the measurement of acoustic emissions in the external ear. Drugs, fatigue, and trauma are used to manipulate the cochlea in the hope of discovering the contribution of individual components of the transducer process.

No longer can the mechanical properties be ascribed to a single, all-important element, the basilar membrane. Attention is now directed toward the role of the tectorial membrane and the hair cells and their stereocilia. Observations of nonlinearities and acoustic emissions suggest active elements in the cochlea and demand substantial modification (8, 15) of previous models of cochlear function (14). Modeling efforts are directed toward increasingly comprehensive representations of the cochlea as they become concerned with micromechanics.

BACKGROUND

The mammalian cochlea is a helical structure encased in bone, in which reside the hair cells, the acoustic sensory transducers. In cross-section, the cochlea consists of three fluid-filled compartments: the scala media, which is a completely sealed duct; and the scala vestibuli and the scala tympani, which are

231

0066-4278/84/0315-0231$02.00

connected through the helicotrema and bound the scala media on either side. Airborne pressure variations are coupled through the middle-ear ossicles to the fluid-filled scala vestibuli and, in turn, to the scala tympani. The subsequent pressure differences between the scala vestibuli and the scala tympani produce displacement of the basilar membrane that separates the two compartments, resulting in activation of the acoustic sensory structure known as the organ of Corti, which rests on the basilar membrane and houses the hair-cell transducers.

The early history of direct observation of cochlear mechanics began in 1928 with the efforts of Georg von Békésy (83). As a young Hungarian engineer, he was assigned the task of improving the telephone system. With great wisdom, von Békésy decided that such a task required an understanding of the hearing organ, and he thus embarked on one of the most illustrious careers in hearing science. Using both genius in instrumentation and remarkable wisdom, he contributed many fundamental observations on the mechanics of the inner ear. He focused attention on the basilar membrane, demonstrating its importance in the translation of pressure changes in the inner ear fluids and showing that the membrane's own, intrinsic characteristics determined its vibratory pattern at different frequencies. His foremost observation was that traveling waves move along the basilar membrane from the basal end toward the apex. Further, he confirmed the mechanical basis for the place principle of frequency analysis by demonstrating that high frequencies produce the greatest displacement of the cochlear partition in the basal region and low frequencies in the apical region.

DIRECT OBSERVATIONS OF COCHLEAR MECHANICS

In the 1950s and 1960s a number of factors led many students of cochlear function to question the credibility of von Békésy's observations. First, most of his observations were made on nonphysiological (dead) cochlear preparations. Second, the technique used to observe the mechanical vibrations of the cochlea (a light microscope with stroboscopic illumination) necessitated the use of intense sound of up to 150 dB sound pressure level, well above the natural range of stimulus intensity. Third, the tuning of the basilar membrane (or cochlear partition), as determined by von Békésy, was much broader than that inferred in psychoacoustic experimentation (e.g. 78) or in recordings from auditory-nerve fibers (e.g. 42). Lastly, it had been estimated, based on extrapolation of the response at relatively high stimulus levels, that the displacement of the basilar membrane at threshold would be on the order of 0.0001 nm (1/100 the diameter of a hydrogen atom). All of these observations puzzled individuals attempting to understand and explain the physics of the inner ear.

The objections raised to von Békésy's measurements were partially overcome when Johnstone & Boyle (33) employed the Mössbauer effect to measure the amplitude of vibration of the basilar membrane in guinea pig. This technique requires the placement of a small radioactive metal foil, a Mössbauer source, on the vibrating structure. The number of gamma-rays from the source passing through an absorbing metal foil is modulated by the source velocity. Velocities as small as 0.1 mm s^{-1} can be measured in this way. Johnstone & Boyle's results generally supported von Békésy's findings but indicated that the basal (high-frequency) region of the guinea-pig basilar membrane was more sharply tuned than previously described. The high-frequency slope of the amplitude-vs-frequency relation for basilar-membrane vibration was shown to be as much as -100 dB per octave. Overall, however, the vibration was broad and could be described as a low-pass filter (34). The use of the Mössbauer technique was extended by Rhode (56–61) to include measurement of both amplitude and phase. When the technique was applied to measure vibration of the squirrel-monkey basilar membrane in the mid-frequency range, a number of important findings were reported: (a) The basilar-membrane/malleus-transfer ratio peaked near the cutoff frequency (the frequency beyond which little energy is transmitted). (b) The high-frequency slope was as much as -140 dB per octave. (c) Beyond the cutoff, a plateau region occurs, characterized by nearly constant amplitude and phase. The phase lag increases to more than 20 radians, confirming von Békésy's observation that the motion must be a traveling wave because a simple resonator would not exhibit more than 2π radians phase difference. (d) The final and probably most significant finding was that basilar-membrane vibration was nonlinear in the region of the peak. This finding created the possibility that the basilar membrane, based on its own intrinsic vibration characteristics, might account for some of the response patterns observable in eighth-nerve fibers.

Conflicting results (90) indicated that the tuning of the basilar membrane was broad and that the vibration was linear. Confounding the conflict was the use of a different animal, the guinea pig, and an alternative measurement technique, the capacitive probe. This device measures changes in capacitance between a 0.15 mm diameter probe and the basilar membrane. It is capable of measuring vibrations down to 0.01 nm (87). These data suggested that the basilar membrane could be characterized as a low-pass filter and paved the way for the formal hypothesis of the existence of a second filter (18) to account for the sharp tuning of auditory-nerve fibers (e.g. 16, 42).

Thus there were two principal differences between Rhode's results and those found for the guinea pig (33, 90): (a) a more peaked (or sharper) frequency response in the squirrel monkey, and, (b) the very marked nonlinear response in the region of the characteristic frequency. One explanation advanced for the discrepancies was the required evacuation of the perilymph from the scala tympani before making capacitive-probe measurements. Robertson (62) demonstrated that this evacuation can eliminate the sharp tuning of cochlear neurons. To counter this criticism, Evans & Wilson (18) measured tuning in auditory-nerve fibers concurrently with partial drainage of the scala tympani; they found fiber tuning to be similar to that found under normal conditions. In contrast, LePage (48) observed a pronounced change in sensitivity and tuning when perilymph was removed from the scala.

Nonlinearity

The finding of nonlinear vibration in the squirrel monkey basilar membrane (56, 58, 60) was not universally accepted as normative. Nevertheless, it had important implications for hearing theory in estimating the threshold displacement of the basilar membrane and in accounting for the sharpening of tuning of the mechanical filter and for the source of distortion products.

The nonlinearity was confined to the region of the characteristic frequency, where it was compressive in nature—that is, increasing the intensity resulted in a broader transfer characteristic, with a lowered peak that was shifted to lower frequencies. Moreover, when measured around the characteristic frequency, phase changes occur in the vibration of the basilar membrane as intensity is varied (21, 58). These changes are compatible with changes of phase observed in auditory-nerve fiber discharges as a function of intensity (2).

The nonlinear nature of basilar-membrane vibration was supported by Mössbauer measurements made using transient stimuli (58, 64, 65). The amplitude of later cycles of the impulse response increased much more slowly as intensity was increased than would have been expected for a linear system.

Rhode (60) did not find any nonlinearity in the vibration of Reissner's membrane in the apical region of the squirrel-monkey cochlea nor in a few measurements performed on the basilar membrane in the guinea-pig basal turn. This led to speculation that the nonlinearity might be species specific and/or location specific.

Recent studies have provided direct evidence of nonlinear basilar-membrane vibration in guinea pig. Le Page (48) found a compressive nonlinearity using a capacitance probe. Sellick et al (72) applied the Mössbauer technique to guinea-pig basilar membrane; the nonlinear behavior they measured was very similar to that reported by Rhode. The nonlinearity was confined to the region of CF, was compressive in nature, and extended to levels as low as 20 dB SPL. Away from CF, either higher or lower frequencies, the vibration was linear.

Tuning

Until recently it was generally accepted that the tuning of auditory-nerve fibers was substantially sharper than the tuning of the basilar membrane (22, 83, 90). Rhode (60) showed fairly good agreement between the two measures in squirrel monkey, but the tip of the mechanical curve was still at least 20 dB lower than the neural FTC. Khanna & Leonard (38) used a laser interferometer in cat to show that nearly exact agreement between the mechanical and neural FTC can be obtained. Sellick et al (72) obtained similar results in guinea pig (Figure 1). These results suggest that the mechanics of the basilar membrane can explain the neural tuning without the need to invoke a second filter hypothesis.

Lability of Tuning

Since von Békésy performed his measurements on dead cochleas, Rhode (57) compared in vivo and postmortem measurements of basilar-membrane vibrations. He found that both amplitude and phase change upon the death of the animal. There is a rapid and progressive decrease in amplitude, a shift of the tuning curve to lower frequencies, and a loss of the peaked nature (i.e.

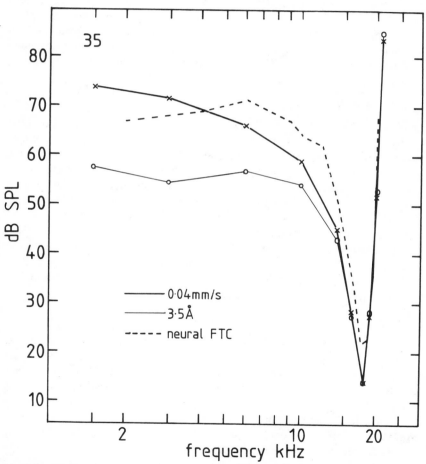

Figure 1   Basilar-membrane iso-velocity and iso-displacement curves compared with a FTC from guinea pig [Sellick et al (72, Fig. 10); by permission of the authors].

broadening of the mechanical filter) of basilar-membrane tuning. Furthermore, the nonlinear behavior of the vibration disappears after death.

In one of the few measurements of the spatial displacement pattern of basilar membrane, Kohllöffel (46) traced postmortem changes by measuring the fuzziness of laser speckle in an excised cochlea. He found progressive changes over a period of a week. The peak of the transfer ratio shifted to a lower frequency at a given basilar-membrane location.

The sensitivity of basilar-membrane tuning to the state of the cochlea has now been extensively documented. Khanna & Leonard (39) vividly describe the pitfalls and problems encountered in making their laser interferometric measurements. Every manipulation of the cochlea results in a progressive loss of sensitivity and tuning. By monitoring the compound action potential while measuring basilar-membrane motion, Sellick et al (72) demonstrated that both decreased progressively after the cochlea was opened to allow placement of the Mössbauer source on the basilar membrane. The nonlinearity of vibration disappeared as the CAP decreased and was absent postmortem.

Nonmammalian Cochlear Tuning

Evidence indicates that in the alligator lizard, the basilar membrane plays little if any role in determining frequency selectivity (85). The fact that the basilar membrane does not increase in width from base to apex, as it does in the mammalian cochlea, may account for this. There are, however, structures that do exhibit systematic morphological changes. The length of the ciliary tufts is longer and varies in the basal region of the cochlea (which is also devoid of a tectorial membrane). The micromechanics of this cochlea could, then, be determined by structures other than the poorly tuned basilar membrane (54).

Further evidence of alternate tuning mechanisms arises from studies in the turtle cochlea (6). Intracellular recordings from cochlear hair cells showed an electrical tuning mechanism. These studies would suggest that a single explanation for cochlear tuning may not suffice across species (84).

Threshold

Von Békésy determined by linear extrapolation that, at behavioral threshold (about 0 dB SPL or 20 uPa in the frequency region of greatest sensitivity), the amplitude of vibration of the human cochlear partition would be about 0.001 nm. Roughly comparable values were estimated in other species upon linear extrapolation over a 60–80 dB range (34, 56). Using the largest observed value for the amplitude of vibration (60), and assuming a behavioral threshold of 0 dB SPL, a threshold vibrational value of 0.01 nm was obtained. But when iso-amplitude curves are compared to neural threshold-tuning curves, as Rhode (60) did for Reissner's membrane vibrations in the apical turn of the squirrel monkey cochlea, a value near 0.1 nm was obtained. Sellick et al (72) found a value of 0.35 nm to be a good estimate of threshold for one eighth-nerve fiber in guinea pig.

In nonmammalian species, two estimates of threshold displacements have been made: a value of 0.2 nm (1 kHz at 30 dB SPL) in alligator lizard (85), and 0.03 nm in turtle (5). These values are "in the same ball park" and suggest that the earlier extrapolations, made over a 70–140 dB range, are in error by one to two orders of magnitude. It appears, then, that we are no longer dealing with a process that operates at amplitudes of 1/100 the diameter of a hydrogen molecule, but one that is very sensitive nonetheless.

INDIRECT OBSERVATIONS OF COCHLEAR MECHANICS

Measurement techniques that do not entail direct observation of the basilar membrane have received extensive attention from a number of laboratories. While all of the direct mechanical measurements are invasive and have been shown to nearly always induce some change in response characteristics, electrophysiological measures such as auditory-nerve fiber responses, cochlear microphonics, and hair-cell recording inflict less damage to the operational environment. The development of mathmatical models of the cochlea has also provided another method of analyzing and understanding this complex system.

These techniques have been utilized to investigate both cochlear tuning and nonlinear mechanisms. Various manipulations of the cochlea such as anoxia or the application of ototoxic drugs [see Evans (17) for review] have been employed to analyze cochlear tuning. Investigations of nonlinear mechanisms have focused on the generation of distortion products, suppression phenomena, acoustic emissions, and echoes.

Numerous early investigations hypothesized a direct relation between basilar-membrane mechanics and the cochlear microphonic or CM (7, 10). The spatial resolution of CM was, however, too limited, and results were often ambiguous. Recent experiments employing auditory-nerve recording and the very difficult but rewarding technique of intracellular recording from hair cells have largely overcome the problems of interpretation common to the CM experiments (13, 66).

Tuning

Von Békésy (83) concluded that the mechanical properties of the basilar membrane largely determine the mechanical properties of the cochlear partition and hence its vibration. More recent manipulations of the cochlea suggest this may not be the entire story. Kiang et al (40) observed abnormal frequency threshold curves (isorate curve at threshold or FTC) in auditory-nerve fibers of cats poisoned with an ototoxic antibiotic, kanamycin. The use of transient hypoxia (17) demonstrated the disappearance of the tip of the tuning curve, while CM recorded at the round window remained normal. This led Evans to conclude that basilar-membrane properties are unaltered by the manipulation. This change in tuning was reversible, as was the loss of the FTC when other ototoxic procedures were tried. This, and other demonstrations, led to the conclusion that there must be a physiologically vulnerable second filter in the cochlea that accounts for the sharp tuning of auditory-nerve fibers.

Examination of the effects of ototoxic drugs on FTCs have suggested interactions between inner and outer hair cells (17, 40). Abnormal FTCs were obtained from nerve fibers believed to innervate regions of the cochlea in which the inner hair cells (IHCs) appeared normal and the outer hair cells (OHCs) were missing. Dallos & Harris (11) used the kanamycin techniques to demonstrate that fibers believed to innervate regions with a nearly pure loss of OHCs could have sharp tuning, despite elevated thresholds. This implied that the sharp tuning characteristics of eighth-nerve fibers were determined by the cochlear mechanics–inner hair cell system while the function of the OHCs was to perform a frequency-dependent boost in the sensitivity of the IHCs. The uncertainty of the site of cochlear innervation of the responding eighth-nerve fibers and their specific relationship to the lesioned region makes these experiments difficult to interpret unequivocally. Robertson et al (63) alleviated this problem by recording FTCs directly from the cell bodies of eighth-nerve fibers, which are situated in the spiral ganglion immediately adjacent to the region of the cochlea that they innervate. They produced a limited lesion of the organ of Corti by driving a 20-micron pipette through the basilar membrane. Neurons from the damaged region of the cochlea were shown to have abnormal FTCs when compared to those of similarly placed neurons in normal cochleas.

Velocity vs Displacement

The majority of auditory-nerve fibers innervate the inner hair cells [95% in cat (80)]. Furthermore, there is no clear physiological evidence for the existence of two populations of eighth-nerve fibers. This would indicate that all auditory–nerve fiber recordings are from the afferents that synapse on inner hair cells. The cilia of the outer hair cells appear to be attached to the tectorial membrane (50), and basilar-membrane displacement is probably the effective stimulus, while the cilia of the inner hair cells do not appear to be attached to the tectorial membrane and may rely on viscous drag of the surrounding fluid [but see (19)]. Dallos et al (9), relying on cochlear microphonic data, suggested that the IHCs respond to the velocity of the basilar membrane. Intracellular recordings demonstrated that inner hair cells respond to basilar membrane velocity at low frequencies (53, 67).

Because of the variability of the data and the complex effects of intensity, frequency, and species on the phase characteristics, it is difficult to determine whether the auditory-nerve output is proportional to basilar-membrane velocity at all frequencies in all species. Sellick et al (73) suggest that FTCs and basilar-membrane iso-velocity curves are in good agreement. Comparing the low-frequency portion of the displacement and velocity curves to the FTC (Fig. 1), it appears that the iso-velocity curve has a different slope than the FTC while, if the displacement curve is shifted vertically, it is closer to the FTC. In both Rhode's (60) and Khanna & Leonard's (38) results, displacement curves are in closer agreement with FTCs than velocity curves when shifted vertically. Similarly, recently obtained basilar-membrane iso-amplitude curves are nearly parallel to the intracellularly obtained iso-amplitude curves from inner hair cells, while the iso-velocity curves clearly are not (74).

Distortion Products

Many psychoacoustic studies have concentrated on the nonlinear aspects of cochlear function. One such nonlinear property is reflected in the combination-tone response. When two tones of frequencies f_1 and f_2 are presented simultaneously, distortion products can be seen at frequencies $mf_1 \pm nf_2$ (m and n are integers) with the most prominent component at $2f_1 - f_2$ (cubic difference tone, CDT). Goldstein & Kiang (25) demonstrated that auditory-nerve fibers can respond to $2f_1 - f_2$ even when the primary tones (f_1 and f_2) were outside of the response region of the fiber. This result suggested that the nonlinear mechanism generating these combination-tone responses must exist in the peripheral stages of the auditory system. Smoorenburg (79) suggested that in order for combination components to be seen in auditory-nerve discharges, the cochlear nonlinearity should be coupled to the basilar membrane. Furthermore, he suggested that this might be accomplished if the compliance of the stereocilia on the hair cells changed with the initiation of an action potential. While this is not necessarily the exact mechanism, the suggestion would seem to be a good one in the light of recent investigations of hair cells (e.g. 19, 31, 35). Smoorenburg also suggested a nonlinear hair-cell coupling of the basilar membrane to the tectorial membrane. He observed that by placing the primary tones in the region of loss (in a subject possessing a dip in his auditory threshold curve) no combination tones were perceived. This implied that the integrity of the hair cells was necessary for the nonlinear mechanism to function. Smoorenburg also suggested that two other nonlinear features of the system, distortion and suppression effects, might be explained by a compressive power-law nonlinearity with an exponent that depends on level.

There has been little evidence for combination tones in basilar-membrane motion (59, 89). Rhode (59) reported the level of CDTs in basilar-membrane vibrations to be at least -40 dB relative to the primaries; however, due to the relative insensitivity of the Mössbauer technique, he had to use primaries of 100–120 dB SPL. This was probably self-defeating, because a number of studies have now demonstrated the lability of cochlear function and nonlinear behavior, particularly in response to high-intensity stimuli.

CM studies led Dallos et al (10) to conclude that there are no mechanically propagated distortion products (components generated in the region of the primaries that propagate to their appropriate cochlear location) for intensities below 70–80 dB and that distortion products in CM are localized to the region of the primary tones. Gibian & Kim (24) optimized conditions for producing distortion products in CM waveforms and observed them in the appropriate region of the cochlea for intensities below 70 dB SPL. They offer arguments that reconcile their measurements and models with the earlier data of Dallos.

Pfeiffer & Kim (55) developed a technique of recording from a large population of nerve fibers in order to make a cochlear map of particular response features. The response component of each fiber, to a particular frequency, is plotted as a function of each fiber's characteristic frequency. The distribution, a link between the spatio-temporal characteristics of basilar-membrane motion and single-fiber response, is obtained without disturbing the cochlea. Based on these efforts, this group took a strong stance regarding the generation and propagation of distortion components (45, 76). They concluded that the distortion products $(f_2 - f_1)$ and $(2f_1 - f_2)$ are mechanically propagated along the basilar membrane in much the same way they would have had they been introduced externally. They also demonstrated reversible alteration of the amplitude of $f_2 - f_1$ by measurements before and after a fatiguing stimulus. Of significance is the fact that the fatiguing stimulus does not have to be very intense: 80–90 dB SPL tones, 1 minute in duration, were sufficient to produce a reduction of $f_2 - f_1$ that recovered within one minute. These results suggest that the intense tones used in direct mechanical measurements could easily have altered the nonlinear properties of the cochlea.

Cochlear Emissions and Echoes

Further evidence of cochlear nonlinearities rests on observations that healthy human ears can emit narrow-band noises spontaneously at one or more frequencies that can be audible as weak tonal tinnitus (88). Kemp (36) showed that stimulated acoustic emissions (those elicited by external stimuli) or echoes are exhibited by the majority of normal human ears. The strongest echoes are observed near frequencies at which spontaneous emissions are found. When two tones are presented simultaneously, combination tones (distortion products) may be present in the emissions. The emissions exhibit strongly nonlinear behavior at low stimulus levels and become insignificant at intensities above 40 dB SL.

Emissions are reduced by stimulation of the crossed olivocochlear bundle (51) or by stimulation with loud sounds (43, 77). They are absent in ears with sensorineural hearing loss.

Suppression

Two-tone suppression in auditory-nerve fibers has been extensively studied (4, 27, 32, 42, 68). Sellick & Russell (75) found analogous suppression in the hair-cell receptor potential, indicating that the source of the nonlinearity is in the cochlea itself. A mechanical correlate was reported by Rhode (59) in the basilar membrane, which showed maximum suppression for a frequency ratio of about 1.1 and little suppression below CF. Neural measures indicate suppression both above and below CF, however, with the maximum suppression at CF (e.g. 32). The discrepancy between the neural and mechanical measurements could arise due to the use of intense tones in making the mechanical measurements and the demonstrated effect this has on nonlinear processes (76).

Another method of studying two-tone suppression uses a very low-frequency signal (25–40 Hz) while applying a probe stimulus at the CF of the unit to determine the biasing effect of the basilar-membrane position on single-unit sensitivity. The data of Lepage (48) and Sellick et al (73) indicate that motion of the basilar membrane towards the scala vestibuli tends to be excitatory, while motion towards the scala tympani has the opposite effect. However, Schmiedt (70) obtained the opposite result in gerbils. These results are dependent on the stimulus frequency, intensity, and possibly species (47, 69, 73). Dallos et al (12) have demonstrated that two-tone suppression is dependent on the presence of outer hair cells.

Other experiments have shown that very-low-frequency maskers suppress auditory-nerve-fiber responses to CF tones much more than they suppress off-CF tone responses. This agrees with the tip of the FTC being more susceptible than the rest of the FTC to anoxia and cochlear injury (23, 32, 41, 71).

Efferents

The crossed olivocochlear bundle (COCB) forms the primary efferent input to the cochlea. Electrical stimulation of the COCB has been shown to alter the sensitivity and selectivity (e.g. 86) of auditory-nerve fibers. The effect appears to be strongest in the vicinity of the tip of the tuning curve. Stimulation of the COCB has also been shown to produce changes in cochlear mechanics (51). The changes observed were manifested as a reduction of the difference tone ($f_2 - f_1$) measured as an acoustic emission in the guinea-pig ear canal. Stimulation of efferents to the turtle cochlea (3) can eliminate tuning completely and raise the threshold by 60 dB or more. An important point to note in considering the mammalian cochlea is that the efferents of the COCB primarily innervate the outer hair cells, while the afferents from which recordings were made must all innervate inner hair cells (49, 80). This again implicates the outer hair cells in the alteration of cochlear mechanics and may relate to the nonlinear behavior seen in the cochlea (12). Others have confirmed these observations (76).

Models of Cochlear Mechanics

While it is impossible here to completely review cochlear modeling (20), it is important to note the role it plays in understanding cochlear mechanics, especially when hypotheses can be explored that may be difficult or impossible to study experimentally [e.g. (82)].

Our principal concern is the recent interaction of models and experimental measurements. Early attempts using nonlinear transmission-line models (26, 30) or nonlinear differential equations (44) incorporated nonlinear damping. They were able to mimic many of the principal nonlinear mechanical and physiological observations, including the compressional nonlinearity in a narrow-frequency band near the characteristic frequency (CF), intensity-dependent phase shifts near CF, distortion products, and shift of the peak of the amplitude envelope toward the apex with increasing intensity.

Attention is being increasingly focused on what is now termed cochlear micromechanics (1, 91). It is generally recognized that the basilar membrane does not exclusively determine the excitation of the hair cells. The factors that may affect basilar-membrane mechanics and the displacement of the stereocilia of the hair cells have certainly not all been resolved. Important questions, such as whether the tectorial membrane is firmly attached to the organ of Corti or to the stereocilia, are still debated (29, 50). Zwislocki & Kletsky (92) proposed a model in which sharpening of the basilar membrane response occurs through the different mechanical propagation constants of the tectorial and basilar membranes. It is also known that the height of the stereocilia increases in length from base to apex. Furthermore, it has been suggested (31) that calcium ions may affect the stiffness of the stereocilia. Because of the many indications of the importance of the stereocilia, Zwislocki (91) incorporated a reed model of them in a cochlear model; he demonstrated that this element could sharpen the mechanical response of the cochlea.

The discovery of acoustic emissions, echoes, and the significance of the microstructure in audiograms by Kemp (36, 37) has influenced recent modeling activities.

Using an active cochlear model with negative damping Kim et al obtained good agreement with Rhode's mechanical measurements for both normal and postmortem conditions (45, 52). Their results suggest that an active element underlies normal cochlear response and is responsible for obtaining much sharper tuning than in a conventional, passive model. This is compatible with the idea of a bidirectional coupling of energy in the cochlea (84).

COMMENT

Von Békésy (83) noted long ago that the great variety of models of cochlear function was inversely proportional to the available data. In the future, direct measurements of cochlear mechanics will be oriented toward tuning, thresholds, effects of COCB stimulation, and the multitude of nonlinear phenomena: combination tones, suppression, and acoustic emissions. The great progress made in cochlear physiology is closely correlated with the development of measurement techniques (81). New techniques, such as electronic speckle interferometry, may overcome some of the limitations of previous techniques and yield a three-dimensional view of the vibration of the cochlear partition in motion (28). The integration of new data, arising from myriad sources, species, and conditions will not be easy, but the reward of understanding cochlear function is certainly worth the effort.

ACKNOWLEDGMENT

The preparation of this manuscript was supported by grant NS12732 from NINCDS. I thank my colleagues C. D. Geisler, J. Hind, P. Smith, and R. Stanny for their assistance.

Literature Cited

1. Allen, J. 1980. Cochlear micromechanics—a physical model of transduction. *J. Acoust. Soc. Am.* 68:1660–70
2. Anderson, D. J., Rose, J. E., Hind, J. E., Brugge, J. F. 1971. Temporal position of discharges in single auditory nerve fibers within the cycle of a sine-wave stimulus: frequency and intensity effects. *J. Acoust. Soc. Am.* 49:1131–39
3. Art, J. J., Crawford, A. C., Fettiplace, R., Fuchs, P. A. 1982. Efferent regulation of hair cells in the turtle cochlea. *Proc. R. Soc. London* 216:377–84
4. Arthur, R. M., Pfeiffer, R. R., Suga, N. 1971. Properties of 'two-tone inhibition' in primary auditory neurones. *J. Physiol.* 212:593–609
5. Crawford, A. C., Fettiplace, R. 1980. The frequency selectivity of auditory nerve fibres and hair cells in the cochlea of the turtle. *J. Physiol.* 306:79–125
6. Crawford, A. C., Fettiplace, R. 1981. An electrical tuning mechanism in turtle cochlear hair cells. *J. Physiol.* 312:377
7. Dallos, P. 1973. Cochlear potentials and cochlear mechanics. In *Basic Mechanisms in Hearing*, ed. A. R. Moller, pp. 335–76. New York: Academic
8. Dallos, P. 1981. Cochlear physiology. *Ann. Rev. Psychol.* 32:153–90
9. Dallos, P., Cheatham, M. A. 1976. Production of cochlear potentials by inner and outer hair cells. *J. Acoust. Soc. Am.* 60:510–12
10. Dallos, R., Billone, M. C., Durrant, J. D., Wang, C. Y., Raynor, S. 1972.

Cochlear inner and outer hair cells: functional differences. *Science* 177:356–58
11. Dallos, P., Harris, D. 1978. Properties of auditory nerve responses in absence of outer hair cells. *J. Neurophysiol.* 41:365–83
12. Dallos, P., Harris, D., Relkin, E., Cheatham, M. A. 1980. Two-tone suppression and intermodulation distortion in the cochlea: Effect of outer hair cell lesions. In *Psychophysical, Physiological, and Behavioural Studies in Hearing*, ed. G. van den Brink, F. A. Bilsen, pp. 242–52. Delft, Netherlands: Delft Univ. Press
13. Dallos, P., Santos-Sanchi, J., Flock, A. 1982. Intracellular recordings from outer hair cells. *Science* 218:582–84
14. Davis, H. 1965. A model for transducer action in the cochlea. *Cold Spring Harbor Symp. Quant. Biol.* 30:181–90
15. Davis, H. 1983. An active process in cochlear mechanics. *Hearing Res.* 9:79–90
16. Evans, E. F. 1972. Does frequency sharpening occur in the cochlea? In *Symp. on Hearing Theory 1972*, Ipo Eindhoven, pp. 27–34
17. Evans, E. F. 1975. Normal and abnormal functioning of the cochlear nerve. *Symp. Zool. Soc. Lond.* 37:133–65
18. Evans, E. F., Wilson, J. P. 1975. Cochlear tuning properties: Concurrent basilar membrane and single nerve fiber measurements. *Science* 180:1218–21
19. Flock, A., Cheung, H. C., Flock, B.,

Utter, G. 1981. Three sets of actin filaments in sensory cell of inner ear. Identification and functional orientation determined by gel electrophoresis, immunofluorescence, and electron microscopy. *J. Neurocytology* 10:133–47

20. Geisler, C. D. 1976. Mathematical models of the mechanics of the inner ear. In *Handbook of Sensory Physiology, Auditory System,* ed. W. D. Keidel, W. D. Neff, pp. 391–415. New York: Springer-Verlag.

21. Geisler, C. D., Rhode, W. S. 1982. The phases of basilar-membrane vibrations. *J. Acoust. Soc. Am.* 71:1201–3

22. Geisler, C. D., Rhode, W. S., Kennedy, D. T. 1974. The responses to tonal stimuli of single auditory nerve fibers and their relationships to basilar membrane motion in the squirrel monkey. *J. Neurophysiol.* 37:1156–72

23. Geisler, C. D., Sinex, D. G. 1980. Responses of primary auditory fibers to combined noise and tonal stimuli. *Hearing Res.* 3:317–34

24. Gibian, G. L., Kim, D. O. 1982. Cochlear microphonic evidence for mechanical propagation of distortion products (f_1-f_2) and ($2f_1$-f_2). *Hearing Res.* 6:35–59

25. Goldstein, J. L., Kiang, N. Y. S. 1968. Neural correlates of the aural combination tone $2f_1$-f_2. *Proc. IEEE* 56:981–92

26. Hall, J. L. 1974. Two-tone distortion products in a non-linear model of the basilar membrane. *J. Acoust. Soc. Am.* 56:1818–28

27. Hind, J. E., Anderson, D. J., Brugge, J. F., Rose, J. E. 1967. Coding of information pertaining to paired low-frequency tones in single auditory nerve fibers of the squirrel monkey. *J. Neurophysiol.* 30:794–816

28. Hogmoen, K., Lokberg, O. J. 1977. Detection and measurement of small vibrations using electronic speckle pattern interferometry. *Appl. Opt.* 16:1869–75

29. Hoshino, T. 1977. Contact between the tectorial membrane and the cochlear sensory hairs in the human and the monkey. *Arch. Oto-Rhino-Laryngol.* 217:53–60

30. Hubbard, A. E., Geisler, C. D. 1972. A hybrid-computer model of the cochlear partition. *J. Acoust. Soc. Am.* 51:1895–1903

31. Hudspeth, A. J., Jacobs, R. 1979. Stereocilia mediate transduction in vetebrate hair cells. *Proc. Natl. Acad. Sci. USA* 76:1506–09

32. Javel, E. 1981. Suppression of auditory nerve responses I: Temporal analysis, intensity effects and suppression contours. *J. Acoust. Soc. Am.* 69:1735–45

33. Johnstone, B. M., Boyle, A. J. F. 1967. Basilar membrane vibration examined with the Mössbauer technique. *Science* 158:389–90

34. Johnstone, B. M., Taylor, K. J., Boyle, A. J. 1970. Mechanics of the guinea pig cochlea. *J. Acoust. Soc. Am.* 47:504–9

35. Jorgensen, J. M. 1982. Microtubles and laminated structures in inner ear hair cells. *Acta Oto–Laryngol.* 94:241–48

36. Kemp, D. T. 1978. Stimulated acoustic emmissions from within the human auditory system. *J. Acoust. Soc. Am.* 64:1386–91

37. Kemp, D. T. 1979. Evidence for a new element in cochlear mechanics. *Scand. Audiol. Suppl.* 9:35–47

38. Khanna, S. M., Leonard, D. G. B. 1982. Basilar membrane tuning in the cat cochlea. *Science* 215:305–6

39. Khanna, S. M., Leonard, D. G. B. 1982. Basilar membrane response properties in damaged cochleas of cats. In *Mathematical Modeling of the Hearing Process,* ed. M. H. Holmes, L. A. Rubenfeld, pp. 70–83. New York: Springer-Verlag

40. Kiang, N. Y. S., Moxon, E. C., Levine, R. A. 1970. Auditory-nerve activity in cats with normal and abnormal cochleas. In *Sensorineural Hearing Loss,* ed. G. E. W. Wolstenholme, J. Knight, pp. 241–68. London: Churchill

41. Kiang, N. Y. S., Moxon, E. C. 1974. Tails of tuning curves of auditory-nerve fibers. *J. Acoust. Soc. Am.* 55:620–30

42. Kiang, N. Y. S., Watanabe, T., Thomas, E. C., Clark, L. F. 1965. *Discharge Pattern of Single Fibers in the Cat Auditory Nerve,* Monogr. 35. Cambridge: MIT Press. 151 pp.

43. Kim, D. O. 1980. Cochlear mechanics: implications of electrophysiological and acoustical observations. *Hearing Res.* 2:297–317

44. Kim, D. O., Molnar, C. E., Pfeiffer, R. R. 1973. A system of nonlinear differential equations modeling basilar membrane motion. *J. Acoust. Soc. Am.* 54:1517–29

45. Kim, D. O., Molnar, C. E., Matthews, J. W. 1980. Cochlear mechanics: Nonlinear behavior in two-tone responses as reflected in cochlear-nerve fiber responses and in ear-canal sound pressure. *J. Acoust. Soc. Am.* 67:1704–21

46. Kohllöffel, L. U. E. 1972. A study of basilar membrane vibrations II. The vibratory amplitude and phase pattern along the basilar membrane (postmortem). *Acustica* 27:66–81

47. Konishi, T., Nielsen, D. W. 1978. The temporal relation between basilar mem-

brane motion and nerve impulse initiation in auditory nerve fibers of guinea pig. *Jpn. J. Physiol.* 28:291–307

48. Le Page, E. L. 1981. The Role of Nonlinear Mechanical Processes in Mammalian Hearing. PhD thesis. Univ. Western Australia.

49. Liberman, M. C. 1982. Single-neuron labeling in the cat auditory nerve. *Science* 216:1239–41

50. Lim, D. J. 1980. Cochlear anatomy related to cochlear micromechanics. *J. Acoust. Soc. Am.* 67:1686–95

51. Mountain, D. C. 1980. Changes in endolymphatic potential and crossed olivocochlear bundle stimulation alter cochlear mechanics. *Science* 210:71–72

52. Neely, S. T., Kim, D. O. 1983. An active cochlear model showing sharp tuning and high sensitivity. *Hearing Res.* 9: 123–30

53. Nuttall, A. L., Brown, M. C., Masta, R. I., Lawrence, M. 1981. Inner hair cell responses to the velocity of basilar membrane motion in the guinea pig. *Brain Res.* 211:171–74

54. Peake, W. T., Ling, A. 1980. Basilar-membrane motion in the alligator lizard: Its relation to tonotopic organization and frequency selectivity. *J. Acoust. Soc. Am.* 67:1736–45

55. Pfeiffer, R. R., Kim, D. O. 1975. Cochlear nerve fiber responses: Distribution along the cochlear partition. *J. Acoust. Soc. Am.* 58:867–69

56. Rhode, W. S. 1971. Observations of the vibration of the basilar membrane in the squirrel monkey using the Mössbauer technique. *J. Acoust. Soc. Am.* 49:1218–31

57. Rhode, W. S. 1973. An investigation of post-mortem cochlear mechanics using the Mössbauer effect. In *Basic Mechanisms of Hearing*, ed. A. R. Møller, pp. 49–67. New York: Academic

58. Rhode, W. S. 1974. Evidence for nonlinear vibration in the cochlea from Mössbauer investigations. *J. Acoust. Soc. Am.* 55:588–96

59. Rhode, W. S. 1977. Some observations on two-tone interaction measured with the Mössbauer effect. In *Psychophysics and Physiology of Hearing*, ed. E. F. Evans, J. P. Wilson, pp. 27–38. New York: Academic

60. Rhode, W. S. 1978. Some observations on cochlear mechanics. *J. Acoust. Soc. Am.* 64:158–76

61. Rhode, W. S. 1980. Cochlear partition vibration—Recent views. *J. Acoust. Soc. Am.* 67:1696–703

62. Robertson, D. 1974. Cochlear neurons: Frequency selectivity altered by perilymph removal. *Science* 186:153–55

63. Robertson, D., Cody, A. R., Bredberg, G., Johnstone, B. M. 1980. Response properties of spiral ganglion neurons in cochleas damaged by direct mechanical trauma. *J. Acoust. Soc. Am.* 67:1295–303

64. Robles, L., Rhode, W. S. 1974. Nonlinear effects in transient response of the basilar membrane. In *Facts and Models in Hearing*, ed. E. Zwicker, E. Terhardt, pp. 287–98. Berlin: Springer-Verlag

65. Robles, L., Rhode, W. S., Geisler, C. D. 1976. Transient response of the basilar membrane measured in squirrel monkeys using the Mossbauer effect. *J. Acoust. Soc. Am.* 59:926–39

66. Russell, I. J., Sellick, P. M. 1978. Intracellular studies of hair cells in the mammalian cochlea. *J. Physiol.* 284: 261–90

67. Russell, I. J., Sellick, P. M. 1981. The responses of hair cells to low frequency tones and their relationship to the extracellular receptor potentials and sound pressure level in the guinea pig cochlea. In *Neuronal Mechanisms of Hearing*, ed. Josef Syka, Aitkin Lindsay, pp. 3–15. New York: Plenum

68. Sachs, M. B., Kiang, N. Y. S. 1968. Two-tone inhibition in auditory-nerve fibers. *J. Acoust. Soc. Am.* 43:1120–28

69. Sachs, M. B., Hubbard, A. E. 1981. Responses of auditory-nerve fibers to characteristic-frequency tones and low frequency suppressors. *Hearing Res.* 4: 309–24

70. Schmiedt, R. A. 1982. Effects of low-frequency biasing on auditory-nerve activity. *J. Acoust. Soc. Am.* 72:142–50

71. Schmiedt, R. A. 1982. Boundaries of two-tone rate suppression of cochlear-nerve activity. *Hearing Res.* 7:335–51

72. Sellick, P. M., Patuzzi, R., Johnstone, B. M. 1982. Measurement of basilar membrane motion in the guinea pig using the Mossbauer technique. *J. Acoust. Soc. Am.* 72:131–41

73. Sellick, P. M., Patuzzi, R., Johnstone, B. M. 1982. Modulation of responses of spiral ganglion cells in the guinea pig cochlea by low frequency sound. *Hearing Res.* 7:199–221

74. Sellick, P. M., Patuzzi, R., Johnstone, B. M. 1983. Comparison between the tuning properties of inner hair cells and basilar membrane motion. *Hearing Res.* 10:93–100

75. Sellick, P. M., Russell, I. J. 1979. Two-tone suppression in cochlear hair cells. *Hearing Res.* 1:227–36

76. Siegel, J. H., Kim, D. O., Molnar, C. E. 1982. Effects of altering organ of Corti

on cochlear distortion. *J. Neurophysiol.* 47:303–28

77. Siegel, J. H., Kim, D. O. 1982. Efferent neural control of cochlear mechanics? Olivocochlear bundle stimulation affects cochlear biomechanical nonlinearity. *Hearing Res.* 6:171–82

78. Small, A. M. 1957. Pure tone masking. *J. Acoust. Soc. Am.* 31:1619

79. Smoorenburg, G. F. 1972. Combination tones and their origin. *J. Acoust. Soc. Am.* 52:615–32

80. Spoendlin, H. 1969. Innervation patterns in the organ of Corti of cat. *Acta Oto–Laryngol.* 67:239–54

81. Tonndorf, J. 1977. Modern methods for measurements of basilar membrane displacements. *Acta Oto–Laryngol.* 83:113–22

82. Viergever, M. A. 1978. Basilar membrane motion in a spiralshaped cochlea. *J. Acoust. Soc. Am.* 64:1048–53

83. von Békésy, G. 1960. *Experiments in Hearing.* New York: McGraw-Hill. 745 pp.

84. Weiss, T. F., Peake, W. T., Ling, A., Holton, T. 1978. Which structures determine frequency selectivity and tonotopic organization of vertebrate nerve fibers? Evidence from the alligator lizard. In *Evoked Electrical Activity in the Auditory Nervous System,* ed. R. F. Naunton, C. Fernandez, pp. 91–112. New York: Academic

85. Weiss, T. F. 1984. The physiology of hair cells. *Ann. Rev. Physiol.* 46:247–59

86. Wiederhold, M. L. 1970. Variations of the effects of electric stimulation of the crossed olivocochlear bundle on cat single auditory-nerve-fiber responses to tone bursts. *J. Acoust. Soc. Am.* 48:966–77

87. Wilson, J. P. 1973. A sub-miniature capacitive probe for vibration measurements of the basilar membrane. *J. Sound Vib.* 30:483–93

88. Wilson, J. P. 1980. Evidence for a cochlear origin for acoustic re-emissions, threshold fine-structure, and tonal tinnitus. *Hearing Res.* 2:233–52

89. Wilson, J. P., Johnstone, J. R. 1973. Basilar membrane correlates of the combination tone 2f1-f2. *Nature* 241:206–7

90. Wilson, J. P., Johnstone, J. R. 1975. Basilar membrane and middle-ear vibration in guinea pig measured by capacitive probe. *J. Acoust. Soc. Am.* 57:705–23

91. Zwislocki, J. J. 1980. Theory of cochlear mechanics. *Hearing Res.* 2:171–82

92. Zwislocki, J. J., Kletsky, E. J. 1979. Tectorial membrane: A possible effect on frequency analysis in the cochlea. *Science* 204:639–41

Ann. Rev. Physiol. 1984. 46:247–59

RELATION OF RECEPTOR POTENTIALS OF COCHLEAR HAIR CELLS TO SPIKE DISCHARGES OF COCHLEAR NEURONS

T. F. Weiss

Department of Electrical Engineering and Computer Science and Research Laboratory of Electronics, Massachusetts Institute of Technology, 77 Massachusetts Avenue, Cambridge, Massachusetts 02139; and Eaton-Peabody Laboratory of Auditory Physiology, Massachusetts Eye and Ear Infirmary, 243 Charles Street, Boston, Massachusetts 02114

INTRODUCTION

The function of the cochlea is to encode sound-induced vibrations of the middle ear into sequences of action potentials in the cochlear nerve fibers that conduct the encoded sound message to the brain. A major accomplishment of cochlear investigators in the last two decades has been the elucidation of this code, first for simple stimuli such as tones and more recently for complex sounds, including speech (70). While a great deal is now known about this code, we do not understand the cochlear mechanisms responsible for the encoding. An important goal is to determine these encoding mechanisms in terms of underlying mechanical, electrical, biological, and chemical processes at organ, cellular, membrane, and molecular levels. One critical step towards the attainment of this goal has been the development of techniques for measuring the receptor potential of cochlear receptor (hair) cells. The first intracellular recordings were reported in 1970 from hair cells in the lateral-line organ (26) and in 1974 from cochlear hair cells (60, 86). In the subsequent decade, there have been several studies of the receptor potential that now allow comparison between properties of the receptor potential and the spike discharges of coch-

247

0066-4278/84/0315-0247$02.00

lear nerve fibers. From such comparisons we can learn the roles of the intervening mechanisms.

This review is organized around four distinctive properties of the responses to simple sound stimuli: adaptation, nonlinearity, temporal synchronization, and frequency selectivity. These ubiquitous properties of cochlear nerve discharges of vertebrates represent important information-bearing properties of these signals. For each of these properties we will compare the representation of sound stimuli in the receptor potential of cochlear hair cells to that in the discharges of cochlear nerve fibers. Recent related reviews have covered biophysical properties of hair cells (33), cochlear physiology (11), and the representation of sound stimuli in the spike discharges of cochlear nerve fibers (13, 40, 47).

Scope of This Review

We review cochlear hair-cell receptor potentials recorded in three kinds of preparations: (a) in vivo in the basilar papilla of the alligator lizard, *Gerrhonotus multicarinatus*, (4, 30, 31, 60, 86); (b) in vitro in the basilar papilla of the red-eared turtle, *Pseudemys scripta elegans*, (8–10, 18, 19); (c) in vivo in inner hair cells in the mammalian organ of Corti of either guinea pig, *Cavia porcellus*, (61, 67–69, 74–76) or Mongolian gerbil, *Meriones unguiculatus*, (24). For each of these preparations, comparable measurements of receptor potentials and nerve-fiber discharges have been reported. We shall not review the somewhat fragmentary results obtained from mammalian outer hair cells (12, 69, 82) because there are no reports of measurements from cochlear neurons that innervate these hair cells.

Definitions

The receptor potential, $v(t)$, is the hair cell's total membrane potential minus its resting potential. The relation between the acoustic stimulus at the tympanic membrane and the receptor potential is in general nonlinear. Hence, when a pure tone of frequency f and amplitude P is presented to the ear, i.e. $p(t)=P\cos 2\pi ft$, then the steady-state receptor potential can be expanded in a Fourier series with a component at the frequency of the stimulus, f, plus components at DC and at harmonics of f (30):

$$v(t) = V_0(f,P) + \sum_{k=1}^{\infty} |V_k(f,P)| \cos\left[2\pi kft + \sphericalangle V_k(f,P)\right] , \qquad 1.$$

where $|V_k(f,P)|$ and $\sphericalangle V_k(f,P)$ are the magnitude and phase angle respectively of the kth Fourier-series component, both of which may depend upon f and P. The term "DC component" of the receptor potential refers to $V_0(f,P)$, and the term "AC component" of the receptor potential refers to $v(t)-V_0(f,P)$.

The discharge of a cochlear nerve fiber in response to a sound stimulus can be described as a stochastic point process with instantaneous driven discharge rate, or more simply the "spike rate", $\lambda(t)$ (i.e. the instantaneous rate minus the spontaneous discharge rate), which is estimated from a post-stimulus-time histogram of the spike train (38). The steady-state spike rate in response to a tone can be described by a Fourier series (39, 45, 57) in a manner analogous to the description of the receptor potential:

$$\lambda(t) = \Lambda_0(f,P) + \sum_{k=1}^{\infty} |\Lambda_k(f,P)| \cos\left[2\pi kft + \measuredangle\Lambda_k(f,P)\right] , \qquad 2.$$

where $|\Lambda_k(f,P)|$ and $\measuredangle\Lambda_k(f,P)$ are the magnitude and phase angle respectively of the kth Fourier-series component, both of which may depend upon f and P. The "DC component" of the spike rate is the average spike rate, $\Lambda_0(f,P)$; the "AC component" of the spike rate, $\lambda(t) - \Lambda_0(f,P)$ is a time-varying function with fundamental frequency, f, which has also been referred to as the time-locked or synchronized component of the spike rate.

In our comparison of the receptor potential of hair cells with the spike discharges of cochlear nerve fibers we compare features of the temporal waveforms of $v(t)$ to those of $\lambda(t)$ for transient stimuli, and properties of the $V_k(f,P)$ to those of $\Lambda_k(f,P)$ for steady-state responses to tones.

ADAPTATION

By "adaptation" we mean the effects of the history of stimulation on the response to an acoustic stimulus. While numerous phenomena satisfying this definition have been observed in the responses of cochlear neurons, only two have been studied in both hair cells and neurons.

One form of adaptations occurs in the response to acoustic clicks, and we will call it "click adaptation." Both the receptor potential of individual hair cells and the cochlear microphonic potential are independent of the rate of presentation of click stimuli up to rates of at least 100 clicks per second (4). In contrast, for moderate level clicks the amplitude of the instantaneous discharge rate of a cochlear nerve fiber (44) and of the compound action potential of the cochlear nerve (3, 43, 63) decrease as the click rate increases above 10 clicks per second. Thus, click adaptation apparently occurs in the synaptic transmission and/or spike initiation processes.

A second form of adaptation occurs in response to tone- and noise-burst stimuli having constant amplitudes. At the onset of the burst, there is a rapid rise and decline in average discharge rate of a cochlear nerve fiber. This is called rapid adaptation. It is followed by a slower decline with an exponential time course whose time constant is about 40–50 msec—called short-term adaptation—to a steady rate of discharge above the spontaneous rate (44, 81). Apparently, no comparable "overshoot" of the response occurs in the hair-cell receptor potential in response to tone bursts (8, 24, 30, 68, 69). Since post-synaptic potentials of nerve fibers innervating hair cells in the goldfish sacculus exhibit adaptation in response to a tone burst (22), it seems likely that short-term adaptation is a property of transmission at the receptor-neuron junction.

Short-term adaptation appears to be related to several other adaptation phenomena, such as the post-stimulus reduction in spontaneous discharge rate (79) and forward masking (25). Short-term adaptation has a time course that is similar to the time course of click adaptation. Hence, it is likely that the same synaptic mechanism can account for several adaptation phenomena.

NONLINEARITY

Linear, time-invariant systems can be characterized efficiently; knowledge of the response to a sharp pulse, to sinusoids of different frequencies, or to a broadband noise stimulus is sufficient to predict the response to an arbitrary stimulus through the use of powerful mathematical techniques (the superposition integral and the integral transforms). Furthermore, linear, time-invariant systems have a number of simple properties. If the stimulus is multiplied by a constant, then the resulting response is multiplied by the same constant. The response to a sum of stimuli is the sum of the individual responses to the two stimuli presented separately. If the stimulus is a sinusoidal time function, then the response is also a sinusoidal time function at the stimulus frequency. Nonlinear systems are generally not described so efficiently, and their response properties can be much more complex. Thus it is essential to determine whether or not a system we wish to understand, such as the cochlea, can be regarded as linear and time-invariant.

AC and DC Response Components

In response to tones, the steady-state receptor potential of hair cells contains a DC component with an appreciable magnitude (8, 24, 30, 68) for a broad range of tone frequencies and, in some preparations (24, 30, 68), for levels down to the threshold of detection of responses. Similarly, the DC or average component of the spike rate of cochlear nerve fibers is appreciable even at low stimulus levels (44). For example, neural tuning curves, which are iso-DC spike-rate contours of nerve fibers, have minima at sound-pressure levels near the behavioral threshold of the animal (91). Since the DC component of the response to a tone is, by definition, a nonlinear response component, it is apparent that the processes of generation of the hair-cell receptor potential and the cochlear-nerve spike rate are nonlinear in the normal behavioral range of hearing for stimulus levels down to the threshold of detection of sounds.

However, these nonlinearities may not remain effective at arbitrarily low stimulus levels (30, 57), i.e. the peripheral auditory system need not necessarily be regarded as containing an essential nonlinearity.

At low frequencies, the magnitudes of AC and DC distortion components of the receptor potential (30) and of the spike rate (39) become more prominent relative to the fundamental component as the stimulus level increases. As frequency increases, the magnitudes of all AC receptor-potential (30, 68, 69) and AC spike-rate (1, 39, 57) components decrease relative to their DC components. Both the receptor potential and the spike rate consist largely of their DC components as the tone frequency increases into the kHz range (see section on Temporal Synchronization).

Thus the dependences on tone frequency and level of AC and DC response components of the receptor potential of hair cells are qualitatively similar to those of the spike rates of cochlear neurons. The AC component of the receptor potential is presumably the precursor of the AC component of the spike rate. The DC component of the receptor potential has a positive (depolarizing) polarity that apparently produces excitation of nerve fibers that innervate the hair cell (72). Hence, it seems likely that the DC component of the receptor potential contributes to the production of the DC component of the spike rate. It is also probable that the processes of synaptic transmission and nerve excitation involve rectification so that the AC component of the receptor potential also contributes to the DC component of the spike rate.

Dependence on Stimulus Level

The dependence of the amplitude of a response component of the receptor potential or of the spike rate on the sound-pressure level is called a "level function." Level functions of the AC and DC components of both the receptor potential (30) and the spike rate (39) have at least two ranges: a low-level range in which the level function increases rapidly as the sound-pressure level is increased, and a high-level range where the level function increases less rapidly and may saturate. At still higher levels (approximately 90–100 dB SPL), nonmonotonic behavior has been reported for DC level functions of the spike rate (41). In order to understand the role of hair cells in the coding of the intensity of a stimulus, we will need to know the relation between level functions of the receptor potential and the spike rate components.

In the low-level range and for frequencies that differ appreciably from the frequency of maximum sensitivity of the hair cell (the characteristic frequency or CF), families of level functions obtained at different frequencies are approximately parallel; the slope of the AC level function is near 1 and the slope of the DC level function is 1–2 (24, 30, 80). For frequencies near CF, the slopes of the level functions of the receptor-potential components are significantly lower than they are for frequencies away from CF (24, 30), which indicates the presence of a compressive nonlinear mechanism that occurs for frequencies near the CF of the hair cell[1]. The relation between the rate of growth of the receptor-potential and spike-rate components in the low-level range is not known quantitatively, although frequency-dependent, compressive nonlinear phenomena similar to those seen in the receptor-potential level functions occur in level functions of the DC components of the spike rates of cochlear nerve fibers (27, 71). In addition, for frequencies below CF, the slope of the AC level function of the spike rate is apparently also near 1 (57).

Both the receptor potential and the spike rate tend toward saturation at high stimulus levels. Does the spike rate saturate because the receptor potential saturates, or is some other factor responsible? The direct measurements of level functions are ambiguous on this point. However, mammalian cochlear neurons with different spontaneous rates have level functions that differ systematically (14, 52, 62), and fibers of different spontaneous rate can apparently innervate the same inner hair cell (53, 54). These results suggest (24, 62) that the shapes of level functions of spike rates are not determined entirely by the shapes of receptor-potential level functions.

Mechanisms

More than one cochlear mechanism may be nonlinear. The motion of the mammalian basilar membrane apparently exhibits a compressive nonlinearity (66). It has been suggested (30) that this compressive nonlinearity originates in the micromechanical properties of the stereociliary tufts of hair cells that may provide a nonlinear mechanical load on the basilar membrane, thus coupling the nonlinear properties into basilar membrane motion. Nonlinear response properties have been found in the transduction from stereociliary displacement to receptor potential of a hair cell (34), and in the electrical properties of hair cells (7, 9, 51). The processes of synaptic transmission and spike initiation may also provide nonlinear mechanisms (36). In order to understand hearing, it will be essential to determine which nonlinear mechanisms have an appreciable effect in the normal physiological range of hearing.

TEMPORAL SYNCHRONIZATION

Cochlear neurons encode temporal features of acoustic stimuli by spike discharges that are time-locked or synchronized to these temporal features. However, there is a limit in the ability of a nerve fiber to synchronize to rapid temporal variations, as demonstrated by the attenuation of the magnitude of the AC component of the spike rate for tone frequencies above 1 kHz (1, 39, 57). Which cochlear mechanisms provide this attenuation? The AC component of

---

[1] This mechanism is apparently not present in the receptor potential of hair cells in the turtle preparation (8, 18), where slopes of AC level functions are near 1 for all frequencies.

the receptor potential of hair cells is also attenuated (30, 68, 69)[2], and this attenuation has been interpreted as resulting from lowpass filtering caused by the membrane capacitance of the hair cell (30, 68, 86). The data are not sufficient to allow us to determine whether attenuation of the AC component of the receptor potential accounts fully for the attenuation of AC components of the nerve spike rate or whether some later stage in the production of spike discharges, such as transmission at the receptor-neuron junction or spike excitation in the neuron, also contributes to the loss of neural synchronization.

The DC component of the hair-cell receptor potential and the DC component of nerve-fiber spike rate persist for high-frequency stimuli for which the AC components are undetectable. These observations suggest a significance of the peripheral nonlinearity giving rise to the DC components. For high-frequency stimuli, the DC components of receptor potentials and spike rates are required so that spectral information can be carried by tonotopically organized cells.

FREQUENCY SELECTIVITY

Cochlear neurons respond with high sensitivity to tones in a restricted frequency range, a property called frequency selectivity. The frequency selectivity of hair cells and cochlear nerve fibers has been assessed from iso-response contours (or tuning curves), which are plots of sound-pressure level vs tone frequency for a "constant response." In the earliest measurements of tuning curves (44, 83), a subjectively determined "response" was held constant. Subsequently, algorithms were developed to make automatic and objective measurements of iso-DC contours, that is iso-average-rate contours (15, 42, 48). There has been only one report (57) of measurements of iso-AC contours, i.e. iso-synchrony contours, and the relation between neural iso-DC and iso-AC contours has not yet been determined, although it appears that both contours show sharp frequency selectivity. The frequency selectivity of hair cells has been assessed by measuring iso-voltage contours of the receptor-potential components, both iso-DC (30, 31, 68) and iso-AC (8, 30, 31, 68) contours. Iso-DC and iso-AC contours differ, but both show sharp frequency selectivity. The receptor potential of hair cells exhibits frequency selectivity that is about as sharp as that shown by cochlear neurons (8, 31, 68). While some questions remain about the relation of frequency selectivity of responses of hair cells and cochlear neurons (31), the available results suggest that sharp frequency selectivity is a property of the mechanical input to the hair cell or of a process intrinsic to each hair cell.

Is this sharp frequency selectivity present in the motion of the basilar membrane, to which the hair cells are attached, or is some other frequency-

---

[2] The electrical properties of the membranes of hair cells in the turtle preparation can apparently not be represented by an equivalent lowpass filter (9).

selective process present? This question has been debated extensively for more than two decades. In mammals, the relation between neural and basilar-membrane frequency selectivity is still unclear (66), and the contributions of processes other than basilar membrane motion, if any, to determining the frequency selectivity of cochlear neurons are unknown.

Micromechanical Resonances of Stereociliary Tufts

The existence of sharp frequency-selective mechanisms intrinsic to hair cells has been demonstrated in lower vertebrates. In the alligator lizard, the frequency selectivity of basilar-membrane motion is not, by itself, sufficient to account for the observed nerve-fiber frequency selectivity or tonotopic organization (64, 89). Clearly in this species, there exists another tonotopically-organized frequency-selective process. Because the frequency-selective properties of cochlear neurons are correlated with changes in morphology of stereociliary-tectorial structures in lizards (31, 84, 87, 89), it was hypothesized (31, 87–89) that micromechanical resonances of the stereociliary-tectorial structures provide the additional tonotopically organized frequency-selective properties. More specifically, it was proposed (31, 88) that for hair cells with free-standing stereocilia, tufts with long stereocilia have low resonance frequencies and those with short stereocilia have high resonance frequencies. This proposal is supported by recently reported direct, in vitro observations of tuft motion in alligator lizard cochleae (20, 21, 29).

Electrical Hair Cell Resonances and/or Bidirectional Transduction?

In in vitro preparations of the turtle cochlea (8–10), the sharp frequency selectivity present in hair-cell responses to sound has also been observed in responses to extrinsic current (i.e. in the electrical impedance of the hair cell). It was proposed (9) that "each hair cell contains it own electrical resonance mechanism which accounts for most of the frequency selectivity of the receptor potential." Such a mechanism is plausible, because electrical resonances in cellular membranes are found in receptor cells in other systems (2, 6, 16) and can result from time-varying membrane ionic conductances (28, 58). This *electrical resonance* mechanism is distinctly different from the *mechanical resonance* mechanism proposed for the alligator lizard, although the measurements in the turtle and the alligator lizard can be interpreted in terms of one underlying mechanism, if the mechanoelectric transduction process of hair cells is bidirectional (85). With a bidirectional mechanism, the resonant frequencies would depend on stereociliary-tectorial dimensions and would be observable in the displacement of the stereocilia as well as in the electrical impedance of the hair cell. Inherent in such a bidirectional process is the capability to produce changes in cochlear mechanical variables in response to electrical changes in hair cells. Bidirectional transduction processes have the capacity to account qualitatively for diverse auditory phenomena (46, 85). These include: mechanical changes resulting from electrical stimulation and metabolic manipulations of the cochlea, lability of cochlear frequency selectivity, and the occurrence of sustained, narrow-band acoustic emissions from the ear.

Generalization

In summary, studies in reptiles have demonstrated that hair cells have intrinsic frequency-selective mechanisms. In the alligator lizard, there is a mechanical resonance of the stereociliary tuft. In the red-eared turtle, there are sharp resonances in the electrical impedance of the hair cell that could result from a purely electrical resonance of the hair-cell membrane or an electro-mechanical resonance involving bidirectional transduction. Studies in amphibians suggest that the mechanical properties of tectorial structures may determine tonotopically organized, frequency-selective properties (50). Although there is no direct evidence that these mechanisms occur in the mammalian cochlea, it appears likely that they might. For example, the correlation of nerve-fiber CF to stereociliary length that has been described for the alligator lizard applies to mammals, since the heights of stereociliary tufts of inner hair cells increase from base to apex (5, 23, 37, 56, 65, 73) and the CFs of radial fibers innervating inner hair cells decrease from base to apex (55). In fact, variations in stereociliary-tectorial structures with position in the auditory receptor organ occur in fish (17), amphibians (49, 76a), reptiles (59, 90), birds (78, 83a), and mammals (5, 23, 56, 73). Spatial variations in these structures are likely to produce a gradient of mechanical input to hair cells in different locations in a receptor organ even if the substrate motion is the same or is absent in all these locations. Spatial variations in these structures may also produce gradients in the electrical properties of hair cells. Thus it appears likely that the mechanical and electrical properties of hair cells vary with location in the receptor organ and that these variations contribute to the tonotopically organized, frequency-selective properties of vertebrate auditory-receptor organs.

PROSPECTS

We now have at least a qualitative view of the relation of the receptor potential of hair cells to the spike discharges of cochlear nerve fibers. In the next decade we can look forward to quantitative, coordinated studies of hair-cell receptor potentials and cochlear nerve spike discharges that will enhance our understanding of the roles of hair-cell and neural mechanisms in determining the neural code. Studies of in vitro preparations of hair-cell receptor organs (7, 32, 34, 35, 77), of isolated hair cells (51), and of isolated hair-cell membrane patches should help to reveal the membrane and molecular bases of hair-cell mechanisms.

ACKNOWLEDGMENTS

I thank my colleagues D. M. Freeman, L. S. Frishkopf, and W. T. Peake for helpful comments on the manuscript. The author's work was supported by Public Health Service Grants 5 P01 NS13126 and 5 K04 NS00113.

Literature Cited

1. Anderson, D. J. 1973. Quantitative model for the effects of stimulus frequency upon synchronization of auditory nerve discharges. *J. Acoust. Soc. Am.* 54:361–64

2. Ashmore, J. F. 1983. Frequency tuning in a frog vestibular organ. *Nature* 304:536–38

3. Baden-Kristensen, K., Weiss, T. F. 1982. Supporting-cell and extracellular responses to acoustic clicks in the free-standing region of the alligator lizard cochlea. *Hearing Res.* 8:295–315

4. Baden-Kristensen, K., Weiss, T. F. 1983. Receptor potentials of lizard hair cells with free-standing stereocilia: responses to acoustic clicks. *J. Physiol.* 335:699–721

5. Bruns, V., Goldbach, M. 1980. Hair cells and tectorial membrane in the cochlea of the greater horseshoe bat. *Anat. Embryol.* 161:51–63

6. Clusin, W. T., Bennett, M. V. L. 1979. The oscillatory responses of skate electroreceptors to small voltage stimuli. *J. Gen. Physiol.* 73:685–702

7. Corey, D. P., Hudspeth, A. J. 1979. Ionic basis of the receptor potential in a vertebrate hair cell. *Nature* 281:675–77

8. Crawford, A. C., Fettiplace, R. 1980. The frequency selectivity of auditory nerve fibres and hair cells in the cochlea of the turtle. *J. Physiol.* 306:79–125

9. Crawford, A. C., Fettiplace, R. 1981. An electrical tuning mechanism in turtle cochlear hair cells. *J. Physiol.* 312:377–412

10. Crawford, A. C., Fettiplace, R. 1981. Non-linearities in the responses of turtle hair cells. *J. Physiol.* 315:317–38

11. Dallos, P. 1981. Cochlear physiology. *Ann. Rev. Psychol.* 32:153–90

12. Dallos, P., Santos-Sacchi, J., Flock, A. 1982. Intracellular recordings from cochlear outer hair cells. *Science* 218:582–84

13. Evans, E. F. 1975. Cochlear nerve and cochlear nucleus. In *Handbook of Sensory Physiology, Auditory System: Physiology and Behavioral Studies, Psychoacoustics*, ed. W. D. Keidel, W. D. Neff, V/2:1–108. Berlin: Springer

14. Evans, E. F., Palmer, A. R. 1980. Relationship between the dynamic range of cochlear nerve fibres and their spontaneous activity. *Exp. Brain Res.* 40:115–18

15. Evans, E. F., Wilson, J. P. 1975. Cochlear tuning properties: concurrent basilar membrane and single nerve fiber measurements. *Science* 190:1218–21

16. Fain, G. L., Gershenfeld, H. M., Quandt, F. 1980. Calcium spikes in toad rods. *J. Physiol.* 303:495–513

17. Fay, R. R., Popper, A. N. 1980. Structure and function in teleost auditory systems. In *Comparative Studies of Hearing in Vertebrates*, ed. A. N. Popper, R. R. Fay, pp. 3–42. New York: Springer

18. Fettiplace, R., Crawford, A. C. 1978. The coding of sound pressure and frequency in cochlear hair cells of the terrapin. *Proc. R. Soc. London B* 203:209–18

19. Fettiplace, R., Crawford, A. C. 1980. The origin of tuning in turtle cochlear hair cells. *Hearing Res.* 2:447–54

20. Frishkopf, L. S. 1981. Mechanical response properties of the basilar papilla in alligator lizard: failure to find a basis for tonotopic organization. *MIT Res. Lab. Elect. Rep. 123*, pp. 206–7

21. Frishkopf, L. S., DeRosier, D. J. Egelman, E. H. 1982. Motion of basilar papilla and hair cell stereocilia in the excised cochlea of the alligator lizard: relation to frequency analysis. *Soc. Neurosci. Abstr.* 8:40

22. Furukawa, T., Matsuura, S. 1978. Adaptive rundown of excitatory post-synaptic potentials at synapses between hair cells and eighth nerve fibres in the goldfish. *J. Physiol.* 276:193–209

23. Garfinkle, T. J., Saunders, J. C. 1983. The morphology of inner hair cell stereocilia in C57BL/6J mice as studied by scanning electronmicroscopy. *Oto-*

laryngol., Head and Neck Surgery. In press

24. Goodman, D. A., Smith, R. L., Chamberlain, S. C. 1982. Intracellular and extracellular responses in the organ of Corti of the gerbil. Hearing Res. 7:161–79

25. Harris, D. M., Dallos, P. 1979. Forward masking of auditory nerve fiber responses. J. Neurophysiol. 42:1083–1107

26. Harris, G. G., Frishkopf, L. S., Flock, A. 1970. Receptor potentials from hair cells of the lateral line. Science 167:76–79

27. Harrison, R. V. 1981. Rate-versus-intensity functions and related AP responses in normal and pathological guinea pig and human cochleas. J. Acoust. Soc. Am. 70:1036–44

28. Hodgkin, A. L., Huxley, A. F. 1952. A quantitative description of membrane current and its application to conduction and excitation in nerve. J. Physiol. 117:500–44

29. Holton, T., Hudspeth, A. J. 1982. Motion of hair-cell stereocilia in the auditory receptor organ of the alligator lizard. Soc. Neurosci. Abstr. 8:40

30. Holton, T., Weiss, T. F. 1983. Receptor potentials of lizard cochlear hair cells with free-standing stereocilia in response to tones. J. Physiol. 345. In press

31. Holton, T., Weiss, T. F. 1983. Frequency selectivity of hair cells and nerve fibres in the alligator lizard cochlea. J. Physiol. 345. In press

32. Hudspeth, A. J. 1982. Extracellular current flow and the site of transduction by vertebrate hair cell. J. Neurosci. 2:1–10

33. Hudspeth, A. J. 1983. Mechanoelectrical transduction by hair cells in the acousticolateralis sensory system. Ann. Rev. Neurosci. 6:187–215

34. Hudspeth, A. J., Corey, D. P. 1977. Sensitivity, polarity, and conductance change in the response of vertebrate hair cells to controlled mechanical stimuli. Proc. Natl. Acad. Sci. USA 74:2407–11

35. Hudspeth, A. J., Jacobs, R. 1979. Stereocilia mediate transduction in vertebrate hair cells. Proc. Natl. Acad. Sci. USA 76:1506–9

36. Ishii, Y., Matsuura, S., Furukawa, T. 1971. An input-output relation at the synapse between hair cells and eighth nerve fibers in goldfish. Japan J. Physiol. 21:91–98

37. Iurato, S. 1967. Submicroscopic Structure of the Inner Ear, pp. 27–28. New York: Pergamon

38. Johnson, D. H. 1978. The relationship of post-stimulus time and interval histograms to the timing characteristics of spike trains. Biophys. J. 22:413–30

39. Johnson, D. H. 1980. The relationship between spike rate and synchrony in responses of auditory-nerve fibers to single tones. J. Acoust. Soc. Am. 68:1115–22

40. Kiang, N. Y. S. 1975. Stimulus representation in the discharge patterns of auditory neurons. In The Nervous System, Human Communication and its Disorders, ed. D. B. Tower, 3:81–96. New York: Raven

41. Kiang, N. Y. S., Moxon, E. C. 1972. Physiological considerations in artificial stimulation of the inner ear. Ann. Otol. Rhinol. Laryngol. 81:714–30

42. Kiang, N. Y. S., Moxon, E. C., Levine, R. A. 1970. Auditory-nerve activity in cats with normal and abnormal cochleas. In Ciba Found. Symp. Sensorineural Hearing Loss, ed. G. E. W. Wolstenholme, J. Knight, pp. 241–73. London: Churchill

43. Kiang, N. Y. S., Peake, W. T. 1960. Components of electrical responses recorded from the cochlea. Ann. Otol. Rhinol. Laryngol. 69:448–58

44. Kiang, N. Y. S., Watanabe, T., Thomas, E. C., Clark, L. F. 1965. Discharge Patterns of Single Fibers in the Cat's Auditory Nerve. Cambridge: MIT Press

45. Kim, D. O., Molnar, C. E. 1979. A population study of cochlear nerve fibers: comparison of spatial distributions of average-rate and phase-locking measures of responses to single tones. J. Neurophysiol. 42:16–30

46. Kim, D. O., Molnar, C. E., Mathews, J. W. 1980. Cochlear mechanics: nonlinear behavior in two-tone responses as reflected in cochlear-nerve-fiber responses and in ear-canal sound pressure. J. Acoust. Soc. Am. 67:1704–21

47. Klinke, R. 1978. Frequency analysis in the inner ear of mammals in comparison to other vertebrates. Verh. Dtsch. Zool. Ges., 71:1–15. Stuttgart: Fischer

48. Klinke, R., Pause, M. 1980. Discharge properties of primary auditory fibres in Caiman Crocodilus: Comparisons and contrasts to the mammalian auditory nerve. Exp. Brain Res. 38:137–50

49. Lewis, E. R. 1981. Suggested evolution of tonotopic organization in the frog amphibian papilla. Neurosci. Lett. 21:131–36

50. Lewis, E. R., Leverenz, E. L., Koyama, H. 1982. The tonotopic organization of the bullfrog amphibian papilla, an auditory organ lacking a basilar membrane. J. Comp. Physiol. 145:437–45

51. Lewis, R. S., Hudspeth, A. J. 1983. Voltage and ion-dependent conductances in solitary vertebrate hair cells. Nature 304:538–41

52. Liberman, M. C. 1978. Auditory-nerve response from cats raised in a low-noise chamber. *J. Acoust. Soc. Am.* 63:442–55

53. Liberman, M. C. 1980. Morphological differences among radial afferent fibers in the cat cochlea: An electron-microscopic study of serial sections. *Hearing Res.* 3:45–63

54. Liberman, M. C. 1982. Single-neuron labeling in the cat auditory nerve. *Science* 216:1239–41

55. Liberman, M. C. 1982. The cochlear frequency map for the cat: Labeling auditory-nerve fibers of known characteristic frequency. *J. Acoust. Soc. Am.* 72:1441–49

56. Lim, D. J. 1980. Cochlear anatomy related to cochlear micromechanics. A review. *J. Acoust. Soc. Am.* 67:1686–95

57. Littlefield, W. M. 1973. *Investigation of the linear range of the peripheral auditory system.* D.Sc. dissertation. Wash. Univ., St. Louis

58. Mauro, A., Conti, F., Dodge, F., Schor, R. 1970. Subthreshold behavior and phenomenological impedance of the squid giant axon. *J. Gen. Physiol.* 55:497–523

59. Miller, M. R. 1980. The reptilian cochlear duct. In: *Comparative Studies of Hearing in Vertebrates,* ed. A. N. Popper, R. R. Fay, pp. 169–204. New York: Springer

60. Mulroy, M. J., Altmann, D. W., Weiss, T. F., Peake, W. T. 1974. Intracellular electric responses to sound in a vertebrate cochlea. *Nature* 249:482–85

61. Nuttall, A. L., Brown, M. C., Masta, R. I., Lawrence, M. 1981. Inner hair cell responses to the velocity of basilar membrane motion in the guinea pig. *Brain Res.* 211:171–74

62. Palmer, A. R., Evans, E. F. 1980. Cochear fibre rate-intensity functions: no evidence for basilar membrane nonlinearities. *Hearing Res.* 2:319–26

63. Peake, W. T., Goldstein, M. H. Jr., Kiang, N. Y. S. 1962. Responses of the auditory nerve to repetitive acoustic stimuli. *J. Acoust. Soc. Am.* 34:562–70

64. Peake, W. T., Ling, A. L. Jr. 1980. Basilar-membrane motion in the alligator lizard: Its relation to tonotopic organization and frequency selectivity. *J. Acoust. Soc. Am.* 67:1736–45

65. Retzius, G. 1884. *Das Gehörorgan der Wirbeltiere. II. Das Gehörorgan der Reptilien, der Vögel und der Säugetiere.* Stockholm: Samson & Wallin

66. Rhode, W. M. 1984. Cochlear mechanics. *Ann. Rev. Physiol.* 46:231–46

67. Russell, I. J., Sellick, P. M. 1977. Tuning properties of cochlear hair cells. *Nature* 267:858–60

68. Russell, I. J., Sellick, P. M. 1978. Intracellular studies of hair cells in the mammalian cochlea. *J. Physiol.* 284:261–90

69. Russell, I. J., Sellick, P. M. 1983. Low-frequency characteristics of intracellularly recorded receptor potentials in guinea-pig cochlear hair cells. *J. Physiol.* 338:179–206

70. Sachs, M. 1984. Neural encoding of complex sounds: speech. *Ann. Rev. Physiol.* 46:261–75

71. Sachs, M. B., Abbas, P. J. 1974. Rate versus level functions for auditory-nerve fibers in cats: tone-burst stimuli. *J. Acoust. Soc. Am.* 56:1835–47

72. Sand, O., Ozawa, S., Hagiwara, S. 1975. Electrical and mechanical stimulation of hair cells in the mudpuppy. *J. Comp. Physiol. A* 102:13–26

73. Saunders, J. C., Garfinkle, T. J. 1981. The morphology of inner hair cell stereocilia in the mouse. *J. Acoust. Soc. Am.* 70:S7–8

74. Sellick, P. M. 1979. Recordings from single receptor cells in the mammalian cochlea. *Trends Neurosci.* 2:114–16

75. Sellick, P. M., Russell, I. J. 1978. Intracellular studies of cochlear hair cells: Filling the gap between basilar membrane mechanics and neural excitation. In *Evoked Electrical Activity in the Auditory Nervous System,* ed. R. F. Naunton, C. Fernández, pp. 113–37. New York: Academic

76. Sellick, P. M., Russell, I. J. 1980. The responses of inner hair cells to basilar membrane velocity during low frequency auditory stimulation in the guinea pig cochlea. *Hearing Res.* 2:439–45

76a. Shofner, W. P., Feng, A. S. 1983. A quantitative light microscopic study of the bullfrog amphibian papilla tectorium: correlation with the tonotopic organization. *Hearing Res.* 11:103–16

77. Shotwell, S. L., Jacobs, R., Hudspeth, A. J. 1981. Directional sensitivity of individual vertebrate hair cells to controlled deflection of their hair bundles. *Ann. NY Acad. Sci.* 374:1–10

78. Smith, C. A. 1981. Recent advances in structural correlates of auditory receptors. In *Progress in Sensory Physiology* 2, ed. D. Ottoson, pp. 135–87. New York: Springer

79. Smith, R. L. 1977. Short-term adaptation in single auditory nerve fibers: some poststimulatory effects. *J. Neurophysiol.* 40:1098–1112

80. Smith, R. L., Frisina, R. D., Goodman, D. A. 1983. Intensity functions and dynamic responses from the cochlea to the cochlear nucleus. In *Hearing—Phys-*

iological Basis and Psychophysics, ed. R. Klinke, R. Hartmann. In press

81. Smith, R. L., Zwislocki, J. J. 1975. Short-term adaptation and incremental responses of single auditory-nerve fibers. *Biol. Cybern.* 17:169–82

82. Tanaka, Y., Asanuma, A., Yanagisawa, K. 1980. Potentials of outer hair cells and their membrane properties in cationic environments. *Hearing Res.* 2:431–38

83. Tasaki, I. 1954. Nerve impulses in individual auditory nerve fibers of guinea pig. *J. Neurophysiol.* 17:97–122

83a. Tilney, L. G., Saunders, J. C. 1983. Actin filaments, stereocilia, and hair cells of the bird cochlea. I. Length, number, width, and distribution of stereocilia of each hair cell are related to the position of the hair cell on the cochlea. *J. Cell Biol.* 96:807–21

84. Turner, R. G., Muraski, A. A., Nielsen, D. W. 1981. Cilium length: influence on neural tonotopic organization. *Science* 213:1519–21

85. Weiss, T. F. 1982. Bidirectional transduction in vertebrate hair cells: a mechanism for coupling mechanical and electrical processes. *Hearing Res.* 7:353–60

86. Weiss, T. F., Mulroy, M. J., Altmann, D. W. 1974. Intracellular responses to acoustic clicks in the inner ear of the alligator lizard. *J. Acoust. Soc. Am.* 55:606–19

87. Weiss, T. F., Mulroy, M. J., Turner, R. G., Pike, C. L. 1976. Tuning of single fibers in the cochlear nerve of the alligator lizard: relation to receptor organ morphology. *Brain Res.* 115:71–90

88. Weiss, T. F., Peake, W. T., Leong, R., Holton, T., Rosowski, J. J., White, J. R. 1981. Mechanical and electrical mechanisms in the ear: Alligator lizard tales. *J. Acoust. Soc. Am.* 70:S50–51

89. Weiss, T. F., Peake, W. T., Ling, A. Jr., Holton, T. 1978. Which structures determine frequency selectivity and tonotopic organization of vertebrate cochlear nerve fibers? Evidence from the alligator lizard. In *Evoked Electrical Activity in the Auditory Nervous System,* ed. R. F. Naunton, C. Fernández, pp. 91–112. New York: Academic

90. Wever, E. G. 1978. *The Reptile Ear.* Princeton, NJ: Princeton Univ. Press

91. Wiener, F. M., Pfeiffer, R. R., Backus, A. S. N. 1966. On the sound pressure transformation by the head and auditory meatus of the cat. *Acta Otolaryngol.* 61:255–69

Ann. Rev. Physiol. 1984. 46:261–73

NEURAL CODING OF COMPLEX SOUNDS: SPEECH

Murray B. Sachs

Department of Biomedical Engineering, Johns Hopkins University School of Medicine, Baltimore, Maryland 21205

INTRODUCTION

Investigations of the neural encoding of "complex" stimuli in the auditory nerve began in the 1960s with investigations of responses to two-tone combinations (9, 11, 14, 19, 24). Although a number of aspects of the response properties to such stimuli are still being worked out (see, for example, 12), a number of investigators have recently turned their attention to the question of how well responses to more complex stimuli, specifically speech, could be predicted on the basis of our knowledge of responses to one- and two-tone stimuli (3, 10, 21, 25, 35). In this review we shall consider the most recently published works dealing with the encoding of various speech features in the discharge patterns of populations of auditory-nerve fibers.

Figure 1 shows a speech stimulus containing many of the important speech features that must be encoded in the auditory-nerve discharge patterns. The stimulus is the consonant-vowel syllable /da/ generated by a digital vocal tract model, which consists of a cascade of tuned circuits (15). The temporal waveform of the syllable is shown in Fig. 1B. This pattern is generated by exciting the vocal tract model with a train of pulses. The rate at which these pulses are delivered is the *pitch frequency* of the speech sound. The major peaks in the speech waveform correspond to this pitch-excitation function. Pitch frequency is plotted vs time in the lower left of Fig. 1A. It is constant at 120 Hz during the first 50 msec; correspondingly, the spacing of major peaks in Fig. 1B during this interval is 8.3 msec. During the last 50 msec, pitch decreases to 116 Hz with a corresponding increase in peak spacing.

The damped oscillations that occur between the major peaks are the response of the vocal tract model to the pitch pulses. Figure 1C shows the first and last 20

261

0066-4278/84/0315-0261$02.00

/da/

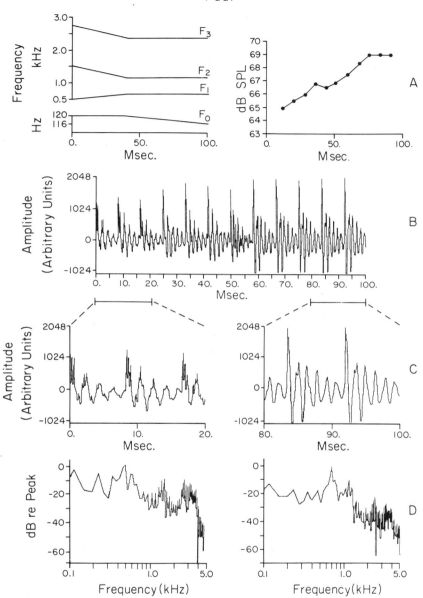

Figure 1 A(*left*): Top three plots show trajectories of the first three formants for the consonant-vowel syllable /da/. The bottom plot shows the trajectory of the fundamental frequency of voicing. A(*right*): Power of the stimulus in dB SPL as a function of time during the stimulus for the experiment on 3/31/81. B: Waveform of the stimulus whose formant trajectories are shown in the top panel. C: Expanded scale version of the first 20 and last 20 msec of the stimulus plotted in B. D: Power spectra derived from the 0–20 msec segment and 80–100 msec segment of the stimulus shown in C. (From Miller & Sachs, 17).

msec of the /da/ on an expanded time scale. Figure 1D shows the Fourier transform magnitudes computed from these same segments. During the first 20 msec there are peaks in the spectrum (within the 50 Hz resolution of the transform) at about 500, 1500, and 2750 Hz. These are the first three *formant frequencies* of the stimulus during this initial time segment. Formant frequencies are the resonant frequencies of the circuits which make up the vocal tract model. The top three plots at left in Fig. 1A show these formant frequencies as a function of time through the stimulus. During the first 50 msec there is a *formant-frequency transition* associated with the stop consonant; during the last 50 msec the formant frequencies are constant and make up the steady-state vowel portion of the syllable. This change in formant frequencies is illustrated by the two spectra in Fig. 1D. The first formant transition is also evident in the time domain representation in Fig. 1C. During the first 20 msec of the stimulus there are four prominent peaks in each pitch period. These peaks reflect the large energy in the stimulus at the fourth harmonic of the pitch; this is the pitch harmonic nearest the first formant frequency. During the last 50 msec there are six peaks per pitch period, reflecting the higher first formant frequency during the steady-state vowel.

In our review we shall emphasize the encoding of the features of stop consonant–vowel syllables like that illustrated in Fig. 1. Specifically, we shall consider the encoding of formant frequencies in steady-state vowels, of formant-frequency transitions associated with stop consonants, and of voice pitch. Where relevant we shall also consider the encoding of fricative consonants.

The population of auditory-nerve fibers can be considered an array of tuned elements whose characteristic frequencies are arranged systematically along the cochlear partition (28). Because the central nervous system has available to it the spike discharge patterns of this whole population, it is reasonable to consider how responses to various speech features are distributed across characteristic frequency. According to what are usually called "place" theories, peaks in the acoustic spectrum of a sound (e.g. formant peaks of a speech sound) would result in peaks in response in the population of auditory-nerve fibers at places along the basilar membrane where characteristic frequencies correspond with the stimulus peaks (formants). Two types of response measures have been used in such place representations. In what we have called "rate-place" representations, the response measure is simply average discharge rate (25). In "temporal-place" representations, the response parameter is some measure of the phase-locking (22) properties of auditory-nerve fibers. We shall first consider rate-place representations.

Representations in Terms of Average Discharge Rate

Figure 2 shows examples of a rate-place representation of steady-state vowels. The spectrum of the vowel (/ɛ/) is shown at top. This vowel is perfectly periodic and thus has energy only at harmonics of the 128 Hz pitch. The bottom two plots show discharge rate in response to /ɛ/ plotted vs characteristic frequency (CF) for a population of 269 fibers recorded in the auditory nerve of a single cat. Each data point comes from a different fiber. As we discuss below, there is good evidence that auditory-nerve fibers with very low rates of spontaneous activity form a separate population (16). For this reason, data from fibers with spontaneous rates less than 1 sec^{-1} are plotted with open square symbols, whereas fibers with higher spontaneous rates are plotted with Xs. Average rate has been normalized in such a way that each fiber's rate increase (above spontaneous rate) to the vowel is plotted as a fraction of its saturation rate (23) to CF tones. The solid line is a windowed average of the data points, which include only the fibers with spontaneous rates greater than one per second. Data for two vowel levels are shown. At 38 dB SPL the rate-place profile (average curve) shows peaks of discharge rate at CFs corresponding with the first three formants of the vowel as required of a rate-place scheme. However, at 78 dB SPL these formant-related peaks are no longer present. The disappearance of these formant peaks can be explained in terms of auditory-nerve nonlinearities (rate saturation and two-tone suppression) (25). The principal effect is rate saturation, which limits the dynamic range of the fibers (23). Because this loss of formant peaks occurs at sound levels within the conversational range, this result could pose serious problems for theories of speech coding based on rate and place. However, these data do not rule out a rate-place code because of a number of factors that we consider next.

First, the low-spontaneous-rate fibers have higher thresholds (16) and wider dynamic ranges (29) than the higher-spontaneous-rate fibers from which the averaged curves in Fig. 2 were computed. Although the data are sparse (because the low-spontaneous-rate fibers form only about 15% of the population), inspection of the open square symbols in Fig. 2 shows that there are clearly formant-related peaks in the rate distribution of these fibers even at 78 dB SPL. Thus, taken as a separate population, these low-spontaneous-rate fibers could code formant frequencies in a rate-place scheme at levels where the high-spontaneous-rate fibers are all saturated (25). Delgutte (5) has presented a simulation in which response rates of low- and high-spontaneous-rate fibers at each CF are combined in a weighted sum. The weighting factors depend only on response rates of fibers at the place (CF) of maximum rate. Such simulations show clear formant peaks at levels as high as 90 dB SPL. Delgutte's simulation does not, however, include effects of two-tone suppression that may restrict the range of levels over which low-spontaneous-rate fibers show second formant peaks (25).

Second, vowels could be discriminated on the basis of gross shape of their rate profiles, even in the absence of formant peaks (25). The gross shapes of the profiles for different vowels are different even at high stimulus levels (27).

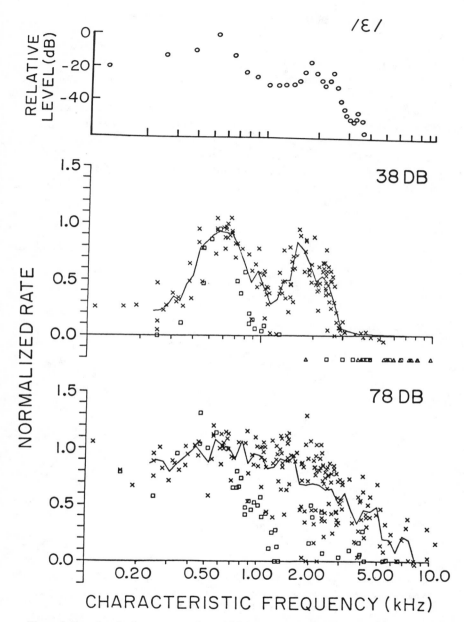

Figure 2 Top: Amplitude spectrum of /ɛ/. *Middle:* Plot of normalized rate vs characteristic frequency for units studied on 11/13/78 with /ɛ/ as the stimulus at 38 dB SPL. *Bottom:* Same as middle but at stimulus level of 78 dB SPL.

Third, the role of the efferent olivocochlear system on encoding at high stimulus levels is unknown. Electrical stimulation of the crossed-olivocochlear bundle can lead to an equivalent "attenuation" of an acoustic stimulus by more than 20 dB (34). The result is that the dynamic part of the fiber-rate functions are moved to higher stimulus levels, which could preserve formant peaks at higher levels than those shown in Fig. 2.

Finally, formant structure during the formant transition of stop consonants is better preserved than that during steady-state vowels, as is shown in Fig. 3 (17, 31). This figure shows profiles of average rate computed over 20 msec intervals throughout the /da/ stimulus. Formant-related peaks are evident during the formant transition (first 50 msec) but not during the steady vowel. This improved performance of rate profiles for consonants is related to the increased

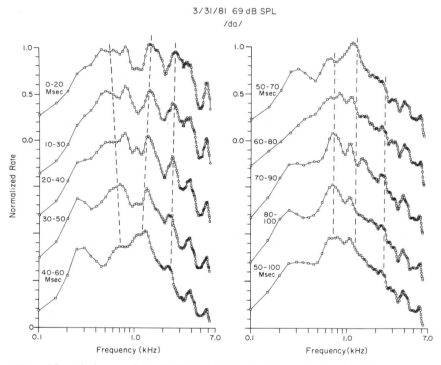

Figure 3 Smoothed averaged rate plots for the /da/ stimulus. The time during which the average rate responses were computed are given in the upper left corner of each plot. The left column represents the response during the formant transitions, the right column is during the steady vowel. All plots were computed from 20 msec segments of the stimulus except the one at the lower right, which is the rate response averaged over the entire 50–100 msec of the steady vowel. The dashed lines show the instantaneous formant frequency trajectories of the first three formant parameters of the synthesizer. (From Miller & Sachs, 17).

dynamic range of auditory-nerve fibers at stimulus onset that has been demonstrated by Smith & Brachman (32).

In contrast to the vowels and voiced consonants, the unvoiced fricative consonants have their major energy at frequencies above 3.0 kHz. Furthermore, they are generated by a noise excitation of the vocal tract, as opposed to the almost periodic pulse trains used to generate the stimuli considered thus far. Delgutte (3, 4) has presented the most extensive study of the fricative consonants. He has shown that for some of the fricatives (e.g. /s/ and /f/) there are clear peaks in rate profiles in CF regions near the fricative-formant frequencies. For others [such as /x/ as in German "Bach" and /š/ (sh)] there are no clear peaks at the places of the formants. Nonetheless, Delgutte has argued that rate profiles for all the fricatives he has studied can be distinguished on the basis either of formant-related peaks or on the basis of other features of the profiles.

Representation in Terms of Temporal (Phase-Locked) Measures

The average rate measures we have discussed thus far discard the fine temporal detail that is present in the discharge patterns of the auditory-nerve fibers. These fibers respond to stimuli in a way that is temporally locked to the stimulus waveform. The instantaneous rate (or probability of discharge) of a fiber responding to stimuli with frequencies below about 6.0 kHz is modulated by a rectified version of the stimulus waveform, as modified by cochlear filtering (1, 11, 22). Figure 4 shows an example. The left panels show bandpass-filtered versions of 20 msec segments of the stimulus waveform for /da/. These waveforms were obtained by filtering the speech waveform with a linear bandpass filter that models basilar-membrane tuning (7). The center frequency of the filter was chosen to correspond to the characteristic frequency (0.57 kHz) of the fiber illustrated in the figure, which is in the range of the first formant frequency for /da/. The center panels show poststimulus-time (PST) histograms for responses of this fiber computed from spikes occurring during the 20 msec segment corresponding to the stimulus at left. The magnitudes of the Fourier transforms of the PST histograms are shown at right. The PST histograms show that the fiber's temporal response was dominated by stimulus energy in the vicinity of CF, as can be judged from a comparison of the histograms and the bandpass-filtered stimuli. During the first 20 msec segment (top row), in both the filtered stimulus and the PST histograms, the most prominent feature is the presence of peaks spaced at intervals corresponding to the period of the first formant, which is close to 500 Hz during this segment (period = 0.5 msec). The Fourier-transform magnitude plot on the right shows a corresponding peak at 500 Hz. During the last 20 msec of the stimulus, the first formant frequency has increased to 700 Hz. The fiber's temporal response has changed correspondingly, resulting in a decrease in peak spacing in the PST histogram and a large 700 Hz component in the Fourier-transform magnitude.

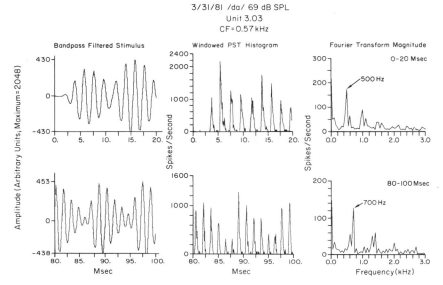

Figure 4 Data for a single fiber studied on 3/31/81. Left column shows 20 msec segments of the bandpass-filtered stimulus waveform for /da/ (see text). The center of the bandpass filter was chosen to be 0.57 kHz, the same frequency as the CF of the unit. Middle column shows PST histograms computed over the interval corresponding to the stimulus segment at left; right column shows the magnitude of the Fourier transform of the PST histogram. The upper plots correspond to the first 0–20 msec segment of the stimulus, the lower plots correspond to the 80–100 msec segment of the stimulus. The Fourier transform is computed with 256 bins and has a resolution of 50 Hz, corresponding to the period of the 20 msec long histograms. The PST and Fourier-transform ordinates are given in absolute rate (spikes sec^{-1}). (From Miller & Sachs, 17).

Temporal patterns such as these have been studied in great detail recently for vowels (3, 21, 35) and for stop consonants (4, 17, 31). The results of all of these studies is that temporal responses of fibers are dominated by frequency components that are large in the stimulus. Furthermore, responses to any stimulus component tend to be largest at places in the population of fibers where CFs correspond with the frequency of that component (17, 35). These properties can be used to advantage to develop a "temporal-place" representation of stimulus spectra as follows. It makes sense (35) to take as a measure of the population response to any stimulus component the amplitude of response at that component frequency, averaged across fibers tuned near that frequency. We have therefore defined such a measure (average localized synchronized rate, ALSR) at any frequency as the average value of the amplitude of the Fourier-transform component ("synchronized rate," expressed in spikes/sec) at that frequency; the average is computed over all fibers whose CF are within ± 0.25 octaves of that frequency. The ALSR reflects both place and temporal information about the population response to a frequency: place because only fibers tuned near that frequency are included in the average; temporal because the measure averaged is synchronized rate.

Figure 5 shows an example of such a temporal-place representation. The top plot shows the spectrum of /da/ computed over the first 25 msec of the stimulus (see Fig. 1). The spectrum has a smooth envelope that has peaks at the formant frequencies. Superimposed on this envelope there is a rapidly varying component with peaks at harmonics of the pitch frequency (120 Hz in this case; arrows at top in Fig. 5) and troughs between. The bottom plot in Fig. 5 shows the ALSR for a population of auditory-nerve fibers in response to this same /da/. PST histograms were computed from spikes occurring over the first 25 msec of the stimulus and the ALSR measure extracted as discussed above. The similarity between the ALSR and stimulus spectrum is clear. Specifically, the ALSR shows peaks at harmonics of the pitch (arrows) and troughs between. The smooth envelope of the ALSR has peaks at the stimulus-formant frequencies.

This temporal-place measure has been shown to provide a robust representation of vowels and stop consonants. Peaks in the ALSR at formant frequencies are maintained for both vowels and consonants at the highest stimulus levels tested (17, 35). Formant frequency transitions in stop consonants are closely tracked by these formant peaks (17, 31). The temporally based ALSR representation is quite resistant to masking by noise (4, 26). Rate-place profiles, on the other hand, deteriorate drastically in the presence of masking noise. We must be careful in interpreting the results of masking studies, however, until the possible role of the efferent system is clarified (see, for example, 6).

The types of stimuli with which we have dealt in this section (vowels and stops) are all generated with a periodic or quasi-periodic excitation of the vocal tract. One must question whether a temporal-place representation could be adequate to encode the features of fricatives that are generated with a noise excitation of the vocal tract. Voigt et al (33) have demonstrated that some stimuli generated with a noise excitation of the vocal tract can be encoded in a temporal-place representation. They studied responses to stimuli that were approximations to whispered vowels. ALSR measures based on interval histograms of response to these whispered vowels showed clear peaks at the formant frequencies of the vowels. However, the vowel formants used were lower than the formants of most fricatives. In fact, the formant frequencies of many fricatives are close to or above the upper bound on significant phase-locking (5–6 kHz; 13). As would be expected, Delgutte (4) has shown that an ALSR type of temporal-place measure for fricatives shows formant-related peaks only for those stimuli with relatively low formant frequencies.

Of the speech features illustrated in Fig. 1, we have thus far considered the encoding only of those related to the vocal tract transfer function, namely formant frequencies and formant-frequency transitions. We now turn to the

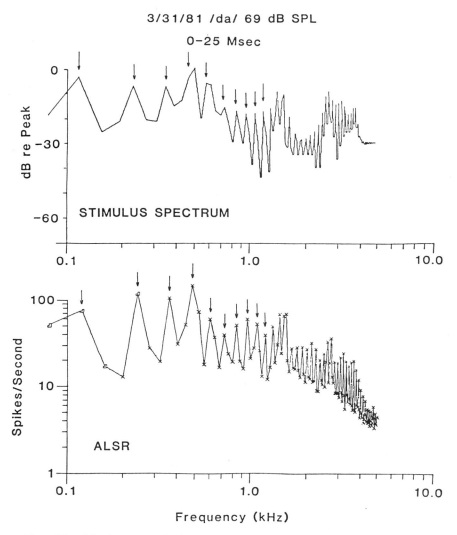

Figure 5 Top: Stimulus spectrum for first 25 msec of /da/. *Bottom:* Average localized synchronized rate for population of auditory-nerve fibers. Arrows point to first 10 harmonics of 120 Hz pitch. (Redrawn from Miller & Sachs, 18).

encoding of the feature related to the source-excitation function, pitch frequency. The mechanisms underlying the perception of the pitch of complex sounds has long been a focus for auditory physiology and psychophysics (2). Two theories have received considerable attention. In the first, pitch is determined by the intervals between the major envelope peaks in the speech waveform

(Fig. 1B–C). As Schouten (30) and Plomp (20) have pointed out, the outputs of cochlear filters will show pitch-related envelope modulations. Examples are shown in outputs of the model cochlear filters shown in Fig. 4. The PST histograms in Fig. 4 show that such envelope modulations are maintained in the auditory-nerve fiber discharge patterns. The histogram envelopes have peaks spaced at intervals equal to the pitch. Such pitch-related envelope modulations occur for fibers with CFs across the population of the auditory nerve (3, 18). Exceptions occur for units tuned very close to the formant frequencies and in the presence of broadband background noise.

According to the second general theory of pitch perception, pitch is determined by the harmonic structure of the spectra of complex stimuli (e.g. 8). This harmonic structure is illustrated by the spectrum in Fig. 5 that, as we have pointed out, has peaks at the harmonics of the pitch frequency. This harmonic structure is clearly maintained in the auditory-nerve fiber responses, as is illustrated by the ALSR plot at bottom in Fig. 5. It should be emphasized that the ALSR maintains this harmonic structure because: (*a*) responses to stimulus harmonics dominate the population responses; and (*b*) responses to any harmonic are largest near the place in the auditory-nerve population where fibers are tuned to that harmonic. Miller & Sachs (17) have shown that pitch can be extracted from ALSR measures with enough precision to allow tracking of small pitch changes such as that illustrated by the stimulus in Fig. 1. On the other hand, rate-place profiles have not been shown to provide spectral resolution fine enough to permit extraction of pitch from harmonic structure (17).

SUMMARY

The studies that we have reviewed here demonstrate that a temporal-place code can represent fine details in the spectra of vowels and stop-consonants. These features include formant frequencies, formant-frequency transitions, and pitch. On the other hand, such a phase locking–based representation may have difficulty with certain fricative consonants. Detailed formant structure of vowels is present in a rate-place code at moderate stimulus levels, but is maintained at high levels only in the small population of low-spontaneous-rate fibers. A rate-place code preserves the formant structure at high stimulus levels better for stop-consonants than for vowels. Formant structure of some fricatives may be represented in a place-rate code in cases where a temporal-place code fails. Voice pitch is well preserved in a temporal code but not in a rate-place code. From this summary we must consider the possibility that the central nervous system utilizes both rate-place and temporal-place information in processing all of the relevant features of speech.

This review points out a number of issues that currently confront us in the coding of complex stimuli. We conclude by briefly summarizing these issues. First, we must attempt to clarify the role of the low-spontaneous-rate, high-threshold fibers in the representation of speech at high-stimulus levels. A second major question that must be addressed is the role of the cochlear efferents in the peripheral encoding of speech, especially in the presence of background noise. Closely related to the role of the efferents may be the role of the middle ear muscles. Finally, if we are to seriously consider a temporal-based code for speech, we must develop quantitative hypotheses about how spectral information might be extracted from temporal patterns in the central nervous system with real neural "hardware."

Literature Cited

1. Brugge, J. F., Anderson, D. J., Hind, J. E., Rose, J. E. 1969. Time structure of discharges in single auditory-nerve fibers of the squirrel monkey in response to complex periodic sounds. *J. Neurophysiol.* 32:386–401
2. de Boer, E. 1976. On the "residue" and auditory pitch perception. In *Handbook of Sensory Physiology*, ed. W. D. Keidel, W. D. Neff, 5:479–583. New York: Springer-Verlag
3. Delgutte, B. 1980. Representation of speech-like sounds in the discharge patterns of auditory-nerve fibers. *J. Acoust. Soc. Am.* 68:843–57
4. Delgutte, B. 1981. *Representation of speech-like sounds in the discharge patterns of auditory-nerve fibers.* PhD thesis. Cambridge: 243 pp.
5. Delgutte, B. 1982. Some correlates of phonetic distinctions at the level of the auditory nerve. In *Representation of Speech in the Peripheral Auditory System*, ed. R. Carlson, B. Granstrom, pp. 131–49. Amsterdam: Elsevier Biomedical Press
6. Dewson, J. H. 1968. Efferent olivocochlear bundle: Some relationships to stimulus discrimination in noise. *J. Neurophysiol.* 31:122–30
7. Duifhuis, H. 1973. Consequences of peripheral frequency selectivity for nonsimultaneous masking. *J. Acoust. Soc. Am.* 54:1471–85
8. Goldstein, J. L. 1973. An optimum processor theory for the central formation of the pitch of complex tones. *J. Acoust. Soc. Am.* 54:1496–516
9. Goldstein, J. L., Kiang, N. Y. S. 1968. Neural correlates of the aural combination tone $2f_1\text{-}f_2$. *Proc. IEEE* 56:981–92
10. Hashimoto, T., Katayama, Y., Murata, K., Taniguchi, L. 1975. Pitch synchronous response of cat cochlear nerve fibers to speech sounds. *Jpn. J. Physiol.* 25:633–44
11. Hind, J. E., Anderson, D. J., Brugge, J. F., Rose, J. E. 1967. Encoding of information pertaining to paired low-frequency tones in single auditory-nerve fibers of the squirrel monkey. *J. Neurophysiol.* 30:794–816
12. Javel, E., McGee, J., Walsh, E. F., Farley, G. R., Gorga, M. P. 1983. Suppression of auditory nerve responses. II. Suppression threshold and growth, Iso-suppression contours. *J. Acoust. Soc. Am.* In press
13. Johnson, D. H. 1980. The relationship between spike rate and synchrony in responses of auditory-nerve fibers to single tones. *J. Acoust. Soc. Am.* 68:1115–22
14. Kim, D. O., Siegel, J. H., Molnar, C. E. 1979. Cochlear nonlinear phenomena in two tone responses. *Scand. Audiol.* 1979 (Suppl. 9):63–82
15. Klatt, D. 1980. Software for a cascade/parallel formant synthesizer. *J. Acoust. Soc. Am.* 67:971–95
16. Liberman, M. C. 1978. Auditory-nerve responses from cats raised in a low-noise chamber. *J. Acoust. Soc. Am.* 63:442–55
17. Miller, M. I., Sachs, M. B. 1983. Representation of stop consonants in the discharge patterns of auditory-nerve fibers. *J. Acoust. Soc. Am.* 74:502–17
18. Miller, M. I., Sachs, M. B. 1983. Temporal and spectral representation of voice pitch in the auditory nerve. *Hearing Res.* Submitted for publication
19. Nomoto, M., Suga, N., Kataski, Y. 1964. Discharge patterns and inhibition of primary auditory nerve fibers in the monkey. *J. Neurophysiol.* 27:768–87
20. Plomp, R. 1966. Aspects of tone sensation. London: Academic. 167 pp.
21. Reale, R. A., Geisler, C. D. 1980. Auditory-nerve fiber encoding of two-tone approximations to steady-state vowels. *J. Acoust. Soc. Am.* 67:891–902
22. Rose, J. E., Brugge, J. F., Anderson, D. J., Hind, J. E. 1967. Phase-locked response to low frequency tones in single

auditory nerve fibers of the squirrel monkey. *J. Neurophysiol.* 30:769–893

23. Sachs, M. B., Abbas, P. J. 1974. Rate vs level functions for auditory-nerve fibers in cats: tone burst stimuli. *J. Acoust. Soc. Am.* 56:1835–47

24. Sachs, M. B., Kiang, N. Y. S. 1968. Two-tone inhibition in auditory-nerve fibers. *J. Acoust. Soc. Am.* 43:1120–28

25. Sachs, M. B., Young, E. D. 1979. Encoding of steady-state vowels in the auditory nerve: representation in terms of discharge rate. *J. Acoust. Soc. Am.* 66:470–79

26. Sachs, M. B., Voigt, H. F., Young, E. D. 1983. Auditory nerve representation of vowels in background noise. *J. Neurophysiol.* 50:27–45

27. Sachs, M. B., Young, E. D., Miller, M. I. 1982. Encoding of speech features in the auditory nerve. In *The Representation of Speech in the Peripheral Auditory System*, ed. R. Carlson, B. Granstrom, pp. 115–130. Amsterdam: Elsevier Biomedical Press

28. Sando, I. 1965. The anatomical interrelationships of the cochlear nerve fibers. *Acta Oto-laryngol.* 59:417–36

29. Schalk, T. B., Sachs, M. B. 1980. Nonlinearities in auditory-nerve fiber responses to bandlimited noise. *J. Acoust. Soc. Am.* 67:903–13

30. Schouten, J. F. 1940. The residue and the mechanism of hearing. *Proc. Kon. Ned. Akad. Wet.* 43:991–99

31. Sinex, D. G., Geisler, C. D. 1983. Responses of auditory-nerve fibers to consonant-vowel syllables. *J. Acoust. Soc. Am.* In press

32. Smith, R. L., Brachman, M. L. 1980. Dynamic responses of single auditory-nerve fibres: Some effects of intensity and time. In *Psychophysical, Physiological, and Behavioral Studies in Hearing*, ed. G. van den Brink, F. A. Bilsen, pp. 312–19. Delft, Netherlands: Delft Univ. Press

33. Voigt, H. F., Sachs, M. B., Young, E. D. 1982. Representation of whispered vowels in discharge patterns of auditory-nerve fibers. *Hearing Res.* 8:49–58

34. Wiederhold, M. L. 1970. Variations in the effects of electric stimulation of the crossed olivocochlear bundle on cat single auditory-nerve fiber responses to tone bursts. *J. Acoust. Soc. Am.* 48:966–77

35. Young, E. D., Sachs, M. B. 1979. Representation of steady-state vowels in the temporal aspects of the discharge patterns of populations of auditory-nerve fibers. *J. Acoust. Soc. Am.* 66:1381–403

Ann. Rev. Physiol. 1984. 46:275–87

NEURAL MECHANISMS FOR SOUND LOCALIZATION

R. Bruce Masterton

Department of Psychology, Florida State University, Tallahassee, Florida 32306

Thomas J. Imig

Department of Physiology, University of Kansas Medical Center, Rainbow Blvd. at 39th, Kansas City, Kansas 66103

INTRODUCTION

In humans there are at least six relatively independent cues for sound localization (84). However, in physiological studies of the central mechanisms for localization, attention has been directed almost entirely to only two of these cues: interaural time and spectrum disparities. For the special case of pure tone stimuli, these reduce to interaural phase and intensity differences. Furthermore, with extended sound durations, pinna and neck muscle reflexes often contribute movement-by-intensity cues as the ears move within the sound field. Although the localization of long duration sounds is interesting in its own right, mechanisms analyzing these scanning cues are probably quite different than those required for sounds that are too brief to allow concurrent ear movement (48). This review is restricted to the central analyses of binaural time and intensity cues that mediate the latter, more demanding, ability.

In the last 30 years, research into the central mechanisms of sound localization has gradually become focused on two problems. (a) Does there exist an "acoustic chiasm" that analyzes the specific binaural cues for sound direction and distributes the product to contralateral auditory and motor centers? And, if so, where is it, and what is its anatomical and physiological basis? (b) Does there exist a topographic map of sound direction? And, if so, where is it, and how is it synthesized? This review is largely confined to these two questions. Other reviews on related topics or with somewhat different orientations are available elsewhere (e.g. 11, 13, 18, 20, 22, 29, 71, 79).

275

0066-4278/84/0315-0275$02.00

STUDIES OF THE ACOUSTIC CHIASM

Evidence for the Existence of a Functional Auditory Chiasm

By the turn of the century, it was known that the anatomical bilaterality of the auditory system begins with the partial decussation of second-order fibers from the cochlear nuclei (40, 64, 75, 92). Some 50 years later, Rasmussen (76) and Stotler (87) showed that many of the largest of the fibers from both cochlear nuclei converge on the superior olivary complex (SOC) in a manner suggesting its involvement in binaural interactions. Rosenzweig and colleagues (78, 80, 81) provided physiological confirmation by showing that, (a) stimulation either of one ear or by a sound in space evokes neural activity on both sides of the auditory pathway from the lateral lemniscus upward, and (b) binaural interactions are not evident in the responses of the second-order fibers, but are clearly evident among the higher-order fibers contained in the lateral lemniscus.

Because at the time it seemed that unilateral lesions of the auditory pathway above the SOC did *not* result in large or permanent deficits in sound localization (e.g. 88), and because the auditory system was known to afford several opportunities for bilateral interaction beyond the trapezoid body, the idea soon developed that the neural representation of a localizable sound source somehow depended on the relative amounts of neural activity on the two sides of the higher levels of the system (e.g. 2, 5, 18, 78, 86).

Recently, however, several observations indicate that this notion of the bilateral representation of sound direction is probably incorrect. First, ablation-behavior studies (15, 59, 65) show that the only commissure necessary for sound localization is the trapezoid body, and that section of higher level commissures has no effect on a cat's ability to localize a sound. This means that a comparison of neural activity on the two sides of the system at any level above the termination of trapezoid body fibers is neither necessary nor sufficient for normal sound localization. Second, unilateral lesions in the auditory pathway above the level of the SOC result in profound and permanent deficits both in reflexive orientation to sound and in instrumental sound localization, which are confined to the hemifield of space contralateral to the lesion (47, 49, 50, 58, 89, 90). These results suggest that contralateral sound directions are represented in one side of the system at levels above the SOC and that any chiasm-like "contralateralization" of the activity evoked by a lateral sound source takes place at or below the level of the inferior colliculus. That this contralateralization does *not* occur before the SOC has also been shown: lesions below the level of the SOC result in ipsilateral or bilateral deficits but not in contralateral ones (16, 47, 49, 59). By this argument, experimentation on the neural mechanisms of the acoustic chiasm or on the analysis of cues for sound direction quickly becomes focused on the SOC.

The Nature of the Acoustic Chiasm

Because in vision or somesthesis the sensory field is topographically represented on the receptor surface, the contralateral representation of the respective hemifields can be achieved by the decussation of the appropriate ascending fibers. In the auditory system, however, a region of cochlea represents a frequency range, not a region of auditory space, hence fiber sorting cannot accomplish the task. It follows that the acoustic chiasm must be fundamentally different from the optic or somatosensory chiasms: whereas the latter are anatomical structures, the acoustic chiasm must be a physiological process.

In abstract, the acoustic chiasm requires a two-stage process: first, the convergence and comparison of afferent activity arising at the two ears, and then the efferent distribution of this analysis to the appropriate side of the system. In the remainder of this section, we describe the anatomical basis, physiological mechanisms, and functional consequences of this two-stage process as it seems to be accomplished by the SOC.

The several nuclei of the SOC are embedded within the fibers of the trapezoid body (45, 66). Three of these nuclei, the lateral (LSO) and medial superior olives (MSO), and the ventral nucleus of the trapezoid body (VTB), gain relatively direct afferents from both ears (via the cochlear nuclei). Their constituent neurons are sensitive to binaural time or spectrum differences (11, 29, 37). A fourth nucleus, the medial nucleus of the trapezoid body (MTB), supplies contralateral afferents to LSO. Because no other nuclei in SOC yield sufficiently short-latency responses to acoustic stimulation or project to the binaurally sensitive nuclei, it is on these four nuclei that current research into the neural mechanisms of the acoustic chiasm is usually directed (11, 29–31, 33).

LSO and MTB

As elegantly demonstrated by Boudreau & Tsuchitani (7, 8) and since verified by others (9, 31, 33), the ipsilateral afferents to LSO are excitatory, while the contralateral afferents (via MTB) are inhibitory. Thus, the response characteristics of LSO cells are said to be "EI"—ipsilateral monaural stimulation *Excites*, contralateral monaural stimulation *Inhibits*. Furthermore, the characteristic (or best) frequencies of the excitatory and inhibitory afferents converging on individual LSO cells are closely matched. This convergence of ipsilateral excitatory and contralateral inhibitory activity matched for frequency specificity means that collectively, the EI cells of LSO perform a binaural spectrum-difference analysis on the sound stimulation reaching the two ears. In effect, each LSO subtracts the sound spectrum reaching its contralateral ear from the spectrum reaching its ipsilateral ear (8). Because this binaural spectrum difference is one of the most important and compelling cues for sound direction, it is clear that the MTB-LSO system makes a crucial contribution to the first or analytic stage of the two-stage chiasmatic process.

Turning to the second stage of the process, the distribution of the binaural spectrum-difference analysis to higher levels of the system, the contribution of LSO is not so obvious. Each LSO projects to the dorsal nucleus of the lateral lemniscus and the central nucleus of the inferior colliculus on *both* sides of the brainstem about equally (1, 12, 19, 24, 27, 82). However, the crossed and uncrossed projections arise from two different subpopulations of cells intermingled within LSO. Retrograde double-labeling experiments (using fluorescent dyes injected into the colliculi) suggest that the number and proportion of auditory cells in the hindbrain projecting bilaterally via axon collaterals is quite small (25, 27). But the same experiments have shown that the subpopulation of LSO cells giving rise to the uncrossed projection is concentrated laterally, while the population giving rise to the crossed projection is concentrated medially. Since LSO is tonotopically organized with low frequencies represented laterally and high frequencies medially, this pattern of labeling means that LSO's binaural analysis of the high-frequency end of the spectrum is projected mostly to the contralateral side, while its analysis of the low-frequency end of the spectrum is projected mostly to the ipsilateral side (26, 27). Since it is known that the interaural spectrum difference set up by a lateral sound source is physically much wider at high frequencies than at low frequencies, the arrangement of LSO's projections suggests that the part of its analysis most useful for sound localization (the high-frequency part) is directed mostly to the contralateral midbrain, while the part least useful for sound localization (the low-frequency part) remains mostly on the ipsilateral side. It remains to be seen if there exists other functional differences between LSO's crossed and uncrossed projections at their lemniscal and collicular targets (e.g. modes of termination, neurotransmitters, excitatory vs inhibitory action).

MSO and VTB

MSO and VTB gain direct projections from both cochlear nuclei. Electrophysiological studies of the response characteristics of MSO units have shown that almost 90% are binaurally sensitive; about 75% of these are of the EE type (excited by stimulation of either ear alone), and the remainder are of the EI type. Among the cells of VTB, about which much less is known, only about 50% seem to be binaural; about 70% of these are of the EE type (30, 31, 33, 34). When the two ears are presented with identical stimuli that are offset in time, the responses of the EE cells are either facilitated or suppressed, depending on the length of the short interval between the two monaural stimuli. For this reason they are often called "delay-sensitive" or simply "delay" cells. This peculiar response characteristic, first discovered by Galambos et al (21), has been verified several times in cats and in dogs (30, 31, 33, 34, 67–70, 83).

Animals with well-developed MSOs (e.g. humans, cats, dogs, monkeys, tree shrews, and elephants) can easily localize a single, brief tone-pip in their own low-frequency range (39, 60). In contrast, animals with poorly developed MSOs (e.g. rats) have great difficulty localizing tone-pips in their low-frequency range. Animals without any MSO at all (e.g. hedgehogs) cannot localize tone-pips in their low-frequency range at all (60). Taken together, electrophysiological and comparative psychophysical studies suggest that at least one part of MSO's (and possibly, VTB's) role in sound localization includes the analysis of binaural time differences.

Studies of glucose metabolism also suggest MSO's contribution to low-frequency sound localization. If labeled 2-deoxyglucose (2-DG) is administered to a monaural cat in the presence of low-frequency sound, the MSO ipsilateral to the remaining ear is labeled more heavily than the contralateral MSO. (This result presumably reflects the somewhat heavier afferent projections received from the ipsilateral cochlear nucleus.) If, however, the 2-DG is administered to a normal cat stimulated with a lateral sound source, the MSO contralateral to the sound source is more heavily labeled than the ipsilateral MSO (28, 58). This reversal in side of labeling given an active "far ear" means that the responses of the EE-delay cells in MSO are either facilitated on the side contralateral to the sound source, or suppressed on the side ipsilateral, or both. Together, the combination of electrophysiological, behavioral, and 2-DG results suggests that MSO encodes interaural time disparities by means of a neural "delay-line" and, further, contributes to the chiasmatic process by its activation contralateral to the sound source (46).

Turning to MSO's contribution to the second stage of the chiasmatic process, the situation is a bit more simple. To begin with, virtually all of MSO's efferent projections (and many of VTB's efferents not descending to cochlear nuclei or cochleae) ascend the *ipsilateral* lateral lemniscus, bypass the ventral nucleus of the lateral lemniscus, and terminate in the ipsilateral dorsal nucleus of the lateral lemniscus and in the dorsolateral (i.e. low-frequency) part of the ipsilateral central nucleus of the inferior colliculus (1, 10, 19, 24, 41, 85). Combining these anatomical results with the results of electrophysiological and 2-deoxyglucose surveys showing that it is the cells in the MSO contralateral to a sound source that are more excited (or less inhibited), it can be concluded that MSO probably projects more neural activity up the lateral lemniscus contralateral to the sound source than up the lemniscus ipsilateral to the sound source. Since we have already seen that the activity in the contralateral lemniscus is usable for sound localization while the activity ipsilateral to the sound source is not, this result suggests that it is only the activation of the contralateral MSO (and, ultimately, the activity at its pontine and midbrain terminals) that contains information used in the representation of the direction of a sound source. Thus, unlike the LSO system, the contralateralization of direction-relevant activity is accomplished on the afferent side of the MSO system. Nevertheless, several questions arise about MSO's efferents: If the activity evoked in ipsilateral MSO is not used for sound localization, what is its fate at the colliculus—and beyond?

Summary

If the evidence for the existence of a functional chiasm in the auditory system and its probable location within the binaural nuclei of the superior olivary complex is accepted, then its anatomical basis would seem to hinge on the convergence of afferents on these nuclei, the physiological analyses and integrations taking place within the nuclei, and the distribution of the integrated responses to the contralateral side of the system. So far the weight of evidence suggests that the binaural spectrum-difference cue is encoded by the EI cells in the LSO and that the most useful (high-frequency) part of this analysis is then projected to the midbrain, mostly contralateral to the sound source. The binaural time-difference cue is probably encoded by delay-line activation of EE cells in the MSO (and VTB), contralateral to the sound source, and then projected to the homolateral midbrain. Thus, both of these systems contribute to the two-stage process of contralateralization and seem to satisfy the requirements of chiasmatic function.

NEURAL REPRESENTATION OF SOUND DIRECTION

The ability to localize sound implies a neural representation of sound direction at least at some level along the sensory-motor dimension of nervous system function. In abstract, a topographic map of sound direction places several requirements on the receptive fields of the constituent neurons. *First,* a neuron's discharge rate must vary systematically as a function of sound direction. *Second,* directional sensitivity must vary among neurons. *Third,* the directional sensitivity of a neuron must remain relatively invariant regardless of changes in sound quality. *Fourth,* some feature of the receptive fields must be ordered topographically along one or more coordinates of auditory space. As yet, published studies providing explicit evidence bearing on this question have been confined mostly to owl, guinea pig, and cat; this section is divided accordingly.

Owl

The midbrain of the barn owl appears to contain a map of sound direction. Some "space-limited" neurons seem to have the requisite receptive field properties (52–54). Their receptive fields are limited to a restricted area of space, the receptive-field centers of different neurons vary in location (both in elevation and azimuth), and the receptive-field locations have been shown to be invariant with respect to some changes in the quality of the stimulus. The size and location of the receptive fields are joint products of central neural analysis and peripheral specializations. Receptive-field locations vary both in elevation and azimuth which, in turn, are functions of two independent cues. The azimuth coordinate depends primarily on interaural time disparities (62, 63). The elevation coordinate depends primarily on interaural intensity differences, a consequence of a vertical disparity in the directional sensitivity of the owl's asymmetrical ears (56).

The lowest level in the owl's auditory pathway containing neurons with space-limited receptive fields is nucleus mesencephalicus lateralis dorsalis (MLD), a homologue of the mammalian inferior colliculus (63). In the antero-lateral "space-mapped" part of MLD, spatial locations of receptive fields vary systematically to produce a two dimensional map of auditory space (53, 54). Once assembled in MLD, this space map is replicated in the optic tectum (52, 55). Thus, receptive-field characteristics and topographic organization suggest that MLD and optic tectum in owl each contains a two-dimensional place map of sound direction and that a particular sound direction is represented as a restricted focus of increased neural activity within the map.

Guinea pig

Although animals lacking asymmetrical ears may not be able to generate two-dimensional space maps using only interaural time and intensity differences, generation of a one dimensional map (i.e. of azimuth alone) is certainly conceivable and may occur in the deep (i.e. motor) layers of the superior colliculus of the guinea pig (72). Many acoustically driven neurons are sensitive to a limited range of azimuths of sound direction, and the azimuth sensitivity varies among neurons throughout the entire 180° of contralateral directions. Directional tuning is relatively unaffected by increases in stimulus intensity in some neurons, although the effect of changes in spectral content is not known. Finally, the azimuths of the receptive fields are topographically ordered. Therefore, as in the owl, sound direction appears to be represented in a place map in the superior colliculus of guinea pig (74).

Cat

For the cat, pinna mobility appears to add an additional complication to the neural representation of sound direction, because a change in pinna orientation will certainly affect binaural intensity differences associated with a particular sound direction. One can conceive of at least three possible solutions to this problem. One strategy is to orient the ears in a standard position relative to the head, thus eliminating the variability of binaural cues associated with different pinna orientations. There are some anecdotal observations that cat's ears do assume a stereotypical position during repeated sound-direction testing (90). A second strategy is to analyze sound direction using pinna-referenced coordinates rather than head-referenced coordinates. A third possible strategy is to analyze sound direction in pinna coordinates and then to integrate this product with a neural representation of concurrent pinna position, producing a map in head-referenced coordinates. These three strategies make quite different predictions of the effect of changes in pinna orientation on a neuron's directional sensitivity. In the first case, a change in pinna orientation shifts the location of directional sensitivity with respect to both the head and the pinna. In the second case, the location shifts with respect to the head, but not the pinna. In the third case, the location shifts with respect to the pinna, but not the head.

INFERIOR COLLICULUS   Rose and his collaborators (77) described "characteristic delay" neurons (much like the delay cells of MSO) whose sensitivity to interaural time differences remain invariant, despite changes in stimulus intensity and frequency. They correctly identified these neurons as appropriate elements for constructing a map of sound direction. About 60% of the collicular neurons sensitive to binaural time differences exhibit a characteristic delay (96). Similarly, many high-frequency (>3 kHz) neurons whose spatial receptive fields have been studied are differentially sensitive to sound direction, although directional sensitivity of some of these neurons may vary with changes in stimulus intensity or frequency. Further, there appears to be a segregation of characteristic delays within an isofrequency lamina (3, 6, 17, 23, 42, 57). Therefore, whether sound direction is topographically represented in the inferior colliculus remains an open question. Certainly, many of the cells exhibit some of the required characteristics.

SUPERIOR COLLICULUS   Gordon studied the properties of the auditory-responsive neurons in the deeper layers of the superior colliculus in paralyzed unanesthetized cats (32, 93). Generally, the neurons were sensitive to sound direction though only the receptive-field border nearest the frontal median plane usually appeared sharply defined. Furthermore, there was a positive correlation between the locations of the medial borders of the auditory and visual receptive fields in bimodally responsive neurons. Since the superior colliculus contains a retinotopic map, this finding suggests that azimuth might be topographically represented as the location of the leading edge or the expanse of neural activity in the superior colliculus (44). However, it remains to be demonstrated that the locations of receptive-field borders are relatively independent of changes in stimulus quality and whether the resulting map is referenced to the head or to the pinna.

Quite a different view of the superior colliculus comes from the work of Harris et al (36), who found auditory receptive fields with well-defined medial and lateral borders. Auditory and visual receptive fields in bimodal neurons had similar azimuth locations, suggesting the existence of a place map similar to that reported in the guinea pig (72). Although differences in these findings could reflect differences in acoustic stimulation or anesthesia, changes in pinna orientation (which were not controlled in the latter case) might have influenced receptive-field location. Therefore, there may exist a place map of sound direction in the deep superior colliculus of cat, although not all the requirements for a strict topographic representation have yet been demonstrated (94, 95).

AUDITORY CORTEX   Many neurons in cortical field AI of the cat are directionally sensitive (35, 61). Three classes of receptive fields, varying in position and size, have been identified within the high frequency (3–20 kHz) representation (61). "Axial" units are generally most sensitive to high frequencies (>12 kHz) and have relatively small, circumscribed receptive fields centered on the acoustical axis of the contralateral pinna. "Hemifield" units are generally most sensitive to lower frequencies (3–12 kHz), have receptive fields that occupy most or all of the contralateral sound field, and, usually, only the receptive-field border near the frontal median plane is sharply delineated. Finally, "omnifield" units have best frequencies ranging from 3–20 kHz and respond both to ipsilateral and contralateral sound directions.

The directional sensitivity and receptive-field size of axial and hemifield neurons bear a similarity to the directional sensitivity of the pinna (61, 73). First, the receptive-field locations of axial cells are dictated by the directional sensitivity of the pinna for high-frequency sounds, as movement of the pinna produces a corresponding movement in the receptive-field location. The effect of pinna movement on the receptive-field locations of omnifield and hemifield units is unknown. Second, receptive-field size may be partly determined by the directional sensitivity of the pinna. For high frequencies (> 12 kHz), the directional-sensitivity gradient of the pinna is steepest, and cortical neurons sensitive to these frequencies have the smallest receptive fields. For lower frequencies, receptive fields are larger and the directional-sensitivity gradient of the pinna is broader. Since most AI (and ventral medial geniculate) units are sensitive to binaural stimulation, the receptive fields of axial and hemifield units appear to be the product of pinna directional sensitivity and prior binaural convergence (4, 14, 43, 86). Therefore, these results suggest that AI does *not* contain a head-referenced place map of sound-direction azimuth similar to that seen in guinea pig tectum or in owl. However, destruction of a restricted part of the frequency representation in AI produces a deficit in sound localization in the corresponding frequency range (on the contralateral side of the head). This suggests that sound direction may well be represented along an isofrequency strip (50). The effects of changes in sound quality and pinna orientation on the neurons directional sensitivity remain to be studied, but if sound direction is topographically represented in AI, it may be represented in the activity profile of several populations of neurons.

Summary

Although the efforts to find a place map of sound direction within the auditory system of mammals has been reinspired by the recent discoveries in owl, progress to date has not been encouraging. Neither the inferior colliculus nor auditory cortex has yielded immediate evidence of such a map, despite ingenious and persistent efforts to find it. Thus, at present, the evidence suggests that a head-referenced map of auditory space is more likely to be found in structures more motor than sensory in function—in the deep layers of the superior colliculus or brainstem tegmentum, for example. Insofar as these structures have been implicated in eye, ear, and head orientation toward a sound source, one might expect that premotor units for orienting would be sensitive to sound direction and thus, collectively, constitute a map of auditory azimuth isomorphic to the map of motor azimuth (91). However, even for these structures, the possibility for significant variation among mammalian species exists. Because many candidate motor structures (such as the deep superior colliculus) receive input from the cerebral cortex, and because the role of auditory cortex in sound localization seems to vary widely among mammals (38, 51) an equal amount of variation in auditory-motor maps may also exist.

Literature Cited

1. Adams, J. C. 1979. Ascending projections to the inferior colliculus. *J. Comp. Neurol.* 183:519–38
2. Bekesy, G. von, 1930. Zur Theorie des Horens. *Physikalische Zeitschrift* 31:857–68. Ed. and transl. E. G. Weaver, 1960, in *Experiments in Hearing.* Chap. 8 New York: McGraw-Hill
3. Benevento, L. A., Coleman, P. D. 1970. Responses of single cells in cat inferior colliculus to binaural click stimuli: combinations of intensity levels, time differences, and intensity differences. *Brain Res.* 17:387–405
4. Benson, D. A., Hienz, R. D., Goldstein, M. H. Jr. 1981. Single-unit activity in the auditory cortex of monkeys actively localizing sound sources: spatial tuning and behavioral dependency. *Brain Res.* 219:249–67
5. Benson, D. A., Teas, D. C. 1976. Single unit study binaural interaction in the auditory cortex of the chinchilla, *Brain Res.* 103:313–38
6. Bock, G. R., Webster, W. R. 1974. Coding of spatial location by single units in the inferior colliculus of the alert cat. *Exp. Brain Res.* 21:387–98
7. Boudreau, J. C., Tsuchitani, C. 1968. Binaural interaction in the cat superior olive S-segment. *J. Neurophysiol.* 31:442–54
8. Boudreau, J. C., Tsuchitani, C. 1970. Cat superior olive s-segment cell discharge to tonal stimulation. In *Contributions Sensor Physiology,* ed. W. D. Neff, 4:143–213. New York: Academic
9. Brownell, W. E., Manis, P. B., Ritz, L. H. 1979. Ipsilateral inhibitory responses in the cat lateral superior olive. *Brain Res.* 177:189–93
10. Brugge, J. F., Anderson, D. J., Aitkin, L. M. 1970. Response of neurons in the dorsal nucleus of the lateral lemniscus of the cat to binaural tonal stimulation. *J. Neurophysiol.* 33:441–58
11. Brugge, J. F., Geisler, C. D. 1978. Auditory mechanisms of the lower brainstem. *Ann. Rev. Neurosci.* 1:363–94
12. Brunso-Bechtold, J. K., Thompson, G. C., Masterton, R. B. 1981. HRP study of the organization of auditory afferents ascending to central nucleus of inferior colliculus in cat. *J. Comp. Neurol.* 197:705–22
13. Busnel, R. G., Fish, J. F. 1980. *Ani-*

mal Sonar Systems. New York: Plenum. 1135 pp.

14. Calford, M. B., Webster, W. R. 1981. Auditory representation within principal division of cat medial geniculate body. *J. Neurophysiol.* 45:1013–28

15. Casseday, J. H., Neff, W. D. 1975. Auditory localization: Role of auditory pathways in brainstem of the cat. *J. Neurophysiol.* 38:842–58

16. Casseday, J. H., Smoak, H. A. 1981. Effects of unilateral ablation of anteroventral cochlear nucleus on localization of sound in space. In *Symposium on Neuronal Mechanisms of Hearing*, ed. J. Syka, L. Aitkin, pp. 277–82. New York: Plenum

17. Chan, J. C., Yin, T. C. T. 1982. Topographic relationships along the isofrequency laminae of the cat inferior colliculus: correlation with the anatomical lamination and representation of binaural response properties. *Soc. Neurosci. Abstr.* 8:348

18. Colburn, H. S., Durlach, N. I. 1978. Models of binaural interactions. In *Handbook of Perception IV Hearing*, ed. E. C. Carterette, M. P. Friedman, pp. 467–518. New York: Academic

19. Elverland, H. H. 1978. Ascending and intrinsic projections of the superior olivary complex in the cat. *Exp. Brain Res.* 32:117–34

20. Erulkar, S. D. 1972. Comparative aspects of spatial localization of sound. *Physiol. Rev.* 52:237–360

21. Galambos, R., Schwartzkopff, J., Rupert, A. 1959. Microelectrode studies of superior olivary nuclei. *Am. J. Physiol.* 197:527–36

22. Gatehouse, R. W., ed. 1982. *Localization of Sound: Theory and Applications*. Groton, Conn: Amphora Press. 288 pp.

23. Geisler, C. D., Rhode, W. S., Hazelton, D. W. 1969. Responses of inferior colliculus neurons in the cat to binaural acoustic stimuli having wide-band spectra. *J. Neurophysiol.* 32:960–74

24. Glendenning, K. K., Brunso-Bechtold, J. K., Thompson, G. C., Masterton, R. B. 1981. Ascending auditory afferents to the nuclei of the lateral lemniscus. *J. Comp. Neurol.* 197:673–704

25. Glendenning, K. K., Bull, M. S., Masterton, R. B. 1981. A fluorescent double labeling study of ascending auditory projections to inferior colliculus of cat. *Soc. Neurosci.* 7:57

26. Glendenning, K. K. Masterton, R. B. 1982. Functional asymmetry in efferent projections of lateral superior olive in cat. *Anat. Rec.* 202:64–65

27. Glendenning, K. K., Masterton, R. B. 1983. Acoustic chiasm: efferent projections of the lateral superior olive. *J. Neurosci.* 3:1521–37

28. Glendenning, K. K., Skeen, L. C., Masterton, R. B. 1978. Activity of hindbrain auditory nuclei in response to a localizable sound. *Anat. Record* 190:402–3 (Abstr.)

29. Goldberg, J. M. 1974. Physiological studies of auditory nuclei of the pons. In *Handbook of Sensory Physiology*, ed. W. D. Keidel, W. D. Neff, 2:109–44. New York: Springer

30. Goldberg, J. M., Brown, P. B. 1968. Functional organization of the dog superior olivary complex: An anatomical and electrophysiological study. *J. Neurophysiol.* 31:639–56

31. Goldberg, J. M., Brown, P. B. 1969. Response of binaural neurons of dog superior olivary complex to dichotic tonal stimuli: some physiological mechanisms of sound localization. *J. Neurophysiol.* 32:613–36

32. Gordon, B. 1973. Receptive fields in deep layers of cat superior colliculus. *J. Neurophysiol.* 36:157–78

33. Guinan, J. J. Jr., Norris, B. E., Guinan, S. S. 1972. Single auditory units in the superior olivary complex: II. Locations of unit categories and tonotopic organization. *Int. J. Neurosci.* 4:147–66

34. Hall, J. L. II. 1965. Binaural interaction in the accessory superior-olivary nucleus of the cat. *J. Acoust. Soc. Am.* 37:814–23

35. Hall, J. L., Goldstein, M. H. Jr. 1968. Representation of binaural stimuli by single units in primary auditory cortex of unanesthetized cats. *Acoust. Soc. Am.* 43:456–61

36. Harris, L. R., Blakemore, C., Donaghy, M. 1980. Integration of visual and auditory space in the mammalian superior colliculus. *Nature* 288:56–59

37. Harrison, J. M. 1978. Functional properties of the Auditory System of the Brain Stem. In *Handbook of Behavioral Neurobiology*, ed. R. B. Masterton, 1:409–51. New York: Plenum

38. Heffner, H. E., Masterton, R. B. 1975. Contribution of auditory cortex to sound localization in the monkey. *J. Neurophysiol.* 38:1340–58

39. Heffner, R. S., Heffner, H. E. 1982. Hearing in the elephant: absolute sensitivity, frequency, discrimination, and sound localization, *J. Comp. Psychol.* 91:926–44

40. Held, H. 1893. Die Zentrale Gehorleitung. *Arch. Anat. Physiol., Anat. Abt.,* 17:201–48

41. Henkel, C. K., Spangler, K. M. 1982. Organization of medial superior olivary

projections to the inferior colliculus in the cat. *Soc. Neurosci. Abstr.* 8:151

42. Hind, J. E., Goldberg, J. M., Greenwood, D. D., Rose, J. E. 1963. Some discharge characteristics of single neurons in the inferior colliculus of the cat. II. Timing of the discharges and observations on binaural stimulation. *J. Neurophysiol.* 26:321–41

43. Imig, T. J., Adrian, H. O. 1977. Binaural columns in the primary field (AI) of cat auditory cortex. *Brain Res.* 138:241–57

44. Irvine, D. R. F., Wise, L. Z. 1983. The neural representation of auditory space. *Proc. Aust. Physiol. Pharmacol. Soc.* 14: In press

45. Irving, R., Harrison, J. M. 1967. The superior olivary complex and audition: a comparative study. *J. Comp. Neurol.* 130:77–86

46. Jeffress, L. A. 1948. A place theory of sound localization. *J. Comp Physiol. Psychol.* 41:35–39

47. Jenkins, W., Masterton, R. B. 1979. Contralateral representation of auditory hemifield in upper levels of brainstem auditory system. *Anat. Rec.* 193:575–76

48. Jenkins, W. M., Masterton, R. B. 1979. Sound localization in pigeon *(Columbia livia)*. *J. Comp. Physiol. Psychol.* 93:403–13

49. Jenkins, W. M., Masterton, R. B. 1982. Sound localization: effects of unilateral lesions in central auditory system. *J. Neurophysiol.* 47:987–1016

50. Jenkins, W. M., Merzenich, M. M. 1981. Lesions of restricted frequency representational sectors within primary auditory cortex produce frequency dependent sound localization deficits. *Soc. Neurosci. Abstr.* 7:392

51. Kelly, J. B. 1980. Effects of auditory cortical lesions on sound localization by the rat. *J. Neurophysiol.* 44:1161–74

52. Knudsen, E. I. 1982. Auditory and visual maps of space in the optic tectum of the owl. *J. Neurosci.* 2:1177–94

53. Knudsen, E. I., Konishi, M. 1978. A neural map of auditory space in the owl. *Science* 200:795–97

54. Knudsen, E. I., Konishi, M. 1978. Space and frequency are represented separately in auditory midbrain of the owl. *J. Neurophysiol.* 41:870–84

55. Knudsen, E. I., Konishi, M. 1978. Center-surround organization of auditory receptive fields in the owl. *Science* 202:778–80

56. Knudsen, E. I., Konishi, M. 1980. Monaural occlusion shifts receptive-field locations of auditory midbrain units in the owl. *J. Neurophysiol.* 44:687–95

57. Leiman, A. L., Hafter, E. R. 1972. Responses of inferior colliculus neurons to free field auditory stimuli. *Exp. Neurol.* 35:431–49

58. Masterton, R. B., Glendenning, K. K., Nudo, R. J. 1981. Anatomical-behavioral analyses of hindbrain sound localization mechanisms. See Ref. 16, pp. 263–75

59. Masterton, R. B., Jane, J. A., Diamond, I. T. 1967. Role of brainstem auditory structures in sound localization. I: Trapezoid body, superior olive, and lateral lemniscus. *J. Neurophysiol.* 30:341–59

60. Masterton, R. B., Thompson, G. C., Brunso-Bechtold, J. K., Robards, M. J. 1975. Neuroanatomical basis of binaural phase-difference analysis for sound localization: A comparative study. *J. Comp. Physiol. Psychol.* 89:379–86

61. Middlebrooks, J. C., Pettigrew, J. D. 1981. Functional classes of neurons in primary auditory cortex of the cat distinguished by sensitivity to sound location. *J. Neurosci.* 1:107–20

62. Moiseff, A., Konishi, M. 1981. Neuronal and behavioral sensitivity to binaural time differences in the owl. *J. Neurosci.* 1:40–48

63. Moiseff, A., Konishi, M. 1982. The nuclei of the owl's auditory brainstem are characterized by unique modes of binaural interaction. *Soc. Neurosci. Abstr.* 8:150

64. Monakow, C. von. 1890. Striae acusticae und untere Schliefe. *Arch. Psychiatr. Nervenkrankh.* 22:1–29

65. Moore, C. N., Casseday, J. H., Neff, W. D. 1974. Sound localization: The role of the commissural pathways of the auditory system of the cat. *Brain Res.* 82:13–26

66. Moore, J. K., Moore, R. Y. 1971. A comparative study of the superior olivary complex in the primate brain. *Folia Primat.* 16:35–51

67. Moushegian, G., Rupert, A. L., Langford, T. L. 1967. Stimulus coding by medial superior olivary neurons. *J. Neurophysiol.* 30:1239–61

68. Moushegian, G., Rupert, A., Whitcomb, M. A. 1964. Brain-stem neuronal response patterns to monaural and binaural tones. *J. Neurophysiol.* 27:1174–91

69. Moushegian, G., Rupert, A., Whitcomb, M. A. 1964. Medial superior-olivary-unit response patterns to monaural and binaural clicks. *J. Acoust. Soc. Am.* 36:196–202

70. Deleted in proof

71. Neff, W. D. 1968. Localization and lateralization of sound in space. In *Ciba Foundation Symposium on Hearing*

Mechanisms in Vertebrates, ed. A. V. S. DeReuch, J. Knight, pp. 207–31. London: Churchill

72. Palmer, A. R., King, A. J. 1982. The representation of auditory space in the mammalian superior colliculus. *Nature* 299:248–49

73. Phillips, D. P., Calford, M. B., Pettigrew, J. D., Aitkin, L. M., Semple, M. N. 1982. Directionality of sound pressure transformation at the cat's pinna. *Hearing Res.* 8:13–28

74. Popelar, J., Syka, J. 1979. Responses of inferior colliculus neurons in guinea-pig to monaural and binaural acoustic stimuli. *Physiol. Bohemoslov.* 28:465

75. Ramon y Cajal, S. 1909. *Histologie du Systeme Nerveux de l'Homme et des Vertebres,* 1:774–838. Madrid: Inst. Ramon y Cajal

76. Rasmussen, G. L. 1946. The olivary peduncle and other fiber projections of the superior olivary complex. *J. Comp. Neurol.* 84:141–219

77. Rose, J. E., Gross, N. B., Geisler, C. D., Hind, J. E. 1966. Some neural mechanisms in the inferior colliculus of the cat which may be relevant to localization of a sound source. *J. Neurophysiol.* 29:288–314

78. Rosenzweig, M. R. 1954. Cortical correlates of auditory localization and of related perceptual phenomena. *J. Comp. Physiol. Psychol.* 47:269–76

79. Rosenzweig, M. R. 1961. Development of research on the physiological mechanisms of auditory localization. *Psychol. Bull.* 58:376–89

80. Rosenzweig, M. R., Amon, A. H. 1955. Binaural interaction in the medulla of the cat. *Experientia* 11:498–500

81. Rosenzweig, M. R., Sutton, D. 1958. Binaural interaction in lateral lemniscus of cat. *J. Neurophysiol.* 21:17–23

82. Roth, G. L., Aitkin, L. M., Anderson, R. A., Merzenich, M. M. 1978. Some features of spatial-organization of central nucleus of inferior colliculus of cat. *J. Comp. Neurol.* 182:661–80

83. Rupert, A., Moushegian, G., Whitcomb, M. A. 1966. Superior-olivary response patterns to monaural and binaural clicks. *J. Acoust. Soc. Am.* 39:1069–76

84. Searle, C. L., Braida, L. C., Davis, M. F., Colburn, H. S. 1976. Model for auditory localization. *J. Acoust. Soc. Am.* 60:1164–75

85. Semple, M. N., Aitkin, L. M. 1979. Representation of sound frequency and laterality by units in central nucleus of cat inferior colliculus. *J. Neurophysiol.* 42:1626–39

86. Starr, A. 1974. Neurophysiological mechanisms of sound localization. *Fed. Proc.* 33:1911–14

87. Stotler, W. S. 1953. An experimental study of the cells and connections of the superior olivary complex of the cat. *J. Comp. Neurol.* 98:401–32

88. Strominger, N. L. 1969. Localization of sound in space after unilateral and bilateral ablation of auditory cortex. *Exp. Neurol.* 25:521–33

89. Thompson, G. C., Cortez, A. M. 1983. The inability of squirrel monkeys to locate sound after unilateral ablation of acoustic chiasm. *Behav. Brain Res.* 8:211–16

90. Thompson, G. C., Masterton, R. B. 1978. Brain stem auditory pathways involved in reflexive head orientation to sound. *J. Neurophysiol.* 41:1183–1202

91. Tunkl, J. E. 1980. Location of auditory and visual stimuli in cats with superior colliculus ablations. *Exp. Neurol.* 68:395–402

92. Warr, W. B. 1982. Parallel ascending pathways from the cochlear nucleus: neuroanatomical evidence of functional specialization. *Sensory Physiology,* 7:1–38. New York: Academic

93. Wickelgren, B. G. 1971. Superior colliculus: some receptive field properties of bimodally responsive cells. *Science* 173:69–72

94. Wise, L. A., Irvine, D. R. F., Pettigrew, J. D., Calford, M. B. 1982. Auditory spatial receptive field properties of neurons in intermediate and deep layers of cat superior colliculus. *Neurosci. Lett.* 8:888

95. Wise, L. Z., Irvine, D. R. F. 1983. Auditory response properties of neurons in deep layers of cat superior colliculus. *J. Neurophysiol.* 49:674–85

96. Yin, T. C. T., Kuwada, S. 1983. Binaural interaction in low frequency neurons in the inferior colliculus of the cat. III. Effects of changing frequency. *J. Neurophysiol.* In press

RENAL AND ELECTROLYTE PHYSIOLOGY

Introduction, Carl W. Gottschalk, *Section Editor*

Determination of the relative importance of glomerular and tubular factors in control of salt and water excretion has been a fascinating but perplexing topic for renal physiologists. It was early recognized that, because of their magnitude, the rates of glomerular filtration (GFR) and tubular reabsorption of salt and water must be tightly coupled to avoid excessive changes in their rates of excretion. It was also early recognized that the inherent error of measurement of the filtration rate, and thus of calculating the rate of reabsorption, generally exceeds the rates at which salt and water are excreted. Most initial investigations of the topic used maneuvers that presumably caused a primary change in GFR. Not surprisingly, the concept arose that almost all changes in salt and water excretion resulted from changes in the filtered load. It was recognized, however, that aldosterone resulted in changes in sodium, potassium, and water excretion through its direct effect on tubular transport processes, presumably located in the latter part of the nephron. It was not until experiments were reported in which the GFR was extremely carefully controlled or reduced that it was generally appreciated that extracellular fluid volume expansion results in a change in tubular reabsorption and that the tubular effect alone can explain changes in rates of excretion independent of a change in filtered load. Although the nature of the "third factor(s)," as it was initially called, has still not been fully elucidated, it is now apparent that changes in rates of tubular reabsorption independent of changes in GFR can be primary determinants of altered rates of excretion of salt and water.

289

The section on Renal Physiology deals with four humoral systems that influence salt and water excretion by the kidney. The presentations elucidate the contributions of filtered load and tubular transport to alterations in salt and water excretion in health and disease. Gibbons, Dzau, Farhi & Barger discuss the interaction of the various signals in the regulation of renin release. They emphasize the importance of making observations in the absence of anesthesia and other factors that disturb homeostasis. Margolius reviews the mechanisms for the effect of the kallikrein-kinin system on renal electrolyte and water excretion and the complex interactions with other hormones and enzyme product systems. Currie & Needleman discuss the cellular localization of renal arachidonic acid metabolism as determined from recent studies of isolated cultured renal cells. They also discuss an interesting pathophysiological model of exaggerated prostaglandin synthesis that appears to involve an immunologic response in the cortex resulting in increased PGE_2 release. Finally, Buckalew & Gruber review recent developments in the characterization of "natriuretic hormone" and its involvement in volume regulation and hypertension.

Ann. Rev. Physiol. 1984. 46:291–308

INTERACTION OF SIGNALS INFLUENCING RENIN RELEASE

G. H. Gibbons, V. J. Dzau, E. R. Farhi, and A. C. Barger

Departments of Physiology and Medicine, Harvard Medical School, and the Hypertension Unit, Brigham and Women's Hospital, Boston, Massachusetts 02115

INTRODUCTION

The various physiological mechanisms that individually modulate the release of renin from the kidney have been reviewed by a number of investigators (18, 27, 68). It is apparent that the juxtaglomerular cells that release renin are influenced by a variety of both stimulatory and inhibitory input signals. The final control mechanisms that govern renin release must process these signals and produce an integrated response. However, the approach to the study of renin release has frequently involved the examination of only a single stimulus, for example renal perfusion pressure, adrenergic activity, or tubular sodium concentration. Moreover, much of this work has been performed with anesthetized animals, immediately following surgery—when the physiologic state is markedly altered—or in isolated tissue lacking many of the control inputs. Although such experiments provide valuable information, we will primarily review how some of the stimuli for renin secretion interact in homeostatic adjustments in the chronic, unanesthetized dog, in order to elucidate the response of the renin-angiotensin system in man in health and disease. In fact, it was the well-known relationship between renal and cardiac diseases and the possible endocrine role of the kidney that motivated Tigerstedt & Bergman (65) in their discovery of renin.

Historical Background

The history of the renin-angiotensin system has been controversial. Even the stimulus for Tigerstedt & Bergman's interest in the kidney as an endocrine

291

0066-4278/84/0315-0291$02.00

organ has often been mistakenly attributed to Richard Bright (11), who first demonstrated the association of kidney disease with hypertension. His clinical and pathological reports, however, were not the immediate impetus for Tigerstedt & Bergman's search for a pressor agent in the kidney. In the first paragraph of their classic paper of 1898 they state that it was Brown-Séquard's early endocrine studies that stimulated them (12):

> The ingenious idea of Brown-Séquard, that various organs release substances into the blood which do not belong to the usual catabolic products, but are formed by specific activity of the tissues and have a basic importance for the over-all functioning of the body, has been brilliantly established through numerous investigations.

Tigerstedt & Bergman subsequently devised a series of experiments to determine whether substances released from the kidney influence the circulatory system. The experiments were imaginatively planned, carefully executed, and sufficiently clear and detailed for other investigators to reproduce. Although the experiments were remarkably successful and published in the prime of Tigerstedt's career, they brought him nothing but criticism and even scorn. The significance of this most innovative and important work of his distinguished career was not recognized for nearly half a century—many years after his death.

In their first experiment Tigerstedt & Bergman reported:

> When one grinds a freshly excised rabbit kidney with glass powder and water (physiological salt solution), filters off the supernatant fluid, and injects 2 cc intravenously into a normal rabbit . . . one gets in a short time definite and considerably long-lasting elevation of the arterial pressure.

They determined that the pressor agent, which they named renin, was characterized by the following properties:

> It exerts a significant activity in very small amounts, . . . is insoluble in absolute and 50% alcohol," and is present only in the cortex. They reasoned that "the injection of several cc of renal venous blood into a normal animal will not have a significant demonstrable [pressor] activity, since the addition of quite a small amount of renin to that already present in the blood in this case, would, according to all probability, be practically without significance. Therefore, we carried out experiments in rabbits from which one or two days previously both kidneys had been extirpated.

By nephrectomy, not only did they lower plasma renin activity but serendipitously elevated renin substrate levels. Under these circumstances, the injection of a small amount of blood into a nephrectomized rabbit produced a gradual and marked rise in blood pressure. The conclusions that they drew from their observations were judiciously and modestly presented:

> Concerning the role these substances normally play in the vascular tonus, we can form only provisional hypotheses, and we have no reason to occupy ourselves with such. We wish only to direct attention to the fact that the pressure-raising substance obtained from the kidneys

may be possibly of importance in the theoretical interpretation of the cardiac hypertrophy occuring in certain renal diseases. Hence, the conclusion cannot be set aside, that, under certain circumstances, this substance could be formed in larger quantities than usual, or that it could be excreted from the body in smaller amounts than ordinary. In that case there would be exerted a stronger and more lasting action than under normal circumstances upon the vascular musculature, and in this manner the resistance to the vessels be constantly raised above the normal level.

The ink was scarcely dry on Tigerstedt & Bergman's publication when the controversy concerning renin began, led by Max Lewandowsky (45) of the Physiological Institute of Berlin, a brilliant scion of a well-known German medical family, who was primarily interested in the sympathetic nervous system. In 1899, he wrote a scathing and sarcastic rebuttal of the paper by Tigertstedt & Bergman. He emphasized that the adrenal medullary extract of Oliver & Schäfer (49) was far more powerful than the pressor substance that was supposedly obtained from the kidney. Moreover, he noted that when the adrenal glands were removed, hypotension and death ensued; on the contrary, no one had demonstrated that the removal of kidneys had led to a significant drop in blood pressure. He concluded that the experiments of Tigerstedt & Bergman "be denounced a priori." Ignoring the sound reasoning of Tigerstedt & Bergman that nephrectomized rabbits be used for testing the pressor activity in renal venous blood, Lewandowsky injected blood into normal rabbits and saw no pressor effect. Then in a grand rhetorical style he asked: "What will become of the blood pressure if so small amounts of venous blood of a perfused kidney, the most productive of all organs of the body, has such colossal effects?"

Although some early investigators were able to reproduce the results reported by Tigerstedt & Bergman [see Bingel & Strauss (7)], others, such as Pearce (51), found primarily depressor substances in kidney extracts. Unfortunately, investigators who reviewed the literature and quoted Pearce's negative results apparently failed to notice that most of Pearce's studies were done with a dried filtrate of an alcoholic extract dissolved in salt solution. Tigerstedt & Bergman had clearly shown that renin was alcohol insoluble. The crowning blow may have come from Janeway (38), the doyen of American internists interested in the kidney. In his review of nephritic hypertension in 1913 he briefly reviewed the work of Tigerstedt & Bergman and tersely concluded: "I think it is reasonable to dismiss them from consideration."

According to those who knew Tigerstedt personally, he apparently did not mention the renin work and may well have wished that his paper be forgotten, because it had brought him nothing but grief. In his *Lehrbuch der Physiologie des Menschen* (63), one of the most popular European textbooks, Tigerstedt devoted only one paragraph to these earlier renin studies. In the American edition of his Textbook of Human Physiology, translated by Murlin (64) in

1906, even this single paragraph was deleted. In the 1924 obituary of Tigerstedt published in the Skandinavisches Archiv für Physiologie, the journal he had edited for many years, no mention of renin was made by his long-time colleague and successor, Santesson (54).

SIGNALS INFLUENCING RENIN RELEASE

Renal Perfusion Pressure Signal

It was Goldblatt's pioneering studies (33) that provided the model that finally led to the appreciation of the role of renin in hypertension. Although Goldblatt first postulated that renal ischemia was responsible for renin release, we now know that reduction in renal perfusion pressure, as first hinted by Blalock & Levy (9), is the important variable. Indeed, moderate reduction of renal perfusion pressure, with no appreciable fall in renal blood flow, may increase renin secretion (58). Tobian (66) proposed the existence of a renal "barorecep-tor" that responds to stretching of the afferent arteriole. According to this hypothesis, renal vasodilatation or an increase in perfusion pressure stretches the wall of the afferent arteriole (and juxtaglomerular cells), thereby decreasing renin secretion. More recently, Fray (26) presented a mathematical stretch receptor model based on his studies of the perfused rat kidney. In his model, renin release is related to the elastic modulus of the afferent arteriole, the internal and external hydrostatic pressures, and more importantly, to the ratio of the internal and external radii of the afferent arteriole. He proposed that vasodilatation (induced by papaverine) or high pressure may stretch the afferent arteriole and depolarize the granular cell membrane, inhibiting renin release, whereas vasoconstriction or low pressure may decrease stretch and thus hyper-polarize the cell and increase renin secretion. However, Keeton & Campbell (41) have challenged Fray's hypothesis, emphasizing that renal artery hypotension is usually accompanied by autoregulatory arteriolar dilatation. Moreover, intrarenal infusion of vasodilators other than papaverine (e.g. dopa-mine, prostaglandins, etc.) stimulate renin secretion. Thus, the mechanism by which reduction in renal perfusion pressure (RPP) stimulates renin secretion is still a subject of controversy.

Although the precise location and nature of the renal baroreceptor is still unknown, it may be functionally (and quantitatively) described by determining the stimulus-response curve relating RPP to plasma renin activity (PRA). Farhi et al (22) have performed such experiments in conscious dogs, maintaining a steady-state RPP by frequent adjustment of an inflatable cuff around the renal artery. As shown in Figure 1, the stimulus-response curve may be divided into two ranges of pressure: one in which renin secretion is relatively unresponsive to lowering of RPP (down to 10–20 mmHg below basal pressure), and another in which PRA is a steep and linear function of RPP. The pressure at which the curve begins to rise abruptly is only slightly below normal systemic pressure. These findings differ from the observations of Cowley & Guyton (16) in the anesthetized animal, who reported a linear relationship between PRA and RPP even at elevated pressures produced by norepinephrine infusion. The differences are probably due to the anesthesia, surgical trauma, and high levels of norepinephrine in the latter experiments. As we discuss later, these factors may shift the stimulus-response curve to the right. Nevertheless, these data indicate that changes in RPP are of primary importance in determining the rate of renin secretion as suggested by Skinner, McCubbin & Page in 1964 (56).

The Sodium Signal

Plasma renin activity varies inversely with dietary intake of sodium in all species examined, but the mechanism by which sodium alters renin secretion

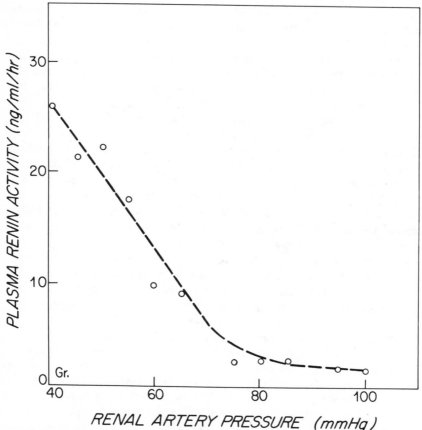

Figure 1   Stimulus-response curve of the renal baroreceptor of a dog on a low-sodium diet.

remains a subject of controversy. The effect may be a direct action of sodium on the juxtaglomerular cells, or an indirect action mediated by neural or humoral signals induced by alterations in extracellular sodium concentration or fluid volume. Of the numerous hypotheses proposed for regulation of renin secretion by sodium intake, the macula densa theory has received the most attention. Thirty years after Goormaghtigh (34) first suggested an endocrine role for the macula densa of the kidney, Vander & Miller (69) proposed that renin secretion was controlled by the flow or composition of intratubular fluid at the level of the macula densa, and that renal venous pressor activity was inversely related to the rate of sodium excretion.

Since it is impossible to perform micropuncture analysis of ionic composition of tubular fluid in the region of the juxtaglomerular apparatus, various indirect methods have been used to test the macula densa thesis. By retrograde microinjection of hypertonic saline into the distal tubule, Thurau et al (62) came to the conclusion that, contrary to Vander & Miller's study, renin secretion was directly related to tubular sodium concentration. In an attempt to determine whether changes in intrarenal sodium concentration altered renin release by a vascular or a tubular mechanism, Shade and colleagues (55) infused hypertonic sodium chloride into the renal artery of caval constricted dogs with a filtering or nonfiltering kidney; in the former, renin release was markedly reduced, but the infusion had little effect in the latter. They concluded, therefore, that a tubular rather than a vascular sensor regulates renin secretion in response to changes in intrarenal sodium. On the other hand, Fray (26) varied the sodium concentration of fluid perfusing isolated rat kidneys from 85 to 204 mM without altering the rate of renin secretion, despite large changes in sodium excretion. Hence, the role of the macula densa in the regulation of renin release is still unclear. In addition, new questions have recently been raised concerning the anatomical and functional characteristics of the macula densa. Taugner and co-workers (59), using freeze-fracture techniques, have demonstrated gap junctions between most of the cellular elements of the juxtaglomerular (JG) apparatus (hydrophilic channels that allow the passage of ions and small molecules from cell to cell without significant leak into the extracellular space). There are, however, no gap junctions between the macula densa cells and other cells of the JG region. This is surprising, because the macula densa is presumed to be the receptor through which changes in distal fluid composition alter renin release.

Although the transport properties of the thick ascending limb and distal convoluted tubule have been established, the transport properties of the interposed macula densa cells remain unknown. In several species Beeuwkes & Rosen (4) have shown, histochemically and by electron probe microanalysis, that the highest levels of (Na^+,K^+)-ATPase activity are found in the thick ascending limb and distal convoluted tubule, while little or no activity is found within the macula densa cells regardless of dietary sodium intake. If the ability to establish high transepithelial ion gradients is required for transduction, then these results are inconsistent with a transducer role for the macula densa cells. Moreover, Sottiurai & Malvin (57), also using the microprobe, have reported that the sodium concentration in the macula densa cells does not vary during maneuvers that change renin release over a wide range. Thus, their study does not support the tenet that alteration of the concentration of sodium in the macula densa cells regulates renin release. At present, then, we do not know the cellular mechanism by which sodium balance affects renin release. Nevertheless, it is possible to examine how sodium balance interacts with other parameters such as renal perfusion pressure and catecholamine concentration in the control of PRA.

The Adrenergic Signal

Electrical stimulation of the renal nerves with sufficient intensity has long been known to increase renin secretion in the anesthetized animal, as has the infusion of pharmacological doses of epinephrine and norepinephrine (67). These effects are attenuated by β-blockers. Under basal conditions, however, the renal efferent-nerve activity in the conscious dog appears to be too low to influence renin release significantly (36). Thus, acute administration of adrenergic blocking agents does not alter PRA in the conscious, salt-replete animal, nor would one expect any significant inhibition of renin release to be reflexly induced. However, even at such low levels of PRA, angiotensin II still plays a significant physiological role in the regulation of circulation. By the use of power-spectrum analysis of heart-rate fluctuations in the conscious, recumbent dog, Akselrod and co-workers have shown that low-frequency alterations are markedly increased when angiotensin converting–enzyme inhibitor is administered intravenously (1). Most of the studies on adrenergic control of renin release have focused on epinephrine and norepinephrine. Recently, several investigators have reported that dopamine may also be a neurotransmitter in the kidney (44, 48). Moreover, Mizoguchi et al (47) have shown that intrarenal infusion of dopamine produces a dose-related increase in renin secretion that is inhibited by specific dopaminergic blocking agents. The controversial subject of α-adrenergic influences on renin release are beyond the scope of this short review.

INTERACTION OF STIMULI INFLUENCING RENIN RELEASE

As described in the previous section, renin secretion can either be inhibited or enhanced by a number of mechanisms. In many physiologic conditions (e.g. during hemorrhage) several signals act simultaneously on the JG cells, which must process the information and produce an integrated response. As with many biological systems, the net response to simultaneous stimulatory and/or inhibitory signals is not always predictable. In the case of two positive signals, for example, the net effect may be a single additive response, a synergistic response, or no net gain over a single response. For these reasons, we have been particularly interested in examining the interaction of several primary stimuli on the release of renin in the conscious dog. In particular, we shall discuss the interaction between sodium balance and the renal baroreceptor, between the renal baroreceptor and adrenergic receptors, and the interaction of all three of these inputs.

Interaction between Sodium Signal and Renal Baroreceptor

After Fray and coworkers (29) demonstrated that basal PRA and the rise in PRA following renal artery constriction were inversely related to salt intake, Farhi et al (23) performed a quantitative analysis of interaction between sodium intake and renal perfusion pressure in the control of renin release in the unanesthetized animal. The stimulus-response relationship was examined in conscious dogs on normal- and low-sodium diets; the results are summarized in Figure 2A. The stimulus-response curve of the dogs on low-salt intake is shifted upward compared to the dogs on normal-salt intake. In fact, the stimulus-response curves are superimposable if the plasma renin activity in the normal-salt dog is multiplied by a constant factor as illustrated in Figure 2B. These data imply that at any two given RPP's the percentage change in PRA will be the same in the two salt states. Fray (29) has shown that, in the salt-loaded animal, both the basal PRA and the response to renal artery constriction are markedly depressed.

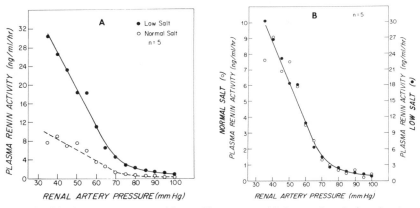

Figure 2 Stimulus-response curves of the renal baroreceptor. (*A*) Averaged results from five dogs on a normal-salt intake (80 meq Na$^+$/day, (○) and on a low-salt diet (●). (*B*) Averaged results from five dogs on a normal-salt diet (○, ordinate on left) and on low-salt diet (●, ordinate on right). The ordinate of the low-salt PRA's is three times that of the normal-salt PRA's. Reproduced with permission from the American Journal of Physiology (23).

By varying the salt intake over a wide range, a family of stimulus-response curves can be obtained.

Interaction of Intrarenal Adrenergic Receptors and Renal Baroreceptors

Numerous laboratories have reported that epinephrine increases renin secretion both in vivo and in vitro. Johnson et al (40) reported that in the conscious dog intravenous infusions of epinephrine, which produced systemic plasma concentrations within the high physiologic range, consistently increased PRA. They noted, however, that intrarenal infusions of epinephrine, which produced similar renal arterial epinephrine concentrations, did not elevate PRA. After a number of further experiments, it appeared that the only significant difference between the two routes of administration was the small drop in systemic pressure produced by the intravenous epinephrine. Since earlier studies of Ayers et al (3) and Eide et al (21) had suggested that isoproterenol was a more potent stimulus for renin secretion at lowered renal arterial pressures, Farhi et al (22) investigated the possibility that the effect of systemic epinephrine infusions on PRA was mediated though an interaction between the renal baroreceptor and intrarenal epinephrine receptors. They determined the stimulus-response curves during graded reduction of RPP with comparable renal arterial levels of epinephrine induced by intravenous or intrarenal infusion. As Figure 3 demonstrates, the stimulus-response curve is similar in the presence of intravenous and intrarenal infusions. In both, the curve is shifted to the right to the same extent, decreasing the amount that the perfusion pressure must be lowered before PRA begins to rise steeply. This figure indicates that once the renal arterial pressure is accounted for, the effect of an intravenous epinephrine infusion can be entirely explained by its action in raising renal epinephrine concentration and, hence, through an action on intrarenal receptors. Thus, as illustrated in Figure 4, concentrations of epinephrine within the physiologic range shift the stimulus-response curve of the renal baroreceptor to the right, whereas sodium depletion produces a change in the gain of the stimulus-response curve. PRA can increase from A (on the normal curve) to a stimulated value, B, either through an increase in the gain of the stimulus-response curve (low-salt curve, broken line), or through a shift of the curve to the right (epinephrine curve, dotted line).

Dopamine also interacts with the renal baroreceptor. Mizoguchi et al (47) reported that an intrarenal infusion rate of 300 ng kg^{-1}min^{-1} of dopamine was necessary to produce a significant rise in PRA in the conscious dog with normal renal arterial pressure (100 mmHg); one tenth the dose at lowered renal arterial pressure of 75 mmHg elevated PRA more than two-fold. This latter concentration of dopamine may well be in the normal, physiological range. These findings of Mizoguchi are consistent with those of other laboratories regarding

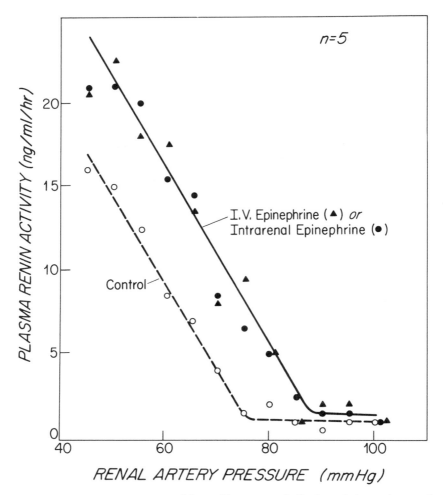

Figure 3   Stimulus-response curves of the renal baroreceptor for five low-salt dogs under control conditions (○) and with infusion of epinephrine into the inferior vena cava (▲) or renal artery (●). Reproduced with permission from Circulation Research (22).

the interaction of the catecholamines and lowered renal arterial pressure (3, 21) and the observations of Thames & DiBona (61) that low-level stimulation of the renal nerves, which did not increase renin secretion at control RPP in the anesthetized animal, did so when RPP was lowered.

Although carotid sinus hypotension increases sympathetic nervous activity to the kidney (36), the role of the carotid sinus in the regulation of PRA has not been clear. In 1964 Skinner et al (56) reported that occlusion of the carotid arteries had no effect on PRA in some anesthetized animals, while in others it

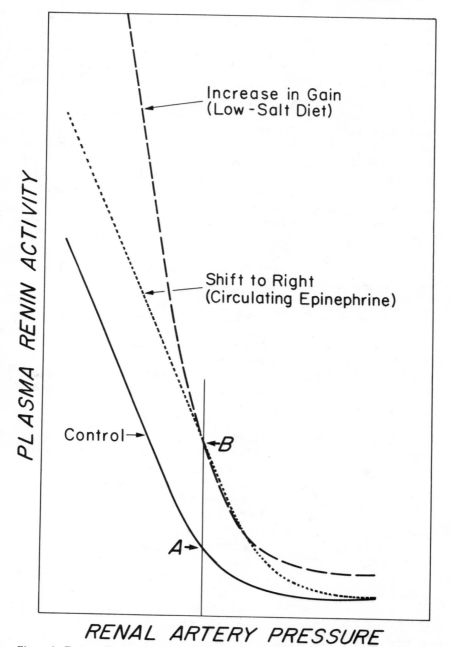

Figure 4   Factors affecting the stimulus-response curve of the renal baroreceptor. See text for explanation. Reproduced with permission of American Journal of Physiology (23).

produced a drop in PRA. In a later study, Bunag and coworkers (13) observed a rise in PRA when RPP was held constant during carotid occlusion. However, Brennan et al (10) were unable to reproduce these latter results. To resolve these conflicts, Rocchini & Barger (52) investigated the interaction of carotid sinus pressure and RPP in the control of PRA in intact, conscious dogs on normal- and low-salt intakes. They found that, regardless of salt state, lowering carotid sinus pressure increased PRA when RPP was kept constant, but not when RPP was allowed to rise with systemic pressure. These observations have been confirmed by Gross et al (35) in the trained dog. They also demonstrated that increased renin secretion may occur in the absence of changes in renal blood flow and that the response is prevented by the infusion of β-blocking agents. Thus, in the unanesthetized animal reduced carotid sinus pressure will stimulate renal release, although this effect may be overcome by the inhibitory rise in renal arterial pressure that normally occurs during carotid occlusion. It is well to emphasize, however, that under most physiologic and pathophysiologic conditions the pressures in the carotid sinus and renal baroreceptors are essentially the same, so that reduction of pressure in both receptors may act synergistically to enhance renin release.

Multiple Interactions Influencing Renin Release

To quantify the relative roles of the various mechanisms regulating PRA and their interactions, ideally one would examine all these factors in the same animal over a period of time. As Farhi and coworkers (22) noted in their repeated studies of the stimulus-response curves of the renal baroreceptor in a conscious dog on a constant salt intake, the baseline PRA and the slope of the curves were stable over periods of days to weeks. Although the curves were qualitatively similar in all the dogs examined, the parameters varied quantitatively from dog to dog. Thus it is difficult, even in trained animals, to determine the relative magnitude of each interacting signal. Nevertheless, certain generalizations can be made in different groups of animals. For example, lowering of RPP by 25–30 mmHg by cuff constriction in dogs on normal salt intake produces only a modest rise in PRA (23); a much larger increment in PRA is produced by a similar reduction in RPP induced by moderate hemorrhage (30 ml kg^{-1}) (42) in dogs on the same sodium intake. In these latter experiments a similar reduction in RPP is accompanied by a rise in plasma epinephrine from 50 to 300 pg ml^{-1}, suggesting a shift to the right of the stimulus-response curve as illustrated in Figure 3. Moreover, with hemorrhagic hypotension, pressure in the systemic arterial baroreceptors is reduced, reflexly increasing renal sympathetic activity to the kidney and thus enhancing the renal baroreceptor stimulation.

The rise in PRA is even larger when arterial pressure is lowered to a lesser degree by inferior vena caval constriction (70). Under these circumstances, in addition to the fall in RPP and rise of catecholamines, we now have an increase in renal venous and interstitial pressure and translocation of blood and extracellular fluid volume, with a further increase in the renal baroreceptor responsiveness. The magnitude of rise in PRA with inferior vena caval constriction is of the same order of magnitude as that obtained during moderate hemorrhage in the salt-depleted dog (42). During such hemorrhage, PRA and epinephrine rise to high levels, and the curves of the changes in concentration of the two hormones are nearly superimposable. This provides further evidence for the importance of the sympathetic nervous system in the modulation of renin release. Conversely, a striking interrelationship between the renin-angiotensin system and the regulation of catecholamine release was noted after hemorrhage, when blood pressure was further reduced by pharmacological means (42). With the administration of the α-blocking agent, phentolamine, the fall in systemic pressure was accompanied by the expected rise in catecholamines and heart rate. However, when the arterial pressure was reduced by administration of angiotensin-converting enzyme inhibitor, catecholamines failed to rise and heart rate fell. This suggests an equally important role of angiotensin II in the facilitation of catecholamine release, as previously suggested by Feuerstein during hemorrhage in anesthetized, nephrectomized cats (24). Thus, under these conditions, not only do the catecholamines enhance renin release, but angiotensin II appears to play an important role in the modulation of adrenergic activity.

CELLULAR MECHANISMS INFLUENCING RENIN RELEASE

A considerable body of evidence has been presented that intracellular calcium (Ca), cyclic AMP (cAMP), and prostaglandins (PGs) may mediate the cellular response to stimuli for renin secretion. Vasodilatator PGs increase renin release when infused into the renal artery (32) or when added to the media bathing kidney slices (71). However, the precise role of the endogenous PGs in the regulation of renin secretion with various physiological pertubations is not clear. In the basal state, the PG cyclo-oxygenase inhibitor, indomethacin, does not affect PRA in the sodium-replete dog (19) but does attenuate (but not suppress) renin release in the salt-depleted dog, particularly when propranolol is administered simultaneously to block the β-adrenergic receptors (19). In most of the published reports, β-adrenergic stimulation of renin release does not appear to involve the PGs. Although Campbell et al (14) noted that both indomethacin and meclofenamate inhibited renin release induced by intravenous isoproterenol infusion in the conscious rat, Berl and coworkers (6) reported that, in the anesthetized dog, the inhibition of PG synthesis did not attenuate the increase in PRA associated with β-adrenergic stimulation with isoproterenol. In the conscious dog, Johnson et al (39) found that indomethacin did not blunt the renin response to intravenous epinephrine. Moreover, in the isolated rat glomerulus, Beierwaltes et al (5) observed that isoproterenol-stimulated renin secretion was not altered by meclofenamate but was inhibited by propranolol. Similarly, the renin secretion produced by low-level renal nerve stimulation in the anesthetized dog is independent of PG synthesis (43). Thus, PGs do not appear to be an integral part of β-receptor–mediated renin release.

The role of endogenous PGs in the control of renal baroreceptor–mediated renin release is even more equivocal. J. L. Data and her coworkers (17) have reported that indomethacin blocked the renin response to renal hypotension in anesthetized dogs with nonfiltering kidneys, suggesting that PGs may mediate the renin release in response to renal baroreceptor stimulation. In agreement with this hypothesis, Berl et al (6) and Blackshear and colleagues (8) observed an attenuated renin secretory response to renal hypotension within the autoregulatory range in anesthetized animals. However, several other groups have been unable to demonstrate an affect of PG synthesis inhibition in baroreceptor-mediated renin release in the sub-autoregulatory range. The work of Freeman et al (31) and Anderson (2) in conscious dogs suggest that PGs are not essential for baroreceptor-mediated renin release in the sodium-replete animal, particularly with low levels of renal blood flow. It is important to recall that the stress of anesthesia and surgery markedly increases the level of endogenous PG synthesis, which may account for the contradictory observations made in the conscious vs the anesthetized dog (60). Further studies of the stimulus-response curves of renin release in the conscious animal, with and without PG synthesis inhibitors, may help to resolve this problem.

The possible role of calcium in the regulation of renin release has received increasing attention. The concept of Ca as a mediator in stimulus-secretion coupling was first developed from the studies of Douglas & Rubin (20) on the adrenal medulla and extended to many other endocrine systems (53). In contrast to most of these systems, in which a positive correlation between Ca influx and hormone secretion was observed, renin secretion from the JG cells appears to be inhibited by inward movement of Ca and stimulated by Ca efflux (27).

In most secretory cells, high concentrations of extracellular K cause depolarization, a rise in intracellular Ca, and hormone secretion. Fishman (25) has shown that juxtaglomerular cells are also depolarized by elevated K. However, in sharp contrast to other secretory cells, recent evidence suggests that K-induced depolarization inhibits renin release and that this effect can be attenuated by the Ca channel–blocking agent, verapamil (50). Similarly, it now appears that agents such as AII, α-adrenergic agonists, vasopressin, and ouabain inhibit renin release by a Ca influx that can also be blocked by verapamil (50). Since JG cells originate from the smooth muscle cells of the afferent arteriole, Fray (28) has postulated that intraluminal pressure may alter the membrane potential of the JG cells in the same manner as that observed in smooth muscle cells. Thus a rise in renal perfusion pressure would cause depolarization, a rise in intracellular (or cytosolic) Ca, and inhibition of renin release. In accord with this hypothesis, Fray has shown that the Ca entry antagonist, verapamil, blocks the inhibitory effect of high perfusion pressure in the isolated, perfused rat kidney (28). Conversely, the stimulatory signal for renin release may be hyperpolarization of the JG cells and a decrease in intracellular (or cytosolic) Ca. Fishman (25) has also reported that epinephrine hyperpolarizes the JG cells. In addition, in the perfused rat kidney, Harada & Rubin (37) have noted that renal nerve stimulation, isoproterenol, and glucagon promote Ca^{45} efflux. Moreover, the blockade of Ca efflux with lanthanum inhibits the renin release provoked by isoproterenol or glucagon (46). Evidence has also been presented that cAMP and dibuteryl-cAMP can cause renin release by sequestration or efflux of intracellular Ca. Since the physiologic effects of β-receptor agonists and glucagon may be mediated by cAMP, these experimental data would suggest an interrelationship between cAMP and the Ca ion as cellular messengers in control of renin release. Hence, it begins to appear that agents that hyperpolarize JG cells and/or increase intracellular cAMP may effect renin release by lowering intracellular Ca.

Recent studies suggest that many of the cellular events controlled by intracellular Ca are mediated by calmodulin, the cellular Ca-binding protein. Churchill & Churchill (15) and Fray and coworkers (30) have examined the effect of the putative calmodulin antagonist, trifluoperazine, on renin secretion. Although this drug inhibits hormone secretion in most systems studied, it produced a dose-dependent *increase* in renin release. Trifluoperazine also blocked the inhibitory effect of K-induced depolarization. These workers have, therefore, suggested that changes in the Ca-calmodulin complex may regulate the role of the Ca ion on renin release and constitute an integral link in the final common pathway controlling renin secretion. With this newer information available, we may now be able to define more precisely the interaction of the various signals in the regulation of renin release.

ACKNOWLEDGMENT

Work in our laboratory has been supported by NIH grants HL19467 and HL02493 and a gift from R. J. Reynolds Industries.

Literature Cited

1. Akselrod, S., Gordon, D., Ubel, F. A., Shannon, D. C., Barger, A. C., Cohen, R. J. 1981. Power spectrum analysis of heart rate fluctuation: a quantitative probe of beat-to-beat cardiovascular control. *Science* 213:220–22
2. Anderson, W. P. 1982. Prostaglandins do not mediate renin release during severe reduction of renal blood flow in conscious dogs. *Clin. Exp. Pharm. Physiol.* 9:259–63
3. Ayers, C. R., Harris, R. H. Jr., Lefer, L. G. 1969. Control of renin release in experimental hypertension. *Circ. Res.* 24/25 (Suppl. 1):103–12
4. Beeuwkes, R. III, Rosen, S. 1979. Renal Na-K-ATPase localization and pharmacological analysis by means of the K^+-dependent phosphatase reaction. In *Cellular Mechanisms of Renal Tubular Ion Transport,* of *Current Topics in Membranes and Transport,* ed. E. Boulpaep, 13:343–54. New York: Academic
5. Beierwaltes, W. H., Schryver, S., Olson, P. S., Romero, J. C. 1980. Interaction of the prostaglandin and renin-angiotensin systems in isolated rat glomeruli. *Am. J. Physiol.* 239:F602–8
6. Berl, T., Henrich, W. L., Erickson, A. L., Schrier, R. W. 1979. Prostaglandins in the beta-adrenergic and baroreceptor mediated secretion of renin. *Am. J. Physiol.* 236:F472–77
7. Bingel, A., Strauss, E. 1909. Uber die blutdrucksteigernde Substanz der Niere. *Deutches Archiv. Klin. Med.* 96:476–92
8. Blackshear, J. L., Spielman, W. S., Knox, F. G., Romero, J. C. 1979. Dissociation of renin release and renal vasodilation by prostaglandin synthesis inhibitors. *Am. J. Physiol.* 237:F20–24
9. Blalock, A., Levy, S. E. 1937. Studies on the etiology of hypertension. *Ann. Surg.* 106:826–47
10. Brennan, L. A., Henninger, A. L., Jochim, K. E., Malvin, R. L. 1974. Relationship between carotid sinus pressure and plasma renin activity. *Am. J. Physiol.* 227:295–99
11. Bright, R. 1836. Tabular views of the morbid appearances in 100 cases connected with albuminous urine. *Guy's Hosp. Rep.* 1:380–400
12. Brown-Séquard, C. E., d'Arsonval. 1892. Des injections souscutanes ou intraveineuses d'extraits liquides de nombre d'organes. *Comptes rendus de l'Academie des Sciences.* 114:1399–405
13. Bunag, R. D., Page, I. H., McCubbin, J. W. 1966. Neural stimulation of renin. *Circ. Res.* 19:851–58
14. Campbell, W. B., Graham, R. M., Jackson, E. K. 1979. Role of renal prostaglandins in sympathetically mediated renin release in the rat. *J. Clin. Invest.* 64:448–56
15. Churchill, P. C., Churchill, M. C. 1983. Effects of trifluoperazine on renin secretion of the kidney slices. *J. Exp. Pharm. Ther.* 224:68–72
16. Cowley, A. W. Jr., Guyton, A. C. 1972. Quantification of intermediate steps in the renin - angiotensin - vasoconstrictor feedback loop in the dog. *Circ. Res.* 30:557–66
17. Data, J. L., Gerber, J. G., Crump, W. J., Frolich, J. C., Hollifield, J. W., Nies, A. S. 1978. The prostaglandin system: a role in canine baroreceptor control of renin release. *Circ. Res.* 42:454–58
18. Davis, J. O., Freeman, R. H. 1976. Mechanisms regulating renin release. *Physiol. Rev.* 56:1–56
19. DeForrest, J. M., Davis, J. O., Freeman, R. H., Seymour, A. A., Rowe, B. P., et al. 1980. Effects of indomethacin and meclofenamate on renin release and renal hemodynamic function during chronic sodium depletion in conscious drugs. *Circ. Res.* 47:99–107
20. Douglas, S. W., Rubin, R. P. 1961. The role of calcium in the secretory response of the adrenal medulla to acetylcholine. *J. Physiol.* 159:40–57
21. Eide, I., Loyning, E., Kiil, F. 1974. Potentiation of renin release by combining renal artery constriction and β-adrenergic stimulation. *Scand. J. Clin. Lab. Invest.* 34:301–10
22. Farhi, E. R., Cant, J. R., Barger, A. C. 1982. Interactions between intrarenal epinephrine receptors and the renal baroreceptor in the control of PRA in conscious dogs. *Circ. Res.* 50:477–85
23. Farhi, E., Cant, J. R., Barger, A. C. 1983. Alteration of renal baroreceptor by salt intake in control of plasma renin activity in the conscious dog. *Am. J. Physiol.* 245:F119–22
24. Feuerstein, G., Boonyaviroj, P., Gutman, Y. 1977. Renin-angiotensin mediation of adrenal catecholamine secretion induced by haemorrhage. *Eur. J. Pharm.* 44:131–42
25. Fishman, M. C. 1976. Membrane potential of juxtaglomerular cells. *Nature* 260:542–44
26. Fray, J. C. S. 1976. Stretch receptor model for renin release with evidence from perfused rat kidney. *Am. J. Physiol.* 231:936–44
27. Fray, J. C. S. 1980. Stimulus secretion coupling of renin: role of hemodynamic and other factors. *Circ. Res.* 47:485–92

28. Fray, J. C. S. 1980. Mechanism by which renin secretion from perfused rat kidneys is stimulated by isoprenaline and inhibited by high perfusion pressure. *J. Physiol.* 308:1–13

29. Fray, J. C. S., Johnson, M. D., Barger, A. C. 1977. Renin release and pressor response to renal arterial hypotension: effect of dietary sodium. *Am. J. Physiol.* 233:H191–95

30. Fray, J. C. S., Lush, D. J., Share, D. S. 1983. Possible role of calmodulin in renin secretion from isolated kidney and renal cells: studies with trifluoperazine. *J. Physiol.* In press

31. Freeman, R. H., Davis, J. O., Dietz, J. R., Villarreal, D., Seymour, A. A., Echtenkamp, S. F. 1982. Renal prostaglandins and the control of renin release. *Hypertension* 4(Suppl II):106–12

32. Gerber, J. G., Keller, R. T., Nies, A. S. 1979. Prostaglandins and renin release: the effect of PGI-2, PGE-2, and 13,14-dihydro PGE-2 on the baroreceptor mechanism of renin release in the dog. *Circ. Res.* 44:796–99

33. Goldblatt, H., Lynch, J., Hanzel, R. F., Summerville, W. W. 1934. The production of persistent elevation of systolic blood pressure by means of renal ischemia. *J. Exp. Med.* 59:347–79

34. Goormaghtigh, N. 1932. Les segments neuromyoarteriels juxtaglomerularies du rein. *Arch. Biol. Leige.* 43:575–91

35. Gross, R., Hackenberg, H.-M., Hackenthal, E., Kirchheim, H. 1980. Interaction between perfusion pressure and sympathetic nerves in renin release by carotid baroreflex in conscious dogs. *J. Physiol.* 313:237–50

36. Gross, R., Kirchheim, H. 1980. Effects of bilateral carotid occlusion and auditory stimulation on renal blood flow and sympathetic nerve activity in the conscious dog. *Pflügers Arch.* 383:233–39

37. Harada, E., Rubin, R. P. 1978. Stimulation of renin secretion and calcium efflux from the isolated perfused cat kidney by noradrenaline after prolonged calcium deprivation. *J. Physiol.* 274:367–79

38. Janeway, T. C. 1913. Nephritic hypertension: clinical and experimental studies. *Am. J. Med. Sci.* 145:625–56

39. Johnson, M. D., Farhi, E. R., Troen, B. R., Barger, A. C. 1979. Plasma epinephrine and control of plasma renin activity: possible extrarenal mechanisms. *Am. J. Physiol.* 236:H854–59

40. Johnson, M. D., Shier, D. N., Barger, A. C. 1979. Circulating catecholamines and control of plasma renin activity in conscious dogs. *Am. J. Physiol.* 236:H463–70

41. Keeton, T. K., Campbell, W. B. 1980. The pharmacologic alteration of renin release. *Pharmacol. Rev.* 32:81–227

42. Kopelman, R. I., Dzau, V. J., Shimabukuro, S., Barger, A. C. 1983. Compensatory response to hemorrhage in conscious dogs on normal and low salt intake. *Am. J. Physiol.* 244:H351–56

43. Kopp, U., Aurell, M., Sjölander, M., Ablad, B. 1981. The role of prostaglandins in the alpha- and beta-adrenoreceptor mediated renin release response to graded renal nerve stimulation. *Pflügers Archiv.* 391:1–8

44. Kopp, U., Bradley, T., Hjemdahl, P. 1983. Renal venous outflow and urinary excretion of norepinephrine, epinephrine, and dopamine during graded renal nerve stimulation. *Am. J. Physiol.* 244:E52–60

45. Lewandowsky, M. 1899. Zur Frage der Nieren Secretion von Nebenniere und Niere. *Z. Klin. Med.* 37:535–45

46. Logan, A. G., Tenyi, I., Peart, W. S., Breathnach, A. S., Martin, B. G. H. 1977. The effect of lanthanum on renin secretion and renal vasoconstriction. *Proc. R. Soc. Lond. Ser. B* 195:327–42

47. Mizoguchi, H., Dzau, V. J., Siwek, L. G., Barger, A. C. 1983. Effect of intrarenal administration of dopamine on renin release in conscious dogs. *Am. J. Physiol.* 244:H39–45

48. Morgunov, N., Baines, A. D. 1981. Renal nerves and catecholamine excretion. *Am. J. Physiol.* 240:F75–81

49. Oliver, G., Schäfer, E. A. 1895. The physiological effects of extracts of the suprarenal capsules. *J. Physiol.* 18:230–76

50. Park, C. S., Han, D. S., Fray, J. C. S. 1981. Calcium in the control of renin secretion: Ca^{2+} influx as an inhibitory signal. *Am. J. Physiol.* 240:F70–74

51. Pearce, R. M. 1909. An experimental study of the influence of kidney extracts and the serum of animals with renal lesions upon the blood pressure. *J. Exp. Med.* 11:430–42

52. Rocchini, A. P., Barger, A. C. 1979. Renin release with carotid occlusion in the conscious dog: role of renal arterial pressure. *Am. J. Physiol.* 236:H108–11

53. Rubin, R. P. 1974. *Calcium and the Secretory Process.* New York: Plenum

54. Santesson, C. G. 1924. Professor Robert Tigerstedt. *Skand. Arch. Physiol.* 45:1–6

55. Shade, R. E., Davis, J. O., Johnson, J. A., Witty, R. T. 1972. Effects of renal arterial infusion of sodium and potassium on renin secretion in the dog. *Circ. Res.* 31:719–27

56. Skinner, S. L., McCubbin, J. W., Page,

I. H. 1964. Control of renin secretion. *Circ. Res.* 15:64–76

57. Sottiurai, V. S., Malvin, R. 1982. Intracellular sodium in macula densa cells and renin release. *J. Surg. Res.* 32:401–9

58. Tagawa, H., Gutman, F. D., Haber, E., Miller, E. D., Samuels, A. I., Barger, A. C. 1974. Reversible renovascular hypertension and renal arterial pressure. *Proc. Soc. Exp. Biol. Med.* 146:975–82

59. Taugner, R., Schiller, A., Kaissling, B., Kriz, W. 1978. Gap junctional coupling between the JGA and the glomerular tuft. *Cell Tiss. Res.* 186:279–85

60. Terragno, N. A., Terragno, D. A., McGiff, J. C. 1977. Contribution of prostaglandins to the renal circulation in conscious, anesthetized, and laparotomized dogs. *Circ. Res.* 40:590–95

61. Thames, M. D., DiBona, G. F. 1979. Renal nerves modulate the secretion of renin mediated by nonneural mechanisms. *Circ. Res.* 44:645–52

62. Thurau, K., Schnermann, J., Nagel, W., Horster, M., Wahl, M. 1967. Composition of tubular fluid in the macula densa segment as a factor regulating the function of the juxtaglomerular apparatus. *Circ. Res.* 20/21 (Suppl. II):79–89

63. Tigerstedt, R. 1902. *Lehrbuch der Physiologie des Menschen,* 2d ed., revised, p. 407. Leipzig: Verlag von S. Hirzel

64. Tigerstedt, R. 1906. *A Text-book of Human Physiology,* (translated from the 3rd ed.), ed. J. R. Murlin. New York: D. Appelton

65. Tigerstedt, R., Bergman, P. G. 1898. Niere und Kreislauf. *Skand. Arch. Physiol.* 8:223–71

66. Tobian, L. 1960. Interrelationship of electrolytes, juxtaglomerular cells, and hypertension. *Physiol. Rev.* 40:280–312

67. Vander, A. J. 1965. Effect of catecholamines and the renal nerves on renin secretion in anesthetized dogs. *Am. J. Physiol.* 209:659–62

68. Vander, A. J. 1967. Control of renin release. *Physiol. Rev.* 47:359–82

69. Vander, A. J., Miller, R. 1964. Control of renin secretion in the anesthetized dog. *Am. J. Physiol.* 207:537–46

70. Watkins, L. Jr., Burton, J. A., Haber, E., Cant, J. R., Smith, F. W., Barger, A. C. 1976. The renin-angiotensin-aldosterone system in congestive failure in conscious dogs. *J. Clin. Invest.* 57:1606–17

71. Weber, P. C., Larsson, C., Anggård, E., Hamberg, M., Corey, E. J., et al. 1976. Stimulation of renin release from rabbit renal cortex by arachidonic acid and prostaglandin endoperoxides. *Circ. Res.* 39:868–74

Ann. Rev. Physiol. 1984. 46:309–26

THE KALLIKREIN-KININ SYSTEM AND THE KIDNEY

Harry S. Margolius

Departments of Pharmacology and Medicine, Medical University of South Carolina, Charleston, South Carolina 29425

INTRODUCTION

Kallikrein (E.C. 3.4.21.8) was first found in mammalian urine more than 70 years ago (1). This urinary enzyme is now known to be synthesized in the kidney, to have biochemical actions and structural features similar to several other mammalian proteinases, and to be regulated by hormones that control important aspects of renal function. The kinin products (kallidin, also known as lysyl-bradykinin, and bradykinin) of this tissue kallikrein's action upon kininogen substrates are extremely potent stimuli to renal biochemical and physiological events. These facts have provoked substantial recent interest in the renal kallikrein-kinin system. This interest is augmented by evidence of system abnormality in renal pathological states and system sensitivity to drugs affecting renal function. Although the functional responsibilities of the renal kallikrein-kinin system are unclear and controversial, there seems no doubt the system has an important role in renal physiology. In this section, the recent findings that support this conclusion are presented. Additional details can be found in recent encyclopedic reviews (16, 89, 94).

COMPONENT CHARACTERIZATION AND LOCALIZATION

Tissue kallikrein is classified as a serine proteinase, indicating the presence of serine at an active catalytic site, and its inhibition by diisopropylflurophosphate (19). Other members of this class include trypsin, thrombin, plasmin, and plasma kallikrein. The latter enzyme differs from tissue kallikrein in molecular weight, other physiochemical characteristics, immunologic specificity, pro-

309

0066-4278/84/0315-0309$02.00

duct formed, and inhibitory profile. The tissue kallikreins of kidney have been purified from dog and rat kidney and the urine of horse, rabbit, rat, pig, and human (19, 20). These kallikreins are acidic glycoproteins with isoelectric points near 4.0 and derived molecular weights of 25,000–48,000. The reasons for this diversity may be differences in carbohydrate content and/or amino acid sequence, but the larger weight may be more accurate, at least for the human enzymes (77, 102). Urine and renal tissue contain an inactive enzyme, prokallikrein, that can be activated by tryptic hydrolysis (86). Phospholipase A_2 and mellitin also activate membrane-bound kallikrein (12, 74, 103, 114). Renal kallikrein seems very similar to the kallikrein found in salivary and sweat glands, pancreas, and gastrointestinal tract of the same species, but considering tissue kallikrein as a single enzyme is an oversimplification. Multiple forms of kallikrein are found in each of these sites, including human urine into which more than 100 micrograms of the immunoreactive enzyme are excreted daily (102). Differences in these forms may exist in the charged carbohydrate moieties as well as in amino acid composition. Structural analyses of tissue kallikreins have now reached a new level, with the determination of the mRNA sequence for rat pancreatic preprokallikrein, a protein of 265 amino acids including a proposed secretory prepeptide (17 amino acids) and an activation peptide (11 amino acids) (113); the cloning and preliminary characterization of a mouse gene family encoding glandular kallikreins (61a); and the determination of the crystal structure of porcine pancreatic kallikrein A and this kallikrein-bovine pancreatic trypsin inhibitor complex (4a, 13a).

Renal kallikrein localization has been of much recent interest, with several approaches taken. Scicli et al (97) measured kinin-generating activity from outer to innermost portions of dog kidney. They found 90% of total activity in the cortex, mostly in the outer cortex, decreasing to less than 5% of total in the medulla and papillae. Histo-chemical efforts have found kallikrein-like immunoreactivity of rat (83, 104) and human (85) kidney to predominate in distal convoluted tubules. Disagreement exists about the extent of observed staining along cortical or medullary collecting duct lumenal membranes, but two groups see "reabsorption droplets" of staining in proximal tubules (85, 103). Ascending thick limb and macula densa staining is prominent for another enzymatic activity thought to be a non–kinin liberating, kallikrein-like esterase (85). In general, histochemical efforts in kidney and salivary glands comment upon the lumenal predominance of staining (83, 85, 103). However, a subcellular localization effort using rabbit kidney cortex showed highest kallikrein activity in lysosomes and lysosome-like particles with low (Na^+,K^+)-ATPase activity, as well as in a nonmicrovillus plasma membrane fraction with high specific activity of (Na^+,K^+)-ATPase (30). More recently, a basolateral membrane–enriched fraction from rat renal cortex was found to contain both a kallikrein and prokallikrein that have some apparent differences from the urinary enzyme

(126). Other studies have shown that renal kallikrein is: enriched in endoplasmic reticulum and plasma membrane fractions of renal cortical tissue (74); oriented as a membrane-bound ectoenzyme with active sites facing the exterior of isolated renal cortical cells in suspension (12); and, entering the urine stream in more distal fractions during stop-flow studies in the dog (96). Tomita et al (115) measured kallikrein-like activity along single-nephron portions from rabbits, and only found aprotinin-inhibitable activity in the granular portion of the distal convoluted tubule. Some more proximal sites contained kallikrein-like activity not inhibitable by aprotinin. This work was extended to show that there is also twice as much inactive vs active enzyme in the granular portions of both distal convoluted and cortical collecting tubule (78).

There is still little known about endogenous inhibitors of renal kallikrein. A principal inhibitor of plasma kallikrein, α_2-macro-globulin, does not inhibit or even bind to the tissue enzymes (117). Recent work has claimed that α_1-antitrypsin, a known slow inactivator of plasma kallikrein, is capable of slowly (i.e. hours) inhibiting human urinary kallikrein (24). In addition, tissue (urinary) kallikrein inhibition was absent in sera of patients with α_1-antitrypsin deficiency (22), and urinary α_1-antitrypsin concentration is said to be inversely correlated with urinary kallikrein activity (35). However, other studies have been unable to show that human α_1-antitrypsin inhibits human urine kallikrein (92). More work is needed before these conflicting findings are resolved.

In the course of some renal kallikrein localization studies, a 4700-dalton polypeptide which seemed to inhibit all tissue and plasma kallikreins (but not trypsin) was found (23). Its importance is not established. Two laboratories have recently studied interactions between renal kallikreins and cations. One study has shown that the in vitro kininogenase activity of purified human urinary kallikrein was increased markedly, but the esterase or amidase activity of the enzyme was decreased, as monovalent cation concentration in the reaction mixture was increased to 100 mM (51). Another study shows that the in vitro preincubation of purified urinary kallikreins with mono- or divalent cations, for 30 min at 37°C, uniformly decreases esterase, kininogenase, and even the immunoreactivity of the enzymes (13). The latter study also found that membrane-bound renal enzyme was almost competely resistant to this cationic inhibitory effect (13). Whether either set of data actually pertains to the modulation of renal membrane-bound or soluble kallikrein activity, in situ, remains to be determined.

The kininogen substrates for kallikrein are acidic glycoproteins present in plasma as either low- or high-molecular-weight forms consisting of heavy and light chains. Tissue kallikreins attack either form, but preferentially the former, to produce kallidin. The primary structures of bovine liver low-molecular-weight kininogens and their mRNAs have been determined (73). Recently, human renal kininogen has been characterized and localized, after first being isolated from human urine with immobilized antibody (87). Urinary kininogen is similar, if not identical, to plasma low-molecular-weight kininogen. However, as its urinary level is 5-fold greater than that expected if it were filtered at a rate similar to albumin, it probably arises from the kidney. This suggestion is supported by the detection of heavy-chain antigen by immunofluorescence in cortical and medullary distal tubules and collecting ducts, the major site of renal kallikrein localization (87).

The widespread pharmacologic activities of the kinin peptides cleaved from kininogen are well known, and include vasodilation, increased capillary permeability, and contraction of a variety of extravascular smooth muscle. The extreme potency of these peptides in relation to certain events (e.g. vasodilation and prostaglandin production) is difficult to reconcile with the presence of enormous productive capacity at certain sites (the renal cortex, salivary glands, or intestinal mucosa). Until recently, the various physiologic and biochemical responses seen after tissue kallikrein activation or administration were universally considered to be the result of kinin formation. Now there are several processes, including prorenin (10) or proinsulin cleavage, renin release, and smooth-muscle contraction, that are thought to result from kallikrein actions independent of kinin release. Those with relevance to the renal enzyme are discussed below. The issue is raised here to emphasize the greatest present liability to understanding the role of renal kallikrein and the kinin it can produce, i.e. the absence of any specific kinin-receptor blocker.

The processes and factors that regulate the formation and release of kinins by renal kallikrein are just beginning to be described. They probably include substrate availability, enzyme concentration and activity, and perhaps, as noted above, local ionic effects. Some recent evidence suggests that urine acidification can decrease urinary kinin while increasing urinary kallikrein excretion (98). Twenty-four-hour urine collections contain microgram quantities of kinins (31). In stop-flow studies, kinins appeared in the urine stream at the level of the distal nephron (99), suggesting they are products formed by the action of membrane-bound or secreted kallikrein at this locale. As the kidney kallikrein that appears in urine forms kallidin, urinary bradykinin is probably a product of urinary aminopeptidase (6), and met-lys-bradykinin is formed by uropepsin, another urinary serine proteinase active at acid pH (31). Since urinary kinin collections are usually made into 0.1 N hydrochloric acid, this kinin is formed in vitro and is of little significance except in artifactually altering measured levels of urinary kinin. A bradykinin binding site has been identified in a crude membrane preparation from guinea pig kidney (39), but studies of this sort are just beginning.

Probably only a fraction of any liberated kallidin is converted to bradykinin by the action of aminopeptidase before being inactivated at the C-terminal end. The enzymes with this hydrolytic inactivating capability are known as kininase

I and II. Kininase I is a carboxypeptidase (also called plasma carboxypeptidase N) with an estimated molecular weight of 280,000 that inactivates kinins by removal of the C-terminal arginine. Its role in limiting the action of renal kallikrein (and the kinin it produces) has been uncertain. Recently, Erdös and colleagues (61) have purified a new kininase I–type enzyme from human urine and kidney that is different in size, inhibitory profile, and immunologic specificity from the plasma enzyme. It is suggested to originate in kidney, but precise localization is unknown.

Kininase II is of widespread interest because it also converts angiotensin I to angiotensin II. Specific inhibitors are being widely used to explore its functions (110–112, 119, 123). Bradykinin or kallidin seem to be preferred substrates with a lower Km than angiotensin I. The enzyme requires a divalent cation cofactor, is activated by chloride ion, and is a glycoprotein. Kininase II is present in the kidney in membrane-bound form in vascular endothelial cells, renal tubular epithelial cells, and glomeruli (17). It is especially concentrated along the proximal tubule and highest concentrations have been found in proximal-tubule brush-border preparations (121, 122). This localization probably accounts for the lack of appearance of arterially infused kinins in urine (71) and the similar disappearance of kinins microperfused into the proximal convoluted tubule (8). Some kininase II activity is also detectable in the distal nephron by histochemical (28) and stop-flow techniques (99). Thus, the actions of any locally formed or injected kinins within the renal vasculature is limited by this endothelial, as well as plasma, enzyme activity. Renal lymph also contains kininase II (34). Any kinin that might be filtered seems subject to the proximal-tubule brush-border enzyme, and peptide entering the tubule lumen at more distal sites may be susceptible to catabolism by distal membrane-bound enzyme or kininases I or II present in the urine (44, 61). It is therefore difficult to explain the presence of large quantities of kinin in excreted urine.

In summary, recent work has identified every essential synthetic and catabolic component of the glandular kallikrein-kinin system within the kidney and urine. The questions now to be addressed concern the relations between these components and renal function.

RENAL HEMODYNAMICS

Studies in normal human subjects (26), anesthetized dogs (124), or isolated perfused kidneys (63) have established that either intravenously or intra-arterially administered bradykinin or kallidin cause renal arteriolar vasodilation. But the fact that pharmacologic doses of kinin produce vasodilation does not prove that the renal kallikrein-kinin system performs this function in situ. As stated by Nasjletti and Colina-Chourio (70): "Inference of physiological roles on the basis of the aforementioned observations [results of infusions of kinins IV or into the renal artery] should be regarded with caution, since probably no route of administration of kinins reproduces the effects evoked by release of kinins intrarenally, in terms of either concentrations achieved at their sites of action, localization of activity, or the sequence of vascular elements affected." If this is kept in mind, along with the available evidence on system component localization and the presence of inhibitory or destructive limits upon kinin viability in plasma, it is not easy to visualize how kinins produced in the kidney can have significant effects upon vascular resistance. Nevertheless, data have been obtained that are consistent with this possibility.

Hilton & Lewis (32) first proposed that a tissue kallikrein-kinin system (in salivary glands) regulated local vasodilation by showing kininogen consumption, kallikrein release, and kinin formation, in conjunction with glandular vasodilation in response to parasympathetic nerve stimulation. Schacter (93) challenged this interpretation by showing this functional hyperemia could be produced by other maneuvers in the absence of changes in levels of components of the kallikrein-kinin system. This dormant controversy is now reactivated by data suggesting that ^{125}I-kallikrein infused back into the rat submandibular gland main duct appears in venous blood (81). Furthermore, intense cervical sympathetic nerve stimulation can release kallikrein from the gland into blood, which produces large increases in venous effluent kinins in captopril-treated animals (100). Several groups have found an immunoreactive tissue kallikrein-like material in plasma (46, 76, 88). Lawton et al (46) showed that the measured immunoreactivity increased six-fold in nephrectomized rats and that salivary gland excision significantly reduced plasma levels. The protein of interest was immunologically identical to purified rat urinary kallikrein but had no activity against kininogen or synthetic substrate. Thus, the antigen may be inhibitor-complexed tissue kallikrein, but the antigen is clearly not active enzyme. Whether this tissue kallikrein ever circulates in an active form, and whether a similar release of renal kallikrein into blood occurs—and in a manner that affects some aspect of renal hemodynamics—are still matters of controversy.

Inferential data support a direct correlation between renal kallikrein-kinin activity and renal blood flow. Kininase II inhibition increases renal blood flow with concomitant increases in renal venous and urinary kinins (62, 70). Acute or chronic renal arterial constriction in the dog decreases urinary kallikrein with an excellent correlation to renal blood flow (43). Kallikrein excretion is also well correlated with renal blood flow in both normal or hypertensive human subjects (50). But in sodium-deprived rats, either saralasin, an angiotensin II–receptor blocker, or captopril produce similar increases in renal blood flow and changes in its intrarenal distribution, suggesting that in this dietary state converting-enzyme inhibition affects renal hemodynamics through inhibition of angiotensin II formation rather than as a result of altered kinin destruction

(67). Another recent study (40), however, showed that kinin infusion does not reduce renal vascular resistance in rats on a chronic low-sodium diet, but would do so if these animals had been pretreated with aprotinin. This suggested to the authors that the activity of the renal kallikrein-kinin system is already maximal in the low-sodium condition. In contrast, in rats on a chronic high-sodium diet, saralasin failed to reduce renal vascular resistance, but captopril did. This effect of captopril could be prevented by aprotinin, suggesting that in the high-sodium circumstance captopril was acting by preventing kinin destruction. Also, in these high-sodium rats, kinins were capable of reducing renal vascular resistance. Collectively, these interesting data infer that renal kinins are somehow exerting control over renal vascular resistance, at least in rats eating a low-sodium diet. Studies of this sort do not differentiate between possible effects of delayed destruction of blood kinins formed by the action of circulating, activated plasma (or tissue) prokallikrein, or those effects possibly induced by kinins produced by the action of renal kallikrein. The use of more specific kallikrein inhibitors (e.g. antibodies) or kinin-receptor blockers may clarify the role of the renal system in hemodynamic events. On the other hand, interpretations of hemodynamic data may become even more complex if a recent report by Nolly & Lama (75), describing an active tissue kallikrein-like enzyme in the arterial wall of the rat, proves to be correct.

RENAL ELECTROLYTE AND WATER EXCRETION

Whether the glandular kallikrein-kinin system participates in the regulation of electrolyte and water excretion as a natriuretic/diuretic or an antinatriuretic/antidiuretic influence is uncertain. The seminal observations of Webster & Gilmore (124) and Gill et al (26) established that injected kinins increase sodium and water excretion. A bradykinin antiserum from rabbit, given intravenously to rats, decreased sodium and water excretion, while control serum had no such effects (60). Some studies of bradykinin injected into the renal artery suggest reduced proximal reabsorption of sodium and water during stop-flow in the dog (7). Other work has shown that intra-arterial kinin does not alter sodium reabsorption in micropunctured, superficial proximal tubules and suggests any kinin-induced natriuresis could be the result of changes in proximal reabsorption in deeper cortical nephrons not available for micropuncture (105). Schneider et al (95) were also unable to detect a bradykinin inhibitory effect on sodium reabsorption by the dog proximal tubule. The suggestion was made that bradykinin also lacked an inhibitory effect on inner as well as superficial proximal-tubule sodium reabsorption. Willis (125) found bradykinin to decrease the medullary osmotic gradient during water diuresis in the anesthetized dog and suggested that a resultant increase in free water clearance is accounted for by this action. This decreased gradient might result from an increase in medullary blood flow or from decreased tubular sodium reabsorption in cortical portions of the distal tubule. An increase in free water clearance without increased sodium excretion was also noted in the isolated blood-perfused kidney subjected to intra-arterial bradykinin (63).

Kauker (42) has done a more direct study by microperfusing bradykinin into the late proximal tubule of rats and measuring ^{22}Na efflux into serially collected urine samples. Urinary recovery of ^{22}Na was increased from 5.84% to 11.02% of injected isotope by bradykinin (100 pg nl^{-1}). This data might suggest a direct kinin effect upon tubular sodium reabsorption in more distal nephron segments, but only one dose of kinin ($\sim 10^{-4}$ M) was used, and this concentration is far above amounts required for other kinin-induced responses.

Nevertheless, the work summarized above and other indirect and correlative studies infer strongly that endogenous kinins augment sodium and water excretion, but whether this means kinins generated in and affecting renal vasculature, or kinins generated in and affecting renal tubular activity, or both, is unclear. The fact that kininase II is localized in the proximal tubule brush border suggests that renal kallikrein and its product kinin(s) affect tubular transport processes downstream of this site. This notion is supported by data showing that bradykinin microinjected into the proximal tubule is destroyed in large part before it reaches the urine. However, the case for a singular influence of kinins to increase renal sodium and water excretion is not as strong as it might seem, because: (a) exogenously administered kinins or agents that increase or decrease kinin levels along with other effects (e.g. kininase II–converting enzyme inhibitors and nonspecific serine-protease inhibitors) may not produce the same effects as activation or inhibition of the endogenous system in situ; (b) the only direct study of kinin effects on sodium recovery through microperfused tubules seems to require enormous quantities of kinin ($\sim 10^{-4}$M) to produce small changes in ^{22}Na delivery; (c) there is a body of evidence that cannot be integrated into a natriuretic/diuretic framework without difficulty.

This evidence includes increased renal and urinary kallikrein activity and quantity, secondary to increased aldosterone activity (25, 45, 49, 58, 66, 91, 120). The relation of aldosterone to kallikrein was noted first in patients with primary aldosteronism (57), the majority of whom have high urinary kallikrein excretion (33, 59). This is also true of patients with Bartter's syndrome (29, 48, 118), and normal volunteers on a low-sodium diet (58), a high-potassium diet (36), or taking synthetic mineralocorticoid (58, 120). Furthermore, either normal subjects whose kallikrein excretion was increased by a low-sodium diet, or patients with primary aldosteronism and high kallikrein excretion, showed a marked decrease in kallikrein during treatment with the specific aldosterone antagonist, spironolactone, concomitantly with increased sodium excretion (58, 59). The suggestion that the system might participate in antina-triuretic/antidiuretic mechanisms arises from this collection of inferential data and the enzyme's localization at aldosterone-sensitive, sodium-reabsorbing sites. It is difficult to understand how these disparate maneuvers and diseases, all of which increase at least urinary and—where measured—renal kallikrein activity and quantity, result in augmented sodium and water excretion secondary to some direct effect of renal kallikrein and its product kinin(s).

Although it is not certain whether the synthesis of renal or other glandular kallikreins is regulated directly by aldosterone, renal cells in suspension elaborate more kallikrein in the presence of high concentrations of aldosterone and less in the presence of spironolactone than usual (41). The hormone also increases kallikrein concentration in rat renal cortical plasma membranes or endoplasmic reticulum (74). Most recently, a chronic low-sodium diet has been shown to increase the rate of renal kallikrein synthesis (65).

There is other evidence that also does not fit well with a natriuretic/diuretic function for the system. First, amiloride is an effective inhibitor of all enzymatic actions of mammalian tissue kallikreins and a kallikrein-like enzyme of the amphibian bladder and skin (56). This diuretic, a monovalent cation at physiological pH, inhibits sodium reabsorption by action(s) at mucosal surfaces of aldosterone-sensitive sites of sodium reabsorption, i.e. the distal nephron, salivary duct, colonic mucosa, and amphibian bladder or skin. Drug concentrations required to inhibit sodium reabsorption at these kallikrein-rich sites are similar to those required to inhibit kallikrein activity (56). It is not known whether kallikrein inhibition is a component of the drug's principal pharmacologic effect. However, it was reported recently that amiloride given intravenously to anesthetized rats decreases both urinary kallikrein and kinin excretion concomitantly with increasing urine solute excretion (98).

Second, aprotinin, a reversible kallikrein inhibitor, or D-phe-D-phe-L-arg-chloromethylketone (DPPA), a recently synthesized irreversible kallikrein inhibitor, reduce short-circuit current (SCC) in *Bufo marinus* urinary bladder in concentrations that reduce bladder kallikrein-like esterolytic activity equivalently (79). Aprotinin decreases sodium reabsorption reversibly and DPPA irreversibly. Both agents are more potent and rapidly acting on the mucosal than the serosal surface. In further studies, it was found that amphotericin B reversed the effects of both inhibitors (80). When initial SCC was completely blocked by mucosal amiloride, the addition of amphotericin B to the mucosal bath induced an amiloride-insensitive SCC that was not affected by high concentrations of either aprotinin or DPPA, but was inhibited by ouabain (80). These data suggest that the kallikrein inhibitors act at some site(s) along the active transport pathway proximal to the ouabain-sensitive site and that removal of the apical barrier by amphotericin B prevents their effect. Thus, the apical barrier seems a likely site of action for these agents to inhibit SCC (and sodium absorption). The data are consistent with the notion that a kallikrein-like serine proteinase is involved in sodium transport across the bladder.

Finally, and perhaps paradoxically, it was shown recently that kinins have only minimal effects upon sodium fluxes across the isolated rat colon. That is, both $J_{SM}Na$ and $J_{MS}Na$ were slightly—but significantly—decreased by kallidin, 10^{-6} M, applied to the antelumenal surface of the colon stripped of serosa and musculature. On the other hand, the large increases in SCC produced by antelumenal addition of the peptide were found to be due principally to augmented net chloride secretion (14, 15, 54). This effect was seen with a kinin concentration 500,000-fold less than that required to affect sodium excretion in the renal tubule in the studies of Kauker, mentioned above. The colon effect is blocked or attenuated by furosemide, inhibitors of prostaglandin synthesis, and verapamil. It seems likely that examination of the effects of kinins on renal tubular chloride movements will be of interest.

Thus, conflicting data and interpretations account for the lack of consensus on the role of the kallikrein-kinin system in renal electrolyte-transporting events. However, the localization of system components along the nephron and in other tissues where transmembrane electrolyte movements are major functional activities, the long-observed effects of kinin peptides on renal electrolyte excretion, and system relations to aldosterone, amiloride, and chloride secretion suggest the role is both important and close to clarification.

Relations of the system to water metabolism are at an earlier stage of research. In the dog and rat, antidiuretic hormone (ADH) increases urinary kallikrein excretion during IV infusion (18). These increases correlate with the expected changes in electrolyte excretion and urine osmolality. In the toad bladder, one study found no effects of kallikrein inhibitors on ADH-stimulated water flow (79), while another found that aprotinin increased and captopril decreased vasopressin-stimulated water flow (9). It was suggested that kallikrein and kinins might be negative modulators of ADH activity (9). This conclusion is consistent with earlier work showing that bradykinin reversibly inhibited vasopressin-stimulated water flow in the toad bladder (21). Preliminary studies in man have shown that urinary kinin excretion can vary directly with urine osmolality, is low in familial neurogenic diabetes insipidus, and can be increased to normal 60 min after a dose of ADH (Pitressin) (90). However, male Brattleboro rats homozygous for hypothalamic diabetes insipidus had levels of urinary and renal kallikrein not generally different from control Long-Evans rats (5). Vasopressin tannate (100 mU per day for 3 days) had no effect on urinary kallikrein excretion in either strain. It seems that more could be learned in relation to ADH activity by simultaneous studies of several system components.

INTERRELATIONS WITH HORMONES AND INTRARENAL BIOCHEMICALS

In the kidney and vasculature, kinins activate prostaglandin synthesis (2, 64, 127). This effect occurs as a result of acylhydrolase (phospholipase A_2) stimulation, which increases available free fatty acids to prostaglandin synthetase. The fact that phospholiphase A_2 can activate membrane-bound renal kallikrein (12, 74) suggests that some interesting feedback relationships might exist. The spectrum of arachidonic acid metabolites produced in response to endogenously generated kinins within the kidney is uncertain. Exogenously administered kinins can stimulate the release of prostacyclin (69) and thromboxane A_2 (68), in addition to the well-known release of prostaglandin (PG) E_2 (72). Greiner et al (27) have done an interesting study of kinin-induced prostaglandin synthesis by rabbit renal papillary-collecting tubule cells in culture. They found that low concentrations of kinins ($\sim 10^{-10}$ M) caused prompt and large increases in immunoreactive PGE_2 production by these cells, as well as significant increases in $PGE_{2\alpha}$, PGD_2, and 6-keto-$PGE_{1\alpha}$. The kinin concentrations required are similar to those that affect prostaglandin-dependent changes in short-circuit current and chloride flux in other tissues (14, 15, 54). In both studies kinins were effective from the serosal (interstitial) surface and collectively provide support for the notion that some endogenous kinin-prostaglandin interaction regulates ion-transporting events along the more distal protions of the nephron (or gastrointestinal tract). No ion-transporting events were measured by Greiner et al (27) in response to kinins, but, interestingly, they did observe that kinins had no effect upon cyclic AMP levels in this system. Although events subsequent to production of PGE_2, $PGF_{2\alpha}$, and PGI_2 induced by bradykinin or kallidin were not measured, Uglesity et al (116) observed this stimulation in rat kidney mesangial cells, and speculated that prostaglandin production might accompany mesangial cell contraction, thereby participating in regulation of glomerular function.

Many studies provide evidence linking kinin-induced effects upon renal function to prostaglandin generation. These have been reviewed recently (72). The locations of these interactions are not defined, but the possibility exists that kinins produced within the tubule travel to more distal medullary sites to affect prostaglandin synthesis within tubular epithelial or interstitial cells (72). Earlier work showing that inhibition of prostaglandin synthesis would reduce renal vasodilation produced by kinin has not been supported in subsequent studies (52, 72, 106). However, bradykinin infusions intrarenally can reduce the vasoconstrictor responses to norepinephrine, sympathetic nerve stimulation, or angiotensin II by an action that is prostaglandin-dependent and abolished by indomethacin (53, 107). Whether these events are linked to the function of an endogenous renal kallikrein-kinin system remains to be determined. The same uncertainty applies to the demonstration of simultaneous bradykinin-induced PGE_2 synthesis and natriuresis, although both can be inhibited by sodium meclofenamate (4). In several clinical and experimental circumstances, sodium-retaining steroid hormones increase urinary kallikrein and PGE_2 concomitantly (72). Paradoxically, these steroids fail to affect urinary kinin excretion (120) and, in one circumstance of aldosterone excess, Bartter's syndrome, urinary kallikrein and PGE_2 are elevated while kinin excretion is low (118). The puzzle of renal kinin-prostaglandin interrelations is well demonstrated by Bartter's syndrome, where not only are urinary kallikrein and PGE_2 elevated, but plasma kinins also seem increased (118). Indomethacin or meclofenamate treatment predictably reduce this prostaglandin level and also decrease the elevated urinary kallikrein and plasma kinins. However, these inhibitors also increase urinary kinins. There must be multiple renal kallikrein-kinin–prostaglandin interrelations, only some of which have been demonstrated; more work is needed to understand their functional significance. It also now seems likely that a spectrum of cycloxygenase and lipoxygenase products could be stimulated in different renal cells to meet a range of kinin—or other hormonal, or neurally regulated—functional responsibilities. This possibility compels a great deal of caution in interpretating kallikrein-kinin–prostaglandin correlations to renal functional events.

Mulrow and colleagues have suggested that purified urinary kallikrein can release renin from rat renal cortical slices (108). This effect is presumably independent of kinin production, because even high doses of bradykinin do not release renin into surrounding media (109). The effect is blocked by aprotinin or amiloride but not by indomethacin or propranolol. Although these results imply some degree of specificity to this action of kallikrein, renin release is also observed when slices are treated with cathepsin D or plasmin but not when treated with trypsin or pepsin. The kallikrein effect on renin release was recently reexamined (15a). It is now suggested that the previous observations resulted from an action of kallikrein that prevented renin destruction in frozen samples prior to assay for renin concentration. Along a similar line, much data has been produced recently on the capability of kallikreins to activate inactive renin. Initial reports (101) have been amended by many studies which show that glandular kallikrein activity upon acid-activated renin in vitro probably does not reflect what is occurring in vivo (37, 38). The findings do not yet eliminate glandular kallikreins from a conceptually fascinating endogenous role in renin activation or release, but data interpretation has become more circumspect recently.

Some additional reports suggest other connections between renal peptide pressor and "depressor" systems. First, pancreatic kallikrein, generally considered identical to the renal enzyme, can attack a human plasma protein fraction to liberate a pressor substance similar to angiotensin II, leading to the proposal of a "kinin-tensin" system involving kallikrein actions on either kininogens or angiotensinogens (3). Second, close structural similarity exists between the protein tonin, which acts upon several substrates to generate pressor peptide, and glandular kallikrein (47).

It seems likely that kinins, and perhaps kallikrein directly (11) via activation of specific membrane receptors (39), affect cellular cyclic nucleotide or free calcium levels. Some evidence for both possibilities has been gathered (16). Of interest is the fact that bradykinin receptor binding is decreased by sodium or low concentrations of calcium (39). Since alterations in calcium movements are involved in responses to kinins (84), it is reasonable to examine in more detail connections between kinin receptors and the regulation of cellular calcium permeability.

To summarize, kinins and kallikreins affect and are affected by other hormones and enzyme-product systems involved in the regulation of renal function. However, these relations haven't defined the functional responsibilities of the renal kallikrein-kinin system. The now well-known abnormalities in the levels of some system components in various hypertensive and renal diseases (55) add clinical relevance to the exploration of these responsibilities.

ACKNOWLEDGMENTS

The author thanks Dr. Donald H. Miller for his critical analysis of this manuscript. Some of the work described was supported by the National Institutes of Health, the Burroughs-Wellcome Fund, and South Carolina State Appropriations for Research.

Literature Cited

1. Abelous, J. E., Bardier, E. 1909. Les substance hypotensives de l'urine humaine normale. *C. R. Soc. Biol.* 66:511–12

2. Antonello, A., Tremolada, C., Baggis, B., Buin, F., Favaro, S., et al. 1978. *In vivo* activation of renal phospholipase activity by bradykinin in the rat. *Prostaglandins* 16:23–29

3. Arakawa, K., Maruta, H. 1980. Ability of kallikrein to generate angiotensin II-like pressor substance and a proposed 'kinin-tensin' enzyme system. *Nature* 288:705–6

4. Blasingham, M. C., Nasjletti, A. 1979. Contributions of renal prostaglandins to the natriuretic action of bradykinin in the dog. *Am. J. Physiol.* 237:F182–87

4a. Bode, W., Chen, Z., Bartels, K., Kutzbach, C., Schmidt-Kastner, G., et al. 1983. Refined 2Å X-ray crystal structure of Porcine pancreatic kallikrein A, a specific trypsin-like serine protinase. *J. Mol. Biol.* 164:237–82

5. Bonner, G., Rascher, W., Speck, G., Marin-Grez, M., Gross, F. 1981. The renal kallikrein-kinin system in Brattleboro rats with hereditary hypothalamic diabetes insipidus. *Acta Endocrinol.* 98:36–42

6. Brandi, C. M. W., Prado, E. S., Prado, M. J., Prado, J. L. 1976. Kininconverting aminopeptidase from human urine: partial purification and properties. *Int. J. Biochem.* 7:335–41

7. Capelo, L. R., Alzamora, F. 1977. A stop-flow analysis of the effects of intrarenal infusion of bradykinin. *Arch. Int. Pharmacodyn. Ther.* 230:156–65

8. Carone, F. A., Pullman, T. N., Oparil, S. N., Nakamura, S. 1976. Micropuncture evidence of rapid hydrolysis of

bradykinin by rat proximal tubule. *Am. J. Physiol.* 230:1420–24

9. Carvounis, C. P., Carvounis, G., Arbeit, L. A. 1981. Role of the endogenous kallikrein-kinin system in modulating vasopressin-stimulated water flow and urea permeability in the toad urinary bladder. *J. Clin. Invest.* 67:1792–96

10. Catanzaro, D. F., Morris, B. J. 1980. Cell-free biosynthesis of renin precursor and activation by kallikrein and trypsin. *IRCS Med. Sci.* 8:495–96

11. Chao, J., Buse, J. B., Shimamoto, K., Margolius, H. S. 1981. Kallikrein-induced uterine contraction independent of kinin formation. *Proc. Natl. Acad. Sci. USA* 78:6154–57

12. Chao, J., Margolius, H. S. 1979. Studies on rat renal cortical cell kallikrein. II. Identification of kallikrein as an ectoenzyme. *Biochim. Biophys. Acta* 570:330–40

13. Chao, J., Tanaka, S., Margolius, H. S. 1983. Inhibitory effects of sodium and other monovalent cations on purified versus membrane-bound kallikrein. *J. Biol. Chem.* 258:6461–65

13a. Chen, Z., Bode, W. 1983. Refined 2.5Å X-ray crystal structure of the complex formed by porcine kallikrein A and the bovine pancreatic trypsin inhibitor. *J. Mol. Biol.* 164:283–311

14. Cuthbert, A. W., Margolius, H. S. 1981. Kinin effects on electrolyte transport in rat colon. *J. Physiol.* 319:45P

15. Cuthbert, A. W., Margolius, H. S. 1982. Kinins stimulate net chloride secretion by the rat colon. *Brit. J. Pharmacol.* 75:587–98

15a. Doi, Y., Hinko, A., Franco-Saenz, R., Mulrow, P. J. 1983. Reexamination of the effect of urinary kallikrein on renin release: evidence that kallikrein does not release renin but protects renin from destruction. *Endocrinology* 113:114–18

16. Erdös, E. G., ed., 1979. *Bradykinin, Kallidin and Kallikrein. Handb. Exp. Pharmacol. XXV Suppl.* Berlin: Springer-Verlag. 817 pp.

17. Erdös, E. G., ed. 1979. Kininases. See Ref. 16, pp. 427–87

18. Fejes-Toth, G., Zahajszky, T., Filep, J. 1980. Effect of vasopressin on renal kallikrein excretion. *Am. J. Physiol.* 239: F388–92

19. Fiedler, F. 1979. Enzymology of glandular kallikreins. See Ref. 16, pp. 103–61

20. Fritz, H., Dietze, G., Fiedler, F., Haberland, G. L., eds. 1982. *Recent Progress on Kinins, Agents and Actions* Suppl., 9:126–83. Basel: Birkhaüser. 708 pp.

21. Furtado, M. 1971. Inhibition of the permeability response to vasopressin and oxytocin in the toad bladder: effects of bradykinin, kallidin, eledoisin, and physalaemin. *J. Memb. Biol.* 4:165–78

22. Geiger, R., König, G., Fruhmann, G. 1981. Inhibition of human tissue (urinary) kallikrein by sera of patients suffering from hereditary α_1-antitrypsin (α_1-proteinase inhibitor) deficiency. *Hoppe-Seylers Z. Physiol. Chem.* 362:1013–15

23. Geiger, R., Mann, K. 1976. A kallikrein-specific inhibitor in rat kidney tubules. *Hoppe-Seylers Z. Physiol. Chem.* 357: 553–58

24. Geiger, R., Stuckstedte, U., Calusnitzer, B., Fritz, H. 1981. Progressive inhibition of human glandular (urinary) kallikrein by human serum and identification of the progressive antikallikrein as α_1-antitrypsin (α_1-protease inhibitor). *Hoppe-Seylers Z. Physiol. Chem.* 362:317–25

25. Geller, R. G., Margolius, H. S., Pisano, J. J., Keiser, H. R. 1972. Effects of mineralocorticoids, altered sodium intake, and adrenalectomy on urinary kallikrein in rats. *Circulation Res.* 31:857–61

26. Gill, J. R. Jr., Melmon, K. L., Gillespie, L. Jr., Bartter, F. C. 1965. Bradykinin and renal function in normal man: effects of adrenergic blockade. *Am. J. Physiol.* 209:844–48

27. Greiner, F. C., Rollins, T. E., Smith, W. L. 1981. Kinin-induced prostaglandin synthesis by renal papillary collecting tubule cells in culture. *Am. J. Physiol.* 241:F94–104

28. Hall, E. R., Kato, J., Erdös, E. G., Robinson, C. J. G., Oshima, G. 1976. Angiotensin I-converting enzyme in the nephron. *Life Sci.* 18:1299–303

29. Halushka, P. V., Wohltmann, H., Privitera, P. J., Hurwitz, G., Margolius, H. S. 1977. Bartter's syndrome: urinary prostaglandin E-like material and kallikrein; indomethacin effects. *Ann. Int. Med.* 87:281–86

30. Heidrich, H. G., Geiger, R. 1980. Kininogenase activity in plasma membranes and cell organelles from rabbit kidney cortex: subcellular localization of renal kallikrein by free-flow electrophoresis and density-gradient fractionation. *Kidney Int.* 18:77–85

31. Hial, V., Keiser, H. R., Pisano, J. J. 1976. Origin and content of methionyl-lysyl-bradykinin, lysyl-bradykinin, and bradykinin in human urine. *Biochem. Pharmacol.* 25:2499–503

32. Hilton, S. M. 1970. The physiological role of glandular kallikreins. In *Bradykinin, Kallidin and Kallikrein, Handb. Exp. Pharmacol. XXV*, ed. E. G. Erdös,

pp. 389–99. Berlin: Springer-Verlag. 768 pp.

33. Holland, O. B., Chud, J. M., Braunstein, H. 1980. Urinary kallikrein excretion in essential and mineralocorticoid hypertension. *J. Clin. Invest.* 65:347–56

34. Horky, K., Rojo-Ortega, J. M., Rodriguez, J., Boucher, R., Genest, J. 1971. Renin, renin substrate, and angiotensin I-converting enzyme in the lymph of rats. *Am. J. Physiol.* 220:307–11

35. Hörl, W. H., Heidland, A. 1981. Inactivation of urinary kallikrein by alpha$_1$-antitrypsin. *Klin. Wochenschr.* 59:761–63

36. Horwitz, D., Margolius, H. S., Keiser, H. R. 1978. Effects of dietary potassium and race on urinary excretion of kallikrein and aldosterone in man. *J. Clin. Endocrinol. Metab.* 47:296–99

37. Hsueh, W. A., Carlson, E. J., Israel-Hageman, M. 1981. Mechanism of acid-activation of renin: role of kallikrein in renin activation. *Hypertension* 3(Suppl. I):22–29

38. Inagami, T., Okamoto, H., Ohtsuki, K., Shimamoto, K., Chao, J., Margolius, H. S. 1982. Human plasma inactive renin: purification and activation by proteases. *J. Clin. Endocrinol. Metab.* 55:619–27

39. Innis, R. B., Manning, D. C., Stewart, J. M., Snyder, S. H. 1981. [^{3}H]-Bradykinin receptor binding in mammalian tissue membranes. *Proc. Natl. Acad. Sci. USA* 78:2630–34

40. Johnston, P. A., Bernard, D. B., Perrin, N. S., Arbeit, L., Lieberthal, W., Levinsky, N. G. 1981. Control of rat renal vascular resistance during alterations in sodium balance. *Circulation Res.* 48:728–33

41. Kaizu, T., Margolius, H. S. 1975. Studies on rat renal cortical cell kallikrein. I. Separation and measurement. *Biochim. Biophys. Acta* 411:305–15

42. Kauker, M. L. 1980. Bradykinin action on the efflux of luminal ^{22}Na in the rat nephron. *J. Pharmacol. Exp.* 214:119–23

43. Keiser, H. R., Andrews, M. J. Jr., Guyton, R. A., Margolius, H. S., Pisano, J. J. 1976. Urinary kallikrein in dogs with constriction of one renal artery. *Proc. Soc. Exp. Biol. Med.* 151:53–56

44. Kobuku, T., Kato, I., Nishimura, K., Yoshida, N., Hiwada, K., Ueda, E. 1978. Angiotensin I-converting enzyme in human urine. *Clin. Chim. Acta* 89:375–79

45. Lawton, W. J., Fitz, A. E. 1977. Urinary kallikrein in normal renin essential hypertension. *Circulation* 56:856–59

46. Lawton, W. J., Proud, D., Frech, M. E.,

Pierce, J. V., Keiser, H. R., Pisano, J. J. 1981. Characterization and origin of immunoreactive glandular kallikrein in rat plasma. *Biochem. Pharmacol.* 30:1731–37

47. Lazure, C., Seidah, N. G., Thibault, G., Boucher, R., Genest, J., Chretien, M. 1981. Sequence homologies between tonin, nerve growth factor γ-subunit, epidermal growth factor–binding protein and serine proteases. *Nature* 292:383–84

48. Lechi, A., Covi, G., Lechi, C., Mantero, F., Scuro, L. A. 1976. Urinary kallikrein excretion in Bartter's syndrome. *J. Clin. Endocrinol. Metab.* 43:1175–78

49. Levy, S. B., Frigon, R. P., Stone, R. A. 1978. The relationship of urinary kallikrein activity to renal salt and water excretion. *Clin. Sci. Mol. Med.* 54:39–45

50. Levy, S. B., Lilley, J. J., Frigon, R. P., Stone, R. A. 1977. Urinary kallikrein and plasma renin activity as determinants of renal blood flow. *J. Clin. Invest.* 60:129–38

51. Lieberthal, W., Oza, N. B., Bernard, D. B., Levinsky, N. G. 1982. The effect of cations on the activity of human urinary kallikrein. *J. Biol. Chem.* 257:10827–30

52. Lonigro, A. J., Hagemann, M. H., Stephenson, A. H., Fry, C. L. 1978. Inhibition of prostaglandin synthesis by indomethacin augments the renal vasodilator response to bradykinin in the anesthetized dog. *Circulation Res.* 43:447–55

53. Malik, K. U., Nasjletti, A. 1979. Attenuation by bradykinin of adrenergically induced vasoconstriction in the isolated perfused rabbit kidney: relationship to prostaglandin synthesis. *Br. J. Pharmacol.* 67:269–75

54. Manning, D. C., Synder, S. H., Kachur, J. F., Miller, R. J., Field, M. 1982. Bradykinin receptor-mediated chloride secretion in intestinal function. *Nature* 299:256–59

55. Margolius, H. S. 1982. Kallikrein and kinins in hypertension. In *Hypertension,* 2nd ed., ed. J. Genest, O. Kuchel, P. Hamet, M. Cantin, pp. 360–73. New York: McGraw-Hill. 1318 pp.

56. Margolius, H. S., Chao, J. 1980. Amiloride inhibits mammalian renal kallikrein and a kallikrein-like enzyme from toad bladder and skin. *J. Clin. Invest.* 65:1343–50

57. Margolius, H. S., Geller, R., Pisano, J. J., Sjoerdsma, A. 1971. Altered urinary kallikrein in human hypertension. *Lancet* 2:1063–65

58. Margolius, H. S., Horwitz, D., Geller, R. G., Alexander, R. W. Jr., Gill, J. R. Jr., Pisano, J. J., Keiser, H. R. 1974. Urinary kallikrein excretion in normal

man: Relationships to sodium intake and sodium-retaining steroids. *Circulation Res.* 35:812–19

59. Margolius, H. S., Horwitz, D., Pisano, J. J., Keiser, H. R. 1974. Urinary kallikrein in hypertension: Relationships to sodium intake and sodium-retaining steroids. *Circulation Res.* 35:820–25

60. Marin-Grez, M. 1974. The influence of antibodies against bradykinin on isotonic saline diuresis in the rat. *Pfluegers Arch.* 350:231–39

61. Marinkovic, D. V., Ward, P. E., Erdös, E. G., Mills, I. H. 1980. Carboxypeptidase-type kininase of human kidney and urine. *Proc. Soc. Exp. Biol. Med.* 165:6–12

61a. Mason, A. J., Evans, B. A., Cox, D. R., Shine, J., Richards, R. I. 1983. Structure of mouse kallikrein gene family suggests a role in specific processing of biologically active peptides. *Nature* 303:300–7

62. McCaa, R. E., Hall, J. E., McCaa, C. S. 1978. The effects of angiotensin I-converting enzyme inhibitors on arterial blood pressure and urinary sodium excretion. Role of the renin-angiotensin and kallikrein-kinin systems. *Circulation Res.* 43(Suppl. I):32–39

63. McGiff, J. C., Itskovitz, H. D., Terragno, N. A. 1975. The actions of bradykinin and eledoisin in the canine isolated kidney: relationships to prostaglandins. *Clin. Sci. Mol. Med.* 49:125–31

64. McGiff, J. C., Terragno, N. A., Malik, K. U., Lonigro, A. J. 1972. Release of a prostaglandin E-like substance from canine kidney by bradykinin. *Circulation Res.* 31:36–43

65. Miller, D. H., Chao, J., Margolius, H. S. 1983. Tissue kallikrein synthesis and its modification by testosterone or low dietary sodium. *Biochem. J.* In press

66. Mimran, A., Baudin, G., Casellas, D., Soulas, D. 1977. Urinary kallikrein and changes in endogenous aldosterone in the rat. *Eur. J. Clin. Invest.* 7:497–502

67. Mimran, A., Casellas, D., Dupont, M. 1980. Indirect evidence against a role of the kinin system in the renal hemodynamic effect of captopril in the rat. *Kidney Int.* 18:746–53

68. Morrison, A. R., Mishikawa, K., Needleman, P. 1978. Thromboxane A_2 biosynthesis in the ureter obstructed isolated perfused kidney of the rabbit. *J. Pharmacol. Exp. Ther.* 205:1–8

69. Mullane, K. M., Moncada, S., Vane, J. R. 1980. Prostacyclin release induced by bradykinin may contribute to the antihypertensive action of angiotensin-converting enzyme inhibitors. In *Advances in Prostaglandin and Thromboxane Research*, ed. B. Sammuelson, P. W. Ramwell, R. Paoletti, pp. 1159–61. New York: Raven

70. Nasjletti, A., Colina-Chourio, J. 1976. Interaction of mineralocorticoids, renal prostaglandins, and the renal kallikrein-kinin system. *Fed. Proc.* 35:189–93

71. Nasjletti, A., Colina-Chourio, J., McGiff, J. C. 1975. Disappearance of bradykinin in the renal circulation of dogs. Effects of kininase inhibition. *Circulation Res.* 37:59–65

72. Nasjletti, A., Malik, K. U. 1981. Renal kinin–prostaglandin relationship: implications for renal function. *Kidney Int.* 19:860–68

73. Nawa, H., Kitamura, N., Hirose, T., Asai, M., Inayama, S., Nakanishi, S. 1983. Primary structures of bovine liver low-molecular-weight kininogen precursors and their two mRNAs. *Proc. Natl. Acad. Sci. USA* 80:90–94

74. Nishimura, K., Alhenc-Gelas, F., White, A., Erdös, E. G. 1980. Activation of membrane bound kallikrein and renin in the kidney. *Proc. Natl. Acad. Sci. USA* 77:4975–78

75. Nolly, H., Lama, M. C. 1982. Vascular kallikrein: a kallikrein-like enzyme present in vascular tissue of the rat. *Clin. Sci.* 63:2495–51

76. Nustad, K., Ørstavik, T. B., Gautvik, K. M. 1978. Radioimmunological measurements of rat submandibular gland kallikrein (RSK) in tissue and serum. *Microvasc. Res.* 15:115–16

77. ole-Moi Yoi, O., Spragg, J., Austen, K. F. 1979. Structural studies of human urinary kallikrein. *Proc. Natl. Acad. Sci. USA* 76:3121–25

78. Omata, K., Carretero, O. A., Scicli, A. G., Jackson, B. A. 1982. Localization of active and inactive kallikrein (kininogenase activity) in the microdissected rabbit nephron. *Kidney Int.* 22:602–7

79. Orce, G. G., Castillo, G. A., Margolius, H. S. 1980. Inhibition of short-circuit current in toad urinary bladder by inhibitors of glandular kallikrein. *Am. J. Physiol.* 239:F459–65

80. Orce, G. G., Castillo, G. A., Margolius, H. S. 1981. Kallikrein inhibitors decrease short-circuit current of inhibiting sodium uptake. *Hypertension* 3(Suppl. II):92–95

81. Ørstavik, T. B., Gautvik, K. M., Nustad, K. 1980. Intraglandular transport of ^{125}I-glandular kallikrein in the rat submandibular salivary gland. *Acta Physiol. Scand.* 109:315–23

82. Deleted in proof

83. Ørstavik, T. B., Nustad, K., Brandtzaeg,

P., Pierce, J. V. 1976. Cellular origin of urinary kallikrein. *J. Histochem. Cytochem.* 24:1037–39

84. Perris, A. D., Whitfield, J. F. 1969. The mitogenic action of bradykinin on thymic lymphocytes and its dependence on calcium. *Proc. Soc. Exp. Biol. Med.* 130:1198–1201

85. Pinkus, G. S., ole-Moi Yoi, O., Austen, K. F., Spragg, J. 1981. Antigenic separation of a nonkinin-generating TAMe esterase from human urinary kallikrein and immunohistochemical comparison of their localization in the kidney. *J. Histochem. Cytochem.* 29:38–44

86. Pisano, J. J., Corthorn, J., Yates, K., Pierce, J. V. 1978. The kallikrein-kinin system in the kidney. *Contrib. Nephrol.* 12:116–25

87. Proud, D., Perkins, M., Pierce, J. V., Yates, K. N., Highet, P. F., et al. 1981. Characterization and localization of human renal kininogen. *J. Biol. Chem.* 256:10634–39

88. Rabito, S. F., Amin, V., Scicli, A. G., Carretero, O. A. 1979. Glandular kallikrein in plasma and urine: evaluation of a direct RIA for its determination. In *Kinins-II: - Advances in Experimental Medicine and Biology*, ed. S. Fujii, H. Moriya, T. Suzuki, 120A:127–42. New York: Plenum. 610 pp.

89. Regoli, D., Barabe, J. 1980. Pharmacology of bradykinin and related kinins. *Pharmacol. Rev.* 32:1–46

90. Robertson, G. L., Conder, M. L. 1980. Regulation of urinary kinin excretion. *Clin. Res.* 28:536A (Abstr.)

91. Robillard, J. E., Lawton, W. J., Weismann, D. N., Sessions, C. 1982. Developmental aspects of the renal kallikrein-like activity in fetal newborn lambs. *Kidney Int.* 22:594–601

92. Sakamoto, W., Nishikaze, O. 1980. α_1-Antitrypsin and α_2-macroglobulin do not inhibit the kinin-releasing activity of kallikreins from human urine and saliva. *Biochim. Biophys. Acta* 633:305–9

93. Schacter, M. 1970. Vasodilation in the submaxillary gland of the cat, rabbit, and sheep. See Ref. 32, pp. 400–8

94. Schacter, M. 1980. Kallikreins (Kininogenases)—A group of serine proteases with bioregulatory actions. *Pharmacol. Rev.* 31:1–17

95. Schneider, E. G., Strandhoy, J. W., Willis, L. R., Knox, F. G. 1973. Relationship between proximal sodium reabsorption and excretion of calcium, magnesium, and phosphate. *Kidney Int.* 4:369–76

96. Scicli, A. G., Carretero, O. A., Hampton, A., Cortes, P., Oza, N. B. 1976.

Site of kininogenase secretion in the dog nephron. *Am. J. Physiol.* 230:533–36

97. Scicli, A. G., Carretero, O. A., Oza, N. B. 1976. Distribution of kidney kininogenases. *Proc. Soc. Exp. Biol. Med.* 151:57–60

98. Scicli, A. G., Diaz, M. A., Carretero, O. A. 1983. Effect of pH and amiloride on the intrarenal formation of kinins. *Am. J. Physiol.* 245:F198–203

99. Scicli, A. G., Gandolfi, R., Carretero, O. A. 1978. Site of formation of kinins in the dog nephron. *Am. J. Physiol.* 234:F36–40

100. Scicli, A. G., Ørstavik, T. B., Rabito, S. F., Murray, R. D. Carretero, O. A. 1983. Blood kinins after sympathetic nerve stimulation of the rat submandibular gland. *Hypertension.* 5(II):I101–6

101. Sealey, J. E., Atlas, S. A., Laragh, J. H., Oza, N. B., Ryan, J. W. 1978. Human urinary kallikrein converts inactive renin to active renin and is a possible physiological activator of renin. *Nature* 275:144–45

102. Shimamoto, K., Chao, J., Margolius, H. S. 1980. The radioimmunoassay of human urinary kallikrein and comparisons with kallikrein activity measurements. *J. Clin. Endocrinol. Metab.* 51:840–48

103. Shimamoto, K., Chao, J., Margolius, H. S. 1982. A method for determination of human urinary inactive kallikrein (prekallikrein). *Tohoku J. Exp. Med.* 137:269–74

104. Simson, J. A. V., Spicer, S. S., Chao, J., Grimm, L., Margolius, H. S. 1979. Kallikrein localization in rodent salivary glands and kidney with the immunoglobulin-enzyme bridge technique. *J. Histochem. Cytochem.* 27:1567–76

105. Stein, J. H., Congbalay, R. C., Karsh, D. L., Osgood, R. W., Ferris, T. F. 1972. The effect of bradykinin on proximal tubular sodium reabsorption in the dog: evidence for functional nephron heterogeneity. *J. Clin. Invest.* 51:1709–21

106. Strand, J. C., Gilmore, J. P. 1982. Prostaglandins do not mediate the renal effects of bradykinin. *Renal Physiol. Basel* 5:286–96

107. Susic, H., Nasjletti, A., Malik, K. U. 1981. Inhibition by bradykinin of the vascular effects of pressor hormones in the canine kidney: relationship to prostaglandins. *Clin. Sci.* 59:145S–48

108. Suzuki, S., Franco-Saenz, R., Tan, S. Y., Mulrow, P. J. 1980. Direct action of rat urinary kallikrein on rat kidney to release renin. *J. Clin. Invest.* 66:757–62

109. Suzuki, S., Franco-Saenz, R., Tan, S.

Y., Mulrow, P. J. 1981. Direct action of kallikrein and other proteases on the renin-angiotensin system. *Hypertension* 3:13–17
110. Swartz, S. L., Williams, G. H., Hollenberg, N. K., Levine, L., Dluhy, R. G., Moore, T. J. 1980. Captopril-induced changes in prostaglandin production. *J. Clin. Invest.* 65:1257–64
111. Swartz, S. L., Williams, G. H., Hollenberg, N. K., Moore, T. J., Dluhy, R. G. 1979. Converting-enzyme inhibition in essential hypertension: the hypotensive response does not reflect only reduced angiotensin II formation. *Hypertension* 1:106–11
112. Sweet, C. S., Gross, D. M., Arbegast, P. T., Gaul, S. L., Britt, P. M., Ludden, C. T., Weitz, D., Stone, C. A. 1981. Antihypertensive activity of N-[(S)-1-(ethoxycarbonyl)-3-phenylpropyl]-L-Ala-L-Pro(MK-421), an orally active converting-enzyme inhibitor. *J. Pharmacol. Exp. Therap.* 216:558–66
113. Swift, G. H., Dagorn, J.-C., Ashley, P. L., Cummings, S. W., MacDonald, R. J. 1982. Rat pancreatic kallikrein in mRNA: nucleotide sequence and amino acid sequence of the encoded preproenzyme. *Proc. Natl. Acad. Sci. USA* 79:7263–67
114. Takaoka, M., Akiyama, H., Ito, K., Okamura, H., Morimoto, S. 1982. Isolation of inactive kallikrein from rat urine. *Biochem. Biophys. Res. Comm.* 109:841–47
115. Tomita, K., Endou, H., Sakai, F. 1981. Localization of kallikrein-like activity along a single nephron in rabbits. *Pflügers Arch.* 389:91–95
116. Uglesity, A., Kreisberg, J. I., Levine, L. 1983. Stimulation of arachidonic acid metabolism in rat kidney mesangial cells by bradykinin, antidiuretic hormone, and their analogues. *Prostaglandins Leukotrienes and Med.* 10:83–93
117. Vahatera, E., Hamburg, U. 1976. Absence of binding of pancreatic and urinary kallikreins to α_2-macroglobulin. *Biochem. J.* 157:521–24
118. Vinci, J. M., Gill, J. R., Jr., Bowden, R. E., Pisano, J. J., Izzo, J. L. Jr., Radfar,

N., Taylor, A. A., Zusman, R. M., Bartter, F. C., Keiser, H. R. 1978. The kallikrein-kinin system in Bartter's syndrome and its response to prostaglandin synthetase inhibition. *J. Clin. Invest.* 61:1671–82
119. Vinci, J. M., Horwitz, D., Zusman, R. M., Pisano, J. J., Catt, K. J., Keiser, H. R. 1979. The effect of converting-enzyme inhibition with SQ 20,881 on plasma and urinary kinins, prostaglandin E, and angiotensin II in hypertensive man. *Hypertension* 1:416–26
120. Vinci, J. M., Zusman, R. M., Izzo, J. L. Jr., Bowden, R. E., Horwitz, D., et al. 1979. Human urinary and plasma kinins. Relationship to sodium-retaining steroids and plasma renin activity. *Circulation Res.* 44:228–37
121. Ward, P. E., Erdös, E. G., Gedney, C. D., Dowben, R. M., Reynolds, R. C. 1976. Isolation of membrane-bound renal enzymes that metabolize kinins and angiotensins. *Biochem. J.* 157:642–50
122. Ward, P. E., Gedney, C. D., Dowben, R. M., Erdös, E. G. 1975. Isolation of membrane-bound renal kallikrein and kininase. *Biochem. J.* 151:755–58
123. Weare, J. A., Stewart, T. A., Gafford, J. T., Erdös, E. G. 1981. Inhibition of human converting enzyme *in vitro* by a novel tripeptide analog. *Hypertension* 3:50–53
124. Webster, M. E., Gilmore, J. P. 1964. Influence of kallidin-10 on renal function. *Am. J. Physiol.* 206:714–18
125. Willis, L. R. 1977. Effect of bradykinin on the renal medullary osmotic gradient in water diuresis. *Eur. J. Pharmacol.* 45:173–83
126. Yamada, K., Erdös, E. G. 1982. Kallikrein and prekallikrein of the isolated basolateral membrane of rat kidney. *Kidney Int.* 22:331–37
127. Zusman, R. M., Keiser, H. R. 1977. Prostaglandin E_2 biosynthesis by rabbit renomedullary interstitial cells in tissue culture: mechanism of stimulation by angiotensin II, bradykinin, and arginine vasopressin. *J. Biol. Chem.* 252:2069–71

Ann. Rev. Physiol. 1984. 46:327–41

RENAL ARACHIDONIC ACID METABOLISM

Mark G. Currie and Philip Needleman

Department of Pharmacology, Washington University School of Medicine, 660 South Euclid Avenue, St. Louis, Missouri 63110

INTRODUCTION

Renal prostaglandin synthesis has been the focus of extensive investigation during the past decade. This chapter reviews the cellular localization of renal arachidonic acid metabolism in view of the substantial recent progress in the isolation and culture of renal cell types. The study of such specific renal cell types permits a more exact correlation of arachidonic acid metabolism, hormonal recognition, and specific kidney functions. In addition, we have chosen to describe a pathophysiological model that exhibits exaggerated prostaglandin (PG) synthesis and demonstrates the impact of nonrenal cells on kidney arachidonate metabolism and function.

RENAL ARACHIDONATE METABOLISM

An overview of arachidonic acid metabolism in cortical or medullary homogenates is shown in Figure 1. The three enzymatic pathways involved in the renal synthesis of eicosanoids (i.e. arachidonic acid metabolites) include cyclooxygenase (prostaglandin endoperoxide synthetase) (27, 66), lipoxygenase (49, 104, 117), and cytochrome P-450 monooxygenase (74, 86, 87) (Figure 1). Cyclooxygenase converts arachidonic acid into the unstable prostaglandin endoperoxides that are in turn enzymatically converted into PGE_2, $PGF_{2\alpha}$, PGD_2, PGI_2 (prostacyclin), and thromboxane A_2 (TxA_2) (27, 66). The renal medulla has a ten-fold greater capacity to produce PGs than the renal cortex (59, 119). Lipoxygenase, especially in the medulla, converts arachidonic acid into noncyclized metabolites, hydroperoxyeicosatetraenoic acids, that are then reduced to the hydroxyeicosatetraenoic acids (HETEs) (117). Hydroperoxy-

327

eicosatetraenoic acids are known inhibitors of prostacyclin synthetase (36, 71, 110) and 15-HPETE has been suggested to be a regulator of medullary blood flow by inhibiting production of the vasodilator prostacyclin (76). Recently, an NADPH-dependent cytochrome P-450 monooxygenase has been described in rabbit renal cortex that metabolizes arachidonic acid (74, 86, 87). This enzyme was inhibited by carbon monoxide (86) and high concentrations of other known cytochrome P-450 inhibitors (74). The products of the monooxygenase are listed in Figure 1. The trihydroxyeicosatrienoic acids are most likely formed by ω- and (ω−1)-hydroxylation of the dihydroxyeicosatrienoic acids (87). The physiological significance of this pathway of arachidonate remains to be determined.

CELLULAR SITES OF PROSTAGLANDIN BIOSYNTHESIS AND RELATIONSHIP TO FUNCTION

Various renal functions are compartmentalized within defined nephron structures; (e.g. the collecting duct system is an important site for the regulation of water reabsorption). Determination of the specific cellular sites of PG production provides an indication of the local function of the metabolite, particularly since PGs are thought to be local hormones. Localization of cyclooxygenase-

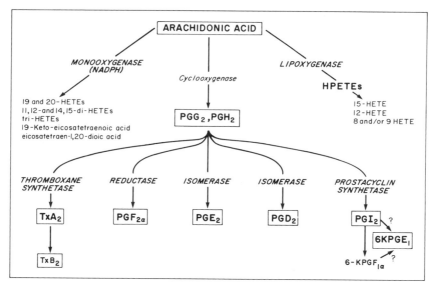

Figure 1 Schematic representation of the pathways for renal arachidonic acid metabolism. The following abbreviations were employed: HETE—hydroxyeicosatetraenoic acid; PG—prostaglandin, Tx—thromboxane; and PGI$_2$—prostacyclin.

containing cells by histochemical (48) and immunohistochemical (97–99) techniques have demonstrated the presence of the enzyme in the cortical and medullary collecting ducts, medullary interstitial cells, vascular endothelial cells, and glomerular cells. Such morphological studies are useful because they indicate the potential for renal PG synthesis, but they neither directly demonstrate PG production nor do they identify the specific PGs produced.

Recent efforts at localization of the renal cellular sites of PG production have utilized cell isolation and culture techniques. A consideration of each cell type that metabolizes arachidonate is presented in the morphological sequence along the nephron. Isolated glomeruli from rat (28, 37, 105) and human (101) produce substantial amounts of 6-keto-PGF$_{1_\alpha}$ (stable metabolite of PGI$_2$), TxB$_2$ (stable metabolite of TxA$_2$), PGE$_2$, and PGF$_{2_\alpha}$. The glomerulus contains four cell types: the glomerular endothelial cell, the mesangial cell, the glomerular epithelial cell, and the glomerular parietal epithelial cell. Studies examining eicosanoid metabolism by cultured partially purified rat glomerular epithelial and mesangial cells indicate that these two cell types produce prostaglandins and thromboxanes (90, 102, 103). The mesangial cell was found to produce ten times more cyclooxygenase products than epithelial cells, with the order of abundance as follows: PGE$_2$>TxB$_2$>PGF$_{2_\alpha}$>6-keto-PGF$_{1_\alpha}$ (102). Recent results obtained with cloned cell lines of epithelial and mesangial cells conflict with the results from the primary cultures of epithelial and mesangial cells. Homogenous glomerular epithelial cells were found to produce ten times more cyclooxygenase products than cloned mesangial cells (57). The glomerular epithelial cells produced predominantly PGI$_2$, whereas mesangial cells produced predominantly PGE$_2$. The differences between the results of the cloned cell lines and partially purified cell cultures may reflect differences in growth conditions and number of passages (57). The glomerular production of the vasodilators PGE$_2$ and PGI$_2$ and the potent vasoconstrictor TxA$_2$ could function to regulate glomerular hemodynamics (2, 8, 92). The glomerulus is also a site of lipoxygenase activity (49, 104). Homogenized rat kidney glomeruli, in the presence of a cyclooxygenase inhibitor, metabolized arachidonate to 12-HETE and 8- and/or 9-HETEs (49). Glomeruli isolated from murine and human renal cortex metabolize arachidonic acid to 12- and 15-HETE (104). Cultured rat glomerular epithelial cells were subsequently shown to be a site of glomerular production of 12-HETE (49). Lipoxygenase metabolites may play a role as mediators of the inflammatory response in glomerular diseases, and HPETEs may regulate glomerular circulation by regulating prostacyclin production.

We have recently found that microdissected isolated rabbit thin limb of Henle produces PGE$_2$ (18). The thin limb of Henle has previously been shown to possess cyclooxygenase antigenicity in the hydronephrotic (but not normal) rabbit kidney (98). The descending portion of the thin limb exhibits increased adenylate cyclase activity in response to both vasopressin and PGE_2 (109). PGE_2 could be released by the thin limb of Henle cells into the luminal space and subsequently transported by urine flow to the PGE_2-sensitive sites along the lumen of the thick ascending limb. PGE_2, administered on the luminal portion of the thick ascending limb, decreases sodium and chloride reabsorption (106).

Partially purified rabbit medullary thick ascending limb cells have been described to produce nearly equal amounts of PGE_2 and PGF_{2_α} (94). The cyclooxygenase activity found in this portion of the nephron is very low and may possibly be due to contamination of the preparation with a small number of medullary collecting tubule cells. We have attempted to measure prostaglandin synthesis in microdissected rabbit thick ascending limb segments but have failed to detect cyclooxygenase activity with sensitive assay techniques (18). Regardless of whether this portion of the nephron produces prostaglandin it does appear to be a site for prostaglandin action. Cyclooxygenase inhibitors enhance NaCl absorption in the thick ascending limb (39), whereas the direct addition of exogenous PGE_2 to either the luminal or basal side inhibits NaCl absorption (106).

Microdissected rabbit connecting tubule segments produce PGE_2 (18). The function of PGs produced by the connecting tubule has not been examined. This portion of the nephron shares some characteristics with both the distal convoluted tubule and the cortical collecting tubule (51). Since PGs appear to regulate water transport by the collecting duct (27, 33), perhaps they serve this function in the connecting tubule as well. The connecting tubule is not only capable of synthesizing PG but also is a site of kallikrein synthesis (81).

The most active site of PG synthesis of the nephron is the collecting tubule system (18). Cortical collecting tubule cells isolated either by microdissection (16) or by the use of monoclonal antibodies directed against this portion of the nephron (30) have recently been grown in cell culture. The predominant PG produced by the collecting tubule cells is PGE_2, with lesser amounts of PGF_{2_α} and PGD_2 being formed (16, 18, 34, 45). PGE_2 has been proposed as both an inhibitor (33, 89) and a mediator (40, 41) of the renal actions of vasopressin. The effect of vasopressin on water transport by the isolated perfused cortical collecting tubule is antagonized by PGE_1 (33). PGE_2 inhibits sodium reabsorption by the cortical collecting tubule (44, 107) and may mediate the inhibitory effect of sustained vasopressin treatment on sodium, chloride, calcium, and phosphorus reabsorption by the cortical collecting tubule (40, 41). Dog cortical collecting tubule cultured cells (30) and isolated rabbit cortical collecting tubules (53) respond to vasopressin with a two-fold increase of PGE_2 synthesis. On the other hand, vasopressin did not stimulate PGE_2 synthesis in cultured rabbit renal papillary collecting tubule cells (34). These results suggest that heterogeneity exists along the collecting duct system with respect to the ability of vasopressin to induce prostaglandin synthesis.

Renal medullary interstitial cells have been the subject of detailed investigation. This cell type is located in the renal papilla, closely associated with the vasa recta, Henle's loop, and collecting duct (51). The synthesis of PGs (predominantly PGE_2 and PGF_{2_α}) by the renal medullary interstitial cells is stimulated by vasopressin, bradykinin, angiotensin, and the removal of potassium from the culture medium (126–129). A possible clinical correlation of the effect of potassium on PGE_2 synthesis in these cells is that Bartter's syndrome patients are typically hypokalemic and produce large amounts of PGE_2 (32). PGs produced by the renal medullary interstitial cells may play a role in the regulation of inner medullary blood flow and tubular water reabsorption (125). The close proximity of the interstitial cells to the vasa recta and the medullary collecting duct suggests a possible interaction between these structures. Stimulation of PGE_2 synthesis by the pressor hormones, angiotensin II and vasopressin, could function to blunt the vasoconstriction of the vasa recta, because PGE_2 is a potent vasodilator (27, 66). Similarly, PGE_1 antagonizes the effect of vasopressin on water transport in collecting duct (33).

Medullary interstitial cells also produce dihomo-PGE_2, which is a metabolite of adrenic acid [7, 10, 13, 16-docosatetraenoic acid] (12, 100). Adrenic acid is formed from arachidonic acid by chain elongation and is found in significant amounts in the adrenal gland, brain, testis, and the renal medulla (55, 112). Of these tissues, only the renal medulla was found to metabolize adrenic acid to dihomo-PGs and -thromboxanes (100).

In summary, the identified sites of PG production in the kidney are the renal vasculature, glomeruli, thin limb of Henle, connecting tubule, collecting ducts, and medullary interstitial cells.

HORMONAL INTERACTIONS WITH THE RENAL PROSTAGLANDIN SYSTEM

Renal arachidonic acid metabolites modify or mediate renal blood flow, renin release, and water and ion reabsorption (27, 66). Many of the effects of the eicosanoids on renal function are linked to complex interactions with other renal hormone systems. Hormonal stimulation (e.g. bradykinin, vasopressin, angiotensin II) of medullary slices elicits a calcium-dependent stimulation of PG synthesis (14, 54, 121, 122) and is associated with increased phosphatidyl-inositol-polyphosphoinositide turnover (5). The calmodulin inhibitor, trifluoperazine, inhibited the calcium-dependent increase of PGE_2 synthesis in the medullary slices (15). Trifluoperazine inhibited acyl hydrolase activity in microsomes, and exogenous calmodulin restored the activity. These results suggest that calmodulin regulates the cleavage of arachidonic acid from the phospholipids by the acyl hydrolase, and thereby regulates renal medullary PG synthesis (15).

RENIN-ANGIOTENSIN SYSTEM– PROSTAGLANDIN INTERACTIONS

The vasoconstrictor activity of angiotensin II is enhanced when PG synthesis is blocked by indomethacin and other nonsteroidal anti-inflammatory agents (1, 66). Angiotensin II stimulates the release of PGE_2 (26, 67, 82, 83) and PGI_2 (77) by the kidney, which subsequently blunts the peptide-induced vasoconstriction (65, 108). The known renal sites at which angiotensin causes PG production are the glomerulus (93), medullary interstitial cells (126–129), and papillary collecting duct cells (34).

Renin release from the juxtaglomerular cells is regulated physiologically by several factors: a decrease in renal perfusion pressure, the adrenergic nervous system, and alterations in ion concentration at the macula densa (21). PGs have been demonstrated to directly stimulate the release of renin from in vivo and in vitro kidney preparations (46). The stimulation of renin release by PGs is thought to be mediated by cyclic AMP (46, 66). In several species, intrarenal infusion of arachidonic acid causes the stimulation of renin release, which is blocked by cyclooxygenase inhibitors (7, 60, 114). PGs mediate the increase in renin release caused by baroreceptor (19, 38) and macula densa stimulation (88). Whether the increase of renin release caused by sympathetic nervous system stimulation is dependent on prostaglandin synthesis is unresolved (46). Some controversy exists as to exactly which cyclooxygenase product is the physiological regulator of renin release. PGE_2, PGI_2, 6-keto-PGE_1, and PGD_2 are all capable of being renin secretogogues (31, 46, 96, 115, 116). PGD_2 is an unlikely candidate since it is a quantitatively minor renal arachidonate metabolite (27, 66). Considerable evidence has been accumulated to support both the role of PGE_2 and PGI_2 as regulators of renin secretion (31, 46, 96, 115, 116). PGI_2 has been observed to be a more potent stimulus of renin release than PGE_2 (115, 116). However, this finding does not necessarily imply that PGE_2 is an unimportant regulator, because it is the predominant arachidonate metabolite produced by the kidney in many species (27, 66). The action of PGI_2 to cause renin release has been proposed to be mediated in part by 6-keto-PGE_1. PGI_2 or 6-keto-PGF_{1_α} may be enzymatically converted into 6-keto-PGE_1 (118). Exogenous 6-keto-PGE_1 is slightly more active than PGI_2 at causing renin release and has a more sustained effect (47, 69). Proof of the temporal and quantitative correlation of intact kidney synthesis of 6-keto-PGE_1 with renin secretion is, however, currently lacking.

RENAL KININ–PROSTAGLANDIN RELATIONSHIP

The interactions between the PGs and the kinin system have recently been reviewed (81). Kinins (e.g. bradykinin, lysylbradykinin) are peptides produced by the action of kallikrein on the plasma protein substrate, kininogen. Kallikreins occur in plasma and in several glandular tissues, including the kidney. Renal kallikrein has been localized in the distal convoluted tubule and the connecting segment. The renal kallikrein acts on low-molecular-weight kininogens to generate lysylbradykinin, which may be subsequently converted to bradykinin by an aminopeptidase. Renal kallikrein is thought to be an ectoenzyme that is released into both the tubular fluid and renal vascular compartment. Large quantities of kallikrein and kinins are found in the urine. The intrarenal infusion of kinins produces renal vasodilation, diuresis, and natriuresis (81). These actions caused by the kinins are attenuated by PG synthesis inhibitors (66, 68), and the intrarenal infusion of arachidonic acid mimics many of the renal effects of the peptide (66, 81). However, the contribution of prostaglandins to the renal vasodilation induced by bradykinin is disputed (64, 81). Bradykinin stimulates the release of PGE_2, $PGF_{2\alpha}$, and PGI_2 from the normal kidney (26, 66, 68, 70, 78). Many of the renal actions of the kinins appear to be mediated by PGE_2 and PGI_2 (66). The renal infusion of either of these PGs causes effects similar to those caused by kinins (66). The known sites of action of kinins to stimulate the release of renal PGs are the endothelial cells (66), medullary interstitial cells (127, 128), and papillary collecting duct cells (34).

VASOPRESSIN-PROSTAGLANDIN INTERACTIONS

Prostaglandins have been proposed to regulate the hydroosmotic effect of vasopressin (33, 89). Many studies examining the relationship of prostaglandins to vasopressin have utilized the toad bladder, a model of the mammalian collecting duct (125). Exogenous PGE_1 and PGE_2 cause a marked suppression of vasopressin-stimulated water flow (89, 111), while treatment of the bladders with cyclooxygenase inhibitors augment the action of vasopressin on water transport (125, 130). Vasopressin has been shown to stimulate the synthesis of PGE_2 by the isolated toad bladder (10, 130), but others have failed to demonstrate this stimulation (6, 29). Endogenous thromboxane synthesis by the toad bladder has been reported and proposed to be a possible mediator of vasopressin-stimulated water transport (10, 11). Thromboxane synthetase inhibitors blunt the hydroosmotic effect of vasopressin (11), while thromboxane analogs stimulate water flow (9).

Investigations with mammalian kidneys have shown that cyclooxygenase inhibitors augment—whereas PGE_2 suppresses—the vasopressin-induced increase in water transport in many species (27, 125). Vasopressin stimulates PGE_2 synthesis in medullary slices (13), medullary interstitial cells (127, 128), cortical collecting tubule cells (30, 53), and isolated perfused rabbit kidneys (124). However, the nonpressor antidiuretic analog of vasopressin, 1-desamino-8-D-arginine vasopressin (dD'AVP), failed to acutely stimulate PGE_2 synthesis from the isolated perfused rabbit kidneys (124), medullary interstitial cells (3, 25), or rat medullary slices (13). Moreover, the stimulation of PGE_2 synthesis in these systems by vasopressin was inhibited by the specific pressor antagonist d-cyclo-o-methyl-tyrosine-arginine vasopressin (13, 124). These findings suggest that vasopressin stimulation of renal PGs is related primarily to its pressor and not its antidiuretic activity.

On the other hand, the chronic administration of either vasopressin or dD'AVP causes enhanced urinary PGE_2 excretion in the intact rat (25, 113). Studies of diabetes insipidus in rats receiving chronic vasopressin or dD'AVP have shown that these agents cause increases in PG excretion in the urine that are correlated with increases in medullary cyclooxygenase activity (25).

ARACHIDONATE METABOLISM AND RENAL PATHOPHYSIOLOGY

Several models of renal disease [e.g. ureter obstruction (hydronephrosis) (72, 84), renal venous constriction (123), and glycerol-induced tubular necrosis (4)] exhibit markedly enhanced arachidonic acid metabolism by the kidney. Furthermore, the nature of the PGs released by the diseased kidney is dramatically changed (73). The isolated perfused normal rabbit kidney releases modest amounts of PGs and undetectable levels of thromboxane in response to the vasoactive peptides bradykinin and angiotensin II (73, 91). In contrast, the perfused rabbit hydronephrotic kidney exhibits augmented PGE_2 and PGI_2 production and a profound thromboxane release in response to these vasoactive peptides (73, 84, 91). The facilitated PG response to bradykinin and angiotensin of the isolated perfused kidneys increases with ex vivo perfusion time and appears to require new protein synthesis (72). Kidney slice experiments demonstrate that the enhanced arachidonic acid metabolism is predominantly localized in the cortex (17). Renal cortical (but not medullary) slices exhibit a time-dependent increase of prostaglandin synthesis that is dependent upon protein synthesis (17, 95). Microsomes isolated from the cortex of hydronephrotic kidneys produce predominantly PGE_2 and TxB_2, whereas microsomes from normal kidney cortex produce PGE_2 to a much lesser degree and form only a trace amount of TxB_2 (83, 119). Both cyclooxygenase and thromboxane synthetase activities increased 20- to 40-fold in cortical microsomes following 3 days of ureter obstruction (119). Surprisingly, PG endoperoxide E_2 isomerase activity was found to be very high in normal kidneys, despite low cyclooxygenase activity, and the isomerase activity was unchanged by ureter obstruction (119). Medullary cyclooxygenase activity increased 2- to 3-fold and thromboxane synthetase activity increased 15-fold following 3 days of ureter obstruction. Cortical and medullary microsomes from hydronephrotic kidneys convert arachidonate into equivalent amounts of PGE_2 and TxB_2. However, renal microsomes incubated in the presence of reduced glutathione produce 10-fold more PGE_2 than TxB_2 (119). Similarly, isolated perfused hydronephrotic kidneys release 10-fold more PGE_2 than TxB_2 (52), suggesting that the intact tissue is dominated by the PG endoperoxide E_2 isomerase and that reduced glutathione may be a key influence on the in vivo synthesis of PG in hydronephrosis. The finding that human hydronephrotic cortical tissue produces increased amounts of thromboxane and prostacyclin compared to normal cortical tissue compliments the studies of rabbit hydronephrotic kidneys (75). Recently, two other models of renal damage, renal venous occlusion (124) and glycerol-induced acute renal failure (4), have been shown to have a marked enhancement of renal PG synthesis and induction of thromboxane production. The finding that several models of renal damage have definite quantitative and qualitative alterations in the PG cascade reflects the importance of this pathway in renal pathophysiology.

The alterations in arachidonic acid metabolism that occur in response to ureter obstruction appear to influence renal function. Following ureter obstruction the rat kidney undergoes a reduction in blood flow and a reduced glomerular filtration rate that are restored to control levels by thromboxane synthetase inhibitors (120). The vascular resistance in perfused rabbit hydronephrotic kidneys appears to be controlled by a balance between the vasodilator PGs and the potent vasoconstrictor TxA_2 (52). The basal resistance in this rabbit model of hydronephrosis was dependent in part on endogenous vasodepressor PG biosynthesis, since indomethacin treatment increased basal perfusion pressure (84). Selective inhibition of thromboxane synthesis by OKY-1581 (sodium-3-[4-(3-pyridylmethyl)phenyl]-2-methylacrylate) revealed that endogenous TxA_2 constricts the renal vasculature of the hydronephrotic kidney (52). Release of ureter obstruction in man often results in postobstructive diuresis, and it has been suggested that this increase in urine output is associated with PG biosynthesis. Recently a model of postobstructive diuresis has been developed in the rabbit. The postobstructive diuresis observed in hydronephrotic rabbit kidneys is greatly reduced by indomethacin treatment (63).

The cellular sites and mechanism of increased PG biosynthesis induced by renal injury have been examined in detail in ureter-obstructed rabbit kidneys. The cellular candidates for the increase of PG production in hydronephrosis are inflammatory cells and fibroblasts that occur in the damaged cortex (79, 80). The demonstration of mononuclear cells in close contact with the cytoplasmic processes of the cortical fibroblasts may have profound implications in the progression of the histologic and metabolic changes involved in the renal injury (79, 80). It has been found that abolition of circulating blood monocytes by antimacrophage serum and steroids substantially delays the appearance of fibroblasts at sites of injury and suppresses the fibroblast proliferation rate (61). The macrophages also appear to actively modulate fibroblast PG biosynthesis. Several investigators have reported that conditioned media obtained from adherent mononuclear cell cultures contain a factor that is mitogenic for fibroblasts (62), and in several instances it has been correlated to a marked stimulation of PGE_2 biosynthesis by dermal fibroblasts (56), by gingival fibroblast-like cells (24), and by synovial cells (22, 23). The presence of a substantial number of macrophages in the damaged cortex of the hydronephrotic kidney introduces the possibility that these mononuclear cells themselves contribute to the arachidonic acid metabolites released by hydronephrotic kidney. Macrophages have been demonstrated to produce PGE_2, TxA_2, PGI_2 and a number of lipoxygenase products (42, 43, 58). Endotoxin has been demonstrated to stimulate PG and thromboxane biosynthesis by cultured peritoneal macrophages (35, 58). The involvement of macrophages in the increased PG synthesis induced by ureter obstruction is demonstrated by the finding that endotoxin stimulates PG and thromboxane release when injected into the perfused hydronephrotic kidney (85). Endotoxin has no effect on PG synthesis in normal kidneys (85). Furthermore, ureter obstruction of the cat kidney causes only a modest increase of PG synthesis and does not induce thromboxane production (85). Histologic examination of the hydronephrotic cat kidney reveals the presence of very few macrophages (85). Vasoactive peptides (20, 50) and endotoxin (50) stimulate PG synthesis in renal cultures derived from rabbit hydronephrotic cortex that contain fibroblasts and macrophages, whereas renal cell cultures derived from normal kidney cortex that contains only fibroblasts release only a slight amount of PGs in response to vasoactive peptides and do not respond to endotoxin.

Thus, ureter obstruction could cause an immunologic stimulus in the cortex that triggers a regional inflammatory response resulting in stimulation of the interstitial cell proliferation and a mononuclear invasion. The macrophages, which are in direct contact with the fibroblasts, are capable of releasing a factor that stimulates: (*a*) fibroblast proliferation; (*b*) cortical microsomal cyclooxygenase activity; and (*c*) PGE_2 release (i.e. intrinsic arachidonate metabolism).

Literature Cited

1. Aiken, J. W., Vane, J. R. 1973. Intrarenal prostaglandin release attenuates the renal vasoconstrictor activity of angiotensin. *J. Pharmacol. Exp. Ther.* 184:678–87
2. Baylis, C., Brenner, B. M. 1978. Modulation by prostaglandin synthesis inhibitors of the action of exogenous angiotensin II on glomerular ultrafiltration in the rat. *Circ. Res.* 43:889–98
3. Beck, T. R., Hassid, A., Dunn, M. J. 1980. The effect of arginine vasopressin and its analogs on the synthesis of prostaglandin E_2 by rat renal medullary interstitial cells in culture. *J. Pharmacol. Exp. Ther.* 215:15–19
4. Benabe, J. E., Klahr, S., Hoffman, M. H., Morrison, A. R. 1980. Production of thromboxane A_2 by the kidney in glycerol-induced acute renal failure. *Prostaglandins* 19:333–47
5. Benabe, J. E., Spry, L. A., Morrison, A. R. 1982. Effects of angiotensin II on phosphatidylinositol and polyphosphoinositide turnover in rat kidney: Mechanism of prostaglandin release. *J. Biol. Chem.* 257:7430–34
6. Bisordi, J., Schlondorff, D., Hays, R. 1980. Interaction of vasopressin and prostaglandins in the toad urinary bladder. *J. Clin. Invest.* 66:1200–10
7. Bolger, P. N., Eisner, G. M., Ramwell,

P. W., Slotkoff, L. M. 1976. Effect of prostaglandin synthesis on renal function and renin in the dog. *Nature* 259:244–45

8. Brenner, B. M., Schor, N. 1983. Studies of prostaglandin action on the glomerular microcirculation. In *Prostaglandins and the Kidney: Biochemistry, Physiology, Pharmacology, and Clinical Applications*, ed. M. J. Dunn, C. Patrono, G. A. Cinotti, 1:125–32. New York: Plenum. 414 pp.

9. Burch, R. M., Halushka, P. V. 1980. Thomboxane and stable prostaglandin endoperoxide analogs stimulate water permeability in the toad urinary bladder. *J. Clin. Invest.* 66:1251–57

10. Burch, R. M., Knapp, D. R., Halushka, P. V. 1979. Vasopressin stimulates thromboxane synthesis in the toad urinary bladder: Effects of imidazole. *J. Pharmacol. Exp. Ther.* 210:344–48

11. Burch, R. M., Knapp, D. R., Halushka, P. V. 1980. Vasopressin-stimulated water flow is decreased by thromboxane synthetase inhibition or antagonism. *Am. J. Physiol.* 239:F160–66

12. Cagen, L. M., Zusman, R. M., Pisano, J. J. 1979. Formation of 1a, 1b dihomo-prostaglandin E_2 by rabbit renal interstitial cell cultures. *Prostaglandins* 18:617–21

13. Campbell, H. T., Craven, P. A., DeRubertis, F. R. 1982. Evidence for independent actions of vasopressin on renal inner medullary cyclic AMP and prostaglandin E production: Relationship of the prostaglandin E response to hormone pressor activity. *Metabolism* 31:1035–41

14. Craven, P. A., Briggs, R., DeRubertis, F. R. 1980. Calcium-dependent action of osmolality on adenosine 3',5' monophosphate accumulation in rat renal inner medulla. Evidence for a relationship to calcium-responsive arachidonate release and prostaglandin synthesis. *J. Clin. Invest.* 65:524–42

15. Craven, P. A., Studer, R. K., DeRubertis, F. R. 1981. Renal inner medullary prostaglandin synthesis: A calcium-calmodulin–dependent process suppressed by urea. *J. Clin. Invest.* 68:722–32

16. Currie, M. G., Cole, B. R., DeSchryver-Kecskemeti, K., Holmberg, S., Needleman, P. 1983. Cell cultures of renal epithelium derived from rabbit microdissected cortical collecting tubules. *Am. J. Physiol.* 244:F724–28

17. Currie, M. G., Davis, B. B., Needleman, P. 1981. Localization of exaggerated prostaglandin synthesis associated with renal damage. *Prostaglandins* 22:933–44

18. Currie, M., Needleman, P. 1983. Sites of prostaglandin synthesis along the rabbit nephron. Submitted for publication

19. Data, J. L., Gerber, J. G., Crump, W. J., Frolich, J. C., Hollifield, J. W., Nies, A. S. 1978. The prostaglandin system: A role in canine baroreceptor control of renin release. *Circ. Res.* 42:454–58

20. Davis, B. B., Thomasson, D., Zenser, T. V. 1983. Renal disease profoundly alters cortical interstitial cell function. *Kidney Int.* 23:458–64

21. Davis, J. O., Freeman, R. H. 1976. Mechanisms regulating renin release. *Physiol. Rev.* 56:1–56

22. Dayer, J.-M., Passwell, J. H., Schneeberger, E. E., Krane, S. M. 1980. Interactions among rheumatoid synovial cells and monocyte-macrophages: production of collagenase-stimulating factor by human monocytes exposed to concanavalin A or immunoglobulin Fc fragments. *J. Immunol.* 124:1712–20

23. Dayer, J.-M., Robinson, D. R., Krane, S. M. 1977. Prostaglandin production by rheumatoid synovial cells. Stimulation by a factor from human mononuclear cells. *J. Exp. Med.* 145:1399–1404

24. D'Souza, S. M., Englis, D. J., Clark, A., Russell, R. G. 1981. Stimulation of production of prostaglandin E in gingival cells exposed to products of human blood mononuclear cells. *Biochem. J.* 198:391–96

25. Dunn, M. J., Beck, T. R., Kinter, L. B., Hassid, A. 1983. The effects of vasopressin and vasopressin analogues upon renal synthesis of prostaglandins. See Ref. 8, pp. 151–66

26. Dunn, M. J., Liard, J. F., Dray, F. 1978. Basal and stimulated rates of renal secretion and excretion of prostaglandins E_2, $F_{2\alpha}$, and 13-14-dihydro-15-keto F_α in the dog. *Kidney Int.* 13:136–43

27. Dunn, M. J., Hood, V. L. 1977. Prostaglandins and the kidney. *Am. J. Physiol.* 233:F169–84

28. Folkert, V. W., Schlondorff, D. 1977. Prostaglandin synthesis in isolated glomeruli. *Prostaglandins* 13:873–92

29. Forrest, J. N., Schneider, C. H., Goodman, D. B. 1982. Role of prostaglandin E_2 in mediating the effects of pH on the hydroosmotic response to vasopressin in the toad urinary bladder. *J. Clin. Invest.* 69:499–506

30. Garcia-Perez, A., Smith, W. L. 1983. Use of monoclonal antibodies to isolate cortical collecting tubule cells: AVP induces PGE release. *Am. J. Physiol.* 244:C211–20

31. Gerber, J. G., Branch, R. A., Nies, A. S., Gerkens, J. F., Shand, D. G., et al. 1978. Prostaglandins and renin release:

II. Assessment of renin secretion following infusion of PGI_2, E_2 and D_2 into the renal artery of anesthetized dogs. *Prostaglandins* 15:81–88

32. Gill, J. R. 1980. Bartter's Syndrome. *Ann. Rev. Med.* 31:405–19

33. Grantham, J., Orloff, J. 1968. Effect of prostaglandin E_1 on the permeability response of the isolated collecting tubule to vasopressin, adenosine 3', 5'-monophosphate, and theophyline. *J. Clin. Invest.* 47:1154–61

34. Grenier, F. C., Rollins, T. E., Smith, W. L. 1981. Kinin-induced prostaglandin synthesis by renal papillary collecting tubule cells in culture. *Am. J. Physiol.* 241:F94–104

35. Halushka, P. V., Cook, J. A., Wise, W. C. 1981. Thromboxane A_2 and prostacyclin production by lipopolysaccharide-stimulated peritoneal macrophages. *J. Reticuloendothelial Soc.* 30:445–50

36. Ham, E. A., Egan, R. W., Soderman, D. D., Gale, P. H., Kuehl, F. A. 1979. Peroxidase-dependent deactivation of prostacyclin synthetase. *J. Biol. Chem.* 254:2191–94

37. Hassid, A., Konieczkowski, M., Dunn, M. J. 1979. Prostaglandin synthesis in isolated rat kidney glomeruli. *Proc. Natl. Acad. Sci. USA* 76:1155–59

38. Henrich, W. L., Schrier, R. W., Berl, T. 1979. Mechanisms of renin secretion during hemorrhage in the dog. *J. Clin. Invest.* 64:1–7

39. Higashihara, E., Stokes, J. B., Kokko, J. P. 1979. Cortical and papillary micropuncture examination of chloride transport in segments of the rat kidney during inhibition of prostaglandin production: A possible role in the chloroeisis of acute volume expansion. *J. Clin. Invest.* 64:495–502

40. Holt, W. F., Lechene, C. 1981. ADH-PGE_2 interaction in cortical collecting tubule. I. Depression of sodium transport. *Am. J. Physiol.* 241:F452–60

41. Holt, W. F., Lechene, C. 1981. ADH-PGE_2 interactions in cortical collecting tubule. II. Inhibition of Ca and P reabsorption. *Am. J. Physiol.* 241:F461–67

42. Hsueh, W., Kuhn, C., Needleman, P. 1979. Relationship of prostaglandin secretion by rabbit alveolar macrophages to phagocytosis and lysosomal enzyme release. *Biochem. J.* 184:354–60

43. Humes, J. L., Sadowski, S., Galavage, M., Goldenberg, M., Subers, E., et al. 1982. Evidence for two sources of arachidonic acid for oxidative metabolism by mouse peritoneal macrophages. *J. Biol. Chem.* 257:1581–95

44. Iino, Y., Imai, M. 1978. Effects of prostaglandins on Na transport in isolated collecting tubules. *Pflügers Arch.* 373:125–32

45. Jackson, B. A., Edwards, R. M., Dousa, T. P. 1980. Vasopressin-prostaglandin interactions in isolated tubules from rat outer medulla. *J. Lab. Clin. Med.* 96:119–28

46. Jackson, E. K., Branch, R. A., Oates, J. A. 1982. Participation of prostaglandins in the control of renin release. *Adv. Prostagl. Thrombox. Res.* 10:255–76

47. Jackson, E. K., Herzer, W. A., Zimmerman, J. B., Branch, R. A., Oates, J. A., Gerkens, J. F. 1981. 6-keto-prostaglandin E_1 is more potent than prostaglandin I_2 as a renal vasodilator and renin secretagogue. *J. Pharmcol. Exp. Ther.* 216:24–27

48. Janszen, F. H., Nugteren, D. H. 1971. Histochemical localization of prostaglandin synthetase. *Histochemie* 27:159–64

49. Jim, K., Hassid, A., Sun, F., Dunn, M. J. 1982. Lipoxygenase activity in rat kidney glomeruli, glomerular epithelial cells and cortical tubules. *J. Biol. Chem.* 257:10244–49

50. Jonas, P. E., Leahy, K. M., DeSchryver, K., Needleman, P. 1983. Inflammatory cells and arachidonic acid metabolism in rabbit renal hydronephrosis. *Fed. Proc.* 42(3):348 (Abstr.)

51. Kaissling, B., Kriz, W. 1979. *Structural Analysis of the Rabbit Kidney*, pp. 1–123 Berlin: Springer-Verlag

52. Kawasaki, A., Needleman, P. 1982. Contribution of thromboxane to renal resistance changes in the isolated perfused hydronephrotic rabbit kidney. *Circ. Res.* 50:486–90

53. Kirschenbaum, M. A., Lowe, A. G., Trizna, W., Fine, L. G. 1982. Regulation of vasopressin action by prostaglandins. Evidence for prostaglandin synthesis in the rabbit cortical collecting tubule. *J. Clin. Invest.* 70:1193–1204

54. Knapp, H. R., Oelz, O., Roberts, L. J., Sweetman, B. J., Oates, J. A., Reed, P. W. 1977. Ionophores stimulate prostaglandin and thromboxane biosynthesis. *Proc. Natl. Acad. Sci. USA* 74:4251–55

55. Komai, K., Farger, S., Paulsrud, J. R. 1975. Analyses of renal medullary lipid droplets from normal, hydronephrotic, and indomethacin treated rabbits. *Lipids* 10:555–61

56. Korn, J. H., Halushka, P. V., LeRoy, E. C. 1980. Mononuclear cell modulation of connective tissue function. Suppression of fibroblast growth by stimulation of endogenous prostaglandin production. *J. Clin. Invest.* 65:543–54

57. Kreisberg, J. I., Kurnovsky, M. J.,

Levine, L. 1982. Prostaglandin production by homogeneous cultures of rat glomerular epithelial and mesangial cells. 1982. *Kidney Int.* 22:355–59

58. Kurland, J. I., Bockman, R. 1978. Prostaglandin E production by human blood monocytes and mouse peritoneal macrophages. *J. Exp. Med.* 147:952–56

59. Larsson, C., Anggard, E. 1973. Regional differences in the formation and metabolism of prostaglandins in the rabbit kidney. *Eur. J. Pharmacol.* 25:326–32

60. Larsson, C., Weber, P., Anggard, E. 1974. Arachidonic acid increases and indomethacin decreases plasma renin activity in the rabbit. *Eur. J. Pharmcol.* 28:391–94

61. Leibovich, S. J., Ross, R. 1975. The role of macrophage in wound repair. A study with hydrocortisone and antimacrophage serum. *Am. J. Pathol.* 78:71–91

62. Leibovich, S. J., Ross, R. 1976. A macrophage-dependent factor that stimulates the proliferation of fibroblasts *in vitro*. *Am. J. Pathol.* 84:501–13

63. Lips, D. L., Lefkowith, J., Needleman, P. 1983. Participation of arachidonic acid metabolites in postobstructive diuresis. *Fed. Proc.* 42(3):349 (Abstr.)

64. Lonigro, A. J., Hagemann, M. H., Stephenson, A. H., Fry, C. L. 1978. Inhibition of prostaglandin synthesis by indomethacin augments the renal vasodilator response to bradykinin in the anesthetized dog. *Circ. Res.* 43:447–55

65. Lonigro, A. J., Terragno, N. A., Malik, K. U., McGiff, J. C. 1973. Differential inhibition by prostaglandins of the renal action of pressor stimuli. *Prostaglandins* 3:595–606

66. McGiff, J. C. 1981. Prostaglandins, prostacyclin, and thromboxanes. *Ann. Rev. Pharmacol. Toxicol.* 21:479–509

67. McGiff, J. C., Crowshaw, K., Terragno, N. A., Lonigro, A. J. 1970. Release of a prostaglandin-like substance into renal venous blood in response to angiotensin II. *Circ. Res.* 27(Suppl. 1):121–30

68. McGiff, J. C., Itskovitz, H. D., Terragno, N. A. 1975. The actions of bradykinin and eledoisin in the canine isolated kidney: Relationships to prostaglandins. *Clin. Sci. Mol. Med.* 49:125–31

69. McGiff, J. C., Spokar, E. G., Wong, P. Y.-K. 1982. Stimulation of renin release by 6-oxo-prostaglandin E_1 prostacyclin. *Br. J. Pharmacol.* 75:137–44

70. McGiff, J. C., Terragno, N. A., Malik, K. U., Lonigro, A. J. 1972. Release of a prostaglandin E-like substance from canine kidney by bradykinin. *Circ. Res.* 31:36–43

71. Moncada, S., Gryglewski, R. J., Bunting, S., Vane, J. R. 1976. A lipid peroxide inhibits the enzyme in blood vessel microsomes that generates from prostacyclin endoperoxides the substance (prostaglandin X) which prevents platelet aggregation. *Prostaglandins* 12:715–37

72. Morrison, A. R., Moritz, H., Needleman, P. 1978. Mechanisms of enhanced renal prostaglandin biosynthesis in ureter obstruction: Role of *de novo* protein synthesis. *J. Biol. Chem.* 253:8210–12

73. Morrison, A. R., Nishikawa, K., Needleman, P. 1977. Unmasking of thromboxane A_2 synthesis by ureter obstruction in the rabbit kidney. *Nature* 269:259–60

74. Morrison, A. R., Pascoe, N. 1981. Metabolism of arachidonate through NADPH-dependent oxygenase of renal cortex. *Proc. Natl. Acad. Sci. USA* 78:7373–78

75. Morrison, A. R., Thornton, F., Blumberg, A., Vaughan, E. D. 1981. Thromboxane A_2 is the major arachidonic acid metabolite of human cortical hydronephrotic tissue. *Prostaglandins* 21:417–81

76. Morrison, A. R., Winokur, T. S., Brown, W. A. 1982. Inhibition of soybean lipoxygenase by mannitol. *Biochem. Biophys. Res. Commun.* 108:1757–62

77. Mullane, K. N., Moncada, S. 1980. Prostacyclin release and the modulation of some vasoactive hormones. *Prostaglandins* 20:25–49

78. Mullane, K. N., Moncada, S., Vane, J. R. 1980. Prostacyclin release induced by bradykinin may contribute to the antihypertensive action of angiotensin-converting enzyme inhibitors. *Adv. Prostagl. Thrombox. Res.* 8:1159–61

79. Nagle, R. B., Bulger, R. E., Cutter, R. E., Jervis, H. R., Benditt, E. P. 1973. Unilateral obstructive nephropathy in the rabbit. I. Early morphologic, physiologic, and histochemical changes. *Lab. Invest.* 28:456–67

80. Nagle, R. B., Johnson, M. E., Jervis, H. R. 1976. Proliferation of renal interstitial cells following injury induced by ureteral obstruction. *Lab. Invest.* 35:18–22

81. Nasjletti, A., Malik, K. V. 1981. The renal kallikrein-kinin and prostaglandin systems interaction. *Ann. Rev. Physiol.* 43:597–609

82. Needleman, P., Kauffman, A. H., Douglas, J. R., Johnson, E. M., Marshall, G. R. 1973. Specific stimulation and inhibition of renal prostaglandin release by angiotensin analogs. *Am. J. Physiol.* 224:1415–19

83. Needleman, P., Wyche, A., Bronson, S. D., Holmberg, S., Morrison, A. R.

1979. Specific regulation of peptide-induced renal prostaglandin synthesis. *J. Biol. Chem.* 254:9772–77

84. Nishikawa, K., Morrison, A. R., Needleman, P. 1977. Exaggerated prostaglandin biosynthesis and its influence on renal resistance in the isolated hydronephrotic rabbit kidney. *J. Clin. Invest.* 59:1143–50

85. Okegawa, T., Jonas, P. E., DeSchryver, K., Kawasaki, A., Needleman, P. 1983. Metabolic and cellular alterations underlying the exaggerated renal prostaglandins and thromboxane synthesis in ureter obstruction in rabbits. Inflammatory response involving fibroblasts and mononuclear cells. *J. Clin. Invest.* 71:81–90

86. Oliw, E. H., Lawson, J. A., Brash, A. R., Oates, J. A. 1981. Arachidonic acid metabolism in rabbit renal cortex. *J. Biol. Chem.* 256:9924–31

87. Oliw, E. H., Oates, J. A. 1981. Rabbit renal cortical microsomes metabolize arachidonic acid to trihydroxyeicosatrienoic acids. *Prostaglandins* 22:863–71

88. Olson, R. D., Skoglund, M. L., Nies, A. S., Gerber, J. G. 1980. Prostaglandins mediate the macula densa stimulated renin release. *Adv. Prostagl. Thrombox. Res.* 8:1135–37

89. Orloff, J., Handler, J. S., Bergstrom, S. 1965. Effect of prostaglandin (PGE_1) on the permeability of response of toad bladder to vasopressin, theophylline, and adenosine 3′,5′-monophosphate. *Nature* 205:397–98

90. Petrulis, A. S., Maramichi, A., Dunn, M. J. 1981. Prostaglandin and thromboxane synthesis by rat glomerular epithelial cells. *Kidney Int.* 20:469–74

91. Reingold, D. F., Waters, K., Holmberg, S., Needleman, P. 1981. Differential biosynthesis of prostaglandins by hydronephrotic rabbit and cat kidneys. *J. Pharmacol. Exp. Ther.* 216:510–15

92. Sakr, H., Dunham, E. W. 1982. Mechanism of arachidonic acid-induced vasoconstriction in the intact rat kidney: Possible involvement of thromboxane A_2. *J. Pharmacol. Exp. Ther.* 221:614–22

93. Schlondorff, D., Roczniak, S., Satriano, J. A., Folkert, V. W. 1980. Prostaglandin synthesis by isolated rat glomeruli: effect of angiotensin II. *Am. J. Physiol.* 238:F486–95

94. Schlondorff, D., Zanger, R., Satriano, A., Folkert, V. W., Eveloff, J. 1982. Prostaglandin synthesis by isolated cells from the outer medulla and from the thick ascending loop of Henle of rabbit kidney. *J. Pharmacol. Exp. Ther.* 223:120–24

95. Schwartzman, M., Raz, A. 1981. Selective induction of *de novo* prostaglandin biosynthesis in rabbit kidney cortex. *Biochim. Biophys. Acta* 664:469–74

96. Seymour, A. A., Davis, J. O., Freeman, R. H., DeForrest, J. M., Rowe, B. P., Williams, G. M. 1979. Renin release from filtering and nonfiltering kidneys stimulated by PGI_2 and PGD_2. *Am. J. Physiol.* 237:F285–90

97. Smith, W. L., Bell, T. G. 1978. Immunohistochemical localization of the prostaglandin-forming cyclooxygenase in renal cortex. *Am. J. Physiol.* 235:F451–57

98. Smith, W. L., Bell, T. G., Needleman, P. 1979. Increased renal tubular synthesis of prostaglandins in the rabbit kidney in response to ureteral obstruction. *Prostaglandins* 18:269–77

99. Smith, W. L., Wilkin, G. G. 1977. Immunochemistry of prostaglandin endoperoxide-forming cyclooxygenases: the detection of the cyclooxygenases in rat, rabbit, and guinea pig kidneys by immunofluorescence. *Prostaglandins* 13:873–92

100. Sprecher, H., Van Rollins, M., Wyche, A., Needleman, P. 1982. Dihomoprostaglandins and -thromboxane: a prostaglandin family from adrenic acid that may be preferentially synthesized in the kidney. *J. Biol. Chem.* 257:3912–18

101. Sraer, J., Ardaillou, N., Sraer, J. D., Ardaillou, R. 1982. *In vitro* prostaglandin synthesis by human glomeruli and papillae. *Prostaglandins* 23:855–64

102. Sraer, J., Siess, W., Dray, F., Ardaillou, R. 1983. Regional differences in *in vitro* prostaglandin synthesis by the rat kidney. See Ref. 8, pp. 41–52

103. Sraer, J., Foidart, J., Chansel, D., Mahieu, P., Kouznetzova, B., et al. 1979. Prostaglandin synthesis by mesangial and epithelial glomerular cultured cells. *FEBS Letters* 104:420–24

104. Sraer, J., Riguad, M., Bens, M., Rabinovitch, H., Ardaillou, R. 1983. Metabolism of arachidonic acid via the lipoxygenase pathway in human and murine glomeruli. *J. Biol. Chem.* 258:4325–30

105. Sraer, J., Sraer, J. D., Chansel, D., Russo-Marie, F., Kouznetzova, B. et al. 1979. Prostaglandin synthesis by isolated rat renal glomeruli. *Mol. Cell. Endocrinol.* 16:29–37

106. Stokes, J. B. 1979. Effect of prostaglandin E_2 on chloride transport across the rabbit thick ascending limb of Henle. *J. Clin. Invest.* 64:495–502

107. Stokes, J. B., Kokko, J. P. 1977. Inhibition of sodium transport by prostaglandin E_2 across the isolated, perfused rabbit

collecting tubule. *J. Clin. Invest.* 59: 1099–1104

108. Suric, H., Nasjletti, A., Malik, K. 1981. Inhibition by bradykinin of the vascular action of angiotensin II in the dog kidney. *J. Pharmacol. Exp. Ther.* 218:103–7

109. Torikai, S., Kurokawa, K. 1981. Distribution of prostaglandin E_2-sensitive adenylate cyclase along the rat nephron. *Prostaglandins* 21:427–38

110. Turk, J., Wyche, A., Needleman, P. 1980. Inactivation of vascular prostacyclin synthetase by platelet lipoxygenase products. *Biochem. Biophys. Res. Commun.* 95:1628–34

111. Urakabe, S. Y., Takamimtsu, Y., Shirai, D., Yuasa, S., Kimura, G., Orita, Y., Abe, H. 1975. Effects of different prostaglandins on permeability of toad urinary bladder. *Comp. Biochem. Physiol.* C52:1–4

112. Vahouny, G. V., Hodges, V. A., Treadwell, C. R. 1979. Essential fatty acid deficiency and adrenal cortical function. *J. Lipid Res.* 20:154–61

113. Walker, L. A., Frolich, J. C. 1980. Dose-dependent stimulation of renal prostaglandin synthesis by deamino-8-D-arginine vasopressin in rats with hereditary diabetes insipidus. *J. Pharmacol. Exp. Ther.* 217:87–91

114. Weber, P., Holzgreve, H., Stephan, R., Herbst, R. 1975. Plasma renin activity and renal sodium and water excretion following infusion of arachidonic acid in rats. *Eur. J. Pharmacol.* 34:299–304

115. Whorton, A. R., Lazar, J. D., Smigel, M. D., Oates, J. A. 1980. Prostaglandin-mediated renin release from renal cortical slices. *Adv. Prostagl. Thrombox. Res.* 8:1123–29

116. Whorton, A. R., Misono, K., Hollifield, J., Frolich, J. C., Inagami, T., Oates, J. A. 1977. Prostaglandins and renin release: I. Stimulation of renin release from rabbit renal cortical slices by PGI_2. *Prostaglandins* 14:1095–1104

117. Winokur, T. S., Morrison, A. R. 1981. Regional synthesis of monohydroxy eicosanoids by the kidney. *J. Biol. Chem.* 256:10221–23

118. Wong, P. Y.-K., Malik, K. U., Desiderio, D. M., McGiff, J. C., Sun, F. F. 1980. Hepatic metabolism of prostacyclin (PGI_2) in the rabbit: Formation of a potent novel inhibitor of platelet aggregation. *Biochem. Biophys. Res. Commun.* 93:486–94

119. Wu, Y. S., Lysz, T. A., Wyche, A., Needleman, P. 1983. Kinetic comparison and regulation of the cascade of microsomal enzymes involved in renal arachidonate and endoperoxide metabolism. *J. Biol. Chem.* 258:2188–92

120. Yarger, W. E., Schocken, D. D., Harris, R. H. 1980. Obstructive nephropathy in the rat. Possible roles for the renin-angiotensin system, prostaglandins, and thromboxanes in postobstructive renal function. *J. Clin. Invest.* 65:400–12

121. Zenser, T. V., Davis, B. B. Effects of calcium on prostaglandin E_2 synthesis by rat inner medullary slices. *Am. J. Physiol.* 4:F213–18

122. Zenser, T. V., Herman, C. A., Davis, B. B. 1980. Effects of calcium and A-23187 on renal inner medullary prostaglandin E_2 synthesis. *Am. J. Physiol.* 238:E371–76

123. Zipser, R., Myers, S., Needleman, P. 1980. Exaggerated prostaglandin and thromboxane synthesis in the rabbit with renal vein constriction. *Circ. Res.* 47:231–37

124. Zipser, R. D., Myers, S. I., Needleman, P. 1981. Stimulation of renal prostaglandin synthesis by the pressor activity of vasopressin. *Endocrinology* 108:495–99

125. Zusman, R. M. 1981. Prostaglandins and water excretion. *Ann. Rev. Med.* 32:359–74

126. Zusman, R. M., Brown, C. A. 1980. The role of phospholipase in the regulation of prostaglandin E_2 biosynthesis by rabbit renomedullary interstitial cells in tissue culture: effects of angiotensin II, potassium, hyperosmolality, dexamethasone, and protein synthesis inhibition. *Adv. Prostagl. Thrombox. Res.* 8:243–48

127. Zusman, R. M., Keiser, H. R. 1977. Prostaglandin biosynthesis by rabbit renomedullary interstitial cells in tissue culture: stimulation by angiotensin II, bradykinin, and arginine vasopressin. *J. Clin. Invest.* 60:215–23

128. Zusman, R. M., Keiser, H. R. 1977. Prostaglandin E_2 biosynthesis by rabbit renomedullary interstitial cells in tissue culture: mechanism of stimulation by angiotensin II, bradykinin, and arginine vasopressin. *J. Biol. Chem.* 252:2069–71

129. Zusman, R. M., Keiser, H. R. 1930. Regulation of prostaglandin E_2 synthesis by angiotensin II, potassium, osmolality, and dexamethasone. *Kidney Int.* 17:277–83

130. Zusman, R. M., Keiser, H. R., Handler, J. S. 1977. Vasopressin stimulated prostaglandin E_2 biosynthesis in the toad urinary bladder. *J. Clin. Invest.* 60:1339–47

Ann. Rev. Physiol. 1984. 46:343–58

NATRIURETIC HORMONE

Vardaman M. Buckalew, Jr. and Kenneth A. Gruber

Departments of Medicine and Physiology and Pharmacology, Bowman Gray School of Medicine of Wake Forest University, Winston-Salem, North Carolina 27103

INTRODUCTION

It is well established that expansion of the extracellular fluid volume (ECFV) leads to increased renal sodium excretion, independent of any changes in glomerular filtration rate (GFR) or aldosterone secretion (82). Despite intense investigation, the mediators of volume-expansion natriuresis have not been fully elucidated. Considerable evidence indicates that volume expansion causes release of a humoral natriuretic factor or factors that is therefore referred to as "natriuretic hormone" or "NH" (8). In this article we review recent developments in the characterization of this putative hormone.

Since the biochemical structure of NH is not known, published reports necessarily deal with biologic activities. There is no assurance that the various activities described are caused by the same substance, and there is no standardized assay that all investigators would agree is the best for demonstrating NH. Despite this difficulty, there is general agreement among workers in the field that plasma volume expansion somehow releases a low-molecular-weight factor (or factors) that causes its biologic effects, at least in part, by inhibiting Na,K-ATPase. In this review we discuss NH as though it were a single, homogeneous entity—with the full realization that proof of that assumption is not yet available. We will confine our remarks to that humoral factor that seems to be associated with ECFV expansion. The recently described atrial natriuretic factor (ANF) (18) has not been shown to circulate in plasma, appears to be distinctly different from NH, and is not considered in this review.

343

0066-4278/84/0315-0343$02.00

CHARACTERIZATION OF NH
AS SUGGESTED BY VARIOUS BIOASSAYS

Natriuresis

A volume-related humoral-natriuretic factor has been demonstrated in three ways (8). First, blood from volume-expanded donor animals cross-circulated to either recipient animals or isolated kidneys has been shown to cause natriuresis in the recipient. Second, blood or urine extracts from volume-expanded subjects has been shown to cause natriuresis in assay animals, usually rats. Third, extracts of kidney tissue removed from volume-expanded rats causes natriuresis in assay rats. Cross-circulation studies by themselves do not determine whether volume expansion causes donor animals to suppress secretion of an antinatriuretic factor or increase secretion of a natriuretic factor. However, plasma and urine extracts from volume-expanded subjects clearly contain a transferable natriuretic principle that is either undetectable or less active in extracts from nonexpanded control subjects.

Cross-circulation experiments show that natriuresis in the recipient animals begins almost immediately following a brief period of expansion of the donor, but requires 1 hour to reach maximum effect (70). Some studies of bolus injections of plasma, urine, or tissue extracts into assay rats are in accord with this observation (33, 78). These studies show an almost immediate increase in sodium excretion, peaking 1–2 hours after the extract injection and followed by a slow dissipation of activity. Other investigators show natriuresis beginning immediately, peaking 30 minutes later but showing effects lasting more than two hours after injection (11). This difference in pattern of natriuresis could be due to differences in assay preparation. However, several groups have reported assays of plasma and urine extracts from volume-expanded subjects in which the onset of natriuresis begins about 20 minutes after extract injection, with a peak effect occuring 2–3 hours after injection (8). Preliminary studies using ultrafiltration and chromatography techniques suggest that the factor with delayed onset has a higher molecular weight than the factor with more rapid onset of action, leading to the hypothesis that the former may be a precursor of the latter (8). The finding that NH activity increased when plasma was incubated for 30 minutes at room temperature (34) supports the presence of a NH precursor.

The prolonged natriuretic effect of NH after a bolus injection suggests either that the factor has a long plasma half-life, or that the biologic half-life is longer than the plasma half-life. Cross-circulation experiments (70) showed a biologic half-life of NH of about 30 minutes, although dissipation of the effect appeared to follow an exponential curve, suggesting that return to baseline sodium excretion would have required several hours. Interestingly, these studies also showed that re-exposure of the donor kidney to NH one hour after interruption of the cross circulation resulted in a more rapid response than was seen on initial exposure. Although a short exposure of toad bladder (10) and isolated tubules (27) to NH shows a rapid return of sodium transport to baseline following washout of the factor, other studies in which anuran membranes are exposed to NH for 60 minutes or more show a more prolonged recovery phase, and do not always show complete return to baseline sodium transport (25, 54).

In light of these observations, and in view of the fact that NH may be an endogenous digitalis-like substance (see below), it is interesting to note the pattern of recovery from the antinatriferic effect of ouabain on toad bladder. Crabbe et al (15) showed that when $5 \times 10^{-5}M$ ouabain was removed after 2 hours of incubation, short-circuit current returned gradually toward baseline, requiring 1–2 hours for complete recovery.

The issue of biologic half-life vs plasma half-life is important in interpretation of studies attempting to correlate biologic effects with blood levels. In addition, multiple bioassays of NH performed sequentially in the same animal or tissue could be misinterpreted if the tissue were "sensitized" somehow to the factor by an initial exposure.

Some of the variability in response of assay rats to the natriuretic effect of NH may be due to interactions between NH and intrarenal factors. Fine et al (28) showed that intrarenal NH injections caused more natriuresis in denervated than intact kidneys. Since baseline sodium excretion was higher in denervated kidneys than in normals, and since the sympathetic nervous system has been shown to increase proximal sodium reabsorption (21), it can be inferred that distal delivery of sodium was enhanced in denervated kidneys. These studies suggest that NH has its primary effect on distal sodium reabsorption and that the magnitude of NH natriuresis is a function of the rate of distal sodium delivery. This may explain why most investigators have found that hydrated rats provide a better assay for NH than hydropenic rats.

Fine et al (28) also showed that NH response was enhanced in uremic rats, perhaps due to a true end-organ hypersensitivity. The mechanism of this effect is not clear and may be the opposite of what one would expect if NH levels are elevated in uremia (28). In fact, the studies of Favre et al (26) suggest that increased basal levels of NH lead to decreased renal response to the factor. In their studies, the percentage increase in response to NH was an inverse function of the salt intake of assay rats. Of particular interest was the fact that assay rats on a high-salt diet (6.55 mEq/day in 170-gm rats or about 38 mEq/day/kg) had no response to NH, despite a basal sodium excretion similar to rats on 3.55 mEq/day sodium intake. Although a very high-salt diet did reduce the absolute response of the kidney to NH, increases in sodium intake within the physiologic range increased absolute sodium excretion in response to NH as a direct function of basal sodium excretion.

Intrarenal natriuretic hormones may play a role in regulating the natriuretic response of the kidney to extrarenal factors. Rudd et al (79) reported that prostaglandin (PG) inhibition with indomethacin and naproxen eliminated the renal response to NH. The response to NH could be restored by a continuous infusion of a subnatriuretic dose of PGE_2. These studies suggest that the renal response to volume expansion is due to a synergism between intrarenal PGs and NH. The effect of PG blockade to prevent inhibition of collecting-duct sodium reabsorption in acutely volume-expanded rats (89) may be due to decreased sensitivity of the kidney to NH.

Na,K-ATPase Inhibition

The earliest observations on NH indicated it had "antinatriferic" activity, meaning it inhibited sodium transport in anuran membrane (8). This suggested that NH caused natriuresis by inhibiting distal sodium transport. The inhibitory effect of NH on transtubular potential difference and lumen-to-bath sodium flux of isolated rabbit collecting tubule is in accord with this hypothesis (27).

Gonick et al (32, 46) were the first to suggest that the natriuretic effect of NH might be due to inhibition of renal Na,K-ATPase. A surge of interest in this hypothesis and its possible consequences has recently occurred.

Gruber et al (38) found that plasma of dogs fractionated on HPLC showed two peaks of Na,K-ATPase–inhibitory activity using isolated hog-brain enzyme. In addition, these investigators found that a factor or factors in these same peaks cross-reacted with antidigoxin antibodies, suggesting not only that NH is an inhibitor of Na,K-ATPase, but that it is an endogenous digoxin-like compound, or "endoxin." There was significantly more Na,K-ATPase inhibition and digoxin immunoreactivity in plasma of volume-expanded dogs compared to hydropenic dogs. It seems likely from these studies that NH levels can be quantitatively assayed using a digoxin RIA.

Similar results have recently been reported by Klingmüller et al (51), who found that urine of salt-loaded human subjects fractionated on Sephadex G25 showed one peak of digoxin-like immunoreactivity that coincided with a peak of natriuretic activity. In addition, immunoprecipitation of urine with antidigoxin antibodies achieved a ten-fold increase in natriuretic activity of their Sephadex fraction. Endogenous digoxin immunoreactivity has also been reported by Godfraind et al (31).

Additional evidence that NH is a Na,K-ATPase inhibitor derives from studies of plasma Na,K-ATPase–inhibitory activity. DeWardener et al (19) studied the effect of high- and low-salt diets on the ability of plasma to inhibit guinea-pig renal Na,K-ATPase, as assayed by a cytochemical assay. Circulating inhibitory activity was approximately 25-fold greater in plasma of subjects on a high-salt than on a low-salt intake. Poston et al (75) found that the natriuretic Sephadex G25 fraction (FIV) of urine from humans following an acute saline infusion caused inhibition of both ouabain-sensitive and ouabain-resistant sodium efflux from human peripheral blood leukocytes. This same urine fraction, as well as plasma from subjects undergoing "escape" from the antinatriuretic effect of mineralocorticoid excess, also inhibited leukocyte sodium efflux. Another suggestion that NH may be digitalis-like was reported by Bohan et al (4). They showed displacement of ^{3}H-ouabain binding to renal Na,K-ATPase by natriuretic extracts of urine from uremic dogs. The displacement curve paralleled that of cold ouabain.

These studies all support the hypothesis that NH is a digitalis-like substance that inhibits Na,K-ATPase in numerous tissues, including kidney. At the very least, these observations provide new and potentially more quantitative ways to assay for NH than had previously been reported. It remains to be determined whether the natriuretic effect of NH is due to inhibition of renal Na,K-ATPase. Ouabain causes natriuresis, apparently by inhibiting Na,K-ATPase in the thick ascending loop of Henle and distal tubule (60). However, renal Na,K-ATPase inhibition could not be demonstrated following acute or chronic salt loading in rats (49).

Considerable interest has developed in the possibility that NH inhibition of Na,K-ATPase in tissues outside the kidney may lead to disease processes. Most exciting is the possibility that NH may be a pressor factor and play a role in the pathophysiology of essential hypertension, discussed in detail below.

BIOCHEMICAL NATURE OF NH

The earliest attempts to define the chemical structure of NH were by Cort and his collaborators. They eliminated catecholamines, steroids, or angiotensin II as possible candidates for NH and demonstrated that structural analogs of oxytocin were able to block natriuretic effects attributable to NH (13). The first direct evidence supporting a peptidic nature for NH was presented by Cort et al, who showed that the natriuretic and antinatriferic activity present in the blood of cats after carotid artery occlusion was abolished by trypsin or chymotrypsin digestion (14).

The use of chromatographic resins, such as Sephadex (5) or Biogel (6), or molecular-size filtration techniques (9) suggest that the natriuretic/antinatriferic activity observed by most investigators was of low molecular weight ($\sim$1000). It is interesting to note that all reports of the chromatographic separtation of NH on Biogel or Sephadex have shown that it elutes in a postsalt peak (conventionally called "fraction IV" by most investigators). This would indicate that it is not being separated on these columns by a true molecular sieve action, but is retained by nonspecific binding. In support of this latter concept author Buckalew demonstrated that 1M acetic acid gave a more consistent recovery of biological activity from Biogel P-2 columns than 0.1M acetic acid (6).

Further evidence for the peptidic nature of NH was provided by authors Gruber & Buckalew (35), who demonstrated that NH isolated by high-performance liquid chromatography (HPLC) was sensitive to trypsin digestion. The chromatographic technique used by these investigators (HPLC on Partisil SCX) also supported the concept that they were isolating a peptide, since the procedure used was first developed for small peptides (76). Other groups have demonstrated enzymatic degradation of biologic activity, suggesting NH is a peptide (8). However, Licht et al do not believe the natriuretic factor they isolated from urine of salt-loaded dogs is a peptide (56), nor does deWardener (personal communication).

The apparent cross-reactivity between NH and antidigoxin antibodies (38) suggests that NH might have a three-dimensional structure with some similarities to cardiac glycosides. NH does not appear to be a steroid because it is separated in aqueous solutions and appears susceptible to acid hydrolysis (39). However, nonpeptide cardiac glycoside-like substances have recently been reported in extracts of mammalian brain (29, 45). The initial reports of this substance (or substances) demonstrated its ability to inhibit isolated Na,K-ATPase and to displace ouabain from its binding site (29, 45). The resistance of this substance to acid hydrolysis indicates it is not a peptide. Subsequent work by Whitmer et al (88) and Kracke (53) have pointed out potential artifacts in the isolation of "ouabain-like" activity from brain tissue. No one has yet demonstrated that the levels of these brain-derived factor(s) can be physiologically manipulated, e.g. by ECFV expansion. Until this is established their relationship to NH is in serious question.

In previous years several classes of brain peptides have been proposed and subsequently rejected as candidates for NH. In the late 1960s Cort et al (13) proposed that an oxytocin analog might be NH. Though both vasopressin and oxytocin are natriuretic, their physiological regulation and in vitro effects on frog-skin sodium transport are the opposite of that which would be expected for a NH. Extending the amino acid sequence of oxytocin at the N-terminal prolonged in vivo activity (13). However, no neurohypophyseal analog has ever had the in vivo and in vitro properties attributed to NH.

Another peptide that has been suggested to function as a physiological natriuretic agent is α melanocyte stimulating hormone (αMSH). Orias & McCann first demonstrated the natriuretic effect of αMSH in rats (65). The stimulus for these studies was the finding of histological changes in the pars intermedia of rats after ingestion of hypertonic saline (23). Orias (64) and Kastin (48) showed that injection or ingestion of hypertonic saline solutions caused a depletion of pituitary αMSH. Sedlakova et al (83) have shown that significant amounts of the natriuretic activity in bovine posterior pituitary is due to αMSH or a related peptide, ACTH[1-13]. One of the problems with consideration of αMSH as a candidate for NH is that under some conditions it can manifest a kaliuretic effect (65), an action never seen with NH extracts from volume-expanded animals (78). In addition, it cannot inhibit active sodium transport systems such as toad bladders or red blood cells. Unlike the previously discussed work on oxytocin, there had been no attempt to ascertain if a small fragment of αMSH might be the source of its natriuretic activity and might possibly be a sodium transport inhibitor in vitro.

We have investigated the possibility that a fragment of ACTH or αMSH might have natriuretic, Na,K ATP-ase–inhibitory, and pressor (i.e. natriuretic hormone-like) activities. There is considerable evidence that chronic infusion of ACTH can induce a hypertensive state (30), though the mechanism of action has yet to be determined (57). An effect on steroidogenesis appears to have been ruled out. In addition, ACTH is natriuretic, kaliuretic, and antidiuretic. When the renal effects of αMSH and acetylated ACTH[1-13] fragments are considered, the antidiuretic effect is lost while the kaliuretic effect may be reduced (65, 69). We therefore postulated that a more "pure" natriuretic peptide might be found in a fragment of αMSH, and that ACTH-induced hypertension might be due to an ACTH fragment. Our choice of which fragment of ACTH to investigate first was suggested by a series of papers by Novales (63) on the mechanism of action of αMSH on melanocytes. He determined the optimal ionic requirements for MSH actions and found that an elevated intracellular sodium was probably required for MSH effects. Studies with metabolic blockers showed that these MSH effects were energy-dependent. He concluded that one possible mechanism of action of αMSH would be the inhibition of an ATP-dependent sodium-extrusion pump. It should be noted that this hypothesis was presented in the very early stages of work demonstrating a specific Na,K-ATPase. Though later work on the mechanism of action of αMSH indicated that it might work through an adenyl cyclase mechanism, the synthesis of super MSH agonists, which cause relatively small increases in cAMP production (80), call into question whether this is the only mechanism of MSH action.

Since the common sequence of amino acids shared by MSH and some of its analogues and ACTH is ACTH/αMSH[4-10] (Met-Glu-His-Phe-Arg-Trp-Gly) we decided to test this peptide in appropriate assays. In preliminary studies we have shown that this peptide inhibits Na,K-ATPase, is natriuretic at low doses, and is hypertensive at higher doses (36). The hypertensive mechanism of action appears to be activation of the sympathetic nervous system, since the pressor effects can be blocked by α-receptor antagonists and the cardio-accelerator effects can be eliminated by β-receptor blockade (50).

The existence of a peptide sequence that inhibits Na,K-ATPase and can function as both a natriuretic and hypertensive substance suggests that the structure of NH may be related to ACTH[4-10] or the related peptide sequence γ_1 MSH[3-9] (Met-Gly-His-Phe-Arg-Trp-Asp). None of the peptides tested thus far were able to displace ^{125}I-digoxin from binding to a specific antibody; nevertheless, they represent the first described class of Na,K ATP-ase–inhibitory peptides with in vitro actions similar to those described for NH.

NH AND VOLUME REGULATION

The role played by NH in the renal response to volume expansion is unclear. Volume-expansion natriuresis is mediated by a complex interaction of many factors, including changes in peritubular Starling forces and alterations in the sympathetic nervous system, the renin-angiotensin aldosterone system, and possibly intrarenal prostaglandins (82).

A possible approach to determining the physiologic contribution of NH to volume regulation would be to examine the response of a model in which NH was deficient. Rats with lesions of the anteroventral third ventricle (AV3V) area showed no release of NH and a reduced ability to excrete sodium following an acute saline infusion (1). However, under basal conditions these rats did not develop edema. This suggests that NH may be necessary for a maximal response to acute volume expansion, but is not critical for the day-to-day regulation of sodium balance, at least under basal conditions of a fixed sodium intake. A similar conclusion is suggested by the studies of Naccarato et al in patients with early cirrhosis of the liver (62). None of these patients had edema or ascites; however, when they were subjected to acute saline loading, marked impairment in sodium excretion was observed and NH was virtually absent from urine.

On the other hand, Buckalew & Lancaster (9) reported evidence that NH played a role in the day-to-day oscillations of sodium excretion in normal dogs on a constant sodium intake. Species variation might explain these apparent discrepancies. It is also possible that plasma NH levels under basal conditions are too low to be detected by the methods used in these studies. This problem needs further investigation when better assays are available.

The quantitative differences between sodium excretion in the AV3V-lesioned animal vs the normal controls is of interest. At maximum response after saline loading equal to 10% body weight, AV3V-lesioned rats excreted only 18% of the load vs 56% in normals. This suggests that about 68% of the response to acute saline loading in the rat is due to NH.

NH AND HYPERTENSION

There is considerable epidemiologic and experimental evidence linking salt ingestion to the pathophysiology of hypertension (40). Recent developments suggest that NH may be involved in the mechanism of the effect of salt on blood pressure regulation.

In retrospect, Dahl et al were the first to suggest this possibility (17). They developed two strains of rats with differing sensitivities to the effect of salt on blood pressure. The sensitive (or S) strain became hypertensive on a high-salt diet while the resistant (or R) strain did not. When the two strains were joined with a parabiotic connection, hypertension could be transferred from the S to the R strain. Since hypertension was clearly induced by salt ingestion, and since the sensitivity to salt was related to some abnormality in kidney function (16), Dahl et al suggested that the hypertension might be caused by a salt-excreting hormone with pressor activity (17). This remarkable suggestion was made before most of the work on NH summarized above was published; it was largely ignored by NH investigators until very recently.

The first suggestion that Na,K-ATPase inhibition by a humoral factor might play an important role in the pathogenesis of hypertension was by Haddy & Overbeck (42). Overbeck et al (68) found a depressed ouabain-sensitive sodium-potassium pump in blood vessels from renal hypertensive dogs, and these investigators proposed that the alterations observed were the result of a circulating factor. They later suggested this unknown factor might be NH (42). In recent years the initial work of Overbeck, Haddy, and their associates has been extended by them and others to include the measurement of both arterial and cardiac Na,K ATP-ase in several models of experimental low-renin hypertension (43). In most of these models the Na,K ATP-ase activity was depressed.

Cort et al (14) were the first to show that plasma extracts containing NH-like activity also had pressor activity. More recently, Plunkett et al (71) investigated the possibility that NH might be a pressor substance. They showed that a plasma extract from acutely volume-expanded dogs with NH-like activity increased reactivity of the rat cremaster microcirculation to norepinephrine, vasopressin, and angiotensin II. This extract also increased blood pressure in assay rats with a time course similar to that observed for the vascular reactivity and natriuretic effects.

Several investigators have reported indirect evidence for elevated circulating plasma levels of a Na,K ATP-ase inhibitor in hypertensive subjects. McGregor et al (58) used a cytochemical technique that measures the ability of plasma to stimulate guinea-pig renal glucose-6-phosphate dehydrogenase activity (G6PD), which is said to be a marker of its ability to inhibit Na,K ATP-ase. The G6PD stimulatory activity was elevated in hypertensive patients, was significantly correlated with blood pressure, and was inversely correlated with plasma renin activity. Poston et al (74) showed that when white blood cells from normotensive subjects were incubated in serum obtained from hypertensive patients, the cells exhibited an impairment of ouabain-sensitive sodium efflux found in white cells of hypertensive patients. Interestingly, plasma from hypertensive patients did not cause an impairment of sodium efflux from red cells of normotensive subjects. Edmundson & MacGregor (24) showed that impairment of white-cell sodium efflux was inversely correlated with plasma renin activity. Poston et al (73) found that the defect in white-cell sodium efflux was corrected by treating hypertensive patients with diuretics.

Evidence has been presented that circulating levels of an endogenous digoxin-like substance as measured by radioimmunoassay are elevated in several models of hypertension. Gruber et al (37) found a direct correlation between mean arterial pressure and "endoxin" levels in normotensive and spontaneously hypertensive rhesus monkeys. They also found elevated endoxin in Vervets with two kidney–one clip renovascular hypertension. Likewise, Metzler et al (6) found elevated plasma endoxin levels during the development of DOC-salt hypertension in the rat. Schreiber et al (81) found elevated levels of an endogenous digoxin in rats with coarctation of the abdominal aorta, using an enzyme immunoassay. More recently, Kojima et al (52) showed that a bolus injection of antidigoxin antibodies in DOC-salt hypertensive rats results in significant lowering of blood pressure for up to one hour.

Additional evidence for the circulating Na,K ATP-ase inhibitor theory was recently reported by Hamlyn et al (44). Using a kinetic assay in which enzymatically hydrolyzed ATP is coupled to the oxidation of NADH, they found that plasma, Na,K ATP-ase inhibitory activity was directly correlated with mean arterial pressure in 20 normal subjects and 26 patients with essential hypertension.

The mechanism by which NH levels might become elevated in hypertensive subjects is not known. Most speculation has focused on some abnormality in renal sodium excretion (20). The possibility that a deficient response of the kidney to the natriuretic effect of NH has been proposed (20) and is compatible with currently available data.

The mechanism by which a circulating Na,K ATP-ase inhibitor may cause hypertension has been the subject of some debate. Haddy (41) has favored electrogenic depolarization of vascular smooth muscle, with subsequent increased calcium entry. In contrast, Blaustein (2) proposed that the increase in vascular smooth muscle intracellular sodium caused by pump supression reverses a membrane sodium-calcium exchange mechanism. The two common features of these theories are that the Na,K ATP-ase pump in vascular smooth muscle of hypertensives must be depressed, resulting in increased intracellular calcium and elevated smooth muscle tone.

A major flaw in these theories is that they fail to explain the numerous reports that Na,K ATP-ase pump activity is increased in some experimental (66) and salt-induced (67, 69) models of hypertension in which a circulating pressor factor, presumably NH, has been implicated. In fact, both Pamnani et al (69) and Overbeck et al (67) agree that in Dahl salt-sensitive hypertensive rats conduit-artery smooth-muscle Na,K ATP-ase activity is increased rather than decreased. The former investigators claim that this demonstrates that Dahl rats have genetically defective cell membranes that possess increased ionic permeability, resulting in elevated intracellular sodium concentration and stimulated sodium pump activity. This is in contrast to the evidence, accumulated by several laboratories (47) including Dahl's (17), strongly suggesting the involvement of a humoral hypertensive agent in this form of hypertension. DeWardener & MacGregor (20) have based their theory on the etiology of essential hypertension solely on the ability of NH to inhibit vascular smooth-muscle Na,K ATP-ase, especially in the Dahl strain of rats, despite direct evidence to the contrary.

We suggest an alternate theory to explain these contradictory results. If the primary effect of NH on the cardiovascular system were mediated through inhibition of neural Na,K ATP-ase, resulting in inhibition of the ouabain-sensitive catecholamine-reuptake system (3), then increased vascular smooth-muscle resting tone would be due to increased presentation of catecholamines. Since catecholamines are thought to increase sodium influx as their mechanism of membrane depolarization in many forms of smooth muscle (55), this effect could not easily be differentiated from a genetically "leaky" membrane and would result in an elevation in intracellular sodium and stimulation of Na,K ATP-ase.

There is an increasing body of evidence that indicates that salt-dependent genetic (86) and experimental (77) hypertension is accompanied by an increase in the activity of the peripheral sympathetic nervous system. Dietz, et al (22) showed recently that a high-sodium diet appeared to cause inhibition of catecholamine reuptake in peripheral sympathetic-nerve terminals in the stroke-prone spontaneously hypertensive rat (SHR). This effect was not only seen in the hypertension-prone strain, but to a lesser degree in the normotensive controls.

As noted above, depressed vascular smooth-muscle Na,K ATP-ase activity has been observed in the established phase of low-renin forms of hypertension (43). There is no ready explanation for this apparent discrepancy. However, it is interesting to note that Songu-Mize et al (84) found stimulation of the vascular sodium pump in the early stages of two kidney–one clip Goldblatt and DOC-salt hypertension, while a depression of the pump was present in the malignant stage of the DOC-salt animals. The initial increase in vascular pump activity and blood pressure in the Goldblatt model was prevented by AV3V lesions (85), which have been shown to attenuate the secretion of NH (1). Metzler et al (60) have recently reported elevated levels of plasma endoxin during the onset of DOC-salt hypertension in rats. These two reports suggest that the initial effect of increased levels of a sodium pump inhibitor is to increase vascular smooth-muscle Na,K-ATPase. The pump depression seen in the latter stages of hypertension in this model could be due to chronic effects of the inhibitor or to the well known vascular pathology that accompanies the malignant stage of DOC-salt hypertension.

The hypothesis we propose would be greatly strengthened by evidence that known, Na,K-ATPase inhibitors constrict vascular smooth muscle mainly by activating the sympathetic nervous system, rather than by a direct effect on the muscle cell. Toda (87) has shown that the ouabain-induced contraction of isolated arterial strips is antagonzied by α-receptor blockade with phentolamine. This observation could be due to inhibition of norepinephrine reuptake by ouabain, or to increased sensitivity of the vascular smooth muscle to the endogenous norepinephrine present in the tissue. Mulvany et al (61) demonstrated that the direct inhibition of vascular smooth-muscle Na,K-ATPase by ouabain did not induce contraction, but ouabain could increase reactivity to norepinephrine.

As noted above, we have recently ascertained that a family of peptides in the central nervous system, whose core sequence is centered around ACTH[4–10]/ β,LPH[47–53] or γ,MSH[3–9], have pressor and cardioaccelerator effects mediated by sympathetic nervous system activation (50). These peptides can act as Na,K-ATPase inhibitors (36), suggesting that the cardiovascular effects could be due to inhibition of catecholamine reuptake; this effect, however, has not yet been fully confirmed. Whether the core sequence in these peptides is similar to that in NH has also not yet been shown; however, they have dose-dependent natriuretic-hypertensive effects that we have predicted would be present in NH (8).

The model of hypertension we propose, based on these considerations, is summarized in Figure 1. Salt ingestion leads to NH release by expansion of the "effective" plasma volume. In nonhypertensive individuals NH, in conjunction with other natriuretic forces, causes increased renal sodium excretion, returning effective plasma volume to normal. Since NH can cause natriuresis with no effect on blood pressure (78), volume can be regulated in normal individuals without hypertension.

In hypertensive subjects, renal response to NH is blunted, causing NH levels to become higher than in normotensive individuals. Pathologically elevated NH leads to increased blood pressure either by activating the sympathetic

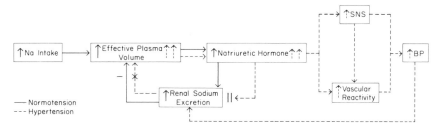

Figure 1   A model for the role of Natriuretic Hormone in the pathophysiology of hypertension is depicted. According to this concept, the development of hypertension is the consequence of an abnormality in volume regulation induced by a defect in the renal response to the natriuretic effect of Natriuretic Hormone.

nervous system, by increasing vascular reactivity directly, or both. The increased blood pressure adds another natriuretic force, helping to overcome the defect in renal sodium excretion. Thus viewed, hypertension is the result of the need to regulate volume in the presence of a defect in renal sodium excretion, as proposed by Coleman & Guyton (12).

We believe this scheme is most relevant to and most easily demonstrated in the early, onset phase of hypertension. In established hypertension, changes in many systems, perhaps occuring secondary to the hypertensive process, might tend to obscure the relatively simple relationships shown in Figure 1.

ACKNOWLEDGMENTS

Dr. Gruber is the recipient of Research Career Development Award 1K04-HL00804 from the National Heart, Lung, and Blood Institute.

The secretarial assistance of Shirley Brandt and the Department of Medicine Satellite Center is gratefully acknowledged.

Literature Cited

1. Bealer, S. L., Haywood, J. R., Gruber, K. A., Buckalew, V. M. Jr., Fink, G. D., et al. 1983. Preoptic-hypothalamic periventricular lesions reduce natriuresis to volume expansion. *Am. J. Physiol.* 244:R51–57
2. Blaustein, M. P. 1977. Sodium ions, calcium ions, blood pressure regulation, and hypertension: a reassessment and a hypothesis. *Am. J. Physiol.* 232:C167–73
3. Bogdanski, D. F., Blaszkowski, T. P., Tissari, A. H. 1970. Mechanisms of biogenic amine transport and storage. IV. Relationship between K^+ and Na^+ requirement for transport and storage of 5-hydroxytriptamine and norepinephrine in synaptosomes. *Biochim. Biophys. Acta* 211:521–32
4. Bohan, T., Potter, L., Bourgoignie, J. J. 1980. Ouabain radioreceptor assay for natriuretic factor. In *Hormonal Regulation of Sodium Excretion*, ed. B. Lichardus, R. W. Schrier, J. Ponec, pp. 393–98. New York: Elsevier
5. Bourgoignie, J. J., Hwang, K. H., Ipakchi, E., Bricker, N. S. 1974. The presence of a natriuretic factor in urine of patients with chronic uremia: the absence of the factor in nephrotic uremic patients. *J. Clin. Invest.* 53:1559–67
6. Buckalew, V. M. Jr. 1978. Column chromatography of plasma antinatriferic activity. In *Natriuretic Hormone*, ed. H. J. Karmer, F. Kruck, pp. 131–40. New York: Springer-Verlag
7. Deleted in proof
8. Buckalew, V. M. Jr., Gruber, K. A. 1983. Natriuretic hormone. In *The Kidney in Liver Disease*, ed. M. Epstein, pp. 479–99. New York: Elsevier. 2nd ed.
9. Buckalew, V. M. Jr., Lancaster, C. D. 1971. Studies of a humoral sodium transport inhibitory activity in normal dogs and dogs with ligation of the inferior vena cava. *Circ. Res. (Suppl II)* 28/29:II44–51
10. Buckalew, V. M. Jr., Martinez, F. J., Green, W. E. 1970. The effect of dialysates and ultrafiltrates of plasma of saline-loaded dogs on toad bladder sodium transport. *J. Clin. Invest.* 49:926–35
11. Clarkson, E. M., Raw, S. M., deWardener, H. E. 1976. Two natriuretic substances in extracts of urine from normal man when salt-depleted and salt-loaded. *Kidney Int.* 10:381–94
12. Coleman, T. G., Guyton, A. C. 1969. Hypertension caused by salt loading in the dog. III. Onset transients of cardiac output and other circulatory variables. *Circ. Res.* 25:153–60
13. Cort. J. H. 1968. The source and chemical nature of the natriuretic activity of plasma evoked by saluretic "volume reflexes." *Can. J. Physiol. Pharmacol.* 46:325–33
14. Cort, J. H., Dousa, T., Pliska, V., Lichardus, B., Safarova, J., et al. 1968. Saluretic activity of blood during carotid occlusion in the cat. *Am. J. Physiol.* 215:921–27

15. Crabbe, J., Fanestil, D. D., Pelletier, M., Porter, G. A. 1974. Effect of ouabain on sodium transport across hormone-stimulated toad bladder and skin. *Pfluegers Arch.* 347:275–96

16. Dahl, L. K., Heine, M. 1975. Primary role of renal homografts in setting chronic blood pressure levels in rats. *Circ. Res.* 36:692–96

17. Dahl, L. K., Knudsen, K. D., Iwai, J. 1969. Humoral transmission of hypertension: evidence from parabiosis. *Circ. Res. 24/25(Suppl. I)*:I21–33

18. deBold, A. J. 1982. Atrial natriuretic factor of the rat heart. Studies on isolation and properties. *Proc. Soc. Exp. Biol. Med.* 170:133–38

19. deWardener, H. E., Clarkson, E. M., Bitensky, L., MacGregor, G. A., Alaghband-Zadeh, J., Chayen, J. 1981. Effect of sodium intake on ability of human plasma to inhibit renal Na^+-K^+-adenosine triphosphatase *in vitro*. *Lancet* 1:411–12

20. deWardener, H. E., MacGregor, G. A. 1980. Dahl's hypothesis that a saluretic substance may be responsible for a sustained rise in arterial pressure: Its possible role in essential hypertension. (Editorial.) *Kidney Int.* 18:1–9

21. Dibona, G. F. 1982. The functions of the renal nerves. *Rev. Physiol. Biochem. Pharmacol.* 94:75–181

22. Dietz, R., Schomig, A., Rascher, W., Strasser, R., Luth, J. B., et al. 1982. Contribution of the sympathetic nervous system to the hypertensive effect of a high sodium diet in stroke-prone spontaneously hypertensive rats. *Hypertension* 4:773–81

23. Duchen, L. W. 1962. The effects of ingestion of hypertonic saline on the pituitary gland in the rat: a morphological study of the pars intermedia and posterior lobe. *J. Endocrinol.* 25:161–68

24. Edmondson, R. P. S., MacGregor, G. A. 1981. Leucocyte cation transport in essential hypertension: its relation to the renin-angiotensin system. *Br. Med. J.* 282:1267–69

25. Favre, H., Hwang, K. H., Schmidt, R. W., Bricker, N. S., Bourgoignie, J. J. 1975. An inhibitor of sodium transport in the urine of dogs with normal renal function. *J. Clin. Invest.* 56:1302–11

26. Favre, H., Louis, F., Gourjon, M. 1979. Role of the basal sodium intake in the rats on their response to a natriuretic factor. *Pfluegers Arch.* 382:73–79

27. Fine, L. G., Bourgoignie, J. J., Hwang, K. H., Bricker, N. S. 1976. On the influence of the natriuretic factor from patients with chronic uremia on the bioelectric properties and sodium transport of the isolated mammalian collecting tubule. *J. Clin. Invest.* 58:590–97

28. Fine, L. G., Bourgoignie, J. J., Weber, H., Bricker, N. S. 1976. Enhanced end-organ responsiveness of the uremic kidney to natriuretic factor. *Kidney Int.* 10:364–72

29. Fishman, M. C. 1979. Endogenous digitalis-like activity in mammalian brain. *Proc. Natl. Acad. Sci. USA* 76:4661–63

30. Freeman, R. H., Davis, J. O., Fullerton, D. 1980. Chronic ACTH administration and the development of hypertension in rats. *Proc. Soc. Exp. Biol. Med.* 163:473–78

31. Godfraind, T., Miller, R. C. 1982. α_1- and α_2-adrenoceptor stimulation and Ca fluxes in isolated rat aorta. *Arch. Int. Pharmacodyn. Ther.* 256:171–72

32. Gonick, H. C., Kramer, H. J., Paul, W., Lu, E. 1977. Circulating inhibitor of sodium-potassium-activated adenosine triphosphatase after expansion of extracellular fluid volume in rats. *Clin. Sci. Mol. Med.* 53:329–34

33. Gonick, H. C., Saldanha, L. F. 1975. A natriuretic principle derived from kidney tissue of volume-expanded rats. *J. Clin. Invest.* 56:247–55

34. Gruber, K. A., Buckalew, V. M. Jr. 1978. Further characterization and evidence for a precursor in the formation of plasma antinatriferic factor. *Proc. Soc. Exp. Biol. Med.* 159:463–67

35. Gruber, K. A., Buckalew, V. M. Jr. 1980. Evidence that natriuretic factor is a cascading peptide hormone system. In *Hormonal Regulation of Sodium Excretion*, ed. B. Lichardus, R. W. Schrier, J. Ponec, pp. 349–55. New York: Elsevier

36. Gruber, K. A., Hennessy, J. F., Buckalew, V. M. Jr., Lymangrover, J. R. 1982. Identification of a heptapeptide with digitalis and natriuretic hormone like properties. *Am. Soc. Neph. Abstr.* p. 77A

37. Gruber, K. A., Rudel, L. L., Bullock, B. C. 1982. Increased circulating levels of an endogenous digoxin-like factor in hypertensive monkeys. *Hypertension* 4:348–54

38. Gruber, K. A., Whitaker, J. M., Buckalew, V. M. Jr. 1980. Endogenous digitalis-like substance in plasma of volume-expanded dogs. *Nature* 287:743–45

39. Gruber, K. A., Whitaker, J. M., Buckalew, V. M. Jr. 1983. Immunochemical approaches to the isolation of an endogenous digoxin-like factor. In *Proc. 3rd Int. Conf. ATP-ase. Curr. Top. Membr. Transp.* In press

40. Haddy, F. J. 1980. Mechanism, preven-

tion, and therapy of sodium-dependent hypertension. *Am. J. Med.* 69:746–58

41. Haddy, F. J. 1981. What is the link between vascular smooth-muscle sodium pumps and hypertension? *Clin. Exp. Hypertension* 3:179–82

42. Haddy, F. J., Overbeck, H. W. 1976. The role of humoral agents in volume expanded hypertension. *Life Sci.* 19: 935–48

43. Haddy, F. J., Pamnani, M. B., Clough, D. L. 1979. Humoral factors and the sodium-potassium pump in volume expanded hypertension. *Life Sci.* 24:2105–18

44. Hamlyn, J. M., Ringel, R., Schaeffer, J., Levinson, P. D., Hamilton, B. P., Kowarski, A. A., Blaustein, M. P. 1982. A circulating inhibitor of ($Na^+ + K^+$) ATP-ase associated with essential hypertension. *Nature* 300:650–52

45. Haupert, G. T., Sancho, J. M. 1979. Sodium transport inhibitor from bovine hypothalamus. *Proc. Natl. Acad. Sci. USA* 76:4658–60

46. Hillyard, S. D., Lu, E., Gonick, H. C. 1976. Further characterization of the natriuretic factor derived from kidney tissue of volume-expanded rats: effects on short-circuit current and sodium-potassium-adenosine triphosphatase activity. *Circ. Res.* 38:250–55

47. Hirata, Y., Tobian, L., Simon, G., Iwai, J. 1983. Humoral factor in Dahl salt sensitive rats: effects of chronic injection of erythrocytes and serum. *Fed. Proc.* 42:A5154

48. Kastin, A. J. 1967. MSH and vasopressin activities in pituitaries of rats treated with hypertonic saline. *Fed. Proc.* 26:A5

49. Katz, A. I. 1982. Renal Na-K-ATP-ase: its role in tubular sodium and potassium transport. *Am. J. Physiol.* 242:F207–19

50. Klein, M. C., Hutchins, P. M., Buckalew, V. M. Jr., Hennessy, J. F., Lymangrover, J. R., Gruber, K. A. 1983. Cardiovascular effects of the ACTH analog $ACTH^{4-10}$ D-PHE-7: an inhibitor of Na^+,K^+-ATPase. *Fed. Proc.* 42:A4266

51. Klingmüller, D., Weiler, E., Kramer, H. J. 1982. Digoxin-like natriuretic activity in the urine of salt-loaded healthy subjects. *Klin. Wochenschr.* 60:1249–53

52. Kojima, I., Yoshihara, S., Ogata, E. 1982. Involvement of endogenous digitalis-like substance in genesis of deoxycorticosterone-salt substance. *Life Sci.* 30:1775–81

53. Kracke, G. R. 1983. Na,K-ATPase inhibitor from guinea-pig brain is not ouabain-like. *J. Lab Clin. Med.* 101:105–13

54. Kramer, H. J., Bäcker, A., Krück, F.

1977. Antinatriferic activity in human plasma following acute and chronic salt-loading. *Kidney Int.* 12:214–22

55. Kuriyama, H., Ito, Y., Suzuki, H., Kitamura, K., Itoh, T. 1982. Factors modifying contraction-relaxation cycle in vascular smooth muscle. *Am. J. Physiol.* 243:H641–62

56. Licht, A., Stein, S., McGregor, C. W., Bourgoignie, J. J., Bricker, N. S. 1982. Progress in isolation and purification of an inhibitor of sodium transport obtained from dog urine. *Kidney Int.* 21:339–44

57. Lohmeier, T. E., Carroll, R. G. 1982. Chronic potentiation of vasoconstrictor hypertension by adrenocorticotropic hormone. *Hypertension* 4 (Suppl. II):II138–48

58. MacGregor, G. A., Fenton, S., Alaghband-Zadeh, J., Markandu, N., Roulston, J. E., deWardener, H. E. 1981. Evidence for a raised concentration of a circulating sodium transport inhibitor in essential hypertension. *Br. Med. J.* 283:1355–57

59. Martinez-Maldonado, M., Allen, J. C., Inagaki, C., Tsaparas, N., Schwartz, A. 1972. Renal sodium-potassium-activated adenosine triphosphatase and sodium reabsorption. *J. Clin. Invest.* 51:2544–51

60. Metzler, C. H., Hennessy, J. F., Buckalew, V. M. Jr. 1982. Evidence for a circulating ATP-ase inhibitor in the development phase of DOC-salt hypertension. *Coun. High Blood Pressure Res. Am. Heart Assoc.*, Abstr. 17

61. Mulvany, M. J., Nilsson, H., Flatman, J. A., Korsgaard, N. 1982. Potentiating and depressive effects of ouabain and potassium-free solutions on rat mesenteric resistance vessels. *Circ. Res.* 51:514–24

62. Naccarato, R., Messa, P., D'Angelo, A., Fabris, A., Messa, M., et al. 1981. Renal handling of sodium and water in early chronic liver disease. Evidence for a reduced natriuretic activity of the cirrhotic urinary extracts in rats. *Gastroenterology* 81:205–10

63. Novales, R. R. 1962. The role of ionic factors in hormone action on the vertebrate melanophore. *Am. Zool.* 2:337–52

64. Orias, R. 1966. Cambios en la concentracion de hormona melanocitoestimulante (MSH) en hipofisis de rata por deshidratracion o soluciones hypertonicas. *Acta Physiol. Lat. Am.* 16(Supp. 1):95

65. Orias, R., McCann, S. M. 1972. Natriuresis induced by alpha and beta melanocyte stimulating hormone (MSH) in rats. *Endocrinology* 90:700–6

66. Overbeck, H. W., Grissette, D. E. 1980. Sodium pump activity in arteries of rats

with Goldblatt hypertension. *Hypertension* 4:132–39

67. Overbeck, H. W., Ku, D. D., Rapp, J. P. 1981. Sodium pump activity in arteries of Dahl salt-sensitive rats. *Hypertension* 3:306–12

68. Overbeck, H. W., Pamnani, M. B., Akera, T., Brody, T. M., Haddy, F. J. 1976. Depressed function of a ouabain-sensitive sodium-potassium pump in blood vessels from renal hypertensive dogs. *Circ. Res.* 38(Suppl. II):II48–52

69. Pamnani, M. B., Clough, D. L., Huot, S. T., Haddy, F. T. 1980. Vascular Na^+-K^+ pump activity in Dahl S and R rats. *Proc. Soc. Exp. Biol. Med.* 165:440–44

70. Pearce, J. W., Veress, A. T., Sonnenberg, H. 1975. Time course of onset and decay of humoral natriuretic activity in the rat. *Can. J. Physiol. Pharmacol.* 53:734–41

71. Plunkett, W. C., Hutchins, P. M., Gruber, K. A., Buckalew, V. M. Jr. 1982. Evidence for a vascular sensitizing factor in plasma of saline-loaded dogs. *Hypertension* 4:581–89

72. Deleted in proof

73. Poston, L., Jones, R. B., Richardson, P. J., Hilton, P. J. 1981. The effect of antihypertensive therapy on abnormal leucocyte sodium transport in essential hypertension. *Clin. Exp. Hypertens.* 3:693–701

74. Poston, L., Sewell, R. B., Wilkinson, S. P., Richarson, P. J., Williams, R., et al. 1981. Evidence for a circulating sodium transport inhibitor in essential hypertension. *Br. Med. J.* 282:847–49

75. Poston, L., Wilkinson, S., Sewell, R. B., Williams, R. 1982. Sodium transport during the natriuresis of volume expansion; a study using peripheral blood leucocytes. *Clin. Sci.* 63:243–49

76. Radhakrishnan, A. M., Stein, S., Licht, A., Gruber, K. A., Udenfriend, S. 1977. High-efficiency cation-exhange chromatography of polypeptides and polyamines in the nanomole range. *J. Chromatogr.* 132:552–55

77. Rascher, W., Schomig, A., Dietz, R., Weber, J., Gross, F. 1981. Plasma catecholamines, noradrenalin metabolism, and vascular response in desoxycorticosterone acetate hypertension of rats. *Eur. J. Pharmacol.* 75:255–63

78. Rudd, M. A., Gruber, K. A., Buckalew, V. M. Jr. 1981. The effect of an endogenous digoxin-like substance on renal sodium excretion. *Fed. Proc.* 40:A2191

79. Rudd, M. A., Gruber, K. A., Buckalew, V. M. Jr. 1982. Prostaglandins (PG) blockade inhibits the natriuretic effect of the natriuretic hormone (NH). *Fed. Proc.* 41:A4216

80. Sawyer, T. K., Hruby, V. J., Darman, P. S., Hadley, M. E. 1982. [Half-Cys^4, half-Cys^{10}]-α-Melanocyte-stimulating hormone: A cyclic α-melanotropin exhibiting superagonist biological activity. *Proc. Natl. Acad. Sci. USA* 79:1751–55

81. Schreiber, V., Kolbel, F., Stepan, J., Gregorova, I., Pribyl, T. 1981. Digoxinlike immunoreactivity in the serum of rats with cardiac overload. *J. Mol. Cell Cardiol.* 13:107–10

82. Schrier, R. W., deWardener, H. E. 1971. Tubular reabsorption of sodium ion: influence of factors other than aldosterone and glomerular filtration rate. *N. Engl. J. Med.* 285:1231–43, 1292–1303

83. Sedlakova, E., Prusik, Z., Skopkova, J., Barth, T., Kluh, I., Cort, J. H. 1974. Isolation of a tridecapeptide from natriuretic fractions of bovine posterior pituitary. *Eur. J. Clin. Invest.* 4:285–92

84. Songu-Mize, E., Bealer, S. L., Caldwell, R. W. 1983. Biphasic changes in vascular Na^+ - pump activity during development of deoxycorticosterone acetate (DOCA)-salt hypertension in rats. *Fed. Proc.* 42:A5140

85. Songu-Mize, E., Bealer, S. L., Caldwell, R. W. 1983. Effect of anteroventral third ventricle lesions on vascular sodium-pump activity in two kidney Goldblatt hypertension. *Hypertension* 5(Suppl. I):I89–93

86. Takeshita, A., Mark, A. L. 1978. Neurogenic contribution to hindquarters vasoconstriction during high sodium intake in Dahl strain of genetically hypertensive rat. *Circ. Res.* 43 (Suppl. I):I86–91

87. Toda, N. 1980 Mechanisms of ouabain-induced arterial muscle contraction. *Am. J. Physiol.* 239:H199–205

88. Whitmer, K. R., Wallick, E. T., Epps, D. E., Lane, L. K., Collins, J. H., Schwartz, A. 1982. Effects of extracts of rat brain on the digitalis receptor. *Life Sci.* 30:2261–75

89. Wilson, D. R., Honrath, U., Sonnenberg, H. 1982. Prostaglandin synthesis inhibition during volume expansion: Collecting duct function. *Kidney Int.* 22:1–7

GASTROINTESTINAL PHYSIOLOGY

John G. Forte, *Section Editor*

Over the past decade the exploitation of cellular and subcellular model systems has provided new insight and mechanistic detail for many functional processes of the gastrointestinal tract. In this section, focus is directed on the recent advances that have been made through the study of gastrointestinal model systems. Both the advantages and limitations of the in vitro approach should be appreciated by the student of physiology, with the goal that tissue and organ function be brought to light.

In the first article, J. A. Williams reviews the physiological advances that have been made using isolated acini from salivary and pancreatic glands. Receptors and second messengers that control electrolyte and macromolecular secretion by these organs have now been clearly established. Future directions are indicated toward the molecular characterization of receptors, as well as the definition of the cellular mechanisms for activating machinery.

Just as the isolated acini have provided an expansive model to study secretion by the tubular-alveolar glands, the preparation of isolated gastric glands, pioneered by T. Berglindh, has redirected investigative attention to the cell physiology of gastric secretion. Here, Dr. Berglindh reviews the methodological advantages and limitations of these in vitro microstomachs, with particular emphasis on acid secretion. He points out the insights that studies on gastric glands have brought to receptor identification and energetic secretion, and he suggests that future advances concerning the mode of stimulus-secretion coupling will rely heavily on the isolated gland preparation.

Using data from isolated cell and gland models, S. J. Hersey, S. H. Norris & A. J. Gibert note the similarities between pepsin secretion by the gastric chief cell and other zymogenic cells of the gastrointestinal tract. Evidence suggests at least two different receptor-mediated pathways for secretion: one clearly involving cyclic AMP and the other possibly involving Ca^{2+}. These authors also direct attention to future research into the mechanisms of cell and membrane activation associated with the secretory event.

In the previous volume, the entire section on Gastrointestinal and Nutritional Physiology was devoted to the physiology of lipid absorption and metabolism, with the emphasis on total body integration and regulation. In this volume, T. M. Forte reviews recent developments in lipid metabolism using primary hepatocyte cell cultures. These model systems have allowed a differentiation of functional attributes between hepatocytes and other liver cells (e.g. Kupfer cells). Sustained in vitro secretory capacity and demonstrated responsiveness to hormones indicate the potential value of primary hepatocyte cultures to the cell biology of lipid metabolism.

The last two articles deal with processes of intestinal absorption. In his review of active Na^+ transport by the colon, S. G. Schultz analyzes the electrophysiological data that characterizes the mechanisms of Na^+ movement across the limiting absorptive barriers, the apical and basolateral cell membranes. He develops the hypothesis that regulation of transepithelial Na^+ flux is the result of a dynamic interaction between these limiting membranes, through which the activity of the Na^+ pump at the basolateral membrane and the number of Na^+ entry channels at the apical membrane are mutually interactive in regulating Na^+ absorption with minimal perturbation of the intracellular milieu.

In the last article, B. R. Stevens, J. D. Kaunitz & E. M. Wright review the processes of amino acid and sugar absorption by the small intestine. They examine the transport properties of brush border and basolateral membrane vesicles isolated from intestinal enterocytes. They point out the clear distinctions that are possible from the analysis of specific pathways, characteristics of Na^+-dependence, and detailed mechanisms for amino acid and sugar transport in these simple membrane systems. Physically determined kinetic parameters are used to reconstruct models for amino acid and sugar absorption across the enterocyte.

Ann. Rev. Physiol. 1984. 46:361–75

REGULATORY MECHANISMS IN PANCREAS AND SALIVARY ACINI

John A. Williams

Departments of Physiology and Medicine, University of California, San Francisco, California 94143; and Cell Biology Laboratory, Mount Zion Hospital and Medical Center, San Francisco, California 94120

METHODOLOGICAL CONSIDERATIONS

A major advance in studying gastrointestinal physiology has been the use of in vitro cell systems. Early in vitro studies of pancreatic and salivary function generally used either gland slices or fragments, or were carried out using tissue from young animals so that the whole gland could be incubated. Although significant data was obtained, major problems existed in terms of tissue viability, representational sampling, diffusional barriers, and the presence of multiple cell types. Over the last decade a number of preparations of isolated cells and acini from the pancreas and salivary glands have been described that have obviated many of these problems. Directly related to this advance has been a large increase in the knowledge of pancreatic and salivary cellular function. By reducing diffusion barriers and allowing reproducible sampling of purified cell types, the use of isolated cells and acini has made possible studies of the receptors, second messengers, and effector systems that together make up the cellular regulatory mechanisms. Furthermore, isolated cells can be placed in primary culture, making it possible to study longer-term regulatory mechanisms such as differential control of the synthesis of various secretory molecules. This review will first discuss the cellular models used to study regulation in pancreas and salivary glands, briefly cover the physiological processes being regulated, and then focus on the various steps in cell regulation.

361

0066-4278/84/0315-0361$02.00

Isolated Cells

Isolated monodispersed pancreatic acinar cells were first prepared by Amsterdam & Jamieson using enzyme digestion, divalent cation chelation, and mechanical shearing (1). The enzymes used were crude collagenase (containing other proteases) and hyaluronidase, and the procedure was modeled on one previously used for the dissociation of hepatocytes. Subsequently, in order to obtain more reproducible results, the method was modified to use purified collagenase and chymotrypsin in place of the crude collagenase (2). Isolated parotid cells were similarly prepared with collagenase and hyaluronidase, but it was necessary to include a second enzymatic digestion step with trypsin (35). Of the various treatments, the collagenase acts to digest the basement membrane and connective tissue stroma, while Ca^{2+} chelation separates desmosomes and alters the structure of tight junctions. Mechanical shearing completes the cell separation (2). Subsequently, a number of studies have been carried out using minor modifications of this method to prepare isolated cells from pancreas, parotid, and submaxillary glands (11, 21, 28, 43–45, 60). As expected from the proportions of cells in the gland, pancreatic cells so prepared are > 95% acinar cells, with only a few endocrine and duct cells. Parotid preparations, however, contain more ductular cells, and the cells prepared from submandibular gland are about 40% ductular (45). The preparations are quite viable for 3–5 h based on exclusion of trypan blue, maintenance of ultrastructure integrity, content of Na^+ and K^+, and incorporation of labeled amino acids into protein.

These isolated cell preparations have been used effectively for a variety of studies measuring receptors, cyclic nucleotides, and ion fluxes. By contrast, secretion of macromolecules is variably reduced in the isolated cell preparation and requires higher concentrations of secretagogue (1, 28, 60). For example, amylase release from the perfused rat pancreas is increased 8–20-fold by CCK, whereas it is increased only 2-fold or less from isolated rat acinar cells (28). It is likely that this decreased secretion is due to the fact that secretion of macromolecules by exocytosis requires a specialized membrane domain present in the luminal plasma membrane. In exocrine cells the luminal membrane makes up less than 10% of the plasma membrane, and its distinct nature, such as can be illustrated by freeze-fracture microscopy, is lost when the tight junctions are split by calcium chelation (38). Also, the microfilament network underlying the luminal membrane is lost upon cell isolation (62). Thus it is not surprising that functions of the basolateral membrane (e.g. activation of hormone and neurotransmitter receptors and second-messenger generation) remain intact, while those of the luminal membrane (e.g. exocytosis) are reduced. Moreover, in those isolated cell preparations retaining the most secretory ability, some hallmarks of luminal cytoarchitecture are retained, or not all cells are completely dissociated. Because of the better secretion of macromolecules by isolated acini, isolated cells are not as frequently used at present. However, for some purposes advantages exist for the use of isolated cells; they remain in suspension better, making sampling of identical aliquots easier, and there are no diffusion barriers. To date there have been few attempts to purify specific, isolated cell types. Counterflow sedimentation has been used to separate isolated acinar and duct cells or the rat pancreas (53). Percoll or albumin gradients have also been used for cells from other organs, and these techniques should be applicable.

Isolated Acini and Ducts

In order to overcome the poor secretory response of isolated acinar cells, the preparation procedure was modified by eliminating the calcium chelation and the noncollagenase protease treatment such that isolated acini were produced (52, 61). Although hyaluronidase was used in some early procedures, it is now clear that isolated acini can be produced by incubation with only purified collagenase when followed by mechanical shearing. Such acini consist of 10–30 cells and retain normal luminal structure, including apical tight junctions (52, 61). Enzyme secretion by pancreatic and parotid acini in response to secretagogues is both greater in magnitude and sensitivity than is that of isolated cells and equals or betters results observed for perfused glands or dissected lobules. Because acini maintain most of the other advantages of isolated cells, they have become the most commonly used preparation for studying the in vitro function of pancreatic and salivary acinar cells. With such preparations it is possible to localize secretagogue receptors and study their relation to protein secretion (26, 49, 62, 63). However, more than one cell type may be present in acinar preparations. For example, isolated pancreatic acini contain a small number of centroacinar cells as an integral component.

By contrast to isolated acini, only a few studies have isolated duct fragments from pancreases and salivary glands. The study of duct fragments may require more indirect measures of function (e.g. O_2 consumption), owing to the difficulty in directly studying ion and fluid transport in such a preparation. In one study, however, pancreatic duct fragments were cultured in agarose and shown to reseal and secrete fluid into their lumina (17).

Cultured Pancreatic or Salivary Cells

Studies of long-term cellular regulation have been limited by the relatively short (3–5 h) lifetime of the previously discussed preparations. Several attempts have been made, therefore, to culture cells obtained from pancreas or parotid in a manner in which differentiated function is retained. Isolated cells have been maintained in suspension culture as either cellular aggregates (40) or as isolated acini (31, 32). In these studies the importance of maintaining secretagogues such as carbachol or epinephrine in the medium was emphasized

(32, 40). These results indicate that factors that are typically thought of for their abilities to elicit an acute response, i.e. enzyme secretion, may also have long-term regulatory effects. It is important, therefore, for exocrine secretory cells to be stimulated in order to maintain their differentiated state. The importance of epidermal growth factor (EGF) for maintaining differentiated secretory function in cultured pancreatic acini has also been recently noted (31, 32). By culturing on collagen substrates, monolayers also have been prepared of both adult cat parotid (16) and mouse pancreas cells (C. D. Logsdon & J. A. Williams, unpublished data). The pancreatic monolayers are structurally polarized with recognizable apical and basal surfaces but with a reduced content of zymogen granules. Besides studies of long-term hormonal regulation, the use of monolayer cultures should also be of value for studying the secretion of electrolytes and water by acinar and duct cells.

REGULATION OF PANCREATIC AND SALIVARY FUNCTION

By use of the preparations reviewed above, plus data from earlier in vivo and in vitro studies, it is now obvious that there exists a complex regulation of pancreatic and salivary cells. Neurotransmitters, hormones, and other regulatory molecules affecting pancreatic and salivary function are listed in Table 1. With only a few exceptions, all of these effects are now known to result from direct regulation of target cells. While most of the induced actions relate to secretion of either fluid or macromolecules, a number of trophic and metabolic effects have also been elucidated. Thus, prolonged stimulation of the pancreas by CCK and of salivary glands by epinephrine causes hypertrophy and hyperplasia. It is still not clear whether some of the biological effects listed are physiological; some may be redundant or vestigial. In other cases, as for example the mammalian pancreas responding to the amphibian peptide bombesin (27), there may be a homolog such as the recently described gastrin-releasing peptide. EGF has effects to maintain differentiation in cultured pancreatic cells (31), but the importance of this action in vivo is unknown. Receptors for glucocorticoids and estrogens have been identified in the pancreas (48, 56), but the nature of the regulatory effects of these steroids on the adult pancreas is not established.

Receptors

The initial step in regulation of cellular function by neurotransmitters, hormones, and growth factors involves binding of the ligand to a specific receptor molecule present in limited number on or in the target cell. Most of the receptors to be discussed here are either proteins or glycoproteins and are present in the plasma membrane, although receptors for other regulators such

Table 1 Regulatory molecules influencing pancreatic and salivary gland function

Organ	Regulator	Actions	Second messenger	Reference
Pancreas	ACh, CCK, Gastrin	Digestive enzyme secretion, Cl$^-$ rich pancreatic juice from acini, digestive enzyme synthesis, trophic effects, increased cellular metabolism	Ca^{2+}	26, 29, 49, 59
	Bombesin, Substance P	Digestive enzyme secretion	Ca^{2+}	25, 27
	VIP, Secretin	HCO$_3^-$ rich pancreatic juice from ducts, potentiation of enzyme secretion from acini, potentiation of trophic effect	cAMP	14, 54
	Insulin	Potentiation of digestive enzyme secretion, trophic effect on amylase, increased cellular metabolism	Unknown	19, 41, 62
	IGF$_1$, IGF$_2$	Insulin-like effects on acinar cell metabolism	Unknown	59a
	EGF	Maintenance of differentiated function	Unknown	30, 31
	Somatostatin	Inhibition of pancreatic secretion in vivo (action site unknown)	Unknown	10
Parotid	ACh, α-Adrenergic, Sub. P	Salivary juice production, enzyme secretion (limited), increased cellular metabolism	Ca^{2+}	8, 42
	β-Adrenergic, VIP	Enzyme secretion, increased cellular metabolism	cAMP	8, 42
Submaxillary	ACh, α-Adrmg.	Salivary juice production	Ca^{2+}	42, 45
	β-Adrenergic	Mucin secretion	cAMP	42, 45
	VIP	Enhanced blood flow, potentiation of the effect of ACh to induce secretion	Unknown (Prob. cAMP)	34

as steroid and thyroid hormones are also present intracellularly. Following occupancy by its specific regulatory molecule, the receptor complex is able directly or via a second messenger to activate an effector system that brings about a cellular response.

Receptors on pancreas and parotid, as is true for other cells, can be described and categorized based on (*a*) differences in the induced biological response, (*b*) the use of specific inhibitors, (*c*) characterization of binding of radiolabeled ligand, or (*d*) by isolation and molecular characterization. Specific inhibitors exist for cholinergic, adrenergic, and CCK receptors such as atropine, propranolol, and dibutyryl cyclic GMP, respectively. Recently, most work has focused on characterizing receptors in terms of ligand binding properties and relating receptor occupancy to the induced biological response. However, the molecular phase that has developed in other systems for the nicotinic-cholinergic and insulin receptor, is now starting to be applied to pancreatic receptors.

Regulatory molecules whose receptors have been characterized by ligand binding in the pancreas and salivary glands are listed in Table 2. In general, neurotransmitter receptors have been studied using radiolabeled antagonists. Hormones, meanwhile, have been studied with radiolabeled agonists or analogs that, in the case of the peptides, have been radioiodinated to high specific activity. Isolated cells and acini have been studied most frequently, because in these preparations it is generally possible to relate receptor occupancy to effects on secretion. In studies where whole glands have been homogenized to prepare plasma membranes or cytosol, it is also less obvious whether receptors are localized to a particular cell type. In these studies data have been collected as to the number and affinity of receptors, analog specificity, pH optimum, and ionic dependence.

Part of the evidence that ligand-binding sites are indeed receptors is the fact that a relationship exists between receptor occupancy and the induced biological response. Usually this means that both receptor occupancy and biological effects follow saturation kinetics. When the percent of maximal biological effect or receptor occupancy is plotted against the log of the ligand concentration, the curves are sigmoid and either overlap or are parallel with the biological-effect dose-response curve to the left (occuring at lower ligand concentration). The latter case is usually taken to indicate "spare receptors", in that only a fraction of receptors need be occupied to induce the full biological effect. Such relations have been studied for a number of regulators of pancreatic acinar function. Insulin receptor occupancy and stimulation of leucine incorporation into pancreatic acinar cell protein are almost superimposable (51). EGF-induced increase in pancreatic leucine incorporation into protein and maintenance of CCK-stimulated amylase occur at slightly lower concentrations than receptor occupancy (31). Stimulation of pancreatic amylase release by bombe-

Table 2 Demonstration by ligand binding of receptors for neurotransmitters, hormones, and other regulatory molecules

Organ	Regulatory molecule	Where demonstrated	Ligand	Reference
Pancreas	Acetylcholine	acinar cells	^{3}H-QNB, ^{3}H-methylscopolamine	29
	Cholecystokinin	isolated acini	^{125}I-CCK$_{33}$, ^{125}I-CCK$_8$	26, 49, 50
		acinar plasma membrane		
	VIP	acinar cells	^{125}I-VIP	11
	Secretin	acinar cells	^{125}I-VIP, ^{125}I secretin	11, 23
		isolated acini		
	Insulin	isolated acini	^{125}I-insulin	18, 51
	IGF$_1$, IGF$_2$	isolated acini	^{125}I-IGF	59a
	EGF	isolated acini	^{125}I-EGF	31
	Bombesin	isolated acini	^{125}I-Tyr$_4$-Bombesin	27
	Substance P	isolated acini	^{125}I-Physalaemin	25
	Somatostatin	pancreatic cytosol	^{125}I-Tyr-Somatostatin	46
	Estrogen	pancreatic cytosol	^{3}H-estradiol	48
	Cortisol	pancreatic cytosol	^{3}H-cortisol	56
Salivary Glands	Acetylcholine	dispersed cells	^{3}H-QNB	9, 33, 43
	β-Adrenergic	membrane particles	^{3}H-dihydroalprenolol	3, 9, 33
		membranes particles	^{125}I-iodohydroxybenzylpindolol	
	α-Adrenergic	dispersed cells	^{3}H-dihydroergocryptine	9, 55
		membrane particles	^{3}H-prazosin	
	Substance P	dispersed cells	^{125}I-physalaemin	44

sin and physalaemin are parallel to receptor occupancy but require respectively only 25% and 45% receptor occupancy for the full biological effect (25, 27). Thus a certain amount of spare receptors would appear to exist for these regulators. Regulation of pancreatic function by CCK and cholinergic analogs is more complicated. Amylase-release curves are biphasic, with supramaximal concentrations of agonist-inducing submaximal amylase release (29, 49). By contrast, stimulation of glucose transport is monophasic but requires higher concentrations of agonist (49). Both CCK and cholinergic agonists appear to interact with two classes of receptors of higher and lower affinity (29, 49, 50). One possible model has been presented in which occupancy of the high-affinity receptor stimulates amylase release; by contrast the low-affinity receptor inhibits amylase release and stimulates glucose uptake (49). In another model the receptor is conceptualized as having two sites where occupancy of the second results in desensitization and reduced secretion (12). High doses of secretagogues also induces morphological changes in the cells, and this may be a response to high intracellular concentrations of Ca^{2+} (6).

It is generally assumed that receptors for polypeptide hormones and neurotransmitters are localized on the plasma membrane and, in the case of exocrine cells, on the basal or lateral membrane. Electron microscope autoradiography of labeled hormones has localized the initial site of binding to isolated pancreatic acini for insulin and CCK to the basolateral plasma membrane (18, 63). When ^{125}I-insulin was injected into rats it also was found to localize in a saturable manner in the pancreas over basolateral membranes of acinar cells, with a lesser amount over duct cells (Sakamoto, Goldfine & Williams, unpublished data). Subsequently in all cases, some of the bound hormone was internalized. The importance of the internalized hormones either for hormone action or degradation is unknown. That the pattern of intracellular localization of internalized hormone in acinar cells was different for insulin and CCK suggests some specificity and that internalization may represent more than just a housekeeping function (18, 63).

Little is yet known of the molecular characteristics of pancreatic and salivary gland receptors. It seems likely that adrenergic, muscarinic-cholinergic, and insulin receptors will be similar to these receptors on better studied target cells, as is the case for their binding specificity. In the case of the insulin receptor on pancreatic plasma membranes, crosslinking studies have revealed a protein of apparent $M_r = 135,000$ that is similar to the α-subunit of other insulin receptors (19). In the case of GI hormones and other peptide secretagogues, the only receptor studied to date is the pancreatic CCK receptor. That receptor is clearly a protein, in that binding was abolished by treatment with trypsin. When radiolabeled CCK was covalently crosslinked to its receptor by ultraviolet radiation (57) or chemically with disuccinimidyl suberate (47), the predominate labeled species under reducing conditions had a M_r of 80,000. In the nonreduced state, a 120,000 M_r band was labeled that was converted to the 80,000 M_r band by dithiothreitol, without the appearance of smaller labeled bands (47a). Since CCK itself has $M_r = 4,000$, a 76,000 M_r presumptive receptor is linked by disulfide bonds to a 40,000 M_r membrane protein that is probably not exposed externally and might be a transduction protein. Further studies of this type may also help explain differences in the binding specificity of CCK receptors in the pancreas, brain, and stomach (59).

Second Messengers

Although the second-messenger concept arose to explain the role of cyclic AMP, it has been broadened to include other molecules or changes in cells that serve an informational function coupling the plasma membrane to an effector or biological response. The best-studied second messengers are cyclic AMP and cytosolic-free Ca^{2+}. Other possible messenger-like systems include membrane depolarization, cytosolic pH, phospholipids, and cyclic GMP. Second messengers in the pancreas, parotid, and submaxillary gland are included in Table 1. In cases where cyclic AMP is listed, the plasma membrane contains adenylate cyclase, and the criteria originally proposed by Sutherland have been met (8). Criteria for establishing Ca^{2+} as a second messenger and its role in the pancreas and parotid have been reviewed recently (8, 54, 58). In the pancreas and to a lesser extent in the parotid, intracellular stores of Ca^{2+} are present and play a role both in buffering cytoplasmic Ca^{2+} and as a "trigger" mechanism for acutely stimulating acinar function. Until recently a major deficit was experimental data directly measuring cytosolic-free Ca^{2+} in cells. A recent study with Ca^{2+}-sensitive microelectrodes in mouse pancreas has indicated a normal resting cytosolic Ca^{2+} concentration around 0.4 µM, which increased to a maximum of 1.0 µM upon stimulation with acetylcholine (39). The exact relationships between receptor occupancy, the rise in cytosolic Ca^{2+}, and induced biological responses, however, still remains to be elucidated.

An important consideration is that specific second messengers are not directly linked in a stereotyped manner to specific biological effects. Thus Ca^{2+} is the major intracellular messenger stimulating enzyme release from pancreatic acinar cells, whereas in the parotid Ca^{2+} largely mediates stimulation of fluid secretion (8, 58). By contrast, cyclic AMP predominately mediates macromolecular secretion from salivary glands, but fluid secretion from pancreas. The two messengers may potentiate the effects of each other, which is especially true in the pancreas. A recent unique effect is the report that VIP acts on submandibular gland to increase the affinity of muscarinic receptors (34). VIP and acetylcholine appear to coexist in the same neuron and are released together. VIP also increases pancreatic and salivary blood flow, which can be a limiting factor for secretion (14). A second consideration is that the effects of more than one extracellular regulator may be mediated in a single cell type by the same second messenger. In most cases of this type, the biological effects of all these regulators is similar, and the data can be explained by distinct receptors coupled to a common mechanism for generating the second messenger. However, contradictory behavior is shown by bombesin and CCK, both of which elicit digestive enzyme secretion from pancreatic acinar cells via Ca^{2+} as second messenger (Table 1). Whereas the dose response for bombesin is monophasic, that for CCK is biphasic (26, 27, 49). A more extreme case is seen for the action of secretin and VIP on guinea pig pancreatic acini. Both act to increase cellular cyclic AMP, with secretin being more effective, whereas VIP is a more potent stimulator of enzyme release (11, 23). These two cases suggest the possibility of subcellular compartments for second messengers, or that more than one messenger is involved.

A number of other phenomena related to cell activation may also play a second-messenger role in pancreas and salivary gland. Changes in phospholipid metabolism have been well studied (30) since the original demonstration that secretagogues increased phospholipid turnover in the pancreas (20a). Specific phenomena include the breakdown of phospholidylinositol and polyphosphoinositides, increased synthesis of phosphatidic acid, release of arachidonic acid with possible synthesis of prostaglandins and thromboxanes, and phospholipid methylation (30). Some of these changes may be involved in the generation of second messenger; for example phosphatidyl inositol breakdown may be involved in gating mechanisms that increase cytosolic-free Ca^{2+} (30). Other changes such as arachidonic acid release may be induced by Ca^{2+} and/or cyclic nucleotides. However, the possibility exists of the generation of an additional second messenger. The formation of diacylglycerol may act in concert with Ca^{2+} to activate a specific protein kinase (see next section).

Membrane depolarization has been considered as a second messenger in the sense that it could function as a transduction mechanism. Many of the secretagogues acting on pancreas and salivary glands induce changes in membrane potential (42). However, changes in membrane potential do not mimic the biological response and at least for pancreatic acini are induced by the rise in Ca^{2+} and are therefore probably a tertiary phenomenon. Cyclic GMP is increased in both pancreas and parotid, but again this appears to be an effect of Ca^{2+} rather than a true second messenger (54). Moreover, artificially increasing intracellular cyclic GMP does not mimic any of the tested biological effects of secretagogues on the pancreas (20). Thus cyclic GMP is still a messenger in search of a function.

A number of hormones and neurotransmitters are listed in Table 1 as having no known second messenger. Several of these, including insulin and EGF, act on membrane receptors, but are then internalized. Of recent interest is that receptors for these molecules have intrinsic tyrosine-specific protein-kinase activity that is activated by the hormones. Although not yet studied in exocrine glands, such activity could be involved in certain actions of these agents. In the case of somatostatin, an intracellular receptor has been described. Occupancy of this receptor activates a protein phosphatase (46). Thus the possibility exists that somatostatin could be its own second messenger.

While regulatory molecules such as acetylcholine, CCK, and catecholamines clearly have acute effects on secretion and metabolism using well characterized second messengers, they also have longer-term effects on cellular differentiation and protein synthesis that are not well understood. At present it is not clear whether these long-term effects use the same or different second messengers as acute effects. For example, it is not known whether the trophic effect of CCK on the pancreas is mediated by a transient or by a maintained increase in cytosolic Ca^{2+}.

Effectors

An effector system can be defined as the molecular machinery that serves to bring about a biological response. At present, considerably less is known about effector systems than of receptors or second messengers. For actions at the plasma membrane, an effector such as a transport protein could be directly activated by an occupied receptor. Most biological responses are, however, controlled by a second messenger, and as the second messenger is thought of as an informational molecule, this necessitates the existence of an effector mechanism.

The best studied class of effectors are the protein kinases that have been demonstrated and studied in pancreas and salivary gland and are similar to those in other tissues. Cyclic AMP–activated protein kinase has been demonstrated in the parotid glands of several species, and a cyclic AMP–binding protein has also been reported (8). In guinea pig pancreas, separate cAMP- and cGMP-activated kinases can be identified using ion exchange chromatography and exogenous histone as substrate (24). In mouse pancreatic acini a cyclic AMP–activated kinase could be identified based on phosphorylation of a specific set of endogenous proteins (7). Recently, descriptions of Ca^{2+}-activated kinases have also appeared. Calcium-activated kinases tend to be more substrate specific than cyclic nucleotide–activated kinases. Two soluble Ca^{2+}-activated kinases have been identified in pancreas, one requiring phosphatidyl serine as a cofactor and the other calmodulin (7, 64). These two kinases and the cAMP-activated kinase all phosphorylate different subsets of cytosolic proteins (7). Both the calmodulin-activated and cyclic AMP–activated kinase strongly phosphorylate a protein of $M_r = 94,000$ in cytosol.

Consistent with this data are a number of reports of altered patterns of protein phosphorylation in intact acinar cells. In the parotid, β-adrenergic agonists and dibutyryl cyclic AMP increased the phosphorylation of proteins variously reported in the range of $M_r = 29–35,000$ (4, 15, 22). Jahn et al localized this protein to the smooth membrane fraction and proposed a role in exocytosis (22). In mouse parotid lobules, carbachol also increased phosphorylation of the same protein as isoproterenol. This is significant because in this species cholinergic receptors strongly stimulate amylase release (22). By contrast, Freedman & Jamieson localized a protein of comparable size to rough membranes and identified it as ribosomal subunit S6 (15). Because of variability in protocol and difficulty in estimating molecular weights it is not definite whether the same protein is being studied.

In rat pancreas, Freedman & Jamieson also found a 29,000 dalton phosphoprotein similar to that in parotid, whose phosphorylation was increased by CCK_8, carbachol, or secretin (15). Burnham & Williams, using mouse pancreatic acini, found not only a particulate protein (M_r = 32,500) whose phosphorylation was increased but also found four soluble proteins whose phosphorylation was altered (5). Of these, dephosphorylation of proteins of M_r = 20,500 and 21,000 correlated most closely with amylase release. Furthermore, phosphorylation of the 32,500-dalton protein was also influenced by insulin, which by itself is not a secretagogue. At present, however, neither the further identity of these proteins is known, nor is the mechanism by which they are related to various cellular responses. Control of exocytotic secretion could involve phosphorylation of granule or plasma membrane or activation of contractility by phosphorylation of the light chain of myosin.

Another recently discovered effector system is the Ca^{2+}-activated monovalent cation–selective channel present in pancreatic basolateral plasma membranes (36, 37). Using the technique of "patch clamping," Maruyama & Petersen showed that the frequency of opening of these channels was increased when the inside of the membrane was exposed to Ca^{2+} (36). CCK applied to the outside of intact acini activated the same set of channels that could be subsequently activated by internal Ca^{2+} after the patch was excised from the cell (37). The opening of these channels will then lead to the influx of Na^+ and Ca^{++} and efflux of K^+ that depolarizes the cell. Thus depolarization is revealed to be the electrical consequence of this ion flux rather than a second messenger. Another probable effector mechanism presented in the basolateral membrane is a $Na^+ - Cl^-$ cotransport entry mechanism that may also be activated by Ca^{2+} (13, 54). In both cases the influx of Na^+ would activate the (Na^+,K^+)-ATPase, which would increase the active efflux of Na^+; this latter phenomenon has been demonstrated by studying the rate of [^{3}H] ouabain binding to the (Na^+,K^+)-ATPase in isolated pancreas acinar cells (21). In one current model, the anion then exits across the luminal membrane, while Na^+ that has been pumped by the (Na^+,K^+)-ATPase into the lateral intracellular space follows through the paracellular pathway, passing through the tight junction (13).

SUMMARY

Pancreas and salivary glands have highly developed regulatory mechanisms for the acute control of secretion of macromolecules and electrolytes, although other longer-term biosynthetic functions are also clearly regulated. The concepts of receptors and second messengers are clearly established, although receptors as molecular entities are just beginning to be characterized. While the functions activated are clearly organ or cell specific, the control systems clearly are not. The molecular mechanisms or effectors by which secretion is stimulated are still largely unkown. In the case of macromolecular secretion, emphasis is currently focused on cyclic AMP and Ca^{2+}-activated phosphorylation of cellular substrates. In the case of electrolyte secretion, attention is centered on the ion channels and carriers by which ions enter cells and on the energy dependent Na-K pump which carries out active ion extrusion.

Literature Cited

1. Amsterdam, A., Jamieson, J. D. 1973. Structural and functional characterization of isolated pancreatic exocrine cells. *J. Cell Biol.* 69:3028–32

2. Amsterdam, A., Jamieson, J. D. 1974. Studies on dispersed pancreatic exocrine cells. I. Dissociation techniques and morphologic characteristics of separated cells. *J. Cell Biol.* 63:1037–56

3. Au, D. K., Malbon, C. C., Butcher, F. R. 1977. Identification and characterization of beta$_1$-adrenergic receptors in rat parotid membranes. *Biochim. Biophys. Acta* 500:361–71

4. Baum, B. J., Freiberg, J. M., Ito, H., Roth, G. S., Filburn, C. R. 1981. β-Adrenergic regulation of protein phosphorylation and its relationship to exocrine secretion in dispersed rat parotid gland acinar cells. *J. Biol. Chem.* 256:9731–36

5. Burnham, D. B., Williams, J. A. 1982. Effects of carbachol, cholecystokinin, and insulin on protein phosphorylation in isolated pancreatic acini. *J. Biol. Chem.* 257:10523–28

6. Burnham, D. B., Williams, J. A. 1982. Effects of high concentrations of secretagogues on the morphology and secretory activity of the pancreas: a role for microfilaments. *Cell Tiss. Res.* 222:201–12

7. Burnham, D. B., Williams, J. A. 1983. Activation of protein kinase activity in isolated pancreatic acini by calcium and cyclic AMP. *Am. J. Physiol.* In press

8. Butcher, F. R., Putney, J. W. 1980. Regulation of parotid gland function by cyclic nucleotides and calcium. *Adv. Cyclic Nucleotide Res.* 13:215–49

9. Bylund, D. B., Martinez, J. R., Camden, J., Jones, S. B. 1982. Autonomic receptors in the developing submandibular glands of neonatal rats. *Arch. Oral. Biol.* 27:945–50

10. Chariot, J., Roze, C., Vaille, C. Debray, C. 1978. Effects of somatostatin on the external secretion of the pancreas of the rat. *Gastroenterology* 75:832–37

11. Christophe, J. P., Conlon, T. P., Gardner, J. D. 1976. Interaction of porcine vasoactive intestinal peptide with dispersed acinar cells from the guinea pig. Binding of radioiodinated peptide. *J. Biol. Chem.* 251:4629–34

12. Collins, S. M., Abdelmoumene, S., Jensen, R. T., Gardner, J. D. 1981. Cholecystokinin-induced persistent stimulation of enzyme secretion from pancreatic acini. *Am. J. Physiol.* 240:G459–65

13. DePont, J. J. H. M., Jansen, J. W. C. M., Kuijpers, G. A. J., Bonting, S. L. 1982. A model for pancreatic fluid secretion. In *Electrolyte and Water Transport Across Gastrointestinal Epithelia*, ed. R. M. Case, A. Gardner, L. A. Turnberg, J. A. Young, pp. 11–17. New York: Raven

14. Fahrenkrug, J. 1981. Physiological role of VIP in digestion. In *Gut Hormones*, ed. S. R. Bloom, J. M. Polak, pp. 385–91. Edinburgh/New York: Churchill Livingstone

15. Freedman, S. D., Jamieson, J. D. 1982. Hormone-induced protein phosphorylation II. Localization to the ribosomal

fraction from rat exocrine pancreas and parotid of a 29,000-dalton protein phosphorylated *in situ* in response to secretagogues. *J. Cell Biol.* 95:909–17

16. Fritz, M. E., LaVeau, P., Nahimas, A. J., Weigel, R. J., Lee, F. 1980. Primary cultures of feline acinar cells: dissociation, culturing, and viral infection. *Am. J. Physiol.* 239:G288–94

17. Githens, S. III, Holmquist, D. R. G., Whelan, J. F., Ruby, J. R. 1980. Ducts of the rat pancreas in agarose matrix culture. *In Vitro* 16:797–808

18. Goldfine, I. D., Kriz, B. M., Wong, K. Y., Hradek, G., Jones, A. L., Williams, J. A. 1981. Insulin action in pancreatic acini from streptozotocin-treated rats. III. Electron microscope autoradiography of ^{125}I-insulin. *Am. J. Physiol.* 240:G69–G75

19. Goldfine, I. D., Williams, J. A. 1983. Receptors for insulin and CCK in the acinar pancreas: relationship to hormone action. *Int. Rev. Cytol.* In press

20. Gunther, G. R., Jamieson, J. D. 1979. Increased intracellular cyclic GMP does not correlate with protein discharge from pancreatic acinar cells. *Nature* 280:318–20

20a. Hokin, L. E., Hokin, M. R. 1955. Effects of acetylcholine on the turnover of phosphoryl units in individual phospholipids of pancreas slices and brain cortex slices. *Biochim. Biophys. Acta* 18:102–10

21. Hootman, S. R., Ernst, S. A., Williams, J. A. 1983. Secretagogue regulation of Na^+/K^+ pump activity in pancreatic acinar cells. *Am. J. Physiol.* 245:G339–46

22. Jahn, R., Söling, H.-D. 1981. Phosphorylation of the same specific protein during amylase release evoked by β-adrenergic or cholinergic agonists in rat and mouse parotid glands. *Proc. Natl. Acad. Sci. USA* 78:6903–6

23. Jensen, R. T., Charlton, C. G., Adachi, H., Jones, S. W., O'Donohue, T. L., Gardner, J. D. 1983. Use of ^{125}I-secretin to identify and characterize high-affinity secretin receptors on pancreatic acini. *Am. J. Physiol.* 245:G186–G195

24. Jensen, R. T., Gardner, J. D. 1978. Cyclic nucleotide-dependent protein kinase activity in acinar cells from guinea pig pancreas. *Gastroenterology* 75:806–17

25. Jensen, R. T., Gardner, J. D. 1979. Interaction of physalaemin, substance P, and eledoisin with specific membrane receptors on pancreatic acinar cells. *Proc. Natl. Acad. Sci. USA* 76:5679–83

26. Jensen, R. T., Lemp, G. F., Gardner, J. D. 1980. Interaction of cholecystokinin with specific membrane receptors

on pancreatic acinar cells. *Proc. Natl. Acad. Sci. USA* 77:2079–83

27. Jensen, R. T., Moody, T., Pert, C., Rivier, J. E., Gardner, J. D. 1978. Interaction of bombesin and litorin with specific membrane receptors on pancreatic acinar cells. *Proc. Natl. Acad. Sci. USA* 75:6139–43

28. Kondo, S., Schulz, I. 1976. Calcium ion uptake in isolated pancreas cells induced by secretagogues. *Biochim. Biophys. Acta* 419:76–92

29. Larose, L., Dumont, Y., Asselin, J., Morisset, J., Poirier, G. G. 1981. Muscarinic receptor of rat pancreatic acini: [3H] QNB binding and amylase secretion. *Eur. J. Pharmacol.* 76 :247–54

30. Laychock, S. G., Putney, J. W. 1982. Roles of phospholipid metabolism in secretory cells. In *Cellular Regulation of Secretion and Release,* ed. P. M. Conn, pp. 53–105. New York: Academic

31. Logsdon, C. D., Williams, J. A. 1983. Epidermal growth factor binding and biological effects on mouse pancreatic acini. *Gastroenterology:* 85:339–45

32. Logsdon, C. D., Williams, J. A. 1983. Pancreatic acini in short-term culture: regulation by EGF, carbachol, insulin, and corticosterone. *Am. J. Physiol.* 244:G675–82

33. Ludford, J. M., Tulamo, B. R. 1980. β-Adrenergic and muscarinic receptors in developing rat parotid glands. *J. Biol. Chem.* 255:4619–27

34. Lundberg, J. M., Hedlund, B., Bartfai, T. 1982. Vasoactive intestinal polypeptide enhances muscarinic ligand binding in cat submandibular salivary gland. *Nature* 295:147–49

35. Mangos, J. A., McSherry, N. R., Butcher, F. R., Irwin, K., Barber, T. 1975. Dispersed rat parotid acinar cells I. Morphological and functional characterization. *Am. J. Physiol.* 229:553–59

36. Maruyama, Y., Petersen, O. H. 1982. Single-channel currents in isolated patches of plasma membrane from basal surface of pancreatic acini. *Nature* 299:159–61

37. Maruyama, Y., Petersen, O. H. 1982. Cholecystokinin activation of single-channel currents is mediated by internal messenger in pancreatic acinar cells. *Nature* 300:61–63

38. Meldolesi, J., Castiglioni, G., Parma, R., Nassivera, N., De Camilli, P. 1978. Ca^{++}-dependent disassembly and reassembly of occluding junctions in guinea pig pancreatic acinar cells. *J. Cell Biol.* 79:156–72

39. O'Doherty, J., Stark, R. J. 1982. Stimulation of pancreatic acinar secretion: increases in cytosolic calcium and

sodium. *Am. J. Physiol.* 242:G513–21

40. Oliver, C. 1980. Isolation and maintenance of differential exocrine gland acinar cells *in vitro*. *In Vitro* 16:297–305

41. Otsuki, M., Williams, J. A. 1982. Effect of diabetes mellitus on regulation of enzyme secretion by isolated rat pancreatic acini. *J. Clin. Invest.* 70:148–56

42. Petersen, O. H. 1980. *The Electrophysiology of Gland Cells*. London: Academic

43. Putney, J. W., Van de Walle, C. M. 1980. The relationship between muscarinic receptor binding and ion movements in rat parotid cells. *J. Physiol.* 299:521–31

44. Putney, J. W., Van de Walle, C. M., Wheeler, C. S. 1980. Binding of ^{125}I-physaelamin to rat parotid cells. *J. Physiol.* 301:205–19

45. Quissel, D. O., Barzen, K. A., Lafferty, J. L. 1981. Role of calcium and cAMP in the regulation of rat submandibular mucin secretion. *Am. J. Physiol.* 241:C76–85

46. Reyl-Desmars, F., Lewin, M. J. M. 1982. Evidence for an intracellular somatostatin receptor in pancreas: a comparative study with reference to gastric mucosa. *Biochem. Biophys. Res. Commun.* 109:1324–31

47. Sakamoto, C., Williams, J. A., Wong, K. Y., Goldfine, I. D. 1983. The CCK receptor on pancreatic plasma membranes: binding characteristics and covalent crosslinking. *FEBS Lett.* 151:63–66

47a. Sakamoto, C., Goldfine, I. O., Williams, J. A. 1983. Characterization of CCK receptor subunits on pancreatic plasma membranes. *J. Biol. Chem.* 258:12707–11

48. Sandberg, A. A., Rosenthal, H. E. 1974. Estrogen receptors in the pancreas. *J. Steroid Biochem.* 5:969–76

49. Sankaran, H., Goldfine, I. D., Bailey, A., Licko, V., Williams, J. A. 1982. Relationship of CCK receptor binding to regulation of biological functions in pancreatic acini. *Am. J. Physiol.* 242:G250–57

50. Sankaran, H., Goldfine, I. D., Deveney, C. W., Wong, K. Y., Williams, J. A. 1980. Binding of cholecystokinin to high affinity receptors on isolated rat pancreatic acini. *J. Biol. Chem.* 255:1849–53

51. Sankaran, H., Iwamoto, Y., Korc, M., Williams, J. A., Goldfine, I. D. 1981. Insulin action in pancreatic acini from streptozotocin-treated rats. II. Binding of ^{125}I-insulin to receptors. *Am. J. Physiol.* 240:G63–68

52. Schultz, G. S., Sarras, M. P., Gunther, G. R., Hull, B. E., Alicea, H. A. et al. 1980. Guinea pig pancreatic acini prepared with purified collagenase. *Exp. Cell. Res.* 130:49–62

53. Schulz, I. 1980. Bicarbonate transport in exocrine pancreas. *Ann. N.Y. Acad. Sci.* 341:191–209

54. Schulz, I., Stolze, H. H. 1980. The exocrine pancreas: the role of secretagogues, cyclic nucleotides, and calcium in enzyme secretion. *Ann. Rev. Physiol.* 42:127–56

55. Strittmatter, W. J., Davis, J. N., Lefkowitz, R. J. 1977. α-Adrenergic receptors in rat parotid cells. I. Correlation of [³H] dihydroergocryptine binding and catecholamine-stimulated potassium efflux. *J. Biol. Chem.* 252:5472–77

56. Svec, F., Rudis, M. 1981. Glucocorticoid hormone receptors in rat pancreas. *Biochim. Biophys. Acta* 674:30–36

57. Svoboda, M., Lambert, M., Furnelle, J., Christophe, J. 1982. Specific photoaffinity crosslinking of [^{125}I] cholecystokinin to pancreatic plasma membranes. Evidence for a disulfide-linked M_r 76,000 peptide in cholecystokinin receptors. *Regulatory Peptides* 4:163–72

58. Williams, J. A. 1980. Regulation of pancreatic acinar cell function by intracellular calcium. *Am. J. Physiol.* 238:G269–79

59. Williams, J. A. 1982. Cholecystokinin: a hormone and a neurotransmitter. *Biomed. Res.* 3:107–21

59a. Williams, J. A., Bailey, A., Humble, R., Goldfine, I. D. 1984. Insulin-like growth factors (IGF) bind to specific receptors in isolated pancreatic acini. *Am. J. Physiol.* 246: in press

60. Williams, J. A., Cary, P., Moffat, B. 1976. Effects of ions on amylase release by dissociated pancreatic acinar cells. *Am. J. Physiol.* 231:1562–67

61. Williams, J. A., Korc, M., Dormer, R. L. 1978. Action of secretagogues on a new preparation of functionally intact, isolated pancreatic acini. *Am. J. Physiol.* 235:E517–24

62. Williams, J. A., Sankaran, H., Korc, M., Goldfine, I. D. 1981. Receptors for cholecystokinin and insulin in isolated pancreatic acini: hormonal control of secretion and metabolism. *Fed. Proc.* 40:2497–2502

63. Williams, J. A., Sankaran, H., Roach, E., Goldfine, I. D. 1982. Quantitative electron microscope autoradiographs of ^{125}I-cholecystokinin in pancreatic acini. *Am. J. Physiol.* 243:G291–96

64. Wrenn, R. W., Katoh, N., Kuo, J. F. 1981. Stimulation by phospholipid of calcium-dependent phosphorylation of endogenous proteins from mammalian tissues. *Biochim. Biophys. Acta* 676:266–69

Ann. Rev. Physiol. 1984. 46:377–92

THE MAMMALIAN GASTRIC PARIETAL CELL IN VITRO

Thomas Berglindh

Department of Physiology, University of California, Los Angeles and CURE, VA Wadsworth Hospital Center, Bldg. 115, Room 217, Los Angeles, California 90073

INTRODUCTION

After almost a century of research on the mechanisms underlying gastric acid secretion, using whole animal or whole tissue preparations, in the last decade the use of subtissue or subcellular models of this process has virtually revolutionized our understanding. Looking back at the development of cellular model systems derived from the stomach, there are really no techniques applied today that were not available earlier. Instead I believe that progress in this area is to a substantial extent a state of mind and that the concept "small is beautiful" had many brain barriers to cross before subtissue models were accepted as an adequate tool for physiological studies. To state this is by no means to take anything away from the studies of whole animal or intact tissue physiology, because any discoveries made in a simplified system must be validated under proper physiological conditions, an approach often lacking in current literature. I believe, however, that the astonishing progress in gastric research in the last decade would not have taken place without in vitro model systems.

This brief overview centers around the gastric mammalian parietal cell in vitro. In a subsequent paper Dr. Hersey describes the peptic cell.

Background

It might seem surprising to readers unfamiliar with the gastric field that only recently was the parietal cell directly identified as the source of the largest ion gradient known in mammalian biology (6). In histological studies close to a century ago, however, this cell was implicated as responsible for hydrochloric acid secretion (27). In the light of recent discoveries that H^+ ion gradients seem to drive a number of biological processes in addition to the well-known

377

0066-4278/84/0315-0377$02.00

chemi-osmotic system in the mitochondria (36, 48), the parietal cell is a valid model of interest to others outside the gastric field.

Based on the morphology of the acid-secreting part of the gastric mucosa, two different subtissue preparations can be obtained: glands and cells. On the average in most mammals, 3–4 glands are associated with each gastric pit into which the glandular content is emptied. Since the mucosa and the pits are covered by a thick layer of mucus, it has always bothered this author how the watery secretion enters the stomach. Presumably a powerful enough jet stream would penetrate this layer, but since the mucus gel seems to form a fairly strong confluent layer, a "plopp-plopp" mechanism where droplets containing the acid and pepsin are shuttled through the gel would seem to be a more appropriate system. The answer to this fairly trivial question has yet to be researched.

With the large output of fluid from the stomach, the mucosa must be very well vascularised. In fact a dense network of capillaries run along and across the glands. By performing a vascular perfusion of these under high pressure, a mechanical separation of the glands will be induced (10). This will in turn facilitate the subsequent collagenase breakdown of the mucosa. Thus, after 40–60 minutes in the rabbit, the whole mucosa is broken down to glands and cells. Typically the glands are 500–1000 μ long and 50 μ wide at this stage. If handled with love and care, their size can be maintained. In glands obtained from some animals, (e.g. man) the perfusion step must be omitted; this will prolong the necessary collagenase digestion time to more than two hours. In spite of this, the glands are relatively responsive to stimulation (29). Glands represent almost a doubling of the percentage parietal cells obtained as compared to the intact mucosa, because all the surface epithelial cells are gone.

GLAND AND CELL PREPARATION

In order to prepare cells, a number of different techniques have been outlined; (a) prolonged collagenase digestion, followed by mechanical disruption of cell clusters (21); (b) pronase digestion of minced mucosa pieces (38); (c) a mixture of pronase and collagenase digestion of minced pieces (9); (d) pronase added to the outside of an everted, tied-off stomach (39); (e) intermittent treatment of mucosa pieces with collagenase and EDTA respectively (52); (f) same as E, but starting from isolated glands (Berglindh, unpublished observation).

To date glands have been prepared from the following species: rabbit (10), man (29), guinea pig (Berglindh, unpublished observation), rat (25), and dog (Berglindh, unpublished observation). In addition to the above species, cells have also been prepared from necturus (16) and frog (44).

Measurement of Parietal Cell Activity

Isolated cells or cell clusters that secrete proteins or enzymes can be easily studied if an assay for that product is available. Examples of these are pancreatic acinar cells (amylase) or gastric chief cells (pepsinogen). But how do we measure H^+ secretion in a gland or cell suspension, when H^+ ions are coming out through the apical membrane and HCO_3^- through the basolateral membrane in equal amounts? In isolated glands we could, theoretically, cannulate the lumen and directly measure acid secretion. Such work is actually in progress. In order to get an average signal from a large number of glands or cells, however, we have to use indirect methods to determine acid formation (or secretion).

Since the glands and all routinely used cell preparations (crude cells) consist of a mixed cell population, parietal cell–specific probes have to be used. The following have been shown to correlate well with the secretory status of the parietal cell.

(a) Oxygen consumption: The parietal cell is extremely rich in mitochondria, which will occupy 30–40% of the cell volume as compared to 5% for the chief cells (30). Thus it is highly likely that any major changes in respiratory activity must mainly reflect changes in parietal cell metabolism (10, 52). This can be checked by agents selectively affecting the parietal cell (e.g. histamine) that at least in the rabbit will only stimulate the parietal cell. Determination of oxygen consumption is probably a good measurement of the turnover of the hydrogen pump, in contrast to some other methods listed below that reflect changes in pH.

(b) Recently the formation of $^{14}CO_2$ from ^{14}C-glucose has been successfully used for determination of metabolic activity in parietal cells from the dog (22). The basis and usefulness of this analysis is the same as for respiration.

(c) Accumulation of weak bases: These can be used to determine sequestered acid, because they will accumulate in membrane-bound acid spaces. They can either be radiolabeled or optically active. The background for this approach is the following: A weak base that is lipid soluble in its uncharged form will rapidly equilibrate across membranes. If the environment on the trans side has a pH at or below its pK_a, the base will be protonated and thus charged. Ideally this charged species will have lost its membrane-penetrating capability and thus will accumulate. Knowing the volume of the space where the weak base has accumulated will enable us to calculate an accumulation ratio (R). From the pK_a of the weak base and the external pH (pH_o), we can now calculate the pH in the acid space (pH_i) using the formula $R = 1 + 10^{(pK_a-pH_i)} / 1 + 10^{(pK_a-pH_o)}$.

From this formula it is obvious that a weak base will not start to accumulate until the pH_i falls below that of the medium or cytoplasm, regardless of the pK_a or the pH_o. With a fluorescent weak base like acridine orange (AO), which has a pK_a of 10.45, we would anticipate an accumulation ratio of 100 at $pH_i=5$ and $pH_o=7$. However there are several structures in a cell where the pH can be around 5, (e.g. lysosomes and granules). It is thus important to choose a weak base with the appropriate pK_a for measurement of HCl secretion in the parietal cell. Fortunately, in the case of AO we can microscopically visualize the accumulation site (6). Accordingly, to ensure that the weak base accumulation we obtain in gastric glands or cells is a true reflection of sequestered HCl, the pk_a of the weak base should be 6 or lower. Since the pH in the space into which acid is secreted should be below 2 (pH in the stomach is 0.8), large amounts of weak base will be accumulated. The other requirement is that the protonated species be highly impermeable. If there is an accumulation limit at which a breakthrough, (i.e. backflux) of ionized weak base takes place, the ratios measured are misleading, and the weak base will act as an uncoupler of the proton pump. Obviously a base with a low pK_a will not as easily reach such a breakthrough point, but chemical considerations such as charge delocalization will also play a role in the permeability of the protonated species. One weak base that comes close to these criteria is aminopyrine (AP) (N,N,-dimethyl antipyrine) with a pK_a of 5.0 (8).

Site of Weak Base Accumulation

It is important to remember that this type of weak base is not a pH indicator as such. It has to penetrate through membranes to accumulate; it is the accumulation that is an index of a pH gradient, not an absolute measure of actual pH in the accumulation compartment. Therefore, it cannot be concentrated by simply diffusing down the lumen of a gland or into the secretory channel of a parietal cell—even if these contain acid—but instead has to travel through the basolateral membrane, through the cytoplasm, and finally cross the apical membrane in order to sense the presence of a transmembrane pH gradient.

Glands and to a lesser extent cells show a basal AP accumulation. This is not sensitive to histamine H_2-receptor antagonists or antimuscarinic agents, *but* can be inhibited by thiocyanate (SCN^-) (47) and substituted benzimidazoles (timoprazole, picoprazole, and omeprazole) (23) as well as mitochondrial inhibitors like oligomycin (43), cyanate, and azide (7). The source for these H^+ ions in a resting preparation is puzzling. Looking at a resting parietal cell by regular transmission electron microscopy reveals a cytoplasmatic space filled with round or elongated smooth surface structures, the so called tubulovesicles. Upon stimulation to secrete acid, these disappear and are replaced by secretory channels packed with long microvilli. All evidence indicates that these two membrane pools originate from the same source and that they are interconvertible. Thus the H^+-generating machinery should be in place whether the cells are resting or not; therefore, it is possible that some acid is secreted into the tubulovesicles in a resting cell and that this acid compartment is detected by the weak base. It is also quite likely that some acid is secreted into the resting secretory channel (characterized by small stubby microvilli).

The transformation from the resting to the secretory state has for a long time been considered to be via a fusion process where the tubulovesicles merge and form the villi in the extended secretory channel. The background for such a proposal has been electron microscopy studies. The problem with these, however, is that we do not know if we are looking at the true morphology, or if this has been altered by the fixation process. Based on studies in living gastric glands some years ago, we suggested that the tubulovesicles actually were collapsed channels, like branches on a tree, that would expand into the secretory channel and microvilli upon osmotic expansion (6). This theory was deduced from the following very simplistic reasoning: (a) Upon stimulation an increased influx of K^+ and Cl^- through selective pathways into the canalicular or vesicular space will take place. (b) Most of the K^+ will be exchanged for H^+ by the gastric (H^+, K^+)-ATPase located at the canalicular membrane, leading to an accumulation of HCl. (c) Since the K^+ is pumped back into the cytoplasm, a continous inward K^+ gradient will persist and lead to an increased osmolarity in the acid-containing space that in turn will draw excess water and osmotically expand the space.

What precipitated this idea was our finding that addition of 1 mM exogenous aminopyrine was accumulated in the parietal cells to such an extent that large vacuoles appeared in apparently resting cells, as viewed by Nomarski optics in living gastric glands and electron microscopy of fixed glands (6). These vacuoles were most abundant when the glands were incubated in a medium of 108 mM K^+, but this was not a prerequisite because the same structures could be induced in resting glands incubated in *regular medium*. The hypothesis that the morphological transformation of the parietal cell from a resting to a stimulated appearance could be partly due to an osmotic force generated a lot of interest as well as criticism. From regular EM micrographs, as well as freeze-fracture replicas, no collapsed network of tubuli could be seen in resting parietal cells. In an attempt to study the osmotic process more closely, Gibert & Hersey (26) repeated the gland experiments and confirmed the formation of vacuoles after addition of aminopyrine. However, they also made morphometric measurements of the areas occupied by tubulovesicular as well as canalicular membrane. In a normal resting cell we have a large pool of tubulovesicular membrane that upon stimulation is decreased and replaced by an apparently equal area of secretory membrane. Gibert & Hersey (26) only saw a doubling of the area occupied by secretory membrane in spite of the "stimulated" appearance of the parietal cells after the aminopyrine treatment. The area occupied by the tubulovesicles did not change. Based on these findings they dismissed the osmotic component of the parietal cell transformation. It is important, however, to remember that the aminopyrine-induced transformation only would occur in areas where sufficient acid is not only present *but actively secreted*. The reason for this is that if an enclosed volume contained, for example, 150 mM HCl, but no additional acid secretion took place, aminopyrine would only accumulate up to 150 mM and then stop. Only via additional secretion could an osmotic effect be expected that in turn would expand that space. *Secondly,* it is very unlikely that the artificially induced osmotic effect could mimic more than a portion of the events taking place upon histamine stimulation of the parietal cell. Thus, it has been convincingly shown that the cytoskeleton plays a significant role for the morphological transformation of the parietal cell and its ability to secrete acid (15). Actin has been shown to be associated with the secretory membrane of the canaliculi and the role of microtubules has been implied due to the effect of microtubule-disrupting agents on the morphology and secretion (15, 46). It is conceivable that the cytoskeleton is essential to give the microvilli of the secretory channel a more rigid structure.

Recently Ito (35) showed that if cells are rapidly frozen in liquid nitrogen prior to fixation for electron microscopy, the appearance of the resting cell is quite different. It was then almost exclusively filled with tubules, although they did not seem to have any openings to the apical membrane. This finding might indicate two things: the vesicles seen following regular fixation might be an artefact; and because no connection can be seen between the tubule and secretory channel, some kind of fusion process might be needed—at least at that stage. We recently studied (Berglindh & Helander, manuscript in preparation) the effect of electrolytes on the morphological transformation induced by histamine. At low intracellular K^+ in the absence of Na^+, limited morphological transformation occured, and this was further inhibited by addition of Na^+. The absence of Cl^- had no effect on the morphological change. Similar effects of electrolytes were recently reported by Logsden & Machen (40). These findings are hard to reconcile with a pure fusion process. It is possible, therefore, that the existence of a combined osmotic and fusion process will ultimately be shown in the mammalian parietal cell, as has been recently suggested in the frog gastric mucosa (41).

Secretagogues Stimulation

One major field where the use of isolated preparations has shown to be invaluable is our understanding as to how the different physiological secretagogues stimulate and interact at the level of the parietal cell. This topic as well as the mechanism by which they seem to work on the intracellular level has been covered in a number of articles and reviews (47, 54, 56), I therefore intend to be very brief on this subject. It is clear from a number of cell and gland studies that histamine and acetylcholine do stimulate via adenylcyclase activation (20) and Ca^{++} influx (12, 47, 54) respectively, and that these mechanisms interact beyond the receptor level, leading to a potentiated response (3). It is also clear that in the dog, gastrin is an additional, albeit poor, direct secretagogue (52–54). In no other species tested, including man, has there been any reports of direct gastrin stimulation of a subtissue preparation under similar circumstances. In rabbit glands a gastrin-dependent response can be obtained in the presence of Isobutyl-Methyl-Xanthine (IMX) (12, 47) and, as originally shown by Chew et al (19), in the presence of the sulfhydryl-reacting agent dithiothreitol (DTT) without IMX. In our hands both these gastrin-dependent responses were totally blocked by 100 μM cimetidine, whereas Chew et al (19) found a small residual response persisting at 10 μM cimetidine. In the presence of DTT a small transient potentiation between histamine and gastrin was also reported. In the dog parietal cells this potentiation was more pronounced (54, 55) and did not need the background of sulfhydryl-reducing agents. Recently we have started to prepare glands from the dog gastric mucosa and subsequently have confirmed the findings of Soll (54) that a small, cimetidine-insensitive response to gastrin is present in most but not all preparations. However, further preliminary data indicate that this response is strongly potentiated by IMX—similar to that in the rabbit, including its sensitivity to cimetidine (Berglindh, unpublished observation). Thus, as far as the rabbit system is concerned, we can state with some certainty that the major gastrin pathway involves histamine as an absolutely essential constituent. For the dog cells and tentatively for the dog glands there is a partial pure gastrin response, coupled to what looks like an important histamine component. These differences between rabbit and dog can only be ascribed at this point to species variation.

The Endogenous Histamine Component

In the rabbit gastric glands, the histamine involved in the gastrin as well as the acetylcholine-dependent response must come from cells within the glands. Histochemical staining has not revealed the presence of any mast cells within the glandular body. In spite of that, rabbit glands contain 5–10 μg histamine g^{-1} wet weight. As first shown by Bergqvist & Obrink (13), the glands have a basal release of histamine; this release can be significantly and dose-dependently increased by gastrin and acetylcholine (13, 14). The source for this histamine is presently unknown, but small endocrine cells in the glands may be involved (14). With a few exceptions (e.g. rat, mouse) the mammalian stomach is considered to have a low histamine-forming capacity (HFC), (i.e. low histidine-decarboxylase activity). However, there might be enough to explain the histamine found associated with the glands. Alternatively, an uptake and storage of exogenous histamine in specialized cells, from which it could be released following the proper stimuli, could be suggested. This possibility seems less likely; it will be discussed in some detail later. Among isolated cells obtained from the dog gastric mucosa, an atypical population of mast cells has been found and purified (2, 57). These mast cells will not release histamine in response to compound 48/80. Nor will histamine be released by gastrin or acetylcholine. Soll et al suggested, based on these findings, that the gastric mast cells, which would be located in the connective tissue outside the glands, could continuously release some histamine. Thus the parietal cell would have a constant histamine background against which gastrin and acetylcholine directly could elicit their stimulatory power (57). This is an interesting suggestion, but it remains to be shown that such an unregulated mechanism could constitute the histamine component of stimulation in the dog gastric mucosa or if also the dog glands will show histamine-containing cells.

Histamine Uptake

A potent histamine uptake system has been found in the rabbit glands (11, 20) as well as in isolated guinea-pig gastric cells (1). This uptake is dependent on Na^+ and on oxidative metabolism (11). The radiolabeled histamine taken up will be accumulated in the glands, and the accumulated product cannot be washed away or chased by addition of excess unlabeled histamine. Thin-layer chromatography of extracts of this accumulated product showed that 95% of the radioactivity recovered was not histamine but a methylated derivative (11). Recently this compound has been positively identified in guinea-pig cells to be tele-methyl-histamine (1). The parietal cell seemed to be the main site for this uptake-conversion mechanism, as judged by autoradiography (11) and positive correlation to the presence of parietal cells (1). Histamine-Methyl-Transferase (the enzyme responsible for the tele-methylation of histamine) has been found in isolated dog cells, and from coincidental studies the preferential localization appears to be the parietal cell (2). It is therefore fairly safe to conclude that the main target cell for histamine in the gastric mucosa has the ability to remove and inactivate one of its key stimulants. The uptake and accumulation of radiolabeled histamine is of such a magnitude that, at an exogenous histamine concentration of 1 μM, the intracellular water will contain 20–30 μM converted histamine after 1 hour (11). Based on that, it is understandable that both the detection of histamine receptors using radiolabeled compounds as well as the localization of an additional uptake pathway for the storage of unconverted histamine in specialized cells, as discussed earlier, are extremely difficult. Previously published binding studies using histamine in rat and guinea-pig gastric cells, showing K_d of 10 μM when the physiological $K_{0.5}$ is found to be 1 μM, could be explained by this uptake mechanism.

Endogenous Gastric Secretory Inhibitors

Based on findings from in vivo studies, a number of gastrones (natural inhibitors of gastric acid secretion) have been suggested. Most of these have been disqualified because the doses needed to inhibit the secretion were much higher then could be expected to exist under physiological circumstances. Among these we find secretin and GIP. Bulbogastrone, neurotensin, VIP, somatostatin, and urogastrone are more likely candidates, but in most cases we await final proof. In the different subtissue systems we will only detect direct effects on the parietal cell and possibly the inhibition of histamine release. If we do not see effects of known inhibitors in these preparations, we have to look for neuronal, secondary hormonal or blood-flow effects. In a recent paper Chew (18) described the inhibitory effect of somatostatin, a hormone found both in the antrum as well as in the fundus. Somatostatin inhibited the gastrin response in the glands (under DTT influence) most potently, $K_i \sim 10^{-9} M$, but also the direct stimulation by histamine. It was suggested, based on these findings, that somatostatin could interact with both the histamine release as well as the histamine effect on the parietal cell, the former antagonizing direct gastrin effects more potently than the latter. Binding of somatostatin has been reported to occur in isolated rat parietal cells (45); it was hard, however, to displace all of the bound hormone using excess unlabeled somatostatin, which might be due to internalization of the label.

In isolated dog cells from the fundic mucosa, somatostatin-containing cells have been partially purified, and preliminary cultures established (59). Somatostatin could be released by adrenalin; this was counteracted by acetylcholine. Thus the somatostatin cell might be under a complex regulatory control, where the cholinergic influence acts like the on/off switch.

Yet another natural inhibitor could be the urogastrone (17), which seems to be very similar to Epidermal Growth Factor (EGF). In preliminary experiments with rabbit gastric glands, EGF very potently inhibited histamine-induced secretion with a K_i around 10 μg l^{-1}. In contrast, the response to dibuturyl-cyclic AMP (db-cAMP) did not show any sign of inhibition until after 40 μg l^{-1} (Berglindh, unpublished observation). Thus EGF might either specifically interact with the histamine receptor or, as has been suggested, increase the production of prostaglandins, which in turn would affect the histamine response in a manner discussed below. Some morphological studies of intact mucosa have indicated that EGF might affect the cytoskeleton and thereby inhibit the secretion (28). If that were the only effect, however, it is unlikely that the histamine response would be singled out.

Prostaglandins of the E-type as well as prostacyclin (PGI$_2$) have been known for a long time to inhibit acid secretion. Since the inhibitory effect of these was found to be associated with an increase in the cAMP content of the gastric mucosa, the mechanisms behind the inhibition remained obscured because the stimulation of acid secretion was also correlated with an increase in cAMP. Again only with the use of isolated cells could this issue be even partially resolved. In partially purified dog parietal cells, the prostaglandins at low concentrations inhibited the histamine-induced production of cAMP in an apparent parallel fashion to the prostaglandin-dependent inhibition of acid formation (53). At higher prostaglandin concentrations the expected overall increase in cAMP was seen. However, this did not seem to correlate with the presence of parietal cells. The cAMP increase might thus reflect activation of adenylcyclase in other cells. Such a set of events would readily explain the results obtained in vivo and in intact tissue.

The precursor to prostaglandins, arachidonic acid, has also been shown to inhibit aminopyrine accumulation in isolated dog cells; this inhibition could be overcome by the cyclo-oxygenase inhibitor indomethacin (51). In fact, using radiolabeled arachidonic acid at least four different prostaglandins [6-keto PGF_{1a} (a hydrolysis product of PGI_2), PGF_{2a}, PGE_2, and PGD_2] were shown to be synthesized (50). Both cell suspensions enriched in parietal cells ($\sim 75\%$) as well as parietal-cell depleted fractions produced these prostaglandins. Until a pure parietal cell fraction is obtained, the cellular source for the different prostaglandins cannot be determined, nor whether the parietal cell itself can produce these compounds. However, we can safely conclude that prostaglandins play a crucial role in the everyday life of the gastric mucosa, shutting down acid production and increasing mucus and HCO_3 secretion in response to injury.

Electrolytes of the Parietal Cell

Another advantage of the cell systems is the ability to measure and manipulate the intracellular ion content. Such maneuvers have extended and confirmed findings from the isolated frog gastric mucosa, which was the first to be subjected to these studies. It is quite clear from our studies in isolated gastric glands that Na^+, K^+, and Cl^- play essential roles in the process of acid secretion (4, 5, 37). Both K^+ (5) and Cl^- (4) are absolutely required for the secretion of acid, whereas Na^+ has an inhibitory effect (37). Removal of extracellular K^+ will inhibit both basal as well as stimulated secretion. If, however, both K^+ and Na^+ are removed, some secretion can, oddly enough, still occur. The reason found for this is that there is a substantial amount of K^+ left in the cells, even after extensive washings in K^+, Na^+-free medium. In the absence of inhibitory Na^+, therefore, even small amounts of intracellular K^+ can drive secretion. The only way glandular K^+ could be depleted was by treatment of glands with the pore-forming ionophore amphotericin B in the presence of ouabain. Once the intracellular level of K^+ was decreased below 5 mM, very little acid was produced, and the dose-dependency of K^+ readdition could be studied. It could now be shown that the sensitivity to K^+ was different for resting as compared to stimulated glands (37). Thus the apparent $K_{0.5}$ for K^+ decreased from 18 mM to 11 mM in the presence of histamine. With Na^+ present these curves were shifted to the right, and more so for the resting glands—indicating that part of the Na^+ inhibition could be of a competitive nature (interacting with the same site(s) as K^+.) In this respect it is of interest that the hydrogen ion transport seen in vesicles containing the gastric (H^+, K^+)-ATPase is inhibited by Na^+ on the cytosolic face. The finding of an increased sensitivity for the K^+-induced secretion under stimulated conditions also fits with the observations of Wolosin & Forte (58) that membranes isolated from stimulated gastric mucosa show an ionophore and pre-equilibration-independent, KCl-driven H-ion transport.

The Cl^- content of parietal cell is much simpler to manipulate; repeated washings in Cl^--free medium is sufficient to totally deplete the cells. Under such conditions the glands will not secrete any acid, but oddly enough the oxygen consumption will increase in response to secretagogues (4). The nature of this apparent uncoupling between metabolism and actual appearance of acid in the secretory channels is highly interesting, but at present we can only speculate about it. In a recent, more detailed study over the Cl^- requirement in gastric glands Malinowska et al (42) determined the intracellular Cl^- levels in resting and stimulated glands, as well as the intracellular $K_{0.5}$ for Cl^- under these conditions. They found that stimulated glands had a higher intracellular steady-state level (80 mM), but that even under apparent resting conditions the intracellular Cl^- levels were high (60 mM). Unless cell potentials were remarkably low, this would suggest that Cl^- is not at electrochemical equilibrium in the gastric gland model. At low extracellular Cl^-, the glands seemed in fact to accumulate Cl^-. In the presence of regular extracellular K^+ and Na^+, the intracellular $K_{0.5}$ for Cl^- was 18 mM under db-cAMP stimulated conditions. In the absence of extracellular Na^+ this value decreased to 11 mM, a figure very similar to that seen for the K^+ requirement under similar conditions. The fact that the Cl^--induced secretion was inhibited by Na^+ (42) just like the K^+-driven secretion indicates strongly that Cl^- and K^+ movements are coupled, because the most likely site for Na^+ inhibition would be the K^+ site.

Metabolism of the Parietal Cell

A large amount of energy is needed to transport H ions uphill against a gradient of at least 4 million. As mentioned earlier, the parietal cell is probably the body cell richest in mitochondria. One would assume, therefore, that the ATP generated by the mitochondria would be the natural energy source. However, for different reasons this issue has been a topic for research and debate in the gastric field for decades. Two main possibilities were discussed. One was a redox process that would donate protons in the form of XH_2, which would convert to $X + 2H^+ + 2e^-$. The electrons would then be taken up by an appropriately oriented acceptor system, and ultimately O_2 would be reduced. The alternative process was that ATP was inducing acid transport via an ATP:ase. With the finding of the unique potassium-dependent, apically located, H^+-transporting ATP:ase, the latter possibility was strongly favored. Naturally that finding does not exclude the existence of a combined ATP and redox–driven hydrogen-ion pump. One of the main difficulties in properly studying these alternatives lay in the obvious problem of getting exogenous ATP into the cells under conditions where the mitichondrial ATP production was shut off. A couple of years ago we managed to permeabilize glands using an electric-shock technique that lead to a dielectric membrane breakdown, allowing at least medium-sized molecules (up to 5000 Mw) to penetrate into the cell (7). By changing the extracellular medium to resemble intracellular composition, we were able to obtain acid formation—as measured by accumulation of aminopy-rine—by addition of exogenous ATP. Inhibitors of mitochondrial activity like azide, cyanide, and amytal did not prohibit this ATP-induced acid formation. As in the intact glands, the secretion was dependent on K^+ and could be inhibited by SCN^-. Removing oxygen by the use of nitrogen combined with glucose oxidase did not seem to inhibit the process. In a similar study where Malinowska et al (43) used digitonin to permeabilize, the glands were first inhibited with oligomycin and then incubated under O_2-free conditions. These studies showed more conclusively that ATP was sufficient to drive the proton formation in these non-stimulated glands. A detailed dose-response curve to K^+ in the digitonin-permeabilized glands showed that the half maximum concentration needed was very close to that found in intact glands (43).

The frog gastric mucosa, which is one of the best studied from a metabolic standpoint because it is possible to optically measure intracellular cytochromes while determining the acid secretion, showed very unusual patterns. The cytochromes went to a reduced state upon stimulation of acid secretion, in contrast to what would be expected upon increased metabolic demand (31). Amytal inhibition of frog gastric acid secretion was shown to be associated with a drop in ATP and phosphocreatine levels (32). Bypassing the amytal block by menadione restored ATP levels and the short-circuit current but not the acid secretion. This would indicate that ATP is not sufficient to drive acid secretion in the frog or possibly that different pools of ATP are used for the separate functions. As mentioned above, the AP accumulation in the permeabilized rabbit glands could be restored by ATP addition even after amytal (7).

In biopsies obtained from the dog gastric mucosa under different stages of HCl secretion, little differences were seen in the ATP/ADP ratio; phospho-creatinine, in fact, increased (49). Although metabolic changes in glycolytic as well as Krebs-cycle intermediates were obtained, no definite discrimination between redox and ATP-driven processes could be determined.

In mammals [e.g. isolated piglet gastric mucosa (24) and isolated rabbit gastric glands (33, 34)] an absolute dependence of acid secretion upon exo-genous substrates is said to exist. The piglet seems to prefer carbohydrates, whereas the rabbit could be classified as a scavanger, being able to metabolize carbohydrates as well as fatty acids (33). Hersey suggested that the main importance for the glucose pathway is to produce pyruvate equivalents and not to generate ATP via the Embden-Meyerhoff pathway (34). Thus both fatty acids and carbohydrates would go via acetyl-CoA and the Krebs cycle. Hersey has also shown that a number of substrates increase oxygen consumption without changing the ATP content of the glands (33). Unfortunately he did not measure aminopyrine accumulation under the same conditions. It turns out that although substrates like butyrate and succinate can increase both resting as well as stimulated respiration, there is no change in the AP accumulation. If the stimulated glands are inhibited by substituted benzimidazoles, which will lead to a decrease in both AP accumulation and respiration, the exact same changes in oxygen consumption (i.e. μl O_2) are seen regardless of the substrate-dependent respiratory rate (23). Thus only the respiration associated with acid secretion was affected. It is therefore doubtful that metabolic preferences can be deduced from respiratory measurements. Recently it was shown, however, that the inhibitor of Na^+-independent glucose transport, phloretin, inhibited glucose oxidation as well as histamine-stimulated AP accumulation in the glands (34). As expected, this inhibition could be overcome by substrates like pyruvate, butyrate, acetate, and 3-Br-butyrate, the last of which has been shown to reduce glandular ATP content (33).

SUMMARY

To summarize the metabolic status of the parietal cell:

(a) There does not seem to be a close relationship between cellular ATP levels and acid secretion.

(b) Acid secretion is absolutely dependent on oxygen, and oxygen consumption will increase in direct proportion to the rate of acid secretion. However, the absolute rate of respiration is not closely related to the formation of acid in the subtissue systems.

(c) Acid formation can be driven directly by addition of ATP in permeabilized glands, even under apparent anoxic conditions. This correlates well with the presence of the gastric (H^+, K^+)-ATPase in the parietal cell.

(d) If ATP is the main source of energy for the acid secretion, it is quite possible that the relevant ATP pool is compartmentalized (33) and that the content in this pool has a high turnover rate, whereas the ATP used for other cellular functions would be spared.

(e) A pure redox mechanism in the gastric mucosa is not possible. However, it remains to be shown that a redox component is not involved in the secretory process. The acid formation measured by AP accumulation in the gastric glands is not an indication of secretory rate. Thus even though ATP appears to restore acid formation in permeabilized glands, this effect has been mainly studied in nonstimulated systems. A detailed study over the energy requirement in the permeabilized resting cell remains to be done.

(f) In the mammals we only have information so far about the piglet and the rabbit in terms of substrate preference. The differences between the two could either be due to species or age difference.

(g) In both mammals and amphibia, there is no evidence to suggest that acid secretion results in an increase in oxygen consumption purely due to a state IV to III transition of mitochondrial respiration. Rather, increased Krebs-cycle activity would appear to be the major metabolic result of stimulation.

FUTURE TRENDS IN GASTRIC GLAND AND CELL RESEARCH

With further developments in cell technology, a number of exciting new fields will open up for the gastric reseacher. Several attempts to culture parietal cells have been made, but so far this highly differentiated cell has been resistant. Since the parietal cell does not divide, cells have to be seeded out, polarized, and a monolayer formed. The development of specific antagonists of the gastric ATPase promises a better understanding of the electrophysiology of the intact tissue. Modern electrical approaches to isolated cells or membranes such as suction clamp, patch clamp, and excised patch clamp should help resolve many of the issues of the electrical properties of the parietal cell. Further developments in our understanding of isolated vesicles derived from resting or stimulated tissue, and of the mechanism of the ATPase itself, will also advance the field. A particular shortfall in our understanding of stimulus secretion coupling is the site of action of second messengers such as Ca^{++} and cAMP. As we begin to understand the differences between "active" and "inactive" membranes, this problem should also become amenable to experimentation.

ACKNOWLEDGMENT

Different parts of this review have been the result of support by The Swedish Medical Res. Council, CFN., Uppsala University, and NIH.

Literature Cited

1. Albinus, M., Sewing, K.-Fr. 1981. Histamine uptake and metabolism in intact isolated parietal cells. *Agents and Actions* 11:223–27
2. Beaven, M. A., Soll, A. H., Lewin, K. J. 1982. Histamine synthesis by intact mast cells from canine fundic mucosa and liver. *Gastroenterology* 82:254–62
3. Berglindh, T. 1977 Potentiation by carbachol and aminophylline of histamine and db-cAMP-induced parietal cell activity in isolated gastric glands. *Acta Physiol. Scand.* 99:75–84
4. Berglindh, T. 1977. Absolute dependence of chloride for acid secretion in isolated gastric glands. *Gastroenterology* 73:874–80
5. Berglindh, T. 1978. The effects of K^+ and Na^+ on acid formation in isolated gastric glands. *Acta Physiol. Scand. Spec. Suppl.* pp. 55–68
6. Berglindh, T., DiBona, D. R., Ito, S., Sachs, G. 1980. Probes of parietal cell function. *Am. J. Physiol.* 238:G165–76
7. Berglindh, T., DiBona, D. R., Pace, C. S., Sachs, G. 1980. The ATP dependence of H^+ secretion. *J. Cell Biol.* 85:392–401
8. Berglindh, T., Helander, H. F., Obrink, K. J. 1976. Effects of secretagogues on oxygen consumption, aminopyrine accumulation, and morphology in isolated gastric glands. *Acta Physiol. Scand.* 97:401–14
9. Berglindh, T., Obrink, K. J. 1973. Isolation of parietal cells from the gastric mucosa. *Acta Physiol. Scand.* 87:21A–22A (Abstr.)
10. Berglindh, T., Obrink, K. J. 1976. A method for preparing isolated glands from the rabbit gastric mucosa. *Acta Physiol. Scand.* 96:150–59
11. Berglindh, T., Sachs, G. 1979. Histamine uptake and release from isolated gastric glands. In *Hormone Receptors in Digestion and Nutrition*, ed. G. Rosselin, et al. pp. 373–82. Elsevier: North Holland Biomed.
12. Berglindh, T., Sachs, G., Takeguchi, N. 1980. Ca^{2+}-dependent secretagogue stimulation in isolated rabbit gastric glands. *Am. J. Physiol.* 239:G90–94

13. Bergqvist, E., Obrink, K. J. 1979. Gastrin—Histamine as a normal sequence in gastric acid stimulation in the rabbit. *Upsala J. Med. Sci.* 84:145–54
14. Bergqvist, E., Waller, M., Hammar, L., Obrink, K. J. 1980. Histamine as the secretory mediator in isolated gastric glands. In *Hydrogen Ion Transport in Epithelia*, ed. I. Schulz, et al. pp. 429–37. Elsevier: North Holland Biomed.
15. Black, J. A., Forte, T. M., Forte, J. G. 1982. The effects of microfilament disrupting agents on the HCl secretion and ultrastructure of piglet gastric oxyntic cells. *J. Membrane Biol.* 67:113–24
16. Blum, A. L., Hirschowitz, B. I., Helander, H. F., Sachs, G. 1971. Electrical properties of isolated cells of Necturus gastric mucosa. *Biochim. Biophys. Acta* 241:261–72
17. Bower, J. M., Camble, R., Gregory, H., Gerring, E. L., Willshire, I. R. 1975. The inhibition of gastric acid secretion by epidermal growth factor. *Experentia* 31:825–26
18. Chew, C. S. 1983. Somatostatin inhibition of acid secretion in isolated gastric glands and parietal cells. *Am. J. Physiol.* 245:G221–29
19. Chew, C. S., Hersey, S. J. 1982. Gastrin stimulation of isolated gastric glands. *Am. J. Physiol.* 242:G504–12
20. Chew, C. S., Hersey, S. J., Sachs, G., Berglindh, T. 1980. Histamine responsiveness of isolated gastric glands. *Am. J. Physiol.* 238:G312–20
21. Croft, D. N., Ingelfinger, F. J. 1969. Isolated parietal cells: Oxygen consumption, electrolyte content and intracellular pH. *Clin. Sci.* 37:491–501
22. Davidson, W. D., Klein, K. L., Kurokawa, K., Soll, A. H. 1981. Instantaneous and continous measurement of ^{14}C-labeled substrate oxidation to $^{14}CO_2$ by minute tissue speciments: An ionization chamber method. *Metabolism* 30:596–600
23. Fellenius, E., Elander, B., Wallmark, B., Helander, H. F., Berglindh, T. 1982. Inhibition of acid secretion in isolated gastric glands by substituted benzimidazoles. *Am. J. Physiol.* 243:G505–10
24. Forte, J. G., Black, J. A., Forte, J. G. Jr. 1980. Substrate dependency for HCl secretion by isolated piglet gastric mucosa. *Am. J. Physiol.* 238:G353–57
25. Gespach, C., Bataille, D., DuPont, C., Rosselin, G., Wunsch, E., Jaeger, E. 1980. Evidence for a cyclic AMP system highly sensitive to secretin in gastric glands isolated from the rat fundus and antrum. *Biochim. Biophys. Acta* 630:433–41
26. Gibert, A. J., Hersey, S. J. 1982. Morphometric analysis of parietal cell membrane transformations in isolated gastric glands. *J. Membrane Biol.* 67:113–24
27. Golgi, C. 1893. Sur la fine organization des glandes pepticues des mammiferes. *Arch. Biol.* 19:448–53
28. Gonzalez, A., Garrido, J., Vial, J. D. 1981. Epidermal growth factor inhibits cytoskeleton-related changes in the surface of parietal cells. *J. Cell Biol.* 88:108–14
29. Haglund, U., Elander, B., Fellenius, E., Rehnberg, O., Olbe, L. 1982. The effects of secretagogues on isolated human gastric glands. *Scand. J. Gastroenterol.* 17:455–60
30. Helander, H. F. 1969. Ultrastructure and function of gastric parietal cells in the rat during development. *Gastroenterology* 56:35–52
31. Hersey, S. J. 1974. Interactions between oxidative metabolism and acid secretion in frog gastric mucosa. *Biochim. Biophys. Acta* 244:157–203
32. Hersey, S. J. 1977. Influence of amytal and menadione of high energy phosphates and acid secretion in frog gastric mucosa. *Biochim. Biophys. Acta* 496:359–66
33. Hersey, S. J. 1981. Energy source of secretion in gastric glands. *Fed. Proc.* 40:2511–18
34. Hersey, S. J., Miller, M., Owirodu, A. 1982. Role of glucose metabolism in acid formation by isolated gastric glands. *Biochim. Biophys. Acta* 714:143–51
35. Ito, S. 1981. Functional gastric morphology. In *Physiology of the Gastrointestinal Tract*, ed. L. R. Johnson, pp. 517–50. New York: Raven
36. Johnson, R. G., Scarpa, A. 1979. Protonmotive force and catecholamine transport in isolated chromaffin granules. *J. Biol. Chem.* 254:3750–60
37. Koelz, H. R., Sachs, G., Berglindh, T. 1981. Cation effects on acid secretion in rabbit gastric glands. *Am. J. Physiol.* GI&L 241:G431–42
38. Lewin, M. J. M., Cheret, A. M., Sachs, G. 1982. Separation of individual cells from the fundic gastric mucosa. In *Cell Separation: Methods and Selected Applications*, 1:223–45. New York: Academic
39. Lewin, M. J. M., Cheret, A., Soumarmon, A., Girodet, J. 1974. Methode pour l'isolement et le tri des cellules de la muqueuse fundique de rat. *Biol. Gastroenterol.* 7:139–44
40. Logsdon, C. D., Machen, T. E. 1982. Ionic requirements for H^+ secretion and membrane elaboration in frog oxyntic cells. *Am. J. Physiol.* GI&L 242:G388–99

41. Logsdon, C. D., Machen, T. E. 1982. Ultrastructural changes during stimulation of amphibian oxyntic cells viewed by scanning and transmission electron microscopy. *Anat. Rec.* 202:73–83

42. Malinowska, D., Cuppoletti, J., Sachs, G. 1983. The Cl⁻ requirement of acid secretion in isolated gastric glands. *Am. J. Physiol.* 245:G573–81

43. Malinowska, D. H., Koelz, H. R., Hersey, S. J., Sachs, G. 1981. Properties of the gastric proton pump in unstimulated permeable gastric glands. *Proc. Natl. Acad. Sci. USA* 78:5908–12

44. Michelangeli, R. 1976. Isolated oxyntic cells: Physiological characterization. In *Gastric Hydrogen Ion Secretion*, ed. D. K. Kasbekar, et al, pp. 212–36. New York: Dekker

45. Reyl, F., Silve, C., Lewin, M. J. M. 1979. Somatostatin receptors on isolated gastric cells. See Ref. 37, pp. 391–400

46. Rosenfield, G. C., McAllister, E., Thompson, W. J. 1981. Cytochalasin inhibition of isolated rat gastric parietal cell function. *J. Cell Physiol.* 109:53–7

47. Sachs, G., Berglindh, T. 1981. Physiology of the parietal cell. See Ref. 21, pp. 567–602

48. Sachs, G., Faller, L. D., Rabon, E. 1982. Proton/Hydroxyl transport in gastric and intestinal epithelia. *J. Membrane Biol.* 64:123–35

49. Sarau, H. M., Foley, J., Moonsamy, G., Wieberhaus, V. D., Sachs, G. 1977. Metabolism of dog gastric mucosa. II. Levels of glycolytic citric acid cycle and other intermediates. *J. Biol. Chem.* 252:8572–81

50. Skoglund, M. L., Gerber, J. G., Murphy, R. C., Nies, A. S. 1980. Prostaglandin production by intact isolated gastric parietal cells. *Eur. J. Pharmacol.* 66:145–48

51. Skoglund, M. L., Nies, A. S., Gerber, J. G. 1982. Inhibition of acid secretion in isolated canine parietal cells by prostaglandins. *J. Pharmacol. Exp. Ther.* 220:371–74

52. Soll, A. H. 1978. The actions of secretagogues on oxygen uptake by isolated mammalian parietal cells. *J. Clin. Invest.* 61:370–80

53. Soll, A. H. 1980. Specific inhibition by prostaglandins E_2 and I_2 of histamine-stimulated ¹⁴C aminopyrine accumulation and cyclic adenosine monophosphate generation by isolated canine parietal cells. *J. Clin. Invest.* 65:1222–29

54. Soll, A. H. 1981. Physiology of isolated canine parietal cells: Receptors and effectors regulating function. See Ref. 21, pp. 673–91

55. Soll, A. H. 1980. Secretagogue stimulation of [¹⁴C] aminopyrine accumulation by isolated canine parietal cells. *Am. J. Physiol.* 238:G366–75

56. Soll, A. H., Grossman, M. I. 1981. The interaction of stimulants on the function of isolated canine parietal cells. In *The Control of Secretion. Phil. Trans. R. Soc. London Ser. B* 296:5–15

57. Soll, A. H., Lewin, K., Beaven, M. A. 1979. Isolation of histamine-containing cells from canine fundic mucosa. *Gastroenterology* 77:1283–90

58. Wolosin, J. M., Forte, J. G. 1981. Changes in the membrane environment of the $(K^+ + H^+)$-ATPase following stimulation of the gastric oxyntic cell. *J. Biol. Chem.* 256:3149–52

59. Yamada, T., Soll, A. H., Park, J., Elashoff, J. 1983. Autonomic regulation of somatostatin release: Studies with primary cultures of canine fundic mucosal cells. *J. Clin. Invest.* In press

Ann. Rev. Physiol. 1984. 46:393–402

CELLULAR CONTROL OF PEPSINOGEN SECRETION

S. J. Hersey, S. H. Norris, and A. J. Gibert

Department of Physiology, Emory University, Atlanta, Georgia 30322

INTRODUCTON

A general model for the secretion of pepsin by the stomach was postulated by Langley (21) in 1881—more than 100 years ago. His model featured synthesis of pepsin by gastric chief cells, storage of pepsin in granules, and release of the granular contents upon appropriate stimulation of the chief cell. This original model was based upon simple light microscopic observations, but the sophisticated techniques of the intervening century have only added minor details to Langley's model, while confirming its general features. Although confirmation of the general model and addition of details have advanced our understanding of this secretory process, many major questions remain unanswered. What are the specific neural and hormonal factors responsible for initiating and maintaining pepsinogen secretion? Which intracellular mechanisms are involved in stimulus-secretion coupling? What is the basic mechanism for release of granular contents?

Progress towards understanding the cellular basis of pepsinogen secretion has been very slow, in large part due to the lack of appropriate cellular models for studying these basic questions. As a result, our understanding of pepsinogen secretion relies heavily on analogy with other zymogen-secreting systems, e.g. pancreas and salivary gland, where mechanistic questions have been studied using cellular models. Within the past two years, however, significant progress has been achieved in developing in vitro models for studying pepsinogen secretion and in utilizing these models to answer some of the basic questions. The results of these studies have confirmed some suspected similarities with other zymogen-secreting systems but also have revealed some unique features of the gastric chief cell.

393

0066-4278/84/0315-0393$02.00

This paper reviews the recent progress made by using cellular models for pepsinogen secretion. Because these developments are very recent, much of the information is still "in press" or has been published only as abstracts. Nevertheless, the significance of these reports warrants a review even at this very early stage. The reader should treat this report as preliminary, however, and consider the conclusions as tentative until future experimentation provides confirmation or revision.

CELLULAR MODELS

The vast majority of studies concerning pepsinogen secretion have employed in vivo models or in situ preparations of intact stomach. Reports of in vitro measurement of pepsinogen secretion have been relatively rare. Even in these cases the preparations employed, intact amphibian esophagus (30) and organ-cultured rabbit gastric mucosa (33), do not appear to be ideal models for studying cellular mechanisms. The disadvantages of previous models lie in their complexity, their limitations in environmental manipulation, and their inability to obtain multiple samples for biochemical analysis. Many of these problems have been overcome with the development of cellular models (e.g. isolated gastric glands, dispersed gastric cells, and cultured chief cells). The most significant progress has been made using a preparation of isolated gastric glands obtained from rabbit or rat. This preparation was first described by Berglindh & Obrink (2), and has been used extensively for studying the cellular basis of gastric acid secretion (2, 6).

The gastric glands consist primarily of the acid-secreting parietal cells and chief cells. In addition, there are a small number of endocrine-like cells and a few mucus cells. The cells retain their association through cell junctions, and form a tubule with a central lumen (2). The presence of mixed cell types creates some interpretative problems for certain biochemical measurements. But the ability to measure two physiological parameters (i.e. acid and pepsinogen secretions) in the same preparation allows for some interesting comparisons. A variation of the gastric gland preparation, obtained by brief exposure of the glands to Ca^{2+}-chelating agents (6), yields a preparation of isolated gastric cells. This preparation has not been studied extensively, but dispersed gastric cells have been used as a starting material for separation of cell types, and preliminary attempts to isolate a purified population of chief cells have been reported (35). An alternative approach to isolating chief cells is the very promising development of monolayer cultures. As reported recently (1), monolayer cultures of gastric cells become highly enriched with chief cells, and these cells retain some responsiveness. It remains to be determined whether the culturing procedures modify the cells relative to properties found in non-cultured cells.

Until suitable preparations of purified chief cells are available, the gastric gland remains the most suitable preparation for studying cellular mechanisms of pepsinogen secretion. The glands contain adequate amounts of pepsinogen, show a stable and reasonably low rate of spontaneous release, and respond to a variety of stimuli with a 2–15-fold increase in secretion (8, 19). In addition, the amount of biological material obtained from a single preparation permits multiple sampling for both physiological and biochemical determinations.

SECRETAGOGUES

A wide variety of physiological and pharmacological agents have been shown to stimulate pepsinogen secretion by cellular preparations. Not all preparations respond to the same stimuli, and questions of species differences and preparation differences remain. This report is confined to those stimuli for which there is substantial support, and takes note of some significant differences as reported.

Neurotransmitters

The most widely accepted stimuli for pepsinogen secretion by cellular preparations are cholinergic agents (18, 19, 27). The stimulation is specifically inhibited by atropine, indicating a muscarinic receptor mechanism. These observations are consistent with the many in vivo studies showing the importance of vagal, cholinergic control of pepsinogen secretion (17). A more novel finding is the observation that the β-adrenergic agonist, isoproterenol, is an effective stimulus in gastric glands (19). The adrenergic stimulation was found to be inhibited by propranolol but not by atropine or cimetidine (19). Stimulation of pepsinogen secretion by cholinergic and adrenergic agents appeared to be additive, indicating separate mechanisms for the two types of neurotransmitters. Another significant finding was that histamine, a potent stimulus for acid secretion, does not stimulate pepsinogen secretion by chief cells from rabbit (19) or dog (31). In contrast, isoproterenol, which stimulates pepsinogen secretion, does not stimulate acid formation in gastric glands (19). Thus histamine and isoproterenol appear to be cell-specific agents. Cholinergic agents, on the other hand, stimulate both acid and pepsinogen secretions (5).

Peptide Hormones

Cholecystokinin-octapeptide (CCK-OP) and the related peptide, caerulein, were found to be effective stimuli for pepsinogen secretion in gastric glands (13, 18). Stimulation by these peptides was not inhibited by atropine, propranolol or cimetidine but was found to be antagonized competitively by dibutyryl cyclic GMP (13, 15). The potency but not efficacy of stimulation by the peptides is highly dependent upon the presence of a sulfated tyrosine residue, because the desulfated peptides are about two log orders less potent (13). The related, and presumed physiologically active peptide, gastrin, is less potent than CCK-OP or caerulein (13, 18). The characteristics of peptide stimulation of pepsinogen secretion differ from those for acid secretion in at least two important ways: the stimulation of acid formation is relatively independent of peptide sulfation (11); and stimulation of acid formation by CCK-OP is not inhibited by dibutyryl cyclic GMP (13). These differences suggest that gastric cells contain more than one kind of receptor for CCK-like peptides, and that the chief cell receptor is very similar to the pancreatic CCK receptor.

Among other peptide hormones tested, secretin and VIP (vasoactive intestinal peptide) have been reported to stimulate pepsinogen secretion in gastric glands (26) and cultured chief cells (31). Stimulation by secretin was originally reported using a crude secretin preparation (19). Negative results were obtained with pure secretin, and it was postulated that a contaminant of the crude preparation, possibly CCK, was responsible for the activity. More recent reports have shown that purified, synthetic secretin will stimulate pepsinogen secretion (26). Since the responses to secretin and VIP are additive to those of CCK-OP (26), it appears that the chief cell possesses at least two different peptide receptors.

Cyclic Nucleotides

Cyclic AMP and its dibutyryl and 8-bromo derivatives were found to stimulate pepsinogen secretion (14, 15). No stimulation was observed with AMP, ATP, or adenosine (15), indicating that an adenosine receptor is not involved in the response to the cyclic nucleotides. 8-Bromo cyclic IMP was almost as potent a stimulus as 8-br cAMP while 8-br cGMP was found to be a weak stimulus (15). Neither cyclic GMP nor dibutyryl cyclic GMP stimulates pepsinogen secretion. However, as discussed above, dibutyryl cyclic GMP acts as a competitive antagonist of CCK-like peptides. In addition to the adenosine cyclic nucleotides themselves, two agents which are believed to act via increasing cellular cyclic AMP, forskolin and cholera toxin, have been shown to stimulate pepsinogen secretion (16, 28).

Other Agents

A variety of compounds have been tested for pepsinogen secretory activity. Most of them have yielded negative results. Two agents in addition to those listed above, however, have been reported to stimulate secretion in gastric glands. The alleged calcium ionophore A23187 produced a moderate stimulation of secretion in rat gastric glands (26). The addition of 200 mM mannitol to the incubation medium stimulates pepsinogen secretion in gastric glands (9). This stimulation is most likely related to the increased osmolarity, because it can be produced by similar concentrations of sucrose or NaCl. The mechanism for response to hyperosmolarity, however, remains unknown.

STIMULUS-SECRETION COUPLING

As discussed above, pepsinogen secretion may be stimulated by a number of secretagogues. Evidence reviewed below suggests that stimulated secretion is mediated by at least two separate intracellular regulatory mechanisms. This situation also appears to be the case in pancreatic amylase secretion, in which the two regulatory pathways are suggested to involve cyclic AMP and calcium (8, 34). With respect to pepsinogen secretion by the gastric chief cell, it appears that cyclic AMP mediates the response to some secretagogues, but the regulatory role of calcium, if any, is poorly understood.

Cyclic AMP

β-Adrenergic stimulation of a number of cell types is believed to be mediated through activation of adenylyl cyclase and an elevation of cytoplasmic cyclic AMP (22). In studies on rabbit gastric glands, isoproterenol caused a doubling of gland cyclic AMP content and was found to activate adenylyl cyclase in gland homogenates (19). Isoproterenol stimulation of both pepsinogen secretion and cyclic AMP content was inhibited by the β-adrenergic antagonist, propranolol (19). One point which has not been demonstrated is that the isoproterenol-induced change in glandular cyclic AMP content is localized to the chief cell. It has been found, however, that when preparations of dispersed gastric cells were depleted with respect to parietal cell content, isoproterenol-stimulated adenylyl cyclase activity increased. This suggests at least, that isoproterenol-sensitive adenylyl cyclase was not associated with parietal cells (19).

Preliminary studies on canine chief cell monolayers have shown a stimulation of pepsinogen release by synthetic secretin (32). In addition, it has been reported that secretin caused an elevation of cellular cyclic AMP content in dispersed canine gastric cells (35). It was observed that secretin-stimulated cyclic AMP content co-eluted with pepsinogen content of fractions derived from centrifugal elutriation of the dispersed mixed cell population. This suggests that secretin-stimulated changes in cyclic AMP levels were localized to the chief cells.

Forskolin, which activates adenylyl cyclase from several tissues (29), causes pepsinogen secretion in rabbit gastric glands and greatly stimulates both adenylyl cyclase activity in gland homogenates and cyclic AMP levels in intact glands (16, 23). Forskolin-stimulated adenylyl cyclase activity and cyclic AMP content were found to be greater than either histamine-stimulated or isoproterenol-stimulated levels. These observations, along with the fact that forskolin also stimulates acid formation in gastric glands (16), suggest that forskolin is non-specific activator of adenylyl cyclase. As a result, it is likely that forskolin stimulated levels of cyclic AMP reflect increases in the cyclic AMP content of number of cell types. A direct demonstration of an effect of forskolin on chi cell cyclic AMP content will require the use of highly enriched preparations of chief cells.

Derivatives of cyclic AMP, namely 8-bromo cyclic AMP and dibutyryl cyclic AMP, have been shown to cause a dose-dependent stimulation of pepsinogen secretion in gastric glands (15, 19, 23). Dibutyryl cyclic AMP has also been found to stimulate pepsinogen secretion in canine chief cell mono-layers (27, 32).

Considering the evidence reviewed above, a cyclic AMP-dependent regulatory pathway appears to be involved in the mediation of pepsinogen secretory responses to a number of secretagogues. Isoproterenol, synthetic secretin, and forskolin have each been shown to stimulate adenylyl cyclase and to cause an increase in cyclic AMP content of gastric gland cells. Furthermore, responses to these secretagogues may be mimicked by cyclic AMP derivatives, suggesting that the secretagogue-induced elaboration of endogenous cyclic AMP is capable of activating the secretory machinery.

The manner in which cyclic AMP may pass along the secretory stimulus in the chief cell remains purely speculative. By analogy with other systems (20, 22), it may be that cyclic AMP activates membrane-bound or free protein kinases in the chief cell, and that subsequent phosphorylation of key proteins activates the secretory machinery. Studies on cyclic AMP–dependent protein kinases from several tissues have shown a similarity in the order of potency of different cyclic nucleotides to activate the enzymes (20), and this was cyclic AMP > cyclic IMP > cyclic GMP. Stimulation of pepsinogen secretion in gastric glands by cyclic nucelotide derivatives exhibits the same order of potency (15). This observation is consistent with the involvement of cyclic AMP-dependent protein kinase in the mediation of stimulation by cyclic nucleotides, as well as by secretagogues which elevate cyclic AMP content.

Calcium

There are a number of pepsinogen secretagogues which do not appear to be mediated by cyclic AMP. These include cholecystokinin-like peptides and cholinergic agonists. Doses of CCK-OP, caerulein, and gastrin, which are maximal for stimulation of pepsinogen secretion in gastric glands, have been shown not to cause activation of adenylyl cyclase in gland homogenates (6, 13). Also, gastrin stimulation is not associated with a change in cyclic AMP content (6). Similarly, carbachol does not alter cyclic AMP content of gastric glands (5). Further evidence supporting the notion that CCK-OP and carbachol stimulations are not mediated by cyclic AMP comes from the observations that CCK-OP and carbachol-stimulated responses are additive with responses presumed to be mediated by cyclic AMP. For example, in gastric glands, responses to doses of CCK-OP which are maximal for pepsinogen secretion are additive with responses to maximal doses of either 8-bromo cyclic AMP or isoproterenol (13, 15). Also, responses to carbachol and epinephrine have been shown to be additive (19). However, responses to CCK-OP and carbachol are less than additive (13). Thus, CCK-OP and carbachol stimulations may share a common mechanism which is not mediated by cyclic AMP.

Extensive studies on pancreatic amylase secretion suggest that CCK-OP and carbachol stimulations are both mediated by calcium (8, 34). That calcium might mediate CCK-OP and carbachol-stimulated responses in the chief cell has not been demonstrated conclusively. Incubation of isolated gastric glands in calcium-free medium has been found to inhibit pepsinogen secretion in response to CCK-OP, caerulein, and carbachol (13, 19). This could be interpreted as consistent with the suggestion that calcium mediated the normal response. However, incubation of glands in calcium-free medium has also been found to inhibit pepsinogen secretion stimulated by isoproterenol (19). The latter observation raises the question of whether calcium plays a regulatory role or perhaps just a permissive one.

If physiological levels of cellular calcium are indeed regulatory, one might expect to find changes in calcium content and/or mobilization of calcium in glands in response to CCK-OP and carbachol, as seen in pancreatic acinar cells (34). Such issues have not been addressed experimentally in gastric glands or in isolated chief cells. However, preliminary studies using canine chief cell monolayers have been reported in which both chlorpromazine, a calmodulin inhibitor, and N,N,-(diethylamino)octyl 3,4,5-trimethoxybenzoate (TMB-8), believed to inhibit mobilization of intracellular calcium, inhibited carbachol-stimulated pepsinogen release (27). Also, the calcium ionophore, A23187, has been found to stimulate pepsinogen secretion in gastric glands (18), although it was not demonstrated that the stimulation required extracellular calcium. Whereas the actions of chlorpromazine, TMB-8, and A23187 may be characterized in other tissues, it should not be assumed that these agents will affect the gastric chief cell in the same manner. Direct evidence that calcium is mobilized by chief cells in response to secretagogues or A23187 would greatly facilitate an interpretation of studies using these alleged "calcium-active" agents.

SECRETORY MECHANISM

The presumed mechanism for pepsinogen release is exocytosis. Exocytotic figures have been demonstrated with electron microscopy in chief cells of gastric glands isolated from rabbit (9). Helander (12) reported that, in rat gastric cells fixed by perfusion, granules were released singly, and no granule-to-granule fusions could be observed. Gibert & Hersey found, however, that granule fusions were commonly observed in isolated gastric glands, sometimes forming large intracellular cisternae (9). Granule-to-granule fusions are called compound exocytosis, and have been described in other cell types.

In a number of systems it has been shown that exocytosis has a requirement for calcium, but the source of the ion can be either extracellular, as with cells of neural origin, or intracellular, as with cells of exocrine glands (7). The precise role that calcium plays is unknown, but it may bind the granule membrane to the inner plasma membrane, initiating the fusion process (36). In gastric chief cells there is still insufficient evidence that calcium is required for exocytosis, but a few studies discussed above (13, 19, 26, 27), indicate that it may play a part. It is probable that intracellular calcium pools in chief cells are sufficient to sustain pepsinogen seceretion at least over the experimental periods employed for in vitro studies.

Osmotic swelling of the granules may be an essential event in the exocytotic process, possibly triggering fusion of the granular and plasma membranes (25) or initiating extrusion of the granular contents (3). A loss of electron density of the granules is characteristic of chief cell exocytosis (9). Such a loss of electron density has been interpreted in other systems as evidence of osmotic swelling of the granules (3). Because of the role of osmotic forces in the exocytotic process, attempts have been made to interrupt it using hyperosmolar medium. Some cell types are inhibited by hyperosmolar medium (25), but gastric chief cells, like pancreatic cells (4), are stimulated to secrete by hyperosmolar medium. This secretion has been shown with electron microscopy to be an exocytotic process (9). If the granules do, in fact, swell during exocytosis, then some mechanism must be operating, even in hyperosmolar medium, to increase the osmolarity of the granular contents.

It has been proposed that changes in ionic concentrations in the granules might alter the osmolarity of the granules, either by accumulating in the granules (25), or by altering the paracrystalline structure of proteins in the granules, permitting them to decondense (3). Investigations of the effect of various ions, ionophores, and inhibitors of ion transport on gastric chief cells have been reported in preliminary communications. Ouabain was reported to inhibit stimulation by 8-bromo cyclic AMP, forskolin, and hyperosmolarity, but not CCK-OP (10). The ionophore amphotericin partially inhibited all secretagogues tested, but was most effective on cyclic AMP-mediated secretion (24). Also, secretion was reported to be sensitive to pH (23) and sodium concentration (10). The apparent stimulus-specific ionic sensitivity could be the result of effects on specific enzymes in the cyclic AMP pathway. On the other hand, the results may reflect stimulus-specific membrane transport mechanisms.

PROSPECTUS

The recent progress in understanding the control of pepsinogen secretion, made through the use of cellular models, has allowed us to develop a working hypothesis. Tests of this hypothesis, and the formulation of a detailed model, must await future experimentation. The current view which has evolved for the gastric chief cell shows a high degree of similarity with the pancreatic and salivary gland acinar cells. The chief cell appears to possess a multitude of receptors, including adrenergic, cholinergic, and two types of peptide receptors (secretin and CCK-like peptides). The receptor stimulation appears to be mediated by at least two different intracellular mechanisms. Reasonable evidence exists for the hypothesis that cyclic AMP mediates the actions of adrenergic agents and secretin, as well as those of the non-physiological agents, forskolin and cholera toxin. The stimulation by CCK-like peptides and cholinergic agents does not appear to be mediated by cyclic AMP. The suggestion that these secretagogues act via changes in intacellular calcium has been made, but direct evidence is still lacking. The basic mechanism for release of pepsinogen involves a compound type of exocytosis. The general features of multiple receptors, of more than one intracellular mechanism, and of a compound-exocytotic release of zymogen granules are common to the pancreatic and salivary gland acinar cells. However, the gastric chief cell appears to be unique in terms of the exact receptors which it possesses.

The initial results using cellular models for pepsinogen secretion clearly point out specific directions for future research. Among the most significant unknowns requiring investigation are: the exact role of calcium in secretion; the nature of the process which leads to granular fusion and release of contents; and, the physiological significance of the many receptors exhibited by the chief cell. Answers to these questions will probably require the development of additional techniques for isolating chief cells and for studying the nature and properties of the pepsinogen granules.

ACKNOWLEDGMENT

The authors wish to thank those investigators who kindly shared pre-publication information. This work was supported in part by NIH grants AM28459 and AM14752.

Literature Cited

1. Ayalon, A., Sanders, M. J., Thomas, L. P., Amirian, D. A., Soll, A. H. 1982. Electrical effects of histamine on monolayers formed in culture from enriched canine gastric chief cells. *Proc. Natl. Acad. Sci. USA* 79:7009–13
2. Berglindh, T., Obrink, K. J. 1976. A method for preparing isolated glands from the rabbit gastric mucosa. *Acta Physiol. Scand.* 96:150–59
3. Bilinski, M., Plattner, H., Matt, H. 1981. Secretory protein decondensation as a distinct, Ca^{2+}-mediated event during the final steps of exocytosis in Paramecium cells. *J. Cell Biol.* 88:179–88
4. Case, R. M., Clausen, T. 1973. The relationship between calcium exchange and enzyme secretion in the isolated rat pancreas. *J. Physiol.* 235:75–102
5. Chew, C. S., Hersey, S. J. 1980. cAMP and secretagogue interactions in isolated gastric glands. In *Advances in Physiological Science: Nutrition, Digestion, Metabolism*, ed. T. Gati, L. G. Szollar, Gy. Ungvary, 12:149–56. New York: Pergamon
6. Chew, C. S., Hersey, S. J. 1982. Gastrin stimulation of isolated gastric glands. *Am. J. Physiol.* 242:G504–12
7. Douglas, W. W. 1974. Involvement of calcium in exocytosis and the exocytosis-vesiculation sequence. *Biochem. Soc. Symp.* 39:1–28
8. Gardner, J. D., Jensen, R. T. 1981. Regulation of pancreatic exocrine secretion *in vitro:* the action of secretagogues. *Phil Trans. R. Soc. London B.* 296:17–26
9. Gibert, A. J., Hersey, S. J. 1982. Exocy-

tosis in isolated gastric glands induced by secretagogues and hyperosmolarity. *Cell Tissue Res.* 227:535–42

10. Gibert, A. J., Hersey, S. J., Norris, S. H. 1983. Pepsin exocytosis by gastric glands *in vitro*. Ionic requirements and ouabain inhibition. *Fed. Proc.* 42:591 (Abstr.)

11. Gregory, R. A., Tracy, H. J. 1964. The constitution and properties of two gastrins extracted from hog antral mucosa. *Gut* 5:103–17

12. Helander, H. F. 1965. Quantitative ultrastructural studies on rat gastric zymogen cells under different physiological and experimental conditons. *Cell Tissue Res.* 189:287–303

13. Hersey, S. J., May, D., Schyberg, D. 1982. Stimulation of pepsinogen release from isolated gastric glands by cholecystokininlike peptides. *Am. J. Physiol.* 244:G192–97

14. Hersey, S. J., Miller, M., May, D. 1982. Acid and pepsinogen secretion by isolated gastric glands. *Fed. Proc.* 41:1498 (Abstr.)

15. Hersey, S. J., Miller, M., May, D., Norris, S. H. 1983. Lack of interaction between acid and pepsinogen secretion in isolated gastric glands. *Am. J. Physiol.* In press

16. Hersey, S. J., Owirodu, A., Miller, M. 1983. Forskolin stimulation of acid and pepsinogen secretion by gastric glands. *Biochim. Biophys. Acta.* 755:293–99

17. Hirschowitz, B. I. 1976. Secretion of pepsinogen. *Hand. Physiol. Alimentary Canal.* 50:889–918

18. Kasbekar, D. K., Jensen, R. T., Gardner, J. D. 1983. Pepsinogen secretion from dispersed glands from rabbit stomach. *Am. J. Physiol.* 244:G392–96

19. Koelz, H. R., Hersey, S. J., Sachs, G., Chew, C. S. 1982. Pepsinogen release from isolated gastric glands. *Am. J. Physiol.* 243:218–25

20. Kuo, J. F., Greengard, P. 1969. Cyclic nucleotide-dependent protein kinases. *Proc. Natl. Acad. Sci. USA* 64:1349–55

21. Langley, J. N. 1881. On the histology and physiology of pepsin-forming glands. *Philos. Trans. Soc. London Ser. B.* 172:664–711

22. Liddle, G. W., Hardman, J. G. 1971. Cyclic adenosine monophosphate as a mediator of hormone action. *New Engl. J. Med.* 285:560–66

23. Norris, S. H., Hersey, S. J. 1983. pH dependence of pepsinogen and acid secretion in isolated gastric glands. *Am. J. Physiol.* In press

24. Norris, S. H., Hersey, S. J., Gibert, A. J. 1983. Pepsinogen secretion by rabbit isolated gastric glands: effect of amphotericin. *Fed. Proc.* 42:591 (Abstr.)

25. Pollard, H. B., Pazoles, C. J., Creutz, C. E., Zinder, O. 1979. The chromaffin granule and possible mechanisms of exocytosis. *Int. Rev. Cytol.* 58:197

26. Raufman, J. P., Kasbekar, D. K., Jensen, R. T., Gardner, J. D. 1983. Potentiation of pepsinogen secretion from dispersed glands from rat stomach. *Am. J. Physiol.* In press

27. Sanders, M. J., Amirian, D. A., Soll, A. H. 1983. Stimulus-secretion coupling of pepsinogen release in canine chief cell monolayers. *Fed. Proc.* 42:591

28. Schafer, D. E., Garshfield, G. N. 1982. Cholera enterotoxin stimulates marked pepsinogen secretion by isolated gastric fundic glands. *Fed. Proc.* 41:1432 (Abst.)

29. Seamon, K. B., Padgett, W., Daley, J. W. 1981. Forskolin: unique diterpene activator of adenylate cyclase in membranes and in intact cells. *Proc. Natl. Acad. Sci. USA* 78:3363–67

30. Simpson, L., Goldenberg, D., Hirschowitz, B. I. 1980. Pepsinogen secretion by the frog esophagus *in vitro*. *Am. J. Physiol.* 238:G79–84

31. Soll, A. H., Amirian, D. A., Sanders, M. J., Ayalon, A. 1983. Secretagogue stimulation of pepsinogen release by canine chief cells in primary monolayer culture. *Am. J. Physiol.* In press

32. Soll, A. H., Amirian, D. A., Thomas, L., Ayalon, A. 1982. Secretagogue stimulation of pepsinogen release by canine chief cells in primary monolayers culture. *Gastroenterology* 82:1184 (Abst.)

33. Sutton, D. R., Donaldson, R. M. 1975. Synthesis and secretion of protein and pepsinogen by rabbit gastric mucosa in organ culture. *Gastroenterology* 69:166–74

34. Williams, J. A. 1980. Regulation of pancreatic acinar cell function by intracellular calcium. *Am. J. Physiol.* 238:G269–79

35. Wollin, A., Soll, A. H., Samloff, I. M. 1979. Actions of histamine, secretin, and PGE_2 on cyclic AMP production by isolated canine fundic mucosal cells. *Am. J. Physiol.* 237:E437–43

36. Zimmerberg, J., Cohen, F. S., Finkelstein, A. 1980. Fusion of phospholipid vesicles with planar phospholipid bilayer membranes. I. Discharge of vesicular contents across the planar membrane. *J. Gen. Physiol.* 75:241–50

Ann. Rev. Physiol. 1984. 46:403–15

PRIMARY HEPATOCYTES IN MONOLAYER CULTURE: A MODEL FOR STUDIES ON LIPOPROTEIN METABOLISM

Trudy M. Forte

Donner Laboratory, University of California, Berkeley, California 94720

INTRODUCTION

The pioneering studies of Berry & Friend (8) on isolation of hepatocytes and that of Bissell et al (9) on culturing hepatocytes in nonproliferating monolayers demonstrated the feasibility of using isolated parenchymal cells to study functional aspects of the liver. The obvious advantage of such a system is that one can study metabolic events in a defined, easily manipulated population of cells for periods of hours or even days. This review focuses on nonproliferating hepatic parenchymal cells in monolayer culture as a model for investigating lipoprotein synthesis and degradation.

STRUCTURAL-FUNCTIONAL ASPECTS

Two rather comprehensive studies on the ultrastructure of hepatocyte mono-layers as a function of time in culture have been carried out (16, 59), and both have shown that within 24 hrs in culture, parenchymal cells are flattened and polygonal and re-establish biliary polarity. Qualitatively the cells appear similar to in situ liver cells, because they possess osmiophilic very low density lipoprotein (VLDL)–sized particles within the Golgi and secretory vesicles. Studies with rat hepatocyte monolayers also suggest that these cells possess clathrin-coated pits on their free surfaces and cytoplasmic receptosomes that contain osmiophilic particles in the size range of small VLDL (31). Cytoimmunochemical techniques on intact liver demonstrated that apolipoproteins (apo) B and C of VLDL are present in rat liver ribosomes and that these apolipopro-

403

teins associate with the lipid moiety at the junction of smooth and rough endoplasmic reticulum (1, 11). The elegant molecular approach of Siuta-Mangano & Lane (53) with chick hepatocyte monolayers demonstrated that not only is apoB synthesized on polysomes and translocated into the endoplasmic reticulum lumen but also that the complete process of chain elongation and translocation of this large molecule takes place within 7.5–9 min. Furthermore, partial nascent apoB chains could be trapped on the polysomes with cyclohex-imide and subsequently discharged into the lumen with puromycin. This technique could be a powerful tool for probing the effects of co- and posttrans-lational modification of apoB and other apolipoproteins on lipoprotein assem-bly and function.

Glycosylation, the final step in lipoprotein synthesis, takes place within the Golgi (21); however, this step does not appear to be a strict requirement for transport of lipoproteins out of the cell. Struck et al (57) treated chick hepato-cyte monolayers with tunicamycin, an inhibitor of glycosylation, and found that although incorporation of [^{3}H]-glucosamine into apoB was almost com-pletely blocked, secretion of apoB-containing lipoproteins into the medium was not inhibited. Similar results were obtained with rat monolayer cultures (7), where tunicamycin blocked carbohydrate incorporation into apoB, E, and C-III-3, yet secretion of VLDL, low density lipoprotein (LDL), and high-density lipoprotein (HDL) was not altered. It remains to be seen, however, whether the physiological function of these particles is altered, because it is known that carbohydrate residues have a profound effect on metabolism of other glycoproteins.

SYNTHESIS AND SECRETION OF LIPOPROTEINS UNDER BASAL CONDITIONS

Very Low Density Lipoproteins

The first attempt to utilize nonproliferating rat hepatocyte monolayers to study lipoprotein secretion revealed that rat hepatocytes incubated with [^{14}C]-glycerol secreted labeled triglycerides into the medium (42). No conclusion could be drawn on the protein nature of the secretory product, however, since apolipoproteins could not be identified either qualitatively or quantitatively. This most likely reflected the difficulties inherent in using a limited number of monolayers for carrying out assays. Later investigations on chick (58) and rat hepatocyte cultures (18) provided sound evidence that triglyceride was secreted as a lipoprotein.

Unlike plasma VLDL, the ratio of free to esterified cholesterol was elevated in VLDL isolated from culture media in the investigations of Davis et al (18) and Dashti et al (17); however, VLDL cholesteryl ester content approached plasma values in the rat hepatocyte studies reported by Bell-Quint & Forte (5).

These differences may be the consequence of increased cellular acyl-CoA:cholesterol acyltransferase (ACAT) activity in the latter studies, with the net result of increased cholesteryl ester secreted in the nascent VLDL.

VLDL secreted by monolayer cultures have a particle size range and structure similar to plasma counterparts (5, 18, 19). The major plasma apolipoproteins, apoB and -E, are major proteins in culture-medium VLDL; however, the presence of C-apolipoproteins was only reported by one group of investigators (5). C-apolipoproteins have been clearly identified in rat liver perfusion studies (26, 35, 45, 47), where they form a not insignificant part of the total protein content. The apparent absence of the apoC's in the studies of Davis et al (18) is not readily explained except that these proteins may have been dissociated from the lipoprotein particles during isolation procedures.

The reported values for net rate of VLDL secretion by nonproliferating hepatocyte cultures varies considerably, as summarized in Table 1; the large differences between these values may reflect differences in experimental design and culture media composition. It is also apparent that the rate of VLDL secretion by cultured cells is less than that reported in perfused rat liver studies. Two contributing factors that may in part explain this discrepancy are: (a) Perfusion studies commence immediately and are of short duration. Therefore, some fraction of the secreted VLDL undoubtedly represents the release of preformed VLDL. Cultured cells, on the other hand, are preincubated up to 24 hr, followed by a medium change, before secretory studies are undertaken. This manipulation may result in a new steady state for the cells quite different from that of the intact perfused liver. (b) VLDL production in monolayer cultures may be underestimated due to trapping of VLDL within the intercellular spaces of the closely apposed cells, as suggested by Bell-Quint & Forte (5).

The rate of VLDL secretion in nonproliferating cultures is not constant over extended periods of time, as demonstrated by time-course studies of lipoprotein secretion in rat hepatocyte monolayers (5). In this study VLDL—but not LDL and HDL—that was recovered from the media fell to extremely low levels after 17 or more hours in culture. This decrease of media VLDL may result from hydrolysis of VLDL with the formation of more dense particles. The secretion of hydrolytic enzymes, including both hepatic and lipoprotein lipase, has been demonstrated in chick hepatocyte cultures (39). Alternatively, endocytosis and catabolism of VLDL by the cells may account for some of the loss. Since the media VLDL carry the appropriate apolipoproteins (apoB and -E) for recognition by receptor sites, this latter mechanism cannot be discounted, although definitive studies remain to be carried out.

Low Density Lipoproteins

Evidence for de novo LDL secretion by monolayers is limited and conflicting. While the experiments of Davis et al (18) indicate that LDL are not synthesized

Table 1 Basal rates (mg/g cell protein/hr) of lipoprotein secretion: hepatocyte cultures *vs* liver perfusion

| | Lipoprotein fraction | | | |
	VLDL	LDL	HDL	References
Culture medium	0.285	—	—	18
	0.801	—	0.333[a]	17
	0.767	0.333	0.433	5
	—	—	0.389[a]	51
Liver perfusate	1.13	0.375	0.200	44[b]
	1.19	0.010	0.275	47[b]
	2.02	—	—	37[b]

[a]Estimate based on particle consisting of 38% protein, where 50% is apo AI.

[b]Where data was recorded as mg/g liver the assumption was made that 20% of the liver wet weight is protein. The lipid weight assumed for various lipoproteins is 90%, 75%, and 50% for VLDL, LDL, and HDL, respectively.

by cells in culture, others have shown (5) that LDL with physico-chemical properties similar to plasma LDL can be recovered from the medium. The rate of LDL production in the latter study is similar to the rate of LDL secretion in the perfused rat liver (44) (see Table 1). Identification of media LDL as de novo synthesized LDL is not unequivocal, as degradation of VLDL to LDL in the media cannot be entirely ruled out. That de novo synthesis of LDL occurs is strengthened by the recent observation that LDL from monolayer cultures contain predominantly a high-molecular-weight form of apoB (345,000 daltons, B345), whereas VLDL possess mainly a small-molecular-weight form of apoB (242,000 daltons, B242) (6).

Several laboratories have shown that rat livers secrete two forms of apoB (one heavy and one light) and that the heavy apoB (B345) is associated with more dense particles (55, 60). Elovson et al (24) were able to isolate heavy (PI) and light (PIII) apoB components from both microsomes and Golgi vesicles of rat livers. The PI (B345) species migrated mainly with smaller lipoprotein particles, while the PIII (B242) species migrated mainly with VLDL. Immunologic and peptide-mapping studies indicated that the two apoB forms are similar but not identical. A key question remaining to be resolved is whether the two forms of apolipoproteins are synthesized under separate genetic control or whether there is one gene product and posttranslational modification produces two variants.

Control mechanisms for the synthesis and secretion of various apoB forms have not been extensively investigated. Studies with cultured hepatocytes from fasted vs fed rats provide evidence that B242 is linked to triglyceride synthesis and secretion (6). Opposite results were reported by Boogaerts et al (10), who found that cultured hepatocytes from sucrose-fed rats had increased rates of triglyceride synthesis but decreased incorporation of [³H]-arginine into B242.

Recent investigations on the effect of oleic acid on triglyceride and apoB synthesis by rat hepatocyte cultures from chow-fed rats indicated that, although triglyceride synthesis is increased 2- to 3-fold by oleic acid, synthesis of B242 and B345 was not affected (20). Since these results were obtained on short-term cultures and it is known that exogenous oleic acid can sustain elevated triglyceride synthesis for several days, it will be important to determine whether apoB synthesis can be induced during longer incubation periods. Clearly, systematic studies on culture protocols and physiological and nutritional variables are indicated in order to determine how B345 and B242 syntheses are regulated.

High Density Lipoproteins

HDL particles isolated from the culture medium are spherical structures morphologically similar to plasma components (5). The spherical morphology and high ratio of esterified to free cholesterol (3.5) in the isolated HDL suggested that LCAT was present in the medium, and it has been shown that rat hepatocyte suspension cultures do secrete LCAT (48). Most studies on hepatocyte monolayers have not described HDL particles, but apoA-I in the incubation medium has been reported (17, 51). Assuming that this protein is associated with HDL-like particles, the estimated rates of HDL synthesis in the latter two studies are comparable to that reported by Bell-Quint & Forte (5) (see Table 1) and are approximately 1.5–2.0-fold higher than that of the perfused liver (Table 1), indicating that monolayers may be an ideal system in which to study regulation of HDL synthesis.

HDL isolated from rat hepatocyte cultures contain reduced amounts of apoE and no apoA-IV (5). Both these apolipoproteins are normally associated with rat plasma HDL. Another characteristic of hepatocyte monolayers HDL is the presence of apoB (5, 6), although a similar phenomenon has been noted for perfused rat liver HDL (25, 45). Increased HDL triglyceride parallels apoB appearance in such cases, but it is unclear whether the liver secretes a unique triglyceride-rich, apoB-containing, high-density particle, or whether this particle represents a catabolic product.

PHYSIOLOGICAL FACTORS INFLUENCING SECRETION

Hepatocytes isolated from fasted donors maintain the nutritional characteristics of the donor; thus, it has been shown that hepatocytes from fasted rats (5) and chicks (58) secrete low levels of triglyceride and VLDL into the medium. Refeeding donors reverses this effect; moreover, secretion can be augmented by feeding animals sucrose-enriched diets. Sucrose feeding (5) produced a 10-fold increase in VLDL secretion compared with fasted hepatocytes. Rather than increasing, LDL decreased under these conditions, suggesting that separate control mechanisms may exist for VLDL and LDL synthesis and secretion, a suggestion reinforced by the presence of different apoB forms on the VLDL and LDL particles (6) and differences in specific activity of [^{3}H]-leucine in apoB of VLDL and LDL (5).

Triglyceride synthesis in fasting or basal conditions can be greatly accelerated by adding free fatty acid (bound to albumin) to the culture medium. Oleic acid added to the medium has been shown to stimulate VLDL secretion 2–10-fold (5, 17, 19); this stimulation is concentration-dependent. Hepatocyte monolayers also appear to be sensitive to the molecular species of fatty acid, and unsaturated fatty acids are generally more effective than saturated ones in stimulating triglyceride secretion (20, 42). Studies with hepatocyte suspensions suggest that exogenous fatty acids stimulate diacylglycerol acyltransferase, the only enzyme exclusively involved in triglyceride synthesis (34); moreover, it is possible that the structure of the fatty acid influences activity of this enzyme.

Control of cholesterol metabolism in hepatocyte cultures has been demonstrated by dietary manipulations as well as by culture-media manipulations (19, 22, 23). 25-Hydroxycholesterol, a potent inhibitor of 3-hydroxy-3-methylglutaryl CoA (HMG-CoA) reductase, added to the culture medium, reduces HMG-CoA reductase activity and simultaneously increases cellular ACAT activity and cellular cholesteryl ester content. 25-Hydroxycholesterol and mevalonolactone in the medium also increased cholesteryl ester content (150%) in newly secreted VLDL (22). Hepatocytes obtained from cholesterol-fed donors are functionally similar to those treated exogenously with 25-hydroxycholesterol, because they show a 67-fold increase in cellular cholesteryl ester and almost complete inhibition of de novo cholesterol synthesis (19). During cholesterol feeding, cellular triglyceride synthesis is maintained but secretion is greatly reduced. The net result is that VLDL rich in cholesteryl ester and poor in triglyceride are secreted. It appears that diet plays a critical role in determining intracellular pool sizes of triglyceride and cholesteryl ester, which in turn dictate the composition of the VLDL to be exported. Investigations on the effects of dietary or media cholesterol have focused primarily on intracellular levels of cholesteryl ester and VLDL cholesteryl ester content; alterations in synthesis and secretion of other lipoprotein classes have not been addressed and are an area for future studies on hepatocyte cultures.

The hormones, insulin and glucagon are also important regulators of lipogenesis in hepatocyte cultures. These two hormones modulate important hepatic enzymes involved in lipid synthesis; a comprehensive review of this topic has recently been published (32). Chick hepatocyte cultures require insulin for VLDL secretion (58), because removal of this hormone results in a parallel decline in acetyl-CoA carboxylase activity and VLDL synthesis. Enzymatic function could be restimulated by preincubating monolayers for 2–3 days with insulin; this reversal suggests that insulin may act by inducing de novo synthesis of the enzyme. Fasted rat hepatocytes showed similar induction effects (15), because it was necessary to preincubate cells for 20 hr with insulin before glucose stimulated acetyl-CoA carboxylase. Both glucose and insulin at physiological concentrations added to nonfasted rat hepatocyte cultures were found to stimulate acetyl-CoA–carboxylase activity (40). Since these authors found that inhibitors of protein synthesis block insulin and glucose activity, it is suggested that both hormone and substrate are involved in the induction of new enzyme synthesis. Insulin may also be involved in the induction of apolipoprotein synthesis, because preliminary studies with neonatal pig hepatocytes show an increase in apoA-I in the presence of insulin (36). Stimulation of VLDL secretion by insulin can be blocked by the addition of glucagon (58), which inhibits acetyl-CoA carboxylase activity. It is thought that glucagon achieves this by modulating the degree of phosphorylation of acetyl-CoA carboxylase. In its phosphorylated state this key enzyme is inhibited. Insulin and glucagon also play a role in regulating cholesterol synthesis in isolated hepatocytes by regulating phosphorylation and dephosphorylation of HMG-CoA reductase (38). Short-term effects on lipoprotein metabolism by both insulin and glucagon are most likely related to their ability to regulate dephosphorylation and phosphorylation, respectively, of key lipogenic enzymes, while long term effects involve induction of new enzymes.

Estrogen is a hormone known to stimulate hepatic VLDL production. Early studies with rat hepatocyte cultures in which estrogen was introduced into the medium showed that this hormone stimulated cellular glycerol kinase activity, increased the incorporation of [^{14}C]-glycerol into cellular triglycerides and phospholipids, and increased secretion of labeled triglyceride into the medium (42). In investigations where chicks were pre-treated with estrogen (58), donor hepatocytes responded with increased incorporation of [^{3}H]-leucine into VLDL; radioactivity was specifically increased in apolipoproteins corresponding to apoB and apoC. These studies suggest that estrogen plays a major role in regulating not only lipid synthesis but also protein synthesis. How estrogen effects LDL and HDL synthesis and secretion remains to be established.

CATABOLISM OF LIPOPROTEINS BY HEPATOCYTE MONOLAYERS

Chylomicrons, Very Low Density Lipoproteins, and Remnants

Rat hepatocyte monolayer culture studies have demonstrated that chylomicrons have relatively little effect on regulation of hepatic lipoprotein metabolism, because there is little binding and uptake of these large particles (27, 28). Normal rat VLDL incubated with homologous cells have a varied response, according to the experience of several investigators. Breslow et al (12) reported a stimulation of HMG-CoA reductase with normal VLDL, while others have found that VLDL had no effect on sterol metabolism in rat hepatocytes (13, 56). Such conflicting results may reflect differences in cell isolation procedures, media, and physiological states of the animal used. Unlike normal VLDL, VLDL from hypercholesteremic animals show a marked ability to down-regulate HMG-CoA reductase (12, 13, 54). These hypercholesteremic VLDL are enriched in cholesteryl ester and apoE and are taken up by the apoB-E receptor found on liver membranes (41, 43).

Chylomicron remnants produced in vivo or in vitro in the presence of serum become depleted in apoA-I and triglyceride and are concomitantly enriched in apoE and cholesteryl ester. These particles are capable of binding to cultured cells in a saturable manner (27–29, 46), are internalized and degraded, and suppress HMG-CoA reductase and stimulate ACAT. Hydrolysis, but not binding and uptake, can be blocked by chloroquine (lysosomal inhibitor) and colchicine (microtubule inhibitor), which suggests that remnants are normally internalized by an endocytic mechanism, probably through the clathrin-coated regions seen in electron microscopy. Endocytic vesicles fuse with primary lysosomes in which hydrolysis of proteins and lipids is accomplished. Remnants added to cultures obtained from hypercholesteremic rats or from normal cells pre-incubated with mevalonolactone show a suppression of remnant uptake (30). Because under both of these conditions cellular cholesteryl ester is elevated, one can speculate that intracellular pools of cholesteryl ester play a crucial role in regulating receptor function as well as lipoprotein synthesis.

Low Density Lipoproteins

Several laboratories have demonstrated that LDL bind to cultured rabbit and pig hepatocytes in a saturable manner that requires Ca^{++} and the presence of unaltered lysyl and arginyl residues (3, 4, 50, 54, 56). These properties indicate that LDL are removed by high affinity binding sites on liver cells that are similar to those on fibroblasts. LDL degradation suppresses HMG-CoA reductase activity and synthesis of new receptors. The use of heterologous serum LDL with monolayer cultures has provided conflicting results: in some instances such LDL elicited no changes in HMG-CoA reductase activity (2, 12), but in another instance there was a 40% decrease in activity (13). Inconsistencies of this nature suggest that caution must be exercised in interpreting data using heterologous serum lipoproteins; the conclusions drawn may be misleading.

The studies of Attie et al (2), using lactosylated LDL (Lac-LDL) of human origin on rat hepatocytes, indicate that in the rat there are two compartments for intracellular processing of LDL. Native human LDL are taken up by a low-affinity mechanism, are degraded slowly, and do not alter HMG-CoA reductase activity. On the other hand, Lac-LDL enter the cell rapidly—even at low concentration—through the galactose-specific receptor, indicating that high-affinity receptors target the particle for rapid degradation by lysosomes, a process which ultimately suppresses HMG-CoA reductase activity. The route of entry of LDL particles (and probably other lipoproteins as well) into the cell dictates its metabolic fate and capacity to regulate sterol metabolism. A similar conclusion can be drawn from recent studies of Bachorik et al (4) with homologous LDL on cultured pig liver hepatocytes. Pig [^{125}I]-LDL are bound with high affinity to one site that is Pronase sensitive, requires recognition of LDL lysine groups, and is sensitive to lysosomal inhibitors. This LDL-specific binding site has been termed "LDL degradation site." A second site was also demonstrated, which binds [^{125}I]-LDL but does not degrade it. HDL and methyl-LDL compete for binding to this latter site but do not interfere with [^{125}I]-LDL degradation mediated through the LDL-specific site. The second LDL-binding site is probably analogous to the low-affinity site of the rat and has little impact on sterol regulation.

Recent investigations on hepatocyte cultures from Watanabe heritable hyperlipidemic (WHHL) rabbits reveal the potential for developing model cellular systems in which to study metabolic abnormalities similar to those in humans (3). The WHHL mutants lack high affinity LDL receptors and have extremely elevated plasma cholesterol levels and spontaneous atherosclerosis. Hepatocytes of WHHL rabbits take up LDL by a nonspecific, nonsaturable mechanism that is not inhibited by chloroquine and colchicine and that does not down-regulate HMG-CoA reductase. These metabolic abnormalities are very similar to those in human homozygous familial hypercholesteremia and offer hope that the precise metabolic defect in the complex series of enzyme reactions governing sterol synthesis may one day be resolved.

High Density Lipoproteins

High-density lipoproteins have been shown to play a dual role in hepatic lipid metabolism. Studies with homologous HDL added to rat monolayers revealed that HMG-CoA reductase activity is stimulated (12, 13, 56) rather than suppressed. The stimulatory effect can be ascribed to the ability of HDL to effect a net efflux of cholesterol from cells (49, 52). In other studies specific fractions of HDL, such as HDL$_2$, have been shown to be taken up by a saturable mechanism (33) and are therefore able to suppress HMG-CoA reductase activity (52). Saturation kinetics for the uptake of rat HDL$_2$ suggest that these particles may be taken up by the apoB-E receptor, because the less dense region of rat HDL contains apoE. Recent evidence from studies with pig hepatocyte cultures suggest that pig [^{125}I]-HDL of d 1.12–1.16 g ml^{-1} can be bound and proteolyzed by a high-affinity, saturable receptor mechanism. However, since these HDL contain no apoE, the classical apoB-E receptor is not involved (4).

This HDL receptor, as mentioned earlier, is capable of binding LDL and methyl-LDL but not of degrading LDL. No direct feedback on the control of the HDL receptor synthesis is evident, because the presence or absence of lipoproteins in the medium does not affect uptake and degradation of pig non-apoE-HDL. The physiological significance of the non-apoE-HDL receptor (apoA receptor?), particularly its effect on sterol and protein synthesis, remains to be elucidated.

SUMMARY

Primary hepatocyte cultures are ideal models in which to investigate regulation of lipoprotein synthesis and catabolism by the liver. Not only can one regulate the physiological and nutritional state of the donor animal, but one can also manipulate the culture milieu. A possible problem that arises in prolonged incubations is the accumulation of metabolites in the culture media, which may alter the function of the cells. Studies using more novel culturing techniques such as "perifusion" (14) may resolve this technical problem. This review indicates that caution must be used in analyzing data based on studies employing heterologous sera; additionally, closer attention should be given to the role of lipoprotein subfractions in regulating lipoprotein metabolism. It is now known that lipoprotein classes are heterogeneous with respect to metabolic origin and lipid and apolipoprotein content, hence they may have diverse physiological roles in hepatic lipid metabolism.

ACKNOWLEDGMENT

I wish to thank Dr. Paul A. Davis for his helpful comments on the manuscript and Diana Morris for preparation of the manuscript.

Literature Cited

1. Alexander, C. A., Hamilton, R. L., Havel, R. J. 1976. Subcellular localization of B apoprotein of plasma lipoproteins in rat liver. *J. Cell Biol.* 69:241–63
2. Attie, A. D., Pittman, R. C., Steinberg, D. 1980. Metabolism of native and of lactosylated human low density lipoprotein: evidence for two pathways for catabolism of exogenous protins in rat hepatocytes. *Proc. Natl. Acad. Sci. USA* 77:5923–27
3. Attie, D. A., Pittman, R. C., Watanabe, Y., Steinberg, D. 1981. Low density lipoprotein receptor deficiency in cultured hepatocytes of the WHHL rabbit: further evidence of two pathways for catabolism of exogenous proteins. *J. Biol. Chem.* 256:9789–92
4. Bachorik, P. S., Franklin, F. A., Virgil, D., Kwiterovich, P. O. 1982. High-affinity uptake and degradation of apolipoprotein E free high density lipoprotein and low density lipoprotein in cultured porcine hepatocytes. *Biochemistry* 21: 5675–84
5. Bell-Quint, J., Forte, T. 1981. Time-related changes in the synthesis and secretion of very low density, low density, and high density lipoproteins by cultured rat hepatocytes. *Biochim. Biophys. Acta* 663:83–98
6. Bell-Quint, J., Forte, T., Graham, P. 1981. Synthesis of two forms of apolipoprotein B by cultured rat hepatocytes. *Biochem. Biophys. Res. Commun.* 99: 700–6

7. Bell-Quint, J., Forte, T., Graham, P. 1981. Glycosylation of apolipoproteins by cultured rat hepatocytes: effects of tunicamycin on lipoprotein secretion. *Biochem. J.* 200:409–14

8. Berry, M. N., Friend, D. S. 1969. High-yield preparation of isolated rat liver parenchymal cells. A biochemical and fine structural study. *J. Cell. Biol.* 43:506–20

9. Bissell, D. M., Hammaker, L. E., Meyer, U. A. 1973. Parenchymal cells from adult rat liver in nonproliferating monolayer culture. I. Functional studies. *J. Cell Biol.* 59:722–34

10. Boogaerts, J. R., McNeal, M. M., Davis, R. A. 1981. Dissociation of triglyceride and apo-B secretion in cultured rat hepatocytes. *Arteriosclerosis* 1:375a

11. Bouma, M-E., Amit, N., Infante, R. 1979. Ultrastructural localization of apoB and apoC binding to very low density lipoproteins in rat liver. *Virchows Arch. B Cell Pathol.* 30:161–80

12. Breslow, J. L., Lothrop, D. A., Clowes, A. W., Lux, S. E. 1977. Lipoprotein regulation of 3-hydroxy-3-methylglutaryl coenzyme A reductase activity in rat liver cell cultures. *J. Biol. Chem.* 252:2726–33

13. Calandra, S., Tarugi, P., Battistini, N., Ferrari, R. 1979. Cholesterol synthesis in isolated rat hepatocyte: effect of homologous and heterologous serum lipoproteins. *Metab. Clin. Exp.* 28:843–50

14. Capuzzi, D. M., Lackman, R. D., Pietra, G. G. 1981. Stimulated secretion of esterified lipids and VLDL by perifused hepatocytes. *J. Cell. Physiol.* 108:185–94

15. Caro, J. F., Amatruda, J. M. 1982. The regulation of lipid synthesis in freshly isolated and primary cultures of hepatocytes from fasted rats: the primary role of insulin. *Metab. Clin. Exp.* 31:14–18

16. Chapman, G. S., Jones, A. L., Meyer, U. A., Bissell, D. M. 1973. Parenchymal cells from adult rat liver in nonproliferating monolayer culture. II. Ultrastructural studies. *J. Cell Biol.* 59:735–47

17. Dashti, N., McConathy, W. J., Ontko, J. A. 1980. Production of apolipoproteins E and A-I by hepatocytes in primary culture. *Biochim. Biophys. Acta* 618:347–58

18. Davis, R. A., Engelhorn, S. C., Pangburn, S. H., Weinstein, D. B., Steinberg, D. 1979. Very low density lipoprotein synthesis and secretion by cultured rat hepatocytes. *J. Biol. Chem.* 254:2010–16

19. Davis, R. A., McNeal, M. M., Moses, R. L. 1982. Intrahepatic assembly of very low density lipoprotein: competition by cholesterol esters for the hydrophobic core. *J. Biol. Chem.* 257:2634–40

20. Davis, R. A., Boogaerts, J. R. 1982. Intrahepatic assembly of very low density lipoproteins: Effects of fatty acids on triacylglycerol and apolipoprotein synthesis. *J. Biol. Chem.* 257:10908–13

21. Dolphin, P. J., Rubinstein, D. 1977. Glycosylation of apoproteins of rat very low density lipoprotein during transit through the hepatic golgi apparatus. *Can. J. Biochem.* 55:83–90

22. Drevon, C. A., Engelhorn, S. C., Steinberg, D. 1980. Secretion of very low density lipoproteins enriched in cholesteryl esters by cultured rat hepatocytes during simulation of intracellular cholesterol esterification. *J. Lipid Res.* 21:1065–71

23. Drevon, C. A., Weinstein, D. B., Steinberg, D. 1980. Regulation of cholesterol esterification and biosynthesis in monolayer cultures of normal adult rat hepatocytes. *J. Biol. Chem.* 255:9128–37

24. Elovson, J., Huang, Y. O., Baker, N., Kannan, R. 1981. Apolipoprotein B is structurally and metabolically heterogeneous in the rat. *Proc. Natl. Acad. Sci. USA* 78:157–61

25. Fainaru, M., Felker, T. E., Hamilton, R. L., Havel, R. J. 1977. Evidence that a separate particle containing B-apoprotein is present in high density lipoproteins from perfused rat liver. *Metab. Clin. Exp.* 26:999–1004

26. Felker, T. E., Fainaru, M., Hamilton, R. L., Havel, R. J. 1977. Secretion of the arginine-rich and A-I apolipoproteins by the isolated perfused rat liver. *J. Lipid Res.* 18:465–73

27. Floren, C-H., Nilsson, Ä. 1977. Degradation of chylomicron remnant cholesteryl ester by rat hepatocyte: inhibition by chloroquine and colchicine. *Biochem. Biophys. Res. Commun.* 74:520–28

28. Floren, C-H., Nilsson, Ä. 1977. Binding interiorization and degradation of cholesteryl ester-labeled chylomicron-remnant particles by rat hepatocyte cultures. *Biochem. J.* 168:483–94

29. Floren, C-H., Nilsson, Ä. 1978. Uptake and degradation of iodine-labeled chylomicron remnant particles by monolayers of rat hepatocytes. *Biohem. J.* 174:827–38

30. Floren, C-H., Nilsson, Ä. 1981. Effects of hypothyroidism and cholesterol feeding on the clearance of chylomicron remnants *in vivo* and by rat hepatocyte monolayers. *Eur. J. Clin. Invest.* 11:11–18

31. Forte, T. M., Bell-Quint, J. 1981.

Lipoprotein synthesis and secretion by rat hepatocytes cultures: structural-functional interrelationships. In *Advances in Physiological Science,* ed. J. Salanki, 3:225–28. New York: Pergamon

32. Geelen, M. J. H., Harris, R. A., Beynen, A. C., McCune, S. A. 1980. Short term hormonal control of hepatic lipogenesis. *Diabetes* 29:1006–22

33. Ghiselli, G. C., Angelucci, R., Regazzoni, A., Sirtori, C. R. 1981. Metabolism of HDL_2 and HDL_3 cholesterol by monolayers of rat hepatocytes. *FEBS Lett.* 125:60–64

34. Haagsman, H. P., Van Golde, L. M. G. 1981. Synthesis and secretion of very low density lipoproteins by isolated rat hepatocytes in suspension: role of diacylglycerol acyltransferase. *Arch. Biochem. Biophys.* 208:395–402

35. Hamilton, R. L., Williams, M. C., Fielding, C. J., Havel, R. J. 1976. Discoidal bilayer structure of nascent high density lipoproteins from perfused rat liver. *J. Clin. Invest.* 58:667–80

36. Hughes, T., Gwynne, J. 1981. Hormone regulation of swine hepatic apolipoprotein A-I secretion. *Arteriosclerosis* 1: 380a

37. Ide, T., Ontko, J. A. 1981. Increased secretion of very low density lipoprotein triglyceride following inhibition of long chain fatty acid oxidation in isolated rat liver. *J. Biol. Chem.* 256:10247–55

38. Ingebritsen, T. S., Geelen, M. J. H., Parker, R. A., Evenson, K. J., Gibson, D. M. 1980. Modulation of hydroxymethylglutaryl-CoA reductase activity, reductase kinase activity and cholesterol synthesis in rat hepatocytes in response to insulin and glucagon. *J. Biol. Chem.* 254:9986–89

39. Jensen, G. L., Baly, D. L., Brannon, P. M., Bensadoun, A. 1980. Synthesis and secretion of lipolytic enzymes by cultured chicken hepatocytes. *J. Biol. Chem.* 255:11141–48

40. Katz, N. R., Ick, M. 1981. Induction of acetyl-CoA carboxylase in primary rat hepatocyte cultures by glucose and insulin. *Biochem. Biophys. Res. Commun.* 100:703–9

41. Kovanen, P. T., Bilheimer, D. W., Goldstein, J. L., Jaramillo, J. J., Brown, M. S. 1981. Regulatory role for hepatic low density lipoprotein receptors *in vivo* in the dog. *Proc. Natl. Acad. Sci. USA* 78:1194–98

42. Lamb, R. G., Wood, C. K., Landa, B. M., Guzelian, P. S., Fallon, H. J. 1977. Studies of the formation and release of glycerolipids by primary monolayer cultures of adult rat hepatocytes. *Biochim. Biophys. Acta* 489:318–29

43. Mahley, R. W., Hui, D. Y., Innerarity, T. L. 1981. Two independent lipoprotein receptors on hepatic membranes of dog, swine, and man: apo-B, E, and apo-E receptors. *J. Clin. Invest.* 68:1197–206

44. Marsh, J. B. 1974. Lipoproteins in a non-recirculating perfusate of rat liver. *J. Lipid Res.* 15:544–50

45. Marsh, J. B. 1976. Apoproteins of the lipoproteins in a nonrecirculating perfusate of rat liver. *J. Lipid Res.* 17:85–90

46. Nilsson, Å., Ehnholm, C., Floren, C. H. 1981. Uptake and degradation of rat chylomicron remnants, produced *in vivo* and *in vitro*, in rat hepatocyte monolayers. *Biochim. Biophys. Acta* 663:408–20

47. Noel, S-P., Wong, L., Dolphin, P. J., Dory, L., Rubinstein, D. 1979. Secretion of cholesterol-rich lipoproteins by perfused livers of hypercholesterolemic rats. *J. Clin. Invest.* 64:674–83

48. Nordby, G., Berg, T., Nilsson, M., Norum, K. R. 1976. Secretion of lecithin: cholesterol acyltransferase from isolated rat hepatocytes. *Biochim. Biophsy. Acta* 450:69–77

49. O'Malley, J. P., Soltys, P. A., Portman, O. W. 1981. Interaction of free cholesterol and apoproteins of low- and high density lipoproteins with isolated rabbit hepatocytes. *J. Lipid Res.* 22:1214–24

50. Pangburn, S. H., Newton, R. S., Chang, C-M., Weinstein, D. B., Steinberg, D. 1981. Receptor-mediated catabolism of homologous low density lipoproteins in cultured pig hepatocytes. *J. Biol. Chem.* 256:3340–47

51. Patsch, W., Franz, S., Schonfeld, G. 1981. Synthesis and secretion of apolipoproteins in primary rat liver cell cultures. *Arteriosclerosis* 1:385a

52. Ray, E., Bellini, F., Stoudt, G., Hemperly, S., Rothblat, G. 1980. Influence of lecithin:cholesterol acyltransferase on cholesterol metabolism in hepatoma cells and hepatocytes. *Biochim. Biophys. Acta* 617:318–34

53. Siuta-Mangano, P., Lane, M. D. 1981. Very low density lipoprotein synthesis and secretion. Extrusion of apoprotein B nascent chains through the membrane of the endoplasmic reticulum without protein synthesis. *J. Biol. Chem.* 256:2094–97

54. Soltys, P. A., Portman, O. W. 1979. Low density lipoprotein receptors and catabolism in primary cultures of rabbit hepatocytes. *Biochim. Biophys. Acta* 574:505–20

55. Sparks, C. E., Marsh, J. B. 1981. Meta-

bolic heterogeneity of apolipoprotein B in the rat. *J. Lipid Res.* 22:519–27

56. Stange, E. F., Fleig, W. E., Schneider, A., Nother-Fleig, M., Alavi, M., Preclik, G., Ditschuneit, H. 1982. 3-Hydroxy-3-methylglutaryl CoA reductase in cultured hepatocytes: regulation by heterologous lipoproteins and hormones. *Atherosclerosis* 41:67–80

57. Struck, D. K., Siuta, P. B., Lane, M. D., Lennarz, W. J. 1978. Effect of tunicamycin on the secretion of serum proteins by primary cultures of rat and chick hepatocytes. Studies on transferrin, very-low-density lipoprotein and serum albumin. *J. Biol. Chem.* 253:5332–37

58. Tarlow, D. M., Watkins, P. A., Reed, R.

E., Miller, R. S., Zwergel, E. E., Lane, M. D. 1977. Lipogenesis and the synthesis and secretion of very-low density lipoprotein by avian liver cells in nonproliferating monolayer culture. Hormonal effects. *J. Cell Biol.* 73:332–53

59. Wanson, J-C., Drochmans, P., Mosselmans, R., Ronveaux, M-F. 1977. Adult rat hepatocytes in primary monolayer culture. Ultrastructural characteristics of intercellular contacts and cell membrane differentiations. *J. Cell Biol.* 74:858–77

60. Wu, A-L., Windmueller, H. G. 1981. Variant forms of plasma apolipoprotein B. Hepatic and intestinal biosynthesis and heterogeneous metabolism in the rat. *J. Biol. Chem.* 256:3615–18

Ann. Rev. Physiol. 1984. 46:417–33

INTESTINAL TRANSPORT OF AMINO ACIDS AND SUGARS: ADVANCES USING MEMBRANE VESICLES

Bruce R. Stevens, Jonathan D. Kaunitz, and Ernest M. Wright

Departments of Physiology and Medicine, UCLA School of Medicine, Los Angeles, California 90024

INTRODUCTION

The small intestine is the primary site of amino acid and glucose absorption into the blood. These solutes are transported by three processes: simple diffusion, facilitated diffusion, and "active" transport. Simple diffusion occurs via the paracellular and cellular routes, whereas mediated transport occurs solely through the cell. Transport across the enterocyte involves (*a*) uptake from the gut across the brush-border membrane, (*b*) diffusion through the cytoplasm, and (*c*) exit to the portal blood across the basolateral membrane. Topologically, the brush border faces the outside of the body, and is therefore the interface barrier between the glucose and amino acid pools of the organism and the foodsource. The brush borders contain unique transport properties, while the basolateral membranes are very similar to plasma membranes of nonepithelial cells. The "active" transport of sugars and amino acids across the intestine is a consequence of this polarity of the epithelium. In this review, we will focus on the differential transport properties of isolated brush-border and basolateral membranes, which will enable us to propose a composite model of transcellular movement of amino acids or sugars.

Crane (4) in 1961 proposed that uphill transport of glucose across the brush border occured via a Na-glucose-carrier complex driven by the transmembrane Na gradient. In the ensuing two decades many experiments using intact intestinal tissues confirmed and refined Crane's hypothesis for glucose, and extended it to amino acids. Further advances, however, have been limited by

417

problems of unstirred layers, paracellular shunts, and metabolism of natural sugars and amino acids. The reader is directed elsewhere for reviews of transport across the intact epithelium (18, 26, 35).

A landmark in intestinal physiology was the introduction of brush-border membrane vesicles by Hopfer and co-workers in 1973 (9). The impact was twofold: it confirmed the Crane hypothesis of Na-glucose cotransport, and it provided a stimulus for further experiments using intestinal brush-border and basolateral-membrane vesicles. Vesicles circumvent the problems listed above for intact epithelial studies and offer some experimental advantages over intact cell and tissue preparations (see 29).

Membrane Vesicles

Brush-border vesicles are readily prepared from intestinal cells by the method of Ca^{++} or Mg^{++} differential centrifugation. This procedure produces 100–150 nM diameter vesicles of normal orientation, based on the electronmicrographic distribution of the actin microvillus core material and the glycocalyx (15). Purity is customarily judged by the enrichment of brush-border markers relative to those for other subcellular organelles (e.g. sucrase enriched 22X over the initial cell homogenate). The isolation procedure for basolateral membranes has involved density gradient and differential centrifugation (24, 25). The basolateral membranes are enriched with (Na^+,K^+)-ATPase 13–19X compared to the initial cell homogenate, but are depleted of brush-border and mitochondrial markers (see 22 for a discussion of membrane markers).

Transport properties of vesicles have been measured using radioactive tracers and a rapid mixing–filtration procedure (9, 17), where time points of 1 second are possible even with manual techniques. Recently, an optical probe technique has been introduced to study the kinetics of Na-coupled transport processes (33). These two techniques are currently employed to measure the kinetics of sugar and amino acid transport, where *cis* and *trans* solute concentrations are well controlled. Readers are referred to Murer & Kinne (29) and Sachs et al (32) for some technical aspects of vesicle experiments.

AMINO ACID TRANSPORT

It has been recognized for 25 years that amino acids are transported across plasma membranes by a multiplicity of carriers. Christensen and his colleagues (see 1, 2) have played a leading role in the classification of these carriers in a wide variety of nonepithelial cell types. Six fundamental categories have been described: the *A, ASC, L, y^+*, β, and the *glycine* transport systems. In our studies of intestinal transport, we have retained and expanded the Christensen classification. The characteristics of the transport pathways occuring in enterocytes are summarized in Table 1 and are discussed below. Enterocyte vesicles

Table 1 Amino acid transport pathways in jejunal membrane vesicles

Pathway	Occurrence	Na-dependent	Typical substrates	Notable excluded substrates	Comments
Diffusion	brush border & basolateral	—	—	—	passive non-saturable transport
NBB	brush border	yes	most neutral amino acids	MeAIB, β-alanine	found exclusively in brush-border membrane
IMINO	brush border	yes	imino acids, proline, MeAIB	glycine, most amino acids	highly selective for imino acids & Na
PHE	brush border	yes	phenylalanine, methionine	—	—
y^+	brush border	no	lysine, arginine, cationic amino acids	—	inhibition by neutral amino acids + Na; probably also in basolaterals
L	brush border & basolateral	no	leucine, BCH, branched & ringed amino acids	β-alanine	Na-independent; broadly selective for most neutral amino acids
A	basolateral	yes	MeAIB, short-chained polar amino acids	—	broadly selective for many neutral amino acids
ASC	basolateral	yes	3 and 4 carbon neutral amino acids; alanine serine, cysteine	MeAIB, glycine, phenylalanine	highly selective for L–stereo isomers & Na; the protonated carrier shows Na–independent inhibition by anionic amino acids in hepatocytes (39).

Systems A and ASC were defined originally for nonepithelial unicellular membranes (see 1, 2, 21) and were subsequently revealed in rat jejunal basolateral vesicles (24). Systems y^+ (changed nominally from Ly^+; 45) and L (1, 2) were also defined for unicellular systems and have been identified in rat basolateral and rabbit brush-border membranes (see 24, 39). Systems NBB, IMINO, and PHE were originally characterized in rabbit jejunal brush-border membrane vesicles (39).

lack the β system, which can transport β-alanine and taurine, and lack the *glycine* system, which is restricted to Na-dependent transport of glycine and sarcosine in nonepithelial cells.

Brush-Border Membranes

Amino acids enter the rabbit jejunal brush-border membrane vesicles via three major transport routes (39): nonsaturable simple diffusion, Na-independent carriers, and Na-dependent carriers.

PASSIVE DIFFUSION   When the passive permeability coefficients (P) of amino acids are ranked, the sequence is very similar to nonepithelial membranes, including artificial liposomes (39). For instance, the lipophilic neutral phenylalanine diffuses faster (P $= 1.4$ $\mu l \cdot mg^{-1} \cdot min^{-1}$) than the cationic lysine (P $= 0.6$ $\mu l \cdot mg^{-1} \cdot min^{-1}$). The measured permeability sequence is: phenylalanine $>$ β-alanine $>$ mannitol $>$ alanine $>$ α-methyl aminoisobutyric acid (MeAIB) $>$ proline $>$ glycine $>$ lysine.

It is noteworthy that jejunal brush borders are unique among membranes, in that the sole pathway for β-alanine uptake is via passive diffusion. The pI of β-alanine (6.9) is greater than the pI of L-alanine (6.0), and therefore β-alanine exists in a greater fraction of the zwitterion form at the luminal pH of 7.4. This effectively increases the partition coefficient and allows it to diffuse across the brush-border membrane nearly twice as fast as L-alanine. Teleologically, the absence of the β carrier suggests that jejunal passive uptake adequately meets the organism's nutritional demand for β-amino acids.

Na-INDEPENDENT CARRIERS   There are two major Na-independent carrier systems in brush-border membrane vesicles. One is the *L* system originally described in the Ehrlich ascites tumor cell (2) and found in all eukaryotic cell types. In enterocyte brush borders this system transports neutral amino acids and favors lipophilic amino acids such as phenylalanine, leucine, and the analogue 2-amino-2-norbornanecarboxylic acid hemihydrate (BCH). Although the *L* system was historically defined by BCH transport, this analogue is now known to interact with other systems (1, 2, 39). The *L* system J_{max} is about 2 $nmol \cdot mg^{-1} \cdot min^{-1}$, and the K_t values for phenylalanine and alanine are about 0.3 mM.

The second carrier handles cationic amino acids such as lysine (26, 39). This has been designated y^+ for nonepithelial cells (45). There is evidence that some neutral amino acids such as glycine and alanine are transported by the cationic carrier in rat (26).

Na-DEPENDENT CARRIERS   Sigrist-Nelson et al (38) were the first to demonstrate Na-dependent uphill transport of amino acids in intestinal brush-border vesicles. They additionally showed, using K^+ and H^+ diffusion potentials, that uptake was sensitive to membrane potentials (E_m). Recently, our group (33) has used a potential-sensitive dye to show that amino acid/Na cotransport depolarizes E_m. Amino acid uptake is coupled to Na uptake, with a coupling coefficient ($J^{Na}/J^{nonelectrolyte}$) of 1 or greater, depending on the specific carrier mechanism (40, 46). Na affects the carrier affinity (K_t), not the J_{max} (33, 40), and behaves as an obligatory activator. In the absence of Na, uptake via other Na-independent carrier(s) prevails.

Based on uptake kinetics and cross-inhibitions, Stevens et al (39) have shown that the brush-border membrane transports amino acids via at least three Na-dependent carrier systems (see Table 1). Each of these pathways are unique to brush-border membranes (none conform to classical pathways observed in other membranes). (a) The *NBB* system (*N*eutral *B*rush *B*order) transports most neutral amino acids (i.e. primarily the zwitterion at pH 7.5) and shows some interaction with BCH. It does not interact with MeAIB, and therefore is not the *A* system found in other cell membranes; and it is not the *ASC* system because it serves glycine and phenylalanine. (b) The *PHE* system handles primarily phenylalanine and methionine. (c) The *IMINO* system exclusively transports imino acids (proline, hydroxyproline) and MeAIB. Although the *IMINO* system is the sole carrier for MeAIB uptake in brush-border membranes, it is different from the *A* system because it excludes alanine and other short-chained amino acids.

Hayashi et al (6) measured proline and MeAIB uptake in guinea pig intestinal brush-border vesicles and tentatively concluded that the brush-border membrane contained the *A* and *ASC* systems. However, they did not test for *A* system interactions using cross-inhibition profiles of MeAIB against a wide range of other amino acids, nor did they test the interaction of phenylalanine and glycine with proline uptake (to check for *ASC* interactions). The guinea pig proline kinetics (6) were very similar to those obtained in rabbit (39). For example, each species showed strictly Na-dependent proline uptake with the same J_{max} ($\sim 10\ \mathrm{nmol \cdot mg^{-1} \cdot min^{-1}}$), similar K_t values ($\sim 0.6\ \mathrm{mM}$), and similar permeability coefficients ($P \sim 1.0\ \mathrm{\mu l \cdot mg^{-1} \cdot min^{-1}}$). Hence, it is likely that the proline transport in guinea pig occurs via the same *IMINO* system found in rabbit brush-border membrane. There is no exclusive proline/glycine interaction in either species.

RELATIVE IMPORTANCE OF THE PATHWAYS   We have computed the percent contribution of known phenylalanine uptake pathways at various phenylalanine concentrations (see Figure 1). Phenylalanine enters the brush-border membrane vesicle via diffusion ($P = 1.4\ \mathrm{\mu l \cdot mg^{-1} \cdot min^{-1}}$), via the Na-independent system ($K_t = 0.3\ \mathrm{mM}$, $J_{max} = 1.8\ \mathrm{nmol \cdot mg^{-1} \cdot min^{-1}}$), and via a Na-dependent mode ($K_t = 9\ \mathrm{mM}$, $J_{max} = 37\ \mathrm{nmol \cdot mg^{-1} \cdot min^{-1}}$). Diffusion provides a

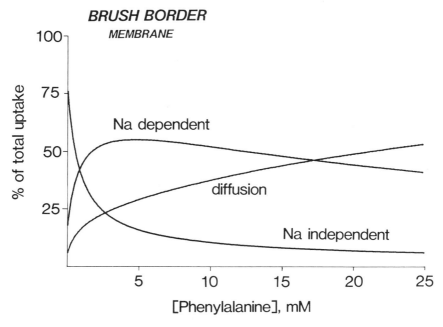

Figure 1   Relative contributions of transport pathways available for L-phenylalanine uptake in brush-border membrane vesicles. The kinetic parameters of each system are presented in the text.

significant pathway in membrane vesicles at physiological concentrations. For example, uptake via diffusion is about 25% of the total uptake at 2.5 mM, providing about the same percent as the Na-independent carrier. At 17 mM, uptake by diffusion exceeds uptake via all carrier pathways and accounts for about 45% of the total uptake. At concentrations below 2.5 mM, carriers are required for sufficient uptake across the brush border. At phenylalanine concentrations ≲ 1 mM, uptake via the Na-independent carrier dominates (up to 75% of the total). Above 2.5 mM this system becomes the pathway contributing least to total uptake.

RENAL *VS* INTESTINAL CARRIERS   Some similarities are shared by renal and jejunal brush-border membranes (23, 33). These similarities include (*a*) the apparent absence of any Na-dependent carriers that are found in nonepithelial membranes (e.g. no *A* or *ASC*), (*b*) a distinct *IMINO* carrier, and (*c*) several carriers for PHE and ALA. The most notable disparity is that renal membranes possess a Na-stimulated β system while intestinal membranes have no detectable β-alanine carrier. Quantitative comparisons made between renal and intestinal membranes prepared from the same animals indicate that transport rates are less in jejunal than in renal membranes (41).

Basolateral Membranes

Hopfer et al (11, 28) pioneered the comparison of transport properties between brush-border and basolateral membranes. Later, Mircheff et al (24), using rat membranes, contributed to current knowledge of neutral amino acid transport at the basolateral surface. Transport across basolateral membranes occurs via passive diffusion and the Na-independent (L) and Na-dependent (A, ASC) carriers found universally in nonepithelial membranes (see Table 1).

PASSIVE DIFFUSION   The basolateral membrane is more permeable to amino acids than is the brush-border membrane. For example, the P for alanine is about 4.5 $\mu l \cdot mg^{-1} \cdot min^{-1}$ in basolateral membranes (24), and 1 $\mu l \cdot mg^{-1} \cdot min^{-1}$ in brush-border membranes (39). The leaky nature of this membrane allows accumulated amino acid to diffuse readily from the enterocyte to the blood, consistent with autoradiographic observations in intact tissue (30). However, carrier-mediated pathways aid in the exodus as well as provide for uptake into the enterocyte when gut luminal amino acid concentrations are low.

Na-INDEPENDENT CARRIERS   The L system provides a major transport route for neutral amino acids (11, 24). For alanine it is the predominant mode and contributes about 50% of the total flux over the concentration range 0.5–1 mM. Above 1 mM, however, diffusion predominates. This L system ($K_t = 0.7$ mM, $J_{max} = 5.3$ nmol·mg^{-1}·min^{-1}) is unresponsive to either Na or E_m. Na-independent carriers for lysine and proline have also been observed at the basolateral surface of intact epithelium (5, 26).

Na-DEPENDENT CARRIERS   At lower concentrations (<20 μM), alanine transport via Na-dependent pathways constitutes about 30% of the total jejunal basolateral transport. This probably provides the enterocyte with amino acids for its own maintenance and metabolism at times of low amino acid concentrations in the gut lumen. At alanine concentrations above 150 μM, transport via Na-dependent routes becomes less significant (<10%). An A-like system serves neutral amino acids with a high affinity (alanine $K_t = 40$ μM) but low capacity ($J_{max} = 0.26$ nmol·mg^{-1}·min^{-1}). An ASC-like system has also been demonstrated by cross-inhibition.

Clinical Correlations

Clinically observed specific amino acid malabsorption syndromes can be explained as genetic disorders of membrane-transport carriers. The transport defects are often simultaneously manifested in renal and gastrointestinal tissues, which suggests a mutation of a common gene locus (34). For example Hartnup's disease, characterized by reduction in intestinal uptake of neutral amino acids, probably is a defect in the L and/or Na-dependent neutral amino acid carriers *NBB* and *PHE*. Prolinuria is probably an intestinal defect of the *IMINO* system, and hyperdibasicaminoaciduria is a likely defect in the y^+ system in enterocytes and renal membranes. It is generally not known whether brush-border and basolateral-membrane carriers are both involved, nor is the role of feedback to the nucleus (e.g. repression of carrier synthesis) known in these diseases. Studies using intact segments of jejunal biopsies obtained from patients with lysinuric protein–intolerance syndrome, however, have suggested that a basolateral membrane defect may be implicated in lysine malabsorption (5).

Summary

Some general observations can be made regarding amino acid transport. (*a*) Diffusion contributes significantly to transport in both brush-border and basolateral membranes. The significance varies with each amino acid and depends on factors such as the structure (i.e. partition coefficient) and the degree of interactions with high-capacity (high J_{max}) carriers. (*b*) Both membranes possess Na-dependent and Na-independent carriers. Only one carrier type, the *L* system, is common to both membranes. This *L* system is ubiquitous in eukaryotic plasma membranes. (*c*) The basolateral-membrane pathways are very similar to those found randomly distributed on nonepithelial cell membranes such as hepatocytes, reticulocytes, and fibroblasts. These pathways include *L*, *A*-like, and *ASC*-like carriers. (*d*) The brush-border membrane Na-dependent pathways (*NBB, IMINO, PHE*) are unique, not observed in any nonepithelial cell membrane. Several similarities are shared with renal brush-border membranes, however.

D-GLUCOSE TRANSPORT

Brush-Border Membranes

The first experiments using brush-border vesicles confirmed the Na-glucose cotransport hypothesis by showing that uphill glucose transport could be energized by Na gradients, i.e. the so-called overshoot phenomenon (9, 27). The kinetics of glucose transport have since been explored by two techniques. One is the rapid uptake procedure to obtain initial rates under defined *cis, trans,* and E_m conditions (3, 13, 14, 16, 17). The second is the equilibrium isotope-exchange method exploited by Hopfer's group (7, 8). In the latter case, the half time of ^{3}H-glucose exchange between vesicles and medium is measured with identical solutions (Na + glucose) at the *cis* and *trans* sides of the membrane.

Under both zero *trans* and equilibrium exchange conditions, glucose transport occurs by at least two pathways: a Na-dependent saturable system, and a "leak," or diffusional, pathway. In steer and rabbits (14) the leak pathway exhibits first-order kinetics between 0–20 mM glucose ($P \sim 1$–4 $\mu l \cdot mg^{-1} \cdot min^{-1}$).

In rats, however, Ling et al (20) found saturation at much higher (> 50mM) glucose concentrations, indicating a low-affinity facilitated-diffusion system.

The kinetic parameters for the Na-dependent saturable system are summarized in Table 2. Under equilibrium exchange conditions, the K_t is 2–4 mM and the J_{max} ~ 35 nmoles·mg^{-1}·min^{-1} in rabbit. Lower values for K_t (0.1–0.3mM) and J_{max} (5–11 nmoles·mg^{-1}·min^{-1}) are obtained from zero-*trans* experiments.

Some of the variation among the zero *trans* results is explainable by methodological differences. One difference is the variation in E_m. *Cis* NaSCN produces a more negative E_m compared to NaCl, and decreases K_t while increasing J_{max} (17). This is consistent with studies using intact enterocytes (18) but contrary to those for renal-vesicle succinate transport (48). An additional difference is that Kaunitz & Wright (14) measured uptakes over a wider glucose-concentration range (0.01–20 mM vs 20–400 μM). Over the wider range they found three systems in rabbit vesicles: (a) diffusion (see above); (b) a major, low affinity system (J_{max} = 11 nmole·mg^{-1}·min^{-1}, K_t = 0.34 mM); and (c) a minor, high affinity system (J_{max} = 3 nmole·mg^{-1}·min^{-1}, K_t = 0.03 mM) (see also 3). In steer brush borders they also find three systems, with the J_{max} and K_t of the high-affinity system about one order of magnitude lower than the low-affinity system.

EFFECTS OF Na   Under equilibrium exchange conditions, increasing NaSCN from 1 to 100 mM had little effect on K_t, but increased J_{max} by 15–20-fold (7, 8). However, with zero-*trans* conditions, noncompetitive-type kinetics were obtained (16), i.e. as Na was raised from 5 to 100 mM, J_{max} increased and K_t

Table 2   Kinetics of Na/glucose transport in brush-border membranes

Animal	[Na] (mM) cis	[Na] (mM) trans	K_t (mM)	J_{max} (nmol·mg^{-1}·min^{-1})	Salt	Notes
Rat	100	100	14	—	NaSCN	a
Rabbit	100	100	2.4	—	NaSCN	b
	200	200	—	36	NaSCN	c
	100	0	0.08	11	NaSCN	d
	100	0	0.18	5	NaCl	d
	100	0	0.34	11	NaCl	e
	100	100	3.7	35	NaCl	d
Cow	100	0	0.1	9	NaCl	f

All kinetic parameters were calculated for the major Na–dependent system when more than one cotransporter was resolved.
[a] 15°C, sucrase enriched 22× (7);
[b] 15°C, sucrase enriched 25× (8);
[c] 25°C (10);
[d] 20°C, 20–400 μM glucose, sucrase enriched 20–25×, no control of E_m (17);
[e] 22°C, 10 μM–20mM glucose, and sucrase enriched 19× (14);
[f] 22°C, 100 μM–20mM glucose and sucrase enriched 15× (14).

decreased. These results are subject to uncertainty, due to variations in E_m and a limited range of glucose concentrations (20–500 μM). Similar uncertainties exist with Crane & Dorando's experiments (3). We found that Na acts as a competitive-type activator of the major carrier in steer, i.e. Na affects K_t but not J_{max} (14). *Trans* Na inhibition of glucose uptake (14, 16) may be due mainly to a reduction in J_{max}. This *trans* Na inhibition is relieved by *trans* glucose (16).

COUPLING RATIO   The number of Na^+ ions cotransported with each glucose molecule (coupling ratio) is required to assess the energetics of uphill transport (18). The coupling ratio has been directly and indirectly measured in rabbit (13) and bovine (14) brush borders. When the carrier-dependent initial rates of ^{22}Na and ^{3}H-glucose were compared, a ratio of 3:1 (Na:glucose) was found. Indirect estimates of the coupling were also obtained by varying external Na and measuring the initial rate of glucose uptake using zero-*trans*, voltage-clamped conditions in the presence of fixed glucose. In this case, a sigmoidal Na activation curve was obtained with a Hill coefficient of 1.9, consistent with at least two Na binding sites. In more extensive bovine-vesicle experiments, Kaunitz & Wright (14) found that the Hill coefficient changed from 2.0 to 1.2 when the *cis* glucose concentration was raised from 0.01 mM to 0.5 mM. These observations are explained by a major, 1:1 Na:glucose high-capacity system and a low-capacity, high-affinity system requiring multiple Na^+ ions. The cosubstrate-dependent intial influx of Na was ~2.5 times the influx of glucose at 30 mM Na and 0.5 mM glucose, consistent with a 1:1 and 3:1 carrier operating in parallel. These results compare with those of Turner & Moran (44), who found two Na-glucose transporters in renal brush-border vesicles with differing affinities, capacities, and coupling ratios, and may explain the discrepancies with previous studies performed with whole tissue, enterocytes, or vesicles (8, 18, 35).

EVIDENCE FOR CARRIER ASYMMETRY   Semenza's laboratory (37) has shown that proteases and p-chloromercuribenzene sulfonate inhibit Na-dependent phlorizin binding to brush borders only when vesicles are disrupted with deoxycholate. They concluded that these inhibitions resulted from differences between the exposed portions of the Na-glucose transporter at each membrane face. More recently, Kessler & Semenza (16) have shown that *trans* glucose, Na, and negative E_m each inhibited Na-coupled glucose influx, but the inhibition was relieved by *trans* glucose. *Trans* solute and E_m affected efflux much less than influx, indicative of a functional asymmetry of the cotransporter.

TRANSPORT MECHANISM   Transport mechanisms have been modeled after enzyme mechanism paradigms (36). Hopfer & Groseclose (8) used equilibrium isotope exchange to study the effect of Na concentration on glucose influx, and vice-versa. Biphasic activation curves were seen, with enhancement of uptake at low substrate concentrations and inhibition at high concentrations, similar to patterns seen in an ordered enzyme kinetic system (i.e. obligate binding of one solute prior to the addition of the other solute). Hopfer & Groseclose concluded that under equilibrium exchange conditions, Na and glucose add to the transporter in an ordered fashion. Based on zero-*trans* experiments, Crane & Dorando (3) presented a random model (no obligate order of reactant binding) for Na-glucose transport in rabbit jejunal vesicles, while Kessler & Semenza (16) proposed a semirandom "preferred" (rather than obligate) binding of Na before glucose. The latter model was based largely on observations (42) that both phlorizin binding and glucose transport required *cis* Na and E_m (vesicle interior negative) for maximal velocity. These investigators concluded that E_m-sensitive Na binding must be the first step of phlorizin binding and glucose transport.

Kaunitz & Wright (14) have formulated a model system based on observation made under zero-*trans* conditions, when $E_m = 0$. Contrary to the intact tissue studies of Goldner et al (see 35), but in agreement with findings derived from other cotransport systems, *cis* Na affected the K_t but not the J_{max} of glucose influx in vesicles. Assuming that translocation of the loaded carrier is rate limiting (rapid equilibrium assumption), it is predicted from classical kinetic analysis (36) that an ordered system is present with Na adding first (Iso Ordered Bireactant system). The velocity equation is:

$$ J = \frac{J_{max}\,[G]}{K_G(1 + K_{Na}/[Na]) + [G]} $$

where K_{Na}, K_G, [Na], and [G] are the relative dissociation constants and concentrations of Na and glucose. The velocity equation only describes the effect of varying *cis* substrates on Na-dependent glucose influx. The complete rate equation, which takes into account translocation rates of all substrate-carrier complexes, effect of E_m, and solute binding and debinding is more complex (see 43).

RELATIVE IMPORTANCE OF THE PATHWAYS   Using measured kinetic parameters, we calculated the relative contribution of the diffusive and both saturable-transport systems to the overall uptake rate. The high-affinity system predominates when the glucose concentration is < 0.5 mM, giving way to the high-capacity system at higher concentrations. Above 2 mM, the diffusive system is more important.

Basolateral Membranes

As in the case of amino acids, glucose transport across intestinal basolateral membranes has been subjected to far less scrutiny than the brush border. Essentially, the major conclusion drawn from all studies thus far is that glucose basolateral transport occurs by simple plus facilitated diffusion (11, 20, 28, 47).

In rat basolaterals (47), kinetics of L-glucose were linear from 10–150 mM, with $P = \sim 2$ $\mu l \cdot mg^{-1} \cdot min^{-1}$, and a temperature coefficient of 3 $kcal \cdot mol^{-1}$. D-glucose transported by the saturable system exhibited all the features of facilitated glucose diffusion in red blood cells: stereospecificity, saturation kinetics (K_t 44 mM and J_{max} 120 $nmoles \cdot mg^{-1} \cdot min^{-1}$ at 10°C), and inhibition by structural analogs (e.g. D-galactose) and transport inhibitors (phloretin and cytochalasin B). The only major inconsistency is that Wright et al (47) found that all sugars with the D-glucose chair conformation, except α-methyl-D-glucoside, inhibited glucose uptake, while Ling et al (20) found that only glucose and galactose competed for the sugar carrier. The reason for this discrepancy is unclear, but our results are consistent with those on intact enterocytes (18) and are in agreement with the properties of the glucose carrier found in such diverse tissues as placenta, red cell, and choroid plexus. The specificity of the facilitated-diffusion system is quite distinct from that for Na-cotransport in brush borders. The latter is restricted to hexoses with an equatorial –OH group on carbon 2 (see 4). The work by Ling et al (20) also suggests that a Na-independent glucose carrier is in brush-border and basolateral membranes.

Summary

(a) Glucose crosses the intestinal brush border via one diffusive and two saturable systems. (b) Under zero-*trans* conditions, the major saturable system has the characteristics of an Iso Ordered Bireactant system with one Na binding and, additionally, shows the properties of *trans* inhibition by Na and sensitivity to E_m. (c) An additional high-affinity saturable system exists with a K_t in the micromolar range and has the capacity for binding multiple Na^+ ions. (d) Biochemical and transport studies indicate that the brush-border Na-glucose cotransporter may be asymmetric with respect to the inner and outer membrane face. (e) The Na-independent glucose carrier found in enterocyte basolateral membranes strongly resembles the facilitated glucose carrier found in other membranes.

CONCLUSION

Transepithelial Transport

A general scheme for transcellular alanine and glucose transport, based on data obtained with rabbit jejunal brush borders and rat basolateral membranes, is

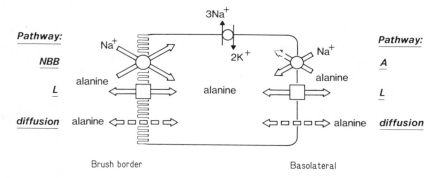

Figure 2   Transepithelial L-alanine transport. The composite model is based on transport experiments using jejunal brush-border and basolateral membrane vesicles, with the kinetic parameters described in Table 3.

presented in Figures 2 and 3. The major transport pathways for each solute are shown in the figure, and the estimates of the kinetic parameters are listed in Tables 3 and 4.

There are three systems for alanine transport across the brush border. At low mucosal concentrations the largest contributor is the Na-dependent *NBB* system, but as the luminal alanine concentration rises, diffusion predominates. As the intracellular alanine concentration rises, efflux across the brush-border membrane by simple diffusion and the *L* carrier reduces the efficiency of the *NBB* system. Furthermore, alanine also diffuses out of the cell by simple plus facilitated diffusion (*L* carrier) across the basolateral membrane, resulting in net absorption. The higher permeability and high capacity of the basolateral *L* system ensures that a larger fraction of the cell's free amino acid leaves via the basolateral membrane rather than the brush-border membrane. Only in the case

Table 3   Kinetic parameters of alanine transport

	Brush border (rabbit)
System *NBB*	J_{max} = 6 nmol·mg^{-1}·min^{-1} (0.4 μmol·cm^{-2}·hr^{-1}) K_t = 9 mM
System *L*	J_{max} = 2 nmol·mg^{-1}·min^{-1} (0.1 μmol·cm^{-2}·hr^{-1}) K_t = 0.3 mM
Diffusion	P = 1.1 μl·mg^{-1}·min^{-1} (0.06 cm·hr^{-1})
	Basolateral (rat)
System *A*	J_{max} = 0.26 nmol·mg^{-1}·min^{-1} (0.02 μmol·cm^{-2}·hr^{-1}) K_t = 0.04 mM
System *L*	J_{max} = 5 nmol·mg^{-1}·min^{-1} (0.3 μmol·cm^{-2}·hr^{-1}) K_t = 0.73 mM
Diffusion	P = 4.5 μl·mg^{-1}·min^{-1} (0.27 cm·hr^{-1})

Transport via various pathways (24, 39) at 23°C are expressed either as vesicle units [nmol·(mg vesicle protein)$^{-1}$·min^{-1}], or converted to standard intact epithelium units (μmol·cm^{-2}·hr^{-1}), as described in the text.

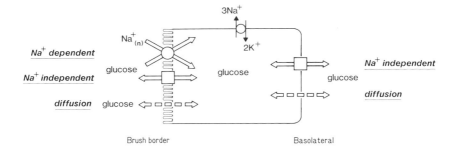

Figure 3 Transepithelial D-glucose transport. The model is based on transport in jejunal brush-border and basolateral membrane vesicles, and the kinetic parameters are described in Table 4.

of very low (< 10 μM) plasma-alanine concentrations will the basolateral *A* system produce intracellular accumulation.

To enable direct comparison of the vesicle data with that from intact epithelial preparations, we have also converted the transport rates from $nmol \cdot (mg\ protein)^{-1} \cdot min^{-1}$ to $\mu mol \cdot cm^{-2} \cdot hr^{-1}$, where the area refers to the serosal surface area. The conversion factors were obtained (41) from the epithelial cell protein (4×10^{-7} mg/cell), cell density (1×10^7 cells cm^{-2}), and membrane-vesicle protein enrichment (19X brush borders, 14X basolateral membranes). For brush borders and basolaterals, one mg of membrane protein is roughly equivalent to one cm^2 of serosal surface. The jejunal brush-border alanine uptakes may be compared with those reported for the intact rabbit ileum (see 31). The values for total carrier-mediated alanine uptake in vesicles ($J_{max} = 0.5$ $\mu mol \cdot cm^{-2} h^{-1}$) measured at 22°C, and the Na-dependent K_t (9mM) are remarkably close to those obtained in intact epithelial preparations at 37°C. Nonetheless, the extrapolation should be viewed with caution, given the differences in methodologies.

Table 4 Kinetic parameters of glucose transport

	Brush border (rabbit)
Na–dependent system	Major $J_{max} = 11\ nmol \cdot mg^{-1} \cdot min^{-1}$ ($0.7\ \mu mol \cdot cm^{-2} \cdot hr^{-1}$)
	$K_t = 0.34$ mM
	Minor $J_{max} = 3\ nmol \cdot mg^{-1} \cdot min^{-1}$ ($0.2\ \mu mol \cdot cm^{-2} \cdot hr^{-1}$
	$K_t = 0.03$ mM
Diffusion	$P = 2\ \mu l \cdot mg^{-1} \cdot min^{-1}$ ($0.12\ cm \cdot hr^{-1}$)
	Basolateral (rat)
Na–independent system	$J_{max} = 80–120\ nmol \cdot mg^{-1} \cdot min^{-1}$ ($5\ \mu mol \cdot cm^{-2} \cdot hr^{-1}$)
	$K_t = 40–80$ mM
Diffusion	$P = 2\ \mu l \cdot mg^{-1} \cdot min^{-1}$ ($0.12\ cm \cdot hr^{-1}$)

The measured diffusion component for glucose concentrations < 20 mM may also contain a contribution of a low–affinity ($K_t < 50$ mM) facilitated–diffusion system (Table 2; 20, 47).

Similar conclusions can be drawn from glucose vesicle experiments. The major uphill transport of glucose across the brush border occurs by the high-capacity, low-affinity Na cotransporter. The efficiency of the process is limited by the parallel diffusion pathways. Diffusion, simple and facilitated, also accounts for glucose exit across the basolateral membrane. Thus the asymmetrical distribution of glucose carriers between the two plasma membranes explains net glucose absorption even in the absence of transepithelial driving forces.

Future Trends

One goal is to identify, purify, and characterize the peptides responsible for transport in plasma membranes of the intestinal epithelium. So far, attempts have been made to identify and/or reconstitute into liposomes the glucose carriers of the intestine and renal proximal tubule. Progress has been slow because the Na/glucose cotransporter probably accounts for less than 1% of the membrane protein, and detergents apparently irreversibly denature the transporters.

The most successful advances are those of Hosang et al (12), who were able to demonstrate phlorizin-analogue photoaffinity labeling of an intestinal brush-border 72,000 m.w. polypeptide, and Koepsell et al (19), who showed a correlation between enrichment of a 52,000 m.w. protein and Na-dependent glucose transport in proteoliposomes reconstituted from renal brush borders. Future work along these lines should lead to a thorough understanding of the mechanism of Na-dependent transport.

Literature Cited

1. Christensen, H. N. 1975. *Biological Transport.* Reading, Mass: W. A. Benjamin. 2nd ed. 514 pp.
2. Christensen, H. N. 1979. Exploiting amino acid structure to learn about membrane transport. *Advan. Enzymol.* 49:41–101
3. Crane, R. K., Dorando, F. C. 1982. The kinetics and mechanism of Na$^+$ gradient-coupled glucose transport. In *Membranes and Transport,* ed. A. Martinosi, 2:153–60. New York: Plenum
4. Crane, R. K., Miller, D., Bihler, I. 1961. The restrictions on possible mechanisms of active transport of sugars. In *Membrane Transport and Metabolism,* ed. A. Kleinzeller, A. Kotyk. Prague: Czech. Acad. Sci.
5. Desjeux, J. F., Rajantie, J., Simell, O., Dumontier, A-M., Perheentupa, J. 1980. Lysine fluxes across the jejunal epithelium in lysinuric protein intolerance. *J. Clin. Invest.* 65:1382–87
6. Hayashi, K., Yamamoto, S-I., Ohe, K., Miyoshi, A., Kawasaki, T. 1980. Na$^+$-

gradient-dependent transport of L-proline and analysis of its carrier system in brush border membrane vesicles of the guinea-pig ileum. *Biochim. Biophys. Acta* 601:654–63
7. Hopfer, U. 1977. Kinetics of Na$^+$-dependent D-glucose transport. *J. Supramol. Structure* 7:1–13
8. Hopfer, U., Groseclose, R. 1980. The mechanism of Na$^+$-dependent D-glucose transport. *J. Biol. Chem.* 255:4453–62
9. Hopfer, U., Nelson, K., Perotto, J., Isselbacher, K. J. 1973. Glucose transport in isolated brush border membrane from rat small intestine. *J. Biol. Chem.* 248:25–32
10. Hopfer, U., Provencher, S. W. 1982. Estimation of heterogeneity and initial velocity of transport in vesicles by inverse laplace transformation of transport data. *Biophys. J.* 37:339a (Abstr.)
11. Hopfer, U., Sigrist-Nelson, K., Ammann, E., Murer, H. 1976. Differences in neutral amino acid and glucose transport between brush border and basolater-

al plasma membrane of intestinal epithelial cells. *J. Cell. Physiol.* 89:805–10

12. Hosang, M., Gibbs, E. M., Diedrich, D. F., Semenza, G. 1981. Photoaffinity labeling and identification of (a component of) the small-intestinal Na$^+$, D-glucose transporter using 4-azidophlorizin. *FEBS Lett.* 130:244–48

13. Kaunitz, J. D., Gunther, R. D., Wright, E. M. 1982. Involvement of multiple sodium ions in intestinal D-glucose transport. *Proc. Natl. Acad. Sci. USA* 79:2315–18

14. Kaunitz, J. D., Wright, E. M. 1983. Heterogeneity of the intestinal sodium-D-glucose carrier. *Fed. Proc.* 42(5):1287 (Abstr.)

15. Kessler, M., Acuto, O., Storelli, C., Murer, H., Muller, M., et al. 1978. A modified procedure for the rapid preparation of efficiently transporting vesicles from small intestinal brush border membranes. Their use in investigating some properties of D-glucose and choline transport systems. *Biochim. Biophys. Acta* 506:136–54

16. Kessler, M., Semenza, G. 1983. The small intestinal Na$^+$, D-glucose cotransporter: An asymmetric gated channel (or pore) responsive to $\Delta\Psi$. *J. Membr. Biol.* 76:27–56

17. Kessler, M., Tannenbaum, V., Tannenbaum, C. 1978. A simple apparatus for performing short time (1–2 seconds) uptake measurements in small volumes; its application to D-glucose transport studies in brush border vesicles from rabbit jejunum and ileum. *Biochim. Biophys. Acta* 509:348–59

18. Kimmich, G. A. 1981. Intestinal absorption of sugar. In *Physiology of the Gastrointestinal Tract*, ed. L. R. Johnson, pp. 1035–72. New York: Raven

19. Koepsell, H., Menuhr, H., Ducis, I., Wissmuller, T. F. 1983. Partial purification and reconstitution of the Na-D-glucose cotransport protein from pig renal proximal tubules. *J. Biol. Chem.* 258:1888–94

20. Ling, K. Y., Im, W. B., Faust, R. G. 1981. Na$^+$-independent sugar uptake by rat intestinal and renal brush border and basolateral membrane vesicles. *Int. J. Biochem.* 13:693–700

21. Makowske, M., Christensen, H. N. 1982. Hepatic transport systems interconverted by protonation from service for neutral to service for anionic amino acids. *J. Biol. Chem.* 257:14635–38

22. Mircheff, A. K. 1983. Empirical strategy for analytical fractionation of epithelial cells. *Am. J. Physiol* 244:G347–56

23. Mircheff, A. K., Kippen, I., Hirayama,

B., Wright, E. M. 1982. Delineation of sodium-stimulated amino acid transport pathways in rabbit kidney brush border vesicles. *J. Membr. Biol.* 64:113–22

24. Mircheff, A. K., van Os, C. H., Wright, E. M. 1980. Pathways for alanine transport in intestinal basal lateral membrane vesicles. *J. Membr. Biol.* 52:83–92

25. Mircheff, A. K., Wright, E. M. 1976. Analytical isolation of plasma membranes of intestinal epithelial cells: Identification of Na, K-ATPase rich membranes and the distribution of enzyme activities. *J. Membr. Biol.* 28:309–33

26. Munck, B. G. 1981. Intestinal absorption of amino acids. In *Physiology of the Gastrointestinal Tract*, ed. L. R. Johnson, pp. 1097–1122. New York: Raven

27. Murer, H., Hopfer, U. 1974. Demonstration of electrogenic Na$^+$ dependent D-glucose transport in intestinal brush border membranes. *Proc. Natl. Acad. Sci. USA* 7:484–88

28. Murer, H., Hopfer, U., Kinne-Safran, E., Kinne, R. 1974. Glucose transport in isolated brush-border and lateral-basal plasma-membrane vesicles from intestinal epithelial cells. *Biochim. Biophys. Acta* 345:170–79

29. Murer, H., Kinne, R. 1980. The use of isolated membrane vesicles to study epithelial transport processes. *J. Membr. Biol.* 55:81–95

30. Paterson, J. Y. F., Sepulveda, F. V., Smith M. W. 1982. Amino acid efflux from rabbit ileal enterocytes. *J. Physiol.* 331:537–46

31. Preston, R. L., Schaeffer, J. F., Curran, P. F. 1974. Structure-affinity relationships of substrates for the neutral amino acid transport system in rabbit ileum. *J. Gen. Physiol.* 64:443–67

32. Sachs, G., Jackson, R. J., Rabon, E. C. 1980. Use of plasma membrane vesicles. *Am. J. Physiol.* 283:G151–64

33. Schell, R. E., Stevens, B. R., Wright, E. M. 1983. Kinetics of sodium-dependent solute transport by rabbit renal and jejunal brush border vesicles using a fluorescent dye. *J. Physiol.* 335:307–18

34. Schriver, C. R., Chesney, R. W., McInnes, R. R. 1976. Genetic aspects of renal tubular transport: Diversity and topology of carriers. *Kidney Int.* 9:149–71

35. Schultz, S. G., Curran, P. F. 1970. Coupled transport of sodium and organic solutes. *Physiol. Rev.* 50:637–718

36. Segel, I. H. 1975. *Enzyme Kinetics.* New York: Wiley. 957 pp.

37. Semenza, G. 1982. The small intestinal Na$^+$/D-glucose carrier is inserted asymmetrically with respect to the plane of the

brush border membrane. See Ref. 3, pp. 175–82

38. Sigrist-Nelson, K., Murer, H., Hopfer, U. 1975. Active alanine transport in isolated brush border membranes. *J. Biol. Chem.* 250:5674–80

39. Stevens, B. R., Ross, H. J., Wright, E. M. 1982. Multiple transport pathways for neutral amino acids in rabbit jejunal brush border vesicles. *J. Membr. Biol.* 66:213–25

40. Stevens, B. R., Wright, E. M. 1983. The effect of Na^+ on proline transport kinetics in jejunal brush border membrane vesicles. *Fed. Proc.* 42:1287 (Abstr.)

41. Stevens, B. R., Wright, S. H., Hirayama, B. S., Gunther, R. D., Ross, H. J., et al. 1982. Organic and inorganic solute transport in renal and intestinal membrane vesicles preserved in liquid nitrogen. *Membr. Biochem.* 4:271–82

42. Toggenburger, G., Kessler, M., Semenza, G. 1982. Phlorizin is a probe of the small intestinal Na^+, D-glucose cotransporter. A Model. *Biochim. Biophys. Acta* 688:557–71

43. Turner, R. J. 1981. Kinetic analysis of a family of cotransport models. *Biochim. Biophys. Acta* 649:269–80

44. Turner, R. J., Moran, A. 1982. Further studies of proximal tubular brush border membrane D-glucose transport heterogeneity. *J. Membr. Biol.* 70:37–46

45. White, M. F., Christensen, H. N. 1982. Cationic amino acid transport into cultured animal cells. *J. Biol. Chem.* 257: 4450–57

46. Wright, E. M., Gunther, R. D., Kaunitz, J. D., Stevens, B. R., Harms, V., et al. 1983. Mechanisms of sodium transport across brush border basolateral membranes. In *Intestinal Transport*, ed. M. Gilles-Baillien, R. Gilles, pp. 122–32. Berlin: Springer-Verlag

47. Wright, E. M., Van Os, C. H., Mircheff, A. K. 1980. Sugar uptake by intestinal basolateral membrane vesicles. *Biochim. Biophys. Acta* 597:112–24

48. Wright, S. H., Hirayama, B. H., Kaunitz, J. D., Kippen, I., Wright, E. M. 1983. Kinetics of sodium-succinate cotransport across renal brush border membranes. *J. Biol. Chem.* 258:5456–62

Ann. Rev. Physiol. 1984. 46:435–51

A CELLULAR MODEL FOR ACTIVE SODIUM ABSORPTION BY MAMMALIAN COLON

Stanley G. Schultz

Department of Physiology & Cell Biology, University of Texas Medical School, P.O. Box 20708, Houston, Texas 77025

INTRODUCTION

The functions of mammalian colon[1] in the alimentary canal may be likened to those of the distal nephron of the kidney. After the small intestine has carried out the "obligatory" isotonic absorption of the bulk of the water, electrolytes, and virtually all of the nutrients that enter the canal, the colon performs the final act of conserving salt and water in a manner that appears to be responsive to bodily needs ("facultative absorption").

The overall transport functions of the colon have recently been reviewed in considerable detail (c.f. 48, 54) and are only briefly summarized here.

Normally, sodium (Na) is actively absorbed from the lumen against a considerable electrochemical-potential difference. This absorptive process is rapidly and reversibly inhibited by the pyrazine diuretic, amiloride, is stimulated by aldosterone, and appears to be primarily, if not entirely, responsible for the transepithelial electrical-potential difference (5–20 mV, serosa- or plasma-positive with respect to the lumen) and the "short-circuit" current in vitro (11, 48, 54). Thus, in many major respects, Na absorption by colonic mucosa resembles that observed in other well-studied epithelia such as amphibian skin and urinary bladder (40).

Potassium (K) is secreted into the lumen. This secretory process is enhanced by aldosterone (48, 54) and must be driven, at least in part, by the transepithelial electrical-potential difference (52). However, there is a growing body of

---

[1]In recent years it has become clear that in some species there are regional differences along the length of the large intestine (c.f. 14, 73). This review is largely concerned with data derived from studies on the distal (descending) portion of rabbit colon, which has been most extensively studied in vitro. There is reasonable evidence that the properties of this preparation resemble those of the distal colon of rat and man.

435

0066-4278/84/0315-0435$02.00

compelling evidence that at least under some conditions an active secretory process is also involved (41, 68).

Chloride (Cl) is absorbed by what appears to be an electrically "silent" or "neutral" process, and there is reasonable evidence that this silence is due to the coupling of Cl absorption to the secretion of bicarbonate (HCO_3), (25, 48, 54). Both Cl absorption and HCO_3 secretion are inhibited by the carbonic anhydrase inhibitor, acetazolamide (47).

Under some conditions, the colon may also secrete fluid and electrolytes. As in a number of other secretory epithelia (10, 48), active Cl secretion appears to be the propelling force, and an elevation of intracellular cyclic-AMP and/or calcium (Ca) appears to be the stimulant (9, 10, 48). Further, elegant optical studies recently reported by Welsh et al (67) have established, beyond reasonable doubt, that cells located in the crypts of the colonic mucosa are responsible for this secretory process, whereas it seems certain that the columnar cells that populate the surface of the mucosa are responsible for active Na absorption. The physiological agonists that evoke secretion by the colon have not, as yet, been clearly defined, but it would not be surprising if humoral agents and/or neurotransmitters were involved (48).

In recent years, the cellular processes responsible for active Na absorption by the mammalian colon[1] have been elucidated, largely through the use of micro-electrophysiological techniques, to the point where the individual properties of the apical and basolateral membranes, as well as the intervening intracellular compartment, have been sufficiently well defined to permit a coherent, consistent, and reasonably complete description of this process at the membrane level, thereby opening the way for studies at the molecular level. The purpose of this review is to summarize these findings, briefly, and to refer the reader interested in more detailed accounts to the relevant literature. I will also draw upon the results of studies on closely related epithelia, particularly frog skin and toad urinary bladder, when appropriate. I take a reductionist approach that presupposes the validity of the Koefoed-Johnsen-Ussing double-membrane model (28). In short, I assume that active transcellular Na transport is the result of interactions among the apical and basolateral membranes and the intervening intracellular compartment and that a coherent picture of this process can be constructed from an understanding of behavior and properties of these individual elements. Evidence accrued during the quarter of a century since this model was introduced abundantly supports this supposition and approach (40, 51).

THE APICAL MEMBRANE

The Mechanism of Na Entry Across the Apical Membrane

It is generally agreed that, under physiological conditions, Na entry across the apical membrane is the rate-limiting step in transcellular Na transport in a variety of "tight" or "moderately tight" Na-absorbing epithelia[2], inasmuch as under these conditions the basolateral pump appears to operate far from saturation (13, 40). [The "tightness" of an epithelium generally reflects the transepithelial resistance that, in turn, is largely a function of the resistance of paracellular pathways. Examples of "tight" Na-absorbing epithelia are amphibian skin and urinary bladder, where the transepithelial resistance may be several thousand ohms·cm[2]. The distal colon is a "moderately tight" epithelium, with resistances of approximately 200–300 ohm·cm[2]. The resistances of "leaky" epithelia such as small intestine, gallbladder, and renal proximal tubule are generally less than 100 ohm·cm[2] and may be as low as 5 ohm·cm[2] (55).]

In rabbit descending colon the resistance of the apical membrane is 4–5 times that of the basolateral membrane, and when Na entry is blocked by amiloride the resistance of the apical membrane is approximately 9–10 times that of the basolateral membrane (56, 60, 61). These findings indicate that while the apical membrane is predominantly permeable to Na, there is also a significant conductance to other ions (59, 70). The identity of these other conductive channels across the apical membrane has not been established conclusively, but evidence has been presented for the presence of K channels in this barrier (72).

Recent studies have shown that the relation between the rate of Na entry across the apical membrane and the electrical-potential difference across that barrier, when intracellular Na activity is constant, conforms to the Goldman-Hodgkin-Katz "constant field" equation (16, 22) for the simple diffusion of a cation (60) (Figure 1); similar findings have been reported for several other "tight" Na-absorbing epithelia (15, 44, 59). Further, noise analysis of the amiloride-inhibitable Na entry step across the outer membrane of frog skin (36) and the apical membrane of toad urinary bladder (45) are consistent with the notion that each membrane site that mediates Na entry can transfer approximately 10^6 Na ions per sec. This high single-site conductance is similar to the values that have been reported for single-channel conductances of pore-forming ionophores (e.g. Gramacidin) incorporated into lipid bilayers (21) but is 3–4 orders of magnitude greater than the conductances or "turn-over times" of known "carriers," artificial (29) or natural (24).

Thus, it seems certain that Na entry into the surface columnar cells of rabbit descending colon is the result of simple electrodiffusion through relatively homogenous[2] pores or channels. It follows that the rate of entry at any moment

---

[2]Conformity with the Goldman-Hodgkin-Katz flux equation suggests that an ion moving through a pore is confronted with a large number (continuum) of equal energy barriers, so that the total energy barrier can be treated as if it is distributed symmetrically about the midpoint of the channel—hence the descriptive term "homogenous" (53).

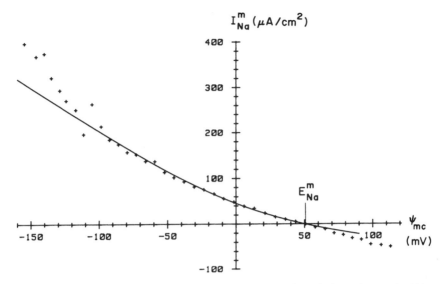

Figure 1   The relation between the rate of Na entry across the apical membrane of rabbit descending colon (I_{Na}^m) and the electrical-potential difference across the barrier (ψ^{mc}). The points are the experimental data, and the solid curve is that predicted by the Goldman-Hodkin-Katz "constant field" flux equation (60). The "reversal potential," E_{Na}^m, corresponds to a cell Na activity of approximately 10 mM.

will be determined by the number of open pores, the electrochemical-potential difference acting across this population of open pores, and the single-channel conductance of each pore. As we will see, for the conditions examined to date, the latter appears to be invariant.

Factors That Influence Na Entry Across the Apical Membrane

As mentioned above, Na entry across the apical membrane of mammalian colon is rapidly and reversibly inhibited by amiloride, as is the case for a number of other "tight" Na-absorbing epithelia (40). The precise mechanism of action of this positively-charged guanidinium derivative is unknown. It is unclear whether this agent interacts directly with and blocks (plugs) the Na channels or whether it interacts with nearby, regulatory sites and indirectly inactivates the Na channels. The kinetics of inhibition in rabbit descending colon appears to be of the "mixed" type, with a 1:1 stoichiometry for the interaction between amiloride and the Na entry mechanism (64). This matter is discussed below.

There are a number of other factors that influence the permeability of the apical membrane to Na, including: (*a*) the Na activity in the luminal or mucosal solution, $(Na)_m$; (*b*) the intracellular Na activity, $(Na)_c$; (*c*) aldosterone; (*d*) certain anions; and (*e*) sulfhydryl-reactive agents. These are discussed, briefly, in turn.

(*a*) Increasing the concentration of Na in the mucosal solution results in a decrease in the permeability of the apical membrane to Na (65) (Figure 2). This "self-inhibition" was first described for frog skin (15, 34), and noise analysis has revealed that increasing the Na concentration of the solution bathing the outer ("apical") membrane of this epithelium results in a decrease in the number of open channels without affecting the transport capacity of individual channels (65). The mechanism of this self-inhibition is unclear. Because it is a relativey slow process, Lindemann (35, 37) has suggested that it is the result of an interaction between Na and nearby regulatory sites, rather than with the Na channel directly. In any event, the physiological usefulness of this regulatory process is immediately apparent when one considers its inverse; i.e. the permeability of the apical membrane to Na *increases* as the luminal Na concentration *decreases*. Clearly, such a regulatory process is ideally suited for an epithelium whose function is to conserve Na by reducing the concentration of this cation in the luminal contents to minimal values (54). Thus, as the luminal Na concentration falls, three events take place: (*i*) the electrical-potential difference across the apical membrane hyperpolarizes (i.e. cell interior becomes more negative with respect to the mucosal solution (c.f. 56, 59); (*ii*) the intracellular Na activity declines (64); and (*iii*) the number of open Na channels in the apical membrane increases. All contribute to the ability of this epithelium to extract Na from the luminal contents.

(*b*) There also appears to be an inverse relation between intracellular Na activity and the permeability of the apical membrane to that cation ("negative feedback") such that an increase in $(Na)_c$ resulting from inhibition of the basolateral Na pump brings about a decrease in apical membrane Na permeability. Conversely, depletion of cell Na results in an increase in apical Na permeability (62). The underlying mechanism is not yet completely established, but there is strong, suggestive evidence derived from studies on other epithelia that the direct mediator of this effect is cell Ca. There is evidence for the presence of a carrier-mediated Na-Ca countertransport mechanism in the basolateral membrane of several epithelia (1, 4, 5, 18, 20, 30, 57), by which the downhill movement of Na into the cell energizes the uphill extrusion of Ca from the cell (2). Thus, an increase in $(Na)_c$ would reduce the electrochemical-potential difference for that ion across the basolateral membrane and, in turn, the energy available for Ca extrusion. This could lead to a higher steady-state

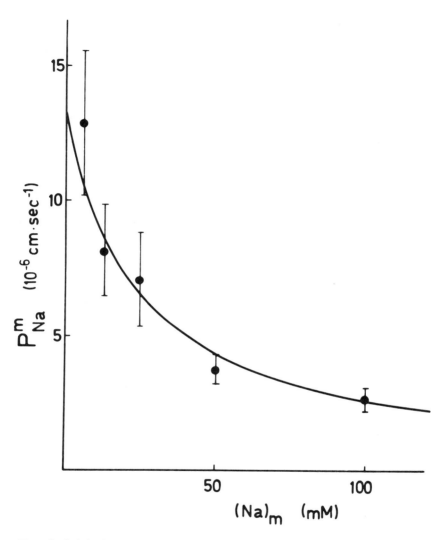

Figure 2   Relation between $(Na)_m$ and the permeability of the apical membrane of rabbit descending colon to Na, P_{Na}^m, when the electrical-potential difference across that barrier is "clamped" at zero (65).

level of cell Ca, $(Ca)_c$, that might directly reduce the apical Na permeability. The plausibility of this hypothesis is given strong support by the findings that: removal of Na from the serosal solution leads to an increase in $(Ca)_c$ in renal proximal tubule (30); treatment of renal proximal tubules with ouabain results in simultaneous increases in $(Na)_c$ and $(Ca)_c$ (38); and, Ca in the micromolar range inhibits amiloride-sensitive Na uptake by apical membrane vesicles from toad urinary bladder (5). Compelling evidence is lacking, however, that this purported mechanism exerts a significant regulatory effect on apical Na permeability under physiological conditions.

The ability of cell Na to regulate, directly or indirectly (via cell Ca), the Na-permeability of the apical membrane also has obvious physiologic utility. Clearly, such a mechanism can "gear" the rate of Na entry across the apical membrane to the rate of pump-mediated active Na extrusion across the basolateral membrane and protect the cell against inordinate changes in $(Na)_c$ in response to changes in basolateral-pump activity. Thus, a slowing of pump activity (for whatever reason) would lead to an increase in cell Na that, in turn, would result in a decrease in the ease with which Na can enter the cell. Conversely, a primary increase in pump activity (e.g. glucocorticoids, see below) would lead to a decrease in cell Na that, in turn, would result in an increase in the ease with which Na can enter the cell. Additionally, a low $(Na)_c$, due to the presence of a low mucosal (luminal) Na concentration (see Figure 3), would contribute to maximizing the ease with which Na can enter the cell from a dilute mucosal solution; under these conditions [i.e. low $(Na)_m$ *and* low $(Na)_c$] the permeability of the apical membrane to Na approaches its maximum (65).

Finally, it is of interest that an increase in $(Na)_c$ also appears to decrease the effectiveness of amiloride; i.e. when $(Na)_c$ is presumably increased by partial inhibition of the pump with ouabain, the fractional inhibition of Na entry by amiloride decreases (64). The mechanism underlyng this effect is unclear, but the data are consistent with the notion that the effects of elevated $(Na)_c$ and amiloride are exerted via a regulatory site (see below).

(*c*) Sodium absorption by mammalian colon is stimulated by aldosterone in vivo (48, 54) as well as in vitro (12). This appears to be, at least in part, attributable to an increase in apical Na permeability resulting from the activation of additional Na channels without affecting the single-channel conductance (45). Recent finding on toad urinary bladder suggest that these channels are actually already present in the apical membrane and that the mineralocortocoid somehow activates them (15a). As discussed below, there is compelling evidence that aldosterone also results in an increase in the number of Na-pump units in the basolateral membrane.

(*d*) The replacement of Cl in the mucosal solution with a number of anions such as sulfate, isethionate, and several organic-sulfonic acid derivatives results in a prompt and marked stimulation of Na absorption, due to an increase in apical Na permeability (62). Similar findings have been reported for toad urinary bladder (56a). The mechanism of action of these anions is not established, but it may simply involve "screening" of positively-charged groups in

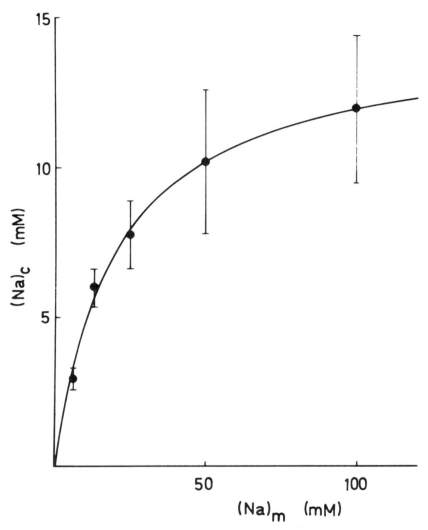

Figure 3   Relation between $(Na)_m$ and $(Na)_c$ when rabbit descending colon is exposed to a high-K serosal solution and the electrical-potential difference across the apical membrane is "clamped" at zero (65).

the vicinity of the Na channels, thereby in effect increasing the Na activity in that interfacial region ("double-layer").

(*e*) Gottlieb et al (17) found that p-chloromercuribenzene-sulfonate blocks and reverses the inhibitory effect of amiloride on Na entry across the apical membrane of rabbit descending colon. These observations were extended by Luger & Turnheim (39) to include two other sulfhydryl-reactive organic mercurials, mersalyl and p-chloromercuribenzoate. Luger & Turnheim also found that those agents inhibit Na entry when the rate is above a mean value of approximately 2–3 $\mu Eq/cm^2 hr$ *but* stimulate entry when the spontaneous rate is below that value. In addition, these agents appear to inhibit the negative-feedback effect of $(Na)_c$ on apical Na permeability (39). Thus it seems as if these agents "freeze" the Na conductance of the apical membrane at some mean value. Further, Luger & Turnheim (39) presented compelling evidence that these effects are due to interactions with high-affinity sulfhydryl groups located superficially in the apical membrane.

The Regulation of Na Entry

From the above considerations it should be clear that although Na entry is the result of electrodiffusion through pores or channels, the process can hardly be considered "simple." Instead, this entry process is influenced by a number of factors that appear to act by regulating the number of open pores extant at any given time.

Thus, as shown in Figure 4 *(left)*, Na entry across the apical membrane saturates with increasing $(Na)_m$. From the work of van Driessche & Lindemann (66) on frog skin, it seems reasonable to conclude that this is the result of a decrease in the number of open channels with increasing $(Na)_m$ and presumably $(Na)_c$. It is apparently not the result of saturation of the Na current through single channels, although this is a common characteristic of channels. [Ion movements across lipid membranes doped with some pore-forming ionophores (e.g. Gramacidin A) exhibit saturation with increasing concentration (21). Ionic diffusion across a membrane containing such channels would not be expected to conform to the Goldman-Hodgkin-Katz equation over a wide range, inasmuch as that formalism assumes that permeability coefficients are independent of concentration.] Aldosterone appears to indirectly elicit an increase in the number of pre-existing channels in the apical membrane that are in the "open configuration" (15a).

The important point is that the properties of the individual channels appear to be invariant; the seminal variable is the number of such channels that are operant at any given time.

A central question to be resolved is whether the factors that influence the number of open Na channels, including amiloride, do so by interacting *directly* with these channels or with a regulatory mechanism or modifying-site that is close to, but spatially distinct from, these channels. Turnheim et al (64) have raised a number of arguments suggesting that the effects of stimulators [aldosterone, certain anions, low $(Na)_m$ and low $(Na)_c$] and inhibitors [amiloride, high $(Na)_m$ and high (Na_c)] act through a separate regulatory mechanism that is blocked by sulfhydryl-reactive agents. This notion, which resembles the "floating receptor" model suggested by Lindemann (33, 37), is intriguing and awaits further testing.

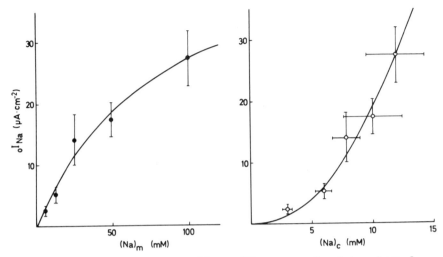

Figure 4 (*left*) Relation between (Na)$_m$ and the rate of Na entry across the apical membrane, $_oI_{Na}$. (*right*) Relation between (Na)$_c$ and "pump rate" across the basolateral membrane. Data were obtained on short-circuited segments of rabbit descending colon exposed to a high-K serosal solution (65). Thus, the electrical potential differences across both the apical and basolateral membranes were "clamped" at zero mV. Clearly, under steady-state conditions, the rate of Na diffusion into the cell across the apical membrane must be equal to the rate at which it is pumped out of the cell across the basolateral membrane.

Clearly, while the mechanism of Na entry seems reasonably well established, the determinants of the fraction of channels in the apical membrane that are "open" or "closed" over any given time interval, as well as the underlying reasons for "openedness" and "closedness," await clarification at the microscopic level.

THE INTRACELLULAR COMPARTMENT

The relation between the Na activity in the mucosal solution, (Na)$_m$, and the intracellular Na activity, (Na)$_c$ in rabbit distal colon, is illustrated in Fig. 3. This relation conforms closely with simple saturation kinetics of the Michaelis-Menten type, with a maximum (Na)$_c$ of 15 mM and a half-maximal (Na)$_c$ achieved when (Na)$_m$ = 20 mM. These values, determined from the reversal potentials of current-voltage relations similar to that shown in Fig. 1, are within the range of values determined on other Na-absorbing epithelia using Na-selective microelectrodes. [The "reversal" or "equilibrium" potential of an ion whose movement is due entirely to simple diffusion (i.e. that electrical-potential difference at which the ionic current is zero) is given by the Nernst equation. Thus knowing the extracellular Na activity, (Na)$_m$, and the reversal potential, one can readily calculate the intracellular Na activity, (Na)$_c$ (53).]

The intracellular K activity, $(K)_c$, in rabbit descending colonic cells, determined using K-selective microelectrodes, is approximately 75 mM (70; M. Duffey & S. G. Schultz, unpublished observations). This value is considerably greater than that predicted for an equilibrium distribution of K across the basolateral membrane, leaving no doubt that K is actively accumulated by the cell, and is in good agreement with the values reported for other mammalian epithelia.

Further, this value is in reasonable agreement with estimates of cell K concentration determined chemically, assuming an activity coefficient of approximately 0.7, suggesting that there is no significant "tight binding" or sequestration of this cation within the cell (52).

THE BASOLATERAL MEMBRANE

The basolateral membrane of rabbit colonic epithelial cells possess the ubiquitous, ouabain-inhibitable Na-K exchange pump in parallel with relatively low resistance leak pathways. Studies by Wills et al (69) indicate that although this barrier is somewhat permeable to Na and Cl, by far the predominant permeant ion is K; the permeability ratios estimated by these investigators are: $P_{Na}/P_K = 0.04$ and $P_{Cl}/P_K = 0.06$. These estimates are consistent with the finding that elevation of the K activity in the solution bathing the serosal surface of the tissue to a value that approximates that in the cell results in a marked reduction in the resistance of the basolateral membrane and essentially abolishes the electrical-potential difference across that barrier (60).

The properties of the ouabain-inhibitable Na-K pump in the basolateral membrane resemble those characterized in a number of nonepithelial cells as well as some "tight" epithelia. The relation between the rate of pump-mediated Na extrusion from the cell and $(Na)_c$ is illustrated in Fig. 4 *(right)*. This relation is clearly sigmoidal, and the curve closely corresponds to the predictions of the Hill equation for a strongly cooperative interaction of 2–3 Na ions with each pump unit. The value of the maximum pump rate is approximately 6 μEq/cm^2hr in excellent agreement with the value observed when the apical membrane is made higly porous to Na by exposure to the "pore-forming" antibiotic, Amphotericin B (13). It is of interest that similar maximum rates are observed in the presence of stimulatory anions (62) and following treatment with aldosterone (12), suggesting that these agents can increase the Na conductance of the apical membrane to the point where the basolateral pump mechanism is saturated. The value of $(Na)_c$ at which pump-rate is half-maximal is 24 mM; this value is in excellent agreement with that reported for Na extrusion by human erythrocytes (24). Further, Jorgensen (26) has reported that the activity of purified renal Na-K-ATPase is half-maximal in the presence of

26 mM Na. Finally, based on very general theoretical considerations, it can be shown that all of the electrophysiologic data accumulated on rabbit colon are consistent with the notion that the stoichiometry of the Na-K exchange pump is 3Na:2K (52).

In short, the basolateral Na-K pump in rabbit descending colon appears to be rheogenic ("current-generating"), as indicated directly by the findings of Wills et al (70), with kinetic properties that closely resemble those reported for several other epithelial (6, 7, 27, 31, 32, 42, 43) as well as nonepithelial cells (23, 58). However, because of the low resistance of this barrier, the contribution of this current generation to the electromotive force and potential difference across the basolateral membrane is small (2–4 mV) (61, 70), so that these parameters are scarcely affected by changes in pump rate.

There is evidence suggesting that total Na-pump activity in rat colon, as reflected by total Na-K ATPase activity, increases in response to mineralocorticoids as well as chronic glucocorticoid administration (c.f. 3) and that these changes are correlated with changes in ion transport in vivo. Recently, Sellin & De Soignie (personal communication) have demonstrated that treatment of rabbits with methylprednisolone *or* deoxycorticosterone-acetate for two days prior to sacrifice markedly increases the basal rate of Na absorption as well as the maximum transport capacity of segments of distal colon studied in vitro.

Thus aldosterone not only increases the number of open channels in the apical membrane but also the number of Na-K pump units in the basolateral membrane. This "dual action" of aldosterone offers a reasonable explanation for the observaton of Wills & Lewis (71) that the urinary bladders of rabbits maintained on a Na-free diet display a marked increase in the rate of Na absorption but no significant increase in $(Na)_c$. Petty et al (46) have recently presented intriguing evidence that the increase in pump units in rabbit cortical collecting tubules 2–3 hours after treatment with aldosterone may be secondary to an increase in the rate of Na entry across the apical membrane, inasmuch as in increase in Na-K ATPase is not observed if the animals are also treated with amiloride, which blocks Na entry.

Finally, Na-K ATPase activity in rat colon is also increased by chronic K loading, which seems to elicit active K secretion by this epithelium (8). Further, this increase was also observed in adrenalectomized rats, *suggesting* that it is not mediated by mineralo- or glucocorticoids; however, in these studies, the "completeness" of adrenolectomy was not firmly established.

THE CELL

Having considered some of the individual properties of the apical and basolateral membranes and the intracellular compartment of rabbit descending colon, I will now attempt to combine these elements to form a working model of the absorptive cell; such a model is illustrated in Figure 5 for the condition

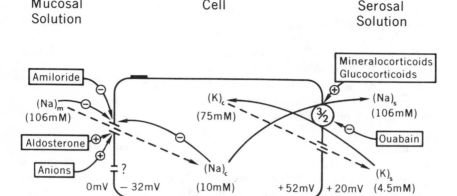

Figure 5 Cellular model for active Na absorption by rabbit descending colon, *in vitro*, bathed on both surfaces with a mammalian "Ringer's solution."

in which the tissue is bathed on both surfaces with a normal Ringer's solution having a Na *activity* of 106 mM.

The electrical-potential difference across the apical membrane, ψ^{mc}, under these conditions is approximately -32 mV (56, 60), and the chemical-potential difference for Na across that barrier, E^m_{Na}, is approximately 60 mV, corresponding to a 10-fold difference in Na activities. Thus the total driving force for the entry process is approximately 90 mV. It is of interest that spontaneous variations in Na entry at fixed-luminal Na activity appear to be entirely attributable to spontaneous variations in the conductance of the apical membrane to that cation; that is to say, the thermodynamic driving force at fixed $(Na)_m$, $(E^m_{Na}-\psi^{mc})$, is constant (60, 65). The mechanism(s) responsible for maintaining this driving force constant at constant $(Na)_m$ is (are) not clear but the physiological implications of these findings are interesting. As discussed above, inasmuch as entry takes place through discrete Na-selective channels, the total Na current across the apical membrane is given by $I^m_{Na} = Ni^m_{Na}$, where N is the number of open channels, and i^m_{Na} is the Na current through each channel. The latter is given by $i^m_{Na} = g^m_{Na}(E^m_{Na}-\psi^{mc})$ where g^m_{Na} is the single-channel conductance; thus, the total conductance is given by $G^m_{Na} = N\,g^m_{Na}$. Since $(E^m_{Na}-\psi^{mc})$ is constant at fixed $(Na)_m$ and since the single-channel transport capacity appears to be invariant (45, 66) it follows that the only variable responsible for spontaneous variations in Na absorption is N. Clearly an issue of major physiological importance is the molecular mechanism(s) that determines the total number of channels present in the apical membrane, the probability that any one will be in open configuration at any given time, and the duration of the "open state." The "patch clamp" technique that has opened the way to the direct analysis of single-channel currents (19) is the most promising approach toward resolving this issue.

Having crossed the apical membrane, Na enters a relatively small "Na-transport pool" (40) that appears to interact with the basolateral Na-K pump in a highly cooperative manner (65). The sharply sigmoidal relation between $(Na)_c$ and pump activity permits relatively large changes in the latter with minimal pertubation in the former; on intuitive grounds, this feature would seem to be of value in terms of homocellular regulation of ionic composition (51).

From these data it is possible to draw some inferences regarding the energetics of the Na-K pump. Given the values for $(Na)_c$, $(K)_c$, the electrical potential difference across the basolateral membrane, and the activities of Na and K in the serosal solution (see Fig. 5), and assuming a 3Na:2K stoichiometry, it can be readily shown that the reversible work performed by the pump per cycle is approximately 380 mV. The free energy of ATP hydrolysis is not known with certainty, but assuming a reasonable range of 9–12 kCal mole^{-1} or 390–520 mV, it seems that the pump efficiency is 75%–95%.

Finally, one of the most striking features that emerges from this attempt to reconstruct the Na-absorbing cell from its most basic elements is the capacity for dynamic interaction between the two limiting membranes via an intracellular dialogue. Clearly, the properties of these two barriers with respect to transcellular Na transport are neither static nor independent of one another. Thus, primary changes in basolateral Na-pump activity will affect the number of open Na channels in the apical membrane, and it may very well be that primary changes in the rate of Na entry across the apical membrane influences the number of active Na-K pump units at the basolateral membrane. In addition to this intracellular dialogue, there is interaction between the electrical properties of the two membranes mediated by the paracellular pathway (50, 56). Indeed, we may find that, in the face of these interactions, the notion that one membrane or the other is "rate limiting" is ambiguous and that under physiological conditions both membranes act in concert to permit varying rates of Na absorption with minimal pertubation of the ionic composition of the intracellular milieu (51).

It should be emphasized that throughout this paper I have assumed that the behavior of rabbit distal colon is representative of mammalian descending colon and have drawn heavily on results of studies on other epithelia (particularly frog skin and toad urinary bladder). I believe there are a sufficient number of similarities shared by these epithelia to warrant such extrapolations. Time will tell whether these liberties were entirely justifiable.

ACKNOWLEDGMENTS

Research from the author's laboratories reported in this review was supported by grants from the NIH-NIAMDDK. The author gratefully acknowledges the collaborative efforts of Drs. R. A. Frizzell, S. M. Thompson, and K. Turnheim in much of this work.

Literature Cited

1. Arruda, J. A. L., Sabatini, S., Westenfelder, C. 1982. Serosal Na/Ca exchange and H and Na transport by the turtle and toad bladders. *J. Membr. Biol.* 70:135–46

2. Blaustein, M. P. 1974. The interrelationship between sodium and calcium fluxes across cell membranes. *Rev. Physiol. Biochem. Pharmacol.* 70:33–82

3. Charney, A. N., Kinsey, M. D., Myers, L., Giannella, R. A., Gots, R. E. 1975. Na-K activated adenosine triphosphatase and intestinal electrolyte transport. Effects of adrenal steroids. *J. Clin. Invest.* 56:653–60

4. Chase. H. S. Jr., Al-Awqati, Q. 1981. Regulation of the sodium permeability of the luminal border of toad urinary bladder by intracellular sodium and calcium. *J. Gen. Physiol.* 77:693–712

5. Chase, H. S. Jr., Al-Awqati, Q. 1983. Calcium reduces the sodium permeability of luminal membrane vesicles from toad urinary bladder: Studies using a fast reaction apparatus. *J. Gen. Physiol.* 81:643–65

6. Eaton, D. C. 1981. Intracellular sodium activity and sodiumion transport in rabbit urinary bladder. *J. Physiol.* 316:527–44

7. Eaton, D. C., Frace, A. M., Silverthorn, S. U. 1982. Active and passive Na fluxes across the basolateral membrane of rabbit urinary bladder. *J. Membr. Biol.* 67:219–29

8. Fisher, K. A., Binder, H. J., Hayslett, J. P. 1976. Potassium secretion by colonic mucosal cells after potassium adaption. *Am. J. Physiol.* 231(4):987–94

9. Frizzell, R. A. 1977. Active chloride secretion by rabbit colon: Calcium-dependent stimulation by ionphore A23187. *J. Membr. Biol.* 35:175–87

10. Frizzell, R. A., Field, M., Schultz, S. G. 1979. Sodium-coupled chloride transport by epithelial tissues. *Am. J. Physiol.* 236(5):F1–8

11. Frizzell, R. A., Koch, M. J., Schultz, S. G. 1976. Ion transport by rabbit colon. I. Active and passive components. *J. Membr. Biol.* 27:297–316

12. Frizzell, R. A., Schultz, S. G. 1978. Effect of aldosterone on ion transport by rabbit colon, *in vitro. J. Membr. Biol.* 39:1–26

13. Frizzell, R. A., Turnheim, K. 1978. Ion transport by rabbit colon. II. Undirectional sodium influx and the effects of amphotericin B and amiloride. *J. Membr. Biol.* 40:193–211

14. Fromm, M., Hagel, U. 1978. Segmental heterogeneity of epithelial transport in rat large intestine. *Pfluegers Arch.* 378:71–83

15. Fuchs, W., Larsen, E. H., Lindemann, B. 1977. Current-voltage curve of sodium channels and concentration dependence of sodium permeability in frog skin. *J. Physiol.* 267:137–66

15a. Garty, H., Edelman, I. S. 1983. Amiloride sensitive trypsinization of apical sodium channels. Analysis of hormonal regulation of sodium transport in toad bladder. *J. Gen. Physiol.* 81:785–803

16. Goldman, D. E. 1943. Potential, impedance, and rectification in membranes. *J. Gen. Physiol.* 27:360

17. Gottlieb, G. P., Turnheim, K., Frizzell, R. A., Schultz, S. G. 1978. p-Chloromercuribenzene sulfonate blocks and reverses the effect of amiloride on sodium transport across rabbit colon *in vitro. Biophys. J.* 22:125–29

18. Grinstein, S., Erlij, D. 1978. Intracellular calcium and the regulation of sodium transport in the frog skin. *Proc. R. Soc. London Ser. B* 202:353–60

19. Hamill. O. P., Marty, A., Neher, E., Sakmann, B., Sigworth, F. J. 1981. Improved patch-clamp techniques for high-resolution current recording from cells and cell-free membrane patches. *Pflueger's Arch.* 391:85–100

20. Hidmann, B., Schmidt, A., Murer, H. 1982. Ca transport across basal-lateral plasma membranes from rat small intestinal epithelial cells. *J. Membr. Biol.* 65:55–62

21. Hladky, S. B. 1974. Pore or carrier? Gramacidin A as a simple pore. In *Drugs and Transport Processes*, ed. B. A. Callingham, pp. 193–210. Baltimore: University Park

22. Hodgkin, A. L., Katz, B. 1949. The effect of sodium ions on the electrical activity of the giant axon of the squid. *J. Physiol.* 108:37–77

23. Hoffman, J. F., Kaplan, H., Callahan, T. J. 1979. The Na:K pump in red cells is electrogenic. *Fed. Proc.* 38:2440–41

24. Hoffman, J. F., Kennedy, B. G., Lunn, G. 1981. Modulation of red cell Na/K pump rates. In *Erythrocyte Membranes 2: Recent Clinical and Experimental Advances*, pp. 5–9. New York: Liss.

25. Hubel, K. A. 1968. The ins and outs of bicarbonate in the alimentary tract. *Gastroenterology* 54:647–51

26. Jorgensen, P. L. 1980. Sodium and potassium ion pump in kindey tubules. *Physiol. Rev.* 60:864–917

27. Kirk, K. L., Halm, D. R., Dawson, D. C. 1980. Active sodium transport by turtle colon via an electrogenic Na-K exchange pump. *Nature* 287:237–39

28. Koefoed-Johnsen, V., Ussing, H. H. 1958. The nature of the frog skin potential. *Acta Physiol. Scand.* 42:298–308

29. Laüger, P. 1972. Carrier-mediated ion transport. *Science* 178:24–30

30. Lee, C. O., Taylor, A., Windhager, E. E. 1980. Cytosolic calcium ion activity in epithelial cells of *Necturus* kidney. *Nature* 287:859–61

31. Lewis, S. A., Wills, N. K. 1981. Interaction between apical and basolateral membranes during sodium transport across tight epithelia. In *Ion Transport by Epithelia,* ed. S. G. Schultz, pp. 93–107. New York: Raven

32. Lewis, S. A., Wills, N. K., Eaton, D. C. 1978. Basolateral membrane potential of a tight epithelium: Ionic diffusion and electrogenic pumps. *J. Membr. Biol.* 41: 117–48

33. Lindemann, B. 1977. Steady-state kinetics of a floating receptor model for the inhibition of sodium uptake by sodium in frog skin. In *Renal Function,* ed. G. H. Giebisch, E. F., Purcell, pp. 110–31. New York: Macy Found.

34. Lindemann, B., Gebhardt, U. 1973. Delayed changes of Na permeability in response to steps of (Na) at the outer surface of frog skin and frog bladder. In *Transport Mechanisms in Epithelia,* ed. H. H. Ussing, N. A. Thorn, pp. 115–30. Copenhagen: Munksgaard

35. Lindemann, B., van Driessche, W. 1978. The mechanism of Na uptake through Na-selective channels in the epithelium of frog skin. In *Membrane Transport Processes,* ed. J. Hoffman, 1:155–78. New York: Raven

36. Lindemann, B., van Driessche, W. 1977. Sodium-specific membrane channels of frog skins are pores: Current fluctuations reveal high turnovers. *Science* 195:292–94

37. Lindemann, B., Voute, C. 1976. Structure and function of the epidermis. In *Frog Neurobiology,* ed. R. Llinas, W. Precht, pp. 169–210. Berling: Springer-Verlag

38. Lorenzen, M., Lee, C. O., Windhager, E. E. 1981. Effect of quinidine and ouabain on intracellular calcium and sodium activities in isolated perfused proximal tubules of *Necturus* kidney. *Kidney Int.* 21:281a

39. Luger, A., Turnheim, K. 1981. Modification of cation permeability of rabbit descending colon by sulphydryl reagents. *J. Physiol.* 317:49–66

40. Macknight, A. D. C., DiBona, D. R., Leaf, A. 1980. Sodium transport across toad urinary bladder: A model tight epithelium. *Physiol. Rev.* 60:615–715

41. McCabe, R., Cooke, H. J., Sullivan, L. P. 1982. Potassium transport by rabbit descending colon. *Am. J. Physiol.* 242: C81–86

42. Nielsen, R. 1979. A 3 to 2 coupling of the Na-K pump responsible for the transepithelial Na transport in frog skin as disclosed by the effect of Ba. *Acta Physiol. Scand.* 107:189–91

43. Nielsen, R. 1982. Effect of ouabain, amiloride, and antidiuretic hormone on the sodium-transport pool in isolated epithelia from frog skin (Rana temporaria). *J. Membr. Biol.* 65:221–26

44. Palmer, L. G., Edelman, I. S., Lindemann, B. 1980. Current-voltage analysis of apical sodium transport in toad urinary bladder: Effects of inhibitors of transport and metabolism. *J. Membr. Biol.* 57:59–71

45. Palmer, L. G., Li, J. H.-Y., Lindemann, B., Edelman, I. 1982. Aldosterone control of the density of sodium channels in the toad urinary bladder. *J. Memb. Biol.* 64:91–102

46. Petty, K. J., Kokko, J. P., Marver, D. 1981. Secondary effect of aldosterone on Na-K ATPase activity in the rabbit cortical collecting tubule. *J. Clin. Invest.* 68: 1514–21

47. Phillips, S. F., Schmalz, P. F. 1970. Bicarbonate secretion by the rat colon: Effect of intraluminal chloride and acetazolamide. *Proc. Soc. Exp. Biol. Med.* 135:116–22

48. Powell, D. W. 1979. Transport in large intestine. In *Transport Across Biological Membranes,* ed. G. Giebisch, D. C. Tosteson, H. H. Ussing, 4:781–809. Berlin: Springer-Verlag

49. Deleted in proof

50. Schultz, S. G. 1972. Electrical potential differences and electromotive forces in epithelial tissues. *J. Gen. Physiol.* 59: 794–98

51. Schultz, S. G. 1981. Homocellular regulatory mechanisms in sodium-transporting epithelia: avoidance of extinction by "flush-through." *Am. J. Physiol.* 241:F579–90

52. Schultz, S. G. 1981. Potassium transport by rabbit colon, *in vitro. Fed. Proc.* 40:2408–11

53. Schultz, S. G. 1980. *Basic Principles of Membrane Transport,* pp. 21–39. New York: Cambridge University.

54. Schultz, S. G. 1981. Ion Transport by Mammalian Large Intestine. In *The Physiology of the Digestive Tract,* ed. L.

R. Johnson,. pp. 991–1002. New York: Raven

55. Schultz, S. G., Fromm, M. 1982. The permselective properties of paracellular pathways across "ultraleaky" epithelia and a "moderately tight" epithelium. In *The Paracellular Pathway,* ed. S. E. Bradley, E. Prucell, pp. 3–9. New York: Macy Found.

56. Schultz, S. G., Frizzell, R. A., Nellans, H. N. 1977. Sodium transport and the electrophysiology of rabbit colon. *J. Membr. Biol.* 33:351–84

56a. Singer, I., Civan, M. M. 1971. Effects of anions on sodium transport in toad urinary bladder. *Am. J. Physiol.* 221: 1019–26

57. Taylor, A. 1981. Role of cytosolic calcium and sodium-calcium exchange in regulation of transepithelial sodium and water absorption. In *Ion Transport by Epithelia,* ed. S. G. Schultz, pp. 233–59. New York: Raven

58. Thomas, R. C. 1972. Electrogenic sodium pump in nerve and muscle cells. *Physiol. Rev.* 52:563–94

59. Thomas, S. R., Suzuki, Y., Thompson, S. M., Schultz, S. G. 1983. The electrophysiology of *Necturus* urinary bladder: I. "Instantaneous" current-voltage relations in the presence of varying mucosal sodium concentrations. *J. Membr. Biol.* 73:157–75

60. Thompson, S. M., Suzuki, Y., Schultz, S. G. 1982. The electrophysiology of rabbit descending colon. I. Instantaneous transepithelial current-voltage relations and the current-voltage relation of the Na-entry mechanism. *J. Membr. Biol.* 66:41–54

61. Thompson, S. M., Suzuki, Y., Schultz, S. G. 1982. The electrophysiology of rabbit descending colon. II. Current-voltage relations of the apical and basolateral membranes and paracellular pathway. *J. Membr. Biol.* 66:55–61

62. Turnheim, K., Frizzell, R. A., Schultz, S. G. 1977. Effect of anions on amiloride-sensitive, active sodium transport across rabbit colon, *in vitro. J. Membr. Biol.* 37:63–84

63. Turnheim, K., Frizzell, R. A., Schultz, S. G. 1978. Interaction between cell sodium and the amiloride-sensitive sodium entry step in rabbit colon. *J. Membr. Biol.* 39:233–56

64. Turnheim, K., Luger, A., Grasl, M. 1981. Kinetic analysis of the amiloride-sodium entry site interaction in rabbit colon. *Mol. Pharm.* 20:543–50

65. Turnheim, K., Thompson, S. M., Schultz, S. G. 1983. Relation between intracellular sodium and active sodium transport in rabbit colon. *J. Membr. Biol.* In press

66. van Driessche, W., Lindemann, B. 1979. Concentration dependence of currents through single sodium-selective pores in frog skin. *Nature* 282:519–20

67. Welsh, M., Smith, P., Fromm, M. J., Frizzell, R. A. 1982. Crypts are the site of intestinal fluid and electrolyte secretion. *Science* 218:1219–21

68. Wills, N. K., Biagi, B. 1982. Active potassium transport by rabbit descending colon epithelium. *J. Membr. Biol.* 64: 195–203

69. Wills, N. K., Eaton, D. C., Lewis, S. A., Ifshin, M. S. 1979. Current-voltage relationship of the basolateral membrane of a tight epithelium. *Biochem. Biophys. Acta* 555:519–23

70. Wills, N. K., Lewis, S. A., Eaton, D. C. 1979. Active and passive properties of rabbit descending colon: A microelectrode and nystatin study. *J. Membr. Biol.* 45:81–108

71. Wills, N. K., Lewis, S. A. 1980. Intracellular Na activity as a function of Na transport rate across a tight epithelium. *Biophys. J.* 30:181–86

72. Wills, N. K., Zeiske, W., van Driessche, W. 1982. Noise analysis reveals K channel conductance fluctuations in the apical membrane of rabbit colon. *J. Membr. Biol.* 69:187–97

73. Yau, W. M., Maklouf, G. M. 1975. Comparison of transport mechanisms in isolated ascending and descending rat colon. *Am. J. Physiol.* 228:191–95

CELL AND MEMBRANE PHYSIOLOGY

Introduction, Joseph F. Hoffman, *Section Editor*

The theme of the papers contained in this year's section on Cell and Membrane Physiology is membrane channels. The reason for this is easy to understand, given there have been in recent years major revisions of our concepts of aqueous-filled pores that had previously provided explanations for so-called passive permeability phenomena. Indeed, the advances as well as the sophistication in our understanding in molecular terms of the properties of single channels have already furthered the field considerably.

It is hoped that the present series of articles will be useful to the reader both in scope and in depth, since different types of approaches are described for the study and characterization of single-channel activity. In addition, the several contributions also survey various types of channels in different types of tissues. It is certainly tacitly assumed that these articles will stimulate further analysis in other areas not only in establishing physiologically relevant channel properties, but by elaborating in detail the molecular mechanisms involved.

Ann. Rev. Physiol. 1984. 46:455–72

PATCH CLAMP TECHNIQUES FOR STUDYING IONIC CHANNELS IN EXCITABLE MEMBRANES

B. Sakmann and E. Neher

Max-Planck-Institut für Biophysikalische Chemie, 3400 Gottingen, Federal Republic of Germany

INTRODUCTION

Availability of techniques largely influences the choice of preparations in electrophysiological research. To study basic mechanisms of electrical excitability, usually the squid axon or giant snail neurons are used for technical reasons, or more simply, because they are large. For other reasons one would very often prefer to use mammalian cells, but they are much smaller and more difficult to handle. Recently, more freedom of choice was introduced by the so-called patch clamp techniques, which resulted from the technical challenge that the measurement of single-channel currents presented. It is evident that the smallness of these quantities required that the measurement be restricted to very small structures—small patches of membrane or very small cells. This led to the development of new techniques well suited for studying membrane currents from cells of any size and particularly suited to study small cells in culture.

This review aims to describe the uses of the technique and to emphasize those results that use features specific to the various configurations of the patch clamp. We do not intend to present technical details, which can be found in the original literature (32, 74).

BASIC PRINCIPLE AND VARIANTS OF THE PATCH CLAMP METHOD

The original goal was to resolve the current contributions of individual ionic channels in a biological membrane. This was achieved by placing heat-polished

455

micropipettes onto the surface of enzymatically cleaned cells and measuring the current flowing through the pipette (57). The pipettes had openings somewhat larger than conventional microelectrodes (0.5–1 μm) and, in contrast to microelectrodes, were filled with normal saline. The major technical difficulty was to establish an electrical seal between pipette and membrane. Without such a seal, the current flowing through the pipette was not identical to the current flowing through the membrane covered by the pipette. In addition, the shunt conductance between the pipette interior and the bath was the dominating noise source. The pipette had to be held at the bath potential at all times to avoid large leakage currents through the shunt.

A major advance in this respect was the observation that the pipette-membrane seal can be improved by a factor of 100 to 1000 when clean pipettes are used and, upon contact, slight suction is applied to the pipette (32, 81). Thereby, a small patch of membrane is sucked into the pipette interior, forming an omega-shaped semivesicle. This, in an all-or-nothing way, seals tightly to the inner pipette wall. The electrical resistance across the seal is then on the order of 10–100 gigaohms, and the membrane is firmly attached to the pipette walls. The high seal resistance can be exploited to perform high-resolution current measurements and to apply voltages across the membrane (and the seal). The firm attachment allows a certain number of mechanical manipulations to be performed, which will be described below.

Figure 1 schematically illustrates the different measurement configurations that can be obtained with patch pipettes. The diagram starts at the top with the "cell-attached" configuration. This is the case of a pipette placed and sealed onto an intact cell, as described above. Three simple mechanical manipulations can be performed after this stage has been reached: rupture of the membrane patch by a brief pulse of suction, withdrawal of the pipette, and brief exposure of the pipette to air by shortly lifting the pipette out of solution. For all three manipulations the pipette membrane seal stays intact during a relatively high proportion of trials, thus leading to well-defined configurations.

Rupturing the membrane patch establishes an electrical connection between the pipette and the cell interior. The pipette-cell assembly is well insulated ($R_{shunt} > 10\ G\Omega$) from the bath. This configuration, which we call "whole-cell measurement," is very similar to a conventional microelectrode penetration, but it seems to be more gentle, yielding good recordings in cells as small as red blood cells. Pipettes should be filled with high-K^+, low-Ca^{2+} solution if the aim is to penetrate the cell.

Withdrawal of the pipette starting from the cell-attached configuration usually leads to an intermediate stage where a closed vesicle is sealed into the pipette tip (32). During withdrawal, a cytoplasmic bridge surrounded by membrane is first pulled from the cell. This becomes more and more narrow as the separation between pipette and cell increases, until it collapses, leaving behind an intact cell and a closed structure inside the pipette. The vesicle is not suitable for

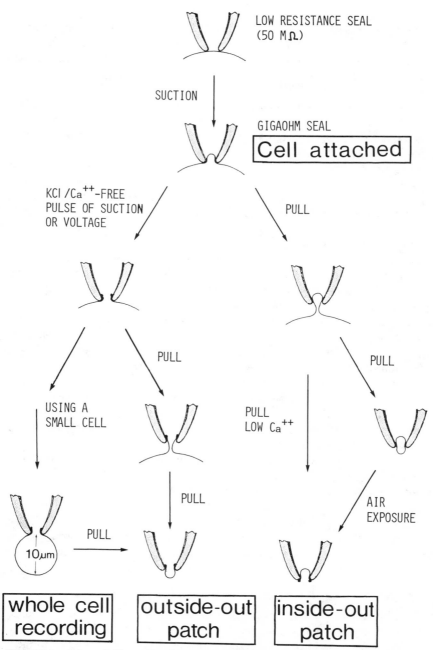

FIGURE 1. Schematic illustration of the different configurations of the patch clamp and of the manipulations that lead to them. From Hamill et al (32), by permission of Springer-Verlag, Heidelberg.

electrical measurement. However, short air exposure will break the outer half of it, resulting in an "inside-out" patch (34). This name was chosen because the former cytoplasmic surface of the membrane now faces the bath solution. Inside-out patches (also called "excised patches") can be obtained directly without air exposure if the withdrawal is performed in Ca-free media (36).

The complementary configuration, an "outside-out" patch, can be obtained when the pipette is withdrawn from a "whole-cell" configuration. Inside-out and outside-out patches are complementary techniques in the sense that it is always easy to change the solution in the bath, whereas carefully designed arrangements have to be used for changing the pipette solution during an experiment (18).

In the following section we will discuss the different configurations, pointing out the specific scientific problems for which they are best adapted.

THE CELL-ATTACHED PATCH CONFIGURATION

This configuration probably disturbs least the structure and environment of the cell membrane. It provides a current resolution several orders of magnitude larger than previous current measurements. The membrane voltage can be changed without intracellular microelectrodes, and both transmitter- and voltage-activated channels can be studied in their normal ionic environment. Because the solution in the pipette contacts only a small area, which is a fraction of the whole cell surface, ionic gradients can be set up across the membrane patch that are advantageous for studying a particular type of ion channel but that might be harmful if the entire cell were exposed to it. Finally, the limitation of the current measurement to a small part of the surface permits one to study mechanisms where different parts of the cell membrane interact with each other via an intracellular signal.

In cell-attached patch recording, the cells' resting membrane conductance is assumed to "clamp" the internal potential of the patch. One has to realize, however, that small cells can have input resistances on the order of 10 GΩ. Because of the cell's high resistance, which is in series with the patch plus seal resistance, the applied pipette voltage may only partially appear across the patch membrane. This is a severe limitation to the use of this configuration. Large single-channel currents can discharge the cell membrane capacitance leading to current waveforms with a relaxing time course (22).

Membrane Perturbation by Gigaseal Formation

The formation of a high-resistance seal usually involves an omega-shaped deformation of the cell surface membrane when suction is applied to the pipette interior (32, 73). Suction is normally released once the seal has formed; however, the membrane remains deformed. Possible alterations in the channel function may result from: (*a*) local leaks (22); (*b*) increased mobility of the receptors or channels due to detachment from the cytoskeleton as it is observed in membrane blebs (83); (*c*) formation of a bottleneck or a cytoplasmic bridge between the membrane in the pipette-tip and the cell-surface membrane; and (*d*) ill-defined voltage gradients in the membrane area forming the high-resistance seal (rim effects). Whereas formation of a bottleneck and recording from the seal area can be recognized in most cases just by inspecting the current records (heterogeneous current amplitudes, rounded rising phases), the possible alterations due to local leaks or to detachment have not been assessed so far. The available evidence on systems that have been well studied both by patch clamp and by conventional techniques suggests, however, that channel function in a more or less normal way (15, 78, 81). On the other hand, it has been reported that voltage-sensitive inward-rectifying K^+ channels cease to function after about 20 command pulses (25). It is not clear whether this was related to seal formation itself. In summary, possible alterations in channel properties by gigaseal formation cannot be excluded, and for each type of channel this has to be shown by comparing single-channel recordings with conventional current measurements.

High-Resolution Current Recording: Limits of Resolution and New Features

At variance with most of the models invoked to interpret noise measurements, the current through an activated channel does not have, as it appeared from the initial single-channel current recordings (57), the shape of a simple rectangular pulse. In most single-channel current records three types of "new" phenomena are observed: (*a*) The current is very often interrupted by brief, mostly not completely resolved fluctuations towards the baseline, followed by a reopening (Nachschlag). (*b*) It shows fluctuations to one or several current levels intermediate between those of the fully closed and fully open channel (substate). (*c*) The rms noise of the current recording is increased when current is flowing through a channel (open-channel current noise). In the following section the occurrence of these phenomena and possible interpretations will be reviewed.

Figure 2a shows a recording of the current through a single endplate channel activated by acetylcholine (ACh). The current flow is interrupted by a brief closing gap. This type of current waveform is observed in all transmitter-activated ionic channels (14, 15, 19–21, 59, 72, 75) and in some voltage-activated channels (13, 16, 62, 78). For interpretation of these closing gaps in transmitter-activated channels, it is assumed that it represents the closing and reopening of the channel during a single ligand-receptor occupancy (12). Using this simple hypothesis the rates of channel opening and agonist dissociation have been derived (14, 15, 19–21, 75). Interestingly, different ACh-receptor agonists yielded different dissociation and channel-opening rates but relatively similar closing rates (15, 82). For ACh the channel-opening rate is larger than the agonist-dissociation rate. This implies that one of the assumptions made previously to interpret current fluctuation experiments—that of a single rate-limiting step—does not hold.

Figure 2b shows an example of another single-channel current recorded from the frog endplate. Following the opening of the channel, the current jumps transiently to an intermediate level. Intermediate current levels occurring during a channel opening, preceding or following it, have been observed in both transmitter- and voltage-gated channels (2, 3, 31, 33, 80, 84). Their functional significance is unclear at present. Similar substates of conductance have been observed in lipid bilayers doped with alamethicin (34a) or with membrane fragments containing a Cl^--selective channel from Torpedo electrocytes (56a).

Figure 2c illustrates another new phenomenon apparent in high resolution single-channel current recordings. It demonstrates a difference in the noise amplitude of the recording before and after opening of a single channel. It is obvious that the rms noise is increased when current is flowing through the open channel. The size and the spectral characteristics of "open-channel noise" have been analyzed so far only in ACh-activated single-channel currents of rat myoballs (79), and the source generating it is as yet unclear. Possible mechanisms include "shot noise" from ion permeation and short, unresolved gaps. Slow fluctuations are also observed, which might arise from structural fluctuations of the AChR channel protein (F. Sigworth, personal communication).

Apart from these new phenomena, which are observed after the channel has undergone a transition from closed to open, the analysis of channel open times and of the intervals between channel openings has led to new kinetic schemes describing the activation and inactivation of ionic channels. For transmitter-activated channels, it has become clear that the three-state scheme originally proposed by del Castillo & Katz (20a) is not sufficient to describe channel activation. In most single-channel current recordings, an excess of short events is found (14, 20, 41, 75). It was suggested that the receptor can open the channel from different states of occupancy (e.g. mono- or biliganded), which differ in their respective reaction rates. Multiple components in the distribution of closed times have been attributed to desensitization steps (15, 18, 76).

Bursting behavior, which is characterized by closed-time distributions having more than one exponential component, was first observed in voltage-activated channels by Conti & Neher (16) for K^+ channels, and was subsequently reported also for Ca^{2+} channels (7, 23, 29, 69). Reaction rates for three-state systems were derived. In most cases the data were not consistent with a Hodgkin-Huxley–type power law of activation (see, however, 24).

In conclusion, high-resolution single-channel current recordings have yielded new information on the mechanisms of channel gating. From the

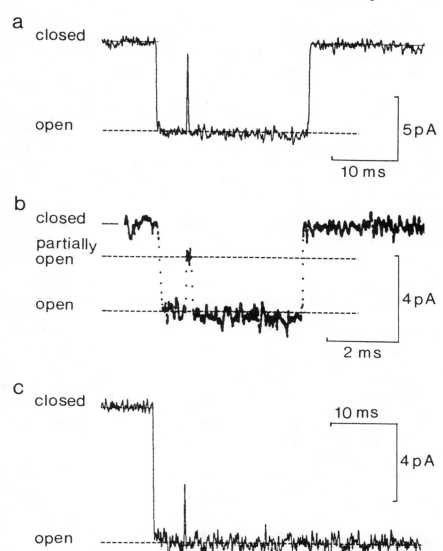

FIGURE 2.   High-resolution current recording of single-channel currents activated by low concentrations (<500 nM) of acetylcholine at the neuromuscular endplate of frog muscle fibers. The three traces show the new features, which are explained in the text. *A*: The open channel current is interrupted by a brief closing gap, which is followed by reopening of the channel (Nachschlag). *B*: The opening is followed by a brief current step towards a substate of conductance where the channel is only partially open (conductance substate). *C*: While the channel is open, the trace shows increased "noisiness" (open channel current noise).

statistical analysis of the intervals between openings, reaction rates leading to and from the open state have been determined. Analysis of the open state has led to the suggestion that channels can have more than one fully open state, they can adopt substates where the channel is partially open, and they may fluctuate in their structure.

Increased Flexibility with Respect to Choice of Electrolytes

Single-channel currents were initially studied in a normal ionic environment, i.e. pipettes were filled with physiological saline. These studies included ACh-receptor channels (40, 57, 59, 71), glutamate-activated channels (65), GABA-activated channels (41), and electrically excitable Na^+ and K^+ channels (16, 48, 81). However, the patch pipette offers the advantage that it isolates a small part of the cell's membrane that then can be exposed to an "unphysiological" extracellular ion composition. Such media have been used to study both voltage- and transmitter-dependent channels in the cell-attached configuration.

INWARD-RECTIFYING K^+ CHANNELS: These channels are present in muscle membrane, tunicate egg membrane, and in the heart cell membrane. Since their conductance shows very pronounced inward rectification, it becomes most easily measurable with high extracellular K^+. So far three reports with single-channel current measurements have shown that the empirical $g \sim \sqrt{K_o}$ relationship is a property of the single open channel. There are, however, pronounced differences both in the conductance values and the voltage-dependent gating kinetics between embryonic muscle (61), tunicate eggs (25, 26), and heart ventricular cells (77, 86). It might well turn out that inwardly rectifying K^+ channels that are thought to mediate the resting membrane potential are rather heterogeneous in their properties.

Ca^{2+} CHANNELS: Current flow through single voltage-activated Ca^{2+} channels has been measured in several preparations. In all of these studies the extracellular concentration of Ca^{2+} was raised to 40 mM Ca^{2+} (47), or Ca^{2+} was replaced by Ba^{2+} at a concentration of 70–100 mM to improve the signal-to-noise ratio of the recording. Under these conditions currents flowing through single Ca^{2+} channels were recorded from chromaffin cells (23), Helix neurones (7, 47), heart cell cultures (69), dorsal root ganglion cells (7), and tumor cells (29). In all these studies it was found that the Ca^{2+} channel shows burst kinetics when Ba^{2+} is the charge carrier. However, Ba^{2+} is known to alter the gating behavior of Ca^{2+} channels (70).

ACETYLCHOLINE-ACTIVATED K^+ CHANNELS: In pacemaker cells of the mammalian heart, ACh operates a largely K^+-selective channel that shows strong inward rectification. To improve the signal-to-noise ratio, high extracellular K^+ in the pipette was used to measure the gating properties of this channel (75).

TRANSMITTER-GATED Cl^- CHANNELS: Postsynaptic inhibition is mediated by a transmitter-dependent increase in the Cl^--conductance of the postsynaptic membrane. Because in most preparations Cl^- is close to its electrochemical equilibrium at the cell's resting potential, the patch membrane potential must be shifted in the depolarizing direction to measure a net current flow. However, voltage-dependent K^+ channels are also present in most neuronal membranes, so that both Cl^- and K^+ outward currents appear in the patch current. By performing the measurement with pipettes filled with high K^+ solution and clamping to near the (shifted) K^+ equilibrium potential, GABA and glycine-dependent single channel Cl^- currents have been measured in cultured spinal cord neurones (72), hippocampal neurones (6), and ACh-dependent Cl^- channels in *Aplysia* (2).

Spatial Resolution of Receptor-Channel Coupling on the Cell Membrane

The tight diffusion barrier between pipette solution and bath solution offers a new way to study receptor-channel interactions between different regions of a cell. A number of transmitters or hormones are believed to liberate an intracellular signal after binding to an extracellular receptor. This second messenger diffuses to other parts of the cell membrane, "modulating" membrane channels from the cytoplasmic face. The patch clamp technique is ideally suited to study such interactions between spatially separated receptors and channels. Figure 3 illustrates this sort of experiment in the case of the modulation of membrane channels by transmitters that act via cyclic-AMP.

Patch current measurements with second-messenger activation have so far been performed on glandular cells (54, 55, 66, 67) with cholecystokinin and acetylcholine as modulators of cationic channels, on *Aplysia* neurones (11, 78) using serotonin as a modulator of K^+ channels, and on embryonic heart cells (10) using 8-bromocyclic AMP as a modulator of Ca^{2+} channels. In all preparations it was reported that channel currents of normal conductance could be recorded from the patch, while agonist application was restricted to non-patch area. Serotonin was shown to modulate the number of active channels in the patch, whereas 8-bromo-cyclic AMP appeared to affect the opening and closing rates of Ca^{2+} channels.

THE INSIDE-OUT PATCH FOR STUDYING MECHANISMS CONTROLLED BY CYTOPLASMIC COMPONENTS

Techniques for forming inside-out patches have been described that involve air exposure (34) or solutions free of divalent ions (36; see above). An alternative

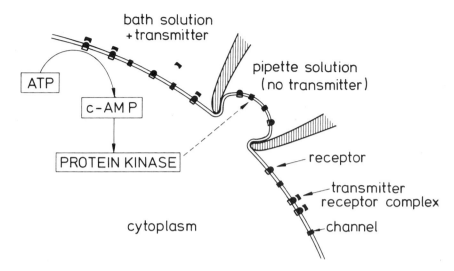

FIGURE 3. Schematic diagram illustrating the suitability of the cell-attached patch current recording mode to investigate channel regulation by transmitters acting via second messengers. By applying the transmitter to the cell membrane area outside the pipette opening, the modulation of membrane channels in the membrane patch in the pipette tip opening can be examined. In this example the hypothetical pathway of K^+-channel regulation by serotonin in *Aplysia* sensory neurones (78) or Ca^{2+}-channel regulation by adrenaline in heart cells is illustrated.

method is to touch an immersed oil droplet (Marty, personal communication) or a Sylgard surface (53). After patch formation, the solution in contact with the intracellular surface is typically changed repeatedly in order to study its influence on membrane currents. A special arrangement for rapid and easy change of solution has been described by Yellen (89).

Channels Dependent on Intracellular Ca^{2+}

Most of the work so far involving inside-out patches has concerned the role of intracellular Ca^{2+}. This is probably due to the fact that in many preparations a very prominent K^+ channel is activated in inside-out patches, unless special care is taken to keep the Ca^{2+} concentration on the cytoplasmic surface low. This Ca^{2+}-dependent K^+ channel was first identified by Marty (50) in bovine chromaffin cells. It has a conductance of 180 pS in symmetrical isotonic K^+ solutions and its gating behavior is very much influenced by the Ca^{2+} concentration on the inner side of the membrane. At low Ca^{2+} concentrations ($<10^{-7}$ M) very large depolarizations are required for voltage-dependent activation. Increasing Ca^{2+} concentration activates the channel at progressively less depolarized voltage levels; at 1 mM Ca^{2+} the channel switches randomly between open and closed in an almost voltage-independent fashion. At a given voltage, the opening probability changes with the second or third power of Ca^{2+} concentration. Extracellular Ca^{2+}, in contrast, influences the switching behavior very little. The kinetics were analyzed in more detail in a similar channel observed in cultured muscle cells (5, 56, 62). The dependence of open and closed times on voltage and Ca^{2+} has been described in terms of an activation/blockade mechanism (56) or, alternatively, as a mechanism involving a minimum of two open states and four closed states (63). Channels with similar characteristics have been observed in cells originating from the anterior pituitary (88), from spinal cord (42), from hippocampus (42), in sympathetic neurones (1), and in smooth muscle cells (87). They are also very similar to channels originating from skeletal muscle membranes incorporated into lipid bilayers (see chapter by Latorre, Coronado & Vergara, this volume, for a detailed description). A remarkable feature of these channels is that they are very ion-selective (45a, 62) despite their large conductance (see discussion by O. Andersen, this volume).

Another type of K^+ channel requiring both voltage and Ca^{2+} for activation was observed in snail neurones (48). Its main distinction with respect to the channel described above is its relatively small conductance ($\sim$ 19 pS.)

Apart from K^+ channels, a specific dependence on intracellular Ca^{2+} concentration was also observed for a nonspecific cationic channel in neonatal heart cells (13), neuroblastoma cells (89), and pancreatic acinar cells (54). This channel does not discriminate strongly between monovalent cations and is also permeable to Ba^{2+}.

Hormone-Regulated Channels and Second Messengers

A nonspecific cation channel of the type described above was identified by Murayama & Petersen (55, 66, 67) to underlie the depolarization induced by the peptide hormone cholecystokinin and by acetylcholine in pancreatic acinar cells. The channels can be decoupled from the regulatory action of the hormone in an inside-out patch by controlling the concentration of Ca^{2+} on the cytoplasmic face (55). This experiment provides evidence complementary to that from cell-attached measurements such as shown in Fig. 3.

A number of other channels are modulated by diffusible intracellular substances (27). Most prominent among these is the Ca^{2+} channel in heart cells and some other preparations (see 68; and the article by Reuter, this volume). It is interesting to note in this respect that it has not been possible so far to record single Ca^{2+} channel currents in isolated patches for extended periods of time (23, 53). Obviously patch isolation disrupts some of the control mechanisms, most probably by depletion of diffusible intracellular components. This is not surprising, considering the drastic procedures involved. The more surprising fact is that many other channels seem to function in a normal way after patch isolation.

Control of Ionic Milieu

Control over the composition of the solutions on both sides of the membrane has in the past only been possible with quite involved techniques such as internal perfusion (4) or internal dialysis (35, 43, 46). Patch isolation is a simple way to achieve the same goal. This has been exploited for permeability studies (38, 51, 71a), and for exposing the inner surface of electrically excitable membranes to agents that remove Na^+-channel inactivation (64).

THE OUTSIDE-OUT PATCH CONFIGURATION

The outside-out patch configuration is best if one wants to examine ionic channels controlled by externally located receptors. The extracellular solution can be changed easily, allowing testing of the effects of different transmitter substances or permeating ions. Similar to the case discussed above, formation of an outside-out patch may involve major structural rearrangements of the membrane, and the effect of isolation on channel properties should be determined. In one case (the AChR-channel in rat myotubes), outside-out patch formation was reported to slightly alter channel kinetics (85).

The outside-out patch configuration has been used to measure the dependence of conductance states of the AChR channel in embryonic cells on the permeating ion (33). The effect of different acetylcholine analogues on channel gating properties was studied by Sine & Steinbach (82).

Outside-out patches were also used to identify and isolate *transmitter-gated* Cl^- channels in the soma membrane of spinal cord neurones (31, 72), in *Aplysia* neurones (2), and in the muscle membrane of *Ascaris* (49). In spinal cord neurones, two putative transmitters—GABA and glycine—were applied to the same patch to identify the properties of their respective ionic channels. It was found that both agonists activate Cl^--selective channels with different conductance values. Both channels possibly share lower conductance substates (31). In *Ascaris* muscle and in *Aplysia* neurones, the outside-out patch was used to unequivocally identify the observed current step as GABA or ACh-dependent respectively.

THE WHOLE-CELL CONFIGURATION: VOLTAGE CLAMP AND DIALYSIS OF SMALL CELLS

A conductive pathway as low in resistance as 2–10 MΩ develops between pipette and cell when a membrane patch is broken by a short pulse of suction

(32). This configuration when established on a *large* cell can be used to measure membrane potential in the conventional way. When applied to very *small* cells, it, in addition, provides the conditions for a high-quality voltage clamp and for the dialysis of the cell interior (22, 53). Consider, for instance, a chromaffin cell of 10 μm diameter. It has an input resistance in the resting state as high as several gigaohms, and active currents are in the range of several hundred picoamperes. For these values, a 5 MΩ access resistance R_s presents negligible series resistance problems. To voltage-clamp a cell, then, requires nothing more than to apply a voltage to the pipette and to measure the current. Also, a step command produces a capacitive transient settling with a time constant of only 25 μsec (T = R_s C, where C is the membrane capacitance of approximately 5 pF). It should be appreciated, however, that series resistance can become a problem when cells are only slightly larger. Series resistance compensation will then be necessary to extend the usefulness of this approach.

The configuration described here can be considered a microversion of the dialysis techniques originally developed for large neurons (43, 46) and later adapted to smaller cells (45, 46). It was shown (22) that the potassium contents of the cell interior exchange for sodium in the pipette within 20 sec if care is taken to maintain a low resistance access (< 4 MΩ). Therefore, many of the points raised in the above discussion on inside-out patches also apply to this configuration. These include the technical advantages that are offered by control over the intracellular milieu as well as the danger of losing important intracellular components through diffusive depletion.

Contrary to conventional intracellular electrodes, the pipettes are filled with a medium of the ionic strength of physiological saline (but see 39 for an exception) in order to prevent massive loading of the cell with KCl. Therefore, diffusion potentials (35a) or Donnan-type potentials (after diffusional equilibration of small, mobile ions) in the pipette tip may not be negligible. This can result in apparent displacements along the voltage axis of the characteristics of electrically excitable cells (53). This disadvantage may turn out to be relatively minor in view of clear evidence of drastic changes in membrane parameters of small cells due to KCl leakage from standard microelectrodes (5a).

Ionic Currents in Small Cells

Whole-cell recording allows conventional voltage-clamp–type records to be obtained from cells as small as red blood cells (30). Many other cell types, particularly cells in tissue culture, can for the first time be studied under voltage-clamp conditions in this way. Among them are bovine chromaffin cells (22, 23), the pituitary cell line GH$_3$ (28), isolated sinoatrial node cells from rabbit heart (75), pancreatic islet cells (52), cultured neonatal heart cells (9), and ciliary ganglion cells (60).

Ca^{2+} Currents in Small Cells

Ca^{2+} currents are difficult to characterize in many preparations because they are usually contaminated by K^+ currents; they have fast turn-off kinetics and small single-channel conductance. Some of the features of the whole-cell configuration are ideally suited to overcome these difficulties. It allows the intracellular milieu to be controlled for suppression of K^+ currents; it is fast, and has high resolution that allows noise analysis of the currents. These advantages have been used by several investigators to study Ca^{2+} currents in small cells like bovine chromaffin cells (23), rat clonal pituitary cells (28), and inner segments of rod photoreceptor cells (17). The properties of Ca^{2+} currents in these preparations are discussed by Reuter (this volume). With regard to the method it should be pointed out that Ca^{2+} currents decline rather rapidly (rundown) after a recording period of approximatey 10 min. This phenomenon was also observed using other techniques of internal dialysis (8, 44). It is probably related to the washout of intracellular components (see discussion above).

CONCLUSIONS

Each of the four different patch clamp configurations has properties that are useful for studying different kinds of problems. Recording from cell-attached patches imposes very little perturbation on the cell under study. It allows single-channel currents from nearly all of the known types of ionic channels to be resolved. The cell-free configurations inside-out and outside-out have similarly high current resolution and provide control over the ionic milieu on both sides of the membrane. The solution on one side (the side facing the bath) can be easily changed. Thus, an outside-out configuration is indicated when a mechanism controlled by a receptor on the outer surface is to be studied. An inside-out configuration is indicated when a mechanism involving intracellular components, e.g. Ca^{2+}, is present. Both cell-free patch configurations, as well as whole-cell measurements, may suffer from the fact that cellular components necessary for the functioning of channels are being depleted. This, on the other hand, may lead to the identification of these components. The whole-cell configuration allows conventional voltage-clamp and current-clamp measurements to be performed on very small cells while the intracellular milieu is dialysed against the solution inside the pipette. Patch clamping seems to be universally applicable, with the only restriction that the membrane under study has to be exposed for direct contact with the pipette.

Acknowledgment

This work was supported in part by the Deutsche Forschungsgemeinschaft (DFG).

Literature Cited

1. Adams, P. R., Constanti, A., Brown, D. A., Clark, R. B. 1982. Intracellular Ca^{2+} activates a fast voltage-sensitive K^+ current in vertebrate sympathetic neurones. *Nature* 296:746–49
2. Ascher, P., Erulkar, S. 1983. Cholinergic Cl^- channels in snail neurones. See Ref. 74, pp. 401–8
3. Auerbach, A., Sachs, F. 1983. Flickering of a nicotinic ion channel to a subconductance state. *Biophys. J.* 42:1–10
4. Baker, P. F., Hodgkin, A. L., Shaw, T. I. 1961. Replacement of the protoplasm of a giant nerve fibre with artificial solutions. *Nature* 190:885–87
5. Barrett, J. N., Magleby, K. L., Pallotta, B. S. 1982. Properties of single calcium-activated potassium channels in cultured rat muscle. *J. Physiol.* 331:211–30
5a. Blatt, M. R., Slayman, C. L. 1983. KCl leakage from microelectrodes and its impact on the membrane parameters of a nonexcitable cell. *J. Membrane Biol.* 72:223–34
6. Bormann, J., Sakmann, B., Seifert, W. 1983. Isolation of GABA-activated single-channel Cl^- currents in the soma membrane of rat hippocampal neurones. *J. Physiol.* 341:9–10P
7. Brown, A. M., Camerer, H., Kunze, D. L., Lux, H. D. 1982. Similarity of unitary Ca^{2+} currents in three different species. *Nature* 299:156–58
8. Byerly, L., Hagiwara, S. 1982. Calcium currents in internally perfused nerve cell bodies of Limnea stagnalis. *J. Physiol.* 322:503–28
9. Cachelin, A. B., de Peyer, J. E., Kokubun, S., Reuter, H. 1983. Sodium channels in cultured cardiac cells. *J. Physiol.* In press
10. Cachelin, A. B., de Peyer, J. E., Kokubun, S., Reuter, H. 1983. Calcium channel modulation by 8-bromo-cyclic AMP in cultured heart cells. *Nature* 304:462–64
11. Camardo, J. S., Siegelbaum, S. A. 1983. Single channel analysis in *Aplysia* neurons: A specific K^+ channel is modulated by serotonin and cyclic AMP. See Ref. 74, pp. 409–23
12. Colquhoun, D., Hawkes, A. 1977. Relaxation and fluctuations of membrane currents that flow through drug-operated ion channels. *Proc. R. Soc. London Ser. B.* 199:231–62
13. Colquhoun, D., Neher, E., Reuter, H., Stevens, C. F. 1981. Inward current channels activated by intracellular Ca in cultured cardiac cells. *Nature* 294:752–54
14. Colquhoun, D., Sakmann, B. 1981. Fluctuations in the microsecond time range of the current through single acetylcholine receptor ion channels. *Nature* 294:464–66
15. Colquhoun, D., Sakmann, B. 1983. Bursts of openings in transmitter-activated ion channels. See Ref. 74, pp. 345–64
16. Conti, F., Neher, E. 1980. Single channel recordings of K^+ currents in squid axons. *Nature* 285:140–43
17. Corey, D. P., Dubinsky, J., Schwartz, E. A. 1982. The calcium current of rod-photoreceptor inner segments recorded with a whole-cell patch clamp. *Soc. Neurosci. Abstr.* 8:944
18. Cull-Candy, S. G., Miledi, R., Parker, I. 1981. Single glutamate-activated channels recorded from locust muscle fibres with perfused patch electrodes. *J. Physiol.* 321:195–210
19. Cull-Candy, S. G., Parker, I. 1982. Rapid kinetics of single glutamate-receptor channels. *Nature* 295:410–12
20. Cull-Candy, S. G., Parker, I. 1983. Experimental approaches used to examine single glutamate receptor ion channels in locust muscle fibres. See Ref. 74, pp. 389–400
20a. Del Castillo, I., Katz, B. 1957. Interaction at end-plate receptors between different choline derivatives. *Proc. R. Soc. London Ser. B* 146:369–81
21. Dionne, V. E., Leibowitz, M. D. 1982. Acetylcholine receptor kinetics. *Biophys. J.* 39:253–61
22. Fenwick, E. M., Marty, A., Neher, E. 1982. A patch-clamp study of bovine chromaffin cells and of their sensitivity to acetylcholine. *J. Physiol.* 331:577–97
23. Fenwick, E. M., Marty, A., Neher, E. 1982. Sodium and calcium channels in bovine chromaffin cells. *J. Physiol.* 331:599–635
24. Fukushima, Y. 1981. Identification and kinetic properties of the current through a single Na^+ channel. *Proc. Natl. Acad. Sci. USA* 78:1274–77
25. Fukushima, Y. 1981. Single channel potassium currents of the anomalous rectifier. *Nature* 294:368–71
26. Fukushima, Y. 1982. Blocking kinetics of the anomalous potassium rectifier of tunicate egg studied by single channel recording. *J. Physiol.* 331:311–31
27. Greengard, P. 1978. Phosphorylated proteins as physiological effectors. *Science* 199:146–52
28. Hagiwara, S., Ohmori, H. 1982. Studies of calcium channels in rat clonal pituitary

cells with patch electrode voltage clamp. *J. Physiol.* 331:231–52

29. Hagiwara, S., Ohmori, H. 1983. Studies of single calcium channel currents in rat clonal pituitary cells. *J. Physiol.* 336:649–61

30. Hamill, O. P. 1983. Potassium and chloride channels in red blood cells. See Ref. 74, pp. 457–71

31. Hamill, O. P., Bormann, J., Sakmann, B. 1983. Activation of multiple conductance state chloride channels in spinal neurones by glycine and GABA. *Nature.* 305:805–8

32. Hamill, O. P., Marty, A., Neher, E., Sakmann, B., Sigworth, F. J. 1981. Improved patch-clamp techniques for high-resolution current recording from cells and cell-free membrane patches. *Pflügers Arch.* 391:85–100

33. Hamill, O. P., Sakmann, B. 1981. Multiple conductance states of single acetylcholine recptor channels in embryonic muscle cells. *Nature* 294:462–64

34. Hamill, O. P., Sakmann, B. 1981. A cell-free method for recording single-channel currents from biological membranes. *J. Physiol.* 312:41–42P

34a. Hanke, W., Boheim, G. 1980. The lowest conductance state of the alamethicin pore. *Biochem. Biophys. Acta* 596:456–62

35. Hille, B., Campbell, D. T. 1976. An improved vaseline gap voltage clamp for skeletal muscle fibres. *J. Gen. Physiol.* 67:265–93

35a. Hironaka, T., Morimoto, S. 1979. The resting membrane potential of frog sartorius muscle. *J. Physiol.* 297:1–8

36. Horn, R., Patlak, J. 1980. Single channel current from excised patches of muscle membrane. *Proc. Natl. Acad. Sci. USA* 77:6930–34

37. Deleted in proof

38. Horn, R., Patlak, J., Stevens, C. F. 1981. The effect of tetramethylammonium. *Biophys. J.* 36:321–27

39. Hume, J. R., Giles, W. 1981. Ionic currents in single isolated bullfrog atrial cells. *J. Gen. Physiol.* 81:153–94

40. Jackson, M. B., Lecar, H. 1979. Single postsynaptic channel currents in tissue cultured muscle. *Nature* 282:863–64

41. Jackson, M. B., Lecar, H., Mathers, D. A., Barker, J. L. 1982. Single channel currents activated by γ-aminobutryic acid, muscimol, and (−)pentobarbital in cultured mouse spinal neurons. *J. Neuroscience* 2:889–94

42. Jackson, M. B., Lecar, H., Morris, C. E., Wong, B. S. 1983. Single channel current recording in excitable cells. In *Current Methods in Cellular Neurobiology*, ed. J. L. Barker, J. F. Mckelvy. New York: Wiley. In press

43. Kostyuk, P. G., Krishtal, O. A. 1977. Separation of sodium and calcium currents in the somatic membrane of mollusc neurones. *J. Physiol.* 270:545–68

44. Kostyuk, P. G. 1980. Calcium ionic channels in electrically excitable membrane. *Neuroscience* 5:945–59

45. Krishtal, O. A., Pidoplichko, V. I. 1980. A receptor for protons in the nerve cell membrane. *Neuroscience* 5:2325–27

45a. Latorre, R., Miller, C. 1983. Conduction and selectivity in potassium channels. *J. Membr. Biol.* 71:11–30

46. Lee, K. S., Akaike, A., Brown, A. M. 1980. The suction pipette method for internal perfusion and voltage clamp in small excitable cells. *J. Neurosci. Methods* 2:51–78

47. Lux, H. D., Nagy, K. 1981. Single channel Ca^{2+} currents in *Helix pomatis* neurons. *Pflügers Arch.* 391:252–54

48. Lux, H. D., Neher, E., Marty, A. 1981. Single channel activity associated with the calcium-dependent outward current in *Helix pomatia*. *Pflügers Arch.* 389:293–95

49. Martin, R. J. 1983. GABA single channel currents from *Ascaris* muscle. *J. Physiol.* 336:36P

50. Marty, A. 1981. Ca-dependent K channels with large unitary conductance in chromaffin cell membranes. *Nature* 291:497–500

51. Marty, A. 1983. Blocking of large unitary calcium-dependent potassium currents by internal sodium ions. *Pflügers Arch.* 396:179–81

52. Marty, A., Neher, E. 1982. Ionic channels in cultured rat pancreatic islet cells. *J. Physiol.* 326:36–37P

53. Marty, A., Neher, E. 1983. Tight seal whole-cell recording. See Ref. 74, pp. 107–22

54. Maruyama, Y., Petersen, O. H. 1982. Single-channel currents in isolated patches of plasma membrane from basal surface of pancreatic acini. *Nature* 299:159–61

55. Maruyama, Y., Petersen, O. H. 1982. Cholecystokinin activation of single-channel currents is mediated by internal messenger in pancreatic acinar cells. *Nature* 300:61–63

56. Methfessel, C., Boheim, G. 1982. The gating of single calcium-dependent potassium channels is described by an activation/blockade mechanism. *Biophys. Struct. Mech.* 9:35–60

56a. Miller, C. 1982. Open-state substructure of single chloride channels from Torpedo electroplax. *Philos. Trans. R. Soc. London. Ser. B* 299:401–11

57. Neher, E., Sakmann, B. 1976. Single-channel currents recorded from membrane of denervated frog muscle fibres. *Nature* 260:799–802

58. Deleted in proof.

59. Nelson, D. J., Sachs, F. 1979. Single ionic channels observed in tissue-cultured muscle. *Nature* 282:861–63

60. Ogden, D. C., Gray, P. T. A., Colquhoun, D., Rang, P. 1983. Kinetics of acetylcholine activated ion channels in chick ciliary ganglion neurones grown in tissue culture. *Pflügers Arch.* In press

61. Ohmori, H., Yoshida, S., Hagiwara, S. 1981. Single K^+ channel currents of anomalous rectification in cultured rat myotubes. *Proc. Natl. Acad. Sci. USA* 78:4960–64

62. Pallotta, B. S., Magleby, K. L., Barrett, J. N. 1981. Single channel recordings of Ca^{2+}-activated K^+ currents in rat muscle cell culture. *Nature* 293:471–74

63. Palotta, B. S., Magleby, K. L. 1983. Calcium-dependence of open and shut interval distributions of calcium-activated potassium channels in cultured rat muscle. *Biophys. J.* 41:57a

64. Patlak, J., Horn, R. 1982. Effect of N-bromoacetamide on single sodium channel currents in excised membrane patches. *J. Gen. Physiol.* 79:333–51

65. Patlak, J. B., Gration, K. A. F., Usherwood, P. N. R. 1979. Single glutamate-activated channels in locust muscle. *Nature* 278:643–45

66. Petersen, O. H., Maruyama, Y. 1983. What is the mechanism of the calcium influx to pancreatic acinar cells evoked by secretagogues? *Pflügers Arch.* 396: 82–84

67. Petersen, O. H., Maruyama, Y. 1983. Cholecystokinin and acetylcholine activation of single channel currents via second messenger in pancreatic acinar cells. See Ref. 74, pp. 425–35

68. Reuter, H. 1983. Calcium channel modulation by neurotransmitters, enzymes, and drugs. *Nature* 301:569–74

69. Reuter, H., Stevens, C. F., Tsien, R. W., Yellen, G. 1982. Properties of single calcium channels in cardiac cell culture. *Nature* 297:501–4

70. Saimi, Y., Kung, C. 1982. Are ions involved in the gating of calcium channels? *Science* 218:153–56

71. Sakmann, B. 1978. Acetylcholine-induced ionic channels in rat skeletal muscle. *Fed. Proc.* 37:2654–59

71a. Sakmann, B., Bormann, J., Hamill, O. 1983. Ion transport by single receptor channels. *Cold Spring Harbor Symp.* 48. In press

72. Sakmann, B., Hamill, O. P., Bormann, J. 1983. Patch clamp measurements of elementary chloride currents activated by the putative inhibitory transmitter GABA and glycine in mammalian spinal neurons. *J. Neural Transm.* 18 (Suppl.):83–95

73. Sakmann, B., Neher, E. 1983. Geometric parameters of pipettes and membrane patches. See Ref. 74, pp. 37–51

74. Sakmann, B., Neher, E. 1983. *Single Channel Recording*. New York: Plenum. 496 pp.

75. Sakmann, B., Noma, A., Trautwein, W. 1983. Acetylcholine activation of single muscarinic K^+ channels in isolated pacemaker cells of the mammalian heart. *Nature* 303:250–53

76. Sakmann, B., Patlak, J. B., Neher, E. 1980. Single acetylcholine-activated channels slow burst kinetics in the presence of desensitizing concentrations of agonist. *Nature* 286:71–73

77. Sakmann, B., Trube, G. 1984. *J. Physiol.* In press

78. Siegelbaum, S. A., Camardo, J. S., Kandel, E. R. 1982. Serotonin and c-AMP close single K^+ channels in *Aplysia* sensory neurones. *Nature* 299: 413–17

79. Sigworth, F. J. 1982. Fluctuations in the current through open ACh-receptor channels. *Biophys. J.* 37:309A

80. Sigworth, F. J. 1983. An example of an analysis. See Ref. 74, pp. 301–21

81. Sigworth, F. J., Neher, E. 1980. Single Na^+ channel currents observed in cultured rat muscle cells. *Nature* 287:447–49

82. Sine, S. M., Steinbach, J. H. 1983. Apparent channel opening and agonist dissociation rates of acetylcholine receptor BC IH1 cells. *Biophys. J.* 41: 133A

83. Tank, D. W., Wu, E., Webb, W. W. 1982. Enhanced molecular diffusibility in muscle membrane blebs: Release of lateral constraints. *J. Cell. Biol.* 92:207–17

84. Trautmann, A. 1982. Curare can open and block ionic channels associated with cholinergic receptors. *Nature* 298:272–75

85. Trautmann, A., Siegelbaum, S. A. 1983. The influence of membrane patch isolation on single ACh-channel current in myotubes. See Ref. 74, pp. 473–80

86. Trube, G., Sakmann, B., Trautwein, W. 1981. Inward-rectifying potassium currents recorded from isolated heart cells by the patch clamp method. *Pflügers Arch.* 391:R7

87. Walsh, J. F. Jr., Singer, J. J. 1983. Identification and characterization of a Ca^{++}-activated K^+ channel in freshly dissociated, vertebrate smooth muscle cells using the patch-clamp technique. *Biophys. J.* 41:56a

88. Wong, B. S. Lecar, H., Adler, M. 1983. Single calcium-dependent potassium channels in clonal anterior pituitary cells. *Biophys. J.* 39:313–17

89. Yellen, G. 1982. Single Ca^{2+}-activated nonselective cation channels in neuroblastoma. *Nature* 296:357–59

Ann. Rev. Physiol. 1984. 46:473–84

ION CHANNELS IN CARDIAC CELL MEMBRANES

Harald Reuter

Department of Pharmacology, University of Berne, 3010 Berne, Switzerland

INTRODUCTION

The electrophysiology of cardiac muscle is notoriously complicated. In the past, some of the difficulties in interpreting voltage clamp data arose from the complex morphology of cardiac tissues and from inadequate tools for unequivocal separation of the various ionic current components (2, 13). However, new methods have been developed. Single cardiac cells can be voltage-clamped and internally dialyzed (51, 54), and single ion channels can be identified and analyzed by the patch clamp method (34). First attempts to reconstitute cardiac sarcolemmal ion channels have been successful (24). Specific binding of radioligands to ion channels emerges as an additional method for identifying the channels (31, 49). Some of the previous results obtained in intact cardiac tissue and some older concepts have been confirmed, and important new insight has been gained by the new techniques. Although the molecular analysis of ion channels in the heart is still in its early infancy, some initial developments in this field are discussed in this review. In some instances new results from cardiac cells are compared with those from other cells, in order to indicate possible similarities between ion channels in various biological tissues. Because of space limitations, only a few of the many pertinent papers can be discussed. Important new developments in the field of junctional channels and tissue impedance (16, 17, 55) are beyond the scope of this review.

Table 1 gives an overview of the various currents and the respective identified channels observed in cardiac cell membranes. The variety of channels is puzzling, a feature that cardiac muscle shares with other excitable tissues, e.g. molluscan neurons (1).

473

0066-4278/84/0315-0473$02.00

Table 1 Ion channels in cardiac cell membranes

Current	Charge carrier	Activation mechanism	Single channel conductance (pS)	Function
Inward currents:				
I_{Na}	Na^+	voltage	$15(s.)^a$ (137 $[Na]_0$; 9)	AP–upstroke
I_{Ca} (I_{si})	Ca^{2+}	voltage	$9-25(s.)^a$ $6.5(c.)^b$ (10–95 $[Ba]_0$,$[Ca]_0$; 15, 66, 69, 73)	AP–plateau, pacemaker, e.c.–coupling
I_t (TI)	$NA + K^+$	$[Ca^{2+}]_i$	$30-40(c.)^a$ (140 $[Na]_0$, $[K]_0$; 23)	after–depolarization
I_f (I_h)	$Na + K^+$	voltage	? 28 $(c.)^c$ (100 $[K]_0$; 24)	pacemaker
Outward currents:				
I_{K_1}	K^+	voltage	$6-35(s.)^a$ (11–150 $[K]_0$; 74, 79)	resting potential, repolarization
I_{x_1}	$K^+(+Na^+)$	voltage	? 28 $(c.)^c$ (100 $[K]_0$; 24)	repolarization
$I_{K(ACh)}$	K^+	acetyl-choline	$5-39(s.)^a$ (20–70 $[K]_0$; 74, 77) $3.7(c.)^b$ (3 $[K]_0$;76)	hyperpolarization, inhibition
$I_{K(Ca)}$	K^+	$[Ca^{2+}]_i$	?	repolarization
I_{Cl}	Cl^-	voltage (?)	$55(c)^c$ (100$[Cl]_0$; 24)	?

In parentheses: c. = chord conductance; s. = slope conductance; concentrations of charge carriers (mM); references.
[a] direct single–channel recording.
[b] noise analysis.
[c] reconstituted channels.

INWARD CURRENT CHANNELS

Na^+ Channels

The recent rapid progress in the analysis of the Na^+ conductance (g_{Na}) in cardiac muscle is primarily due to the development of more suitable preparations and improved conditions for voltage clamping. Experiments in rabbit Purkinje fibers (P-fibers) with wide intercellular clefts (3, 19, 21, 22), in cell cultures (28), and in isolated single mammalian ventricular cells (5, 6, 53, 54) have provided useful information. Differences between the kinetics of g_{Na} in cardiac cells and in other excitable tissues seem to be minor, with the possible exception of slower recovery kinetics of the channels from inactivation (6, 21). Furthermore, the experiments in P-fibers have confirmed a pronounced non-linear relation between g_{Na} and $\dot{V}_{max}$ of the action potential (AP) (3) as earlier suggested from calculations of g_{Na} and $\dot{V}_{max}$ in nerve (3, 20). The nonlinearity presumably arises primarily from relatively slow activation kinetics of g_{Na}, which prevents it from ever attaining a steady state during the rapid upstroke of the AP (3). This result may also, at least partly, explain the pronounced voltage-dependent shift of the dose-response curve of tetrodotoxin (TTX) observed in $\dot{V}_{max}$ measurements (19, 72), an effect not seen in voltage clamp experiments (19). On the other hand, use-dependence and low potency (72) of TTX action in cardiac cells have been confirmed in voltage-clamp experiments and have been interpreted in terms of mutual interactions between channel gating and TTX binding (19). Like in nerve (62), TTX must have access to its receptor from the external surface of the membrane, because it does not block Na^+ channels from the inside (9). Therefore, differences in the accessibility of the binding site from the outside and/or structural differences of the receptor may account for the discrepancies in binding kinetics of TTX in cardiac cells and nerve. Radioligand binding and biochemical analysis of the binding site may be useful tools (49, 73b) to solve this question. It is interesting to note that, in contrast to TTX, the effects of lidocaine and quinidine on g_{Na} are very similar in cardiac muscle and nerve (3, 22, 53).

Direct single Na^+-channel recordings by means of the patch-clamp method (34) strongly suggest a close similarity of Na^+ channels in various excitable cells. Single Na^+-channel slope conductance at 16–18°C is about 15 pS in cultured cardiac cells from neonatal rat hearts (9), a value similar to that obtained in cultured muscle cells (38, 75), neuroblastoma cells (67), and chromaffin cells (30). Gating of the channels, i.e. their opening, closing, and inactivation properties as a function of voltage, is also very similar for all cell types (9, 30, 38). Channel open times increase with depolarization (9, 30, 75). Ensemble averages of hundreds of single-channel records yield mean currents, I, identical to the macroscopic Na^+ currents obtained from whole-cell recordings (9, 38, 75). Inactivation of the channels during depolarization and, in the steady-state, after conditioning clamp steps results from a reduced opening probability, p, and not from a decrease of single-channel current, i, (9, 38, 75). It seems that inactivation can occur without preceding channel opening, in which case activation and inactivation would be independent processes (38). Na^+ channels can be recorded in cell-attached as well as in excised inside-out or outside-out membrane patches (9, 30, 38). The Na^+-channel density per surface area ranges from about 1–2 channels μm^{-2} in cultured cardiac cells to about 16 μm^{-2} in isolated cells from adult rat hearts (9), which is comparable to other tissues [5–15 μm^{-2} in chromaffin cells (30), about 10 μm^{-2} in myoballs (75), and 17 μm^{-2} in neuroblastoma cells (67)].

Ca^{2+} Channels

Basic properties of voltage-dependent single Ca^{2+} channels, like those of Na^+ channels, appear to be very similar in various tissues (7). Ca^{2+} currents and channels have been extensively discussed in previous reviews (33, 59, 68, 69,

81), so I shall confine my discussion to a few new developments pertinent to cardiac muscle.

Ca^{2+} current (I_{Ca}) measurements in single cardiac myocytes have supported many of the previous results obtained in multicellular cardiac preparations (59, 68), although there are important quantitative differences. In single myocytes, I_{Ca} density seems to be considerably larger than in multicellular preparations (42, 81; but see 39), and the activation and inactivation kinetics are faster (39, 42, 81). Part of this discrepancy may be due to series resistance problems in the intact preparations (42), but other possibilities (see e.g. 55) have not been excluded. Another property of I_{Ca} originally discovered in intact preparations (68, 70)—its relatively negative reversal potential (V_0), which does not coincide with the much more positive Ca^{2+} equilibrium potential (V_{Ca})—has also been confirmed in single cardiac cells (39, 51, 61). In internally dialyzed cells it could be shown that the negative shift of V_0 with respect to V_{Ca} results from a small permeability of K^+ ions through Ca^{2+} channels (51), as previously suggested for intact preparations (70).

In agreement with earlier results (68, 69, 71), β-adrenoceptor agonists increase I_{Ca} in single myocytes without changing its kinetics (42). Moreover, injection or dialysis of cAMP (41, 78) or of the catalytic subunit of cAMP-dependent protein kinase (65) in single cardiac cells have effects identical to those seen with the β-adrenoceptor agonists. This is strong support for the hypothesis (68, 80) that cAMP-dependent phosphorylation reaction is involved in the modulation of Ca^{2+} channels by β-adrenergic neurotransmitters and drugs.

Ca^{2+} channels can be blocked by various organic compounds. The mechanisms of action of some of these Ca^{2+} channel blockers have recently been analyzed in multicellular (60) and single cell (52) cardiac preparations. Verapamil and its derivatives block Ca^{2+} channels predominantly from the inside surface of the membrane (35) by entering the channel preferentially when it is open (52). The same applies to diltiazem (52). The blocking potencies of these charged tertiary amines depends on membrane potential (voltage dependence) and on the rate of stimulation (use dependence) (52, 60). This contrasts with the effects of the 1, 4-dihydropyridines (nifedipine, nitrendipine, nisoldipine), which are uncharged at physiological pH and do not show voltage and use dependencies (52, 44). Important discrepancies, however, exist if one compares the blocking effects of 1, 4-dihydropyridines on I_{Ca} (52) with radioligand binding (31, 37) of this class of compounds to putative Ca^{2+} channels in homogenates or crudely purified particulate fractions of cardiac sarcolemma. The K_D value estimated from the blocking potency of I_{Ca} by nitrendipine is 2–3 orders of magnitudes higher (52) than the K_D values obtained in radioligand binding studies (31, 37). Furthermore, while in the electrophysiological experiments Ca^{2+} ions compete with nitrendipine at its binding site (52), to my knowledge no such effect has been reported for radioligand binding (31).

Ca^{2+} and other divalent cations in the micro- to millimolar range even facilitate ^{3}H-nitrendipine and ^{3}H-nimodipine binding (31).

Recordings of single Ca^{2+} channels from cultured neonatal rat heart cells (73) and from adult guinea pig ventricular cells (15) by means of the patch clamp method yielded very similar results. Channel openings often occur in bursts separated by longer intervals of closures. Single-channel slope conductance with 90–96 mM Ba^{2+} in the pipette ranges from 15–25 pS (15, 69, 73), while with 50 mM Ca^{2+} or Ba $^{2+}$ it is 9–10 pS (15). The current-voltage (i/V) relationship is approximately ohmic over a rather wide potential range (15, 73), in agreement with earlier results obtained from tail-current analysis (70). The relationship between open state probability, p, and voltage seems to saturate at levels p <1 (15, 69, 73). With Ba^{2+} as charge carriers, there is voltage-dependent inactivation resulting from a decrease in p with conditioning depolarization (15, 73). However, it is quite possible that an additional, Ca^{2+}-dependent inactivation mechanism (33, 81) exists if Ca^{2+} ions are the current carriers. There is a considerable overlap between the voltage ranges of activation and inactivation of I_{Ca} (59, 68, 70), resulting in a steady-state "window current." The steady-state current fluctuations have been analyzed by power spectra and yielded a single-channel conductance of 6.5 pS [10 mM $BaCl_2$; (66)]. Mean open times, $\bar{t}_o$ (0.6–1.1 msec), of Ca^{2+} channels are exponentially distributed, while mean closed times can be described by two exponentials: a fast one with mean closed time, $\bar{t}_{C1}$ (0.6–1.3 msec); and a slow one with $\bar{t}_{C2}$ (3–20 msec) (10, 15, 73). These results are similar to those described for chromaffin cells (30) and snail neurons (56) and can be quantitatively analyzed in terms of a kinetic model (30) that assumes two closed states, C_1 and C_2, and one open state, O, of the channel:

$$C_1 \underset{k_{-1}}{\overset{k_1}{\rightleftharpoons}} C_2 \underset{k_{-2}}{\overset{k_2}{\rightleftharpoons}} O,$$

where the transitions between the states are determined by four voltage-dependent rate constants. Most probably this reaction scheme is an oversimplification, since it does not take into account an inactivated state. However, it has been useful in analyzing the effects of isoproterenol (69, 73) and 8-br-cAMP (10) on Ca^{2+} channels, both of which enhance the channel opening probability primarily by increasing the forward rate constants k_1 and k_2 and by slightly decreasing k_{-2} (10, 69, 73). In contrast to Na^+ channels, Ca^{2+} channels do not function in isolated membrane patches (15, 30, 69). The density of Ca^{2+} channels in cardiac cell membranes has been estimated as 1000–10000 channels per cell, or 0.5–5 channels μm^{-2} (4, 69).

Ca^{2+}-Activated, Nonselective Channels

Under certain conditions cardiac cells develop oscillatory depolarizing after-potentials (for review see 25). After-depolarizations (ADs) sometimes reach threshold to fire off action potentials and can thus initiate ectopic extrasystoles and severe arrhythmias of the heart (25). In view of the clinical impact of ADs it is not surprising that considerable effort has been extended to elucidate the cellular mechanisms of their origin. The conditions under which ADs develop seem to have one factor in common: they raise the free intracellular Ca^{2+} concentration, $[Ca^{2+}]_i$, transiently above the normal diastolic value after an action potential (29, 46). These conditions include high cardiac glycoside concentrations, high $[Ca^{2+}]_o$, low $[Na^+]_o$, $[K^+]_o$, or $[caffeine]_o$ (18, 29, 43, 46). High caffeine concentrations suppress ADs (43, 48). ADs are not confined to pacemaker tissues like P–fibers (29, 45–47, 50), but have also been described for ventricular myocardial fibers (29, 36, 43) or cultured ventricular cell aggregates from chick hearts (18).

A transient inward current, I_t (TI) (50), has originally been found responsible for ADs in P-fibers treated with toxic concentrations of strophanthidin (46, 47, 50). It could be shown that I_t is different and independent from other current components in the heart and sometimes shows oscillatory behavior, probably resulting from an oscillatory Ca^{2+} release from intracellular stores (45–47, 58). Intracellular injection of EGTA abolishes I_t (45, 58), providing evidence for the requirement of a rise of $[Ca^{2+}]_i$ for the activation of this membrane-current component. Further extensive analysis in P-fibers has led to the suggestion that Na^+ and K^+, but not Cl^-, could be the respective charge carriers of I_t (47). The reversal potential, V_0, of this current was found to be around -5 mV in P-fibers (46, 47). No clear reversal of the current could be observed in ferret papillary muscles, although extrapolation of the I-V relation led to a similar value of V_0 as in P-fibers (43).

Spectral analyses of current or voltage fluctuations resulting from the activation of I_t have been performed both in P-fibers (45) and in single ventricular myocardial cells (58). In both studies the power spectra show peak resonant frequencies consistent with the periodicities of I_t. The current fluctuations are cross-correlated with corresponding fluctuations in contractile force (45) and are suppressed by EGTA injection into the cells (45, 58), pointing to an oscillatory release of Ca^{2+} from intracellular stores as a common source for the fluctuations (45, 58).

Two different mechanisms for the genesis of I_t have been discussed: an electrogenic Na-Ca exchange, or a nonselective cation channel (43, 47). So far, there is little direct evidence in favor of the first mechanism, but considerable evidence for the second one. Application of the patch-clamp method to cultured cardiac cells revealed a new type of ion channel that has precisely the properties required for the genesis of I_t (23). The channels can be measured in intact cells as well as in excised membrane patches. In inside-out patches they can be activated by $[Ca^{2+}]_i > 0.5$ μM. With long exposures to high $[Ca^{2+}]_i$ the channels seem to desensitize. The charge carriers for the current flowing through open channels are Na^+ and K^+, which are both equally permeable. The reversal potential with equal concentrations of both ions on either side of the membrane patch is 0 mV. Anions do not permeate the channel. The opening and closing kinetics of the channels are complex, with open and closed times ranging from a few msec to many sec. The open-close equilibrium of the channels depends very little on voltage and, therefore, the predominant gating mechanism is the fluctuation of the free $[Ca^{2+}]_i$. The single channel chord conductance is ohmic, (about 35 pS at 26°C), and appears to be rather temperature-sensitive. The channels do not seem to dwell at intermediate conductance levels. We have found these channels also in guinea-pig myocytes where, however, they seem to be much more sparse than in cultured rat heart cells (A. Cachelin, J. de Peyer & H. Reuter, unpublished). Meanwhile these channels have also been observed in neuroblastoma cells (82) and in pancreatic acinar cells (57). In the latter cells they seem to be regulated by hormones that are known to induce secretion (57).

What is the physiological role of the Ca^{2+}-activated, nonselective cation channels in the heart? Here I can only speculate. They may be particularly important in pacemaker tissue like sinus node and atrio-ventricular node. These tissues have a low maximal diastolic potential, although the K^+ equilibrium potential is about 20–30 mV more negative (32). Because there is a considerable Ca^{2+} influx during each action potential into these relatively small cells (40), the resulting fluctuating free $[Ca^{2+}]_i$ may periodically activate a certain fraction of the channels and thereby depolarize V_m and help maintain pacemaker activity.

Pacemaker Current

The pacemaker current, I_f, in P-fibers, originally described as a deactivating K^+ current (I_{K_2}) (63), has recently been reexamined and found to be rather an inward current activated during hyperpolarization negative to about -50 mV (26). V_0 depends on both Na^+ and K^+ and, at physiological concentrations of both ions, has a value near -10 mV (27). The earlier failure to identify I_f as a nonselective current seems to be due to complications arising from accumulation and depletion of K^+ in the narrow extracellular clefts of ungulate P-fibers (2, 26, 27, 55). Meanwhile, measurement of I_f in disaggregated single P-fiber cells, i.e. without narrow clefts, has confirmed the view of a nonselective current (11). I_f, however, was first discovered in the sinoatrial node (8, 40) and has also been found in the atrio-ventricular node (48). This implies that the same current component could be involved in the spontaneous activity of various pacemaker tissues of the mammalian heart.

Single-channel recordings of I_f have not been reported so far. However, it is clear that the nonselective channels described in the previous section cannot account for I_f. These channels show little voltage dependence, while I_f activation depends steeply on potential (26, 27). On the other hand, the nonselective cation channels have an absolute requirement of $[Ca^{2+}]_i$ for their activation, while I_f has not (13, 23). Whether any of the recently reconstituted ion channels (24) meets the requirements for producing I_f remains to be seen.

OUTWARD CURRENT CHANNELS

Inward-Rectifying Channels

An important outward current in cardiac cells is a K^+ current that exhibits inward-going rectification (I_{K_1}) (for review see 13). I_{K_1} is a major determinant of the resting potential and decreases upon depolarization (inward rectification), thus facilitating the occurrence of the long plateau phase of cardiac action potentials. The current can be blocked by Cs^+ or Ba^{2+} and is enhanced by external K^+ (12, 13). In contrast to previous beliefs, I_{K_1} does not seem to be time-independent (12).

The information on single-channel currents related to I_{K_1} is still relatively sparse. In ventricular myocardial and a.-v. nodal cells, a K^+-selective channel has been described with mean open times $\bar{t}_0$, of about 50–100 msec (22–32°C) near V_K (74, 79). Single-channel current, i, increases and $\bar{t}_0$ decreases upon hyperpolarization. Single-channel conductance depends on $[K^+]_0$ (Table 1). Both single-channel conductance and opening probability decrease upon depolarization from V_K (79), which accounts for inward rectification of the macroscopic current I_{K_1}. The channels are blocked by Cs^+ and Ba^{2+} (79). The few data available at present do not allow a direct comparison with properties of inward rectifying K^+ channels in other tissues.

It has long been known that acetylcholine (ACh), by binding to muscarinic receptors, increases g_K in certain cardiac tissues (76). Recent extensive analyses of the effect (see review 76) have provided information concerning the mechanism of action. ACh activates K^+ channels that show inward rectification, like I_{K_1} channels (74, 76). It has indeed been suggested (64) that ACh simply modulates the current flowing through I_{K_1} channels. However, although both channel types have certain properties in common (inward rectification, K^+ dependence, and size of single channel conductance), they seem to be different entities. The voltage-dependent kinetics are very different, and ACh has no effect on membrane patches where only I_{K_1} channels are present (74). However, the possibility still exists that one population of I_{K_1} channels is not coupled to muscarinic receptors and therefore cannot be activated and/or modulated by the neurotransmitter.

Other Outward Currents

I can only briefly mention the other outward current components observed in various cardiac tissues (for review see 13). They include the delayed rectifier current that is mainly carried by K^+ (I_{x_1}) (13, 39). Data from patch-clamp analysis on single-channel properties of this current component are not yet available. However, one population of ion channels reconstituted from cardiac sarcolemma in planar bilayers has features that could be consistent with I_{x_1} (24). The permeability ratio $P_K/P_{Na} = 5$ for this channel, and the single-channel chord conductance is 28 pS (100 mM KCl). The channel is activated by voltage over a potential range of about 80 mV. It will be interesting to see whether a channel with those properties can also be identified in intact cells. Other K^+ conductances in the heart are thought be activated by $[Ca^{2+}]_i$ (see 13 for review). In contrast to other cells (34), no patch-clamp results on Ca^{2+}-activated K^+ channels have so far been reported for cardiac myocytes. A Ca^{2+}-activated $^{86}Rb^+$ flux has been observed in cardiac sarcolemmal vesicles (14) which, however, could also be related to I_t.

None of the current components in the heart can be clearly assigned to a Cl^- conductance (13), although a Cl^- channel has been reconstituted from cardiac sarcolemma (24).

ACKNOWLEDGMENT

Support by the Swiss National Science Foundation is gratefully acknowledged.

Literature Cited

1. Adams, D. J., Smith, S. J., Thompson, S. H. 1980. Ionic currents in molluscan neurons. *Ann. Rev. Neurosci.* 3:141–67
2. Attwell, D., Cohen, I. 1977. The voltage clamp of multicellular preparations. *Progr. Biophys. Mol. Biol.* 31:201–45
3. Bean, B. P., Cohen, C. J., Tsien, R. W. 1982. Block of cardiac sodium channels by tetrodotoxin and lidocaine: sodium current and V_{max} experiments. In *Normal and Abnormal Conduction in the Heart*, ed. A. Paes de Carvalho, B. F. Hoffman, M. Lieberman, pp. 198–206. Mount Kisco, NY: Futura
4. Bean, B. P., Nowycky, M. D., Tsien, R. W. 1983. Electrical estimates of Ca channel density in heart cell membranes. *Biophys. J.* 41:295A
5. Bodewei, R., Hering, S., Lemke, B., Rosenshtraukh, L. V., Undrovinas, A. I., Wollenberger, A. 1982. Characterization of the fast sodium current in isolated rat myocardial cells: simulation of the clamped membrane potential. *J. Physiol.* 325:301–15
6. Brown, A. M., Lee, K. S., Powell, T. 1981. Sodium current in single rat heart muscle cells. *J. Physiol.* 318:479–500
7. Brown, A. M., Camerer, H., Kunze, D. L., Lux, H. D. 1982. Similarity of unitary Ca^{2+} currents in three different species. *Nature* 299:156–58
8. Brown, H., Di Francesco, D. 1980. Voltage-clamp investigations of membrane currents underlying pacemaker activity in rabbit sino-atrial node. *J. Physiol.* 308:331–51
9. Cachelin, A. B., de Peyer, J. E., Kokubun, S., Reuter, H. 1983. Sodium channels in cultured cardiac cells. *J. Physiol.* 340:389–401
10. Cachelin, A. B., de Peyer, J. E., Kokubun, S., Reuter, H. 1983. Calcium channel modulation by 8-bromo-cyclic AMP in cultured heart cells. *Nature.* 304:462–64
11. Callewaert, G., Carmeliet, E., van der Heyden, G., Vereecke, J. 1982. The pacemaker current in a single cell preparation of bovine cardiac Purkinje fibres. *J. Physiol.* 326:66P
12. Carmeliet, E. 1982. Induction and removal of inward-going rectification in sheep cardiac Purkinje fibres. *J. Physiol.* 327:285–308
13. Carmeliet, E., Vereecke, J. 1979. Electrogenesis of the action potential and automaticity. In *Handbook of Physiology, The Cardiovascular System*, Vol. I, ed. R. M. Berne, pp. 269–334. Baltimore: Am. Physiol. Soc.
14. Caroni, P., Carafoli, E. 1982. Modulation by calcium of the potassium permeability of dog heart sarcolemmal vesi-

cles. *Proc. Natl. Acad. Sci. USA* 79: 5763–67

15. Cavalié, A., Ochi, R., Pelzer, D., Trautwein, W. 1983. Elementary currents through Ca^{2+} channels in guinea-pig myocytes. *Pflügers Arch.* 398:284–97

16. Clapham, D. E., De Felice, L. J. 1982. Small signal impedance of heart cell membranes. *J. Membr. Biol.* 67:63–72

17. Clay, J. R., De Felice, L. J., De Haan, R. L. 1979. Current noise parameters derived from voltage noise and impedance in embryonic heart cell aggregates. *Biophys. J.* 28:169–84

18. Clusin, W. T. 1983. Caffeine induces a transient inward current in cultured cardiac cells. *Nature* 301:248–50

19. Cohen, C. J., Bean, B. P., Colatsky, T. J., Tsien, R. W. 1981. Tetrodotoxin block of sodium channels in rabbit Purkinje fibers. *J. Gen. Physiol.* 78:383–411

20. Cohen, I., Attwell, D., Strichartz, G. 1981. The dependence of the maximum rate of rise of the action potential upstroke on membrane properties. *Proc. R. Soc. London B* 214:85–98

21. Colatsky, T. J. 1980. Voltage clamp measurements of sodium channel properties in rabbit cardiac Purkinje fibres. *J. Physiol.* 305:215–34

22. Colatsky, T. J. 1982. Mechanism of action of lidocaine and quinidine on action potential duration in rabbit cardiac Purkinje fibers. An effect on steady-state sodium currents? *Circ. Res.* 50:17–27

23. Colquhoun, D., Neher, E., Reuter, H., Stevens, C. F. 1981. Inward current channels activated by intracellular Ca in cultured cardiac cells. *Nature* 294:752–54

24. Coronado, R., Latorre, R. 1982. Detection of K^+ and Cl^- channels from calf cardiac sarcolemma in planar lipid bilayer membranes. *Nature* 298:849–52

25. Cranefield, P. F. 1977. Action potentials, afterpotentials, and arrhythmias. *Circ. Res.* 41:415–23

26. Di Francesco, D. 1981. A new interpretation of the pace-maker current in calf Purkinje fibres. *J. Physiol.* 314:359–76

27. Di Francesco, D. 1981. A study of the ionic nature of the pace-maker current in calf Purkinje fibres. *J. Physiol.* 314:377–93

28. Ebihara, L., Shigeto, N., Lieberman, M., Johnson, E. A. 1980. The initial inward current in spherical clusters of chick embryonic heart cells. *J. Gen. Physiol.* 75:437–56

29. Eisner, D. A., Lederer, W. J. 1979. Inotropic and arrhythmogenic effects of potassium depleted solutions on mammalian cardiac muscle. *J. Physiol.* 294:255–77

30. Fenwick, E. M., Marty, A., Neher, E. 1982. Sodium and calcium channels in bovine chromaffin cells. *J. Physiol.* 331:599–635

31. Glossmann, H., Ferry, D. R., Lübbecke, F., Mewes, R., Hofmann, F. 1982. Calcium channels: direct identification with radioligand binding studies. *Trends Pharmacol. Sci.* 3:431–37

32. Grant, A. O., Strauss, H. C. 1982. Intracellular potassium activity in the sinoatrial node: evaluation during spontaneous activity and arrest. *Fed. Proc.* 41:1503a

33. Hagiwara, S., Byerly, L. 1981. Calcium channel. *Ann. Rev. Neurosci.* 4:69–125

34. Hamill, O. P., Marty, A., Neher, E., Sakmann, B., Sigworth, F. J. 1981. Improved patch-clamp techniques for high-resolution current recording from cells and cell free membrane patches. *Pflügers Arch.* 391:85–100

35. Hescheler, J., Pelzer, D., Trube, G., Trautwein, W. 1982. Do organic calcium channel blockers act from inside or outside of the cardiac cell membrane? *Pflügers Arch.* 393:287–91

36. Hiraoka, M., Okamoto, Y., Sano, T. 1981. Oscillatory afterpotentials in dog ventricular muscle fibers. *Circ. Res.* 48:510–18

37. Holck, M., Thorens, S., Haeusler, G. 1982. Characterization of ^3H-nifedipine binding sites in rabbit myocardium. *Eur. J. Pharmacol.* 85:305–15

38. Horn, R., Patlak, J., Stevens, C. F. 1981. Sodium channels need not open before they inactivate. *Nature* 291:426–27

39. Hume, J. R., Giles, W. 1983. Ionic currents in single isolated bullfrog atrial cells. *J. Gen. Physiol.* 81:153–94

40. Irisawa, H. 1978. Comparative physiology of the cardiac pacemaker mechanism. *Physiol. Rev.* 58:461–98

41. Irisawa, H., Kokubun, S. 1983. Modulation by intracellular ATP and cyclic AMP of the slow inward current in isolated single ventricular cells of the guinea pig. *J. Physiol.* 338:321–37

42. Isenberg, G., Klöckner, V. 1982. Calcium currents of isolated ventricular myocytes are fast and of large amplitude. *Pflügers Arch.* 395:30–41

43. Karagueuzian, H., Katzung, B. G. 1982. Voltage-clamp studies of transient inward current and mechanical oscillations induced by ouabain in ferret papillary muscle. *J. Physiol.* 327:255–71

44. Kass, R. S. 1982. Nisoldipine: a new,

more selective calcium current blocker in cardiac Purkinje fibers. *J. Pharmacol. Exp. Ther.* 223:446–56

45. Kass, R. S., Tsien, R. W. 1982. Fluctuations in membrane current driven by intracellular calcium in cardiac Purkinje fibers. *Biophys. J.* 38:259–69

46. Kass, R. S., Lederer, W. J., Tsien, R. W., Weingart, R. 1978. Role of calcium ions in transient inward currents and after contractions induced by strophanthidin in cardiac Purkinje fibres. *J. Physiol.* 281:187–208

47. Kass, R. S., Tsien, R. W., Weingart, R. 1978. Ionic basis of transient inward current induced by strophanthidin in cardiac Purkinje fibres. *J. Physiol.* 281:209–26

48. Kokubun, S., Nishimura, M., Irisawa, H. 1982. Membrane currents in the rabbit atrioventricular node cell. *Pflügers Arch.* 393:15–22

49. Lazdunski, M., Renaud, J. F. 1982. The action of cardiotoxins on cardiac plasma membranes. *Ann. Rev. Physiol.* 44:463–73

50. Lederer, W. J., Tsien, R. W. 1976. Transient inward current underlying arrhythmogenic effects of cardiotonic steroids in Purkinje fibres. *J. Physiol.* 263:73–100

51. Lee, K. S., Tsien, R. W. 1982. Reversal of current through calcium channels in dialysed single heart cells. *Nature* 297:498–501

52. Lee, K. S., Tsien, R. W. 1983. Mechanism of calcium channel blockade by verapamil, D600, diltiazem, and nitrendipine in single dialyzed heart cells. *Nature* 302:790–94

53. Lee, K. S., Hume, J. R., Giles, W., Brown, A. M. 1981. Sodium current depression by lidocaine and quinidine in isolated ventricular cells. *Nature* 291:325–27

54. Lee, K. S., Weeks, T. A., Kao, R. L., Akaike, N., Brown, A. M. 1979. Sodium current in single heart muscle cells. *Nature* 278:269–71

55. Levis, R. A., Mathias, R. T., Eisenberg, R. S. 1983. Electrical properties of sheep Purkinje strands. Electrical and chemical potentials in the clefts. *Biophys. J.* In press

56. Lux, H. D., Nagy, K. 1981. Single channel Ca^{2+} currents in Helix pomatia neurons. *Pflügers Arch.* 391:252–54

57. Maruyama, Y., Petersen, O. H. 1982. Cholecystokinin activation of single-channel currents is mediated by internal messenger in pancreatic acinar cells. *Nature* 300:61–63

58. Matsuda, H., Noma, A., Kurachi, Y., Irisawa, H. 1982. Transient depolari-

zation and spontaneous voltage fluctuations in isolated single cells from guinea-pig ventricles. *Circ. Res.* 51:142–51

59. McDonald, T. F. 1982. The slow inward calcium current in the heart. *Ann. Rev. Physiol.* 44:425–34

60. McDonald, T. F., Pelzer, D., Trautwein, W. 1980. On the mechanism of slow calcium channel block in heart. *Pflügers Arch.* 385:175–79

61. Mitchell, M. R., Powell, T., Sturridge, M. F., Terrar, D. A., Twist, V. W. 1982. Action potentials and second inward current recorded from individual human ventricular muscle cells. *J. Physiol* 332:P51–52

62. Narahashi, T., Anderson, N. C., Moore, J. W. 1966. Tetrodotoxin does not block excitation from inside the nerve membrane. *Science* 153:765–67

63. Noble, D., Tsien, R. W. 1968. The kinetics and rectifier properties of the slow potassium current in cardiac Purkinje fibres. *J. Physiol.* 195:185–214

64. Ojeda, C., Rougier, O., Toneur, Y. 1981. Effects of Cs on acetylcholine induced current. Is i_{K_1} increased by acetylcholine in frog atrium? *Pflügers Arch.* 391:57–59

65. Osterrieder, W., Brum, G., Hescheler, J., Trautwein, W., Flockerzi, V., Hofmann, F. 1982. Injection of subunits of cyclic AMP-dependent protein kinase into cardiac myocytes modulates Ca^{2+} current. *Nature* 298:576–78

66. Osterrieder, W., Yang, Q.-F., Trautwein, W. 1982. Conductance of the slow inward channel in the rabbit sinoatrial node. *Pflügers Arch.* 394:85–89

67. Quandt, F. N., Narahashi, T. 1982. Modification of single Na^+ channels by batrachotoxin. *Proc. Natl. Acad. Sci. USA* 79:6732–36

68. Reuter, H. 1979. Properties of two inward membrane currents in the heart. *Ann. Rev. Physiol.* 41:413–24

69. Reuter, H. 1983. Calcium channel modulation by neurotransmitters, enzymes and drugs. *Nature* 301:569–74

70. Reuter, H., Scholz, H. 1977. A study of the ion selectivity and the kinetic properties of the calcium-dependent slow inward current in mammalian cardiac muscle. *J. Physiol.* 264:17–47

71. Reuter, H., Scholz, H. 1977. The regulation of the Ca conductance of cardiac muscle by adrenaline. *J. Physiol.* 264:49–62

72. Reuter, H., Baer, M., Best, P. M. 1978. Voltage dependence of tetrodotoxin action in mammalian cardiac muscle. In *Biophysical Aspects of Cardiac Muscle,*

ed. M. Morad, pp. 129–42. New York: Academic

73. Reuter, H., Stevens, C. F., Tsien, R. W., Yellen, G. 1982. Properties of single calcium channels in cardiac cell culture. *Nature* 297:501–04

73a. Reuter, H., Cachelin, A. B., de Peyer, J. E., Kokubun, S. 1983. Modulation of calcium channels in cultured cardiac cells by isoproterenol and 8-Bromo-cAMP. *Cold Spring Harbor Symp. Quant. Biol.* 48: In press

73b. Rogart, R. B., Regan, L. J., Dziekan, L. C., Galper, J. B. 1983. Identification of two sodium channel subtypes in chick heart and brain. *Proc. Natl. Acad. Sci. USA* 80:1106–10

74. Sakmann, B., Noma, A., Trautwein, W. 1983. Acetylcholine activation of single muscarinic K^+ channels in isolated pacemaker cells of the mammalian heart. *Nature.* 303:250–53

75. Sigworth, F. J., Neher, E. 1980. Single Na^+ channel currents observed in cultured rat muscle cells. *Nature* 287:447–49

76. Trautwein, W. 1982. Effect of acetylcholine on the s.-a. node of the heart. In

Cellular Pacemakers, Vol. 1, ed. D. O. Carpenter, pp. 127–60. New York: Wiley

77. Trautwein, W., Sakmann, B., Noma, A. 1982. Single K channels activated by acetylcholine in isolated AV nodal cells. *Pflügers Arch.* 394:R14 (Suppl.)

78. Trautwein, W., Taniguchi, J., Noma, A. 1982. The effect of intracellular cyclic nucleotides and calcium on the action potential and acetylcholine response of isolated cardiac cells. *Pflügers Arch.* 392:307–14

79. Trube, G., Sakmann, B., Trautwein, W. 1981. Inward rectifying potassium currents recorded from isolated heart cells by the patch clamp method. *Pflügers Arch.* 391:R7 (Suppl.)

80. Tsien, R. W. 1977. Cyclic AMP and contractile activity in heart. *Adv. Cycl. Nucl. Res.* 8:363–420

81. Tsien, R. W. 1983. Calcium channels in excitable cell membranes. *Ann. Rev. Physiol.* 45:341–58

82. Yellen, G. 1982. Single Ca^{2+}-activated nonselective cation channels in neuroblastoma. *Nature* 296:357–59

Ann. Rev. Physiol. 1984. 46:485–95

K+ CHANNELS GATED BY VOLTAGE AND IONS

Ramon Latorre, Roberto Coronado[1], and Cecilia Vergara

Department of Physiology and Biophysics, Harvard Medical School, Boston, Massachusetts 02115

INTRODUCTION

Several different potassium channels are present in membranes of nerve, muscle, and other types of cells (50, 59, 75, 79). These channels come in all sorts of sizes and shapes. K^+ channels range from the tiny (2 pS) delayed rectifier of *Helix* neuron (72) to the huge Ca^{2+}-activated K^+ channel (200 pS) ubiquitously distributed in many cells and tissues (50, 75). Besides the classical K^+ channel (delayed rectifier) of axon membranes (47) in striated and cardiac muscle, and in the egg cell membrane of the tunicate and the starfish, we find the inward or anomalous rectifier (48, 65, 81). This channel allows the passage of large inward K^+ currents, but only small outward currents. In the neurosomata of a marine snail, in addition to the usual early Na^+ and delayed K^+ channels, there is an early K^+ current that inactivates (38). Also, in excitable and non-excitable cells, Ca^{2+}-activated K^+ channels are present (50, 60, 75). It is in great part the interplay of these different K^+ channels, involved in such a variety of processes as repetitive firing (20, 59) and pacemaker activity (34, 35, 76), that allows the appropriate information to flow through the nervous system.

The patch-clamp (43, 64) and channel reconstitution techniques (62) now make possible analysis of these potassium conductances at the single-channel level. The delayed rectifier (23, 24), the inward rectifier (29, 30, 68), and the Ca^{2+}-activated K^+ channel (2, 49, 51, 55, 57, 70, 83) have been detected by patch-clamp and/or incorporation into planar lipid bilayer membranes. The success of these two techniques opens a whole new dimension towards the understanding of channels at the molecular level.

This review focuses on the gating characteristics of the potassium-selective channels described above and the modulation of these characteristics by voltage

---

[1]All correspondence should be addressed to Dr. Roberto Coronado, Department of Pharmacology, University of North Carolina School of Medicine, Chapel Hill, NC 27514

0066-4278/84/0315-0485$02.00

and ions. In this context, we first discuss the delayed rectifier as a voltage-modulated channel. Second, we discuss the inward rectifier as a channel with a gating controlled by both ions and voltage. Third, we examine the Ca^{2+}-activated K^+ channel as a chemically gated channel. In this case, the binding of the agonist, Ca^{2+}, is modulated by voltage.

DELAYED RECTIFIERS

Delayed rectifiers comprise a population of K^+ channels that specialize in repolarizing the cell membrane during the late phase of the action potential. Voltage-clamp analysis of outward K^+ currents, in crab giant axons (71), molluscan neurons (5), and muscle fibers of several kinds (see 79), shows that K^+ repolarizing channels behave differently, depending on cell type and species. Not all delayed rectifiers, therefore, conform to the properties described by Hodgkin & Huxley (47) in squid axons.

Bursting Kinetics of Squid Single K^+ Channels

Patch-clamp experiments showed that the squid K^+ channel displays bursting behavior: grouping in time of opening events, separated by relatively long segments of inactivity (23). Single channel amplitudes correspond to 17 pS under conditions in which the K^+ gradient is reversed (low internal K^+, high external K^+). Open channels have a mean duration of 3.5 ms. On the average, there are 2.8 openings per burst, with a mean duration of 12 ms. The squid delayed rectifier bursting behavior carries an important implication for the mechanism of channel opening, inasmuch as channel flickering is in excess of that predicted by the Hodgkin & Huxley (47) n^4 model (23). A linear form of the n^4 model has been used to describe the macroscopic kinetics of K^+ channel activation (10, 11).

$$C_4 \underset{\beta}{\overset{4\alpha}{\rightleftarrows}} C_3 \underset{2\beta}{\overset{3\alpha}{\rightleftarrows}} C_2 \underset{3\beta}{\overset{2\alpha}{\rightleftarrows}} C_1 \underset{4\beta}{\overset{\alpha}{\rightleftarrows}} 0 \quad , \qquad\qquad 1.$$

where α and β correspond to the macroscopic rate constants, C denotes a closed and O an open state. Bursts of single channel openings are expected in such a scheme at voltages in which α is small and β is large (hyperpolarizing voltages). However, a calculation (23) of the mean number of flickers per burst revealed that single channels flicker about 10-fold more often than predicted by scheme 1. Under the same conditions described in (23), using the cut-open axon preparation (53), Llano & Bezanilla observed bursts of K^+ channels due to activation of 1–5 simultaneously open channels (54). They found a channel conductance of 16 pS.

Coronado et al (24) described in planar bilayers that single K$^+$ channels from lobster axon membranes show bursting behavior similar to that of squid delayed rectifiers. Channels recorded using the lipids prevailing in the cell membrane at 12°C have a conductance of 40 pS. The mean burst duration is 4.5 ms, containing an average of 3.5 closures per burst. Depolarizing voltages increase the frequency of bursts and, to a lesser extent, the duration of bursts.

K$^+$ Gating Currents

For large depolarizations, gating currents *(Ig)* in squid axons show a component too slow to be associated with Na$^+$ channel opening (13). Gilly & Armstrong (32) demonstrated that part of the slow *Ig* is due to K$^+$ channels, because a fraction of slow *Ig* decreases after irreversible loss of functional K$^+$ channels by perfusion of axons with K$^+$-free media. Further, dibucaine blocks Na$^+$ gating and ionic currents, leaving K$^+$ currents and slow *Ig* intact. The bulk of the K$^+$ gating currents was measured by Bezanilla et al (16) after warming the axon to 20°C. Potassium *Ig* shows a raising phase and an exponential decay. The maximum amount of charge moved was 500 e/μ^2, which is only one third of the charge moved for Na$^+$ channels. Seven electronic charges per open K$^+$ channel were recorded (16). The strongest evidence that this component of *Ig* is due to K$^+$ channels is the observed Cole-Moore shift in *Ig* with hyperpolarizing prepulses. With a conditioning hyperpolarizing prepulse, $\bar{g}_K$ shifts along the time axis (85).

Gating current data and macroscopic kinetics (33) do not support the n^4 model shown in scheme 1. First, a six-state model with four of the "on" rate constants equal and only one slower than the rest was used to account for the slowing effect of divalent cations on the channel opening kinetics (33). The slow step could be located anywhere in the sequence except for the last step leading to opening, which is comparatively fast. Second, *Ig* shows a predominant raising phase which can only be understood if there exists in the sequence a slower rate-determining step (15). Bezanilla & White (15) suggested that the slow step is the first one (scheme 2). Third, the decay time constant of g_K is the same as the time-constant of the "off" gating current, while scheme 1 predicts that the ionic current should decay four times faster, inasmuch as only one closed particle shuts the ionic current (15). A model of squid K$^+$ channel opening that considers these findings is (15):

$$\underset{\text{slow}}{C_n} \; \rightleftharpoons \; \overset{\text{fast}}{\overline{\left[C_{n-1} \; \ldots \; C_{n-i} \; \ldots \; C_1 \right]}} \; \overset{\text{very fast}}{\rightleftharpoons} 0 \quad , \qquad 2.$$

where n can be as large as 15 (Bezanilla & White, unpublished results). Although the macroscopic activation is insensitive to the location of the slow process, the shape of the gating currents demands its location at the beginning of the sequence (15).

Effect of Permeant Ions on K^+ Channel Gating

Removal of K^+ ions from the inside of squid axons results in the irreversible loss of K^+ ionic currents (8, 18) and a component of gating currents (8, 32). In Mixicola, K^+ conductance is lost in perfusion experiments but not in dialysis experiments. This implies that an internal component other than ions may be necessary for channel stability (73). The loss of K^+ currents in squid is prevented by high external concentrations of K^+, Rb^+, NH_4, and Cs^+ (8), or by internal Cs^+ (18), indicating that K^+ channels are stabilized by cations inside the channel (8).

The question of the kinetic state of channels and their degree of occupancy by ions has been recently examined in several systems (1, 9, 17, 31, 56, 58, 78, 80). In squid, external K^+ and Rb^+ slow down K^+ channel closing (80). This phenomena can be accounted for by introducing in the reaction sequence a transition from open-ion-unloaded to an open-ion-loaded state (e.g. 56). If a loaded channel cannot close, the lifetime of the open conformation becomes a function of permeant ion concentration.

Subpopulations of K^+ Channels

Multiexponential tail current kinetics and noise anaylsis data have been taken to indicate that at least two populations of K^+ channels exist in the node of Ranvier (22, 28). A two-barrier model of channel gating can reproduce these characteristics (17); thus, in this system, it may not prove necessary to postulate two types of K^+ channels. Two very distinct K^+ channels have been found by Quinta-Ferreira et al (71) after analysis of the outward currents in crab axons. An early component inactivates similar to the I_A currents of neurons (5, 21, 41). A second component is roughly similar to the squid K^+ channel but shows at least four times less voltage sensitivity.

INWARD RECTIFIERS

Macroscopic Conductance

The resting membrane of muscle, tunicates, and starfish eggs is predominantly permeable to K^+. This K^+ conductance system shows anomalous or inward rectification (40, 48, 65, 81). Recently it has become clear that in cell membranes of starfish (42) and frog skeletal muscle (45, 52), inward rectification depends only on membrane potential and external $[K^+]$ and not on $V - V_K$ as traditionally postulated for these channels (48). The inward rectifier steady-state conductance is proportional to the square root of the $[K^+]$ (40, 52, 66).

Kinetic Characteristics

The currents associated with frog muscle inward rectification decline under hyperpolarization. Depending on the degree of hyperpolarization, current inactivation may be due to depletion of K^+ from the transverse tubular system or to blocking of the channel by external Na^+ (3, 4, 6, 7, 77). This K^+ current activates, with hyperpolarization, with a time course faster than the inactivation due to K$^+$ depletion and Na$^+$ block (45, 52). The inward rectifier activation kinetics shows instantaneous as well as time-dependent components. The time-dependent component changes along an exponential time course. Both steady-state and instantaneous components show inward rectification. Similar behavior is shown by the inward rectifier of tunicates and starfish egg membranes (39, 66). However, in oocytes of *Neanthes*, channel activation follows an S-shaped time course (36). In tunicate, initial K$^+$ currents are smaller in Na-free solution (66), indicating that Na$^+$ can not only block this channel but can also activate it. Further, in starfish egg, internal Na$^+$ is necessary for activation of inward rectification (42).

Single-Channel Studies

NOISE MEASUREMENTS   Under large hyperpolarizations, external Na$^+$ blocks the inward rectifying K$^+$ conductance in skeletal muscle (7, 77). Analysis of the current noise associated with the Na$^+$ block in a tunicate egg indicates that the channel conductance changes according to the square root of the external [K$^+$] (66). The channel conductance was 10 pS in 100 mM K$^+$. Thus, the K$^+$-dependent conductance change found macroscopically is due to a property of the open channel. These studies were extended to a series of blockers which included Cs$^+$, hydrazine, Sr^{2+}, and Ba^{2+}. Approximately the same conductance ($\sim$10 pS) for the inward rectifier channel was found (67).

In frog skeletal muscle, current noise was induced by using Cs$^+$ as the blocking ion (74). The channel conductance was 7.8 pS at 0.2 mM Cs$^+$, and 2.1 at 10 mM Cs$^+$. Extrapolation to zero [Cs$^+$] yielded a single-channel conductance of 10 pS in 120 mM K$^+$. Ba^{2+} ions have also been used to introduce current fluctuations (25), and a channel conductance of 8 pS in symmetrical 120 mM K$^+$ was obtained. Thus, the inward rectifier channels of muscle and invertebrates have the same conductance.

At small negative potentials the current noise spectrum can be fitted by a Lorentzian function plus an additional $1/f$ component (26). By interpreting the noise results with a model that includes a closed-open transition for the gating kinetics and a correction for instantaneous rectification of the channel, the channel conductance was found to be 9 pS. Current noise induced by the channel gating system of the inward rectifier has also been measured in *Neanthes* oocytes (37). The spectral noise was interpreted on the basis of a three-state model for inward rectification (see below). The single channel conductance obtained in 40 mM external K$^+$ was 8 pS.

DIRECT SINGLE-CHANNEL MEASUREMENTS   Currents induced by opening of single inward rectifier channels have been measured with the patch clamp technique (29, 30, 68). In rat myotubes (68), the channels were completely activated and current fluctuations were induced by the addition of Ba^{2+} to the medium. The channel conductance was 10 pS when the external K^+ was 155 mM. In tunicate egg membranes, single channel fluctuations were induced with Na^+ or Cs^+ (29, 30). The channel conductance was found to be proportional to the square root of the $[K^+]$ as predicted from the macroscopic conductance and current noise measurements. Channel conductance was 5 pS in 100 mM K^+. The channel conductance of the inward rectifier in tunicate egg membrane is larger in Na^+-containing than in Na^+-free solutions. This facilitatory effect of Na^+ on the K^+ conductance explains the Na^+ activation found when measuring macroscopic conductances (66).

Inward Rectifier Gating Models

The inward rectifier conductance in starfish, tunicate, and muscle can be described in terms of $\bar{g}_K\, n$ where $\bar{g}_K$ as well as n are functions of membrane potential. The channel gating kinetics can be represented by (26, 39):

$$C \underset{\beta}{\overset{\alpha}{\rightleftharpoons}} 0 \;, \qquad\qquad 3.$$

where the rate constants α and β are in general voltage dependent.

For the inward rectifier of *Neanthes* oocytes, the activation kinetics are best described by a three-state linear kinetic model consisting of two closed and one open state (36, 37). "Instantaneous" rectification arises because the transition closed-to-open is too fast to be measured. Other models for the origin of the instantaneous and steady-state rectification shown by the inward rectifier have been proposed (12, 19, 46, 84).

Ca^{2+}-ACTIVATED K^+ CHANNELS

Ca^{2+} and Voltage Modulate Activation of Ca^{2+}-Dependent Currents

Ca^{2+}-activated K^+ currents ($I_{K,Ca}$) have been described in many different cell types, including some non-excitable cells (75). These are repolarizing currents whose activation is a function of both membrane potential and intracellular $[Ca^{2+}]$. Meech (59) proposed that the voltage dependence of $I_{K,Ca}$ was indirect and reflected the voltage dependence of Ca^{2+} ion movement through voltage dependent Ca^{2+} channels. Therefore, Ca^{2+}-activated K^+ channels could be considered as "agonist-gated" (59). Single-channel studies discussed below have shown clearly that this is not the case.

Two Types of Ca^{2+}-Activated K^+ Channels

Single-channel studies revealed that Ca^{2+}-activated K^+ channels can be divided into two general groups: high conductance (100–200 pS) (2, 49, 51, 57, 61, 63, 70, 82, 83) and low conductance (10–20 pS) (44, 55).

HIGH CONDUCTANCE CHANNELS   Single-channel records show openings and closings of durations in the millisecond range (bursts of activity) interrupted by quiescent periods that last several hundred msec. Depolarizing membrane potentials and increasing intracellular $[Ca^{2+}]$ increase the fraction of time that the channel is in the open state within a burst of activity. Also, within bursts of activity, very fast openings and closings (flickers) occur (14, 61, 63, 69). An open state with approximately half the conductance of the full open state is also observed for the different preparations (14, 61, 63). The $[Ca^{2+}]$ and voltage dependence is not the same for the different channels studied (c.f. 63, 83).

A KINETIC MODEL FOR HIGH-CONDUCTANCE CHANNEL ACTIVATION
Methfessel & Boheim (61) in myoballs and Moczydlowski & Latorre (63) in lipid bilayers analyzed the openings and closings within a burst of activity after exclusion of the fast flickers. Under these conditions a single exponential distribution for the open and closed dwell times was found. Both groups followed the same approach for the identification of a kinetic scheme consistent with the experimental data. First, they identified the number of Ca^{2+} ions involved in the gating reaction. The data from the two groups are consistent with a minimum of two Ca^{2+} ions (but see 14, 83). Next they analyzed the $[Ca^{2+}]$ dependence of the mean open ($\bar{\tau}_o$) and mean closed ($\bar{\tau}_c$) times. Both groups found that $\bar{\tau}_o$ is a linear function of $[Ca^{2+}]$ while $\bar{\tau}_c$ is a linear function of $1/[Ca^{2+}]$. The schemes proposed are the following:

$$C + Ca \underset{}{\overset{M}{\rightleftharpoons}} C \cdot Ca \underset{\beta(V)}{\overset{\alpha(V)}{\rightleftharpoons}} 0 \cdot Ca + \quad gate^{2-}; \quad Ca + gate^{2-} \overset{L}{\rightleftharpoons} \quad gate^0 \qquad 4.$$

$$C + Ca \underset{K_1(V)}{\rightleftharpoons} C \cdot Ca \underset{\beta}{\overset{\alpha}{\rightleftharpoons}} 0 \cdot Ca \underset{Ca}{\overset{Ca}{\underset{K_4(V)}{\rightleftharpoons}}} 0 \qquad 5.$$

Although schemes 4 and 5 are formally equivalent with respect to the $[Ca^{2+}]$ dependence of $\bar{\tau}_o$ and $\bar{\tau}_c$, for reaction scheme 4, it was *assumed* (61) that the voltage dependence of the gating reaction resides in the open/closed conformational change having voltage-independent Ca^{2+} binding reactions M and L. Activation takes place by the binding of Ca^{2+} to a negatively charged gate that normally blocks the channel (61). On the other hand, Moczydlowski & Latorre (63) found that in the zero and infinite $[Ca^{2+}]$ limits, $\bar{\tau}_o$ and $\bar{\tau}_c$ at *all* voltages converged to $1/\alpha$ and $1/\beta$, respectively. The slopes of the linear function of $\bar{\tau}_o$ vs $[Ca^{2+}]$ and $\bar{\tau}_c$ vs $1/[Ca^{2+}]$ are exponential functions of voltage. Based on these results, they concluded that in scheme 5 the conformational transition rates (α and β) are voltage-independent while the two Ca^{2+} binding reactions $[K_1(V), K_4(V)]$ of their scheme 5 are voltage-dependent.

More recently, Pallotta & Magleby (69) analyzed the single-channel activation kinetics, including the flickers in their analysis. They suggested that at least three closed states and two open states are required to explain the data.

In summary, the activation of high conductance Ca^{2+}-activated K^+ channels involves Ca^{2+} ions and membrane potential. Two mechanisms have been proposed: modulation by membrane potential of the binding of Ca^{2+} ions to the activating site (63), and an inactivation/blockade mechanism (61).

LOW CONDUCTANCE CHANNEL   A 12 pS Ca^{2+}-activated K^+ channel has been identified in *Helix* neurons by Lux et al (55). In this preparation, current noise and current relaxation measurements indicate that channel activation is a complex process involving at least one open and two closed states (44).

Regulation of Channel Activity

Preliminary data indicate that the probability of opening the *Helix* Ca^{2+}-activated K^+ channel in an isolated membrane patch increases after perfusing the patch with catalytic subunit of protein kinase (I. Levittan, personal communication). Macroscopic current measurements suggest a change in the Ca^{2+} sensitivity of the $I_{K,Ca}$ after perfusing the same enzyme into an individual *Helix* neuron (27). It appears, then, that phosphorylation of the channel or of a closely related component can change its activation properties.

CONCLUSIONS

Nature has provided us with a great variety of K^+ channels that serve numerous physiological functions. K^+ channels show, in general, complex kinetics of activation. Several closed states and a rate-limiting step at the beginning of the kinetic sequence are necessary to explain the gating currents, single channel data, and macroscopic kinetics of the delayed rectifier channel. Activation of the Ca^{2+}-activated K^+ channel needs a minimal model consisting of two closed and two open states. At least two different Ca^{2+}-activated channels have been described and, in some cases, the channel gating kinetics appear to be modulated by metabolism. Although activation of the inward rectifier can be explained on the basis of a two-state model in several preparations, studies in other cells show that this is not a general phenomena. In all three channels discussed here, ions appear to modulate gating.

Literature Cited

1. Adams, D. J., Nonner, W., Dwyer, T. M., Hille, B. 1981. Block of endplate channels by permeant cations in frog skeletal muscle. *J. Gen. Physiol.* 78: 593–615
2. Adams, P. R., Constanti, A., Brown, D. A., Clark, R. B. 1982. Intracellular Ca^{2+} activates a fast voltage-sensitive K^+ current in vertebrate sympathetic neurones. *Nature* 246:746–49
3. Adrian, K. H., Chandler, W. K., Hodgkin, A. L. 1970. Slow changes in potassium permeability in skeletal muscle. *J. Physiol.* 208:645–68
4. Adrian, R. H., Freygang, W. H. 1962. Potassium conductance of frog muscle membrane under controlled voltage. *J. Physiol.* 163:104–14
5. Aldrich, R. W., Getting, P. A., Thompson, S. H. 1979. Inactivation of delayed outward current in molluscan neurone somate. *J. Physiol.* 291:507–30
6. Almers, W. 1972. Potassium conductance changes in skeletal muscle and the potassium concentration in the transverse tubule. *J. Physiol.* 225:33–56
7. Almers, W. 1972. The decline of potassium permeability during extreme hyperpolarization in frog skeletal muscle. *J. Physiol.* 225:58–83
8. Almers, W., Armstrong, C. M. 1980. Survival of K^+ permeability and gating currents in squid axons perfused with K^+-free media. *J. Gen. Physiol.* 75:61–78
9. Arhem, P. 1980. Effects of rubidium, caesium, strontium, barium, and lanthanum on ionic currents in myelinated nerve fibers from *Xenopus laevis*. *Acta Physiol. Scand.* 108:7–16
10. Armstrong, C. M. 1969. Inactivation of the potassium conductance and related phenomena caused by quaternary ammonium injection in squid axons. *J. Gen. Physiol.* 54:553–75
11. Armstrong, C. M. 1971. Interaction of tetraethylammonium ion derivatives with the potassium channel of giant axons. *J. Gen. Physiol.* 58:413–37
12. Armstrong, C. M. 1975. K^+ pores of nerve and muscle. In *Membranes, A Series of Advances*, ed. G. Eisenman, 3:325–58. New York: Marcel Dekker
13. Armstrong, C. M., Bezanilla, F. 1977. Inactivation of the sodium channel. II. Gating current experiments. *J. Gen. Physiol.* 70:557–90
14. Barrett, J. N., Magleby, K. L., Pallotta, B. S. 1982. Properties of single Ca^{2+}-activated K^+ channels in cultured rat muscle. *J. Physiol.* 331:211–30
15. Bezanilla, F., White, M. M. 1983. Properties of ionic channels in excitable membranes. In *Physiology of Membrane Disorders*, ed. T. E. Andreoli, et al. In press. 2nd ed.
16. Bezanilla, F., White, M. M., Taylor, R. E. 1982. Gating currents associated with potassium channel inactivation. *Nature* 296:657–59
17. Cahalan, M. D., Pappone, P. A. 1983. Chemical modification of potassium channel gating in frog myelinated nerve by trinitro benzene sulfonic acid. *J. Physiol.* In press
18. Chandler, W. K., Meves, H. 1970. Sodium and potassium currents in squid axons perfused with fluoride solutions. *J. Physiol.* 211:623–52
19. Ciani, S., Krasne, S., Migarashi, S., Hagiwara, S. 1978. A model for anomalous rectification: Electrochemical-potential-dependent gating of membrane channels. *J. Membr. Biol.* 44:103–34
20. Connor, J. A. 1975. Neural repetitive firing: A comparative study of membrane properties of crustacean walking leg axon. *J. Neurophysiol.* 38:922–32
21. Connor, J. A., Stevens, C. F. 1971. Voltage clamp studies of a transient outward membrane current in gastropod neural somata. *J. Physiol.* 213:31–53
22. Conti, F., Hille, B., Nonner, W. 1982. Properties of K^+ current fluctuations in frog nerve. *Biophys. J.* 37:16a
23. Conti, F., Neher, E. 1980. Single channel recordings of K^+ currents in squid axons. *Nature* 285:140–43
24. Coronado, R., Latorre, R., Mautner, H. G. 1983. Potassium channels in bilayers with delayed rectifier single channel behavior. *Biophys. J.* In press
25. DeCoursey, T. E., Hutter, O. F. 1983a. Potassium current noise induced by barium ions in skeletal muscle. *J. Physiol.* In press
26. DeCoursey, T. E., Hutter, O. F. 1983b. Inward rectifier current noise in skeletal muscle. *J. Physiol.* In press
27. De Peyer, J. E., Cachelin, A. B., Levitan, I. B., Reuter, H. 1982. Ca^{2+}-activated K^+ conductance in internally perfused snail neurons is enhanced by protein phosphorylation. *Proc. Natl. Acad. Sci. USA* 79:4207–11
28. Dubois, J. M. 1981. Evidence for the existence of three types of potassium channels in the frog Ranvier node membrane. *J. Physiol.* 318:297–316
29. Fukushima, Y. 1981. Single channel

potassium currents of the anomalous rectifier. *Nature* 294:368–71

30. Fukushima, Y. 1982. Blocking kinetics of the anomalous rectifier of tunicate egg studied by single channel recording. *J. Physiol.* 331:311–31

31. Gage, P. W., Van Helden, D. 1979. Effects of permeant monovalent cations on end-plate channels. *J. Physiol.* 288:509–28

32. Gilly, W. F., Armstrong, C. M. 1980. Gating currents and potassium channels in the giant axon of the squid. *Biophys. J.* 29:485–92

33. Gilly, W. F., Armstrong, C. M. 1982. Divalent cations and the activation kinetics of potassium channels in squid giant axons. *J. Gen. Physiol.* 79:965–96

34. Gorman, A. L. F., Hermann, A. 1982. Quantitative differences in the currents of bursting and beating molluscan pacemaker neurones. *J. Physiol.* 333:681–99

35. Gorman, A. L. F., Hermann, A., Thomas, M. V. 1982. Ionic requirements of membrane oscillations and their dependence on the Ca^{2+} concentration in a molluscan pacemaker neuron. *J. Physiol.* 327:185–217

36. Gunning, R., Ciani, S. 1983. Inward rectification in *Neanthes* oocytes. *Biophys. J.* 41:149a

37. Gunning, R., Ciani, S. 1983. Steady-state current noise from intrinsic gating of inward rectifier channels in *Neanthes* oocytes. *Biophys. J.* 41:48a

38. Hagiwara, S., Kusano, K., Saito, N. 1961. Membrane changes of onchidium nerve cell in potassium-rich media. *J. Physiol.* 155:470–89

39. Hagiwara, S., Miyazaki, S., Rosenthal, N. P. 1976. Potassium current and the effect of cesium on this current during anomalous rectification of the egg cell membrane of a starfish. *J. Gen. Physiol.* 67:621–38

40. Hagiwara, S., Takahashi, K. 1974. The anomalous rectification and cation selectivity of the membrane of starfish egg cell. *J. Membr. Biol.* 18:61–80

41. Hagiwara, S., Yoshida, S., Yoshii, M. 1981. Transient and delayed potassium currents in the egg cell membrane of the coelenterate, *Renilla koellikeri*. *J. Physiol.* 318:123–41

42. Hagiwara, S., Yoshii, M. 1979. Effects of internal potassium and sodium on the anomalous rectification of the starfish egg as examined by internal perfusion. *J. Physiol.* 292:251–65

43. Hamill, O. P., Marty, A., Neher, E., Sakmann, B., Sigworth, F. J. 1981. Improved patch-clamp techniques for high-resolution current recording from cells and cell-free membrane patches. *Pflugers Arch.* 391:85–100

44. Hermann, A., Hartung, K. 1982. Noise and relaxation measurements of the Ca^{2+}-activated K^+ current in *Helix* neurones. *Pflugers Arch.* 393:254–61

45. Hestrin, S. 1981. The interaction of potassium with the activation of anomalous rectification in frog muscle membrane. *J. Physiol.* 317:497–508

46. Hille, B., Schwarz, W. 1978. Potassium channels as multi-ion single-file pores. *J. Gen. Physiol.* 72:409–42

47. Hodgkin, A. L., Huxley, A. F. 1952. A quantitative description of membrane current and its application to conduction and excitation in nerve. *J. Physiol.* 117:500–44

48. Katz, B. 1949. Les constantes electriques de la membrane du muscle. *Arch. Sci. Physiol.* 3:285–300

49. Krueger, B. K., French, R. I., Blaustein, M. B., Worley, J. F. 1982. Incorporation of Ca^{2+}-activated K^+ channels from rat brain into planar lipid bilayers. *Biophys. J.* 37:170a

50. Latorre, R., Miller, C. 1983. Conduction and selectivity in potassium channels. *J. Membr. Biol.* 71:11–30

51. Latorre, R., Vergara, C., Hidalgo, C. 1982. Reconstitution in planar lipid bilayers of a Ca^{2+}-dependent K^+ channel from transverse tubule membranes isolated from rabbit skeletal muscle. *Proc. Natl. Acad. Sci. USA* 79:805–9

52. Leech, C. A., Stanfield, P. R. 1981. Inward rectification in frog skeletal muscle fibres and its dependence on membrane potential and external potassium. *J. Physiol.* 319:295–309

53. Llano, I., Bezanilla, F. 1980. Current recorded from a cut-open giant axon under voltage clamp. *Proc. Natl. Acad. Sci. USA* 77:7484–86

54. Llano, I., Bezanilla, F. 1983. Bursting activity of potassium channels in the cut-open axon. *Biophys. J.* 41:38a

55. Lux, H. D., Neher, E., Marty, A. 1981. Single channel activity associated with the Ca^{2+}-dependent outward current in *H. pomatia*. *Pflugers Arch.* 389:293–95

56. Marchais, D., Marty, A. 1979. Interaction of permeant ions with channels activated by acetylcholine in *Aplysia* neurones. *J. Physiol.* 297:9–45

57. Marty, A. 1981. Ca^{2+}-dependent K^+ channels with large unitary conductance in chromaffin cell membranes. *Nature* 291:497–500

58. Matteson, D. R., Swenson, R. 1982. Permeant cations alter closing rates of K^+ channels. *Biophys. J.* 37:17a

59. Meech, R. W. 1978. Calcium-dependent K⁺ activation in nervous tissues. *Ann. Rev. Biophys. Bioeng.* 7:1–18

60. Meech, R. W., Strumwasser, F. 1970. Intracellular calcium injection activates potassium conductance in *Aplysia* nerve cells. *Fed. Proc.* 29:834a

61. Methfessel, C., Boheim, G. 1982. The gating of single Ca^{2+}-dependent K⁺ channels is described by an activation/blockade mechanism. *Biophys. Struct. Mech.* 9:35–60

62. Miller, C. 1983. Integral membrane channels. Studies in model membranes. *Physiol. Revs.* In press

63. Moczydlowski, E., Latorre, R. 1983. Gating kinetics of Ca^{2+}-activated K⁺ channels from rat muscle incorporated into planar lipid bilayers. Evidence for two voltage-dependent Ca^{2+} binding reactions. *J. Gen. Physiol.* Submitted

64. Neher, E., Sakmann, B. 1976. Single-channel currents from membrane of denervated frog muscle fibers. *Nature* 260:799–802

65. Noble, D., Tsien, R. W. 1968. The kinetics and rectifier properties of the slow potassium current in cardiac Purkinje fibers. *J. Physiol.* 195:185–214

66. Ohmori, H. 1978. Inactivation kinetics and steady-state current noise in the anomalous rectifier of tunicate egg cell membranes. *J. Physiol.* 281:77–99

67. Ohmori, H. 1980. Dual effect of K⁺ ions upon the inactivation of the anomalous rectifier of tunicate egg cell membrane. *J. Membr. Biol.* 53:143–56

68. Ohmori, H., Yoshida, S., Hagiwara, S. 1981. Single K⁺ channel currents of anomalous rectification in cultured rat myotubes. *Proc. Natl. Acad. Sci. USA* 78:4960–64

69. Pallotta, B. S., Magleby, K. L. 1983. Ca^{2+} dependence of open and shut interval distributions of Ca^{2+}-activated K⁺ channels in cultured rat muscle. *Biophys. J.* 41:57a

70. Pallotta, B. S., Magleby, K. L., Barrett, J. N. 1981. Single channel recordings of Ca^{2+}-activated K⁺ currents in rat muscle cell culture. *Nature* 293:471–74

71. Quinta-Ferreira, E., Rojas, E., Arispe, N. 1982. Potassium currents in the giant axon of the crab *Carcinus maenas*. *J. Membr. Biol.* 66:171–81

72. Reuter, H., Stevens, C. F. 1980. Channel conductance and ion selectivity of potassium channel in snail neurones. *J. Membr. Biol.* 57:103–21

73. Schauf, C. L. 1982. Survival of the K⁺ channel in axons externally and internally perfused with K⁺-free media. *Biophys. J.* 40:171–73

74. Schwarz, W., Neumcke, B., Palade, P. T. 1981. K⁺ current fluctuations in inward-rectifying channels of frog skeletal muscle. *J. Membr. Biol.* 63:85–92

75. Schwarz, W., Passow, H. 1983. Ca^{2+}-activated K⁺ channels in erythrocytes and excitable cells. *Ann. Rev. Physiol.* 45:359–74

76. Smith, T. G., Barker, J. L., Gainer, H. 1975. Requirements for bursting pacemaker activity in molluscan neurones. *Nature* 253:450–52

77. Standen, N. B., Stanfield, P. R. 1979. Potassium depletion and sodium block of potassium currents under hyperpolarization in frog sartorious muscle. *J. Physiol.* 294:497–520

78. Stanfield, P. R., Ashcroft, F. M., Plant, T. D. 1981. Gating of a muscle K⁺ channel and its dependence on the permeating ion species. *Nature* 289:509–11

79. Stefani, E., Chiarandini, D. J. 1982. Ionic channels in skeletal muscle. *Ann. Rev. Physiol.* 44:357–72

80. Swenson, R. P., Armstrong, C. M. 1981. K⁺ channels close more slowly in the presence of external K⁺ and Rb⁺. *Nature* 291:427–29

81. Takahashi, K., Miyazaki, S., Kidakora, Y. 1971. Development of excitability in embryonic muscle cell membranes in certain tunicates. *Science* 171:415–18

82. Walsh, G. V., Singer, J. J. 1983. Identification and characterization of a Ca^{2+}-activated K⁺ channel in freshly dissociated, vertebrate smooth muscle cells using the patch-clamp technique. *Biophys. J.* 41:56a

83. Wong, B. S., Lecar, H., Adler, M. 1982. Single Ca^{2+}-dependent K⁺ channels in clonal anterior pituitary cells. *Biophys. J.* 39:313–17

84. Woodbury, J. W. 1971. Eyring rate theory model of the current-voltage relationship of ion channels in excitable membranes. In *Chemical Dynamics: Paper in Honor of Henry Eyring*, ed. J. Hirschfelder, pp. 601–17. New York: John Wiley

85. Young, S. H., Moore, J. W. 1981. Potassium currents in the crayfish giant axon. Dynamic characteristics. *Biophys. J.* 36:723–33

Ann. Rev. Physiol. 1984. 46:497–515

FLUCTUATION ANALYSIS OF SODIUM CHANNELS IN EPITHELIA

Bernd Lindemann

Second Department of Physiology, 6650 Homburg/Saar, West Germany

INTRODUCTION

Up to a few years ago the ion transport properties of epithelial membranes were still expressed in terms of integral quantities, such as permeabilities computed from fluxes, currents, or conductances per unit membrane area. Conceptually this was unsatisfactory when it became known that transport processes of high specificity are mediated by special molecules, typically proteins or peptides, that occupy only a small fraction of the membrane area. The recent advents of fluctuation analysis (3, 96), patch clamp techniques, and reconstitution methods (37, 75, 78) permit a more appropriate description by revealing the transport rates through single molecules as well as the concentration and—in the future perhaps—the turnover of these transporters in the membrane. Thereby a better understanding of the ion translocation itself and of the regulatory mechanisms that control either the performance of single transporters or the availability of these molecules for transport gradually evolves.

While the application of patch clamp techniques to epithelial membranes is only just beginning (73, 74, 89), fluctuation analysis has already been used to study Na and K channels in tight epithelia and K channels in leaky epithelia. The early literature was reviewed previously (62). This paper is concerned with apical Na channels, studied as yet in frog skin, toad urinary bladder, hen coprodaeum, mammalian colon, and mammalian urinary bladder. The Na channels of these tissues are characterized by a high specificity for Li and Na as compared to K ions, and the absence of voltage-dependent gating. The voltage dependence of the translocation rate conforms roughly to the Goldman-

497

Hodgkin-Katz relationship. The rate does not saturate noticeably at physiological Na concentrations. The channels are blocked from the extracellular side by diuretic drugs like amiloride and triamterene. Physiologically the open state of the Na channels is controlled by Na and probably Ca ions, and the availability of the channels by several hormones.

Fluctuation analysis is a kinetic method used in conjunction with other techniques. Below, some features of Na transport worked out with more classical methods will first be reviewed. Against this background the results of noise analysis are discussed.

EPITHELIAL STRUCTURE

The Na channels are typically found in epithelia that more or less conform to the Koefoed-Johnsen Ussing model (48) for frog skin, as depicted in Figure 1A. These Na-conserving tissues are tight in the sense that the paracellular pathway has a high resistance (31, 107). The apical Na permeability, P_{Na}, is high if transport regulation makes many conducting Na channels available. The basolateral membrane has a high K permeability, presumably due to the presence of K channels (112). It also contains a high density of Na pumps (76), and a Na/Ca exchange system (16).

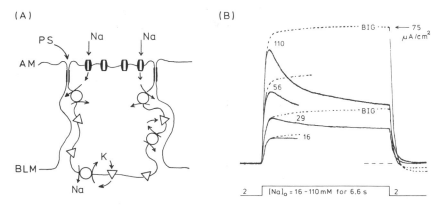

Figure 1(A)   Schematic cross-section through a granular epithelial cell showing the essential features of the Koefoed-Johnsen Ussing model (48). *AM:* apical membrane; *BLM:* basolateral membrane; *PS:* paracellular shunt. Amiloride-blockable Na channels are found predominantly in the apical membrane and K channels (Δ) predominantly in the basolateral membrane, facing the interstitial compartment. This membrane also contains the Na,K pumps. (*B*): Response of I_{Na} (K-depolarised frog skin) to increasing steps of Na_o lasting 6.6 sec in a fast-flow chamber. Unstirred layers 12–15 μm, including the Str. corneum (66). Na_o is indicated as parameter. The dotted curves were obtained in the presence of 0.5 mM BIG, which interferes with the self-inhibition.

As a result of this distribution of transport capacities, net Na movement from the apical solution into the interstitial space becomes possible, while K ions cycle through the basolateral membrane. It is remarkable that thereby the cellular Na concentration can remain relatively small although the Na throughput is large.

CURRENT VOLTAGE RELATIONSHIP

Mucosal application of amiloride in maximal concentrations blocks the Na uptake rapidly and nearly completely (91, 92, 97). The Na current voltage relationship (I_{Na}-V curve) can therefore be obtained, despite the presence of the unspecific paracellular shunt and other ion conducting pathways, by subtracting the currents recorded with 80 μM amiloride from those recorded without amiloride. It is advisable to record the current voltage curves rapidly in order to avoid cellular concentration changes and interference from regulatory processes. Recording may be done under transepithelial voltage clamp if electrical effects of the basolateral membrane can be eliminated by shunting with ionophores (85) or by the use of a high serosal K activity, the so-called K-depolarization (33, 79, 85, 90). Alternatively, microelectrodes may be employed if it can be shown that the impaled cell is still representative of unimpaled cells.

Using K-depolarization, Fuchs et al (33) found that the apical I_{Na}-V curve of frog skin is described by the Goldman-Hodgkin-Katz (GHK) relationship (43) in the voltage range between the reversal potential and about zero mV. It is not clear whether the deviations from the GHK function observed outside of this range reflect properties of the translocation mechanism or interfering effects. However, the voltage range was sufficient to estimate P_{Na} and the cellular Na activity (Na_c) by curve fitting. The same I_{Na}-V curve was obtained with K-depolarized toad urinary bladders (85).

Interestingly, there are indications that the K-depolarization affects the transport regulatory status and perhaps even the regulatory capacity of epithelial cells (24, 44). However, this need not preclude the study of Na-channel properties, as long as enough transporting channels remain in the apical membrane. Microelectrode recordings from frog skin have shed some doubt on the completeness of the K-depolarization (29, 99). However, doubt was also shed on the validity of some microelectrode results obtained in this tissue (80). I_{Na}-V curves of the GHK type were later found by microelectrode recordings from frog skin (93) and from necturus urinary bladder, which has large cells particularly suited for this technique (32, 101). Here the voltage range of conformity to the GHK equation is larger than in the skin of R. esculenta (101). The same I_{Na}-V curves were recorded with microelectrodes from the rabbit colon (102). The voltage range of GHK-behavior is large, and in this tissue K-depolarization was shown to be almost ideally effective (105).

The GHK-type current-voltage curve suggests a particularly simple kind of transfer mechanism. It is compatible with a two-barrier-one-site channel structure (63). It is not compatible with single-filing (40) nor with a high-fixed-charge density at the channel opening (63). Indeed, single-filing was excluded (6a, 82) and a high surface density of fixed charges was not found (6), although one or two titrable negative sites may be present in the channel opening (9, 21, 84, 87, 88, 117). For toad bladder, the selectivity series was estimated to be H>Li>Na $\gg$ K, with a Na/K ratio of 1000 (83). Thus the selectivity is much higher than in Na channels of neuronal origin (39).

REGULATION BY Na AND Ca IONS

When the overall steady-state Na transport is plotted against the mucosal Na activity (Na_o), a saturating function resembling a Michaelis-Menten relationship is usually found (106). With two membranes in series, many effects may cause or contribute to this behavior. It was recognized early, however, that saturation of the active transport step at the basolateral membrane is not involved; rather, tracer experiments showed that the apical permeability, P_{Na}, decreases with increasing Na_o (15). This, in turn, may be caused by a saturation of the apical transport step itself or be achieved by a control mechanism. The latter might be set in effect by Na_o or by Na_c.

Effect of Na_o: The Self-Inhibition

This problem was studied with fast concentration changes in the mucosal solution of K-depolarised frog skin (33, 65, 66). When Na_o was suddenly increased at nearly constant membrane voltage, the Na current rose sharply, passed through a maximum, and then settled down to its much smaller steady-state value within seconds (Figure 1B). The steady-state currents, when plotted against Na_o, showed the familiar saturating curve, but the larger peak currents had a much smaller tendency to saturate (61, 69). These experiments showed that the apical membrane can pass, although transiently, much more current than the saturating steady-state function indicates. Therefore, the saturation cannot be caused by an absolute rate limitation of the transport process itself. The remaining possibility is a regulatory process responding to the increase in Na_o.

In these experiments Na_c was excluded as being instrumental for the change of P_{Na}: thanks to the small unstirred layers of $10-15$ μm (66), the response time was so fast that the Na_o-exposure time could be limited to a few seconds. In this time Na_c increased by less than 2 mM, as evidenced by changes in the Na reversal potential. The reversal potential was obtained from fits of I_{Na}-V curves, recorded at different times of exposure, with the GHK-function (33). Furthermore, the timecourse of I_{Na} remained essentially unchanged when, in the early period of the Na exposure, Na entry was prevented by appropriate manipulations of the holding potential (61).

The fits with the GHK function showed that, during exposure to Na_o, P_{Na} decreased with time. The duration of this transient was in the order of seconds. It appears, therefore, that extracellular Na ions act as effectors, causing P_{Na} to decrease in a relatively slow process that may be called self-inhibition. However, although slow on the scale of chemical reactions (30), this process is faster than the other regulatory processes discussed below.

Agents like benzimidazolyl-guanidine (BIG) and parachloromercury-phenyl-sulfonate (PCMPS) were found to abolish the Na self-inhibition in frog skin when present in the outer solution (21, 25, 33, 117). The effect of BIG on the response of I_{Na} to increasing steps of Na_o is shown in Figure 1B. Although there are indications that PCMPS may in addition release from Na_c-mediated inhibitory effects (11), this explanation is excluded here, because Na_c was shown to remain small.

For *Necturus* urinary bladder, Thomas et al (101) concluded from microelectrode recordings in the steady state that P_{Na} decreases with increasing Na_o, and that this effect is not mediated by changes in Na_c because Na_c was observed to remain constant. In these experiments K-depolarisation was not used. In the K-depolarised mammalian colon P_{Na} was also seen to be downregulated by Na_o (102). Here, however, Na_c increased rather clearly, such that the contribution of Na_c-dependent effects (see below) could not be excluded.

Effect of Na_c: The Feedback Inhibition

Experiments by MacRobbie & Ussing (72), Hviid Larsen (46), and Biber (12) with ouabain-poisoned amphibian skin first indicated a P_{Na} decreasing regulatory process that was shown to require a significant increase in Na_c (27, 51). Today this process is called feedback inhibition. It provides a means for transepithelial Na transport to limit itself (11, 53, 100, 103). Grinstein & Erlij (36) recognized that basolateral Na/Ca exchange is involved, as later confirmed for toad urinary bladder (16). A normal Na gradient at the basolateral membrane would therefore tend to remove Ca from the cell. The rate of Ca elimination would decrease in response to Na loading. Chase & Al-Awqati demonstrated with vesicle preparations that basolateral Na/Ca exchange exists (16) and that cytosolic Ca blocks P_{Na} (17).

For K-depolarized epithelia, where the interstitial Na concentration is small, the Na/Ca exchanger may be expected to draw Ca into the cell if Na_c becomes sufficiently large. Indeed, Garty & Lindemann (35a) found that in toad urinary bladder, feedback inhibition also occurs during K-depolarization. It could be prevented by lowering the serosal Ca concentration to 3 μM. After

Na loading for 40 minutes, feedback inhibition was initiated by increasing the serosal Ca concentration to 10 mM, and the inhibitory rate was estimated from the resulting decrease in conductance. Low rates of about 20% in 10 minutes were observed. In view of these low rates and the requirement for high cellular Na activities, feedback inhibition appears to be a failsafe device that becomes operative when the deviations from normal ion distribution are rather extreme. Noise experiments have shown that feedback inhibition decreases the Na channel density (28), as will be discussed below.

Competition Effects in the Dose-Response Curve of Amiloride

The availability of amiloride as a potent reversible inhibitor of apical Na-transport has been invaluable for analysis both on the membrane level and the molecular level. As reviewed by Cuthbert (22), the macroscopic inhibition constant of this agent (K_A^{ma}) is in some epithelia increased by Na_o, suggesting that competition between at least one type of Na-dependent inhibition and amiloride takes place.

The early demonstration by Cuthbert & Shum (23) of seemingly pure competitive behavior in skins of *R. temporaria* was confirmed for *R. esculenta* (117), and for toad urinary bladder (97). Acèves & Cuthbert (1) found pure competition between Na and the amiloride analogue benzamil in skins of *R. temporaria*. While Benos et al (7) described noncompetitive inhibition for the skins of *R. catesbeiana* and *R. pipiens,* they found mixed inhibition for the skin of *R. temporaria*. In contrast, Takada & Hayashi (98) observed mixed inhibition with the skin of *R. catesbeiana*. In the rabbit descending colon and in the hen coprodaeum, weak competitive inhibition together with a stronger non-competitive component was found (14, 104). Microsomes derived from toad urinary bladder also show competition (49). [Lastly, amiloride is also competitive with Na in its blocking effect on the Na/H exchange (47, 114)]. In short, the type of interaction between channel blockage by Na and amiloride appears variable among species and tissues. A set of two or more modifying sites, which may be expressed in varying combinations (7, 8, 10, 14, 22) depending on the regulatory requirements of the tissue, is conceivable. Notably, for skins of *R. temporaria* and *R. esculenta,* only pure competition or, in one instance, mixed inhibition have been found.

These steady-state studies do not clearly distinguish between inhibition by Na ions from the mucosal and the cellular side of the membrane. However, because in frog skin the competition phenomenon was also found in fast flow experiments (Zeiske & Lindemann, see Figure 6 in ref. 61), with Na_o exposure times that prevent substantial increases of Na_c and thereby the feedback inhibition, it is clear that competition between amiloride and the self-inhibition exists, at least in the tissues thus investigated. In frog skin, toad urinary bladder and mammalian urinary bladder, self-inhibition was noted to express itself in terms of decreased channel densities, as evidenced by noise analysis (54, 60, 70a, 111).

NOISE ANALYSIS
General Remarks

A systematic investigation of the apical Na transport by steady-state noise analysis became possible when appropriate low-noise amplifiers for voltage clamping could be constructed (70, 110), and when it was realized that amiloride may be used as an extrinsic blocker to generate an "induced" Lorentzian in the current power density spectrum, which can readily be interpreted (67).

The structural complexity of epithelia posed some problems. The presence of a series membrane has two major effects: (a) shifting of the holding potential of the membrane investigated with respect to the holding potential of the voltage clamp, and (b) attenuation of the noise signal by a filter network made up essentially of the resistances of membranes and solutions and the membrane capacitances (64, 109).

In principle, the filter effect can be corrected for by analyzing the tissue impedance and computing the tissue current transfer function (membrane→clamp) from it. More elegantly, the voltage transfer function (clamp→membrane) may be estimated, which is already identical with the required current transfer function (membrane→clamp) if the experiment is conducted such that the reciprocity theorem is applicable (64). Up to now, such corrections have not been systematically used.

Instead, in the work with apical Na channels, effects (a) and (b) were often minimized together by depolarising the K-permeable basolateral membrane with a high serosal K-concentration as discussed above. In addition, the apical membrane resistance was increased further above the remaining resistance of the basolateral membrane by the use of high concentrations of amiloride. Thereby, Na_c was kept at low values such that feedback inhibition was presumably inoperative.

The spontaneous current noise arising in epithelia like frog skin and toad urinary bladder is considerably enhanced when Na or Li is present in the mucosal solution. The resulting power density spectrum shows dominance of low-frequency noise essentially proportional to $1/f^2$. It was suggested that this noise component results from spontaneous open/close switching of Na channels due to self-inhibition (68). Unfortunately, the corresponding Lorentzian plateau at very low frequencies has never been convincingly demonstrated under voltage clamp conditions, although the spectra have a tendency to level off below 0.5 Hz. Because of severe stability problems at these low frequencies, it may be best to study low-frequency kinetics with concentration jump techniques. However, the Lorentzian plateau was found in voltage noise spectra (108), and the kinetics of the self-inhibition, as studied with fast concentration steps, imply corner frequencies below 0.2 Hz (33). It is noteworthy that the turnover of membrane channels might also result in low-frequency Lorentzians (18).

Amiloride-Induced Lorentzians

When amiloride is added in maximal concentrations, the Na_o-dependent noise disappears. However, when amiloride is added in submaximal concentrations, the Na_o-dependent noise diminishes at low frequencies, while a new Lorentzian component appears in the 1–50 Hz band (67, 68). Li can substitute for Na (Figure 2B). The plateau power G_o (one-sided spectra) of these "amiloride-induced" Lorentzians decreases, and the corner frequency increases when the amiloride concentration (A_o) is increased. The dependence of corner frequencies (f_c^A) on A_o is linear. Using pseudo–first order kinetics

$$2\pi f_c^A = k_{on} \cdot A_o + k_{off} , \tag{1}$$

the apparent rate constants of amiloride blockage can be obtained from "rate concentration plots" (Figure 2C): k_{on} as the slope, k_{off} as the ordinate intercept. Similar Lorentzians and rate constants are also found during net outward flow of Li ions (Figure 2B) or Na ions (28, 58).

For toad bladder and frog skin of species where competition was demonstrated, the plateaus of amiloride-induced Lorentzians were analyzed in terms of a three-state channel model (57, 59, 60, 68, 86, 111). With N_o designating the density of conducting channels, N_1 channels blocked by Na ions and N_2 channels blocked by amiloride, we obtain the overall, probably simplistic reaction scheme

$$
\begin{array}{ccc}
Na_o & & A_o \\
k_{01} \Big\downarrow & & \Big\downarrow k_{02} \\
N_1 \xrightarrow{} N_o & & \xleftarrow{} N_2 \\
k_{10} & & k_{20}
\end{array}
$$

for pure competitive rather than mixed inhibition. Except for very small Na_o, the stoichiometry of 1 amiloride molecule per blocked channel is justified from the slope of the macroscopic dose-response curves (14, 22) and the Hill coefficient (14, 60, 104). Using the rate constants indicated in the above scheme, the dissociation constants are $K_N = k_{10}/k_{01}$, $K_A = k_{20}/k_{02}$. The sum N $= N_o + N_1 + N_2$ is the density of electrically detectable channels. Cuthbert's interesting alternative, an allosteric model (20, 22), has not yet been tested by noise analysis.

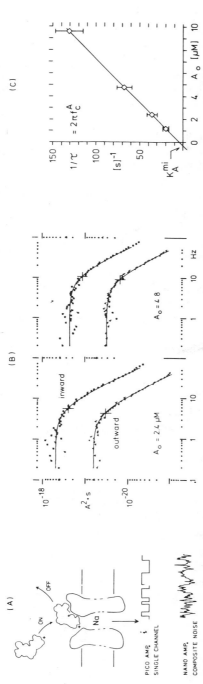

Figure 2(A) Scheme showing how a Na channel might be reversibly blocked by amiloride present in the mucosal solution. As an alternative to this direct block model (21), amiloride might bind to a receptor site outside of the diffusion pathway and trigger a conformational change that closes the channel (9, 10). Below, the single-channel current and the composite noise generated by additive currents from millions of asynchronous blocking events of parallel channels are indicated. (*B*) One-sided power density spectra G(f) computed from composite noise of K-depolarised frog skin, showing amiloride-induced Lorentzians for inward (upper curves) and outward flow of Li-ions. The solid curves are fits with the Lorentzian function, the crosses indicate half plateau powers and corner frequencies (58). (*C*) Rate concentration plot of amiloride, obtained with K-depolarised frog skin. The bars denote standard deviations (57).

The expressions for Lorentzians derived for competitive blockage are complicated (68). Simplifications result when blocker concentrations are in excess with respect to channel concentrations, and when the chemical rate of blockage by amiloride is much larger than that of the blockage by Na. Then $k_{02} = k_{on}$ and $k_{20} = k_{off}$, independent of Na_o. For triamterene k_{off} was shown to be independent of Na_o (45). For amiloride, where the rate of blockage is lower, a small effect of Na_o may be present in K-depolarized frog skin (111) such that $k_{off} \sim k_{20} + k_{01} \cdot Na_o$. However, in view of the large time constants observed macroscopically for the self-inhibition (33), we expect a small value for the Na onrate, $k_{01} \cdot Na_o$, probably no larger than k_{20}.

Hoshiko & Van Driessche noted that in *not K-depolarized* skins the apparent k_{on} of triamterene decreases when Na_o is raised (45). This may mean that Na ions within the channel act as higher rate competitors of triamterene, an effect that would be enhanced when—in this normally polarized, shortcircuited system—the membrane voltage increases the channel occupancy above the value at zero mV. Furthermore, the apical membrane voltage will under these conditions decrease when Na_o is raised. Therefore a voltage dependent k_{on} (38a, 84) might contribute to the phenomenon. Machlup & Hoshiko (71) have developed a "clogging model" to explain this interesting result.

Evidence for competitive behavior is obtained when the Michaelis Menten constant of macroscopic dose-response curves, $K_A^{ma} = K_A (1 + Na_o/K_N)$, is compared with the microscopic rate constant ratio $K_A^{mi} = k_{off}/k_{on}$. For toad urinary bladder it was noted that K_A^{ma} is significantly larger than K_A^{mi} (60). For frog skin the values of five extrinsic blockers, including amiloride and triamterene, were compared (57). The ratio $K_A^{ma}/K_A^{mi} = (1 + Na_o/K_N)/(k_{off}/k_{20})$ was found to have a mean value near seven, indicating dominance of the competitive component over any noncompetitive component that might also be present. This ratio was found to be much smaller in the hen coprodaeum (19), where the competitive component is not dominant (14).

In a structure-activity study the blocking rate constants of 25 structural analogues of amiloride were obtained (55, 56; and Li, Cragoe & Lindemann, in preparation). It was found that the substituents at position 5 and 6 of the pyrazine ring essentially control the offrate and, therefore, the duration of the blocking event. The onrate constant is not affected by halo-substitutions at position 6. The onrate constant is typically much smaller than expected from diffusion-limited encounters. It is not concentration-dependent but differs widely among analogues. According to present evidence this "structure-dependence" of the onrate does not seem to be convincingly explained by changes in steric hindrance. Therefore, the structure-dependence of k_{on} may result from interactions, probably of side-chain ligands, with the channel prior to the actual blocking. Analysis of the corresponding kinetic equations showed that the lifetime of the "encounter complex" must be short if the rate concentration plots are linear, as they are.

Na-Channel Currents

The Lorentzian plateaus[1] were always analyzed with the assumption that one amiloride molecule blocks a channel in an all-or-none manner, such that $I_{Na} = i \cdot N_o$. This assumption seems reasonable since, macroscopically, amiloride blocks Na uptake almost completely (91, 97), and in the epithelia used the Hill coefficient is near unity (14, 60, 104). The channel current can then be estimated from

$$i = 0.25(G_o \cdot 2\pi f_c^A) \cdot (1 + K_A/A_o) \cdot (a \cdot I_{Na})^{-1} \qquad (2)$$

where a is membrane area and $0.25\,(G_o \cdot 2\pi f_c^A)$ the "Lorentzian" variance of I_{Na} resulting from blockage by A_o. (This variance is valid for infinite bandwidth.)

The use of Eq. 2 requires knowledge of K_A. This poses a slight problem, because in case of competition with a lower rate blocking process, only $K_A^{mi} = k_{off}/k_{on}$ ($\geqslant K_A = k_{20}/k_{02}$) is obtained from rate analysis. However, for amiloride acting on frog skin or toad bladder, K_A^{mi} is expected to exceed K_A no more than two-fold (57). This rough numerical estimate of K_A shows that for large A_o values, typically 7–45-fold larger than K_A^{mi}, the ratio K_A/A_o in Eq. 2 tends to vanish. The observed value of f_c^A need not be corrected because it already contains the effect of competition (68).

In K-depolarized frog skin clamped to zero mV, the steady-state value of i was found to increase linearly with Na_o (111). This is expected from the current voltage curves of GHK-type, provided Na_c remains negligible at each Na_o. The linear relationship shows that a saturation of the channel translocation rate is not the cause of the saturation of I_{Na} with increasing Na_o, as already suggested previously (33). For 60 mM Na_o and zero mV, rates close to 10^6 Na ions per second were calculated (67). With voltage i increases more than proportionally and is, at 100 mV, about 4-fold larger than at zero mV (38a). Following Armstrong's well known argument (4, 5), the comparatively high rates of translocation are not compatible with a mobile type carrier mechanism. The rates imply that Na is transported by channels or possibly by a high-rate carrier of the "fixed" type (77). More recent determinations of the flux ratio exponents

---

[1]Na-channel noise was usually analyzed by curve fitting to blocker-induced Lorentzians. It is worth pointing out that the direct estimation of the current variance corresponding to these Lorentzians will yield values for i and N_o more directly: The variance of the total steady-state current flowing at a given Na_o and A_o is computed from the noise record. The "shunt" variance obtained at the same bandwidth and the same Na_o, but with maximal A_o, is subtracted from it. The result should be the integral of a Lorentzian. After correction for bandwidth limitations i is computed with Eq. 2. By this approach (compare 94) rate information is sacrificed, but the need for Lorentzian curve fitting is obviated. Occasional computations of power spectra are advisable as a checkup. For their analysis, the integrated difference spectrum procedure (19) is commendable. Finally, where Lorentzian plateaus are obscured by low-frequency noise, their estimation from the variance difference may lead to a more precise determination of G_o and f_c (63a).

gave values close to unity at different voltages and Na concentrations (6a, 82). These results exclude a carrier both of the mobile type and of the "fixed" type.

Na-channel currents were also computed from amiloride-induced and triamterene-induced Lorentzians obtained from the short-circuited mammalian colon (118) and urinary bladder (70a) and the hen coprodaeum (19). The values are in the range 0.1–0.65 pA (Table 1). The differences are in part explained by differences in temperature (118) and in the apical driving force. When K-depolarisation is not used, the driving force will be larger and increase the value of i.

Competition Effects in Channel Densities

Once i is known, N_o can be estimated as I_{Na}/i. For K-depolarized frog skin, N_o was found to decrease with increasing Na_o (111), while $(N_o + N_2)$ increased with A_o (59), as expected from competition kinetics. In this tissue and in the K-depolarized toad urinary bladder the sum $(N_o + N_2)$ was estimated as $(I_{Na}/i)\cdot(1 + A_o/K_A^{mi})$, using the approximation $K_A = K_A^{mi}$. In the toad bladder $(N_o + N_2)$ also increased with A_o (60), as expected from the competition model. According to the kinetic scheme given above, $(N_o + N_2)$ will increase with A_o at the expense of N_1. Therefore N can be estimated by extrapolating $(N_o + N_2)$ to infinite A_o. The values found are listed in Table 1. For frog skin they are somewhat smaller than those obtained from amiloride and benzamil labeling experiments in this tissue (1, 2).

In frog skin PCMPS and BIG, agents that abolish the Na self-inhibition to a large extent (25, 116), were found to diminish the increase of $(N_o + N_2)$ with A_o (59). For the presence of BIG or PCMPS one would expect that k_{off} is then lowered towards k_{20}. For PCMPS this was actually observed. With 60 mM Na_o, k_{off} decreased from 3.13 ± 0.33 to 2.09 ± 0.27 s^{-1}, implying that $k_{off} = 1.5 \cdot k_{20}$. However, BIG did not decrease k_{off} (59).

Table 1 Na-channel currents (i) and apical channel densities (N) of some Na-retaining epithelia[a]

Species	Rana esculenta	Bufo marinus	Gallus domesticus	Rabbit	Rabbit
Tissue	skin	urinary bladder	copro- daeum	colon descendens	urinary bladder
Blocker[b]	A	A	T	A	A
Na_o (mM)	60	60	130	136	136
K-depol.	yes	yes	no	no	no
Temp. (°C)	20	20	34	27/37	37
i (pA)	0.09–0.3	0.16	0.32	0.09/0.39	0.65
N (μm^{-2})	10–50	1–5	38	3.2/6.1	0.02
Reference	59, 67, 111	60	19	118	54, 70a

[a]Transepithelial voltage: zero mV
[b]Amiloride (A), triamterene (T)

In the not K-depolarized coprodaeum of *Gallus domesticus,* N was found to decrease with increasing Na_o. In this case blockage by Na ions in a way noncompetitive to blockage by triamterene was suggested, since K_T^{ma} is not strongly dependent on Na_o (14, 19). In the not K-depolarised rabbit urinary bladder the channel density also decreases with increasing Na_o (54).

These results from steady-state noise experiments do not show by themselves whether feedback inhibition has contributed to the change in N_o or N with Na_o and of (N_o + N_2) with A_o. It may be argued, however, that with the high blocker concentrations used, Na_c must have been small and, therefore, feedback effects from Na_c minimal. However, when feedback inhibition is provoked by blocking active transport with ouabain and loading the cells with Na from the mucosal side, N is reduced considerably (28). In similar experiments it was noted that Li-loading invokes less feedback inhibition than Na loading (58).

The channel densities were usually expressed per chamber area, total membrane area or apical membrane capacitance. So far it remains unknown whether the channels distribute uniformly over the population of cells, and whether they spread uniformly over the membrane of each cell. Channel clustering and the resulting concentration-polarization would explain the curious observation that i appears to increase with A_o (60), and perhaps the variability that i usually shows.

Ontogenesis and Hormonal Effects on Na Channels

Once i and N_o could be estimated by noise analysis, it became feasible to study the maturing of transport functions in embryos and the effects of Na transport stimulating hormones in terms of these parameters. In the epidermis of larvae of *R. catesbeiana,* stage 10–19, Hillyard, Zeiske & Van Driessche (41) found spontaneously switching channels that pass K, NH_4, Rb, and Cs but not Na and Li ions, and are blocked by Ba and tetraethylammonium. Ba also blocks the apical and basolateral K-channels of adult skins (112, 113). In the presence of amiloride or BIG the embryonic channels show stimulated K- and Cs-transport and now, apparently, also pass Na and Li (41). Larvae in stage 19–24 insert increasing numbers of amiloride blockable Na channels into the apical membrane (42).

In the hen coprodaeum, a low-Na diet causes the appearance of amiloride and triamterene blockable Na channels in the apical membrane (19). The increase in P_{Na} is accompanied by the appearance of conspicuous "rod-shaped" particles in freeze-fracture images of the apical membrane (26). The changeover into a Na retaining epithelium is probably mediated by aldosterone (13).

Aldosterone stimulates Na transport after an induction time of several hours. It induces the synthesis of a set of proteins, of which one, citrate synthase, has been identified (50). Acute experiments did not clarify whether the increase in P_{Na} observed for instance in toad urinary bladder in response to aldosterone application is in part due to de novo synthesis of Na channels. Dietary effects point in this direction (13, 19). Noise analysis of the K-depolarized toad bladder showed that the hormone increases both N_o and N while leaving i essentially unchanged (86). In this respect the response is similar to the effect of ADH, although much slower. The long response time will be due to the fact that metabolic enzymes like citrate synthase have to be synthesized, permitting—possibly through products of energy metabolism—recruitment from an electrically silent pool of Na channels. Indeed, when energy metabolism is impaired, P_{Na} decreases considerably, presumably because N is decreased (35), and during mild metabolic impairment aldosterone is unable to increase P_{Na} although the induction takes place (86). In short, aldosterone causes recruitment of apical Na channels, but this effect depends on, and perhaps is mediated by "energy metabolism."

The fast-acting antidiuretic hormone (ADH) is known to initially increase the cellular concentration of cyclic AMP (81). The resulting stimulation of proteinkinase then leads through a number of unknown steps, possibly involving dephosphorylation of membrane proteins (115), to an increase in P_{Na}. Noise analysis of K-depolarised toad bladder (60) showed that an increase in channel currents is not involved in this process. Rather, N_o increases, but not at the expense of N_1. Instead, the total number of channels, N, is found to be increased in proportion to the increase in P_{Na}. It appears, therefore, that by this hormone more Na channels are recruited for transport and for regulatory inhibition. The nature of the reservoirs drawn upon by hormonal recruitment is being investigated with other techniques (34, 52, 95).

Recruitment of Na channels in response to ADH (+ theophylline) was also reported for the non–K-depolarised skin of *R. pipiens* (38), where blockage by amiloride is noncompetitive (7). The channel current remained unchanged. Inhibition of prostaglandin synthesis produced a large decrease of N that was reversed by subsequent stimulation with ADH + theophylline (38).

On the whole, noise analysis has proven to be particularly suited to follow changes in channel density in the living preparation, and has shown that the variation of channel density is the parameter that controls the rate of apical Na uptake. The channel density results are complementary to those of binding studies, which often yield somewhat higher values (1, 2, 19). The biophysical characterisation of channels by noise analysis awaits parallel studies with single-channel techniques.

SUMMARY

When compiling results obtained with various techniques, it appears that the apical Na translocators are channels of high Na, Li selectivity that permit large transport rates at low driving forces. The concentration dependence of the transport rate is linear at least up to 60 mM Na_o. The voltage dependence is of the Goldman-Hodgkin-Katz type or closely related to it. Outward facing surface charges have little influence. The flux ratio exponent is close to unity, compatible with single-site channels or multisite channels of low occupancy. Noise analysis has proven particularly suited for following changes in the density of conducting channels in the living preparation, and has shown that cellular and hormonal regulatory mechanisms control Na transport by changing the channel density in a variety of ways.

ACKNOWLEDGMENT

I appreciate the helpful remarks of Dr. Jack H.-Y. Li on this review. The English was kindly improved by Dr. T. D. Plant. Experiments in the author's laboratory were supported by the Deutsche Forschungsgemeinschaft through SFB 38, project C1.

Literature Cited

1. Aceves, J., Cuthbert, A. W. 1979. Uptake of [^{3}H] Benzamil at different sodium concentrations. Inferences regarding the regulation of sodium permeability. *J. Physiol.* 295:491–504

2. Aceves, J., Cuthbert, A. W., Edwardson, J. M. 1979. Estimation of the density of sodium entry sites in frog skin epithelium from the uptake of [^{3}H]-benzamil. *J. Physiol.* 295:477–90

3. Anderson, C. R., Stevens, C. F. 1973. Voltage clamp analysis of acetylcholine produced end-plate current fluctuations at frog neuromuscular junction. *J. Physiol.* 235:655–91

4. Armstrong, C. M. 1975. Evidence for ionic pores in excitable membranes. *Biophys. J.* 15:932–33

5. Armstrong, C. M. 1975. Ionic pores, gates, and gating currents. *Q. Rev. Biophys.* 7:179–209

6. Benos, D. J., Latorre, R., Reyes, J. 1981. Surface potentials and sodium entry in frog skin epithelium. *J. Physiol.* 321:163–74

6a. Benos, D. J., Hyde, B. A., Latorre, R. 1983. Sodium flux ratio through the amiloride-sensitive entry pathway in frog skin. *J. Gen. Physiol.* 81:667–85

7. Benos, D. J., Mandel, L. J., Balaban, R. S. 1979. On the mechanism of the amiloride-sodium entry site interaction in anuran skin epithelia. *J. Gen. Physiol.* 73:307–26

8. Benos, D. J., Mandel, L. J., Simon, S. A. 1980. Effects of chemical group specific reagents on sodium entry and the amiloride binding site in frog skin: evi-

dence for separate sites. *J. Membr. Biol.* 56:149–58

9. Benos, D. J., Mandel, L. J., Simon, S. A. 1980. Cation selectivity and competition at the sodium entry site in frog skin. *J. Gen. Physiol.* 76:233–47

10. Benos, D. J., Watthey, J. W. M. 1981. Inferences on the nature of the apical sodium entry site in frog skin epithelium. *J. Pharmacol. Exp. Ther.* 219:481–88

11. Bevevino, L. H., Lacaz-Vieira, F. 1982. Control of sodium permeability of the outer barrier in toad skin. *J. Membr. Biol.* 66:97–107

12. Biber, T. U. L. 1971. Effects of changes in transepithelial transport on the uptake of sodium across the outer surface of frog skin. *J. Gen. Physiol.* 58:131–44

13. Bindslev, N. 1979. Sodium transport in the hen lower intestine. Induction of sodium sites in the brush border by a low-sodium diet. *J. Physiol.* 288:449–66

14. Bindslev, N., Cuthbert, A. W., Edwardson, J. M., Skadhauge, E. 1982. Kinetics of amiloride action in the hen coprodaeum *in vitro*. *Pflügers Arch.* 392:340–46

15. Cereijido, M., Herrera, F. C., Flanigan, W. J., Curran, P. F. 1964. The influence of Na concentration on Na transport across frog skin. *J. Gen. Physiol.* 47:879–93

16. Chase, H. S., Al-Awqati, Q. 1981. Regulation of the sodium permeability of the luminal border of toad bladder by intracellular sodium and calcium. Role of sodium-calcium exchange in the baso-

lateral membrane. *J. Gen. Physiol.* 77: 693–712

17. Chase, H. S., Al-Awqati, Q. 1982. Submicromolar calcium regulates Na permeability of luminal membrane vesicles from toad bladder as measured by flow quench method. *Fed. Proc.* 41:6310 (Abstr.)

18. Chen, Y.-D. 1975. Matrix method for fluctuations and noise in kinetic systems. *Proc. Nat. Acad. Sci. USA* 72:3807–11

19. Christensen, O., Bindslev, N. 1982. Fluctuation analysis of short-circuit current in a warm-blooded sodium-retaining epithelium: site current, density, and interaction with triamterene. *J. Membr. Biol.* 65:19–30

20. Cuthbert, A. W. 1974. Interactions of sodium channels in transporting epithelia: A two state model. *Mol. Pharmacol.* 10:892–903

21. Cuthbert, A. W. 1976. Importance of guanidinium groups for blocking sodium channels in epithelia. *Mol. Pharmacol.* 12:945–57

22. Cuthbert, A. W. 1981. Sodium entry step in transporting epithelia: results of ligand-binding studies. In *Ion Transport by Epithelia*, ed. S. G. Schultz, p. 181. New York: Raven

23. Cuthbert, A. W., Shum, W. K. 1974. Binding of amiloride to sodium channels in frog skin. *Mol. Pharmacol.* 10:880–91

24. Cuthbert, A. W., Wilson, S. A. 1981. Mechanisms for the effects of acetylcholine on sodium transport in frog skin. *J. Membr. Biol.* 59:65–75

25. Dick, H. J., Lindemann, B. 1975. Saturation of Na-current into frog skin epithelium abolished by PCMPS. *Pflügers Arch.* 355:R72 (Abstr.)

26. Eldrup, E., Mollgard, K., Bindslev, N. 1980. Possible epithelial sodium channels visualised by freeze-fracture. *Biochim. Biophys. Acta* 596:152–57

27. Erlij, D., Smith, M. W. 1973. Sodium uptake by frog skin and its modification by inhibitors of transepithelial sodium transport. *J. Physiol.* 228:221–39

28. Erlij, D., Van Driessche, W. 1983. Noise analysis of inward and outward Na current in Ouabain-treated frogs. *Fed. Proc.* 42:1101 (Abstr.)

29. Fisher, R. S., Helman, S. I. 1981. Influence of basolateral $(K)_i$ on the electrical parameters of the cells of isolated epithelia of frog skin. *Biophys. J.* 33:41a (Abstr.)

30. Frieden, C. 1970. Kinetic aspects of regulation of metabolic process. The hysteretic enzyme concept. *J. Biol. Chem.* 245:5788–99

31. Frömter, E., Diamond, J. 1972. Route of

passive ion permeation in epithelia. *Nature* 235:9–13

32. Frömter, E., Higgins, J. T., Gebler, B. 1981. Electrical properties of amphibian urinary bladder epithelia. IV. The current-voltage relationship of the sodium channels in the apical cell membrane. See Ref. 22, p. 31

33. Fuchs, W., Hviid Larsen, E., Lindemann, B. 1977. Current-voltage curve of sodium channels and concentration dependence of sodium permeability in frog skin. *J. Physiol.* 267:137–66

34. Garty, H., Edelman, I. S. 1983. Amiloride-sensitive trypsinisation of apical sodium channels: Analysis of hormonal regulation of sodium transport in toad bladder. *J. Gen. Physiol.* 81:785–803

35. Garty, H., Edelman, I. S., Lindemann, B. 1983. Metabolic regulation of apical sodium permeability in toad bladder in the presence and absence of aldosterone. *J. Membr. Biol.* 74:15–24

35a. Garty, H., Lindemann, B. 1984. Feedback inhibition of sodium uptake in K-depolarized toad urinary bladders. *Biochem. Biophys. Acta.* In press

36. Grinstein, S., Erlij, D. 1978. Intracellular calcium and the regulation of sodium transport in the frog skin. *Proc. R. Soc. Lond. B.* 202:353–60

37. Hamill, O. P., Marty, A., Neher, E., Sakmann, B., Sigworth, F. J. 1981. Improved patch-clamp techniques for high-resolution current recording from cells and cell-free membrane patches. *Pflügers Arch.* 391:85–100

38. Helman, S. I., Cox, T. C., Van Driessche, W. 1983. Hormonal control of apical membrane Na transport in epithelia. *J. Gen. Physiol.* 82:201–20

38a. Henrich, M., Lindemann, B. 1983. Voltage dependence of channel currents and channel densities in the apical membrane of toad urinary bladder. In *Intestinal Absorption and Secretion*, ed. E. Skadhauge, K. Heintze. Lancaster: MTP Press. In press

39. Hille, B. 1975. Ionic selectivity, saturation, and block in sodium channels. A four barrier model. *J. Gen. Physiol.* 66:535–60

40. Hille, B., Schwarz, W. 1978. Potassium channels as multi-ion single-file pores. *J. Gen. Physiol.* 72:409–42

41. Hillyard, S. D., Zeiske, W., Van Driessche, W. 1982. Poorly selective cation channels in the skin of the larval frog (stage≤XIX). *Pflügers Arch.* 394:287–93

42. Hillyard, S. D., Zeiske, W., Van Driessche, W. 1982. A fluctuation analysis study of the development of amiloride-sensitive Na transport in the skin of larval

bullfrogs (Rana catesbeiana). *Biochim. Biophys. Acta* 692:455–61

43. Hodgkin, A. L., Katz, B. 1949. The effect of sodium ions on the electrical activity of the giant axon of the squid. *J. Physiol.* 108:37–77

44. Hoshiko, T., Machlup, S. 1983. Basolateral K effect on total conductance, overshoot response to apical Na, and amiloride inhibition in R. pipiens skin. *Biophys. J.* 41:81a (Abstr.)

45. Hoshiko, T., Van Driessche, W. 1981. Triamterene-induced sodium current fluctuations in frog skin. *Arch. Int. Physiol. Biochim.* 89:P58–60

46. Hviid Larsen, E. 1972. Effect of amiloride, cyanide, and ouabain on the active transport pathway in toad skin. In *Transport Mechanisms in Epithelia*, ed. H. H. Ussing, N. A. Thorn, p. 131. Copenhagen: Munksgaard

47. Kinsella, J. L., Aronson, P. S. 1981. Amiloride inhibition of the Na^+-H^+ exchanger in renal micro villus membrane vesicles. *Am. J. Physiol.* 241:F374–79

48. Koefoed-Johnsen, V., Ussing, H. H. 1958. The nature of the frog skin potential. *Acta Physiol. Scand.* 42:298–308

49. Labelle, E. F., Valentine, M. E. 1980. Inhibition by amiloride of $^{22}Na^+$ transport into toad bladder microsomes. *Biochim. Biophys. Acta* 601:195–205

50. Law, P. Y., Edelman, I. S. 1978. Induction of citrate synthase by aldosterone in the rat kidney. *J. Membr. Biol.* 41:41–64

51. Leblanc, G., Morel, F. 1975. Na and K movements across the membranes of frog skin epithelia associated with transient current changes. *Pflügers Arch.* 358:159–77

52. Lewis, S. A., de Moura, J. L. C. 1982. Incorporation of cytoplasmic vesicles into apical membrane of mammalian urinary bladder epithelium. *Nature* 297:685–88

53. Lewis, S. A., Eaton, D. C., Diamond, I. M. 1976. The mechanism of Na^+ transport by rabbit urinary bladder. *J. Membr. Biol.* 28:41–70

54. Lewis, S. A., Ifshin, M. S., Loo, D. D. F., Diamond, J. M. 1983. Properties of Na channels in the apical membrane of rabbit urinary bladder. *Biophys. J.* 41:80a (Abstr.)

55. Li, J. H.-Y., Cragoe, E. J. Jr., Lindemann, B. 1981. Dual attachement of high potency amiloride analogues to epithelial Na channels. See Ref. 38, p. 184 (Abstr.)

56. Li, J. H.-Y., Lindemann, B. 1979. Blockage of epithelial Na channels by amiloride analogues: Dependence of rate constants on drug structure. *Pflügers Arch.* 379:R18 (Abstr.)

57. Li, J. H.-Y, Lindemann, B. 1983. Competitive blocking of epithelial Na channels by organic cations: the relationship between macroscopic and microscopic inhibition constants. *J. Membr. Biol.* 76:235–51

58. Li, J. H.-Y., Lindemann, B. 1982. Movement of Na and Li across the apical membrane of frog skin. In *Basic Mechanisms in the Action of Lithium*, ed. H. M. Emrich, J. B. Aldenhoff, H. D. Lux, p. 28. Amsterdam: Excerpta Medica

59. Li, J. H.-Y., Lindemann, B. 1983. Chemical stimulation of Na transport through amiloride blockable channels of frog skin epithelium. *J. Membrane Biol.* 75:179–92

60. Li, J. H.-Y., Palmer, L. G., Edelman, I. S., Lindemann, B. 1982. The role of Na-channel density in the natriferic response of the toad urinary bladder to an antidiuretic hormone. *J. Membr. Biol.* 64:77–89

61. Lindemann, B. 1977. A modifier-site model for passive Na transport into frog skin epithelium. In *Intestinal Permeation*, ed. M. Kramer, F. Lauterbach, p. 217. Amsterdam: Excerpta Medica

62. Lindemann, B. 1980. The beginning of fluctuation analysis of epithelial ion transport. *J. Membr. Biol.* 54:1–11

63. Lindemann, B. 1982. Dependence of ion flow through channels on the density of fixed charges at the channel opening. Voltage control of inverse titration curves. *Biophys. J.* 39:15–22

63a. Lindemann, B. 1984. Improved analysis of additively contaminated Lorentzians by integration. *Biophys. J.* In press

64. Lindemann, B., DeFelice, L. J. 1981. On the use of general network functions in the evaluation of noise spectra obtained from epithelia. See Ref. 22, p. 1

65. Lindemann, B., Gebhardt, U. 1973. Delayed changes of Na-Permeability in response to steps of $(Na)_o$ at the outer surface of frog skin and toad bladder. See Ref. 46, p. 115

66. Lindemann, B., Gebhardt, U., Fuchs, W. 1972. A flow chamber for concentration step experiments with epithelial membranes. *T.I.T. J. Life Sci.* 2:15–26

67. Lindemann, B., Van Driessche, W. 1977. Sodium specific membrane channels of frog skin are pores: current fluctuations reveal high turnover. *Science* 195:292–94

68. Lindemann, B., Van Driessche, W. 1978. The mechanism of Na uptake through Na-selective channels in the epithelium of frog skin. In *Membrane Transport Processes*, ed. J. F. Hoffman, 1:115. New York: Raven

69. Lindemann, B., Voute, C. 1976. Struc-

ture and function of the epidermis. In *Frog Neurobiology*, ed. R. Llinas, W. Precht, p. 169. Berlin: Springer

70. Loo, D. D. F. 1983. Using dual JFETs for low noise and low frequency measurements in epithelia. *Biophys. J.* 41:400a (Abstr.)

70a. Loo, D. D., Lewis, S. A., Ifshin, M. S., Diamond, J. M. 1983. Turnover, membrane insertion, and degradation of sodium channels in rabbit urinary bladder. *Science* 221:1288–90

71. Machlup, S., Hoshiko, T. 1982. Sodium and amiloride competition in apical membrane channels: a 3-state model for noise. *Biophys. J.* 37:281a (Abstr.)

72. MacRobbie, E. A. C., Ussing, H. H. 1961. Osmotic behaviour of the epithelial cells of frog skin. *Acta Physiol. Scand.* 53:348–65

73. Maruyama, Y., Petersen, O. H. 1982. Single-channel currents in isolated patches of plasma membrane from basal surface of pancreatic acini. *Nature* 299:159–61

74. Maruyama, Y., Petersen, O. H. 1982. Cholecystokinin activation of single-channel currents is mediated by internal messenger in pancreatic acinar cells. *Nature* 300:61–63

75. Miller, C., Racker, E. 1976. Ca^{++}-induced fusion of fragmented sarcoplasmic reticulum with artificial planar bilayers. *J. Membr. Biol.* 30:283–300

76. Mills, J. W., DiBona, D. R. 1977. On the distribution of Na^+-pump sites in the frog skin. *J. Cell Biol.* 75:968–73

77. Mitchell, P. 1967. Translocations through natural membranes. *Adv. Enzymol.* 29:33–87

78. Montal, M., Darszon, A., Schindler, H. 1981. Functional reassembly of membrane proteins in planar lipid bilayers. *Q. Rev. Biophys.* 14:1–79

79. Morel, F., Leblanc, G. 1975. Transient current changes and Na compartimentalization in frog skin epithelium. *Pflügers Arch.* 358:135–57

80. Nelson, D. J., Ehrenfeld, J., Lindemann, B. 1978. Volume changes and potential artifacts of epithelial cells of frog skin following impalement with microelectrodes filled with 3 M KCl. *J. Membr. Biol.* 40:91–119

81. Orloff, J., Handler, J. 1967. The role of adenosine 3,'5'-phosphate in the action of antidiuretic hormone. *Am. J. Med.* 42:757–68

82. Palmer, L. G. 1982. Na^+ transport and flux ratio through apical Na^+ channels in toad bladder. *Nature* 297:688–90

83. Palmer, L. G. 1982. Ion selectivity of the apical membrane Na channel in the toad urinary bladder. *J. Membr. Biol.* 67:91–98

84. Palmer, L. G. 1983. Voltage dependence of amiloride inhibition of apical membrane Na conductance in toad urinary bladder. *Biophys. J.* 41:186a (Abstr.)

85. Palmer, L. G., Edelman, I. S., Lindemann, B. 1981. Current-voltage analysis of apical Na transport in toad urinary bladder: effects of inhibitors of transport and metabolism. *J. Membr. Biol.* 57:59–71

86. Palmer, L. G., Li, J. H.-Y., Lindemann, B., Edelman, I. S. 1982. Aldosterone control of the density of sodium channels in the toad urinary bladder. *J. Membr. Biol.* 64:91–102

87. Park, C. S., Fanestil, D. D. 1980. Some molecular properties of the epithelial sodium channel. *J. Gen. Physiol.* 76:20 (Abstr.)

88. Park, C. S., Fanestil, D. D. 1983. Chemical-, hormonal-, and metabolic control of Na entry step across the apical membrane of toad urinary bladder. *Fed. Proc.* 42:1282 (Abstr.)

89. Rae, J. L., Levis, R. A. 1983. Single channel currents from frog lens epithelial cells. *Biophys. J.* 41:226 (Abstr.)

90. Rawlins, F., Mateau, L., Fragachan, F., Whittembury, G. 1970. Isolated toad skin epithelium: transport characteristics. *Pflügers Arch.* 316:64–80

91. Rick, R., Dörge, A., Nagel, W. 1975. Influx and efflux of sodium at the outer surface of frog skin. *J. Membr. Biol.* 22:183–96

92. Rick, R., Dörge, A., von Arnim, E., Thurau, K. 1978. Electron microprobe analysis of frog skin epithelium: evidence for a syncytial sodium transport compartment. *J. Membr. Biol.* 39:313–31

93. Schoen, H. F., Erlij, D. 1983. Effects of Ouabain on the apical and basolateral membranes of frog skin. *Fed. Proc.* 42:1101 (Abstr.)

94. Sigworth, F. J. 1980. The variance of sodium current fluctuations at the node of Ranvier. *J. Physiol.* 307:97–129

95. Stetson, D. L., Lewis, S. A., Wade, J. B. 1981. ADH-induced increase in transepithelial capacitance in toad bladder. *Biophys. J.* 33:43a (Abstr.)

96. Stevens, C. F. 1975. Principles and applications of fluctuation analysis: a nonmathematical introduction. *Fed. Proc.* 34:1364–69

97. Sudou, K., Hoshi, T. 1977. Mode of action of amiloride in toad urinary bladder. An electrophysiological study of the drug action on sodium permeability of the

mucosal border. *J. Membr. Biol.* 32: 115–32

98. Takada, M., Hayashi, H. 1980. Interaction of cadmium, calcium, and amiloride in the kinetics of active sodium transport through frog skin. *Jpn. J. Physiol.* 31: 285–303

99. Tang, J., Helman, S. I. 1983. Electrical parameters of apical and basolateral membranes of R. pipiens. *Fed. Proc.* 42:1101 (Abstr.)

100. Taylor, A., Windhager, E. E. 1979. Possible role of cytosolic calcium and Na-Ca exchange in regulation of transepithelial sodium transport. *Am. J. Physiol.* 236:F505–12

101. Thomas, S. R., Suzuki, Y., Thompson, S. M., Schultz, S. G. 1983. Electrophysiology of necturus urinary bladder: I. "Instantaneous" current voltage relations in the presence of varying mucosal sodium concentrations. *J. Membr. Biol.* 73:157–75

102. Thompson, S. M., Suzuki, Y., Schultz, S. G. 1982. The electrophysiology of rabbit descending colon. I. "Instantaneous" transepithelial current-voltage relations and the current-voltage relations of the Na-entry mechanism. *J. Membr. Biol.* 66:41–54

103. Turnheim, K., Frizzell, R. A., Schultz, S. G. 1978. Interaction between cell sodium and the amiloride-sensitive sodium entry step in rabbit colon. *J. Membr. Biol.* 39:233–56

104. Turnheim, K., Luger, A., Grasl, M. 1981. Kinetic analysis of the amiloride-sodium entry site interaction in rabbit colon. *Mol. Pharmacol.* 20:543–50

105. Turnheim, K., Thompson, S. M., Schultz, S. G. 1983. Relation between intracellular sodium and active sodium transport in rabbit colon. *J. Membr. Biol.* 76:299–309

106. Ussing, H. H. 1949. The active ion transport through the isolated frog skin in the light of tracer studies. *Acta Physiol. Scand.* 17:1–37

107. Ussing, H. H., Windhager, E. E. 1964. Nature of shunt path and active sodium transport path through frog skin epithelium. *Acta Physiol. Scand.* 62:484–504

108. Van Driessche, W., Borghgraef, R. 1975. Noise generated during ion transport across frog skin. *Arch. Int. Physiol. Biochim.* 83:140–42

109. Van Driessche, W., Goegelein, H. 1980. Attenuation of current and voltage noise signals recorded from epithelia. *J. Theor. Biol.* 86:629–48

110. Van Driessche, W., Lindemann, B. 1978. Low-noise amplification of voltage and current fluctuations arising in epithelia. *Rev. Sci. Instrum.* 49(1):52–55

111. Van Driessche, W., Lindemann, B. 1979. Concentration-dependence of currents through single sodium-selective pores in frog skin. *Nature* 282:519–20

112. Van Driessche, W., Wills, N. K., Hillyard, S. D., Zeiske, W. 1982. K^+ channels in an epithelial "single membrane" preparation. *Arch. Int. Physiol. Biochim.* 90:P12–14

113. Van Driessche, W., Zeiske, W. 1980. Ba^{2+}-induced conductance fluctuations of spontaneously fluctuating K^+ channels in the apical membrane of frog skin (Rana temporaria). *J. Membr. Biol.* 56: 31–42

114. Vigne, P., Frelin, C., Lazdunski, M. 1982. The amiloride-sensitive Na^+/H^+ exchange system in skeletal muscle cells in culture. *J. Biol. Chem.* 257:9394–400

115. Walton, K. G., DeLorenzo, R. J., Curran, P. F., Greengard, P. 1975. Regulation of protein phosphorylation in sodium transport in toad bladder. *J. Gen. Physiol.* 65:153–77

116. Zeiske, W., Lindemann, B. 1974. Chemical stimulation of Na current through the outer surface of frog skin epithelium. *Biochim. Biophys. Acta* 352:323–26

117. Zeiske, W., Lindemann, B. 1975. Blockage of Na-channels in frog skin by titration with protons and by chemical modification of COO^--groups. *Pflügers Arch.* 355:R71 (Abstr.)

118. Zeiske, W., Wills, N. K., Van Driessche, W. 1982. Na channels and amiloride-induced noise in the mammalian colon epithelium. *Biochim. Biophys. Acta* 688:201–10

Ann. Rev. Physiol. 1984. 46:517–30

VOLTAGE-REGULATED SODIUM CHANNEL MOLECULES

William S. Agnew

Department of Physiology, Yale University School of Medicine, New Haven, Connecticut 06510

INTRODUCTION

Plasma membranes of nerve, muscle, and related cells are sophisticated organelles that control the transduction, integration, and transmission of information in the form of rapidly propagated electrical signals. A strategic experimental objective is the elucidation of the molecular structures and mechanisms that invest the membrane bilayers with their extraordinary properties. Of special significance are the ion transporting channels, including the voltage-regulated sodium channel that produces the early inward currents of the action potential (46). Two experimental approaches can provide information about the sodium channel at the molecular level. The "patch clamp" technique, in its various manifestations, can detect currents through individual channel molecules (4b, 40, 66; and see review by Sakmann & Neher, this volume). In addition, the chemical isolation and direct characterization of the proteins has begun to provide structural information. This article will consider some of the recent advances in the biochemical isolation and characterization of the channel that seem likely to influence our concepts about the molecule. Space restrictions prohibit an extended treatment; fortunately, several recent reviews thoroughly discuss channel biophysics (5, 7, 19, 45) and pharmacology (24, 60, 62, 64).

Functional Design of the Sodium Channel

Four properties are essential to sodium channel function: high rates of ion transport, permeation selectivity, and activation and inactivation gating mechanisms. Single activated channels transport $\sim 10^7$ ions per second at

517

0066-4278/84/0315-0517$02.00

normal membrane potentials, with saturation behavior and temperature coefficients consistent with passive movement through a pore rather than via a carrier mechanism (7, 13, 33, 45, 66). Evidence from single-channel recordings also suggests a conducting pore fluctuating between open and closed states (66). The high single-channel conductances (5–10 pS) allow a channel to efficiently depolarize large areas of membrane. This is consistent with the low surface densities usually encountered [$\sim$50–500 μm^{-2}, or about one channel per $\sim$10^6 Å^2 of membrane (61)]. Another essential property is permeation selectivity. The channel selects among monovalent alkali cations in favor of Li$^+$ and Na$^+$, being less permeable to K$^+$, Rb$^+$ and Cs$^+$ (13, 29, 45). This in part underlies the overall membrane's behavior as an ion-selective "electrode" with rapidly variable ion specificity. Although the channel's ionic preferences are not extraordinary, a membrane passing from a state selective for K$^+$ (resting) to one selective for Na$^+$ (active) may change permeability ratios by several hundred–fold. The resultant voltage excursions of 100,000–200,000 volts/cm are sufficient to modulate channels controlling the excitation cycle, or coupled events.

Channel conductance is regulated by precise time- and voltage-dependent activation and inactivation gating mechanisms (4b, 5, 7, 19, 46). At resting potentials the channel is closed, but on rapid depolarization it is activated to permit ion flux. Responding with slower kinetics, an inactivation mechanism blocks transport, leaving the channel in one or more inactivated states. Thus, at equilibrium, the channel is most likely to be closed at all potentials. It functions specifically to sense and amplify rapid, transient depolarizations. Thus, while allosteric enzymes in central metabolism are continuously regulated for maintenance of steady-state conditions, the sodium channel serves in regenerative signal propagation, suggesting novel conformational mechanisms.

Neurotoxins as Biochemical Markers

Postsynaptic receptors have been evolutionarily co-adapted with their neurotransmitter effectors for allosteric regulation. The sodium channel can be similarly treated as a "receptor" for neurotoxins, although in this case the neurotoxins have been selected to bind at critical sites on the channel to disrupt normal activities. Several classes of toxins have been identified that perturb one or more channel properties (for reviews see 19, 24, 60, 61, 64). Some of these have proven useful as biochemical markers and as probes of channel function.

For application in purification studies a toxin should bind stoichiometrically to the membrane-associated or detergent-solubilized channel, with minimal nonspecific interactions. Binding should parallel pharmacological dose response curves and should occur with high affinity. Even with low nonspecific backgrounds, most assay protocols encourage use of toxins with equilibrium dissociation constants (K_d) of the order of binding site concentrations (e.g. <100 nM). Also, purified, radiolabeled derivatives should be easily prepared.

Of the major classes of sodium channel neurotoxins, only the guanidinium channel blockers tetrodotoxin (TTX), saxitoxin (STX), and their derivatives (6, 14, 30, 31, 38, 39, 47, 63, 69, 72), have been thoroughly shown to satisfy these requirements. They bind reversibly, mutually competitively, and, in most types of excitable cells, with high affinity (Kd~1–10 nM). Binding is to a site accessible from the outside of the membrane, causing blockade of sodium currents. Binding is generally independent of the gating states (but see 32) and is believed to occur at the mouth of the ion pore, with a stoichiometry of one per channel (34, 45).

Alkaloid or alkaloid-like toxins, such as veratridine, aconitine, grayanotoxin, batrachotoxin, and yohimbine, apparently bind mutually competitively to a single class of sites (20, 23) with comparatively low affinities. They tend to alter voltage dependence of activation, delay inactivation, and in some instances alter ion selectivity. These lipid-soluble compounds partition nonspecifically into membranes and detergents. Experiments with labeled veratridine (8) and grayanotoxin derivatives (67) have not revealed specific binding sites in membranes, although [^{3}H]-batrachotoxinin A 20-α-benzoate has been used successfully in binding studies with synaptosomes (18, 28, 75).

A third pertinent category of neurotoxins includes peptides from venoms of certain scorpions and coelenterates (19, 24, 60). Some of these, such as *Leiurus* peptide toxin (ScTX)(21) and *Anemonia* toxin II(ATXII)(25) bind to an external site on the channel, again to slow inactivation, alter voltage-dependence of activation, and, in synergistic action with alkaloids, cause chronic activation (20, 23). Labeled ScTX derivatives have been used in binding studies in cells (20, 23), synaptosomes (27, 70), and membranes (27, 59). Binding of ScTX is voltage-sensitive, with the affinity but not the number of sites being reduced under depolarization (22). It has been reported that one ScTX binds for every 2.8–3.7 STX binding sites (26, 27). These findings were initially suggested to reflect possible functional subunit stoichiometries, an interpretation apparently at odds with the conventional concept of 1 STX per channel. However, ScTX binding was also found to be lost, partially reversibly, on solubilization (27, 68, 70). Binding to purified, reconstituted channels, with nearly unitary stoichiometry, was found to be restored by inclusion of as yet unidentified lipid factors, although without recovery of channel activation (68). Therefore, the modes of peptide toxin–channel interaction are likely to be more involved than first thought. A second class of scorpion toxins from *Tityus* and *Centroides* is also emerging as a source of valuable ligands (12, 58a).

PROGRESS IN SOLUBILIZATION AND ISOLATION

An important finding in 1972 by Henderson & Wang (44) was that the TTX binding component from gar olfactory nerve retained binding activity when solubilized by Triton-X 100. These results were quickly confirmed by Benzer

& Raftery (16). Further progress on the problem of purification, however, was hindered by the lack of a tissue suitable for preparative scale isolation, lack of reliable binding assays, and by the instability of the solubilized preparations. In 1978 Agnew et al (2) described solutions to the major problems surrounding isolation of the protein from the eel electroplax. These were: methods for solubilization with nonionic detergents (2, 4, 55), for convenient quantitative binding assays (2, 50), for stabilization of the soluble protein (1, 2) and for fractionation. Several of the observations made with the eel system have quickly found application in studies with skeletal muscle (9) and brain (27, 41, 49).

The Electroplax TTX Receptor

The main electric organ of the eel *Electrophorus electricus* is a nearly homogeneous tissue consisting of large electroplax cells derived in development from muscle (48, 57). The extrajunctional area of the caudal, innervated surface of each cell contains sodium channels in high densities ($>500 \mu m^{-2}$, 50–100 pmol/g tissue) (2, 4, 54, 55), about 2–3 times the abundance of the acetylcholine receptor (65). Membranes prepared from the tissue, solubilized by nonionic detergents such as Lubrol-PX (4, 55), yielded extracts of 15–30 pmol mg^{-1} protein. This is about 0.5–1% of the theoretical specific activity of the pure protein, assuming one receptor site per ~300,000 dalton protein (2, 10, 12, 42, 51). Abandoning slow equilibrium dialysis techniques in favor of a rapid gel filtration assay (2, 50) reduced the time required for binding measurements from hours to a few minutes, permitting in turn a systematic analysis of the stability characteristics of the protein.

STABILIZATION   The instability of soluble preparations was a formidible barrier to purification. Early studies with degradative enzymes (15, 16) suggested that once released from the protective bilayer, the protein was quickly inactivated by endogenous proteases. Soluble preparations of the eel protein, however, were markedly resistant to proteolytic inactivation (4, 55). The key observation was that the protein was destabilized by merely raising the nonionic detergent concentration (1, 2). These findings suggested that instability resulted from dilution of membrane constitutents into a more extensive micellar "phase." Stability was found to be a quantitative function of the phospholipid to detergent ratio. At molar ratios below 1:15 the protein began to lose stability, and at 1:25 activity was lost in seconds. This phenomenon is not yet explained, although it readily accounts for the failure of early purification attempts. Stability dependent on the lipid-detergent ratio has since been observed with the sarcolemmal and synaptosomal proteins (9, 27, 39), with all nonionic detergents tested, and also with the bile salts cholate and deoxycholate (J. Miller & W. Agnew, unpublished). Some lipid specificity has been reported

(1). The protein is normally fractionated in buffers containing detergent supplemented with low levels of phosphatidylcholine. Ca^{+2} aids the lipid stabilization of the brain and sarcolemmal proteins (9, 41, 27). Tetrodotoxin or saxitoxin occupancy of the binding site also can stabilize by two- to tenfold, depending on conditions used (2; S. Levinson & W. Agnew, unpublished).

PURIFICATION   To reach homogeniety, only about a 200-fold purification was required from the soluble extracts. This could be achieved with two or three conventional steps (2, 3, 36, 54). The solubilized protein bound tightly to anion exchange resins such as DEAE Sephadex. A compound present in the extract, possibly an extracellular acid mucopolysaccharide (2), blocked the uptake of most other proteins. At appropriate ratios of extract to resin, all of the receptor but less than 2% of the total protein was adsorbed. After washing, the TTX receptor was desorbed with 50–70% yield by high salt, giving a 20–40-fold purification. Because of the large Stokes radius of the protein, gel filtration of ion exchange–purified samples yielded preparations of specific activity in the range of 2000 pmol/mg protein, rarely as high as 3300 pmol/mg. With these methods (3, 36, 54), high specific activity preparations have been isolated composed of a single type of polypeptide.

The Sarcolemmal STX Receptor

R. L. Barchi and coworkers have found that in mammalian skeletal muscle toxin binding sites are somewhat less abundant than in the electric organ, (18–20 pmol/gm tissue, 0.15–0.20 pmol/mg protein) (11). Isolation of sarcolemma gave a 20-fold enrichment, and detergent extracts were about 6–9 pmol STX binding sites/mg protein. These workers (9) solubilized the STX binding component from sarcolemma with the detergent Non-Idet P-40, stabilizing with Ca^{+2} and phosphatidylcholine. To purify the protein a low charge density guanidinium ion exchange resin was used in the first step, which gave a 10–20-fold enrichment. An additional 10–20-fold purification was achieved by a wheat germ agglutinin affinity purification. In more recent studies (74), as a third step sucrose density gradient sedimentation was used. Specific activities of 1500–2000 pmol sites/mg protein were reported (9), with values near 3000 pmol/mg sometimes achieved. The final peptide composition was somewhat more complex than that of the eel protein (8a, 9).

The Synaptosomal STX Receptor

Rat brain has also proven to be a good preparative tissue, with the STX binding site abundance being somewhat greater than in muscle, (27, 41). Isolated, osmotically lysed synaptosomal membranes are further enriched, and solubilized extracts have about 2–4 pmol sites/mg protein. Recently, Hartshorne & Catterall (41) reported isolation of the synaptosomal STX receptor after solubilization with Triton X-100. The lipid- and Ca^{+2}-stabilized receptor was fractionated on DEAE Sephadex followed by a step of wheat germ agglutinin affinity chromatography. This was sometimes followed by sucrose gradient sedimentation. In a recent modification, hydroxylappatite chromatography has been added as final step, yielding material of simple and reproducible peptide compositions, with specific activities routinely of ~2000 pmol/mg, occasionally near 3000.

CHARACTERISTICS OF THE TTX/STX BINDING PROTEINS

The Electroplax TTX Receptor Peptide Composition

In the initial report on the electroplax protein, Agnew et al (2) described three peptides: of 46,000 daltons, 57,000 daltons, and an indistinct band on SDS-polyacrylamide gels (SDS-PAGE) of ~300,000 daltons. The majority of the protein was accounted for by the largest peptide, which also correlated closely with the distribution of toxin binding. This was subsequently shown to represent part or all of the TTX binding component (3). More recently Miller et al (36, 54) have isolated preparations of high specific activity composed exclusively of this constituent. Thus the TTX binding site must reside on this peptide, suggesting that it may form the ion channel itself. Also in these studies, mg quantities of the SDS-denatured peptide were prepared and used for analysis of its behavior on gels and determination of its amino acid and carbohydrate compositions. The amino acid composition was similar to that of other membrane proteins such as the acetylcholine receptor. However, the peptide was shown to be a glycopeptide, containing approximately 29% by weight complex carbohydrates, enriched in sialic acids and amino sugars. A marked electrophoretic microheterogeneity was attributed to variations in the carbohydrate substitutents. This was subsequently confirmed by treating the peptide with the endoglycosidase endo-β-N-acetylglucosaminidase F, or Endo F (35). This enzyme cleaved at least two carbohydrate chains, to leave a peptide of ~200,000 daltons (SDS-PAGE), which was no longer heterogeneous (4a; Miller & Agnew, in preparation). The molecular weight could not be accurately determined on gels because the peptide bound disproportionate amounts of SDS. Direct binding experiments have indicated association with 2-4-fold more SDS than binds to conventional peptides.

As described below, the synaptosomal protein appears to include two smaller peptide subunits of 37,000 and 39,000 daltons, one of which is linked to a large peptide by disulfide bonds (43). In contrast, when the eel protein was rapidly isolated in large quantities (0.5–0.6 mg) in the presence of high levels of protease inhibitors, no evidence of a disulfide-linked peptide was found. Smaller, noncovalently linked peptides were not detected either, suggesting for the moment that the electroplax protein may be formed from one or more copies of a very large glycopeptide (4a; J. Miller & W. Agnew, in preparation).

The Sarcolemmal STX Receptor Peptide Composition

Barchi et al (9) initially described three peptides in the purest fractions of sarcolemmal STX receptor: of 53,000, 60,000, and 64,000 daltons. In more recent studies, however, these authors have found peptides of 38,000, 39,000, 45,000 daltons, and an anomalous larger peptide of 130,000–230,000 daltons showing evidence of microheterogeneity and of high free electrophoretic mobility in SDS (8a). There may be authentic distinctions between the molecules from these two tissues, or one or both preparations may have been modified by proteolysis during isolation.

The Synaptosomal STX Receptor Peptide Composition

The first compositional data for the neuronal protein came from photoaffinity labeling experiments with an arylazido derivative of ScTX. Beneski & Catterall (14) showed that in neuroblastoma cells the toxin was specifically cross-linked to a peptide of ~250,000 daltons. Similar labeling with the more enriched synaptosomes revealed a 250,000-dalton peptide and a smaller one of 39,000 daltons, suggesting these peptides may be involved with gating structures. Labeling was blocked by depolarization and omission of batrachotoxin and was not observed in neuroblastoma lines lacking the sodium channel ionophore (14).

After isolation (41), the synaptosomal protein was found most likely to include a large peptide of M_r~270,000 (α subunit) and a smaller peptide, perhaps a doublet, of ~39,000. It was subsequently found (43) that one component of the doublet was due to a peptide of ~37,000 daltons. (β_2 subunit) linked to the α-subunit by disulfides. This peptide was not cross-linked by arylazido ScTX. When released by 2-mercaptoethanol, the apparent size of the α-subunit decreased, opposite to behavior expected from breaking intrapeptide disulfides. When synaptosomes were reacted with the arylazido-ScTX, two labeled bands were seen in absence of reduction (α and β_1), as expected. After reduction, the size of the α peptide subunit again decreased, indicating the release of the covalently linked β_2 peptide subunit. Thus, despite concern about a possible proteolytic origin of the small peptides, these all seem to be present even in the isolated nerve terminals. These rather careful studies, again, raise the question of authentic molecular distinctions between sodium channels from the different tissues.

Molecular Weights

Irradiation inactivation studies using high energy electron bombardment of membrane preparations have yielded molecular weights of 230,000–240,000 daltons for the TTX receptor from electroplax and brain (51). Further, Barhanin et al (12) have found targets of $M_r \sim 266,000$ for receptors for *Centroides* and *Tityus* peptide toxins, and $\sim 260,000$ for the TTX receptor, in synaptosomes. These are interestingly close to the direct size estimations of the major peptides in the purified preparations (3, 14, 43, 54).

Preliminary hydrodynamic analysis has yielded molecular weight estimations of $316,000 \pm 60,000$ and $314,000 \pm 30,000$ daltons for the proteins from synaptosomes (42) and sarcolemma (10), each associated with $\sim 270,000$ daltons of bound lipid and detergent. Although these methods have not been used with the electroplax receptor, the sedimentation coefficient (~ 8 S) and Stokes radius (95 Å) are consistent with those of the other proteins (2).

Functional Reconstitution of Purified Proteins

Recently, progress has been made in the reconstitution of neurotoxin modulated ion transport by relatively purified preparations of the proteins from each of the three tissues. In the first report, Weigele & Barchi (74) supplemented purified samples of the sarcolemmal protein with lipids and removed the nonionic detergent (Non-Idet P-40) by adsorption to polystyrene beads, reforming small liposomes with the protein inserted. The protein was stabilized to elevated temperature and the orientation of the STX binding site was random. When treated with batrachotoxin, veratridine, or aconitine, the vesicles took up labeled Na^+ at enhanced rates. This was blocked 50% by 60–200 nM STX. Evidence for ion-selective flux with some of the activating neurotoxins was provided by rapid quench–flow experiments (71).

Subsequently, Talvenheimo, Tamkun & Catterall (68, 69), with procedures similar to those of Weigele & Barchi, were able to reconstitute the purified synaptosomal protein from Triton X-100, also demonstrating recovery of thermal stability, random orientation, and neurotoxin-mediated ion influx, blocked 50% by 10 nM TTX. They also report an uncharacterized lipid factor from brain required to restore binding of ScTX (68) although not activation of flux.

Most recently Rosenberg, Tomiko & Agnew (59a) have reconstituted the purified electroplax protein, with restoration of thermal stability and neurotoxin-activated sodium flux. Here the Lubrol-PX:phosphatidylcholine solubilized protein was depleted of detergent with polystyrene beads and then fused with sonicated phosphatidylcholine liposomes by freeze-thaw-sonication. Batrachotoxin and veratridine activated transport, which in turn was blocked by TTX precisely in parallel with [^{3}H]-TTX binding ($K_d = 33$ nM). Flux was also blocked by local anesthetics, and the quaternary anesthetic QX-222 apparently blocked by binding to a side of the membrane opposite to the TTX receptor site. These studies with the three different preparations suggest it may soon be possible to assign specific roles to the variously reported polypeptide subunits.

Appearance Under the Electron Microscope

Some general insights into the molecular structure of channel proteins have been provided by high-resolution electron microscopy. This approach has revealed features of acetylcholine receptors and gap junction molecules related to both channel function and orientation in the membrane (73).

Homogeneous samples of the eel sodium channel protein examined by negative staining with uranylacetate contained rod shaped particles (36). These aggregated in highly ordered arrays of up to several thousand particles aligned side-to-side in register, often forming twisted ribbons on the grid. Stereoscopic imaging indicated that these were cylinders of ~40 × 170 Å. The dimensions of the particles yielded an estimated mass of ~257,000 daltons, indicating that each could be formed from one copy of the large peptide.

The shape of these particles did not immediately suggest an ion channel. It was speculated that the molecules might orient with the long axis normal to the membrane, although the 170 Å length is far greater than the thickness of a bilayer. In subsequent studies (37a) purified molecules reconstituted into pure lipid liposomes from either Lubrol-PX or from sodium cholate were examined. Freeze fracture and deep-etch techniques revealed intramembrane particles of ~100 Å diameter, protruding slightly (30–40 Å) beyond the true surface of the vesicles. No rod-shaped structures were seen in any orientation. To reconcile the appearances of the preparations, the soluble material in both Lubrol-PX and cholate were examined with negative staining at various pHs. In both detergents at more acidic pHs (<4), the rod structures were present; those in cholate were irregular in shape and did not aggregate in the ordered arrays always seen in Lubrol. At more neutral pH (>4.5), few rods were seen in either detergent. Resolution of individual particles was better in the cholate suspensions, and in these the aggregates appeared composed of "doughnut"-shaped structures of ~100-Å diameter, exhibiting irregular but pronounced central "pits." Numerous examples of individual doughnuts or clusters of two or three together were found. The relationship of the rod structures to the doughnut particles was not resolved. The latter, however, seem most consistent with the particles found in the reconstituted liposomes. The molecule may be conformationally flexible out of the bilayer environment.

IMMUNOLOGY AND IMMUNOCYTOCHEMISTRY

Biophysical and pharmacological similarities of sodium channels from species as phylogenetically distant as molluscs and vertebrates suggest a highly conserved molecular structure. This might extend to immunological determinants, and heterologous or monoclonal antibodies against even a part of the channel would provide important new reagents for immunochemistry and immunocytochemistry.

Monoclonal antibodies against the electroplax protein (56, 58) have been prepared and used to confirm the identity of the large peptide as a channel constituent; they were not initially explored as immunocytochemical markers. Heterologous antibodies against native eel protein were used by Ellisman & Levinson (37) in immunocytochemical studies. These labeled the innervated but not the noninnervated face of the electroplax, consistent with physiological evidence of channel distribution (48, 57). Myelinated neurons from the eel spinal cord were labeled strongly at the node of Ranvier, an area of high channel density (62). Focal labeling of demyelinated nerves indicated concentrations of antigen only in the node, not in the internode, consistent with physiological (17) and toxin binding data (62). Antibodies to the SDS-denatured peptide (54) precipitated the native (TTX binding) form of the protein and selectively labeled node of Ranvier of myelinated neurons in another fish, *Sternarchus* (M. Ellisman, M. Emerick & W. Agnew, unpublished). Thus antibodies to the electroplax protein appear to recognize the neuronal protein, at least in similar species. Whether they can be applied to other species remains to be explored. In animals immunized with the electroplax protein, no evidence has been reported for experimental autoimmune diseases comparable to *myasthenia gravis* elicited by the acetylcholine receptor (52). However, a systematic search for such disorders may be informative.

SUMMARY

In summary, TTX and STX binding have been used to follow the purification of sodium channel proteins from electric organ, mammalian skeletal muscle, and brain. In each instance they were proteins somewhat larger than the acetylcholine receptor and exhibited stability properties that reflect an intimate interaction with membrane lipids. The principal peptide constituent seems to be a large glycopeptide of ~250,000 daltons. Because this is evidently the only constituent of the electroplax protein, it must contain the TTX receptor site, probably forming the ion pathway itself. Photo-labeling with ScTX and studies with *Tityus* γ toxin (58a) indicate a site involved with gating processes, also associated with the large peptide of the neuronal and electroplax proteins. The smaller peptides are not consistent features of all of the preparations, but may contribute to the molecular ensemble. If, however, the entire channel were formed from a single extremely large peptide, there would be interesting mechanistic implications, because the ion transporting and voltage-sensing mechanisms would be accounted for by domains within the folded polypeptide chain. Clearly, the prospect for combining biochemical isolation and reconstitution with the new biophysical technology offers an exciting experimental conjunction.

ACKNOWLEDGMENTS

The author has been supported by grant number NS17928 from the National Institute of Neurological and Communicative Disorders and Stroke, a grant from the National Multiple Sclerosis Society and a Merck Foundation Faculty Development Award. Mr. M. C. Emerick and Drs. J. A. Miller, R. L. Rosenberg, and S. A. Tomiko are thanked for their helpful comments on the manuscript, and Drs. R. Aldrich, D. Corey, and C. Stevens are thanked for providing preprints of work in press.

Literature Cited

1. Agnew, W. S., Raftery, M. A. 1979. Solubilized tetrodotoxin binding component from the electroplax of *Electrophorus electricus;* Stability as a function of mixed lipid-detergent micelle composition. *Biochemistry* 10:1912–19

2. Agnew, W. S., Levinson, S. R., Brabson, J. S., Raftery, M. A. 1978. Purification of the tetrodotoxin-binding component associated with the voltage-sensitive sodium channel from *Electrophorus electricus* electroplax membranes. *Proc. Natl. Acad. Sci. USA* 75:2606–11

3. Agnew, W. S., Moore, A. C., Levinson, S. R., Raftery, M. A. 1980. Identification of a large peptide associated with the tetrodotoxin binding protein from *Electrophorus electricus*. *Biochem. Biophys. Res. Commun.* 92:860–66

4. Agnew, W. S., Moore, A. C., Levinson, S. R., Raftery, M. A. 1981. Biochemical characterization of a voltage-sensitive sodium channel protein from the electroplax of *Electrophorus electricus*. In *Nerve Membrane*, ed. G. Matsumoto, M. Kotani, pp. 25–44. Tokyo: Univ. Tokyo

4a. Agnew, W. S., Miller, J. A., Ellisman, M. H., Rosenberg, R. L., Tomiko, S. A., Levinson, S. R. 1983. The voltage-regulated sodium channel from the electroplax of *Electrophorus electricus*. *48th Cold Spring Harbor Symp. Quant. Biol.* 48: In press

4b. Aldrich, R. W., Corey, D. P., Stevens, C. F. 1983. A reinterpretation of mammalian sodium channel gating based on single channel recordings. *Nature*. In press

5. Almers, W. 1978. Gating currents and charge movements in excitable membranes. *Rev. Physiol. Biochem. Pharmacol.* 82:96–190

6. Angelides, K. J. 1981. Fluorescent and photoactivatable fluorescent derivatives of tetrodotoxin to probe the sodium channel of excitable membranes. *Biochemistry* 20:4107–18

7. Armstrong, C. M. 1981. Sodium channels and gating currents. *Physiol. Rev.* 61:644–82

8. Balerna, M., Fosset, M., Chicheportiche, R., Romey, G., Lazdunski, M. 1975. Constitution and properties of axonal membranes of crustacean nerves. *Biochemistry* 14:5500–11

8a. Barchi, R. L. 1983. Protein components of the purified sodium channel from rat skeletal muscle sarcolemma. *J. Neurochem.* 40:1377–85

9. Barchi, R. L., Cohen, S. A., Murphy, L. E. 1980. Purification from rat sarcolemma of the saxitoxin binding component of the excitable membrane sodium channel. *Proc. Natl. Acad. Sci. USA* 77: 1306–10

10. Barchi, R. L., Murphy, L. E. 1981. Estimate of the molecular weight of the sarcolemmal sodium channel using H_2O-D_2O centrifugation. *J. Neurochem.* 36:2097–100

11. Barchi, R. L., Weigele, J. B. 1979. Characteristics of saxitoxin binding to the sodium channel of sarcolemma isolated from rat skeletal muscle. *J. Physiol.* 295:383–96

12. Barhamin, J., Schmid, A., Lombet, A., Wheeler, K. P., Lazdunski, M., et al. 1983. Molecular size of different neurotoxin receptors on the voltage-sensitive Na^+ channel. *J. Biol. Chem.* 258:700–2

13. Begenisich, T., Cahalan, M. 1979. Nonindependence and selectivity in sodium channels. In *Membrane Transport Processes, Vol. III, Ion Permeation through Membrane Channels*, ed. C. F. Stevens, R. W. Tsien, pp. 105–12. New York: Raven

14. Beneski, D. A., Catterall, W. A. 1980. Covalent labeling of protein components of the sodium channel with a photoacti-

vatable derivative of scorpion toxin. *Proc. Natl. Acad. Sci. USA* 77:639–42

15. Benzer, T., Raftery, M. A. 1972. Partial characterization of a tetrodotoxin-binding component from nerve membrane. *Proc. Natl. Acad. Sci. USA* 69:3634–37

16. Benzer, T., Raftery, M. A. 1973. Solubilization and partial characterization of the tetrodotoxin binding component from nerve axons. *Biochem. Biophys. Res. Commun.* 51:939–44

17. Bostock, H., Sears, T. A. 1978. The internodal axonal membrane: electrical excitability and continuous conduction in segmental demyelination. *J. Physiol.* 280:273–301

18. Brown, G. B., Tieszen, S. C., Daly, J. W., Warnick, J. E., Albuquerque, E. X. 1981. Batrachotoxinin A 20-α-Benzoate: a new radioactive ligand for voltage-sensitive sodium channels. *Mol. Neurobiol.* 1:19–40

19. Cahalan, M. 1981. Molecular properties of sodium channels in excitable membranes. In *The Cell Surface in Neuronal Function,* ed. C. W. Cotman, G. Poste, G. L. Nicolson, pp. 1–47. Amsterdam: Elsevier

20. Catterall, W. A. 1975. Cooperative activation of the action potential Na ionophore by neurotoxins. *Proc. Natl. Acad. Sci. USA* 72:1782–86

21. Catterall, W. A. 1976. Purification of a toxic protein from scorpion venom which activates the action potential ionophore. *J. Biol. Chem.* 251:5528–36

22. Catterall, W. A. 1977. Membrane potential dependent binding of scorpion toxin to the action potential Na ionophore. Studies with a toxin derivative prepared by lactoperoxidase catalyzed iodination. *J. Biol. Chem.* 252:8660–68

23. Catterall, W. A. 1977. Activation of the action potential Na ionophore by neurotoxins: an allosteric model. *J. Biol. Chem.* 252:8669–76

24. Catterall, W. A. 1980. Neurotoxins that act on voltage-sensitive sodium channels in excitable membranes. *Ann. Rev. Pharmacol. Toxicol.* 20:15–43

25. Catterall, W. A., Beress, L. 1978. Sea anemone toxin and scorpion toxin share a common receptor site associated with the action potential Na ionophore. *J. Biol. Chem.* 253:7393–96

26. Catterall, W. A., Morrow, C. S. 1978. Binding of saxitoxin to electrically excitable neuroblastoma cells. *Proc. Natl. Acad. Sci. USA* 75:218–22

27. Catterall, W. A., Morrow, C. S., Hartshorne, R. P. 1979. Neurotoxin binding to receptor sites associated with voltage-sensitive sodium channels in intact, lysed, and detergent solubilized brain membranes. *J. Biol. Chem.* 254:11379–87

28. Catterall, W. A., Morrow, C. S., Daly, J. W., Brown, G. B. 1981. Binding of Batrachotoxinin A 20-α-Benzoate to sodium channels by the anticonvulsant drugs diphenylhydantoin and carbamazepine. *Mol. Pharm.* 22:627–35

29. Chandler, W. K., Meves, H., 1965. Voltage clamp experiments on internally perfused giant axons. *J. Physiol.* 180:788–820

30. Chicheportiche, R., Balerna, M., Lombet, A., Romey, G., Lazdunski, M. 1979. Synthesis and mode of action on axonal membranes of photactivable derivatives of tetrodotoxin. *J. Biol. Chem.* 254:1552–57

31. Chicheportiche, R., Balerna, M., Lombet, A., Romey, G., Lazdunski, M. 1980. Syntheseis of new, highly radioactive tetrodotoxin derivatives and their binding properties to the sodium channel. *Eur. J. Biochem.* 104:617–25

32. Cohen, C. J., Bean, B. J., Colatsky, T. J., Tsien, R. W. 1981. Tetrodotoxin block of sodium channels in rabbit purkinje fibers: interaction between toxin binding and channel gating. *J. Gen. Physiol.* 78:383–411

33. Conti, F., Hille, B., Neumcke, B., Nonner, W., Stampfli, R. 1976. Conductance of the sodium channel in myelinated nerve fibers with modified sodium channel inctivation. *J. Physiol.* 262:729–42

34. Cuervo, L. A., Adelman, W. J. 1970. Equilibrium and kinetic properties of the interaction between tetrodotoxin and the excitable membrane of the squid giant axon. *J. Gen. Physiol.* 55:309–55

35. Elder, J. H., Alexander, S. 1982. Endo-β - N-Acetylglucosaminidase F: Endoglycosidase from *Flavobacterium meningosepticum* that cleaves both high mannose and complex glycoproteins. *Proc. Natl. Acad. Sci. USA* 79:4540–44

36. Ellisman, M. H., Agnew, W. S., Miller, J. A., Levinson, S. R. 1982. Electron microscopic visualization of the tetrodotoxin binding protein from *Electrophorus electricus. Proc. Natl. Acad. Sci. USA* 79:4461–65

37. Ellisman, M. H., Levinson, S. R. 1982. Immunocytochemical localization of sodium channel (TTX binding protein) distribution in excitable membranes of *Electrophorus electricus. Proc. Natl. Acad. Sci. USA* 79:6707–11

37a. Ellisman, M. H., Miller, J. A., Agnew, W. S. 1983. Molecular morphology of the tetrodoxin binding sodium channel protein from *Electrophorus electricus* in solubilized and reconstituted preparations. *J. Cell Biol.* In press

38. Ghazarossian, R. J., Schantz, E. J., Schnoes, H. H., Strong, F. M. 1976. A biologically active acid hydrolysis product of saxitoxin. *Biochem. Biophys. Res. Commun.* 68:776–80

39. Hafeman, D. R. 1972. Binding of radioactive tetrodotoxin to nerve membrane preparations. *Biochem. Biophys. Acta* 266:548–56

40. Hamill, P., Marty, A., Neher, E., Sakman, B., Sigworth, F. J. 1981. Improved patch clamp techniques for high resolution current recordings in cells and cell free membrane patches. *Pfluegers Arch.* 391:85–100

41. Hartshorne, R., Catterall, W. A. 1981. Purification of the saxitoxin receptor from rat brain. *Proc. Natl. Acad. Sci. USA* 78:4620–24

42. Hartshorne, R. P., Coppersmith, J., Catterall, W. A. 1980. Size characteristics of the solubilized saxitoxin receptor of the voltage-sensitive sodium channel from rat brain. *J. Biol. Chem.* 255:10572–75

43. Hartshorne, R. P., Messner, D. J., Coppersmith, J. C., Catterall, W. A. 1982. The saxitoxin receptor of the sodium channel from rat brain; evidence for two non-identical β-subunits. *J. Biol. Chem.* 257:13888–91

44. Henderson, R., Wang, J. H. 1972. Solubilization of a specific tetrodotoxin binding component from garfish olfactory nerve membranes. *Biochemistry* 11:4565–69

45. Hille, B. 1975. The receptor for tetrodotoxin and saxitoxin: a structural hypothesis. *Biophys. J.* 15:615–19

46. Hodgkin, A. C., Huxley, A. F. 1952. A quantitative description of membrane current and its application to conduction and to excitation in nerve. *J. Physiol.* 117:500–44

47. Kao, C. Y., Walker, S. E. 1982. Active groups of saxitoxin and tetrodotoxin as deduced from actions of saxitoxin analogues on frog muscle and squid axon. *J. Physiol.* 323:619–37

48. Keynes, R. D., Martins-Ferreira, H. 1953. Membrane potentials in the electroplates of the electric eel. *J. Physiol.* 119:315–51

49. Krueger, B. K., Ratzloff, R. W., Strichartz, G. R., Blaustein, M. P. 1979. Saxitoxin binding to synaptosomes, membranes, and solubilized binding sites from rat brain. *J. Membr. Biol.* 50:287–310

50. Levinson, S. R., Curatalo, C. J., Reed, J. K., Raftery, M. A. 1979. A rapid and precise assay for tetrodotoxin binding to detergent extracts of excitable tissues. *Anal. Biochem.* 99:72–84

51. Levinson, S. R., Ellory, J. C. 1972. Molecular size of the tetrodotoxin binding site estimated by irradiation inactivation. *Nature New Biol.* 245:122–23

52. Lindstrom, J. M. 1979. The role of antibodies to the acetylcholine receptor and its component peptides in experimental autoimmune myasthenia gravis in rats. In *Plasmapheresis and the Immunobiology of Myasthenia Gravis*, ed. Peter C. Dau, pp. 3–19. Boston: Houghton-Mifflen

53. Lindstrom, J., Gullick, B., Conti-Traconi, B., Ellisman, M. H. 1980. Proteolytic nicking of the acetylcholine receptor. *Biochemistry* 19:4791–95

54. Miller, J. A., Agnew, W. S., Levinson, S. R. 1983. Principal glycopeptide of the tetrodotoxin/saxitoxin binding protein from *Electrophorus electricus:* isolation and partial chemical and physical characterization. *Biochemistry* 22:462–70

55. Moore, A. C., Agnew, W. S., Raftery, M. A. 1982. Biochemical characterization of the tetrodotoxin binding protein from *Electrophorus electricus*. *Biochemistry* 24:6212–20

56. Moore, H.-P., Fritz, L. C., Raftery, M. A., Brockes, J. P. 1982. Isolation and characterization of a monoclonal antibody against the saxitoxin binding component from the electric organ of *Electrophorus electricus*. *Proc. Natl. Acad. Sci. USA* 79:6707–11

57. Nakamura, Y., Nakajima, S., Grundfest, H. 1965. Analysis of spike electrogenesis and depolarizing K inactivation in *Electrophorus electricus*. *J. Gen. Physiol.* 49:321–49

58. Nakayama, T., Withey, R., Raftery, M. A. 1982. Use of a monoclonal antibody to purify the tetrodotoxin binding component from the electroplax of *Electrophorus electricus*. *Proc. Natl. Acad. Sci. USA* 79:7575–79

58a. Norman, R. I., Schmid, A., Lombet, A., Barhanin, J., Lazdunski, M. 1983. Purification of binding protein for *Tityus* γ toxin identified with the gating component of the voltage-sensitive Na channel. *Proc. Natl. Acad. Sci. USA* 80:4164–68

59. Okamoto, H. 1980. Binding of scorpion toxin *in vitro* and its modification by β-bungarotoxin. *J. Physiol.* 299:507–16

59a. Rosenberg, R. L., Tomiko, S. A., Agnew, W. S. 1984. Reconstitution of neurotoxin modulated ion transport by the voltage-regulated sodium channel isolated from the electroplax of *Elec-*

trophorus electricus. Proc. Natl. Acad. Sci. USA. In press

60. Ritchie, J. M. 1979. A pharmacological approach to the structure of sodium channels in myelinated axons. Ann. Rev. Neurosci. 2:341–62

61. Ritchie, J. M., Rogart, R. B. 1977. The binding of saxitoxin and tetrodotoxin to excitable tissue. Rev. Physiol. Biochem. Pharmacol. 79:1–50

62. Ritchie, J. M., Rogart, R. B. 1977. Density of sodium channels in mammalian myelinated nerve fibers and nature of the axonal membrane under the myelin sheath. Proc. Natl. Acad. Sci. USA 74: 211–15

63. Ritchie, J. M., Rogart, R. B., Strichartz, G. R. 1976. A new method for labeling saxitoxin and its binding to nonmyelinated fibers of the rabbit vagus, lobster walking leg and garfish olfactory nerves. J. Physiol. 261:477–94

64. Rogart, R. 1981. Sodium channels in nerve and muscle membrane. Ann. Rev. Physiol. 43:711–25

65. Schmidt, J., Raftery, M. A. 1972. A simple assay for the study of solubilized acetylcholine receptors. Anal. Biochem. 52:349–54

66. Sigworth, F. J., Neher, E. 1980. Single Na channel currents observed in cultured rat muscle cells. Nature 287:443–49

67. Soeda, Y., O'Brien, R. D., Yeh, J. Z., Narahashi, T. 1975. Evidence that α-dihydrograyanotoxin II does not bind to the sodium gate. Membr. Biol. 23:91–101

68. Talvenheimo, J. A., Catterall, W. A. 1983. Functional reconstitution of the sodium channel purified from rat brain. Biophys. J. 41:142a

69. Talvenheimo, J., Tamkun, M. M., Catterall, W. A. 1982. Reconstitution of neurotoxin stimulated sodium transport by the voltage-sensitive sodium channel purified from rat brain. J. Biol. Chem. 257:11868–71

70. Tamkun, M. M., Catterall, W. A. 1981. Reconstitution of the voltage-sensitive sodium channel of rat brain from solubilized components. J. Biol. Chem. 256: 11457–63

71. Tanaka, J. C., Eccleston, J. F., Barchi, R. L. 1983. Cation selectivity of the purified, reconstituted sodium channel from skeletal muscle sarcolemma. Biophys. J. 41:50a

72. Tsien, R. Y., Green, D. P. L., Levinson, S. R., Rudy, B., Sanders, J. K. M. 1975. A pharmacologically active derivative of tetrodotoxin. Proc. R. Soc. London Ser. B 191:555–59

73. Unwin, P. N. T., Zampighi, G. 1980. Structure of the junction between communicating cells. Nature 283:545–49

74. Weigele, J., Barchi, R. 1982. Functional reconstitution of the purified sodium channel protein from rat sarcolemma. Proc. Natl. Acad. Sci. USA 79:3651–55

75. Willow, M., Catterall, W. A. 1982. Inhibition of binding of [H]Batrachotoxinin A 20-Benzoate to sodium channels by the anticonvulsant drugs diphenylhydantoin and carbamazepine. Mol. Pharm. 22: 627–35

Ann. Rev. Physiol. 1984. 46:531–48

GRAMICIDIN CHANNELS

Olaf Sparre Andersen

Department of Physiology and Biophysics, Cornell University Medical College, 1300 York Avenue, New York, New York 10021

This review summarizes the literature on channels formed by the linear gramicidins.

STRUCTURE

The gramicidins are linear polypeptides (107–109):

$$\text{Formyl–L–XXX–Gly–L–Ala–D–Leu–L–Ala–D–Val–L–Val–D–Val –}$$
$$1 \quad 2 \quad 3 \quad 4 \quad 5 \quad 6 \quad 7 \quad 8$$

$$\text{L–Trp–D–Leu–L–YYY–D–Leu–L–Trp–D–Leu–L–Trp–Ethanolamine,}$$
$$9 \quad 10 \quad 11 \quad 12 \quad 13 \quad 14 \quad 15$$

where XXX denotes Val or Ile, while YYY denotes Trp, Phe, or Tyr in gramicidin A, B, and C respectively. The sequences are among the most hydrophobic known (113), and the alternating L- and D- amino acids permit the molecules to form helical structures with the polar peptide groups lining a central cavity and the nonpolar side chains projecting from the exterior surface (123, 126, 133). This arrangement permits the molecules to be incorporated into lipid bilayer structures and form cation selective channels (52, 71).

The membrane-bound channels are dimers; most dimers, if not all, are conducting channels (17, 134, 135). Gramicidin A also forms dimers in organic solvents (100, 131). Spectroscopic studies show, however, that the major conformer(s) of the membrane-bound dimers are different from the major conformer(s) of the dimers in organic solvents (137).

The solution structures are generally assumed to be intertwined parallel or antiparallel double helices, as suggested by Veatch et al (133). Spectroscopic analysis of gramicidin solutions and detailed comparisons with computed spectra (115) indicate that the predominant structures are antiparallel double helices, but that there are also smaller amounts of head-to-head associated

531

dimeric helices of the type originally proposed by Urry (123), [see also Ramachandran and Chandrasekaran (97)]. This generally accepted structure for the transmembrane channel is the β-helical dimer, in which the channel is formed by two left-handed helices joined by hydrogen bonds at their N-terminal ends. Conclusive experimental support for this picture of the channel was obtained from single-channel and spectroscopic studies on appropriately modified gramicidins (12, 16, 117, 125, 127, 130, 135, 139, 140). Both structural and permeability considerations argue that the channel is the β^6-helical dimer, with 6.3 residues per turn, a uniform luminal diameter of about 4 Å, and a length of about 26 Å (38, 125).

The spectroscopic characteristics of the membrane-bound dimers are the same in both the absence and presence of small monovalent cations (137), while the solvent structures vary considerably upon cation binding (62, 136).

Gramicidin A has been crystallized from organic solvents, and preliminary structural information has been obtained from X-ray diffraction patterns (63, 64). Two different dimeric structures were deduced from the Patterson maps, one for gramicidin crystallized in the absence of salt (length 32 Å, luminal diameter 2 Å), the other for salt- (KSCN or CsSCN) containing crystals (length 26 Å, luminal diameter 3.8 Å). There are two crystallographic cation-binding sites per gramicidin dimer (63). Results of X-ray, NMR, and single-channel investigations are all consistent with the existence of ion-binding sites 2.5 Å from each end of the 26 Å long dimer (8, 63, 127), although there are no clearly distinctive groups in the channel that can function as ion-binding sites. [Ions in the channel are located in energy minima, with positions determined by the superposition of long-range electrostatic forces due to image potentials (57, 58, 77, 92, 93) and local interactions between the ions and the channel wall (e.g. 31, 98). Other factors may also be important, as cations also bind to the C-terminal ends of gramicidin dimers in organic solvents (49)]. The ion-free crystal form has been studied by neutron diffraction, and the structure has been solved to 5 Å (66).

Gramicidin A crystals grown from organic solvents could represent the solvent form(s) or the membrane-bound form(s) of the molecule. (The crystals could grow from a minor conformer in the solution). The ion-free crystals may be solvent forms, while the ion-containing crystals could be of either type. Spectroscopic studies on the mother liquor suggest that the latter crystals may be solvent forms (136, but see also 115). Their dimer dimensions are identical with those obtained from ab initio construction of the peptide backbone for the β^6-helix (65), while a comparison with the dimensions of the proposed solvent structures in Veatch et al (133) shows rather poor agreement.

Gramicidin A has been co-crystallized with phospholipids (61), but it is not known if these crystals represent a membrane-bound form of the molecule.

The major peak in gramicidin A single-channel-amplitude histograms is generally believed to represent channels that have a unique β-helical structure. Published histograms show, however, that a considerable number of channels (up to 50%) fall outside the major peak (e.g. 5, 20, 24, 53). The less frequent channels generally have conductances that are less than the conductances of the channels in the major peak. These minichannels could be due to other channel-forming entities in the gramicidin A samples, or they could represent less frequent conformations of the gramicidin A channel. Some of the minichannels do seem to be formed by gramicidin A (24): one can observe spontaneous state changes (transitions between standard and minichannels) with a frequency that is much too high to be explained by the closing of one channel and the coincidental opening of another. The minis may represent minor variations on the β^6-helical scheme, as the lifetimes of mini and standard channels are comparable (24, 116).

GATING CHARACTERISTICS

The kinetics of channel formation has been investigated by voltage-induced conductance relaxations (15, 17, 18, 43, 141) and current fluctuation (noise) analysis (67, 68, 141). The rate constant for channel formation is estimated to be several orders of magnitude less than the diffusion-controlled limit in a two-dimensional system (17) and dependent upon the lipid composition of the membranes (43, 67, 141). The mechanisms underlying this lipid dependence are not understood. The average single-channel lifetimes also depend on the membrane composition (20, 53, 67, 90, 94, 103, 141). The composition dependence of the lifetimes correlates with changes in membrane surface tension (46, 90, 103), although thickness changes may also play an important role (e.g. 46).

PERMEABILITY CHARACTERISTICS

The wall of a gramicidin channel is lined by the polar groups in the peptide backbone. These polar groups form an array of coordination sites (associated with the carbonyl oxygens) along which ions and H_2O move through the channel. The permeability characteristics of the channel reflect the characteristics of this polar permeation path as well as its narrow and uniform lumen (39). Permeability data were, in fact, decisive for the choice of the β^6-helix as the channel-forming comformation. The luminal diameter of 4 Å is consistent with the channel's permeability to H_2O and small monovalent cations and its impermeability to urea, larger nonelectrolytes, and $N(CH_3)_4^+$ (38, 53, 88). The very high H^+ permeability suggests that the H_2O in the channel forms a continuous phase along which the H^+ can jump (88). The 4 Å luminal diameter restricts the H_2O to form a single row (see also 82), and demands that H_2O and ions other than H^+ move by a single-file mechanism: H_2O and ions cannot pass each other as they move through the channel.

H_2O Permeability

The H_2O permeability of a channel is characterized by two permeability coefficients: p_d (H_2O), the diffusional permeability coefficient; and p_f, the osmotic permeability coefficient (e.g. 39). These two permeability coefficients will generally be different from each other, and the difference provides important insight into the operation of the channel. For a single-filing channel, one finds that the ratio $p_f/p_d(H_2O)$ is equal to N, the average number of H_2O molecules in the channel (40, 76, 99, but see also 83). Both p_f and $p_d(H_2O)$ were determined for gramicidin A channels in bacterial phosphatidylethanolamine membranes (102). Their ratio, N, was 5.3, indicating that 5–6 H_2O occupy the (single-filing part of the) channel. p_f has also been determined in glycerolmonooleate membranes (27). Interestingly, the two estimates for p_f were about 6-fold apart: 10^{-14} and 6×10^{-14} cm^3 s^{-1}. This difference is most likely due to lipid modulation of the channel's permeability characteristics.

Ion-H_2O Interactions

The single-file flux-coupling of ions and H_2O is reflected in electrokinetic phenomena (e.g. streaming potentials and electroosmosis) and the blockage of H_2O movement by permeant ions (27, 80, 81, 101). The electrokinetic phenomena reflect how many H_2O move through the channel each time an ion moves through the channel, while the ion -induced block of H_2O movement should give information about equilibrium ion binding within the channel.

Streaming-potential measurements show, at low salt concentrations, that 7–9 H_2O move through the channel with each ion, while only about 5 H_2O move with an ion at high salt concentrations (80, 101). [Levitt (80) found that the number of H_2O coupled to the movement of Na^+ is about 9, independent of salt concentration.] The general picture of the channel one obtains from these measurements is consistent with that obtained from the comparison of p_f and $p_d(H_2O)$, although the concentration-dependent decrease in the number of H_2O that are coupled to ion movement is not understood. It could result from multiple-ion occupancy, where the H_2O is displaced by the binding of a second ion, but it could also result from the increase in the aqueous solute concentration and consequent decrease in the chemical potential for H_2O, which should tend to decrease the number of H_2O in the channel (39).

If ions bind in the single-filing part of the channel, this should block osmotic H_2O flow measured under open-circuit conditions. This was the case for Li^+, K^+, and Tl^+ (27). The decrease in p_f was a function of the permeant ion concentration. The data were well fitted by assuming that binding of one ion abolished H_2O movement completely. It was possible to estimate dissociation constants between the ions and the channel: 115, 69, and 2 mM for Li^+,

K^+, and Tl^+, respectively. For Na^+ the situation is more complex, as $p_d(H_2O)$ was unaffected by increases in salt concentration (to 2 M) where a 4-fold decrease was predicted (39).

Ion Permeability

Gramicidin A channels appear to be ideally selective for small univalent cations (88, 122), while they are blocked by divalent cations (19). The single-channel conductances for the alkali-metal cations and H^+ are ranked as the aqueous mobilities (5, 53, 91, 122), although the relative conductance variations are larger than the mobility variations (e.g. 51).

The ion permeability of gramicidin channels is abnormally high compared to predictions extrapolated from macroscopic continuum hydrodynamics (e.g. 21). The single-channel conductance in 0.01 M CsCl is about 3 pS (e.g. 7). This value should be compared to the conductance of an aqueous cylinder having the same dimensions as the channel: about 4 pS if the ion size is disregarded, and about 0.002 pS if the steric restrictions and hydrodynamic interactions between the ion and the channel are taken into account. The use of continuum hydrodynamics is unjustified, but these calculations illustrate that the gramicidin channel is not just a water-filled hole! The polar groups that line the wall, solvating ions, and H_2O are critical for the channel's permeability characteristics.

The channels are, in fact, so permeable that single-channel conductances measured at low permeant ion concentrations are significantly affected by ion movement, through the aqueous phases, up to the channel entrance (7). The aqueous convergence permeability, p_a, was estimated from the voltage-independent currents observed at high potentials, low permeant ion concentrations, and high concentrations of impermeant salt (tetraethylammonium chloride, TEACl), to suppress interfacial polarization effects (6, 138). [The use of TEA^+ as an inert cation has been questioned (34), but similar results were obtained in the absence of TEACl if appropriate corrections were made for the interfacial polarization (6)]. For Na^+ through Cs^+, p_a thus estimated was proportional to the aqueous diffusion coefficients for the ions (about 2.6 × 10^{-13} cm^3 s^{-1} for Cs^+), while disproportionately large values were found for NH_4^+, Ag^+, and Tl^+ (7, 9). [For H^+, p_a must also be disproportionately large, at least 2.4 × 10^{-12} cm^3 s^{-1}, to be consistent with the conductance data of Neher et al (91) and Eisenman et al (30)].

The p_a estimate for Cs^+ agrees with the predictions of a simple macroscopic description of diffusion-limited entry of an ion of radius 1.6 Å into a channel of radius 2.0 Å (7, 73), but this cannot be a realistic description. In analogy with solution-complexation kinetics (e.g. 23), ion association with the channel must involve a diffusion-controlled (bimolecular) encounter to form an outer-sphere complex and a series of subsequent (unimolecular) steps in which most of the aqueous solvation shell is replaced by the carbonyl oxygens in the channel wall.

The magnitudes of p_a estimated from voltage-independent currents should therefore reflect the magnitude of the convergence permeability and limitations imposed by voltage-independent steps subsequent to the diffusion-controlled encounter. The concentration variations in the shape of the current-voltage characteristics argue, however, that the major voltage-independent step must be bimolecular (5). Electrostatic calculations show that a substantial fraction of an applied potential difference falls, in the aqueous phases, close to the channel entrances (58–60, 77). Estimates for p_a should thus reflect the magnitude of the aqueous-convergence permeability to the channel entrance, although mechanistic or structural interpretations of the magnitude of p_a are inappropriate at this time. Further insight may come from molecular dynamics simulations (e.g. 82) and experimental studies on the non-noble gas cations.

The gramicidin A single-channel conductance is a saturating function of the permeant ion activity (53, 91, 122). The conductance reaches a plateau at 1–2 M salt (about 100 pS for Rb^+ and Cs^+ in glycerolmonooleate membranes) and decreases slightly at higher concentrations. This behavior suggests that ion binding to the channel is a saturable process and that at least one—most likely two (or more)—ion(s) can occupy the channel. Conductance-activity relations do not provide sufficient information to determine the ion occupancy or kinetics of ion movement through the channel; additional information is necessary (122). The most informative experiments are those sensitive to interactions among permeant ions, as these in principle provide information about the number of ions that simultaneously can occupy the channel. If, for example, the tracer-ion permeability coefficient differs from (is less than) the net ion permeability coefficient obtained from conductance measurements, or if the bi-ionic potential varies as a function of the permeant ion activity, one will generally conclude that the channel can be occupied by more than one ion (39, 44, 48, 55, 80, 99, 105, 121).

Tracer-flux measurements thus show that at least two K^+, Rb^+, Cs^+, or Tl^+ can occupy the channel simultaneously (96, 110, 111; J. Procopio & O. S. Andersen, unpublished observations). The situation for Na^+ is less clear. Schagina et al (111) found that the tracer permeability was significantly less than predicted from the small-signal conductance for channels in membranes formed from mixed brain lipids (the ratio of the two permeabilities was 0.84 ± 0.03 (mean $\pm$ s.e.m.) in 0.1 M NaCl). Procopio & Andersen (96; J. Procopio & O. S. Andersen, unpublished results), however, found the two permeability coefficients to be equal for channels in diphytanoylphosphatidylcholine membranes. (The ratio of the permeability coefficients were 0.99 ± 0.02, 0.99 ± 0.04, and 1.02 ± 0.02 in 0.1, 1.0, and 5.0 M NaCl, respectively). These differences are presently unexplained, but they could possibly reflect profound effects of the lipid environment on the channel characteristics.

Bi-ionic and reversal potential measurements have likewise shown that at least two K^+, Cs^+, NH_4^+ or Tl^+ can occupy the channel (37, 88, 122). The evidence for Na is ambiguous (122).

Additional evidence for multiple-ion occupancy comes from mole–fraction–dependent conductance changes, where single-channel conductances are determined in symmetrical mixtures of two permeant ions. A nonmonotonous conductance variation as a function of the mole fraction of the mixture indicates multiple occupancy by one or both ions (48, 106, 121). Mole–fraction–dependent conductance changes have been observed in mixtures of Tl^+ or Ag^+ and the alkali-metal cations (3, 4, 36, 85, 89).

An alternative, more model-dependent approach is to supplement conductance vs activity data with information gained from concentration-dependent changes in the shape of single- or many-channel current-voltage characteristics. The shape changes reflect changes in the position of the major barrier(s) for ion movement through the channel, which would involve the entry barrier at low ion occupancies (low concentrations) and the exit barrier at high ion occupancies (high concentrations). This approach has been used extensively by Eisenman, Hägglund & Sandblom (32, 33, 35).

Kinetic Models and Interpretation

Kinetic descriptions of ion movement through gramicidin and other ion-conducting channels have with few exceptions (e.g. 79) been developed as Eyring Rate Theory or similar discrete site-and-barrier descriptions (1, 48, 51, 78, 72, 121). These models assume that ions in the channels are located in a few discrete energy wells or sites, which means that it is assumed that the time spent in transitions between sites can be neglected in comparison to the average time spent at the sites. These are reasonable assumptions, but they are probably wrong because comparisons of H_2O and ion permeabilities indicate that ions permeate through gramicidin channels at a rate that is close to the upper limit determined by $p_d(H_2O)$ (28, 39). This means that the barrier to ion movement through the channel interior must be quite small and presumably of considerable spatial extent, in agreement with the electrostatic calculations of Jordan (58–60). Formalisms based upon a diffusive description of ion movement over a barrier (70) may thus be more appropriate than the Eyring Rate Theory descriptions, unless a large number of sites and barriers are used to describe the ion movement through the channel interior. The discrete site-and-barrier descriptions should nevertheless be useful approximations for many purposes, although the neglect of ion-H_2O single-filing interactions may prove to be a serious deficiency.

The simplest description that accounts for the qualitative features of the conductance-activity characteristics, concentration–dependent bi-ionic potentials, and mole fraction–dependent conductances is the two-site–three-barrier model with double occupancy, developed in complete form by Urban & Hladky (121). Single-channel conductance and bi-ionic potential data were used to estimate the kinetic parameters for gramicidin A channels in glycerol-monooleate membranes (122). A striking feature of the fit was the very low dissociation constants for the first ion that binds (between 0.056 mM for Tl^+ and 4.1 mM for Na^+). These high affinities were deduced because the bi-ionic potentials were concentration-dependent at low salt concentrations (1–100 mM), and because single-channel conductance ratios at 10 mM did not equal the permeability ratio deduced from bi-ionic potentials. There are reasons to doubt the interpretation of both findings, because concentration–dependent bi-ionic potentials can arise from aqueous-convergence permeability limitations (7), and because the conductance ratio for K^+ over Na^+ is equal to the permeability ratio if measured at, or close to, the bi-ionic potential (5, 7, 29).

The two-site–three-barrier model is qualitatively acceptable, but it has not, up to now, provided a complete quantitative description of ion movement through the channel. It is not clear whether such a description in fact will be possible within the framework of the discrete site-and-barrier models, but important attempts to achieve such descriptions have been pursued by Eisenman, Hägglund & Sandblom (43a, 105, 106) using models where the channels may be simultaneously occupied by up to 4 ions. The kinetic schemes were solved using simplifying assumptions that were made necessary by the algebraic complexities encountered. The first model assumed that there is a large central barrier and that the two sites at each end of the channel are in equilibrium with each other and with the adjacent aqueous phase (106). A second model assumes that there is a central barrier and that the two sites at each end of the channel are single-filing and in equilibrium with each other, but not in equilibrium with the aqueous phase (43a). The third model assumes that there is a central barrier and that the outer sites at each end of the channel are in equilibrium with the aqueous phases, but not with the inner sites (105). The first model was not compatible with the observed concentration-dependence of the current-voltage characteristics (54). The second model can probably be excluded on the basis of available tracer-flux data (35). The third model accounts quantitatively for the available conductance-activity relations, tracer-flux data, and current-voltage characteristics (33). There is, however, a serious problem: the deduced positions of the ion-binding sites vary with ion type. X-ray diffraction (63), independent single-channel (8), and NMR (127, 130) data all agree that the position of the binding sites should be independent of the ion species. [The interpretation of the single-channel data in (8) is, however, as model-dependent as the interpretation in (33). But the conclusions are in better agreement with the independent determinations.]

LIPID MODULATION OF ION PERMEABILITY

The permeability characteristics of gramicidin channels depend on the composition of the bilayer (see previous section; 11, 20, 42, 67, 90, 116). Conductance changes occur with changes in the polar head groups of phospholipids that have identical fatty acid composition, such as an increase in methylation in going from phosphatidylethanolamine to phosphatidylcholine (20, 90), or the introduction of a net charge (11). Conductance changes may also occur with changes in the fatty acid composition of phospholipids with identical head-groups, c.f. dioleoylphosphatidylcholine (67) and diphytanoylphosphatidyl-choline (11), where the single-channel conductances in 0.1 M salt are about 2-fold larger in the latter lipid. These effects and those of cholesterol (e.g. 84) are poorly understood. It is established, however, that the channels sense changes in surface potentials (2, 11, 116) similar to the changes observed with mobile carriers and hydrophobic ions (e.g. 86), while they only seem to sense a small fraction of interfacial dipole potential changes (4, 116), in agreement with the predictions of Jordan (59). (It is not clear, however, how a dipole potential change will affect the conductance of channels with a small central barrier. The conductance may increase because the rate constant for transloca-tion through the channel interior is increased, or it may decrease because the dissociation rate constant is decreased.)

EQUILIBRIUM ION BINDING

The equilibrium binding of small monovalent cations to gramicidin dimers has been studied in organic solvents (26, 49, 62, 69, 119, 120) and bilayer (132) or micellar structures (50, 128, 129).

The equilibrium selectivity for gramicidin channels is considerable. Veatch & Durkin (132) found by equilibrium dialysis a single set of binding sites for Tl^+ with a dissociation constant of 1–2 mM (this is an upper estimate, as no corrections were made for the Gibbs-Donnan effect on ion distributions across the dialysis membrane), while the values for Na^+ and Rb^+ were undetectably high (>30 mM). Only one Tl^+ bound to the channel—indicating substantial repulsion between the first and second binding ion.

Equilibrium and kinetic aspects of Na^+ binding to gramicidin A dimers and covalently dimerized malonyl gramicidin A in lysophosphatidylcholine micel-les have been studied by $^{23}Na^+$ NMR (128, 129). Two classes of binding sites were observed, with dissociation constants of 10–15 and 300–1000 mM, respectively. This was interpreted to signify double occupany of Na^+ in the dimers. Rate constants for Na^+ dissociation from the tight and weak binding sites were estimated, and it was possible to obtain acceptable predictions of the magnitudes of single-channel currents in glycerolmonooleate membranes using a two-site–three-barrier model, by letting the rate constant for translocation through the channel interior be an adjustable parameter. An independent estimate of the translocation rate constant (for Tl^+) was obtained by dielectric relaxation studies (47).

The dissociation and rate constants estimated by Urry et al (128, 129) agree with the estimates of Urban et al (122) for Na^+ single-channel data in glycerol-monooleate membranes, and they are in general agreement with the tracer-flux data of Schagina et al (111). The dissociation constants differ substantially from the Na^+ data of Veatch & Durkin (132), and the rate constants do not predict the tracer-flux results of Procopio & Andersen (96), as the rate constants lead to the prediction that the tracer permeability coefficient should be less than the net permeability coefficient in 0.1 and 1.0 M NaCl. This may reflect the lipid dependence of the gramicidin A channel characteristics. But it is also possible that there is no double occupancy with Na^+, and that the NMR data reflect the variation in binding affinities and dissociation rate constants among the dimers in the micelles, similar to the variations inferred from the population variation in single-channel conductances (e.g. 24, 116).

The dissociation constant for Tl^+ binding to gramicidin A channels in lysophosphatidylcholine micelles were determined by ^{205}Tl NMR (50). The dissociation constant, 1 mM, agrees with the findings of Veatch & Durkin (132).

CHEMICAL MODIFICATION

Covalently modified gramicidins have been used to establish the general structure of the transmembrane channel, to locate the cation binding sites, to establish the handedness of the helix, and to investigate structure-function relations for a transmembrane channel.

The structural aspects were addressed by altering, or removing, the N- and C-terminal blocking groups to produce compounds with drastic changes in channel characteristics (10, 12, 14, 16, 117, 123, 125). The work with N-pyromellityldesformyl and O-pyromellityl gramicidin (10, 12) and succinyl gramicidin A derivatives (14) is particularly important in this regard, as it demonstrated beyond reasonable doubt that the predominant structure of gramicidin A channels is the head-to-head joined β-helical dimer.

The location of the cation binding sites and the helix sense were determined by studies on gramicidins, where specific carbonyl carbons were enriched in ^{13}C and the ion-induced chemical shifts in ^{13}C NMR were used to locate the carbonyls most exposed to the ions (127, 130). The binding sites are in the vicinity of carbonyl 9, 11, 13, and 15 (close to the aqueous phases), and there were no ion-induced shifts at the formyl, Val-1 and Val-8 carbonyls. The last result shows that the channels are predominantly left-handed.

The relation between side chain structure and single-channel characteristics has received comparatively little attention. This promises to become very informative, because there exist a number of naturally occurring mutants with altered conductances (20), and because semi-synthetic modifications at the

N-terminal end of these molecules can be used to produce highly purified analogs suitable for single-channel studies (8, 84, 87, 104). The molecule is small enough, furthermore, to be conveniently synthesized de novo by conventional techniques (13, 45, 95, 114, 118).

Sample purity becomes crucial in all of these studies, as many modified gramicidins are less potent channel-formers than valine gramicidin A (84, 87, 104). The difference between Tredgold et al (118) and Heitz et al (45) with regards to the single-channel characteristics of 9, 11, 13, 15 destryptophyl-phenylalanyl gramicidin A is, for example, readily explained if the latter compound is a less potent channel-former than gramicidin A and if the gel filtration columns used by Tredgold et al for purification of the reaction products contained some gramicidin A from earlier use (see 45).

The permeability characteristics of gramicidin channels depend on the side chain characteristics. Modifications at position 1 show that the side chain polarity (dipole moment, polarizability) may be an important determinant of the single-channel conductance (84, 104), while the importance of side chain bulk is uncertain. Modifications at the C-terminal end of the molecule have likewise important effects, as the conductance increases when phenylalanine at position 11 is replaced by the more polar tyrosine or tryptophane (20, 45, 84).

MOLECULAR DYNAMICS SIMULATIONS

The permeability characteristics of gramicidin or gramicidin-like channels have recently been investigated by molecular dynamics methods (41, 82).

The simulations of Fischer et al (41) were done on a simplified channel: a rigid hexagonal helix, with carbonyl oxygens that could librate into the channel lumen (e.g. 124). The ion was constrained to move along the center of the channel, which contained no H_2O. This simple model permitted the simulations to be done for sufficiently long times that it became possible to calculate the ion flux through (part of) an infinitely long channel. It was found that an ion vibrates back and forth before it leaves a site and moves over a barrier to an adjacent site and that the (Arrhenius) activation energy for ion movement was less than the activation energy calculated for an array of dipoles that could adjust to the ion such that the potential energy of the system was minimized. This may reflect that the ligand system undergoes thermal fluctuations with fluctuations in barrier height, and the ion will preferentially jump across a barrier when the barrier is low (75).

The simulations of MacKay et al (82) were done on the complete H_2O-filled β^6-helical dimer for 5 psec in simulations where there either were no ions in the channel or where different ions were placed at the channel center or at the center of one of the monomers. In the ion-free channel, the H_2O orientation was highly correlated across the length of the pore: the average dipole moment of all the H_2O in the channel would point in the same direction. The H_2O orientation of the H_2O in the channel interior did not change during the very short simulations, but introduction of an ion into the channel led to a rapid reorientation of the H_2O on either side such that they all pointed the oxygen toward the ion. This has important consequences: first, ion solvation by this one-dimensional H_2O is better than by bulk H_2O. Ions in the middle of the channel will thus be better solvated than expected from short-range (nearest-neighbor) interactions. Second, interactions among ions in the channel will reflect not only the Coulombic interactions between the ions, but also the mutual interactions between ions and H_2O. Third, exit of an ion from the channel will leave the H_2O with the oxygen pointing towards the side to which the ion left and should therefore, for short periods, make the channel asymmetrical. Analysis of ion and peptide backbone motion shows that the ions tend to be off-center and illustrates the libration of the carbonyl oxygens predicted by Urry (124).

The very time-consuming calculations involved in molecular dynamics simulations make approximate calculations attractive. One such approach, Brownian dynamics simulations, is particularly promising (25). Another more analytical approach is to develop mean force models (22, 74, 112), in which the Eyring Rate Theory is used to calculate rate constants for ion movement through the channel interior, based on the microscopic characteristics of the channel structure. The possible modulation of the channel's permeability characteristics by the single-filing H_2O and the importance of the ion entry-exit reactions have not yet received explicit attention in these descriptions.

CONCLUSION

Gramicidin channels have been extensively studied for the last 10–15 years, and the basic channel structure and permeability characteristics are well understood. The relation between structure and function at the single-residue level and the detailed (or even not so detailed) understanding of ion movement through the channel is nonetheless still unavailable. This is, however, mainly a reflection of the level at which the questions are being asked. Gramicidin channels should continue to serve as general models for transmembrane channels, as their small size and experimental accessibility make them uniquely suitable to pursue biophysical investigations of general channel behavior. A particularly important feature of the gramicidin channels is the availability of total or semi-synthetic modifications of channel structure, which allows a freedom to modulate the molecule not available by genetic engineering methods. This should, in conjunction with molecular dynamics simulations, lead to a truly molecular understanding of the structure-function relation.

ACKNOWLEDGMENTS

Preparation of this review was in part supported by N.I.H. grant GM 21342.

Literature Cited

1. Aiytan, S. K., Kalandadze, I. L., Chiz-madjev, Y. A. 1977. Ion transport through the potassium channels of biological membranes. *Bioelectrochem. Bioenerg.* 4:30–44
2. Alvarez, O., Brodwick, M., Latorre, R., McLaughlin, A., McLaughlin, S., Sza-bo, G. 1983. Large divalent cations and electrostatic potentials adjacent to membranes: Experimental results with hex-amethonium. *Biophys. J.* 44:333–42
3. Andersen, O. S. 1975. Ion-specificity of gramicidin A channels. *5th Int. Biophy. Congr.* p. 112 (Abstr.)
4. Andersen, O. S. 1978. Ion transport across simple membranes. In *Renal Function*, ed. G. H. Giebisch, E. F. Purcell, pp. 71–99. New York: Josiah Macy Jr. Found. 322 pp.
5. Andersen, O. S. 1983. Ion movement through gramicidin A channels. Single-channel measurements at very high potentials. *Biophys. J.* 41:119–33
6. Andersen, O. S. 1983. Ion movement through gramicidin A channels. Interfacial polarization effects on single-channel currents. *Biophys. J.* 41:135–46
7. Andersen, O. S. 1983. Ion movement through gramicidin A channels. Studies on the diffusion-controlled association step. *Biophys. J.* 41:147–65
8. Andersen, O. S., Barrett, E. W., Weiss, L. B. 1981. On the position of the alkali metal cation binding sites in gramicidin channels. *Biophys. J.* 33:63a (Abstr.)
9. Andersen, O. S., Procopio, J. 1980. Ion movement through gramicidin A channels. On the importance of the aqueous diffusion resistance and ion-water interactions. *Acta Physiol. Scand. Suppl.* 481:27–35
10. Apell, H.-J., Bamberg, E., Alpes, H., Läuger, P. 1977. Formation of ion channels by a negatively charged analog of gramicidin A. *J. Membrane Biol.* 31:171–88
11. Apell, H.-J., Bamberg, E., Läuger, P. 1979. Effects of surface charge on the conductance of the gramicidin channel. *Biochim. Biophys. Acta* 552:369–78
12. Bamberg, E., Apell, H.-J., Alpes, H. 1977. Structure of the gramicidin A channel: Discrimination between the $\pi_{L,D}$ and the β helix by electrical measurements with lipid bilayer membranes. *Proc. Natl. Acad. Sci. USA* 74:2402–6
13. Bamberg, E., Apell, H.-J., Alpes, H., Gross, E., Morell, J. L., et al. 1978. Ion channels formed by chemical analogs of gramicidin A. *Fed. Proc.* 37:2633–38
14. Bamberg, E., Alpes, H., Apell, H.-J., Bradley, R., Harter, B., et al. 1979. Formation of ionic channels in black lipid membranes by succinic derivatives of gramicidin A. *J. Membrane Biol.* 50:257–70
15. Bamberg, E., Benz, R. 1976. Voltage-induced thickness changes of lipid bilayer membranes and the effect of an electric field on gramicidin A channel formation. *Biochim. Biophys. Acta* 426:570–80
16. Bamberg, E., Janko, K. 1977. The action of a carbonsuboxide dimerized gramicidin A on lipid bilayer membranes. *Biochim. Biophys. Acta* 465:486–99
17. Bamberg, E., Läuger, P. 1973. Channel formation kinetics of gramicidin A in lipid bilayer membranes. *J. Membrane Biol.* 11:177–94
18. Bamberg, E., Läuger, P. 1974. Temperature dependent properties of gramicidin A channels. *Biochim. Biophys. Acta* 367:127–33
19. Bamberg, E., Läuger, P. 1977. Blocking of the gramicidin channel by divalent cations. *J. Membrane Biol.* 35:351–75
20. Bamberg, E., Noda, K., Gross, E., Läuger, P. 1976. Single-channel parameters of gramicidin A, B, and C. *Biochim. Biophys. Acta* 419:223–28
21. Bean, C. P. 1972. The physics of porous membranes—neutral pores. In *Membranes, Macroscopic Systems and Models*, ed. G. Eisenman, 1:1–54. New York: M. Dekker. 333 pp.
22. Brickmann, J., Fischer, W. 1983. Entropy effects on the ion-diffusion rate in transmembrane protein channels. *Biophys. Chem.* 17:245–58
23. Burgess, J. 1978. *Metal Ions in Solution*, pp. 349–52. Chichester, England: Ellis Horwood. 481 pp.
24. Busath, D., Szabo, G. 1981. Gramicidin forms multi-state rectifying channels. *Nature* 294:371–73
25. Cooper, K., Jakobsson, E., Wolynes, P. 1983. Brownian dynamic analysis of ion movement in membranes. *Biophys. J.* 41:47a (Abstr.)
26. Cornelis, A., Laszlo, P. 1979. Sodium binding sites of gramicidin A: Sodium-23 nuclear magnetic resonance study. *Biochemistry* 18:2004–7
27. Dani, J. A., Levitt, D. G. 1981. Binding constants of Li^+, K^+, and Tl^+ in the gramicidin channel determined from water permeability measurements. *Biophys. J.* 35:485–500
28. Dani, J. A., Levitt, D. G. 1981. Water transport and ion-water interactions in the

gramicidin channel. *Biophys. J.* 35:501–8

29. Decker, E. R., Levitt, D. G. 1983. Comparison of the gramicidin A potassium/sodium permeability and single-channel conductance ratio. *Biochim. Biophys. Acta* 730:178–80

30. Eisenman, G., Enos, B., Hägglund, J., Sandblom, J. 1980. Gramicidin as an example of a single-filing ionic channel. *Ann. NY Acad. Sci.* 339:8–20

31. Eisenman, G., Horn, R. 1983. Ionic selectivity revisited: the role of kinetic and equilibrium processes in ionic permeation through channels. *J. Membrane Biol.* 76:196–225

32. Eisenman, G., Hägglund, J., Sandblom, J., Enos, B. 1980. The current-voltage behavior of ion channels: Important features of the energy profile of the gramicidin channel deduced from the conductance-voltage characteristic in the limit of low ion concentrations. *Upsala J. Med. Sci.* 85:247–57

33. Eisenman, G., Sandblom, J. P. 1983. Energy barriers in ionic channels: Data for gramicidin A interpreted using a single-file (3B4S) model having 3 barriers separating 4 sites. In *Physical Chemistry of Transmembrane Ion Motions*, ed. G. Spach, pp. 329–47. Amsterdam: Elsevier. 656 pp.

34. Eisenman, G., Sandblom, J. 1983. TEA and TMA alter the I–V characteristics of the gramicidin channel as if they bind to channel sites at differing depths in the potential field but do not cross. In *The Physiology of Excitable Cells*, ed. A. Grinnell, W. Moody, pp. 191–204. New York: Liss. 604 pp.

35. Eisenman, G., Sandblom, J., Hägglund, J. 1983. Electrical behavior of single-filing channels. In *Structure and Function of Excitable Cells*, ed. D. Chang, I. Tasaki, W. Adelman, R. Leuchtag, pp. 383–413. New York: Plenum

36. Eisenman, G., Sandblom, J., Neher, E. 1977. Ionic selectivity, saturation, binding, and block in the gramicidin A channel: a preliminary report. Metal-ligand Interactions. In *Metal-Ligand Interactions in Organic Chemistry and Biochemistry*, ed. B. Pullman, N. Goldblum, 2:1–36. Dordrecht, Holland: Reidel

37. Eisenman, G., Sandblom, J., Neher, E. 1978. Interactions in cation permeation through the gramicidin channel. Cs, Rb, K, Na, Li, Tl, H, and effects of anion binding. *Biophys. J.* 22:307–40

38. Finkelstein, A. 1974. Aqueous pores created in thin lipid membranes by the antibiotics hystatin, amphotericin B, and gramicidin A: Implications for pores in plasma membranes. In *Drugs and Transport Processes*, ed. B. A. Callingham, pp. 241–50. London: McMillan. 376 pp.

39. Finkelstein, A., Andersen, O. S. 1981. The gramicidin A channel: A review of its permeability characteristics with special reference to the single-file aspect of transport. *J. Membrane Biol.* 59:155–71

40. Finkelstein, A., Rosenberg, P. A. 1979. Single-file transport: Implications for ion and water movement through gramicidin A channels. In *Membrane Transport Processes*, ed. C. F. Stevens, R. W. Tsien, 3:73–88. New York: Raven. 156 pp.

41. Fischer, W., Brickmann, J., Läuger, P. 1981. Molecular dynamics study of ion transport in transmembrane protein channels. *Biophys. Chem.* 13:105–16

42. Frohlich, O. 1979. Asymmetry of the gramicidin channel in bilayers of asymmetric lipid composition: I. Single-channel conductance. *J. Membrane Biol.* 48:365–83

43. Frohlich, O. 1979. Asymmetry of the gramicidin channel in bilayers of asymmetric lipid composition: II. Voltage dependence of dimerization. *J. Membrane Biol.* 48:385–401

43a. Hägglund, J. V., Eisenman, G., Sandblom, J. P. 1983. Single salt behavior of a symmetrical 4-site channel with barriers at its middle and ends. *Bull. Math. Biol.* 45: in press

44. Heckman, K. 1972. Single-file diffusion. In *Biomembranes*, ed. F. Kreuzer, J. F. G. Slegers, 3:127–53. New York: Plenum. 519 pp.

45. Heitz, F., Spach, F., Trudelle, Y. 1982. Single-channels of 9, 11, 13, 15-destryptophyl-phenylalanyl-gramicidin A. *Biophys. J.* 40:87–89

46. Hendry, B. M., Urban, B. W., Haydon, D. A. 1978. The blockage of the electrical conductance in a pore-containing membrane by the *n*-alkanes. *Biochim. Biophys. Acta* 513:106–16

47. Henze, R., Neher, E., Trapane, T. L., Urry, D. W. 1982. Dielectric relaxation studies of ionic processes in lysolecithin-packaged gramicidin channels. *J. Membrane Biol.* 64:233–39

48. Hille, B., Schwarz, W. 1978. Potassium channels as multi-ion single-file pores. *J. Gen. Physiol.* 72:409–42

49. Hinton, J. F., Turner, G. L., Millett, F. S. 1981. A thallium-205 NMR investigation of the thallium(I)-gramicidin complex. *J. Magn. Reson.* 45:42–47

50. Hinton, J. F., Young, G., Millett, F. S. 1982. Thallous ion interaction with gramicidin incorporated in micelles studied by thallium-205 nuclear magnetic resonance. *Biochemistry* 21:651–54

51. Hladky, S. B. 1974. Pore or Carrier? Gramicidin A as a simple pore. In *Drugs and Transport Processes*, ed. B. A. Callingham, pp. 193–210. London: Mcmillan. 376 pp.

52. Hladky, S. B., Haydon, D. A. 1970. Discreteness of conductance change in bimolecular lipid membranes in the presence of certain antibiotics. *Nature* 225: 451–53

53. Hladky, S. B., Haydon, D. A. 1972. Ion transfer across lipid membranes in the presence of gramicidin A. I. Studies of the unit conductance channel. *Biochim. Biophys. Acta* 274:294–312

54. Hladky, S. B., Urban, B. W., Haydon, D. A. 1979. Ion movements in the gramicidin pore. See Ref. 40, pp. 89–103

55. Hodgkin, A. L., Keynes, R. D. 1955. The potassium permeability of a giant nerve fibre. *J. Physiol.* 128:61–88

56. Deleted in proof

57. Jordan, P. C. 1981. Energy barriers for passage of ions through channels. Exact solution of two electrostatic problems. *Biophys. Chem.* 13:203–12

58. Jordan, P. C. 1982. Electrostatic modeling of ion pores. Energy barriers and electric field profiles. *Biophys. J.* 39: 157–64

59. Jordan, P. C. 1983. Electrostatic modeling of ion pores. II. Effects attributable to the membrane dipole potential. *Biophys. J.* 41:189–95

60. Jordan, P. C. 1984. The effect of pore structure on energy barriers and applied voltage profiles. I. Symmetrical channels. *Biophys. J.* Submitted for publication

61. Kimball, M. R., Wallace, B. A. 1981. Co-crystals of gramicidin and phosphatidylcholine: A system for studying ion channel structure and lipid-protein interactions. *Proc. 12th Int. Congr. Crystallogr.*, ed. M. Przybylska, p. 144. Ottawa: LeDroit & LeClerc. (Abstr.)

62. Kimball, M. R., Wallace, B. A. 1982. The effect of monovalent cations on the conformation of gramicidin A in organic solvents. *Biophys. J.* 37:318a (Abstr.)

63. Koeppe, R. E. II, Berg, J. M., Hodgson, K. O., Stryer, L. 1979. Gramicidin A crystals contain two cation binding sites per channel. *Nature* 279:723–25

64. Koeppe, R. E. II, Hodgson, K. O., Stryer, L. 1978. Helical channels in crystals of gramicidin A and of a cesium-gramicidin A complex: an X-ray diffraction study. *J. Mol. Biol.* 121:41–54

65. Koeppe, R. E. II, Kimura, M. 1983. Computer building of -helical polypeptide models. *Biopolymers*. In press

66. Koeppe, R. E. II, Schoenborn, B. P. 1983. 5 A Fourier map of gramicidin A phased by deuterium-hydrogen solvent difference neutron diffraction. *Biophys. J.* 45: in press

67. Kolb, H.-A., Bamberg, E. 1977. Influence of membrane thickness and ion concentration on the properties of the gramicidin A channel. Autocorrelation, spectral power density, relaxation and single-channel studies. *Biochim. Biophys. Acta* 464:127–41

68. Kolb, H.-A., Läuger, P., Bamberg, E. 1975. Correlation analysis of electrical noise in lipid bilayer membranes: Kinetics of gramicidin A channels. *J. Membrane Biol.* 20:133–54

69. Kowalsky, A. 1979. A ^{13}C NMR study of gramicidin interactions with monovalent cations. In *NMR and Biochemistry*, ed. S. J. Opella, P. Lu, pp. 125–37. New York: Dekker

70. Kramers, H. A. 1940. Brownian motion in a field of force and the diffusion model of chemical reactions. *Physica* 7:284–304

71. Krasne, S., Eisenman, G., Szabo, G. 1971. Freezing and melting of lipid bilayers and the mode of action of nonactin, valinomycin, and gramicidin. *Science* 174:412–15

72. Läuger, P. 1973. Ion transport through pores: a rate-theory analysis. *Biochim. Biophys. Acta* 311:423–41

73. Läuger, P. 1976. Diffusion-limited ion flow through pores. *Biochim. Biophys. Acta* 455:493–509

74. Läuger, P. 1982. Microscopic calculation of ion-transport rates in membrane channels. *Biophys. Chem.* 15:89–100

75. Läuger, P., Stephan, W., Frehland, E. 1980. Fluctuations of barrier structure in ionic channels. *Biochim. Biophys. Acta* 602:167–80

76. Levitt, D. G. 1974. A new theory of transport for cell membrane pores. I. General theory and application to red cell. *Biochim. Biophys. Acta* 373:115–31

77. Levitt, D. G. 1978. Electrostatic calculations for an ion channel. I. Energy and potential profiles and interactions between ions. *Biophys. J.* 22:209–19

78. Levitt, D. G. 1978. Electrostatic calculations for an ion channel. II. Kinetic behavior of the gramicidin A channel. *Biophys. J.* 22:221–48

79. Levitt, D. G. 1982. Comparison of Nernst-Planck and reaction-rate models for multiply occupied channels. *Biophys. J.* 37:575–87

80. Levitt, D. G. 1983. Kinetics of movement in narrow channels. In *Ion Channels: Molecular and Physiological Aspects*, ed. W. D. Stein. New York: Academic. In press

81. Levitt, D. G., Elias, S. R., Hautman, J. M. 1978. Number of water molecules coupled to the transport of sodium, potassium, and hydrogen ions via gramicidin, nonactin, or valinomycin. *Biochim. Biophys. Acta* 512:436–51

82. MacKay, D. H. J., Berens, P. H., Wilson, K. R., Hagler, A. T. 1984. Structure and dynamics of ion transport through gramicidin A. *Biophys. J.* Submitted for publication

83. Manning, G. S. 1975. The relation between osmotic flow and tracer solvent diffusion for single-file transport. *Biophys. Chem.* 3:147–52

84. Mazet, J.-L., Koeppe, R. E. II, Andersen, O. S. 1984. Single-channel studies on linear gramicidins with altered amino acid sequences. A comparison of phenylalanine, tryptophane, and tyrosine substitutions at position 1 and 11. *Biophys. J.* 45:263–74

85. McBride, D., Szabo, G. 1978. Blocking of gramicidin channel conductance by Ag^+. *Biophys. J.* 21:25a (Abstr.)

86. McLaughlin, S. 1977. Electrostatic potentials at membrane solution interfaces. In *Current Topics Membranes and Transport*, ed. F. Bronner. A. Kleinzeller, 9:71–144. New York: Academic. 394 pp.

87. Morrow, J. S., Veatch, W. R., Stryer, L. 1979. Transmembrane channel activity of gramicidin A analogs: Effects of modification and deletion of the aminoterminal residue. *J. Mol. Biol.* 132:733–38

88. Myers, V. B., Haydon, D. A. 1972. Ion transfer across lipid membranes in the presence of gramicidin A. II. The ion selectivity. *Biochim. Biophys. Acta* 274:313–22

89. Neher, E. 1975. Ionic specificity of the gramicidin channel and the thallous ion. *Biochim. Biophys. Acta* 401:540–44. Errata, 1977. *Biochim. Biophys. Acta* 469:359

90. Neher, E., Eibl, H.-J. 1977. The influence of phospholid polar groups on gramicidin channels. *Biochim. Biophys. Acta* 464:37–44

91. Neher, E., Sandblom, J., Eisenman, G. 1978. Ionic selectivity, saturation, and block in gramicidin A channels. II. Saturation behavior of single channel conductances and evidence for the existence of multiple binding sites in the channel. *J. Membrane Biol.* 40:97–116

92. Parsegian, A. 1969. Energy of an ion crossing a low dielectric membrane: solutions to four relevant electrostatic problems. *Nature* 221:844–46

93. Parsegian, A. 1975. Ion-membrane interactions as structural forces. *Ann. NY Acad. Sci.* 264:161–74

94. Pope, C. G., Urban, B. W., Haydon, D. A. 1982. The influence of *n*-alkanols and cholesterol on the duration and conductance of gramicidin single channels in monoolein bilayers. *Biochim. Biophys. Acta* 688:279–83

95. Prasad, K. U., Trapane, T. L., Busath, D., Szabo, G., Urry, D. W. 1982. Synthesis and characterization of 1-^{13}C-D.Leu^{12,14} gramicidin A. *Int. J. Peptide Protein Res.* 19:162–71

96. Procopio, J., Andersen, O. S. 1979. Ion tracer fluxes through gramicidin A modified lipid bilayers. *Biophys. J.* 25:8a (Abstr.)

97. Ramachandran, G. N., Chandrasekaran, R. 1972. Studies on dipeptide conformation and on peptides with sequences of alternating L and D residues with special reference to antibiotic and ion transport peptides. In *Progress in Peptide Research*, ed. S. Lande, 2:195–215. New York: Gordon & Breach. 393 pp.

98. Renugopalakrishnan, V., Urry, D. W. 1978. A theoretical study of Na^+ and Mg^{+2} binding to the carbonyl oxygen of N-methyl acetamide. *Biophys. J.* 24:729–38

99. Rickert, H. 1964. Zur Diffusion durch eine lineare Kette (Single-File Diffusion). *Z. Phys. Chem.* 43:129–39

100. Rondelez, F., Litster, J. D. 1979. Light-scattering studies of the monomer-dimer states of gramicidin A. *Biophys. J.* 27:455–60

101. Rosenberg, P. A., Finkelstein, A. 1978. Interaction of ions and water in gramicidin A channels. Streaming potentials across lipid bilayer membranes. *J. Gen. Physiol.* 72:327–40

102. Rosenberg, P. A., Finkelstein, A. 1978. Water permeability of gramicidin A-treated lipid bilayer membranes. *J. Gen. Physiol.* 72:341–50

103. Rudnev, V. S., Ermishkin, L. N., Fonina, L. A., Rovin, Yu. G. 1981. The dependence of the conductance and lifetime of gramicidin channels on the thickness and tension of lipid bilayers. *Biochim. Biophys. Acta* 642:196–202

104. Russell, E. W. B., Weiss, L. B., Navetta, F. I., Koeppe, R. E. II, Andersen, O. S. 1983. Single-channel studies on linear gramicidins with altered amino acid side chains. Effects of altering the polarity of the N-terminal amino acid in gramicidin A. *Biophys. J.* Submitted for publication

105. Sandblom, J., Eisenman, G., Hägglund, J. 1983. Multioccupancy models for single-filing ionic channels: Theoretical behavior of a four-site channel with three

barriers separating the sites. *J. Membrane Biol.* 71:61–78

106. Sandblom, J., Eisenman, G., Neher, E. 1977. Ionic selectivity, saturation, and block in gramicidin A channels: I. Theory for the electrical properties of ion selective channels having two pairs of binding sites and multiple conductance states. *J. Membrane Biol.* 31:383–417

107. Sarges, R., Witkop, B. 1965. Gramicidin A. V. The structure of valine- and isoleucine-gramicidin A. *J. Am. Chem. Soc.* 87:2011–20

108. Sarges, R., Witkop, F. 1965. Gramicidin. VII. The structure of valine- and isoleucine-gramicidin B. *J. Am. Chem. Soc.* 87:2027–30

109. Sarges, R., Witkop, B. 1965. Gramicidin. VIII. The structure of valine- and isoleucine-gramicidin C. *Biochemistry* 4:2491–94

110. Schagina, L. V., Grinfeldt, A. E., Lev, A. A. 1978. Interaction of cation fluxes in gramicidin A channels in lipid bilayer membranes. *Nature* 273:243–45

111. Schagina, L. V., Grinfeldt, A. E., Lev, A. A. 1983. Concentration dependence of bidirectional flux ratio as a characteristic of transmembrane ion transporting mechanism. *J. Membrane Biol.* 73:203–16

112. Schroder, H. 1983. Rate theoretical analysis of ion transport in membrane channels with elastically bound ligands. In *Physical Chemistry of Transmembrane Ion Motions,* ed. G. Spach, pp. 425–36. Amsterdam: Elsevier

113. Segrest, J. P., Feldmann, R. J. 1974. Membrane proteins: amino acid sequence and membrane penetration. *J. Mol. Biol.* 87:853–58

114. Shepel, E. N., Jiordanov, St., Ryabova, I. D., Miroshnikov, A. I., Ivanov, V. T., Ovchinnikov, Yu. A. 1976. Synthesis and antimicrobial properties of new analogs of gramicidin A. *Bioorg. Chem.* 2:581–93

115. Sychev, S. V., Nevskaya, N. A., Jordanov, St., Shepel, E. N., Miroshnikov, A. I., Ivanov, V. T. 1980. The solution conformations of gramicidin A and its analogs. *Bioorg. Chem.* 9:121–51

116. Szabo, G., Busath, D. D. 1983. Ion movement through membrane channels. In *Membrane Biophysics: Physical Methods in the Study of Biophysical Systems,* ed. M. A. Dinno, A. B. Callahan, T. C. Rozzell. New York: Liss. In press

117. Szabo, G., Urry, D. W. 1979. N-acetyl gramicidin: Single-channel properties and implications for channel structure. *Science* 203:55–57

118. Tredgold, R. H., Hole, P. N., Sproule,

R. C., Elgamal, M. 1977. Single channel characteristics of some synthetic gramicidins. *Biochim. Biophys. Acta* 471:189–94

119. Turner, G. L., Hinton, J. F., Koeppe, R. E. II, Parli, J. A., Millett, F. S. 1983. Difference in association of Tl(I) with gramicidin A and gramicidin B in trifluorethanol determined by Tl-205 NMR. *Biochim. Biophys. Acta.* 756:133–37

120. Turner, G. L., Hinton, J. F., Millett, F. S. 1982. Thallium-205 nuclear magnetic resonance study of the thallium(I)-gramicidin A association in trifluoroethanol. *Biochemistry* 21:646–51

121. Urban, B. W., Hladky, S. B. 1979. Ion transport in the simplest single-file pore. *Biochim. Biophys. Acta* 554:410–29

122. Urban, B. W., Hladky, S. B., Haydon, D. A. 1980. Ion movements in gramicidin pores. An example of single file transport. *Biochim. Biophys. Acta* 602:331–54

123. Urry, D. W. 1971. The gramicidin A transmembrane channel: A proposed $\pi_{(L,D)}$ helix. *Proc. Natl. Acad. Sci. USA* 68:672–76

124. Urry, D. W. 1973. Polypeptide conformation and biological function β-helices ($\pi_{L,D}$-helices) as permselective transmembrane channels. In *The Jerusalem Symposium on Quantum Chemistry and Biochemistry,* ed. E. D. Bergmann, B. Pullman, pp. 723–34. Jerusalem: Israel Acad. Sci.

125. Urry, D. W., Goodall, M. C., Glickson, J. D., Mayers, D. F. 1971. The gramicidin A transmembrane channel: Characteristics of head-to-head dimerized $\pi_{(L,D)}$ helices. *Proc. Natl. Acad. Sci. USA* 68:1907–11

126. Urry, D. W., Long, M. M., Jacobs, M., Harris, R. D. 1975. Conformation and molecular mechanisms of carriers and channels. *Ann. NY Acad. Sci.* 264:203–20

127. Urry, D. W., Prasad, K. U., Trapane, T. L. 1982. Location of monovalent cation binding sites in the gramicidin channel. *Proc. Natl. Acad. Sci. USA* 79:390–94

128. Urry, D. W., Venkatachalam, C. M., Spisni, A., Bradley, R. J., Trapane, T. L., Prasad, K. U. 1980. The malonyl gramicidin channel: NMR-derived rate constants and comparisons of calculated and experimental single-channel currents. *J. Membrane Biol.* 55:29–51

129. Urry, D. W., Venkatachalam, C. M., Spisni, A., Läuger, P., Khaled, Md. A. 1980. Rate theory calculation of gramicidin single-channel currents using NMR-derived rate constants. *Proc. Natl. Acad. Sci. USA* 77:2028–32

130. Urry, D. W., Walker, J. T., Trapane, T. L. 1982. Ion interactions in (1-^{13}C)D-val^8 and D-Leu^{14} analogs of gramicidin A, the helix sense of the channel and location of ion binding sites. *J. Membrane Biol.* 69:225–31

131. Veatch, W. R., Blout, E. R. 1974. The aggregation of gramicidin A in solution. *Biochemistry* 13:5257–64

132. Veatch, W. R., Durkin, J. T. 1980. Binding of thallium and other cations to the gramicidin A channel. Equilibrium dialysis study of gramicidin in phosphatidylcholine vesicles. *J. Mol. Biol.* 143:411–17

133. Veatch, W. R., Fossel, E. T., Blout, E. R. 1974. The conformation of gramicidin A. *Biochemistry* 13:5249–56

134. Veatch, W. R., Mathies, R., Eisenberg, M., Stryer, L. 1975. Simultaneous fluorescence and conductance studies of planar bilayer membranes containing a highly active and fluorescent analog of gramicidin A. *J. Mol. Biol.* 99:75–92

135. Veatch, W., Stryer, L. 1977. The dimeric nature of the gramicidin A transmembrane channel: Conductance and fluorescence energy transfer studies of hybrid channels. *J. Mol. Biol.* 113:89–102

136. Wallace, B. A. 1983. Gramicidin A adopts distinctively different conformations in membranes and inorganic solvents. *Biopolymers* 22:397–402

137. Wallace, B. A., Veatch, W. R., Blout, E. R. 1981. Conformation of gramicidin A in phospholipid vesicles: Circular dichroism studies of effects of ion binding, chemical modification, and lipid structure. *Biochemistry* 20:5754–60

138. Walz, D., Bamberg, E., Läuger P. 1969. Nonlinear electrical effects in lipid bilayer membranes. I. Ion injection. *Biophys. J.* 9:1150–59

139. Weinstein, S., Wallace, B. A., Blout, E. R., Morrow, J. S., Veatch, W. 1979. Conformation of gramicidin A channel in phospholipid vesicles: A ^{13}C and ^{19}F nuclear magnetic resonance study. *Proc. Natl. Acad. Sci. USA* 76:4230–34

140. Weinstein, S., Wallace, B. A., Morrow, J. S., Veatch, W. R. 1980. Conformation of the gramicidin A transmembrane channel: A ^{13}C nuclear magnetic resonance study of ^{13}C-enriched gramicidin in phosphatidylcholine vesicles. *J. Mol. Biol.* 143:1–19

141. Zingsheim, H. P., Neher, E. 1974. The equivalence of fluctuation analysis and chemical relaxation measurements: A kinetic study of ion pore formation in thin lipid membranes. *Biophys. Chem.* 2:197–207

Ann. Rev. Physiol. 1984. 46:549–58

ION CHANNELS
IN LIPOSOMES

Christopher Miller

Graduate Department of Biochemistry, Brandeis University, Waltham,
Massachusetts 02254

INTRODUCTION

It may be reasonably argued that of all classes of known cellular proteins, the
ion channels are the least understood biochemically. Of the large number of
channel proteins known from cellular electrical behavior to exist in the membranes of higher organisms, only three—the nicotinic acetylcholine receptor,
the Na^+ channel, and the mitochondrial porin channel—have been obtained in
a relatively purified state (28). Even in these cases, serious questions remain
about the physiologically "correct" functioning of these purified proteins. A
single peculiarity of ion channel proteins explains this unhappy situation: the
lack of a suitable functional assay for integral membrane channels. Seeking to
purify an enzyme, for instance, a biochemist can straightforwardly develop a
specific assay to pursue and eventually to apprehend the protein with a battery
of purification methods. But the only criterion of functionality of an ion
channel is its ability to make a membrane "leaky" to specific ions. To be sure,
this "leak" may be turned on and off in very specific ways and may be modified
pharmacologically, but the fact remains that ion channels, by their very
definition, merely catalyze the passive flow of ions down their thermodynamic
gradients.

It is therefore necessary, in attacking purified channel proteins, to develop a
system in which the flow of ions across a membrane may be detected. Historically, two such model membrane systems have been employed: planar bilayers
and liposomes (10, 22, 26, 27, 32–36). The planar bilayer system has been
largely favored for ion channel work because of its obvious advantages: the
ability to voltage-clamp the model membrane and to measure single channel
current fluctuations, and the easy accessibility to both aqueous phases. But
there are two serious disadvantages in the use of planar bilayers in biochemical

549

reconstitution work: the lack of a generally applicable method for inserting integral membrane proteins into the model membrane (27) and the inability to perform *both* chemical and functional measurements upon the same sample.

The purpose of this review is to discuss the use of liposomes in the reconstitution of ion channels. This model membrane system is often considered inferior to planar bilayers in attacking this problem, mainly because of the electrical inaccessibility of the liposome interior (27). This attitude is, I consider, unjustified. There are several distinct advantages to the use of liposomes in channel reconstitution work, especially in working with purified channel proteins. It is my intention here to illustrate these advantages with a discussion of recent experience with liposome-reconstituted ion channels. Several reviews of ion channel reconstitution, with a larger scope, have recently appeared (26, 27, 32).

CHANNELS RECONSTITUTED IN LIPOSOMES

Liposome Methods: the Good News and the Bad News

Liposomes containing functionally reconstituted membrane proteins can be formed by a variety of methods (10, 29), but the most reliable and generally applicable of these is the detergent-removal method. Crude membrane protein is combined with exogenously added lipids in the presence of a detergent above its critical micelle concentration. The proteins in this micellar solution, thus unlocked from the lipid bilayer, may then be fractionated by standard biochemical procedures. Purified protein fractions, still containing excess lipids, are then subjected to procedures to remove the detergent—simple dialysis being the most straightforward. Detergent removal forces the lipids and membrane protein to self-assemble into a new micellar structure, that of a spherical bilayer, or liposome, now with protein inserted in a thermodynamically "correct" way, i.e. with its hydrophobic surfaces in association with the hydrocarbon region of the bilayer, and its hydrophilic areas in contact with the two aqueous phases on either side of the bilayer. It is not obvious that the protein's solution of the *thermodynamic* insertion problem should automatically lead to a functionally active conformation, but in practice this is often the case. The biochemical literature is now replete with examples of functional reconstitutions of many types of integral membrane proteins via detergent removal techniques. In other words, the detergent-removal method itself solves the problem of protein insertion into the bilayer; the biochemist does not need to cajole the protein in, as he must with planar bilayers.

The liposomes formed in this way are small, at most 200 nm in diameter. This presents a problem unique to the study of ion channels, which display very high turnover rates greater than 10^6 s^{-1}. Consider a liposome of radius r, containing only one functional channel, of conductance γ. Then, we can calculate the time constant, τ, of the exchange of radioactive ions from this liposome at zero voltage (26, 29):

$$\tau = 4\pi r^3 F^2 c/3RT\gamma,$$
1.

where c is the concentration of conducting ion, in mol/ml. Using "typical" values for γ (10 pS), c (0.15 M), and r (50 nm), we find that in a conventional radioactive efflux assay, the ion would leave the liposome with a time constant of 30 ms, if the channel were open all the time. The cubic term in Eq.1 makes the time constant extremely sensitive to liposome size. Thus, special methods of high time resolution are required to follow channel-mediated fluxes in liposomes. We will now examine how recent studies with reconstituted ion channels have tried to overcome the disadvantages and to exploit the advantages of liposomes.

The Nicotinic Acetylcholine Receptor

This is unquestionably the most extensively studied ion channel protein, from the pure phenomenology of synaptic function (1) to the structure of the protein complex itself (21). It is now routinely purified in an apparently functional state from the electric organ of electric fishes (13, 23). It has behaved in an exceptionally vicious manner towards membrane biochemists, who originally used the specific binding of snake toxins to the receptor site as a convenient "functional" assay of the protein; it is now known (19, 23) that toxin binding activity is fully preserved under conditions of total loss of ion transport activity. Epstein & Racker (9) found that the inclusion of excess phospholipids in the detergent solution used to purify the protein is required for the preservation of agonist-dependent $^{22}Na^+$ transport function. The influx assay used to evaluate the function of the reconstituted liposomes is now common: liposomes are mixed with $^{22}Na^+$-containing medium in the presence of agonist, and the influx reaction is subsequently quenched with a large dose of antagonist such as curare. The $^{22}Na^+$ trapped inside the liposomes may then be determined. Although the time resolution of this method is only about 10 seconds, its convenience has given it wide use, mainly as a method to screen numerous samples, allowing for optimization of reconstitution conditions (19, 23), lipid composition (8, 12), and chemical manipulations (7, 20, 24).

As a criterion of channel function, however, the 10-second influx assay is wanting, because under the conditions normally employed (with liposomes of 20–30 nm radius), the time constant of ion influx is expected to be about 3 ms (27). Indeed, the indication of a successful reconstitution using this assay is the *inability* to measure the rapid influx: the liposomes are equilibrated before the first time point can be taken. In spite of this deficiency, this conventional approach has been extremely important in establishing conditions for handling the protein in detergent solution, and for demonstrating that the minimal functional unit of the receptor is the $a_2\beta\gamma\delta$ complex (6, 11, 18, 23), at least to the extent that the assay validly evaluates function. An important result based upon this assay—a result that could not have been obtained in a "native" system—concerns the densensitization of the receptor protein following long application of agonist. It was found (19, 23) that in a liposome system with on the average a single receptor per liposome, as the concentration of agonist is increased, the main effect is an increase in the *number* of liposomes accessible to Na^+. The system behaves as though at low agonist concentrations, most of the receptors desensitize before opening, while the reverse is true at saturating concentrations of agonist. (For a detailed discussion of this point, see 27).

Because of the low time resolution of the usual flux assay, several groups have invested efforts into following fluxes on the millisecond time scale. Walker et al (44) and Huganir & Racker (19) used a rapid quench-flow method of 15 ms resolution, still too slow to determine the time course of ion flow through open channels, but a decided improvement. The receptor desensitization process, however, could be easily followed in the quench-flow system, and was found to agree well with the corresponding behavior in the native *Torpedo* membrane vesicles (44). Wu et al (46) increased the time resolution to about 8 ms by monitoring Tl^+ influx via a fluorescence-quenching technique. Even here, the rate of Tl^+ movement through open channels was too high to measure accurately, but an approximate estimation (employing histrionicotoxin to block open channels partially) showed that the rate was consistent with the known value of channel conductance. The importance of these rapid-flux studies is that they establish that standard detergent-dialysis methods lead to a bulk population of reconstituted receptor proteins that are kinetically competent for agonist activation, desensitization, and ion transport. This result validates the use of the low-resolution assays above.

It is important to realize that the conclusions reached above could not have been validly drawn from similar work using planar bilayers, at least as the technology now stands. It is possible to observe functional acetylcholine receptors in planar bilayers (15, 35, 37), but in these cases, the handful of channels actually observed (in the order of 1–10 channels inserted in a typical experiment) constitute a minute fraction of the population of receptor protein added into the system. In such a situation, there is no way of knowing whether those channels whose properties we can, to be sure, study in such exquisite detail are in any way representative of the whole channel population—whether the 10 channels observed in the bilayer might not be accompanied by another million or so nonfunctional receptor proteins. This problem does not apply with liposomes, since the assay is nearly always carried out on a bulk population of knowable chemical composition.

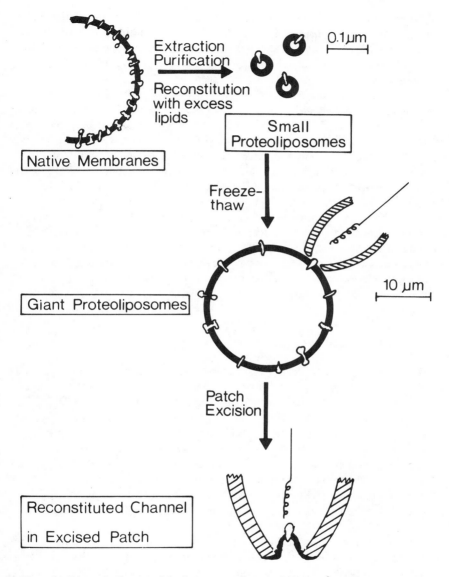

Figure 1   Schematic diagram of the liposome patch method (from 42).

A new liposome reconstitution method has recently been introduced in order to preserve the chemical accessibility of liposome reconstitution while simultaneously exploiting the high resolution of electrical methods. This is the "liposome-patch" technique (41, 42), shown schematically in Figure 1. Here, channel proteins are reconstituted into small liposomes in the usual way. The liposomes are then enlarged up to the 10–50 μm range by freezing and thawing, and are observed in phase-contrast optics. A gigohm seal is formed on one of these giant liposomes with a patch pipette, and a piece of membrane excised by the method of air exposure (14). An inside-out patch is thus established, and single-channel fluctuations may be observed.

This method has been applied successfully to the acetylcholine receptor, among other channels (40–42). Tank et al (40) were able to characterize the purified receptor channel with a resolution not previously possible. In addition to characterizing the activation kinetics with several agonists, these workers found that the dependence of channel conductance on Na^+ concentration follows a rectangular hyperbolic relation quantitatively identical to that found in excised patches of rat cultured muscle (17). Moreover, the kinetics of desensitization of the receptor in the liposome patches could be directly studied. These results provide further strong evidence that the purified receptor protein, reconstituted by the detergent-removal method, is indeed functional. Again, it is important to note that this conclusion could not have been made from planar bilayer work; one aspect of the power of the liposome patch method is its ability to assay a truly random sample of a population of channels, which may be inserted at a known and controllable density into the reconstituted membrane.

Excitable Membrane Na^+ Channel

Like the acetylcholine receptor, the Na^+ channel has long been sought by membrane biochemists. In recent years, the protein has been purified from eel electroplax and from muscle (2–4, 16), using as assay the binding of saxitoxin (STX), a specific inhibitor of the channel. In contrast to the binding of snake toxin to the acetylcholine receptor, STX binding is an activity very easily lost during purification maneuvers. It is this lability (as well as the fact that it is competitive with Na^+) that gives biochemists hope that STX binding is a valid "marker" for the true ion transport function of the channel. It is now clear that the STX-binding activity, and possibly scorpion toxin binding as well, is associated with a large polypeptide of about 270 Kd (4, 5, 31) and possibly with several small protein subunits.

The ultimate demonstration of purified Na^+ channel function must be to show the preservation of voltage-dependent activation and inactivation phenomena as well as ionic selectivity properties consistent with those extensively documented in the physiological system. This goal has not yet been fully achieved, but recent work on the flux properties of liposomes reconstituted with purified Na^+ channels has provided support for the notion that the channel protein is in fact functional. Barchi and colleagues (39, 45) used the alkaloid batrachotoxin as an activator of Na^+ channels in the liposomes and followed the fluxes of a variety of monovalent cations. These workers paid careful attention to problems of using liposomes with reconstituted channels by "pushing" conditions in three ways: by reconstituting at very low protein/lipid ratio, so that liposomes would not contain more than one channel; by using as large liposomes as possible ($\sim$200 nm diameter), and by using a rapid quench-flow technique for measuring influx. Even with these precautions, the influx of Na^+ was found to be faster than the 50 ms time resolution of the assay, as expected from Eq. 1. However, the fluxes of *poorly* permeating cations, such as K^+, Rb^+, and Cs^+, could be clearly resolved (influx half-times of 0.35 s, 2.5 s, and 10 s, respectively). The selectivity sequence of the flux was therefore directly determined: Na^+ ($\sim$1) $> K^+$ (0.14) $> Rb^+$ (0.02) $> Cs^+$ (0.005). This Na^+/K^+ selectivity is fully consistent with that measured in Na^+ channels from reversal potentials in the physiological membrane. Note that permeabilities for Rb^+ and Cs^+ through Na^+ channels are difficult or impossible to measure by electrical methods but are easily determined from the liposome flux technique. This points out another advantage of liposomes: they are of much higher absolute sensitivity than electrical measurements, and they are probably the only system in which very slowly permeating ions can be observed to pass through ion channels.

The Na^+ channel has also been reconstituted in liposomes by several groups using veratridine as activator (38, 39, 43). Veratridine-stimulated Na^+ fluxes are much slower and less ion-selective than batrachotoxin-stimulated fluxes. Barchi's group (39) presented evidence that this is due to a difference in the rate-limiting steps of ion permeation in the two cases: with batrachotoxin, the channels are simply held open, allowing the ion flux through the open channels to be rate-limiting; but with veratridine, channel-opening itself becomes rate-limiting.

At the present, the liposome flux assay of purified Na^+ channels is sufficiently well developed that even in the absence of a demonstration of voltage-activation of the channel, the time is ripe to address questions about the small subunits copurifying with the large channel protein. Only via a reconstitution approach can we find out if these components are essential to channel function or merely detritus of the purification procedure.

Cl^- Channel of Torpedo Electroplax

In a futile attempt to reconstitute acetylcholine receptors in planar bilayers, White & Miller (30, 47) discovered a voltage-dependent, Cl^--specific channel, which they proposed resides in the noninnervated-face membrane of the electroplax cell. This channel has been extensively characterized in planar bilayers (25, 28, 30, 47), but very little could be said about its abundance in the membrane population because of the "blindness" of planar bilayer systems.

Recently, this channel was studied in liposomes after detergent solubilization of *Torpedo* noninnervated-face membranes (42, 43), using the liposome-patch method (Fig. 1). One important consequence of this work is the likelihood that this channel is a major membrane protein and therefore a good target for future purification studies.

This conclusion is based upon studies with giant liposomes formed from detergent extracts of noninnervated-face membranes. When excised patches are formed from these liposomes, Cl^- channels are nearly always observed (42). Occasionally, patches are obtained containing both Cl^- channels and contaminating acetylcholine receptor channels (41). If the Cl^- channel were a minor contaminant of the preparation (a possibility not ruled out by planar bilayer studies), we would not observe it so frequently after solubilization and reconstitution into a bulk population of liposomes. From the number of channels observed per patch, it is possible to estimate that the original channel density in the native membrane is in the order of 500 μm^{-2}. This substantial density of membrane protein is high enough to motivate us to purify the channel, in hopes that the fish has done most of our work for us.

CONCLUSION

The purpose of this survey has been to point out several distinct advantages in the use of liposomes for ion-channel reconstitution. We have seen that only with liposomes can we work on a bulk population of channel protein and thus rigorously relate chemical data with ion transport function. The overwhelming protein insertion problem in planar bilayers simply does not exist with liposome reconstitution, and the detergent-removal method is generally applicable to membrane proteins of all kinds. Liposomes allow rapid screening, at low time resolution, of many samples and reconstitution conditions. Ions poorly permeating through channels can be easily studied in a liposome system, and so ionic selectivity phenomena may be studied at higher sensitivity than with electrical methods. Conclusions about the density of channels in a crude membrane population can be drawn from liposome assays as well.

The main disadvantage of liposomes—low time resolution and electrical inaccessibility—is presently being removed with the elaboration of liposome-patch methods. We may therefore be hopeful that ion channels will soon lose their deserved reputation as a particularly intractable class of membrane protein and will join other types of ion transporters as good candidates for the classic biochemical approach: solubilization, fractionation, purification, and functional reconstitution.

Literature Cited

1. Adams, P. R. 1981. Acetylcholine receptor kinetics. *J. Membr. Biol.* 58:161–74
2. Agnew, W. S., Levinson, S. R., Brabson, J. S., Raftery, M. A. 1978. Purification of tetrodotoxin-binding component associated with the voltage-sensitive sodium channel from *Electrophorus electricus* electroplax membranes. *Proc. Natl. Acad. Sci. USA* 75:2606–10
3. Barchi, R. L. 1982. Biochemical studies of the excitable membrane sodium channel. *Int. Rev. Neurobiol.* 23:69–102
4. Barchi, R. L., Cohen, S. A., Murphy, L. E. 1980. Purification from rat sarcolemma the saxitoxin-binding component of the excitable membrane sodium channel. *Proc. Nat. Acad. Sci. USA* 77:1306–10
5. Barhanin, J., Schmid, A., Lombet, A., Wheeler, K. P., Lazdunski, M. 1983. Molecular size of different neurotoxin receptors on the voltage-sensitive Na$^+$ channel. *J. Biol. Chem.* 258:700–2
6. Changeux, J.-P., Heidmann, T., Popot, J., Sobel, A. 1979. Reconstitution of a functional acetylcholine regulator under defined conditions. *FEBS Lett.* 105:181–87
7. Conti-Traconi, B. M., Dunn, S. M. J., Raftery, M. A. 1982. Functional stability of *Torpedo* acetylcholine receptor. Effects of protease treatment. *Biochemistry* 21:893–99
8. Craido, M., Eibl, H., Barrantes, F. J. 1982. Effects of lipids on acetylcholine receptor essential need of cholesterol for maintenance of agonist-induced state transitions in lipid. *Biochemistry* 21:3622–29
9. Epstein, M., Racker, E. 1978. Reconstitution of carbamylcholine-induced sodium ion flux and desensitization of the acetylcholine receptor from *Torpedo californica*. *J. Biol. Chem.* 253:6660–62
10. Eytan, G. 1982. Use of liposomes for reconstitution of biological functions. *Biochim. Biophys. Acta* 694:185–202
11. Gonzalez-Ros, J. M., Paraschos, A., Martinez-Carrion, M. 1980. Reconstitution of functional membrane-bound acetylcholine receptor from isolated *Torpedo californica* receptor protein and electroplax lipids. *Proc. Nat. Acad. Sci. USA* 77:1796–1800
12. Gonzales-Ros, J. M., Llanillo, M., Paraschos, A., Martinez-Carrion, M. 1982. Lipid environment of acetylcholine receptor from *Torpedo californica*. *Biochemistry* 21:3467–74
13. Gullick, W. J., Lindstrom, J. M. 1982. Structural similarities between acetylcholine receptors from fish. Electric organs and mammalian muscle. *Biochemistry* 21:4563–69
14. Hamill, O. P., Marty, A., Neher, E., Sakmann, B., Sigworth, F. 1981. Improved patch-clamp techniques for high-resolution current recording from cells and cell-free membrane patches. *Pflügers Arch.* 391:85–100
15. Hanke, W., Eibl, H., Boheim, G. 1981. A new method for membrane reconstitution: fusion of protein-containing vesicles with planar bilayer membranes below the phase transition temperature. *Biophys. Struct. Mech.* 7:131–37
16. Hartshorne, R. P., Catterall, W. A. 1981. Purification of the saxitoxin receptor of the sodium channel from rat brain. *Proc. Nat. Acad. Sci. USA* 78:4620–24
17. Horn, R., Patlak, J. B. 1980. Single channel currents from excised patches of muscle membrane. *Proc. Nat. Acad. Sci. USA* 77:6930–34
18. Huganir, R. L., Racker, E. 1980. Endogenous and exogenous proteolysis of the acetylcholine receptor from *Torpedo californica*. *J. Supramol. Struct.* 14:215–21
19. Huganir, R. L., Racker, E. 1982. Properties of proteoliposomes reconstituted with acetylcholine receptor from *Torpedo californica*. *J. Biol. Chem.* 257:9372–78
20. Huganir, R. L., Schell, M. A., Racker, E. 1979. Reconstitution of the purified acetylcholine receptor from *Torpedo californica*. *FEBS Lett.* 108:155–60
21. Kistler, J., Stroud, R. M., Klymowsky, M. W., Lalancette, R. A., Fairclough, R. H. 1982. Structure and function of an acetylcholine receptor. *Biophys. J.* 37:371–83
22. Korenbrot, J. I., Hwang, S. B. 1980. Proton transport by bacteriorhodopsin in planar membranes assembled from air-water interface films. *J. Gen. Physiol.* 76:649–82
23. Lindstrom, J., Anholt, R., Einarson, B., Engel, A., Osame, M., Montal, M. 1980. Purification of acetylcholine receptors, reconstitution into lipid vesicles, study of agonist-induced cation channel regulation. *J. Biol. Chem.* 255:8340–50
24. Lindstrom, J., Gullick, W. J., Conti-Traconi, B., Ellisman, M. 1980. Proteolytic nicking of the acetylcholine receptor. *Biochemistry* 19:4791–95

25. Miller, C. 1982. Open-state substructure of single chloride channels from *Torpedo* electroplax. *Phil. Trans. Roy. Soc. B.* 299:401–12

26. Miller, C. 1983. Reconstitution of ion channels in planar bilayer membranes: a five-year progress report. *Comm. Mol. Cell. Biophys.* 1:413–28

27. Miller, C. 1983. First steps in the reconstruction of ionic channel functions in model membranes. In *Current Methods in Cellular Neurobiology,* ed. J. L. Barker. New York: Wiley. 3:1–37

28. Miller, C. 1984. Integral membrane channels: studies in model membranes. *Physiol. Revs.* In press

29. Miller, C., Racker, E. 1979. Reconstitution of membrane transport functions. In *The Receptors: A Comprehensive Treatise,* ed. R. O'Brien, 3:1–31. New York: Plenum. 345 pp.

30. Miller, C., White, M. M. 1980. A voltage-dependent chloride conductance channel from *Torpedo* electroplax membrane. *Ann. N.Y. Acad. Sci.* 341:534–51

31. Miller, J. A., Agnew, W. S., Levinson, S. A. 1983. Principal glycopeptide of the Tetrodotoxin/saxitoxin binding protein from *Electrophorus elecricus:* isolation and partial chemical and physical characterization. *Biochemistry* 22:462–69

32. Montal, M., Darzon, A., Schindler, H. 1981. Functional reassembly of membrane proteins in planar lipid bilayers. *Quart. Revs. Biophys.* 14:1–79

33. Montal, M., Mueller, P. 1972. Formation of bimolecular membranes from lipid monolayers and a study of their electrical properties. *Proc. Nat. Acad. Sci. USA* 69:3561–66

34. Mueller, P., Rudin, D. O., Tien, H. T., Wescott, W. C. 1962. Reconstitution of cell membrane structure *in vitro* and its transformation into an excitable system. *Nature* 194:979–80

35. Nelson, N., Anholt, R., Lindstrom, J., Montal, M. 1980. Reconstitution of purified acetylcholine receptors with functional ion channels in planar lipid bilayers. *Proc. Nat. Acad. Sci. USA* 77:3057–61

36. Schindler, H. 1980. Formation of planar bilayers from artificial or native membrane vesicles. *FEBS Lett.* 122:77–79

37. Schindler, H., Quast, U. 1980. Functional acetylcholine receptor from *Torpedo*

38. Talvenheimo, J. A., Tankum, M. M., Catterall, W. A. 1982. Reconstitution of neurotoxin-stimulated sodium transport by the voltage-sensitive sodium channel purified from rat brain. *J. Biol. Chem.* 257:11868–71

39. Tanaka, J. C., Eccleston, J. F., Barchi, R. L. 1983. Cation selectivity characteristics of the reconstituted voltage-dependent sodium channel purified rat skeletal muscle sarcolemma. *J. Biol. Chem.* 258:7519–26

40. Tank, D. W., Huganir, R. L., Greengard, P., Webb, W. W. 1983. Patch-recorded single-channel currents of the purified and reconstituted *Torpedo* acetylcholine receptor. *Proc. Nat. Acad. Sci. USA.* 80:5129–33

41. Tank, D. W., Miller, C. 1983. Patch-clamped liposomes: Recording reconstituted ion channels. In *Single-Channel Recording,* ed. B. Sakmann, E. Neher, pp. 91–105. New York: Plenum. 503 pp.

42. Tank, D. W., Miller, C., Webb, W. W. 1982. Isolated-patch recording from liposomes containing functionally reconstituted chloride channels from *Torpedo* electroplax. *Proc. Nat. Acad. Sci. USA* 79:7749–53

43. Villegas, R., Villegas, G. M., Condrescu-Guidi, M., Suarez-Mata, Z. 1980. Characterization of the nerve membrane sodium channel incorporated into soybean liposomes: a sodium channel active particle. *Ann. N.Y. Acad. Sci.* 358:183–203

44. Walker, J. W., Takeyasu, K., McNamee, M. G. 1982. Activation and inactivation kinetics of *Torpedo californica* acetylcholine receptor in reconstituted membranes. *Biochemistry* 21:5384–89

45. Weigele, D. J., Barchi, R. L. 1982. Functional reconstitution of the sodium channel from rat sarcolemma. *Proc. Nat. Acad. Sci. USA* 79:3653–55

46. Wu, W. C. S., Moore, H. P. H., Raftery, M. A. 1981. Quantitation of cation transport by reconstituted membrane vesicles containing purified acetylcholine receptor. *Proc. Nat. Acad. Sci. USA* 78:775–79

47. White, M. M., Miller, C. 1979. A voltage-gated anion channel from electric organ of *Torpedo californica*. *J. Biol. Chem.* 254:10161–66

marmorata in planar membranes. *Proc. Nat. Acad. Sci. USA* 77:3052–56

COMPARATIVE PHYSIOLOGY

Introduction, James Edward Heath, *Section Editor*

The reviews in this section compliment those of the special section on hearing. These deal with the field sensing of animals and their orientation in space by sound. The papers in the special section review the knowledge of the mechanics, transduction, and processing of auditory information largely from exogenous sources. A number of organisms, most notably the bats reviewed here, generate sound pulses and analyze echos to deduce spatial relations and aid in prey capture. Echo location by bats was first suggested by Spallanzani more than 200 years ago. The exquisite sensitivity and sophistication of the process is testament to the power natural selection can bring to bear on sensory systems. A degree of echo location is within the reach of most animals equipped with binaural sensors. This "sonar" has been invented independently by animals as different as fish and birds.

The evolutionary experimentation among fishes with the sensing of electric fields parallels that with hearing. Among sharks, special organs on the snout can sense the fields generated by ion currents in the muscle of their prey. However, these fields are so weak that this sensing system is useful only at short range and in the final stages of prey capture. A degree of sensitivity to electric fields is a fortuitous feature of the lateral line system of fishes and amphibians. Further, the central processing of pressure pulses or sound to the lateral line resembles that of hearing, in that intensity and direction of origin of a disturbance is determined. On this biological framework, some fishes developed a means to synchronize and orient the ion currents of their own muscles so as to produce relatively large electric fields. The pre-existing lateral line sensitivity and auditory-like processing could then be used to process disturbances to the electric field in the vicinity of the fish. The review in this section examines recent advances in the exploration of the diversity and sensitivity of the generation of fields, of the sensing apparatus, and of central processing in weakly electric fish.

Magnetism, in contrast to sound and electric fields, exists in nature as a standing field. The field is strong and readily detectable as to polarity, direction, and dip with primitive mechanical devices. While magnetism has long been philosophized to influence animal behavior and function, only recently has unequivocal magnetic sense been demonstrated in living organisms—and then only in bacteria. There is building evidence that many higher organisms have magnetic sensors and that some of these organisms can sense magnetic fields well enough to use field lines as an aid to navigation. These data are surveyed in the third review of this section. Readers are referred to K. S. Thompson's comparison of the history of the discovery of electric and magnetic field sensing by organisms (Am. Sci. 1983. 71:522–24) for a thoughtful essay on the philosophy of discovery.

Ann. Rev. Physiol. 1984. 46:561–83

THE ELECTRIC SENSE OF WEAKLY ELECTRIC FISH

Walter Heiligenberg

Scripps Institution of Oceanography, University of California at San Diego, La Jolla, California 92093

Joseph Bastian

Department of Zoology, University of Oklahoma, Norman, Oklahoma 73019

INTRODUCTION

The study of electric fish has been particularly rewarding in the areas of sensory and central nervous physiology. Anatomical and physiological similarities between electroreceptors and hair cells in the stato-acoustical system have raised questions about the electrical nature of frequency tuning, and electroreceptors appear to be an excellent model system to study tuning phenomena at the cellular and molecular level. The coordination of behavioral, neurophysiological, and neuroanatomical approaches has been particularly successful in relating central nervous structures to behavioral functions. Fortunately, electric fish display a few rather simple behavioral responses that are sufficiently robust to still function in neurophysiological preparations. The role of individual cells can thus be explored during simultaneous performance of the behavior of the whole organism. Much has been learned about the ethology of electric fish and the function and adaptive significance of specific features of their electric organ discharges (EODs). This knowledge has successfully guided neurophysiological studies, and electric fish thus have become a favorite model system in neuroethology.

Since an extensive review of electroreception was recently written by T. H. Bullock (16), we will concentrate only upon more recent and most promising developments in this field.

THE FREQUENCY TUNING OF ELECTRORECEPTORS

Two major classes of electroreceptors are known in electric fish: ampullary organs, which respond to low-frequency (<40Hz) electric signals; and tuber-

561

ous organs, which are most sensitive in the spectral range of the animal's own EODs [see review by Bullock (16)]. By measuring threshold responses of a tuberous receptor as a function of the stimulating frequency, a V-shaped response characteristic is obtained, and the frequency with the lowest threshold is called the "best frequency" (BF) of the receptor. Hopkins (41) demonstrated that BFs match the predominant spectral frequency of the individual's EOD. Since animals with continual, wave-type EODs, such as *Eigenmannia, Sternopygus, and Apteronotus,* slowly change their fundamental EOD frequency over the course of weeks and months (40), we wonder how the tuning of their tuberous electroreceptors stays in register with their EODs.

The Influence of Steroid Hormones Upon Pacemaker Frequency and Electroreceptor Tuning

Electric fish of the genus *Sternopygus* are sexually dimorphic in the fundamental frequency of their EODs. Mature females have frequencies (120–240 Hz) approximately one octave higher than mature males, while juveniles fire at intermediate frequencies (40). By daily injections of androgens, Meyer (50) was able to lower the pacemaker frequency of either sex by as much as 10% over the course of 1–2 weeks. Injections of estradiol had opposite, although much smaller (1–2%) effects. This finding strongly suggests that the natural sexual difference in EOD frequency, which is typical for this genus, is controlled by differential steroid levels.

Since in normal animals BFs of electroreceptors always approximate the fundamental EOD frequency of the individual, Meyer & Zakon (52) determined the receptor tuning in individuals whose pacemaker frequency was being altered by dihydrotestosterone (DHT) injections. They found that BFs of electroreceptors followed the decrease in pacemaker frequency over days. Electroreceptors remained tuned to the new EOD frequency over the period of steroid injections as well as during the postinjection period (68).

Such receptor plasticity could be due to any of three possible mechanisms. First: Steroids directly affect only the pacemaker frequency, and electroreceptor tuning adjusts itself to the dominant stimulus frequency to which they are exposed, i.e. the animal's own EOD frequency. Second: Steroids directly affect only the BF of electroreceptors, and the pacemaker is entrained to fire within the narrow frequency range at which electroreceptors are most heavily recruited. Third: Steroid hormones simultaneously affect pacemaker frequency and electroreceptor tuning so that both are shifted by approximately the same amount.

By means of a spinal cord transection, the animal's electric organ can be silenced so that its electroreceptors are no longer being driven by its EODs. DHT injections and tests of medullary pacemaker frequency and electroreceptor tuning in such animals so far have demonstrated that only the pacemaker frequency is affected by steroid hormones and that electroreceptor BFs do not shift in the absence of electric fields that substitute for the animal's silenced EODs. By exposing such animals to artificial electric fields, Meyer & Zakon are currently testing whether receptors can be retuned to new frequencies in this manner.

Different mechanisms appear to guide the effect of steroid hormones upon EOD and receptor tuning in mormyrid electric fish. The EODs of these fish are discrete pulses rather than continual sinusoidal discharges, and in some species, the EOD pulse has a sex-specific waveform. Bass & Hopkins (1) found that, in one such species, males have a broader EOD pulse than females and that testosterone or DHT induces females and immature males to produce mature male EODs. Estradiol by contrast has only a weak effect. The changes in EOD waveform take place over a period of 8–10 days, and the EOD of testosterone-treated females is similar to that of natural males. In a related species, which shows no sex difference in the EOD, testosterone has no effect. The effect on the waveform of the EOD seems to take place at the level of the electric organ, because external recordings of the descending spinal volley that excites the electric organ are similar in normal and terstosterone-treated animals.

In mormyrids, as is true in gymnotoids with pulse-type EODs (3), the electroreceptors involved in communications, that is the knollenorgans, are generally tuned to the frequencies at which the power spectrum of their EOD peaks. In those species where the pulse of the male is longer than the pulse of the female and consequently has a power spectrum that peaks at a lower spectral frequency, knollenorgans appear to be tuned to lower spectral frequencies than they are in females. Females that have been treated with androgens apparently lower the BF of their knollenorgans, which is consistent with the decrease observed in the peak power frequency of their EOD (2).

Each EOD cycle, be it of the pulse- or wave-type form, is triggered by a pulse of the pacemaker. Because mormyrids produce EOD pulses at very irregular rates, it is difficult to imagine mechanisms by which receptor tuning could be induced by the activity of the pacemaker (2). Thus, the physiological mechanism guiding the effect of androgens upon receptor tuning may differ from that suggested above for the wave-type discharging gymnotoid, *Sternopygus*.

Electroreceptors as Models for Auditory Hair Cell Tuning

The BF of an electroreceptor is that particular frequency at which it can be driven by minimal stimulation. If an electroreceptor is excited by a short impulse, it rings in the manner of a damped oscillation (13), and the frequency of this oscillation approximates the BF of the receptor when tested by continual sinusoidal stimulation. Electroreceptors thus display physical properties of higher-order electrical filters, and their ringing response offers a convenient, nonintrusive manner of measuring individual receptor tuning via a pipette placed over the receptor pore on the body surface for simultaneous stimulation and recording (52, 65).

Considerable parallels exist between electroreceptors and hair cells, and the V-shaped tuning characteristics of electroreceptors resemble those known from cochlear hair cells in the auditory system. It has been suggested that, in addition to the mechanical tuning provided by the cochlea, a second-stage, electrical filter may enhance the tuning of hair cells (41, 64–66, 68). Much as electroreceptors, auditory hair cells of the turtle cochlea ring at their BF in response to single electrical current pulses (21, 22, 26). The membrane biophysics underlying such electrical tuning phenomena can be investigated most conveniently in electroreceptors, because they are easily accessible and can readily be studied in skin preparations maintained in tissue chambers (Zakon, in preparation).

The Phase Sensitivity of Electroreceptors

Because electroreceptors discriminate the direction of current flow, they are sensitive to the phase function of electric signals. Consequently, electric fish can discriminate electrical pulses with identical power spectra but different phase functions. The most drastic effect is a shift of all phase values by 180°, which is equivalent to a sign inversion of the whole pulse. But even the more subtle effects of much smaller phase shifts are detectable to electric fish (33, 43, 49).

Phase sensitivity offers the fish additional cues for signal detection and discrimination, beyond its ability to distinguish signals on the basis of differences in power spectra. In the case of a species with pulse-type EODs, the animal can readily distinguish its own pulse from those of a neighbor by comparing the timing of electroreceptor firings in different parts of its body surface. So called "Type I" receptors (63) or "PM units" (3) fire a single spike in response to an outward-going current step. As demonstrated in Figure 1, the animal's own EOD pulse, S1, originates in the interior of its body, and the direction of the current with respect to the orientation of the electroreceptors is therefore identical in all parts of the body surface (with the exception of a few receptors at the tip of the tail, where current reenters the body and thus has the opposite sign). The animal's own EOD should therefore trigger a synchronous discharge of its Type I receptors (see spike responses associated with S1 in area A and B of body surface in Fig. 1). Since a neighbor's EOD pulse, S2, has a current source outside the animal, there will be sites on its body surface (A and B in Fig. 1) where the direction of current flow is opposite. As a consequence, Type I spikes triggered by the S2 pulse will fire at different moments in areas A and B. The nonsynchronous spiking of Type I receptors thus indicates the presence of a foreign EOD pulse, and a central evaluation of the timing of Type I firing across the body surface should enable the animal to distinguish its own pulses from those of a neighbor. Moreover, since the direction of the S2 current flow depends upon the direction of the neighbor's longitudinal axis with respect to that of the subject fish, the animal should be able to assess the spatial

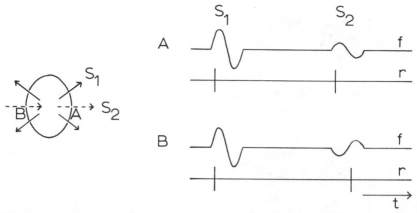

Figure 1 Schematic presentation of current flows associated with EODs of subject fish and neighbor. *Left:* Cross section through fish showing current flow associated with the animal's own EOD (*S1*, solid arrows) and that of a neighbor (*S2*, broken arrows). *Right:* Transepidermal current flow (*f*) and timing (*t*) of associated Type I receptor spike (*r*) in areas *A* and *B* of animal's body surface, in the case of *S1* and *S2* respectively. Since *S1* originates inside the animal, its phase in *A* and *B* is identical, and receptor spikes are synchronous. The opposite holds for *S2*.

orientation of its neighbor. Westby's experiments (67) with electrical dummies strongly support this assumption.

Phase sensitivity is further exploited in the context of species and sex recognition. Hopkins (42) has found approximately 20 sympatric species of mormyrids, in the Ivindo river of Gabon in Africa, that in some cases can be identified more readily on the basis of species-specific EOD features rather than by traditional morphological features (Figure 2). In some species, mature individuals have sex-specific EODs, and Hopkins & Bass (43) have demonstrated by playback experiments that a resident male *Brienomyrus brachyistius* can recognize a mature female of its own species on the basis of EOD features alone. By using a variety of artificial electric signals, these authors could show that a time disparity of approximately 0.4 ms in the firing of Knollenorgan receptors (mormyrid Type I receptor) on opposite sides of the male's body (such as A and B in Fig. 1) is the critical feature for female-EOD recognition and that no other EOD waveform in this habitat can elicit this particular time disparity.

THE INTERPRETATION OF ELECTRORECEPTIVE INPUTS BY COROLLARY DISCHARGES OF THE ELECTRIC ORGAN PACEMAKER

Sensory systems not only respond to stimuli from external or environmental sources but also to stimuli resulting from the animal's own motor activities.

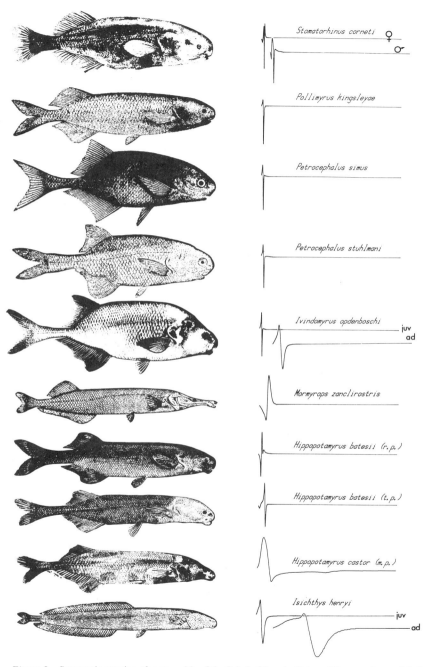

Figure 2 Sympatric species of mormyrids of the Ivindo River in Gabon. The waveform of their

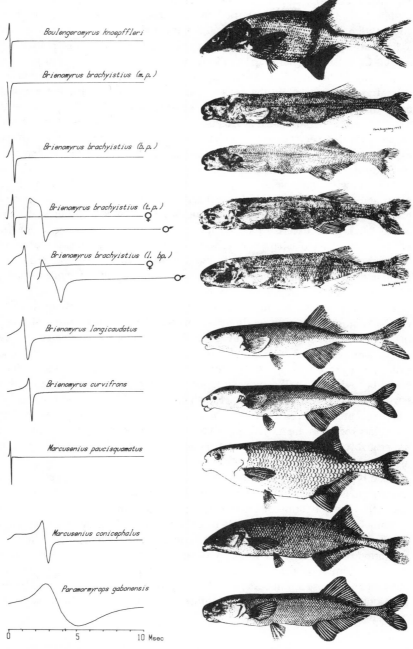

Boulengeromyrus knoepffleri

Brienomyrus brachyistius (m.p.)

Brienomyrus brachyistius (b.p.)

Brienomyrus brachyistius (t.p.) ♀ ♂

Brienomyrus brachyistius (l. bp.) ♀ ♂

Brienomyrus longicaudatus

Brienomyrus curvifrons

Marcusenius paucisquamatus

Marcusenius conicephalus

Paramormyrops gabonensis

0   5   10 Msec

EODs serves in sex and species recognition. (Courtesy of C. D. Hopkins)

This latter category of sensory input, termed reafference by von Holst & Mittelstaedt (39), must be identified and processed appropriately by the nervous system. Failure to do so can result in either the loss of information unique to the reafference or an erroneous evaluation of environmental or "exafferent" inputs. Corollary discharge (61) and efference copy (39) are central nervous system (CNS) signals often associated with mechanisms thought to enable the animal to exploit or avoid the consequences of reafference. It has been proposed that "corollary discharge" be used as a general term describing any signal related to a motor command that affects sensory input. "Efference copy" is then reserved for the special case in which this signal forms a negative image of the expected reafference. This negative image can then be added to the reafference, resulting in its cancellation (11, 48).

Animals with active sensory systems, such as echolocating bats and cetaceans and electrolocating weakly electric fish, rely heavily on the analysis of reafferent inputs to gain information about the environment. Studies of mormyrid weakly electric fish have yielded several important examples of the utility of corollary discharges in processing reafferent inputs. All mormyrid species produce pulse-type EODs of short duration, i.e. high spectral frequency content, and these animals have three types of electroreceptors: knollenorgans, mormyromasts, and ampullary receptors.

The knollenorgans are low-threshold receptors that are most sensitive to EOD-like stimuli. They give a single action potential at a fairly constant latency in response to an adequate stimulus. Since these receptors only produce a single spike, they are unable to encode information about stimulus intensity, and instead they probably signal the presence of the EODs of other fish and mediate social behaviors (62). The mormyromasts respond to adequate stimuli with a burst of action potentials, and burst length is correlated with stimulus intensity. These receptors are well suited to provide information for electrolocation. The ampullary receptors are most responsive to low-frequency (<40Hz) stimuli and are probably used for detecting environmental sources of low-frequency voltages (see 16 for review).

Each type of receptor is activated by an animal's own EOD, yet only the mormyromasts are thought to encode useful information in their responses to the EOD. The activation of the remaining receptor types therefore represents potentially unwanted information that could confound the analysis of appropriate exafferent stimulation of knollenorgans and ampullary receptors. Likewise, activation of an individual's mormyromasts by another fish's EOD will not provide information useful for electrolocation. Studies of the behavior and physiology of these animals show that these problems are circumvented by the interaction of the three categories of receptor inputs with three types of corollary discharges in the CNS.

Physiological Studies of the Interaction of Corollary Discharges and Electrosensory Inputs

Bennett & Steinbach (15) first demonstrated the existence of a corollary discharge of the neural command that controls the mormyrid electric organ. They recorded slow-wave responses in several brain areas that process electrosensory input that were time-locked to the EOD command signal. These responses were found in animals whose EODs were silenced via curare, thereby eliminating the activation of electroreceptors. These authors also showed that CNS responses to direct stimulation of the electrosensory nerves could be inhibited if the stimulation occurred at about the time that the electric organ would normally fire. This result raised the possibility that the corollary discharge was capable of gating electrosensory input. Subsequent single cell studies by Zipser & Bennett (69) showed that a category of neurons, termed principle cells, in the first-order electrosensory processing station, the posterior lateral line lobe (PLLL), received a corollary discharge of the EOD command. This corollary discharge inhibited PLLL cells receiving knollenorgan input and facilitated the majority of cells receiving mormyromast input. This suggests that the animal's CNS will be most responsive to mormyromast inputs due to their own EOD and more sensitive to knollenorgan inputs due to the EODs of neighbors.

More recent studies by Bell (9–11) revealed a remarkable interaction between ampullary receptor inputs and a true efference copy in the PLLL. Ampullary receptors respond best to low-frequency stimuli, and they are thus also driven by the slow repetition rate of the EOD. Bell & Russell (12), however, have provided data suggesting that these receptors do not function in active electrolocation. The ampullary response to the EOD can be quite long, up to 100 ms, and therefore quite disruptive to the detection of environmental sources of low-frequency electrical stimulation. Bell has found that PLLL cells receiving ampullary inputs also receive an efference copy, a negative image of the ampullary response to the EOD. This efference copy, which begins at about the time of the EOD command, is probably integrated with the ampullary response to the EOD, thereby reducing the effect of EOD-generated ampullary activity on higher-order cells. This efference copy is plastic: it changes, in a complementary fashion, as the pattern of ampullary reafference changes, thus insuring minimal exposure of higher-order cells even to slowly changing patterns of EOD-linked sensory input. The efference copy mechanism is far superior to simply inhibiting ampullary inputs for the time that the receptors are active due to the EOD. The duration of this sort of inhibition would need to be quite long and the animal would therefore be insensitive to all stimuli appropriate to the ampullary system for this period of time.

The three categories of electroreceptor input interact with different types of corollary discharges at the level of the PLLL. Each of these interactions enhances the capabilities of the nervous system to utilize the information of different receptor afferents effectively. Knollenorgan information is suppressed during the animal's own EOD, and therefore their responses to the EODs of other fish are selected for analysis. Mormyromast inputs are facilitated immediately following the EOD, insuring that electrolocation is based on responses to the animal's own EOD. Ampullary reafferences are effectively nulled by a complex efference copy, insuring that ampullary sensitivity to relevant stimuli remains high even during an animal's own EOD.

Behavioral Studies of the Effects of Corollary Discharges

Recent behavioral studies support the conclusion that corollary discharges selectively gate inputs from different electroreceptor categories in mormyrids. Heiligenberg (28) showed that *Brienomyrus* displayed reduced abilities to electrolocate when extraneous stimulus pulses were used to jam the animal's electrosensory system. Jamming was only effective, however, when the extraneous pulses coincided with the fish's EODs. Pulses even eight-fold stronger, but presented between EODs, caused minimal decrement in performance. This result supports the physiological data showing that the corollary discharge facilitates or "gates on" mormyromast input only during the EOD, the time at which such inputs are relevant for electrolocation.

Meyer & Bell (51) recently provided results that lend additional support to this gating hypothesis. In their experiments, the EOD was abolished via curare-like drugs, and the spinal motor neuron discharge that drives the electric organ was recorded and used to trigger, at a fixed latency, an artificial EOD (S1) that was applied to the entire fish. This same pulse, reduced in amplitude (S2), was simultaneously applied to a small region of the body via a separate set of narrowly spaced electrodes. By altering the magnitude of S2, Meyer & Bell could modify the pattern of local receptor stimulation, and the fish responded with the "novelty response," a transient increase in EOD rate. These authors found that novelty responses were evoked only if the stimulus was presented during a short time period (12 and 48 ms in two mormyrid species) immediately following the EOD command. Again, this supports the conclusion that mormyromasts input is "gated on," at least for certain types of processing, only at the time of the EOD.

Studies by Moller & Bauer (53, 54) on presumably communicatory behaviors, triggered by knollenorgan receptors, showed that these behaviors were suppressed for a short time following the EOD. This agrees with the physiological data showing that a corollary discharge inhibits knollenorgan input at the time of the animal's discharge.

Behavioral and physiological studies clearly show that the mormyrids utilize corollary discharges to differentially gate various categories of electroreceptor input for higher-order processing. This reliance on corollary discharge mechanisms contrasts sharply with what is known of mechanisms used by gymnotoid pulse-type electric fish to evaluate inputs from different receptor types. No corollary discharges have ever been found in these fish, and behavioral studies show that such mechanisms are not used (30, 34). Instead, these animals appear to rely on a reafferent signal mediated by a rapidly conducting category of electroreceptor afferents to provide the temporal indication of when an EOD occurs. Input from these Type I (63) or PM receptors (3) could encode the timing of an EOD as well as whether the discharge was the fish's own or that of a neighbor. All that is needed is a CNS machinery capable of decoding the different temporal patterns of receptor activation caused by an animal's own EOD vs that of a neighbor as described in the section on the phase sensitivity of electroreceptors.

FUNCTION AND ORGANIZATION OF LAMINATED ELECTROSENSORY STRUCTURES IN THE CNS OF GYMNOTIFORM FISH

The presence of an object in the vicinity of the fish causes local alterations of the transepidermal current flow associated with the animal's EODs (see review in 29), and the pattern of these alterations can thus be considered the electric image of the object. Local transepidermal voltage is monitored by electroreceptors in the animal's skin, and somatotopically organized central nervous projections of electroreceptor afferents and higher-order units provide the substrate for the processing of electric images. The first of these stations, the posterior lateral line lobe (PLLL), has recently been renamed "electrosensory lateral line lobe" (18). Since all literature discussed in this review, however, still uses the old name, we will use it as well.

Primary Afferent Projections to the Posterior Lateral Line Lobe (PLLL)

The somata of primary electroreceptive afferent neurons are located in the anterior lateral line nerve ganglion. Intracellular injection of physiologically identified afferents have shown that ampullary afferents project to the medial portion of the posterior lateral line lobe (PLLL) while each tuberous afferent projects to three separate, additional portions of the PLLL, which are called central-medial, central-lateral, and lateral (Figure 3) (20, 36). All four projections are somatotopically organized, and the enlarged head of each "pisciculus" correlates with the higher density of electroreceptors in this part of the body

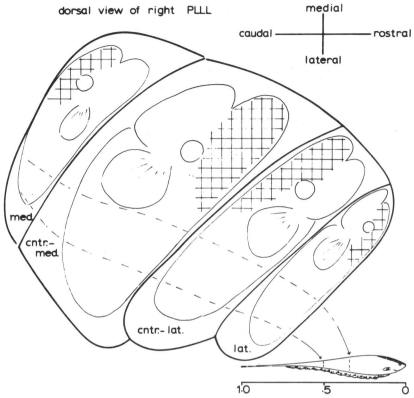

Figure 3 Tuberous and ampullary electroreceptor afferents project somatotopically to the posterior lateral line lobe (PLLL). Whereas ampullary afferents project to the *medial* portion of the PLLL, each tuberous afferent projects to three different maps, located in the *central-medial, central-lateral,* and *lateral* portion of the PLLL. The two classes of tuberous afferents, T and P units, synapse upon different cell types in the PLLL (see Fig. 4) and are in somatotopic register. The hatched area in the four pisciculi represents the dorsal surface of the head. (From 36)

surface. The anatomical separation of ampullary and tuberous projections reflects the difference of the roles of these two modalities in the animal's life.

The two classes of tuberous afferent projections, P and T units, are in somatotopic register but appear to synapse on different cell types in the PLLL. A detailed analysis of the PLLL by Maler et al (47) gives evidence that T units contact spherical cells while P units contact granule, basilar pyramidal, and polymorphic cells (see diagram in Figure 4). It is difficult to confirm these rules by light-microscopic inspection of intracellularly labeled, physiologically identified cells. Preliminary EM studies are largely in agreement with Maler's postulates, and it appears that these rules hold at least in a statistical sense.

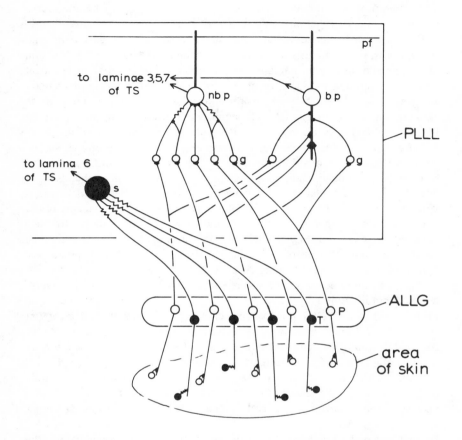

Figure 4 The synaptic organization of primary tuberous electroreceptor afferents in the *PLLL*, as proposed by Maler et al (47). *T*-type afferents *(filled)* form electrical synapses upon spherical cells (*s*), which in turn project to *lamina 6* of the torus (*TS*) (see Fig. 6). *P*-type afferents *(open)* form excitatory chemical synapses upon granule cells (*g*) and upon basilar dendrites of basilar pyramidal cells (*bp*). Basilar pyramidal cells also receive inhibitory input from more distant granule cells, which in turn are excited by *P*-unit inputs from the periphery of the receptive field. The total *P*-type input to the basilar pyramidal cell thus appears to have an excitatory center and inhibitory surround organization. Nonbasilar pyramidal cells (*nbp*), on the other hand, receive inhibitory input from nearest granule cells and electrical synapses from more distant granule cells, with the latter inputs being inhibited by more centrally located granule cells. The total *P*-type input to a nonbasilar pyramidal cell thus appears to have an inhibitory center and excitatory surround organization. Both types of pyramidal cells project most heavily to *laminae 3, 5,* and *7* of the torus (*TS*) (see Fig. 6). The dorsal dendrites of pyramidal cells are contacted by parallel fibers (*pf*) that originate in the lobus caudalis of the cerebellum. *ALLG* is the anterior lateral line nerve ganglion that houses the somata of primary afferent cells.

The nature of the afferent organization of the PLLL can readily be interpreted on the basis of the functional role of P and T units.

For electric fish with continual, sinusoidal EODs, such as *Eigenmannia* and *Apteronotus,* two stimulus variables are of crucial importance for the detection of objects and interfering fields of near neighbors. These variables are local phase and amplitude modulations of the electrical signal on the animal's body surface. Phase modulations, which appear as modulations in the timing of the zero crossing of the sinusoidal EOD signal, are caused by varying capacitive loads associated with the movement of objects (25, 58). Significant phase modulations are further evoked by the interference between the animal's EOD and that of a neighbor of similar frequency. Amplitude modulations are caused by changes in ohmic resistance that characterize the movement of objects (4, 5, 24). Amplitude modulations are also introduced by the interference with a neighbor's EOD, and the form of the joint modulation of phase and amplitude, due to interfering signals, characterizes the sign of the frequency difference between the interfering EODs and thus determines the direction in which the animal must shift its own frequency in order to avoid that of its neighbor [see review of this so-called Jamming Avoidance Response (JAR) in 31].

Phase and amplitude modulations are encoded by T and P units respectively, although not in a mutually exclusive manner. T units fire one spike per EOD cycle, phase-locked to the positive zero crossing of the signal. The latency of firing of some T units, however, is affected by the amplitude of the signal (17, 38), and the timing of firing of such units thus does not reflect phase information unambiguously. T-unit afferents form electric synapses upon the spherical cells in the PLLL (see Fig. 4). Maler et al (47) suggest that the synaptic organization and spike initiation mechanism of these cells are such that only a near synchronous arrival of several T-afferent spikes will result in a single-spike response, whereas T-afferent spikes that arrive out of synchrony may not be transmitted. As a consequence of this mechanism, the spherical cells of the PLLL encode phase by the timing of their firing with even less jitter than do T unit afferents, and, most importantly, the timing of their firing is no longer affected by modulations of stimulus amplitude within naturally occurring ranges (57). We therefore find a purer form of phase representation in the PLLL than at the level of the primary afferent.

Information about amplitude modulations, encoded in the rate of firing of P-unit receptors, is also processed by the PLLL. Whereas the firing of P units, which is statistically linked to the zero crossing of the stimulus, still contains some information about phase, very little phase coupling is seen in the firing of the basilar pyramidal cells, and none is seen in the firing of the nonbasilar pyramidal cells of the PLLL (8). The firing rate of P-unit receptors increases in response to a step increase in stimulus amplitude but partially adapts as the new stimulus amplitude level is maintained (59). The firing of P units thus reflects changes in amplitude more than the amplitude level itself. This phasic response property is even more apparent in the higher-order cells of the PLLL that receive P-unit input: The basilar and nonbasilar pyramidal cells fire at a low spontaneous rate and only respond to changes in stimulus amplitude. Basilar pyramidal cells are excited by an increase in stimulus amplitude and are inhibited by a decrease in stimulus amplitude. The opposite holds for nonbasilar pyramidal cells. These response characteristics were predicted by Maler et al (47) on the basis of synaptic organization (see Fig. 4) and have recently been confirmed by intracellular labeling (56). We thus find that separate types of cells in the PLLL selectively and exclusively encode behaviorally relevant stimulus variables, such as local modulations in stimulus phase and rises and falls in stimulus amplitude. Messages from these cells are relayed to different targets in the CNS, which will be described in following sections.

The triple representation of identical tuberous receptor inputs in the PLLL is mysterious. It is conceivable that three different and mutually incompatible processes of feature extraction occur within the three somatotopically organized maps.

Behavioral experiments have demonstrated that the Jamming Avoidance Response (JAR) in *Eigenmannia* requires stimulus phase comparisons across different parts of the animal's body surface (35). The difference in phase between two areas, A and B, on the body surface is the difference in the timing of the zero crossings of the sinusoidal stimulus in these areas. This phase difference is encoded in the timing difference, t_A-t_B, of T-receptor spikes generated in these two areas. An accurate central nervous representation of the value of t_A-t_B requires that the system compensate for potential conduction time differences if the areas A and B are located at different distances from the CNS. This compensation is partly achieved by higher conduction velocities in primary afferent fibers from more distantly located receptor pores, and the soma size of primary afferents is positively correlated with the conduction velocity of their fibers (36). This compensation for distance-related time disparities at the afferent side parallels a similar compensation at the efferent side, where a synchronous discharge of the electric organ is achieved by higher conduction velocities in efferent fibers to more distant sites of the organ (14).

Projections from PLLL to Torus Semicircularis and Nucleus Praeeminentialis and Recurrent Inputs to the PLLL

The PLLL projects predominantly to the contralateral side of the torus semicircularis, a multilaminated midbrain structure that is related to the inferior colliculus in higher vertebrates (19, 46, 60). The four electrosensory maps of the PLLL merge into one map in the torus (see Figure 5), whose different laminae are vertically in somatotopic register with each other. According to Carr et al (19), the laminae of the torus receive different inputs from the PLLL.

rostral

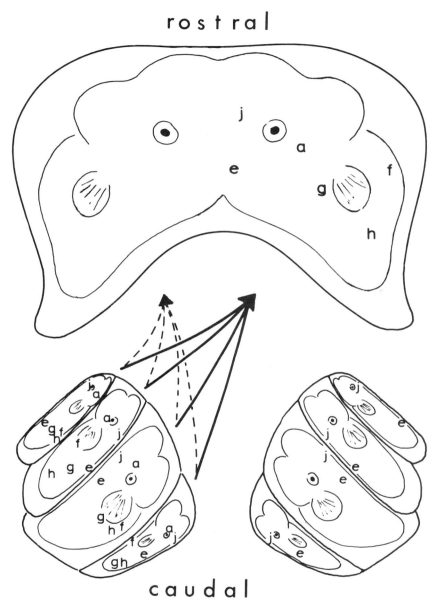

caudal

Figure 5 The PLLL projects predominantly to the contralateral side of the torus semicircularis, shown in dorsal view in the top section of the figure. The four maps of the PLLL merge into one map in the torus, and the region of the head representation is enlarged even further. Letters in the torus map indicate the sites of small vertical injections of horseradish peroxidase (HRP), and the same letters in the PLLL maps indicate retrograde labeling. The maps of the PLLL are ipsilateral representations of the body surface, and the representations of the two sides of the body fuse in the dorsal midline at the level of the torus.

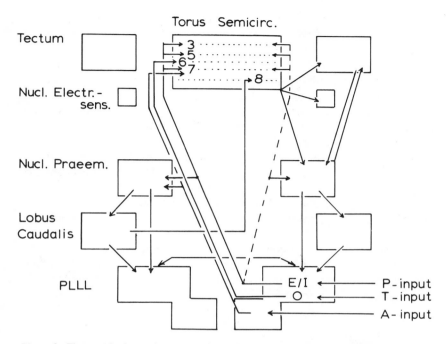

Figure 6 Flow graph of central nervous pathways involved in electroreception. Primary afferents from ampullary receptors *(A-input)* project to the medial portion of the *PLLL* whereas the two types of tuberous afferents, *P* and *T* units, project to the central and lateral portions of the *PLLL*. *T*-type afferents contact spherical cells *(0)* in the *PLLL* that in turn project to lamina *6* of the *torus*. *P*-type afferents control basilar pyramidal cells *(E)* and nonbasilar pyramidal cells *(I)*, which in turn project predominantly to laminae *3, 5,* and *7* of the *torus* and also send collaterals to the *nucleus praeeminentialis*. This nucleus projects back to the *PLLL* as well as to the *lobus caudalis* of the cerebellum, which in turn projects back again to the *PLLL*. Projections of the *PLLL* are largely contralateral and to a lesser extent ipsilateral *(dashed line)*, and the ipsilateral projection gives rise to a potential feedback loop to the *PLLL*. The role of the *PLLL* commissure is still unknown. The *lobus caudalis* projects to the contralateral lamina *8* of the *torus*, and many laminae of the *torus* project to the *tectum, nucleus electrosensorius,* and *nucleus praeeminentialis*. The *tectum* is a potential link in the control of the JAR since its ablation abolishes this response. A very important function of the *tectum* appears to be the composition of visual and electrical images *(6)* of the outside world and the control of oriented behavior in response to moving objects.

The spherical cells (phase coders) of the PLLL project exclusively to lamina 6, while the pyramidal cells (change-in-amplitude coders) project predominantly to laminae 3, 5, and 7 and also send collaterals to the nucleus praeeminentialis (see Figure 6). The four maps of the PLLL are separately represented in this nucleus (46), which in turn sends direct and indirect (via the lobus caudalis of the cerebellum) recurrent input to the PLLL (45).

Very little is known about the physiological implications of these structures and connections. Information about local phase modulations arrives in lamina 6, and the difference in phase between sites on the body surface is computed by cells below lamina 6 (7, 8, 55). Various cell types in deeper laminae of the torus compute local modulations in amplitude in reference to differential phase (55) and thus appear to be vital links in the control of the JAR. A large portion of the neuronal circuitry underlying the JAR is now known, and it is characterized by the following general properties (32): First, parallel processing of inputs from different sources of the body surface by a distributed system of evaluations. Second, a marked absence of so called "pontifical" or "decision" units and instead a more parliamentary and statistical rule by large populations of neurons. Third, detection of specific features by virtue of the activation of statistically defined sets of broadly tuned neurons rather than by the activation of a single class of narrowly tuned specific "feature detectors." Fourth, notable imperfections in the fidelity of sensory coding with, however, negligible behavioral consequences.

   An essential link in the control of the JAR, connecting the torus with a prepacemaker nucleus in the midbrain (37), is still unknown. A massive topographic projection from torus to tectum is the basis for the convergence of electric and visual information.

The Convergence of Electric and Visual Information in the Tectum

The optic tectum (mammalian superior colliculus) is known to receive a variety of sensory inputs in addition to vision. Recent studies in a variety of animals [mice (23), rattlesnakes (27), owls (44), electric fish (6)] show that the organization of nonvisual sensory inputs is also spatiotopically organized and that these sensory projections are largely in register with the visual projection to the tectum. Figure 7a summarizes experiments with the weakly electric fish *Apteronotus albifrons,* in which multiunit activity was recorded from various tectal loci in response to moving visual or electrosensory stimuli. There is a clear relationship between rostro-caudal position of the recording site and the most effective position of the moving stimulus *(center).* The rostral tectum is responsive to visual and electrosensory stimuli near the animal's head, and sequentially more caudal recording sites respond when the stimulus moves toward the animal's tail. The responses to the two types of stimuli are recorded in different tectal layers, but the overall alignment of the projections is very good.

   Studies of single tectal neurons in this same fish (6) show that cells receive both visual and electrosensory input. The interactions between these inputs range from simple linear summation of excitatory and/or inhibitory influences to more complex interactions, such as responses being contingent upon simul-

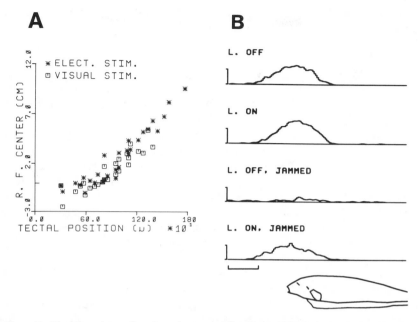

Figure 7 Plot of tectal recording site, microns caudal to the anterior tectal margin, vs the position of a moving visual or electrosensory stimulus at which maximum multiunit activity is evoked. Stimulus movement was parallel to the long axis of the fish. Visual responses were recorded at depths ranging from 100–200 micron below the surface, and electrosensory responses were recorded at depths from 300–500 micron. *B:* Histograms relating the activity of a single tectal neuron to an electrosensory stimulus moving parallel to the long axis of the fish with and without concomitant illumination of the stimulus object. The top trace shows responses of the neuron to the object moving in total darkness *(L-off)*. Illumination of the object *(L-on)* augments this response. The application of a jamming stimulus, a 4 Hz, 2 mV cm^{-1} amplitude modulation of the EOD, strongly suppresses the response *(L-off, jammed)*. Illumination of the object restores the jammed response *(L-on, jammed)*. (After 6)

taneous presentation of both visual and electrosensory stimuli within a restricted receptive field.

The electrosensory responses of the tectum are sensitive to jamming stimuli as are those of lower-order processing stations. The visual and electroreceptive fields of single cells are usually well aligned, and the cell's loss of electrolocation ability due to jamming can be largely compensated for if the stimulus object is made visible (Figure 7b). Jamming the electrosensory system does not influence the visual input, and these bimodal cells therefore insure detection of stimuli having visual and electrosensory components even when the latter system is jammed. In addition to making object detection less vulnerable to jamming, bimodal neurons could also provide the animal with the means of recognizing or identifying stimulus sources providing specific combinations of stimuli as suggested by Hartline et al (27) for the rattlesnake tectum.

SUMMARY

Recent studies of electroreception have been particularly successful in three different areas:

1. Electroreceptors are tuned to the dominant frequency of the animal's EOD, and their tuning follows natural and experimentally induced shifts in EOD frequency. Steroid hormones influence the electric organ pacemaker frequency in the genus *Sternopygus,* and the tuning of electroreceptors will follow hormone-induced frequency shifts only if the receptors experience the animal's EOD. The frequency tuning of electroreceptors reveals properties similar to those of cochlear hair cells, and electroreceptors may be suitable model systems for in vitro studies of cellular and molecular aspects of electrical filter mechanisms in hair cells.

2. In contrast to the South American or gymnotoid electric fish, the African or mormyrid electric fish evaluate electroreceptive information with the help of corollary discharges of their electric-organ pacemaker. The corollary discharge inhibits input from knollenorgan receptors so that, in the context of social communication, the animal only perceives EODs of neighbors but not its own. The corollary discharge at the same time enhances input from most mormyromasts so that the animal, in the context of electrolocation, selectively receives feedback from its own EODs. Finally, responses of ampullary electroreceptors to the animal's own EODs are centrally nulled by an elaborate and modifiable efference copy so that the animal is only informed about "nontrivial", low-frequency events in its environment.

3. Laminated and topographically organized structures in the hindbrain and midbrain of gymnotoid fish are being studied with regard to neuroanatomical fine structure and functional organization. Different laminae and cell types in the hindbrain are specialized for the extraction of specific stimulus features, such as modulations of phase or amplitude in a sinusoidal stimulus regime. This information is passed on to the midbrain for the computation of more complex stimulus variables, such as the difference in phase modulations reported from different parts of the body surface. The torus semicircularis of the midbrain is designed for parallel processing of information from different parts of the body surface and for parallel computation of different stimulus variables for the control of behavioral responses. Electrical and visual information converge in the tectum opticum, which harbors a multimodal representation of sensory space.

ACKNOWLEDGMENTS

We thank Curtis C. Bell, Carl D. Hopkins, Harold H. Zakon, John H. Meyer, and Catherine E. Carr for most helpful suggestions on this manuscript. This work is supported by grants from NSF, NINCDS, and NIMH to the authors.

Literature Cited

1. Bass, A., Hopkins, C. D. 1983. Hormonal control of sexual differentiation: Changes in EOD waveform. *Science*. 220:971–74
2. Bass. A., Hopkins, C. D. 1983. Androgen-related changes in electroreceptor tuning in mormyrid fish. *J. Comp. Physiol*. In press
3. Bastian, J. 1976. Frequency response characteristics of electroreceptors in weakly electric fish (Gymnotoidei) with a pulse discharge. *J. Comp. Physiol*. 112:165–80
4. Bastian, J. 1981. Electrolocation I. How the electroreceptors of *Apteronotus albifrons* code for moving objects and other electrical stimuli. *J. Comp. Physiol*. 144:465–79
5. Bastian, J. 1981. Electrolocation II. The effects of moving objects and other electrical stimuli on the activities of two categories of posterior lateral line lobe cells in *Apteronotus albifrons*. *J. Comp. Physiol*. 144:481–94
6. Bastian, J. 1982. Vision and electroreception: Integration of sensory information in the optic tectum of the weakly electric fish *Apteronotus albifrons*. *J. Comp. Physiol*. 147:287–97
7. Bastian, J., Heiligenberg, W. 1980. Phase sensitive midbrain neurons in *Eigenmannia*: Neural correlates of the jamming avoidance response. *Science* 209:828–31
8. Bastian, J., Heiligenberg, W. 1980. Neural correlates of the jamming avoidance response in *Eigenmannia*. *J. Comp. Physiol*. 136:135–52
9. Bell, C. C. 1981. An efference copy modified by reafferent input. *Science* 214:450
10. Bell, C. C. 1982. Properties of a modifiable efference copy in an electric fish. *J. Neurophysiol*. 47:VI1043–56
11. Bell, C. C. 1983. Effects of motor commands on sensory inflow, with examples from electric fish. In *Comparative Physiology, Sensory Systems*, ed. L. Bolis, R. D. Keynes. Cambridge, Engl.: Cambridge Univ. In press
12. Bell, C. C., Russell, C. J. 1978. Effect of electric organ discharge on ampullary receptors in a mormyrid. *Brain Res*. 145:85–96
13. Bennett, M. V. L. 1967. Mechanism of electroreception. In *Lateral Line Detectors*, ed. P. Cahn, pp. 347–93. Bloomington, Ind.: Indiana Univ.
14. Bennett, M. V. L. 1971. Electric organs. In *Fish Physiology*, ed. W. S. Hoar, D. J. Randall, pp. 347–491. New York: Academic
15. Bennett, M. V. L., Steinbach, A. B. 1969. Influence of electric organ control system on electrosensory afferent pathways in Mormyrids. In *Neurobiology of Cerebellum Evolution and Development*, ed. R. Llinas, pp. 207–14. Chicago: A. M. A.
16. Bullock, T. H. 1982. Electroreception. *Ann. Rev. Neurosci*. 5:121–70
17. Bullock, T. H., Chichibu, S. 1965. Further analysis of sensory coding in electroreceptors of electric fish. *Proc. Natl. Acad. Sci. USA* 54:422–29
18. Bullock, T. H., Northcutt, R. G. 1982. A new electroreceptive teleost: *Xenomystus nigri* (Osteoglossiformes: Notopteridae). *J. Comp. Physiol*. 148:345–52
19. Carr, C. E., Maler, L., Heiligenberg, W., Sas, E. 1981. Laminar organization of the afferent and efferent systems of the torus semicircularis of gymnotiform fish: Morphological substrates for parallel processing in the electrosensory system. *J. Comp. Neurol*. 203:649–70
20. Carr, C. E., Maler, L., Sas, E. 1982. Peripheral organization and central projections of the electrosensory nerves in gymnotiform fish. *J. Comp. Neurol*. 211:139–53
21. Crawford, A. C., Fettiplace, R. 1981. An electrical tuning mechanism in the turtle cochlear hair cells. *J. Physiol*. 312:377–412
22. Crawford, A. C., Fettiplace, R. 1981. Nonlinearities in the response of turtle hair cells. *J. Physiol*. 315:317–38
23. Drager, U. C., Hubel, D. H. 1975. Responses to visual stimulation and rela-

tionship between visual, auditory, and somatosensory inputs in mouse superior colliculus. *J. Neurophysiol.* 38:690–713

24. Enger, P. S., Szabo, T. 1965. Activity of central neurons involved in electroreception in some weakly electric fish (Gymnotidae). *J. Neurophysiol.* 28:800–18

25. Feng, A. S., Bullock, T. H. 1977. Neuronal mechanisms for object discrimination in the weakly electric fish, *Eigenmannia virescens*. *J. Exp. Biol.* 66:141–58

26. Fettiplace, R., Crawford, A. 1978. *Proc. R. Soc. London Ser. B* 203:209

27. Hartline, P. H., Kass, L., Loop, M. S. 1978. Merging of modalities in the optic tectum: Infrared and visual integration in rattlesnakes. *Science* 199:1225–29

28. Heiligenberg, W. 1976. Electrolocation and jamming avoidance in the mormyrid fish *Brienomyrus*. *J. Comp. Physiol.* 109:357–72

29. Heiligenberg, W. 1977. Principles of electrolocation and jamming avoidance. *Studies of Brain Function,* 1:1–85. Berlin: Springer

30. Heiligenberg, W. 1980. The evaluation of electroreceptive feedback in a gymnotoid fish with pulse-type electric organ discharges. *J. Comp. Physiol.* 138:173–85

31. Heiligenberg, W. 1980. The Jamming Avoidance Response in the weakly electric fish *Eigenmannia*. *Naturwissenschaften* 67:499–507

32. Heiligenberg, W. 1983. The Jamming Avoidance Response in an electric fish: Algorithms in sensory information processing and their neuronal organization. In *Advances in Vertebrate Neuroethology,* ed. J. -P. Ewert, D. Ingel, R. Capranica, pp. 669–99. New York: Plenum

33. Heiligenberg, W., Altes, R. 1978. Phase sensitivity in electroreception. *Science* 199:1001–4

34. Heiligenberg, W., Baker, C., Bastian, J. 1978. The jamming avoidance response in gymnotoid pulse-species: A mechanism to minimize pulse-train coincidence. *J. Comp. Physiol.* 124:211–24

35. Heiligenberg, W., Bastian, J. 1980. The control of *Eigenmannia's* pacemaker by distributed evaluation of electroreceptive afferences. *J. Comp. Physiol.* 136:113–33

36. Heiligenberg, W., Dye, J. 1982. Labelling of electroreceptive afferents in a gymnotoid fish by intracellular injection of HRP: The mystery of multiple maps. *J. Comp. Physiol.* 148:287–96

37. Heiligenberg, W., Finger, T., Matsubara, J., Carr, C. 1981. Input to the medullary pacemaker nucleus in the

weakly electric fish, *Eigenmannia* (Sternopygidae, Gymnotiformes). *Brain Res.* 211:418–23

38. Heiligenberg, W., Partridge, B. L. 1981. How electroreceptors encode JAR-eliciting stimulus regimes: reading trajectories in a phase-amplitude plane. *J. Comp. Physiol.* 142:395–408

39. Holst, E. von, Mittelstaedt, H. 1950. Das Reafferenzprinzip. *Naturwissenschaften* 37:464–76

40. Hopkins, C. D. 1972. Sex differences in electric signalling in an electric fish. *Science* 176:1035–37

41. Hopkins, C. D. 1976. Stimulus filtering and electroreceptors in three species of gymnotoid fish. *J. Comp. Physiol.* 111:171–207

42. Hopkins, C. D. 1983. Neuroethology of species recognition in electroreception. See Ref. 32, pp. 871–81

43. Hopkins, C. D., Bass, A. H. 1981. Temporal coding of species recognition signals in an electric fish. *Science* 212:85–87

44. Knudsen, E. I. 1982. Auditory and visual maps of space in the optic tectum of the owl. *J. Neuroscience* 2:1177–94

45. Maler, L., Sas, E. 1983. Organization of descending projections to the posterior lateral line lobe. I: Nucleus Praeeminentialis. *J. Comp. Neurol.* In press

46. Maler, L., Sas, E., Carr, E. C., Matsubara, J. 1982. Efferent projections of the posterior lateral line lobe in gymnotiform fish. *J. Comp. Neurol.* 211:154–64

47. Maler, L., Sas, E., Rogers, J. 1981. The cytology of the posterior lateral line lobe of high frequency weakly electric fish (Gymnotoidei): Dendritic differentiation and synaptic specificity in a simple cortex. *J. Comp. Neurol.* 195:87–140

48. McCloskey, D. I. 1981. Corollary discharges: motor commands and perception. In *Handbook of Physiology, The Nervous System, Vol. II,* ed. V. B. Brooks, 2:1415–47. Bethesda, MD.: Am. Physiol. Soc.

49. Meyer, J. H. 1982. Behavioral responses of weakly electric fish to complex impedances. *J. Comp. Physiol.* 145:459–70

50. Meyer, J. H. 1983. Steroid influences upon the discharge frequency of a weakly electric fish. *J. Comp. Physiol.* Submitted for publication

51. Meyer, J. H., Bell, C. C. 1983. Sensory gating by a corollary discharge mechanism. *J. Comp. Physiol.* 151:401–6

52. Meyer, J. H., Zakon, H. H. 1982. Androgens alter the tuning of electroreceptors. *Science* 217:635–37

53. Moller, P. 1970. Communication in

weakly electric fish, *Gnathonemus niger* (Mormyridae) I. Variation of electric organ discharge (EOD) frequency elicited by controlled electric stimuli. *Animal Behav.* 18:768–86

54. Moller, P., Bauer, R. 1971. "Communication" in weakly electric fish, *Gnathonemus petersii* (Mormyridae) II. Interaction of electric organ discharge activities of two fish. *Animal Behav.* 21:501–12

55. Partridge, B. L., Heiligenberg, W., Matsubara, J. 1981. The neural basis of a sensory filter in the Jamming Avoidance Response: No Grandmother Cells in sight. *J. Comp. Physiol.* 145:153–68

56. Saunders, J., Bastian, J. 1983. In preparation

57. Scheich, H. 1977. Neural basis of communication in the high frequency electric fish, *Eigenmannia virescens* (Jamming Avoidance Response). *J. Comp. Physiol.* 113:181–255

58. Scheich, H., Bullock, T. H. 1974. The detection of electric fields from electric organs. In *Handbook of Sensory Physiology, Vol. III/3*, ed. A. Fessard, pp. 201–56. Berlin: Springer

59. Scheich, H., Bullock, T. H., Hamstra, R. 1973. Coding properties of two classes of afferent nerve fibers: High frequency electroreceptors in the electric fish, *Eigenmannia. J. Neurophysiol.* 36:39–60

60. Scheich, H., Ebbesson, S. O. E. 1981. Inputs to the torus semicircularis in the electric fish *Eigenmannia virescens. Cell Tissue Res.* 215:531–36

61. Sperry, R. W. 1950. Neural basis of the spontaneous optokinetic response produced by visual inversion. *J. Comp. Psychol.* 43:482–89

62. Szabo, T., Enger, P. S., Libouban, S. 1979. Electrosensory systems in the mormyrid fish, *Gnathonemus petersii:* special emphasis on the fast conducting pathway. *J. Physiol.* 75:409–20

63. Szabo, T., Fessard, A. 1974. Physiology of electroreceptors In *Handbook of Sensory Physiology, Vol. III/3*, ed. A. Fessard, pp. 59–124. Berlin: Springer

64. Viancour, T. 1979. Electroreceptors of a weakly electric fish, I and II. *J. Comp. Physiol.* 133:317–38

65. Watson, D., Bastian, J. 1979. Frequency response characteristics of electroreceptors in the weakly electric fish, *Gymnotus carapo. J. Comp. Physiol.* 134:191–202

66. Weiss, T. 1982. Bidirectional transduction in vertebrate hair cells: a mechanism for coupling mechanical and electrical processes. *Hearing Res.* 7:353–60

67. Westby, G. W. M. 1974. Assessment of the signal value of certain discharge patterns in the electric fish, *Gymnotus carapo,* by means of playback. *J. Comp. Physiol.* 92:327–41

68. Zakon, H. H., Meyer, J. H. 1983. Hormone-induced plasticity of electroreceptor tuning in the weakly electric fish, *Sternopygus dariensis. J. Comp. Physiol.* In press

69. Zipser, B., Bennett, M. V. L. 1976. Interaction of electrosensory and electromotor signals in lateral line lobe of a mormyrid fish. *J. Neurophysiol.* 39:693–721

Ann. Rev. Physiol. 1984. 46:585-98

MAGNETIC FIELD SENSITIVITY IN ANIMALS

James L. Gould

Department of Biology, Princeton University, Princeton, New Jersey 08544

INTRODUCTION

The earth's magnetic field provides several pieces of information that many animals find useful. Before reviewing the phenomenology and physiology of the magnetic sense, we must examine the source and nature of magnetic information.

The Earth's Magnetic Field

The earth is, among other things, a large magnet. The field, which measures about 0.5 Gauss (50,000 gamma) in the northeastern United States, is produced primarily in the earth's core. The exact mechanism is a subject of dispute, but most hypotheses invoke a circulation of the earth's molten interior (e.g. 68). The axis of this internal field is only roughly aligned with the planet's axis of rotation; the north magnetic pole is actually near Hudson's Bay in Canada, some 2300 km from the geographic north pole. The magnetic pole is not stable, but instead wanders slowly. Occasionally (every 10,000–100,000 years) the field reverses itself. During these reversals the field felt on the surface decreases in intensity, but never reaches zero. The duration of these low-field interludes is not known; guesses range from days to centuries.

When stable, the earth's magnetic field changes in a more or less regular way from the magnetic equator, where the field lines are horizontal (i.e. parallel to the earth's surface) and the field strength is roughly 25,000 gamma, to the magnetic poles, where the lines are vertical and the strength is 60,000 gamma. Hence there is a gradient of magnetic intensity and field-line angle. In the northeastern United States the dip angle steepens by about $0.01°$ km^{-1} to the NNW while the total field strength increases by roughly 3–5 gamma km^{-1} in the same direction. The intensity of the horizontal and vertical components of

585

0066-4278/84/0315-0585$02.00

the field decrease and increase, respectively, about twice as quickly. Oddly enough, the gradients of these two components are not aligned, but rather differ by 15–30°.

In contrast to the large and relatively static field generated inside the earth, there is a much smaller and more dynamic contribution from the ionosphere: electrically charged particles carried by the jet streams. This flow of ions creates an inductive field, and because the jet streams are displaced north and south each day as the earth is heated and cooled by the sun, there is a regular circadian variation in field strength on the order of 10–100 gamma, depending on season and latitude.

After solar flares and other disturbances associated with sun spots, enormous numbers of charged particles are released from the sun and appear in the jet streams a day or two later. The result is a magnetic "storm" that obliterates the usual circadian patterns by creating both an altered inductive background field as well as magnetic pulses arising from "clumps" of charged particles. Magnetic storms range in intensity up to 3,000 gamma, though storms above 300 gamma are quite rare.

Information in the Earth's Field

DIRECTION   There are three general categories of information of use to animals to be gleaned from the earth's magnetic field. The most obvious is direction. The field lines in the temperate northern hemisphere, for example, point roughly north and down. An animal with a compass sense might find such directional information quite useful, particularly when more obvious cues such as the sun, stars, and familiar landmarks are unavailable. The precision of such a compass is limited by two factors: the declination—the discrepancy between true north and magnetic north—and the sensitivity of the compass sense. The declination is regularly on the order of 5–15° in the northeastern United States, and can be much larger elsewhere. For roughly the same degree of accuracy from a biological magnetic compass (i.e. 5°), a sensitivity of about 1500 gamma (i.e. about 3% of the total field) would be needed.

LOCATION   The second kind of information the earth's field offers is magnetic latitude. Many animals need to know where they are, and an ability to use magnetic cues, particularly when celestial or other information is unavailable or unusable, would be adaptive. Magnetic latitude could be determined from total intensity, vertical intensity, horizontal intensity, or dip angle, but would most likely be useful only for determining *relative* latitude—the distance north or south of some well-known reference point such as home. Even then, any determination would have to depend on measuring local gradient(s) at home and extrapolating them into the world at large. As a result, systematic errors would be expected, reflecting the degree to which the gradients near an animal's home are different from the regional pattern. Using magnetic latitude with an accuracy of, say, 10 km would require a sensitivity of 30–100 gamma (0.06–0.2% of the total field) depending on which component an animal used. Obviously it would be difficult to judge latitude in this way during a severe magnetic storm.

TIME   As far as we know, the only sort of information available in the field is time. Since there is a circadian rhythm to the field, it is theoretically possible that it could serve as a fairly dependable clock, but one that would be useless during magnetic storms. Such a time sense might be useful to animals such as honey bees, whose homes—dark, enclosed cavities—isolate them from the more typical cues like sunrise, sunset, circadian variations in temperature and humidity, and the like. For an accuracy of 0.5 hrs, however, a sensitivity of 5–25 gamma (0.01–0.05% of the total field) would be essential. It is also worth pointing out that since the daily pattern depends on the season, its excursions being compressed in winter and expanded in summer, there is even the possibility of using the circadian variations as a crude calendar.

BEHAVIORAL EVIDENCE

The theoretical possibilities for using the earth's magnetic field are clear enough. What behavioral evidence is there, and what does it suggest about levels of sensitivity, information processing, and receptor mechanisms? Evidence for magnetic-field sensitivity is abundant, though of highly mixed quality. This review will be restricted to the few species or groups of species for which the evidence is at least fairly convincing *and* whose behavior provides information about absolute sensitivity, processing, and/or reception.

Directional Sensitivity

MICROORGANISMS   By far the best evidence for direction sensitivity (if the passive rotation of a microorganism, dead or alive in a magnetic field, merits the term "sensitivity") comes from bacteria (6, 7, 15, 33, 38) and algae (4). A variety of mud-dwelling bacteria are able to follow the earth's field lines (down and north) to their preferred habitat, and predictably alter their direction the instant an artificial field is applied. The accuracy and sensitivity are fairly low, but clearly sufficient for the task. The sensory basis of this ability, now well understood, is discussed later.

HONEY BEES   Although a variety of invertebrates are reported to be magnetically sensitive, only honey bees provide satisfactory behavioral assays. Two behaviors in particular provide clear evidence for directional sensitivity.

One behavior involves the orientation of honeycomb in beehives. When a swarm takes over a suitable cavity, hundreds of worker bees cooperate to build several parallel sheets of comb in almost total darkness. Clearly it would be useful if all the bees could agree on the orientation of the comb in advance. Lindauer (48) reported that in the absence of visual and tactile cues, bees build new comb in the direction of the comb in the parent hive. Although initially no investigator could repeat this result, recently De Jong (11) succeeded, and was able to control the direction in which comb would be built with an artificial field. Although he did not measure a threshold, the average error of 30° (much higher than the two cases reported by Lindauer) suggests that the necessary sensitivity is only about 11,000 gamma (23% of the total field).

The bee's other magnetically influenced behavior has no obvious function. Returning foragers frequently perform dances in the hive to communicate the distance and direction of food that they have discovered. These dances normally take place on the vertical sheets of comb. Vertical is taken to indicate the sun's azimuth: the angle of the dance with respect to vertical corresponds to the angle between the sun and the food. When bees are forced to dance on a horizontal surface, they orient to celestial cues and aim their dances directly at the food. If no celestial cues are provided, they are initially disoriented, but several days later dance to the eight cardinal points of the compass (24, 48). This orientation has nothing to do with the direction of the food, and each bee dances in random order in all eight directions. [This sort of "nonsense" orientation to detectable cues is well known in invertebrates (73).] In a null field the dances are randomly oriented, while in a ten-times-normal field the orientation is more precise than in a normal field. The average error in the earth's field is about 7.6°, which suggests a minimum sensitivity of roughly 3000 gamma (17% of the total field).

The only other insect of interest in this context is the monarch butterfly. Schmidt-Koenig (62) found that this migratory species is able to orient accurately under overcast skies, suggesting that it too may have a magnetic compass.

BIRDS   Many species of reptiles, birds, and fish must navigate over considerable distances under a variety of conditions. The first serious evidence for a compass sense in vertebrates came from studies of caged migratory birds. These animals will orient to celestial cues and spend more time in the part of the cage facing the appropriate migratory direction. To do this, the animals must know how to compensate for the westward movement of the sun from dawn to dusk. Indeed, if a bird's internal clock is reset—"clock-shifted"—by subjecting the animal to artificial dawns, the bird misinterprets the sun's direction and orients incorrectly. In the absence of visual cues, the orientation is much weaker but still significant, providing the data are subjected to second-order analysis (i.e. the mean of the means) (e.g. 5, 13, 27, 85). Rotating the field or canceling it has the expected effects. The direction of orientation is correspondingly rotated or disappears altogether. The most interesting data comes from Wiltschko's study of European robins (85). He was able to show that the birds seem to ignore the polarity of the field, instead taking the direction in which the field lines dip into the earth as north. Hence, they are unable to orient in a field that has no vertical component.

More satisfying evidence comes from data on pigeon homing. In a classic set of experiments, Keeton (34) showed that although pigeons are able to home normally while wearing magnets on sunny days, they are disoriented under overcast skies. This means that the earth's magnetic field provides a backup orientation system. Because the same pigeons are reoriented by clock-shifts—but only on sunny days—the sun or some sun-linked celestial feature must act as the normal compass. Walcott and others (72, 80) have repeated this experiment using small head-mounted, battery-operated coils. Their results suggest that pigeons, like robins (and, for all we know, bees) ignore polarity and use the dip lines as the major directional cue. Recently, Wiltschko (83, 84) has shown that the magnetic compass is first used to calibrate the sun compass.

FISH   Kalmijn (31, 32) has shown that sharks and rays are able to detect an earth-strength magnetic field and can be trained to choose a particular direction in an artificial field. (The sensory basis of this ability, which is well understood, is discussed later.) Along the same lines, tuna have been conditioned to respond to the presence or absence of the earth's magnetic field (82), and there is evidence that salmon are also able to orient magnetically (58, 59, 60).

MAMMALS   Woodmice are reported to be able to keep track of the direction of short displacements performed in the absence of celestial cues (51). Displacements in altered magnetic fields apparently cause the mice to attempt to escape from a 4-arm test chamber in the magnetically appropriate direction. There is also a report that humans can sense magnetic direction (1, 2), but extensive attempts to repeat this work have been uniformly negative (22).

As mentioned earlier, there is (often good) evidence that a variety of other species can use the earth's field to determine direction, but this discussion will be limited to only the ones that are helpful in answering questions about the degree of sensitivity, processing, or the means of detection.

Location Sensitivity

Good evidence that animals can determine location magnetically comes at present only from homing pigeons, although there is preliminary data for several other species of birds and reptiles. The argument for pigeons has been put forward independently by Yeagley (88, 89), Gould (19, 20), Walcott & Lednor (45, 77, 78), and Moore (53). Given that pigeons deprived of form vision can home to within a few km of the loft (63), the necessary sensitivity is on the order of 20–50 gamma. As a result, magnetic storms should affect both initial orientation at the release site as well as homing speed and success. Such appears to be the case. Data from pigeon races in both the United States (10, 88, 89) and Italy (64, 65) show this effect clearly, regardless of whether the sky was clear or overcast. Moreover, the phenomenon appears to be "dosage dependent," in that stronger storms generate larger effects, with a threshold in the 25–50 gamma range. Similar effects have been noted in other species of birds (54, 66, 67).

A second prediction of the magnetic map hypothesis mentioned earlier is that there should be systematic biases in an animal's judgment of location as a consequence of the need to extrapolate local gradients. Just such "release-site biases" have been seen. Birds from Ithaca, N.Y., for instance, show a strong tendency to depart clockwise of the homeward direction when released east of a line running NNW-SSE through Ithaca, and counterclockwise when released to the west (86, 87). The local gradient at Ithaca runs NNW. It is as though Ithaca pigeons "place" home NNW of its true location. A similar pattern is evident in birds from other lofts, including one at Frankfurt (26, 86) where the gradient runs east.

Of course, each release point will differ more or less from even the true regional pattern, so that some release-site biases will be larger than normal while others will be smaller. Nevertheless, magnetic storms should affect all these biases in a dosage-dependent manner, and they do (35). At one well-studied site, a storm of 500 gamma rotates the birds' departure bearing by almost 40°, so that a sensitivity of 10 gamma seems plausible.

In many ways the most convincing evidence for a magnetic location sense comes from Walcott's studies of pigeon orientation at magnetic anomalies in the northeastern United States (76). The field strength at anomalies is 30–3000 gamma too high, and varies irregularly in the vicinity. Pigeons are disoriented in direct proportion to the strength of the anomaly. A similar pattern is evident at German anomalies (36). The data imply a behavioral threshold on the order of 10–20 gamma. Along the same lines, several workers have reported that magnetic topography affects the flight paths of pigeons soon after release (17, 25, 69, 74), though once birds are well oriented they are less disturbed (e.g. 20). This and the evidence from airplane tracking of pigeons (52) suggests that pigeons average incoming map information over at least several minutes.

Time Sense

The best evidence for a magnetic time sense comes from honey bees. Forager bees will return to a food source at the same time each day to look for food. When reared indoors and trained in the absence of light, temperature, or humidity variation, bees are nevertheless able to maintain a circadian foraging rhythm with little sign of the sort of drift evident in most species (46)—in fact, the accuracy is about ± 15 min even after 3 days. During magnetic storms or in a strong, aperiodic field, however, this ability vanishes. The utility of a magnetic time sense for a species that lives in a dark, constant-temperature, and constant-humidity cavity is clear enough.

From a careful examination of daily variations (19, 20), the sensitivity necessary to account for the behavior is better than 3 gamma if absolute field strength is being measured. If they use instead one isolated component of the field, they might be able to get by with a 5-gamma sensitivity, although this would require the bees to measure their position in space—presumably in reference to gravity—with a precision of 0.01% in order to sort out the components. Alternatively, the data could be interpreted to imply a sensitivity to rates of field change on the order of 10–20 gamma hr^{-1} (reviewed in 71).

A curious effect of magnetic fields on the normal vertical-surface dance of bees argues for the rate-of-change alternative. Several alterations of dance or other activity as a result of field changes have been observed (28, 37, 70), but the most dramatic is the relationship between the field and the small (up to 20°) errors in the dance known as "residual misdirection" (47, 48, 50). From empirical curve-fitting, Lindauer and Martin have shown that the magnitude of the error depends on the angle between the magnetic field lines in the plane of the comb and the direction of the dance, *and* the rate of change in field strength (reviewed in 71). As a result, there is no misdirection in a null field or when the dance is parallel to the field lines. From the behavioral data we can estimate that the misdirection effects must depend on an absolute sensitivity of 1–10 gamma or a rate-of-change sensitivity of 6–60 gamma hr^{-1}. Since the misdirection system seems to saturate for field changes faster than 60 gamma hr^{-1}—which is abnormally high even though it represents only a 0.1 change of total field strength per hour—it is more likely that rate of change is the critical parameter. Indeed, the magnitude of the misdirection is no greater in an artificially strong (10×) static field, provided the rates of change are normal.

One curious phenomenon which deserves mention is the so-called "adaptation time" for changes in field strength. It takes roughly 45 min for the misdirection to vanish in a null field (48), or for the cardinal-point tendency of horizontal dances to adjust fully to changes in field strength (50). This is almost certainly a consequence of the "running average" strategy which is employed in honey bee navigation (12, 18, 21). Incoming sensory information is averaged over a 40–50 min "window," probably to suppress noise. Since the phenomenon is clearly evident in sun-compass orientation, it seems unlikely that it tells us anything about the magnetic field detector, although others draw the opposite inference (e.g. 47).

RECEPTOR STRATEGIES

In principle there are only three ways to detect magnetic fields—induction, permanent magnetism, and paramagnetism—and it appears that evolution has tried them all.

Induction

Induction is based on Faraday's law: A conductor moving through a magnetic field will produce an electric potential. Depending on the geometry and the physical environment of the conductor, this potential may either produce a flow of current or maintain a static electric field. Kalmijn has shown both behaviorally and physiologically that induction is the method used by his sharks and rays (31). Current flow (with the surrounding salt water providing an external return path) is detected by the ampullae of Lorenzini (reviewed in 30), and motion as slow as 1 cm sec^{-1} is sufficient to induce a measurable field. Of course the original "purpose" of the ampullae is prey detection by means of "listening" for the AC electric fields given off by other animals. The DC background generated by movement through the earth's magnetic field may be processed separately.

Because of the higher resistivity of the external medium, the system is 100-fold less sensitive in freshwater fish. For terrestrial animals, induction of this sort is unworkable because air would have to act as the return path. Indeed, since the static field of Walcott's head-mounted coil interferes with pigeon orientation, whereas a static field moving with the animal ought not to affect an inductive detector, induction is not considered to be operating in most magnetically sensitive, nonmarine animals.

Paramagnetism

Moving a conductor through a magnetic field induces a current flow, but moving a charged particle creates a magnetic field as well. Electrons spin, and this spin generates the magnetism of permanent magnets and paramagnetic substances. Atoms, of course, have many electrons, but most electrons exist in pairs of opposite spins that produce self-canceling fields. An atom with an unpaired electron has, of necessity, a net magnetic field. If the spins of such unpaired electrons are oriented randomly between atoms in a piece of matter, the fields cancel each other.

A net alignment, however, can come about in two ways. In paramagnetism, an external field (such as the earth's) causes the unpaired electrons to align their own fields with it, thereby amplifying the local magnetic field. This is a statistical process, balancing the slight energetic favorability of being aligned against the energy of thermal "noise" (kT), which tends to randomize the orientation of unpaired electrons. As a result, the strength of the external field controls both the degree and direction of spin alignment. If the external field takes up a new direction, the unpaired electrons track the change almost instantaneously. If the external field is canceled, the electron spins lose their net alignment, and the paramagnetic field disappears.

Paramagnetism has often been suggested as a basis for magnetic-field detection. The transduction of paramagnetic effects could be accomplished along a variety of lines, but a little calculation of the energy of paramagnetic interaction versus thermal noise at physiological temperatures suggests that even several cubic mm of pure, highly paramagnetic organic molecules would not be sufficient for compass orientation (40, 61). This is more than many magnetically sensitive animals possess; it seems unlikely that an organ of this size would have escaped detection even in larger organisms.

Two alternative uses of paramagnetism are more plausible. "Optical pumping," as proposed by Leask (44), would employ the interaction of light and paramagnetic molecules. To date none of the cases of magnetic field sensitivity are known to suffer in the dark. The other alternative is superparamagnetism, discussed following consideration of permanent magnetism.

Permanent Magnetism

Permanent magnetism (reviewed in 40) arises in much the same way as paramagnetism, in that all the unpaired electron spins align in permanent magnets. The atoms with unpaired electrons, however, are arranged in relatively large crystals and spaced in such a way that they generate a self-stabilizing alignment of the spins. This, in turn, produces a strong net magnetic field. Once a critical crystal size has been reached, the field becomes self-stable and no longer depends on an external field. Small permanent magnets could sense the earth's field *if* the torque these particles would feel from the interaction of their magnetic moments with the earth's field could be measured.

Biologically synthesized permanent magnets in the form of magnetite ("lodestone," $FeO \cdot Fe_2O_3$) were first discovered in the dental cappings of chitons (49). The possible link between magnetite and magnetic field detection came in 1978 with the discovery by Gould et al (23) of magnetite in honey bees. Since then, localized concentrations of magnetite have been reported in a variety of animals, and the physics of using magnetite has been carefully explored (40, 90, 91).

MICROORGANISMS   The many species of magnetotactic bacteria all have long chains of electron-dense particles; in the one species studied in detail, these particles are now known to be crystals of magnetite (16). Since magnetite is the densest substance known to be synthesized by organisms, it seems likely that early in evolution the crystals were simply used as "weights" to point the front end of the bacterium down (14). A similar strategy is evident in most positively geotactic bacteria.

INVERTEBRATES   Many honey bees possess about 10^6 mutually aligned, permanently magnetic crystals of magnetite in their abdomens (23). These crystals appear during the pupal stage when no food is ingested, and therefore are probably of biological origin. Iron-staining cells in the abdomen are closely associated with the nervous system (43) and contain large crystals that are probably the iron-storage protein ferrodoxin, the synthetic precursor of magnetite in chitons (41). As we shall see later, bees also possess superparamagnetic domains of magnetite which may be a better candidate for a magnetic field receptor.

Magnetic material has also been discovered in the thorax of monarch butterflies (29) where, as in bees, it appears during the pupal stage when no food is being ingested. Magnetic material is also found in certain migratory crustaceans (9), though not in similar, nonmigratory species. Good data does not yet exist to implicate the magnetite in magnetic sensitivity in invertebrates, nor is there information available about how permanent magnets, if used, are coupled to the nervous system. Several plausible receptor models have been developed (40), however, and some observed behavior matches predictions based on such detectors (39).

BIRDS   Walcott et al (79) discovered localized concentrations of 10^8 crystals of magnetite in pigeons, associated with bone cavities near the midline, roughly between the olfactory bulb and the optic chiasm. For a variety of technical reasons, anatomical analysis has been difficult (75). Magnetic material has also been reported in migratory birds and in neck muscles of pigeons (57). Again there is no good evidence to tie the magnetite to the magnetic sensitivity, though the number of crystals is clearly sufficient to account for even the location sensitivity of birds (40, 91).

FISH AND REPTILES   The best anatomical data come from the tuna. As noted earlier (82), a tuna can be trained to react to the earth's field. The magnetite is located in innervated tissue near the midline between the olfactory bulb and the optic tract in the ethmoid sinuses (81). Magnetite is also found in the heads of migratory turtles (56) and the ethmoid region of the skulls of salmon (42), the fry of which have been reported to be magnetically sensitive (58, 59, 60). The crystals in salmon interact strongly with each other, suggesting that they may be arranged in chains as in bacteria. Magnetic material has also been reported in the vestibular organs of guitarfish (55), though the size and form of the crystals (which are probably magnetite) are such that they probably could not be used for magnetoreception.

MAMMALS   Magnetically sensitive woodmice have a localized concentration of magnetic material in the skull near the dorsal midline at the front of the head (51), a position analagous to that reported in tuna, salmon, and pigeons. Bats also have magnetic deposits (8), as do dolphins (92). In dolphins, the deposit is near the dorsal midline of the skull, but *above* the eyes. Since the breathing apparatus of dolphins is located above rather than below the eyes, it is possible that the exact location will turn out to be analogous to that of most other vertebrates. Finally, humans are reported to have magnetic material in the skull near the front dorsal midline (3).

Superparamagnetism

Magnetite crystals below the critical self-stable size are referred to as superparamagnetic because they behave somewhat like conventional paramagnetic substances. Although these crystals are strongly magnetic on their own—that is, the magnetic moments of the unpaired electrons are well aligned—thermal noise within the crystals causes the direction of the magnetism to wander randomly in a null field. On the other hand, the magnetic axis of the crystal will track an external field such as the earth's. The field of these crystals is quite intense, and nearby grains can therefore interact to affect transduction (40).

Honey bees contain vast numbers (2×10^8) of superparamagnetism grains which fall into the very narrow size range of 300–350Å (24). The misdirection data are best explained in terms of a superparamagnetic detector (24) based on interacting crystals (19, 40). Whether such a detector exists, however, is unknown. The only other animal known to possess substantial numbers of superparamagnetic crystals is the pigeon (79), but few species have been examined, given the much greater difficulty of testing for and measuring superparamagnetic versus permanent crystals.

CONCLUSION

There is now abundant evidence for high-precision magnetic sensitivity in honey bees and homing pigeons, and at least a compass sense in many other species. We can be sure that induction is the receptor strategy used by sharks and rays, while permanent magnetism is employed by microorganisms. Induction is probably ruled out on both theoretical and empirical grounds in terrestrial animals, while the existence of localized concentrations of magnetite crystals in many magnetically sensitive animals suggests that permanent (and, perhaps, superparamagnetic) magnets may be the basis of most receptor systems. As yet, however, the anatomy and physiology of the magnetite-containing cells have not been sufficiently explored. There is also a great deal to be learned behaviorally about receptor mechanisms and information processing strategies, particularly in bees and pigeons. There appears to be a fascinating evolutionary story waiting to be written.

Literature Cited

1. Baker, R. R. 1980. Goal orientation by blindfolded humans after long-distance displacement: possible involvement of a magnetic sense. *Science* 210:555–57
2. Baker, R. R. 1981. *Human Navigation and the Sixth Sense.* London: Hodder & Stoughton. 138 pp.
3. Baker, R. R., Mather, J. G., Kennaugh, J. H. 1983. Magnetic bones in human sinuses. *Nature* 301:78–80
4. Barros, H. G. P. Lins de, Esquivel, D. M. S., Danon, J., Oliveira, L. P. H. de, 1982. Magnetotactic algae. *Acad. Brasileria CBPF Notas Fis.* 48:104–06
5. Bingman, V. P. 1981. Savannah sparrows have a magnetic compass. *Anim. Behav.* 29:962–63
6. Blakemore, R. P. 1975. Magnetotactic bacteria. *Science* 190:377–79
7. Blakemore, R. P., Frankel, R. B. 1981. Magnetic navigation in bacteria. *Sci. Am.* 245:58–65
8. Buchler, E. R., Wasilewski, P. J. 1982. Bats have magnets. *EOS* 63:156
9. Buskirk, R. E. 1981. Magnetic material in marine crustacea. *EOS* 62:850
10. Carr, H. P., Switzer, W. P., Hollander, W. F. 1982. Evidence for interference with navigation of homing pigeons by a magnetic storm. *Iowa State J. Res.* 56:327–40
11. De Jong, D. 1982. The orientation of comb-building by honeybees. *J. Comp. Phys.* 147:495–501
12. Dyer, F. C., Gould, J. L. 1983. Honey bee navigation. *Am. Sci.* 71: In press
13. Emlen, S. T., Wiltschko, W., Demong, N. J., Wiltschko, R., Bergman, S. 1976. Magnetic direction finding: evidence for its use in migratory indigo buntings. *Science* 193:505–8
14. Frankel, R. B. 1981. Bacterial magnetotaxis vs geotaxis. *EOS* 62:850
15. Frankel, R. B., Blakemore, R. P. 1980. Navigational compass in magnetic bacteria. *J. Magn. Magn. Mater.* 15–18:1562–64
16. Frankel, R. B., Blakemore, R. P., Wolfe, R. S. 1979. Magnetite in freshwater magnetic bacteria. *Science* 203:1355–57
17. Frei, U., Wagner, G. 1976. Die Anfangsorientierung von Brieftauben in erdmagnetisch gestörten Gebiet des Mont Jorat. *Rev. Suisse Zool.* 83:891–97
18. Gould, J. L. 1980. Sun compensation by bees. *Science* 207:545–47
19. Gould, J. L. 1980. The case for magnetic sensitivity in birds and bees (such as it is). *Am. Sci.* 68:256–67
20. Gould, J. L. 1982. The map sense of pigeons. *Nature* 296:205–11
21. Gould, J. L. 1984. Processing of sun-azimuth information by honey bees. *Ani. Behav.* 32: In press
22. Gould, J. L., Able, K. P. 1981. Human homing: an elusive phenomenon. *Science* 212:1061–63
23. Gould, J. L., Kirschvink, J. L., Deffeyes, K. S. 1978. Bees have magnetic remanence. *Science* 202:1026–28
24. Gould, J. L., Kirschvink, J. L., Deffeyes, K. S., Brines, M. L. 1980. Orientation by demagnetized bees. *J. Exp. Biol.* 86:1–8
25. Graue, L. C. 1965. Initial orientation in pigeon homing related to magnetic contours. *Am. Zool.* 5:704
26. Grüter, M., Wiltschko, R., Wiltschko, W. 1982. Distribution of release-site biases around Frankfurt. In *Avian Navigation,* ed. F. Papi, H. G. Wallraff, pp. 222–31. Berlin: Springer
27. Gwinner, E., Wiltschko, W. 1978. Endogenously controlled changes in migratory direction of the garden warbler. *J. Comp. Physiol.* 125:267–73
28. Hepworth, D., Pickard, R. S., Overshott, K. J. 1980. Effects of the periodically intermittent application of a constant magnetic field on the mobility in darkness of worker honey bees. *J. Apic Res.* 19:179–86
29. Jones, D. S., McFadden, B. J. 1982. Induced magnetization in the monarch butterfly. *J. Exp. Biol.* 96:1–9
30. Kalmijn, A. J. 1974. The detection of electric fields from inanimate and animate sources other than electric organs. In *Handbook of Sensory Physiology,* ed. A. Fessard. 3:147–200. Berlin: Springer
31. Kalmijn, A. J. 1978. Experimental evidence of geomagnetic orientation in elasmobranch fishes. In *Animal Migration, Navigation, and Homing,* ed. K. Schmidt-Koenig, W. T. Keeton, pp. 347–55 Berlin: Springer
32. Kalmijn, A. J. 1982. Electric and magnetic field detection in elasmobranch fishes. *Science* 218:916–18
33. Kalmijn, A. J., Blakemore, R. P. 1978. Magnetic behavior of mud bacteria. See Ref. 31, pp. 354–55
34. Keeton, W. T. 1971. Magnets interfere with pigeon homing. *Proc. Natl. Acad. Sci. USA* 68:102–6
35. Keeton, W. T., Larkin, T. S., Windsor, D. M. 1974. Normal fluctuations in the earth's magnetic field influence pigeon orientation. *J. Comp. Physiol.* 95:95–103

36. Kiepenheuer, J. 1982. The effect of magnetic anomalies on the homing behavior of pigeons. See Ref. 26, pp. 120–28

37. Kilbert, K. 1979. Geräuschanalyze der Tanzlaute der Honigbiene (Apis mellifica) in unterschiedlichen magnetischen Feldsituationen. J. Comp. Physiol. 132:11–26

38. Kirschvink, J. L. 1980. South-seeking magnetic bacteria. J. Exp. Biol. 86:345–47

39. Kirschvink, J. L. 1981. The horizontal magnetic dance of the honey bee is compatible with a single domain ferromagnetic magnetoreceptor. BioSystems 14:193–203

40. Kirschvink, J. L., Gould, J. L. 1981. Biogenic magnetite as a basis for magnetic field detection in animals. BioSystems 13:181–201

41. Kirschvink, J. L., Lowenstam, H. A. 1979. Mineralization and magnetization of chiton teeth: Paleomagnetic, sedimentologic, and biologic implications of organic magnetite. Earth Planet. Sci. Lett. 44:193–204

42. Kirschvink, J. L., Walker, M. M., Dizon, A. E., Peterson, K. A. 1984. Interacting single-domain magnets in the head of the chinook salmon. J. Comp. Physiol. In press

43. Kuterbach, D. A., Walcott, B., Reeder, R. J., Frankel, R. B. 1982. Iron-containing cells in the honey bee (Apis mellifera). Science 218:695–97

44. Leask, M. J. M. 1977. A physiological mechanism for magnetic field detection by migratory birds and homing pigeons. Nature 267:144–45

45. Lednor, A. J. 1982. Magnetic navigation in pigeons: possibilities and problems. See Ref. 26, pp. 109–19

46. Lindauer, M. 1976. Recent advances in the orientation and learning of honey bees. Proc. 25th Int. Congr. Entomol., 25:450–60

47. Lindauer, M., Martin, H. 1968. Die Schwereorientierung der Bienen unter dem Einfluss der Erdmagnetfelds. Z. Vergl. Physiol. 60:219–43

48. Lindauer, M., Martin, H. 1972. Magnetic effects on dancing bees. In Animal Orientation and Navigation, ed. S. R. Galler, et al, pp. 559–67. Washington DC: USGPO

49. Lowenstam, H. A. 1962. Magnetite in dental capping in recent chitons. Geol. Soc. Am. Bull. 73:435–38

50. Martin, H., Lindauer, M. 1977. Der Einfluss der Erdmagnetfelds und die Schwereorientierung der Honigbiene. J. Comp. Physiol. 122:145–87

51. Mather, J. G., Baker, R. R. 1981. Magnetic sense of direction in woodmice for route-based navigation. Nature 291:152–55

52. Michener, M., Walcott, C. 1967. Homing of single pigeons: an analysis of tracks. J. Exp. Biol. 47:99–131

53. Moore, B. 1980. Is the homing pigeon's map geomagnetic? Nature 285:69–70

54. Moore, F. 1977. Geomagnetic disturbance and the orientation of nocturnally migrating birds. Science 196:682–84

55. O'Leary, D. P., Vilches-Troya, J., Dunn, R. F., Campos-Munõz, A. 1981. Magnets in guitarfish vestibular receptors. Experientia 37:86–88

56. Perry, A., Bauer, G. B., Dizon, A. E. 1981. Magnetite in the green turtle. EOS 62:850

57. Presti, D., Pettigrew, J. D. 1982. Ferromagnetic coupling to muscle receptors as a basis for geomagnetic field sensitivity in animals. Nature 285:99–101

58. Quinn, T. P. 1980. Evidence for celestial and magnetic compass orientation in lake-migrating sockeye salmon fry. J. Comp. Physiol. 137:243–48

59. Quinn, T. P., Brannon, E. L. 1982. Use of celestial and magnetic cues by orienting sockeye salmon smolts. J. Comp. Physiol. 147:547–52

60. Quinn, T. P., Merrill, R. T., Brannon, E. L. 1981. Magnetic field detection in sockeye salmon. J. Exp. Zool. 217:137–42

61. Rosenblum, B., Jungerman, R. L. 1980. Magnetic induction for the sensing of magnetic fields by animals—an analysis. J. Theor. Biol. 87:25–32

62. Schmidt-Koenig, K. 1979. Directions of migrating monarch butterflies in some parts of the eastern United States. Behav. Processes 4:73–78

63. Schmidt-Koenig, K., Walcott, C. 1978. Tracks of pigeons homing with frosted lenses. Anim. Behav. 26:480–86

64. Schriber, B., Rossi, O. 1976. Correlation between race arrivals of homing pigeons and solar activity. Boll. Zool. 43:317–20

65. Schreiber, B., Rossi, O. 1978. Correlation between magnetic storms due to solar spots and pigeon homing performances. IEEE Trans. Magn. 14:961–63

66. Southern, W. E. 1972. Influence of disturbance in the earth's magnetic field on ring-billed gull orientation. Condor 74:102–05

67. Southern, W. E. 1978. Orientation responses of ring-billed gull chicks: a reevaluation. See Ref. 31, pp. 311–17

68. Takeuchi, H., Uyeda, S., Kanamoni, H.

1970. *Debate About the Earth*. San Francisco: Freeman, Cooper & Co. 281 pp.

69. Talkington, L. 1967. Bird navigation and geomagnetism. *Am. Zool.* 7:199

70. Tomlinson, J., McGinty, S., Kish, J. 1981. Magnets curtail honey bee dancing. *Anim. Behav.* 29:307

71. Towne, W. F., Gould, J. L. 1984. Magnetic-field sensitivity in honey bees. In *Magnetite Biomineralization and Magnetoreception in Organisms,* ed. J. L. Kirschvink, D. S. Jones, B. J. Macfadden. New York: Plenum

72. Visalberghi, E., Alleva, E. 1979. Magnetic influence on pigeon homing. *Biol. Bull.* 156:246–56

73. von Frisch, K. 1967. *The Dance Language and Orientation of Bees*. Cambridge, Mass: Harvard Univ. Press. 566 pp.

74. Wagner, G. 1976. Das orientierungsverhalten von Brieftauben im erdmagnetisch gestörten Gebiete des Chasseral. *Rev. Suisse Zool.* 83:883–90

75. Walcott, B., Walcott, C. 1982. A search for magnetic field receptors in animals. See Ref. 26, pp. 338–43

76. Walcott, C. 1978. Anomalies in the earth's magnetic field increase the scatter of pigeons' vanishing bearings. See Ref. 31, pp. 143–51

77. Walcott, C. 1980. Magnetic orientation in homing pigeons. *IEEE Trans. Magn.* 16:1008–13

78. Walcott, C. 1982. Is there evidence for a magnetic map in homing pigeons? See Ref. 26, pp. 99–108

79. Walcott, C., Gould, J. L., Kirschvink, J. L. 1979. Pigeons have magnets. *Science* 205:1027–29

80. Walcott, C., Green, R. P. 1974. Orientation of homing pigeons is altered by a change in the direction of an applied magnetic field. *Science* 184:180–82

81. Walker, M. M., Dizon, A. E. 1981. Identification of magnetite in tuna. *EOS* 62:850

82. Walker, M. M., Dizon, A. E., Kirschvink, J. L. 1982. Yellowfin tuna are easily conditioned to the geomagnetic field. In *Oceans* 82, pp. 755–58. New York: IEEE

83. Wiltschko, R., Nohr, D., Wiltschko, W. 1981. Pigeons with a deficient sun compass use the magnetic compass. *Science* 214:343–45

84. Wiltschko, R., Wiltschko, W. 1981. The development of sun compass orientation in young homing pigeons. *Behav. Ecol. Sociobiol.* 9:135–41

85. Wiltschko, W., Wiltschko, R. 1972. Magnetic compasses of European robins. *Science* 176:62–64

86. Windsor, D. M. 1972. *Directional preferences and their relation to navigation in homing pigeons*. Dissertation. Cornell Univ.

87. Windsor, D. M. 1975. Regional expression of directional preferences by experienced homing pigeons. *Anim. Behav.* 23:335–43

88. Yeagley, H. L. 1947. A preliminary study of a physical basis of bird navigation. *J. Appl. Phys.* 18:1035–63

89. Yeagley, H. L. 1951. A preliminary study of a physical basis of bird navigation, II. *J. Appl. Phys.* 22:746–60

90. Yorke, E. D. 1979. A possible magnetic transducer in birds. *J. Theor. Biol.* 77:101–5

91. Yorke, E. D. 1981. Two consequences of magnetic material found in pigeons. *J. Theor. Biol.* 89:533–37

92. Zoeger, J., Fuller, M. 1981. Magnetic material in the head of the common Pacific dolphin. *Science* 213:892–94

Ann. Rev. Physiol. 1984. 46:599–614

PHYSIOLOGICAL MECHANISMS FOR SPATIAL FILTERING AND IMAGE ENHANCEMENT IN THE SONAR OF BATS

J. A. Simmons and S. A. Kick

Department of Biology, Institute of Neuroscience, University of Oregon, Eugene, Oregon 97403

INTRODUCTION

Bats (Chiroptera) orient themselves with a biological sonar system called *echolocation* (2). They emit ultrasonic sounds and perceive spatial features of targets from acoustic features of echoes received by their ears (2, 14, 19, 21, 27–29, 32). Echolocation serves for locating obstacles to flight and for detecting, locating, and identifying flying insects. The process of intercepting airborne prey is relatively stereotyped across species of bats, although different species use different signal waveforms for this task (19, 21, 27–29). Figure 1 illustrates an interception by the little brown bat, *Myotis lucifugus* (37). There are three stages to the process, a *search* stage (in which the bat emits sonar sounds at 5–20 sounds/sec), an *approach* stage (beginning at distances of 1.5–2 m, during which the bat continuously aims its head at the insect and increases its emission rate to 20–40 sounds/sec), and a *terminal* stage (beginning at a distance of about 30 cm, during which the bat abruptly increases the emission rate to 50–200 sounds/sec as it seizes the target) (5). The entire pursuit maneuver usually takes less than a second, and the bat aims its head at the target with an accuracy of better than ±5° throughout the approach and terminal stages (37).

The distance at which a bat first detects a target depends upon the target's size, the propagation of sound in air, the frequency and intensity of sonar

599

0066-4278/84/0315-0599$02.00

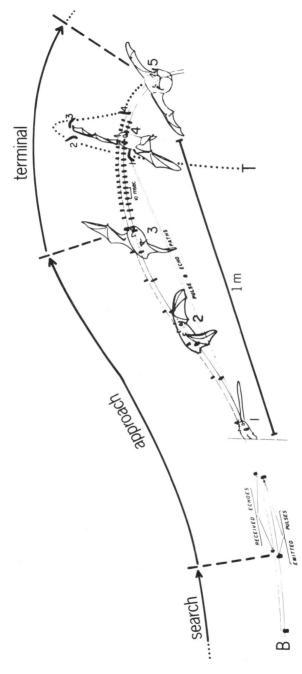

Figure 1 A drawing of the three stages in the interception of an airborne target by the little brown bat, *Myotis lucifugus*. Five numbered positions of the bat (B) on its approach and the target (T, a mealworm) on its trajectory are shown, based upon multiple-exposure stroboscopic photographs of the maneuver, which lasts less than a second (37). The track of the bat illustrates the timing of successive sonar emissions and returning echoes with tic-marks. Note that the bat increases the repetition-rate of its emissions during the approach stage and again, and more abruptly, increases the repetition rate in the terminal stage. The capture occurs in position No. 5 with the bat seizing the mealworm in its tail membrane. The interception process is sufficiently stereotyped in different species that this diagram can be considered typical of airborne captures by bats. Different species do, however, emit different sonar signals throughout the maneuver, indicating that their acoustical strategies for finding prey may be different (27). (Drawing by F. A. Webster; reproduced with permission.)

emissions, and the bat's threshold for hearing echoes (2, 3, 12, 19, 20). The big brown bat, *Eptesicus fuscus,* can detect insect-sized spheres at distances of 3–5 m, several meters further away than the transition from the search to the approach stages (see Figure 1) (11). During the approach stage, the bat evaluates the target's location and decides whether the target is an edible insect (4). The bat also changes the sonar signals it emits to improve its resolution of the target's features (4, 27, 32).

Big brown bats can perceive the distance to a target with an accuracy of 1–2 cm (24), the horizontal direction with an accuracy of 1.5° (30), the vertical direction with an accuracy of 3° (13), and they can perceive the shape of a target with an acuity of fractions of a millimeter (31), probably from echo spectral cues (3) and from the temporal fine structure of complex echoes (25). Much of the bat's ability to perceive the location of targets in space appears to depend upon temporal cues in echoes, such as arrival-time (for range), binaural time differences (for horizontal direction), and echo reverberation in the external ear (for vertical direction) (26). Neurons sensitive to very small binaural time differences have recently been found in bats (6).

One can discern specific functions for the bat's sonar emissions and for the bat's external, middle, and inner ears in promoting or enhancing the acoustic images that bats perceive through echolocation. In addition, specific image-enhancing events have been observed in the bat's auditory nervous system. The collective action of these physiological mechanisms is described below.

SIGNAL PROCESSING IN ECHOLOCATION

The means by which the bat achieves spatial perception of targets from the temporal dimension of echoes is of fundamental interest in hearing. A number of important psychological dimensions of auditory perception arise from neural processing of information about the periodicity of sounds or of parts of sounds, and the perception of target range from echo arrival-time by echolocating bats is scientifically valuable as a particularly clear-cut example. Signal processing related to perception of target range is not restricted to higher levels of the bat's auditory nervous system, however, but occurs in peripheral parts of the auditory system as well.

Control of Signals in Echolocation

The sounds that stimulate the bat's ears during echolocation and the neural activity that represents these sounds in the auditory pathways of the brain are subjected to several kinds of regulatory action which contribute to the quality of the acoustic images that bats perceive. The amount of stimulation reaching the bat's cochlea both from the emitted sonar signals and from the returning echoes is controlled by the external and middle ears. Furthermore, once acoustic stimulation has been transformed into neural impulses representing emissions and echoes, other control mechanisms regulate the flow of these impulses as the spatial information they contain about targets is converted into displays of target features.

CONTROL OF STIMULATION FROM SONAR EMISSIONS   The echolocation sounds emitted by most species of insectivorous bats are extremely intense. Peak-to-peak sound pressures of 90–110 dB SPL are typically observed at distances of about 10 cm from the mouth of species that pursue airborne prey (2, 14, 19, 21). Although this intensity is projected towards the target, the amount of sound directly reaching the ears at the time of emission is significantly smaller (9; Suga, personal communication). The bat's ears, which are located on the sides of the head and off the main axis of the emitted sound beam, receive less sound than is broadcast to the front (21–23). In *Eptesicus fuscus* the bat's emissions are some 15 dB weaker when they reach the ears, for example (Simmons, in preparation). The external ears themselves are directional in their acoustic properties and sounds coming to the ears from the direction of the mouth are received with reduced sensitivity compared to the sensitivity of the ear for echoes from straight ahead or slightly to the side (7, 9, 21, 22). In *Eptesicus fuscus* the emitted sound is discriminated against by about 9 dB, simply because the structures of the external ear partly shield the bat's hearing of sounds being emitted. The combined effect of the directionality of emissions and of hearing reduces the strength of emissions at the eardrum of *Eptesicus fuscus* by 24 dB (Simmons, in preparation).

The middle-ear muscles of bats contract at the same time as activation of the larynx for production of echolocation sounds (8, 16, 35). These contractions occur in synchrony with emissions even at the high repetition rates associated with the late approach and the terminal stages of interception of prey. Contraction of these muscles during vocalization reduces the strength of stimuli reaching the cochlea over the middle-ear system, and relaxation of the middle-ear muscles after vocalization restores the sensitivity of the bat's hearing for subsequent echoes of each emission. The amount of attenuation of vocalizations by middle-ear muscle contractions may be as much as 25–30 dB (35), and this attenuation even occurs during the terminal stage of pursuit because the muscles largely remain in a state of tetanic contraction at high-repetition rates of emission.

CONTROL OF STIMULATION FROM SONAR ECHOES   The directionality of emissions and of hearing affects the amount of stimulation of the cochlea from sonar *echoes,* too. The direction of the target relative to the direction in which the bat aims its head and its sonar sounds determines the amount of sound incident upon the target and, hence, the amount of sound returning in the echo.

The echo arrives at the external ears from the target's direction and is modified by the directional sensitivity of the external-ear system on its way to the eardrum. In *Myotis grisescens* and *Eptesicus fuscus* the combination of the directionality of emissions and of the external ears provides the bat with a zone of greatest sensitivity to targets that is about 40° wide (35; Simmons, in preparation). The combined directionality of emissions and hearing in the horseshoe bat, *Rhinolophus ferrumequinum*, gives a slightly narrower region of greatest sensitivity that is about 30° wide (21). The external ears thus act as spatial filters that concentrate the bat's sensitivity to targets in the direction of the emissions. By the act of aiming its head to track the movement of a target, the bat keeps the target in approximately the most favorable position in the directional receiving pattern for echoes. As long as the bat maintains the aim of its head with the observed accuracy of ±5°, echoes arriving at its ears will not vary as a consequence of the changing horizontal and vertical location of the target with respect to the instantaneous direction of the bat's flight velocity and orientation of its body as a whole.

Contractions of middle-ear muscles accompanying the production of sonar emissions do not disappear immediately upon cessation of the sound; relaxation of the middle-ear muscles from their synchronized contractions takes 5–8 msec (7, 8, 35). The period in which sounds stimulating the cochlea are affected by middle-ear muscle contractions thus extends well past the duration of the emission and into the time when echoes can be expected to occur (7). In *Eptesicus fuscus*, emissions are accompanied by a loss in hearing sensitivity that persists for about as long as the middle-ear muscle contraction (Kick & Simmons, in preparation). Figure 2 shows measurements of the hearing sensitivity of *Eptesicus fuscus* to sonar echoes arriving at delays of 1–6 msec, together with threshold estimates from experiments with spherical targets (11). The magnitude of threshold elevation for echoes arriving at 1 msec delay compared to 6 msec delay is about 30 dB, which correponds well with the total magnitude of attenuations observed in *Myotis lucifugus* from middle-ear muscle contractions (35). There appears to be little in these behaviorally observed threshold shifts that cannot be attributed to middle-ear muscle contractions. There are two physiological consequences of this fact: the threshold shift is achieved by reducing the strength of stimuli reaching the cochlea, and the bat's threshold in the laboratory situation is determined by noise occuring internal to the auditory system rather than from ambient acoustic noise (Simmons, in preparation). Ambient acoustic noise would be reduced along with echoes, and the factor determining whether detection occurs—the signal-to-noise ratio of echoes—would remain unchanged. Instead, middle-ear muscle contractions reduce stimulus strength with respect to a fixed level of internal noise. Possible sources of internal noise must include the current-gating mechanism of hair-cells, the synaptic connections driving auditory-nerve fibers, and even acoustic stimulation generated by mechanical events within the body.

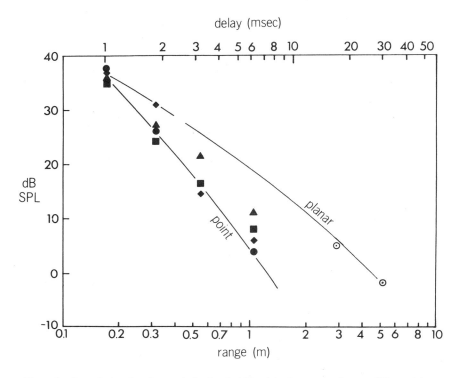

Figure 2   A graph showing changes in the threshold for detecting sonar echoes at different delays (upper horizontal axis) from targets at different distances (lower horizontal axis) by the big brown bat, *Eptesicus fuscus*. The solid data-points show echo-detection thresholds measured directly in four bats (Kick & Simmons, in preparation), and the two open circles show thresholds estimated from the distances at which bats can detect spherical targets 4.8 or 19.1 mm in diameter (11). The line labeled "point" shows the slope of the decline in echo strength from small insect-sized targets at increasing distances from the bat, and the line labeled "planar" shows the corresponding decline in echo strength from larger, flat target surfaces. These data-points show how the bat's thresholds for echo-detection increase by about the same amount as echo strength increases while the bat approaches from a distance of 1.5–2 m to a distance of less than 20 cm. As a result, echoes remain at a steady sensation level throughout the bat's approach (see Figure 1).

Changes in the sensitivity of the bat's hearing for *echoes at different delays* translate into changes in sensitivity for *targets at different ranges*. The bat's threshold for hearing echoes occurring at delays greater than 10 msec appears to be about 0 dB SPL (peak-to-peak) (11). At echo delays shorter than about 10 msec (target ranges shorter than about 1.5–2 m), the bat's thresholds rise by about 11 dB for each halving of range (Fig. 2). The bat's sensitivity thus is nearly inversely proportional to the square of the distance to the target for distances out to 1.5–2 m. Not only do the bat's hearing thresholds increase as targets get nearer, but so do the intensities of echoes from the target. Small objects such as insects, described as point targets, yield echoes that increase in intensity by about 12–13 dB for every halving of range (2, 12, 19). Figure 2 reveals that the bat's hearing thresholds change by the same amount as the intensities of echoes during the bat's approach to a flying insect. Largely through the action of the middle-ear muscles gradually relaxing after each emission, the bat adjusts its sensitivity to echoes to keep them at a constant amplitude relative to hearing thresholds (a constant *sensation level*) throughout the approach and terminal stages of pursuit (Kick & Simmons, in preparation). This regulatory mechanism thus maintains the level of stimulation of hair cells and auditory-nerve fibers by echoes returning from the insect during the course of interception maneuvers at a constant amplitude. The transition from the search to the approach and terminal stages, which previously has been marked by increases in the repetition rate of emissions and the start of tracking head movements by the bat, is now also distinguished by the beginning of adjustments of the bat's hearing sensitivity to regulate the level of echoes stimulating the cochlea. Range-related changes in the strength of echoes as stimuli are cancelled out by the bat.

We see, then, that the peripheral parts of the auditory system of the bat act as *spatial filters* to determine the sensitivity of the bat's hearing for echoes coming from targets in different directions and at different distances. By aiming its head at the target, the bat stabilizes the intensity of echoes even though the target is moving in its horizontal and vertical position with respect to the bat's body axis or its line of flight. By adjusting the sensitivity of its hearing relative to the time of emission of sonar sounds, the bat stabilizes the intensity of echoes even though it is moving progressively nearer to the target all the time. The pursuit process, from the start of the approach stage until the final capture, is characterized by the bat's efforts to prevent changes in the target's position from producing changes in the intensity of echoes as stimuli at the auditory receptors. It thus appears that the approach stage of pursuit requires the bat to perceive features of the target such as location without confusion with features of the target such as size and shape. Both location and size and shape influence the intensity of echoes reaching the bat, and the bat explicitly acts to destroy this influence of location.

CONTROL OF NEURAL SIGNALS REPRESENTING EMISSIONS AND ECHOES   The bat's sonar emission and each echo are converted at the cochlea into volleys of impulses ascending the auditory nerve into the cochlear nucleus. These arrays of impulses spread upward along the auditory pathways to the inferior colliculus, where all ascending brain-stem and midbrain connections converge. The arrays of impulses evoked by each emission and each echo come to represent these stimuli for signal-processing in the auditory nervous system.

The earliest opportunity for control to be exerted on these ascending impulses is in the cochlea, from descending inhibitory fibers of the olivocochlear tracts. It appears at present, however, that this very peripheral neural mechanism does not play any special role in echolocation such as selective suppression of responsiveness of auditory nerve fibers to emissions (9, 35).

Neural control over ascending volleys of nerve impulses representing stimuli for echolocation does take place in the nucleus of the lateral lemniscus (36). Auditory evoked (N_4) responses to the bat's own sonar sounds at the time of vocalization are reduced in amplitude compared to responses to these same sounds subsequently presented after being recorded on tape. The act of vocalization produces neural suppression of activity. Evoked responses from the auditory nerve (N_1) and the olivary complex (N_3) show no such self-induced reduction in amplitude to vocalizations, indicating that many neurons in the nucleus of the lateral lemniscus, which might otherwise respond to emissions, are prevented from responding by a neural mechanism synchronized to vocalizations. Presumably, neurons that do not respond to vocalizations are then available for response to echoes occurring a few milliseconds later, and neurons that do respond to vocalizations are distinguished as responding to the first signal of a pair of signals—the self-vocalized emission rather than the echo. An important class of neurons in the inferior colliculus of bats will only respond to the *second* of a *pair* of sounds, the echo, thus indicating that the bat's nervous system explicitly labels the echo as distinct from the emission (1, 17, 33). The failure of these neurons to respond to the first sounds, which are at least as strong as the second sounds and which precede them, demonstrates a selective suppression of responses at the single-neuron level. Some neural inhibitory mechanism, perhaps also operating in synchrony with emissions, apparently controls the flow of information ascending the auditory pathways by partially segregating impulses evoked by emissions and impulses evoked by echoes into separate groups of neurons in the inferior colliculus. This is bound to be a crucial aspect of information-processing, related to determining whether an echo is present, whether a target is present, and how far away the target is located, for example.

Most neurons in the inferior colliculus of bats respond to short, frequency-modulated (FM) sounds of the type used by most species of bats for echolocation, with one or two impulses marking the time at which the FM sweep passed through the neuron's tuning curve (15, 18, 34). Many of these neurons exhibit sharp tuning curves when stimulated by short-duration FM signals, but exhibit either broad, relatively unselective tuning curves or no response at all when stimulated with short, constant-frequency (CF) signals. The dependence of frequency selectivity upon stimulation with FM or CF sounds reveals the existence of neural interactions that specialize neurons to respond differently to a particular frequency embedded in an FM sweep than when presented alone

(34). The time of occurrence of the discharge represents the time of occurrence of the frequency in the FM sweep, but it does depend upon stimulus intensity. The latency of discharges in auditory-nerve fibers and in other neurons higher in the auditory system changes sytematically with the intensity of stimuli, with stronger stimuli evoking earlier discharges and weaker stimuli evoking later discharges. An important group of neurons in the bat's inferior colliculus responds to FM signals with one (or occasionally two) impulses that change relatively slightly in latency as stimulus intensity changes. The mean latency of the first impulse, which usually is the only impulse in the response, changes by at most 1.5–2 msec for a 40 dB change in stimulus intensity (15, 18, 33). These neurons register the time of occurrence of individual frequencies in FM sweeps, and the activity of many such neurons, each tuned to a different frequency, would represent the time of occurrence of the FM sweep as a whole, and with relatively little variability due to changes in stimulus intensity.

Neural Representation of Images of Targets

Each emission and each echo initially is represented by an array of impulses ascending along auditory-nerve fibers, and these impulses give rise to further arrays of discharges that spread out along the auditory pathways from the cochlear nucleus to other brain-stem auditory nuclei, to the nucleus of the lateral lemniscus, and to the inferior colliculus. At the first level of neural representation, the target's range is coded in terms of the time intervals between impulses evoked by the emission and impulses evoked by the echo. Thus, the arrival-time of echoes is still represented in the time domain in the auditory nerve (26, 34).

NEURAL REPRESENTATION OF ACOUSTIC IMAGES   In first-order fibers of the auditory system, moderate or strong stimulation evokes an increase in the average discharge rate over that which occurs spontaneously in the absence of stimulation (10). This increase takes the form of multiple impulses evoked by each stimulus, with the number of impulses depending upon the intensity and duration of the sound. The level of stimulation reaching the bat's external ears from emissions and echoes certainly is moderate to strong if the bat is within a meter or so of the target. The emission probably reaches the external ear with an intensity of 80–90 dB SPL, and echoes from spheres as large as the insects that bats pursue reach the external ear from a distance of 1–1.5 m with an intensity as much as 25–40 dB SPL. As the bat approaches nearer, echoes can reach amplitudes of 50–70 dB SPL (2, 5, 12, 19). If these sounds were delivered as stimuli to the cochlea, each auditory-nerve fiber would respond with several impulses either to the emission or to the echo. If the time delay of the echo after the emission is not too short, many individual fibers probably would respond to both signals. For shorter delays, however, the echo might well only evoke responses for the most part in fibers that had not responded to the emission. The initial or *on* impulse to the emission or the echo would be the most reliable marker for the time of occurrence of stimulation at the neuron's best frequency (15), but other impulses would follow, because the stimulus would remain within the tuning curve of the neuron for an appreciable time, after first sweeping in frequency down into the tuning curve.

The target's distance is represented by the time interval between the burst of impulses representing the emission and the subsequent burst of impulses representing the echo. These two bursts of impulses would be arrayed across the auditory nerve according to the frequencies in the bat's sonar emissions and the distribution of fibers from different positions along the Organ of Corti within the nerve bundle itself. Figure 3 shows how these burst of impulses might appear if the sounds reaching the bat's external ear were to stimulate the cochlea at their arriving intensities. Hypothetical patterns of impulses in neurons tuned to ultrasonic frequencies in the bat *Eptesicus fuscus* are illustrated for the search, approach, and terminal stages of pursuit. Each diagonal streak of dots on the diagram represents the FM sweep of one of the two or three harmonics in the bat's sonar sounds (27). (The *search* signals sweep from 60 to 25 kHz in the first harmonic, and from 120 to 50 kHz in the second harmonic. The *approach* signals sweep from 45 to 23 kHz in the first harmonic, from 85 to 50 kHz in the second, and around 80 kHz in the third. The *terminal* signals sweep from 25 to 18 kHz, from 50 to 36 kHz, and from 75 to 54 kHz in three harmonics.)

The streaks of dots representing impulses shown in Figure 3 have a sharply defined leading edge, but they extend towards the left in a less well defined manner due to the presence of multiple impulses evoked by the strong emissions and echoes arriving at the external ears. The accuracy of perceiving the position of the target from the echo's arrival time would be reduced by the smearing of these bursts of impulses along the time axis, because only the initial impulses in response to the emission or the echo register the time of occurrence of stimulation with any degree of precision; the rest occur over the duration of stimulation without accurate synchronization to the sound.

ENHANCEMENT OF ACOUSTIC IMAGES   The levels of stimulation representing emissions and echoes arriving at the inner ear are substantially different from the levels reaching the external ear. Emissions are reduced in amplitude by the external ear's directionality and by the contractions of middle-ear muscles at the time of vocalization. Echoes are affected by the direction of the target with respect to the directionality of the external ears, and the bat explicitly controls echo intensity by aiming its head to point at the target when it enters the approach stage. The middle-ear muscles of the bat affect sensitivity to echoes from targets at different ranges as they relax after their contraction synchronized to vocalization. The action of the bat in continuously aiming its

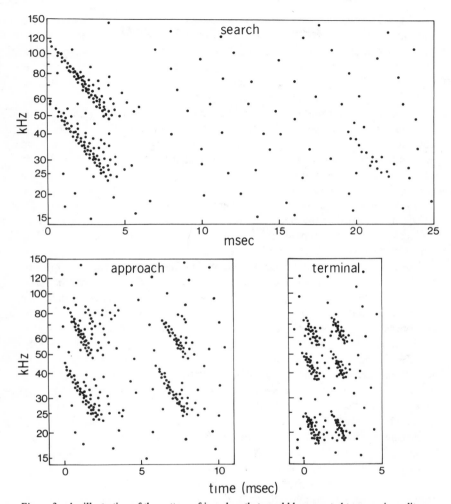

Figure 3 An illustration of the pattern of impulses that would be expected to occur in auditory-nerve fibers of *Eptesicus fuscus* if the sonar emissions and echoes reaching the external ears were to stimulate the cochlea directly. Hypothetical response patterns are shown for the search stage (emission at 0–4 msec, echo at 19–22 msec), the approach stage (emission at 0–2 msec, echo at 6–8 msec), and the terminal stage (emission at 0–1 msec, echo at 2–3 msec). The vertical frequency axes show the frequencies to which the hypothetical auditory-nerve fibers are tuned.

head at the target adjusts the target to a stable, favorable location in the spatial, directional filter constituting the external ears, and the progressive relaxation of the middle-ear muscles regulates the amplitude of echoes at the cochlea to a stable value with respect to the threshold for echo detection at different delays. It is worth repeating that the time-dependent state of contraction of middle-ear muscles acts as a spatial filter for target range analogous in its function to the directional spatial filter consisting of the external ears. These two mechanisms minimize variability in the characteristics of the echoes from an insect as the bat proceeds through the approach and terminal stages of interception. Those variations in echoes that still do occur at the cochlea represent, therefore, changes in the instantaneous characteristics of the *target* itself, not changes related to the distance and direction of the target.

A complex target moving through the air may tumble or turn, changing its effective size and shape to the bat (3, 20). The regulating effects of head aim and the middle-ear muscles on hearing sensitivity "purify" stimulation from echoes to make these target-related changes stand out from those that would otherwise occur due to the closing range and changing direction to the target during the maneuvers that precede capture. Insect wing-beats are a good example of target-related sources of changes in echo features from one moment to the next (20) that the bat does not have to confuse with position-related changes as a result of tracking the target with its head aim and regulating sensitivity to echoes with its middle-ear muscles.

Not only are echoes adjusted to a stable amplitude at the cochlea, but this stable amplitude is rather low compared to the sounds striking the external ears, at least for insect-sized targets. Because echoes from insects stimulate the inner-ear system at levels in the region of 10–30 dB above threshold, the responses of auditory-nerve fibers are somewhat less complicated than would be the case if the sounds impinging upon the external ears were to stimulate the cochlea directly. The most striking consequence of the regulation of echoes to a low amplitude is that most auditory-nerve fibers would only respond with a single impulse when the echo sweeps downward into the neuron's tuning curve near the tip of the response area (10). Occasionally, multiple impulses would be evoked by stronger echoes, and spontaneous activity would result in impulses occurring at random times, but the neural representation of echoes in the auditory nerve would consist largely of the bursts of *on* impulses occurring in those fibers that respond at all to the echoes.

Many of the neurons in the auditory pathways that carry the neural representations of emissions and echoes further into the brain, processing information along the way, exhibit two response properties that further refine the representation of targets as acoustic images. These neurons usually respond to FM stimuli by producing a single impulse (rarely more than one) and they do not show spontaneous activity (15, 33, 34). In fact, the specificity of response of these neurons is such that often one can only find out whether the recording electrode is near such a unit by delivering appropriate FM sounds or even by delivering pairs of sounds if the neuron responds only to echoes. Figure 4 shows how neurons in the bat's auditory pathways might represent sonar emissions and echoes, taking into account the effects described above that collectively result in each emission or echo only evoking a single impulse from a given neuron when the FM stimulus sweeps into its response area.

Figure 4 illustrates the neural representation of acoustic images of targets that ascends into the bat's inferior colliculus. The target's range, for example, is conveyed in the time intervals between the burst of impulses representing the emission and the burst representing the echo, just as in Figure 3. In Figure 4, however, the quality of the representation of range has been improved by the removal of impulses occurring in response to sound after the initial impulses,

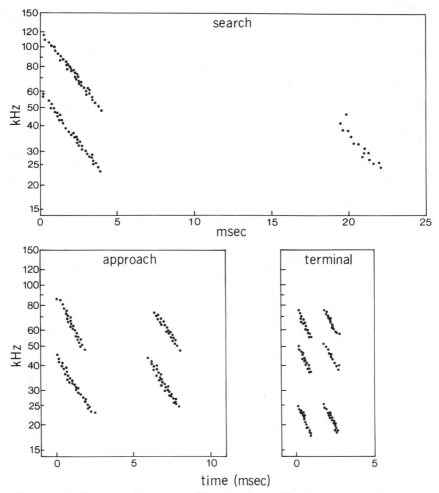

Figure 4 An illustration of the pattern of impulses that would represent sonar emissions and echoes in nerve fibers ascending the auditory pathways of *Eptesicus fuscus,* taking into account the contributions of the external and middle ears and the auditory nervous system in controlling information flow. The enhancement of the neural representations of these signals is evident by comparison with Figure 3.

and spontaneous activity in the background is gone. This dimension of the image has been enhanced by the processing activities of the external and middle ears and of the auditory nervous system. The absence of the temporal smearing of the bursts of impulses representing emissions and echoes ought to promote more accurate perception of target ranges.

Another aspect of the improvement in the quality of the bat's acoustic images is a direct consequence of the stabilization of echo intensity at the cochlea. The latency of nerve impulses after the presentation of a stimulus depends upon stimulus intensity. Changes of 40 dB or so in the strength of sounds can produce shifts of many milliseconds in response latency, but an important class of neurons in the bat's inferior colliculus experience a smaller shift averaging only 1.5–2 msec (15). This shift may seem small from a conventional physiological perspective, but look back to Figure 2 for a moment. As the bat approaches from a distance of 2 m to a distance of 15 cm, echoes from a point target would increase by over 30 dB, an increase that ought to result in a shortening of the most stable neural response latencies by about 1.5 msec. Such a latency shift corresponds to an error in estimating target range of the order of 25–30 cm, which is greater than the actual distance of the target at the end of the bat's approach. By adjusting the strength of echoes to eliminate intensity changes originating in the shortening of target range, the bat avoids experiencing potentially disruptive changes in neural response latency. The benefits of this aspect of enhancement of images seem obvious. Even though the bat captures flying prey in the relatively extensive surface area of the wing or tail membranes (38), a potential ranging error of tens of centimeters seems too big to be ignored.

SEPARATION OF INFORMATION ABOUT THE TARGET FROM INFORMATION ABOUT THE TARGET'S LOCATION   The action of the bat's head in pointing towards the target and of the bat's middle-ear muscles in relaxing in such a way as to regulate effective echo intensity reveal a fascinating mechanism in echolocation. The bat strips from stimuli reaching the cochlea any changes in intensity that would otherwise occur as a result of progressive changes in the target's distance and direction during the pursuit maneuver. This does not deprive the bat of information, however, because it has acoustic cues for distance and horizontal and vertical direction other than echo intensity. True, echo intensity changes can alter the accuracy of perception of these dimensions of target location, but the bat has cancelled them out by its regulatory actions. The bat is left free to perceive echo intensity changes occurring as a consequence of changes in the target itself.

Experiments in which echolocating bats are trained to capture airborne mealworms, which are quite edible, while rejecting airborne objects made of inedible materials, reveal that the intensity of echoes, and changes in intensity of echoes from one moment to the next, may be powerful acoustic cues for identifying targets (3). The regulatory actions of head-aim and middle-ear muscle relaxation make echo intensity variations caused by changes in the target's appearance (due to tumbling in the air or to shape changes such as beating of wings) stand out in isolation from those intensity variations that would otherwise occur due to changes in the target's location with respect to the bat. By using acoustic cues for locating targets that depend principally upon perception of the time of occurrence of echoes (26, 32), the bat may be able to reserve echo intensity as an acoustic cue to examine the target itself.

The bat acquires echo information related to target identification during the approach stage of interception, making its decision to complete the capture just prior to entering the terminal stage (4). By combining field and laboratory observations of the bat's behavior with physiological observations of response properties in the bat's auditory system, we arrive at a unified description of the function of the approach stage of echolocation. It probably does not begin with the bat's detection of the target, which appears to occur at greater distances than those marking the transition into the approach stage, but it does represent a period of time during which the bat is assembling acoustic images to accomplish two distinct tasks: location and tracking of the target, and identification of the target. This highly integrated feature of the anatomy of the bat's behavior during interception of prey depends upon the contributions of the external, middle, and inner ears acting collectively as a *three-dimensional spatial tracking filter* for separating variations in echo intensity due to the target's size and shape from those due to the target's location. This view gives us a useful new framework for interpreting physiological data and for designing new experiments.

ACKNOWLEDGMENTS

This work was supported by NSF Grant No. 80-13170. The authors thank D. R. Griffin, W. M. Masters, A. J. M. Moffat, and N. Suga for their critical comments on these ideas.

Literature Cited

1. Feng, A. S., Simmons, J. A., Kick, S. A. 1978. Echo detection and target-ranging neurons in the auditory system of the bat *Eptesicus fuscus*. *Science* 202:645–48
2. Griffin, D. R. 1958. *Listening in the Dark*. New Haven, CT: Yale Univ. Press. 413 pp.
3. Griffin, D. R. 1967. Discriminative echolocation by bats. In *Animal Sonar Systems: Biology and Bionics*, ed. R.-G. Busnel, 1:273–99. Jouy-en-Josas, France: Lab. Physiol. Acoustique. 1233 pp.
4. Griffin, D. R., Friend, J. H., Webster, F.

A. 1965. Target discrimination by the echolocation of bats. *J. Exp. Zool.* 158:155–68
5. Griffin, D. R., Webster, F. A., Michael, C. R. 1960. The echolocation of flying insects by bats. *Anim. Behav.* 8:141–54
6. Harnischfeger, G. 1980. Brainstem units of echolocating bats code binaural time differences in the microsecond range. *Naturwissenschaften* 67:314–15
7. Henson, O. W. Jr. 1967. The perception and analysis of biosonar signals by bats. In *Animal Sonar Systems: Biology and Bionics*, ed. R.-G. Busnel, 2:949–1003.

Jouy-en-Josas, France: Lab. Physiol. Acoustique. 1233 pp.

8. Henson, O. W. Jr. 1970. The ear and audition. In *Biology of Bats*, ed. W. A. Wimsatt, 2:181–263. New York: Academic 477 pp.

9. Jen, P.H.-S. 1982. Electrophysiological analysis of the echolocation system of bats. In *Contributions to Sensory Physiology*, 6:111–58. New York: Academic

10. Johnson, D. H. 1980. The relationship between spike rate and synchrony in responses of auditory-nerve fibers to single tones. *J. Acoust. Soc. Am.* 68:1115–22

11. Kick, S. A. 1982. Target-detection by the echolocating bat, *Eptesicus fuscus*. *J. Comp. Physiol.* 145:431–35

12. Lawrence, B. D., Simmons, J. A. 1982. Measurements of atmospheric attenuation at ultrasonic frequencies and the significance for echolocation by bats. *J. Acoust. Soc. Am.* 71:585–90

13. Lawrence, B. D., Simmons, J. A. 1982. Echolocation in bats: the external ear and perception of the vertical positions of targets. *Science* 218:481–83

14. Novick, A. 1977. Acoustic orientation. In *Biology of Bats*, ed. W. A. Wimsatt, 3:73–287. New York: Academic. 651 pp.

15. Pollak, G. D. 1980. Organizational and encoding features of single neurons in the inferior colliculus of bats. In *Animal Sonar Systems*, ed. R.-G. Busnel, J. F. Fish, pp. 549–87. New York: Plenum 1135 pp.

16. Pollak, G., Henson, O. W. Jr. 1973. Specialized functional aspects of the middle ear muscles in the bat, *Chilonycteris parnellii*. *J. Comp. Physiol.* 86:167–74

17. Pollak, G. D., Marsh, D., Bodenhamer, R., Souther, A. 1977. Echo-detecting characteristics of neurons in the inferior colliculus of unanesthetized bats. *Science* 196:675–78

18. Pollak, G. D., Marsh, D., Bodenhamer, R., Souther, A. 1977. Characteristics of phasic-on neurons in inferior colliculus of unanesthetized bats with observations relating to mechanisms of echo ranging. *J. Neurophysiol.* 40:926–42

19. Pye, J. D. 1980. Echolocation signals and echoes in air. See Ref. 15, pp. 309–53

20. Schnitzler, H.-U. 1983. The acoustical image of fluttering prey in echolocating bats. In *Ethology and Behavior Physiology*, ed. F. Huber, H. Markl. Heidelberg: Springer. In press

21. Schnitzler, H.-U., Henson, O. W. Jr. 1980. Performance of airborne animal sonar systems. I. Microchiroptera. See Ref. 15, pp. 109–81

22. Shimozawa, T., Suga, N., Hendler, P.,

23. Simmons, J. A. 1969. Acoustic radiation patterns for the echolocating bats, *Chilonycteris rubiginosa* and *Eptesicus fuscus*. *J. Acoust. Soc. Am.* 46:1054–56

24. Simmons, J. A. 1973. The resolution of target range by echolocating bats. *J. Acoust. Soc. Am.* 54:157–73

25. Simmons, J. A. 1979. Perception of echo phase information in bat sonar. *Science* 204:1336–38

26. Simmons, J. A. 1980. The processing of sonar echoes by bats. See Ref. 15, pp. 695–714

27. Simmons, J. A., Fenton, M. B., O'Farrell, M. J. 1979. Echolocation and pursuit of prey by bats. *Science* 203:16–21

28. Simmons, J. A., Howell, D. J., Suga, N. 1975. Information content of bat sonar echoes. *Am. Sci.* 63:204–15

29. Simmons, J. A., Kick, S. A. 1983. Interception of flying insects by bats. See Ref. 20. In press

30. Simmons, J. A., Kick, S. A., Lawrence, B. D., Hale, C., Bard, C., Escudié, B. 1983. Acuity of horizontal angle discrimination by the echolocating bat, *Eptesicus fuscus*. *J. Comp. Physiol.* In press

31. Simmons, J. A., Lavender, W. A., Lavender, B. A., Doroshow, C. F., Kiefer, S. W., et al. 1974. Target structure and echo spectral discrimination by echolocating bats. *Science* 186:1130–32

32. Simmons, J. A., Stein, R. A. 1980. Acoustic imaging in bat sonar: echolocation signals and the evolution of echolocation. *J. Comp. Physiol.* 135:61–84

33. Suga, N. 1970. Echo-ranging neurons in the inferior colliculus of bats. *Science* 170:449–52

34. Suga, N. 1973. Feature extraction in the auditory system of bats. In *Basic Mechanisms in Hearing*, ed. A. Møller, pp. 675–744. New York: Academic. 941 pp.

35. Suga, N., Jen, P.H.-S. 1975. Peripheral control of acoustic signals in the auditory system of echolocating bats. *J. Exp. Biol.* 62:277–311

36. Suga, N., Shimozawa, T. 1974. Site of neural attenuation of responses to self-vocalized sounds in echolocating bats. *Science* 183:1211–13

37. Webster, J. A. 1967. Some acoustical differences between bats and men. In *International Conference on Sensory Devices for the Blind*, pp. 63–87. London: St. Dunstans

38. Webster, F. A., Griffin, D. R. 1962. The role of the flight membrane in insect capture by bats. *Anim. Behav.* 10:332–40

RESPIRATORY
PHYSIOLOGY

Introduction, Robert E. Forster, II, *Section Editor*[1]

The reviews in this section on the development of the lungs and regulation of pulmonary ventilation in the fetus and newborn give an extensive overview of our present knowledge in this field and provide background for possible causes of the abnormalities of pulmonary ventilation seen in this age group.

The first paper, by Burri, outlines the morphology and histological development of the lung, starting with the embryological stage, through the fetal stage and into postnatal development. This discussion is supplemented by helpful diagrams.

Haddad & Mellins initiate the general discussion of the difference in ventilatory control among the fetus, neonate, and adult. Although an increase in inspired P_{CO_2} generally increases ventilation in all, albeit more strongly in the more adult, the companion stimulus of a decrease in inspired P_{O_2} inhibits fetal respiratory movements, produces a biphasic increase followed by a decrease in minute ventilation in the newborn, and does not reach the normal adult response for some weeks after birth. Increasing maturity is accompanied by increasing hyperventilation with hypoxia. The authors have assembled interesting observations on the occurrence of apnea in the newborn.

Harding discusses the generally neglected importance of the larynx and its control in respiration, including both the alteration in its airflow resistance that

[1]Annual Reviews expresses appreciation to former Section Editor Alfred P. Fishman, who planned this section.

can be produced by nervous control and the afferent nervous outflow it sends to the central respiratory center. It appears to increase its resistance during expiration, even in utero, possibly to regulate lung volume. Rigatto reviews in increased detail control of respiration from the fetus to the neonate. (Barcroft's idea that the respiratory system is functional in utero, but inhibited by the central nervous system, seems quite consistent with many modern findings.) Read & Henderson-Smart discuss our knowledge about the influence of behavior on the regulation of respiration in the newborn, particularly the different types of sleep, rapid eye movement (REM) sleep and quiet sleep (nonREM). All apnea is not produced by central inhibition: some arises from airway obstruction, possibly under nervous control. Walker reviews in detail the present knowledge of the development of responses of the peripheral and central chemoreceptors. He points out that although changes in central nervous system activity may explain the increased performance of chemoreflexes in the control of ventilation as the fetus matures, the performance of the peripheral chemoreceptors themselves has not been adequately studied.

The reader is left with the impression that our scientific information in this field, which provides the underpinning for important topics of clinical care, may need more experimental observation to answer key points.

Ann. Rev. Physiol. 1984. 46:617–28

FETAL AND POSTNATAL DEVELOPMENT OF THE LUNG

Peter H. Burri

Section of Developmental Biology, Institute of Anatomy, University of Berne, CH-3000 Berne, Switzerland

INTRODUCTION

In perinatal health care, respiratory distress (RDS) is a frequent life-threatening condition. The syndrome is due to a functional immaturity of the pulmonary surfactant. Our increasing understanding of the pathophysiological mechanisms of RDS and the possibility of preventive therapeutic action have engendered a large number of excellent articles and monographs on the perinatal development of the surfactant system with emphasis on the metabolic maturation of the lung (6, 21–23, 26, 29, 30, 37). Therefore the aim of this article will be to describe particularly the *morphology* of lung development, stressing the fact that the pulmonary structure is still immature at birth.

FETAL LUNG DEVELOPMENT

Human lung development can be subdivided into three chronological periods (Figure 1): an early embryonic period, during which most organs are laid down; a fetal period proper; and a postnatal period, during which the lung matures to the adult form. The fetal period proper is further subdivided into three phases. Called the pseudoglandular, canalicular, and saccular, these names respectively describe the actual morphology of the prospective airways and airspaces. The processes of differentiation during these periods proceed from center to periphery of the lung asynchronously between lobes (33, 34, 39). It is therefore not surprising that there is overlap between the developmental stages, and that, depending on the investigator, the time-table of these steps can slightly differ.

617

0066-4278/84/0315-0617$02.00

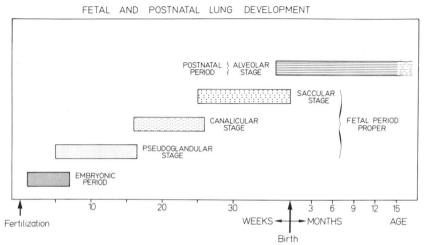

Figure 1 Phases and timing of human lung development.

Embryonic Development of the Lung

The first 5–7 weeks after fertilization[1] correspond to the period of organ development. After the formation of the primitive gut, the lung appears towards the end of the fourth week as a ventral bud of the prospective esophagus (Figure 2). The epithelial components of the lung are hence derived from the endoderm, and the enveloping connective tissue from the mesodermal germ layer. As the bud separates distally from the gut by a deepening, followed by a fusion of the laryngotracheal grooves, it rapidly grows into the surrounding mesenchyme by successive dichotomous divisions. By the end of the sixth week the lobar and segmental portions of the airway tree (and by the end of the seventh week the subsegmental portions) are preformed as tubes of high columnar epithelium. The branching pattern corresponds to the one found later in the corresponding conductive airways. Simultaneously with these early stages of pulmonary organogenesis the development of vascular connections occurs. The pulmonary arteries bud off from the sixth pair of aortic arches and grow down into the mesenchyme, surrounding the lung tubules where they form a vascular plexus. First, this plexus is connected only to systemic veins draining the blood from the proximal gut and the developing trachea. Soon the capillaries also become connected to the pulmonary veins, the main stem of which has grown out as a small tubule from the atrial portion of the heart. During further development the pulmonary vein stem and its first two order branches are incorporated into the left atrium, resulting in four distinct lung veins opening into the left auricle. At the end of seven weeks the lung resembles a small tubulo-acinar gland, giving the ensuing pseudoglandular stage its name.

[1]Dating is based on the time point of ovulation.

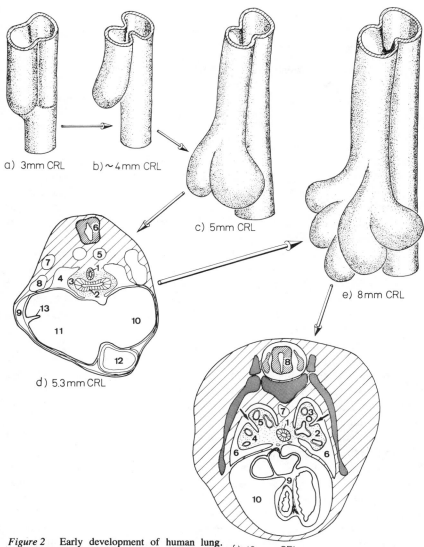

Figure 2 Early development of human lung. Budding of lung primordium from the prospective f) 18mm CRL
esophagus. CRL = Crown Rump Length. CRL of 3 to 5.3 mm correspond to a fetal age of 24–28 days; 8 mm CRL corresponds to ~ 4.5 weeks. (*a*), (*b*), (*c*), and (*e*) represent the epithelial tube formed as a diverticulum from the foregut by deepening of the laryngotracheal grooves. After joining each other the grooves will completely separate the trachea from the esophagus. The tubular sprouts grow into the surrounding mesenchyme, as seen in (*d*) and (*f*), transverse sections of the fetus. (*d*) Age 28 days—1: esophagus; 2: left and right lung buds with tracheal bifurcation; 3: lung mesenchyme; 4: pericardioperitoneal canal; 5: dorsal aorta; 6: neural tube; 7: postcardinal vein; 8: common cardinal vein; 9: pericardial cavity; 10: left atrium; 11: right atrium; 12: conus cordis; 13: right venous valve. (*f*) Age ~ 46 days—1: esophagus; 2: left upper lobe; 3 & 5: lower lobes; 4: middle lobe; 6: pleural cavity; 7: aorta; 8: neural tube; 9: heart; 10: pericardial cavity. Arrows point to oblique fissures. *Figures (d) and (f) drawn after Ref. 24*.

Fetal Period Proper

Following the early organogenetic development, the lung goes through three successive morphologically defined phases to reach, with birth, a stage of functional maturity. Although allowing the organism to survive, this still does not correspond to a state of structural maturity.

1. PSEUDOGLANDULAR STAGE (5–17 WEEKS)   The events of this stage are best described by its two most important outcomes: the formation of all the prospective conductive airways and the appearance of the acinar outlines (8). These outcomes are achieved through a continuous growth and branching process at the outermost periphery of the epithelial tubes (Figure 3a). From experimental data we know that epithelio-mesenchymal interactions play a determining role in regulating growth and branching pattern. Not only have intimate cell contacts between the epithelium and the mesenchymal cells been demonstrated (7), but elegant transplantation experiments have shown that the mesenchyme is directly responsible for a new budding of the epithelial tube. If mesenchyme was removed from the tip of a sprouting tube, further branching was prevented; if on the other hand the removed mesenchyme was placed alongside of a lower order tube, new outgrowth was locally induced (4, 42, 47). Further experimental evidence showed that the presence of collagen was needed for branching (41) and that the amount of mesenchyme influenced the differentiation of the epithelium (35). The observation made by Schneeberger that the epithelial cells in sheep are interconnected with each other by gap junctions indicates that electrical coupling may be responsible for the regulation of cellular differentiation (39). Nexus are present from the early stages of development until the differentiation into type I and type II alveolar cells had occurred in the periphery. Interestingly, the epithelium was also found to form a functionally tight barrier from the very beginning: tight junctions were present as early as they were looked for, at gestational day 69 in sheep (39).

During the pseudoglandular stage the airway tubes are lined proximally by a high columnar and distally by a cuboidal epithelium. Differentiation of the airway wall occurs in a centrifugal direction, so that typical ciliated, nonciliated, goblet, and basal cells appear first in the proximal airways. Cartilage and smooth muscle cells are found in the trachea early in this stage; by the 12th week these tissues extend as far as the segmental bronchi. At this time mucous glands are also present. They have formed as solid sprouts from the epithelial layer and become subsequently canalized; secretory activity was found at 14 weeks gestation in the trachea (11). As may be expected by the close relationship between the airways and the arterial pathways, the accompanying arterial branches are laid down during this phase (28). Because there is only minimal blood flow through these vessels, however, they all remain small and rather inconspicuous.

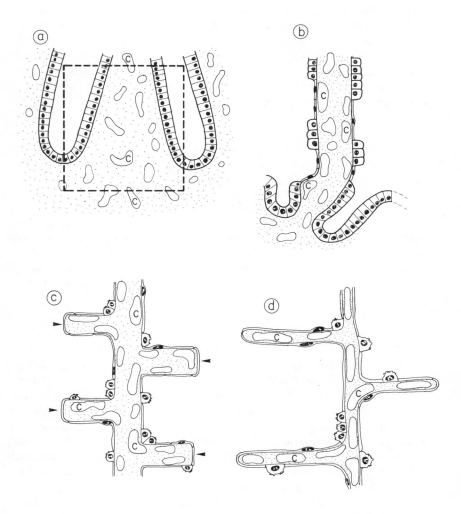

Figure 3 Fetal and postnatal development of lung parenchyma. (*a*) Pseudoglandular stage: epithelial tubes push into the mesenchyme, which contains a loose capillary network (c). (*b*) Further development of structures in frame of Figure 3*a*. Intervening mesenchyme is reduced; capillaries (c) arrange around epithelial tubes. At sites of epithelio-capillary contacts, thin air-blood barrier portions develop. Formation of type I and type II pneumocytes. In the periphery, the cuboidal epithelium still allows for further growth and branching. (*c*) Perinatally secondary septa are developing (arrow heads) from primary septa. All septa are of the primitive type, containing a double capillary network (c) and a central layer of connective tissue. (*d*) Mature lung. Interalveolar septa contain a single capillary network (c) meandering through the interstitium.

Towards the end of the pseudoglandular stage the most peripheral tubules, together with their surrounding tissue, represent the future acini of the gas exchanging parenchyma, as has been shown by the sequential reconstruction studies of Boyden (8). Immunofluorescent investigations, which permit identification of the precursors of type II pneumocytes at the corresponding stage in mice, agree with the above interpretation (43). Thus, all the preacinar airways, as well as the arteries and veins, are present in a pattern corresponding to that of adult age.

2. CANALICULAR STAGE (17–26 WEEKS)   The canalicular stage encompasses the early development of the pulmonary parenchyma. At the end of week 17 we find the newly delineated acinus composed of a stem tubule, the prospective terminal bronchiole, 2–4 future respiratory bronchioles, and some small clusters of short tubules and buds. The acinar borders can be recognized because of a rarefaction of the mesenchymal envelope, visualized by a lighter rim around such a unit. In the subsequent weeks the originally compact clusters grow by further peripheral branching, by lengthening of each tubular branch, and, last but not least, by a marked widening of the distal airspaces at the expense of the intervening mesenchyme (Figures 3a and 3b). It is therefore appropriate to define these new airways (about three orders of branching) as canaliculi. This peripheral growth is accompanied by an increase in capillarization. The capillaries, which previously formed a loose network within the mesenchyme, begin to arrange themselves around the airspaces, subsequently establishing in many places a close contact with the overlying cuboidal epithelium. These contact points are the sites where the epithelial cells decrease in height, develop attenuated cytoplasmic processes, and become invisible (except for the perinuclear region) in the light microscope: we witness the formation of the first thin air-blood barrier portions (Figure 3b). The close apposition of capillaries to the epithelium and the epithelial flattening are intimately related phenomena. It is still unclear which of the two processes induces the other. The formation of thin air-blood barriers starts peripherally but does not involve the terminal segment of the last tubule branch, because the undifferentiated or cuboidal epithelium is needed for further growth and branching (Figure 3b). Electron microscopic investigations of serially sectioned epithelial cells demonstrated that the reliable criterion to ascertain the forthcoming differentiation into type I pneumocytes was the formation of a cytoplasmic attenuation (36) and not the lack of lamellar bodies. Indeed, it seems that before differentiation most cells contain lamellar bodies independently of their destiny. There is good evidence that type II cells, or, more cautiously expressed, "cells containing lamellar bodies," can incorporate tritiated thymidine, divide, loose their granules, and transform to type I cells (2, 31, 32). The same sequence was observed in adult lungs after damaging the alveolar epithelium (1, 14, 20). It is therefore

accepted today that the secretory Type II cells of the alveolar wall are also the stem cells of the alveolar epithelium. Interestingly, it appears that the secretory cell type of the bronchioles (Clara cells) also represents the progenitor cells of the bronchiolar epithelium (19).

With type I cell differentiation, glycogen-rich cuboidal cells develop an increasing amount of lamellar bodies. These bodies represent the intracellular storage form of the surface active material (25) present shortly thereafter in the prospective airspaces. In man, lamellar bodies appear during the sixth month of pregnancy, i.e. $\sim$ 60% of the gestation duration, and the process then propagates slowly through the parenchyma. In most mammals investigated, however, surfactant production starts later, at 80–85% of gestation time, but then usually spreads more rapidly.

3. SACCULAR STAGE (24th WEEK TO BIRTH)   At the beginning of this stage the airways end in clusters of relatively thin-walled terminal saccules. This structure was the reason for calling this phase saccular, or the terminal sac stage. These saccules produce by term the last generations of airways: some further prospective alveolar ducts and, at the outermost periphery, the alveolar sacs. This developmental sequence means that each branch of this pathway, with the exception of the last branch, goes through the stages of being a saccule, then a smooth-walled channel, and after birth, when alveoli have formed, a typical alveolar duct. In view of the highly changeable morphology of these structures, I propose to affix them with the term "transitory." The saccules present at any time until birth shall be called *transitory* saccules: they are transformed by further distal growth and division into *transitory* ducts, and eventually, after alveolization, into definitive alveolar ducts.

The tremendous expansion of the prospective respiratory airspaces during the saccular period leads to a marked decrease in interstitial tissue, which has important consequences for the capillary arrangement. The capillary networks surrounding the airspaces provide a kind of mantle around each airway channel and form a capillary bilayer in the intersaccular septa as the airspaces approach each other (Figures 3b and c). Compared to the mature lung, the capillaries are embedded in a broad interstitial layer that is very cellular but has a low content of extracellular fibers. Soon, however, elastin is deposited underneath the epithelium in bays of interstitial cells. Elastin formation plays an important role in the further morphological development of the lung as the initiating step for alveolar formation (17). As a consequence, shortly before birth the pulmonary parenchyma is prepared for the last developmental step, the postnatal alveolization.

After the formation of the type I and type II pneumocytes in the previous stage, increasing amounts of tubular myelin in the airspaces hint at the growing secretory activity of the type II cells. Tubular myelin has been shown to form directly from lamellar bodies and is considered to correspond to the reserve pool of surface-active material (38). Clearly, with the development and maturation of the surfactant system during the saccular stage, the chances of the human fetus to survive, when born prematurely, increase with every day.

During both the canalicular and the saccular stages, the blood vessels grow in length and diameter. Along with the expansion of the prospective respiratory tissue, new arterial and venous vessels are formed. From caliper measurements on arteriograms of lungs at various fetal and postnatal ages, it appears that the diameter of a vessel is dependent on its distance from the capillary bed (28). Practically, in an early fetal lung a vessel will supply a relatively large portion of a lung lobe, whereas as the lung grows an artery of comparable size will irrigate a progressively smaller area. In later fetal life proximal arteries are of the elastic type as in adults; more distally they are muscular, but further out only partially muscular (spiral muscular tract). Unfortunately, there is no *precise* relationship between wall structure and vessel diameter, since transitions between vessel types occur at various levels depending on the branching pathway (28).

POSTNATAL LUNG DEVELOPMENT

At birth the lung of most mammals investigated is structurally far from being just a miniaturized version of the adult lung. Whereas the number of airway generations is complete at birth and their branching pattern is definitively established, the morphology of the pulmonary parenchyma transforms greatly within the subsequent months to years. Indeed, in man more than 90% of all alveoli are formed after birth. If the adult human lung has on average 300 million alveoli (46), less than 20 million are counted in the newborn lung (15) and even this number is controversial (8). Besides the problem of defining an alveolus *in statu nascendi* (corresponding to a shallow depression), counting alveoli is a very difficult undertaking in two dimensional sections and is therefore subject to great error (27). Alveolar formation has been investigated morphologically in a number of mammals (3, 5, 9, 12, 13, 16, 40). Our own investigations performed in the rat have established the sequence of structural transformations leading to the formation of the alveoli (12, 13). At birth the pulmonary parenchyma of the rat consists of smoothly contoured transitory ducts and saccules (Figure 4a). The walls of these airspaces, called primary septa, are relatively thick and characteristically contain a capillary network on each side of a central sheet of connective tissue (Figure 3c). Within the first postnatal week (probably under the influence of elastic fiber formation), the bulging of new so-called secondary septa can be observed. These septa incompletely partition the originally smooth channels and saccules, transforming them into alveolar ducts and sacs and thus giving birth to the alveoli (Figures 4 and 5). By this process the alveolar surface area increases sharply, as morphometric studies showed (13). The primary septa and the newly added secondary ones, however, do still not resemble the adult interalveolar septa. They are still thick and exhibit the double capillary network (Figure 3c). In the rat, these primitive septa are transformed into the slender mature form within the next two weeks by a process which is still not fully understood. From the observation of the continuous reduction of the intersitial tissue between the airspaces (Figure 3), one may assume that the process of capillary apposition finds an end during postnatal development with the fusion of the two septal capillary networks. Simultaneously the interalveolar septa greatly increase in height, giving the alveoli their classical appearance. The reduction of the interstitial compartment observed during these events is probably also at the origin of the formation of the pores of Kohn. In mice, where postnatal lung development closely matches the description in the rat, the pores of Kohn appear after the second week.

According to Boyden & Tompsett (9, 10), there seems to be an additional mechanism of alveolar formation. Counting the generations of conductive airways, they noticed a decrease in number during late fetal and early postnatal life. From this observation they concluded that the gas exchange region

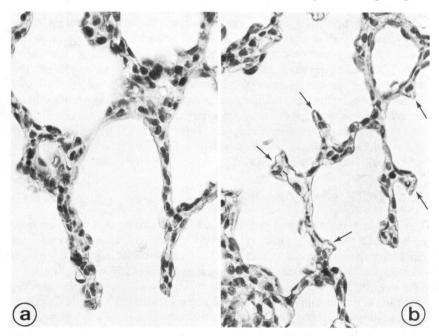

Figure 4   (*a*) Rat lung, age 4 days. Parenchyma contains smooth primary septa that delineates channels and saccules. Magnification 425 ×.(*b*) Rat lung, age 7 days, at same magnification: secondary septa (arrows) have formed, subdividing the airspaces into alveoli.

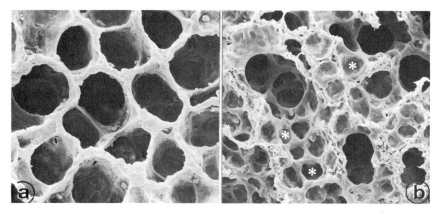

Figure 5   Demonstration of postnatal alveolar formation in rat lung by scanning electron microscopy. Magnification 230 ×.(*a*) Age 4 days: large and smoothly contoured airspaces.(*b*) Age 8 days:
crests and ridges have appeared (secondary septa), delineating shallow alveoli (asterisks).

extended centripetally, resulting in the transformation of respiratory bronchioles into alveolar ducts and of terminal bronchioles into respiratory ones.

So far no systematic ultrastructural and morphometric studies have been
performed on the child's lung, so we lack precise information about the mode
of alveolar formation and about an eventual capillary remodeling in man. In
view of the congruent observations in different animal species, it is probably
justified to assume, as has been done tacitly in recent reviews (44, 45), that the
human lung undergoes the same postnatal changes. On the other hand, we still
do not know how far into childhood the period of alveolar formation extends.
From alveolar counting it has been postulated that new alveoli are added up to
the age of 8 years (18). In view of the great variability of the alveolar counts and
of our own morphological observations it would appear that alveolar formation
is likely to be completed much earlier, maybe as early as 1–2 years.

SUMMARY

The life of a human lung can be subdivided into five distinct phases:
embryonic, pseudoglandular, canalicular, saccular, and alveolar. The
embryonic period, during which the lung primordium is laid down as a
diverticulum of the foregut, lasts for about seven weeks. From the 5th to the
17th week the lung looks much like a tubulo-acinar gland, with epithelial tubes
sprouting and branching into the surrounding mesenchyme. In the last week of
this pseudoglandular stage the prospective conductive airways have been
formed, and the acinar limits can be recognized. The events of the subsequent
canalicular phase (17th–26th week) can be summarized as the widening of the

peripheral tubules, the differentiation of the cuboidal epithelium into type I and type II cells, the formation of the first thin air-blood barriers, and the start of surfactant production. During the saccular stage, which follows and lasts until birth, the growth of the pulmonary parenchyma, the thinning of the connective tissue between the airspaces, and the further maturation of the surfactant system are the most important steps towards life. At birth, although already functional, the lung is structurally still in an immature condition, because alveoli, the gas exchange units of the adult lung, are practically missing. The airspaces present are smooth-walled transitory ducts and saccules with primitive type septa that are thick and contain a double capillary network. During the first 1–3 years of postnatal life, alveoli are formed through a septation process that greatly increases the gas exchange surface area. The primitive septa with their capillaries undergo a complete remodeling, gaining the mature slender morphology found in the adult lung.

ACKNOWLEDGMENTS

The author thanks Dr. Kevin Conley for critically reading the manuscript and Ms. R. M. Fankhauser for typing the text. He is grateful to Mr. Karl Babl for technical assistance. This work was supported by grant No. 3.129–0.81 of the Swiss National Science Foundation.

Literature Cited

1. Adamson, I. Y. R., Bowden, D. H. 1974. The type 2 cell as progenitor of alveolar epithelial regeneration. A cytodynamic study in mice after exposure to oxygen. *Lab. Invest.* 30:35–42

2. Adamson, I. Y. R., Bowden, D. H. 1975. Derivation of type I epithelium from type 2 cells in the developing rat lung. *Lab. Invest.* 32:736–45

3. Alcorn, D. G., Adamson, T. M., Maloney, J. E., Robinson, P. M. 1981. A morphologic and morphometric analysis of fetal lung development in the sheep *Anat. Rec.* 201:655–67

4. Alescio, T., Cassini, A. 1962. Induction *in vitro* of tracheal buds by pulmonary mesenchyme grafted on tracheal epithelium. *J. Exp. Zool.* 150:83–94

5. Amy, R. W. M., Bowes, D., Burri, P. H., Haines, J., Thurlbeck, W. M. 1977. Postnatal growth of the mouse lung. *J. Anat.* 124:131–51

6. Ballard, P. L. 1977. Glucocorticoid receptors in the fetal lung. See Ref. 30, pp. 419–42

7. Bluemink, J. G., van Maurik, P., Lawson, K. A. 1976. Intimate cell contacts at the epithelial/mesenchymal interface in embryonic mouse lung. *J. Ultrastr. Res.* 55:257–70

8. Boyden, E. A. 1977. Development and growth of the airways. See Ref. 30, pp. 3–35

9. Boyden, E. A., Tompsett, D. H. 1961. The postnatal growth of the lung in the dog. *Acta Anat.* 47:185–215

10. Boyden, E. A., Tompsett, D. H. 1965. The changing patterns in the developing lungs of infants. *Acta Anat.* 61:164–92

11. Bucher, U., Reid, L. 1961. Development of the mucus-secreting elements in human lung. *Thorax* 16:219–25

12. Burri, P. H. 1974. The postnatal growth of the rat lung. III. Morphology. *Anat. Rec.* 180:77–98

13. Burri, P. H., Dbaly, J., Weibel, E. R. 1974. The postnatal growth of the rat lung. I. Morphometry. *Anat. Rec.* 178:711–30

14. Crapo, J. D., Barry, B. E., Foscue, H. A., Shelburne, J. 1980. Structural and biochemical changes in rat lungs occurring during exposures to lethal and adaptive doses of oxygen. *Am. Rev. Respir. Dis.* 122:123–43

15. Davies, G., Reid, L. 1970. Growth of the alveoli and pulmonary arteries in childhood. *Thorax* 25:669–81

16. Dingler, E. C. 1958. Wachstum der

Lunge nach der Geburt. *Acta Anat.* 32: 1–86

17. Dubreuil, G., Lacoste, A., Raymond, R. 1936. Observations sur le développement du poumon humain. *Bull. Histol. Appl. Phys.* 13:235–45

18. Dunnill, M. S. 1962. Postnatal growth of the lung. *Thorax* 17:329–33

19. Evans, M. J., Cabral-Anderson, L. J., Freeman, G. 1978. Role of the Clara cell in renewal of the bronchiolar epithelium. *Lab. Invest.* 38:648–55

20. Evans, M. J., Cabral, L. J., Stephens, R. J., Freeman, G. 1975. Transformation of alveolar type II cells to type I cells following exposure to NO_2. *Exp. Mol. Pathol.* 22:142–50

21. Farrell, P. M., ed. 1982. *Lung Development: Biological and Clinical Perspectives*, Vols. 1, 2. New York: Academic. 407 pp., 307 pp

22. Farrell, P. M., Hamosh, M. 1978. The biochemistry of fetal lung development. *Clin. Perinatol.* 5:197–229

23. Farrell, P. M., Morgan, T. E. 1977. Lecithin biosynthesis in the developing lung. See Ref. 30, pp. 307–47

24. Gasser, R. F. 1975. *Atlas of Human Embryos*, p. 79, 215. New York: Harper & Row. 318 pp.

25. Gil, J., Reiss, O. K. 1973. Isolation and characterization of lamellar bodies and tubular myelin from rat lung homogenates. *J. Cell Biol.* 58:152–71

26. Hallman, M., Teramo, K., Kankaanpää, K., Kulovich, M. V., Gluck, L. 1980. Prevention of respiratory distress syndrome: Current view of fetal lung maturity studies. *Ann. Clin. Res.* 12:36–44

27. Hansen, J. E., Ampaya, E. P. 1974. Lung morphometry: a fallacy in the use of the counting principle *J. Appl. Physiol.* 37:951–54

28. Hislop, A., Reid, L. 1981. Growth and development of the respiratory system— Anatomical development. In *Scientific Foundations of Paediatrics*, ed. J. A. Davies, J. Dobbing, pp. 390–432. London: William Heinemann. 2nd ed.

29. Hitchcock, K. R. 1980. Lung development and the pulmonary surfactant system: Hormonal influences. *Anat. Rec.* 198:13–34

30. Hodson, W. A., ed. 1977. *Development of the Lung: Lung Biology in Health and Disease*, Vol. 6. New York: Dekker. 646 pp.

31. Kauffmann, S. L. 1980. Cell proliferation in the mammalian lung. *Int. Rev. Exp. Pathol.* 22:131–91

32. Kauffmann, S. L., Burri, P. H., Weibel, E. R. 1974. The postnatal growth of the rat lung. II. Autoradiography. *Anat. Rec.* 180:63–76

33. Kikkawa, Y., Kaibara, M., Motoyama, E. K., Orzalesi, M. M., Cook, C. D. 1971. Morphologic development of fetal rabbit lung and its acceleration with cortisol. *Am. J. Pathol.* 64:423–42

34. Kotas, R. V., Farrell, P. M., Ulane, R. E., Chez, R. A. 1977. Fetal rhesus monkey lung development: Lobar differences and discordances between stability and distensibility. *J. Appl. Physiol.* 43: 92–98

35. Master, J. R. W. 1976. Epithelial-mesenchymal interaction during lung development: The effect of mesenchymal mass. *Dev. Biol.* 51:98–108

36. Mercurio, A. R., Rhodin, J. A. G. 1976. An electron microscopic study on the type I pneumocyte in the cat: Differentiation. *Am. J. Anat.* 146:255–72

37. Perelman, R. H., Engle, M., Farrell, P. 1981. Perspectives on fetal lung development. *Lung* 159:53–80

38. Sanders, R. L., Hassett, R. J., Vatter, A. E. 1980. Isolation of lung lamellar bodies and their conversion to tubular myelin figures *in vitro. Anat. Rec.* 198:485–501

39. Schneeberger, E. E. 1979. Barrier function of intercellular junctions in adult fetal lungs. In *Pulmonary Edema*, ed. A. P. Fishmann, E. Renkin, pp. 21–37. Bethesda: Am. Physiol. Soc.

40. Short, R. H. D. 1950. Alveolar epithelium in relation to growth of the lung. *Phil. Trans. R. Soc. London Biol.* 235: 35–87

41. Spooner, B. S., Faubion, J. M. 1980. Collagen involvement in branching morphogenesis of embryonic lung and salivary gland. *Dev. Biol.* 77:84–102

42. Spooner, B. S., Wessells, N. K. 1970. Mammalian lung development: Interactions in primordium formation and bronchial morphogenesis. *J. Exp. Zool.* 175: 445–54

43. Ten Have-Opbroek, A. A. W. 1981. The development of the lung in mammals: An analysis of concepts and findings. *Am J. Anatomy* 162:201–19

44. Thurlbeck, W. M. 1975. Postnatal growth and development of the lung. *Am. Rev. Respir. Dis.* 111:803–44

45. Thurlbeck, W. M. 1977. Structure of the lungs. In *Respiratory Physiology II: International Review of Physiology*, ed. J. G. Widdicombe, 14:1–36. Baltimore: University Park Press. 321 pp.

46. Weibel, E. R. 1963. *Morphometry of the Human Lung.* Berlin/Göttingen/Heidelberg: Springer. 151 pp.

47. Wessells, N. K. 1970. Mammalian lung development: Interactions in formation and morphogenesis of tracheal buds. *J. Exp. Zool.* 175:455–66

Ann. Rev. Physiol. 1984. 46:629–43

HYPOXIA AND RESPIRATORY CONTROL IN EARLY LIFE

Gabriel G. Haddad and Robert B. Mellins

Department of Pediatrics (Pulmonary Division), Columbia University, College of Physicians and Surgeons, New York, New York 10032

INTRODUCTION

Available data on the response to respiratory stimuli in the fetus, newborn infant, and adult (human or animal) suggest that the mechanisms that control the respiratory function of the lung develop well before birth (9–11, 13, 14, 33, 71). For example, there is little doubt that fetal breathing movements exist in utero (10, 13, 33, 71). However, the fetal breathing pattern is typically episodic and is characterized by long silent periods, lasting minutes to hours, during which there are no respiratory movements (10, 33). Once separated from the placenta and delivered into a world of intense sensory stimulation, however, the newborn infant breathes continuously—but often in an irregular pattern, especially if preterm. This contrasts with the more regular pattern of breathing in the adult.

That the respiratory control system is not fully mature at birth is evident from the immaturity of the various components of this control system, including the neurophysiologic, metabolic, and mechanical components (4, 19, 20, 37, 48, 51). One important result of the immaturity of this control system is that the newborn is prone to wide and rapid fluctuations in arterial partial pressure of oxygen (PaO_2) and the development of hypoxemia (45). There are several critical features of this system with regard to the control of PaO_2. First, there are relatively small O_2 stores in the lungs of premature or full-term newborn infants compared to the large amount of O_2 they consume per body weight (19, 52). Second, the immaturity of the central nervous system and more specifically the lack of excitatory axo-dendritic synapses (82) as well as the immaturity of the peripheral chemoreceptors (carotid bodies) (4, 21, 58, 75) increase the susceptibility of the very young to develop long respiratory pauses or apneic spells.

629

0066-4278/84/0315-0629$02.00

During such respiratory pauses, not only is O_2 consumed without replenishment but the functional residual capacity (FRC) of the lungs is decreased—further reducing the O_2 stores (19). Third, the decreased elastic recoil of the lung and chest wall in newborn infants can lead to closure of airways during normal tidal breathing and impairment of gas exchange (19).

If the very young are susceptible to hypoxemia, especially during sleep (45), one may ask whether premature and full-term infants (*a*) sense low O_2 tensions, (*b*) respond to these low tensions, and (*c*) if so, how, and what mechanisms are operative in the young? In this chapter, we examine the ventilatory response to hypoxia and the interaction between ventilation and metabolic rate during hypoxia in early life. Respiratory muscle fatigue and the ability of the newborn to sustain respiratory loads during hypoxia are also reviewed in the light of new findings. In addition, the relation between hypoxia, sleep, and arousal responses is discussed. Possible neurotransmitters or modulators of hypoxic responses is described briefly. Finally, the clinical implications and future directions for research in this area are presented.

VENTILATORY RESPONSE TO HYPOXIA

Two kinds of studies have been performed. The first consists of examining the response to hypoxia immediately after either a step function or progressive decrease in inhaled O_2 concentration, usually over a period of a few minutes (75). We term this transient ventilatory response to hypoxia. In the seond type of study, a continuous steady level of hypoxia is imposed and the response evaluated is the one occurring *after* the initial transient response (42). We term this steady-state ventilatory response to hypoxia.

The transient ventilatory response to hypoxia is a good illustration of how the response to a respiratory stimulus matures from fetal to adult life. Although the fetus stops initiating respiratory movements when arterial PO_2 is lowered (9, 89), the adult has a brisk increase in ventilation that levels off after several minutes (56, 76, 80). The newborn infant's response to a reduction in inspired O_2 concentration, however, is different from those of the fetus and adult. Cross et al (29) and subsequently Brady et al (16) and Rigatto et al (75, 76, 80) describe the newborn infant's response to hypoxia as biphasic since it consists of an initial increase in minute ventilation (V) followed by a return of V to baseline and, in most instances, by a decrease in V below normoxic baseline levels. The initial increase in V in response to hypoxia results from an increase in both tidal volume and respiratory frequency, while the subsequent decrease is brought about mainly by a decrease in respiratory frequency and an increase in respiratory pauses (75, 76).

All infants, preterm or full term, exhibit this biphasic response when challenged with hypoxia in the early neonatal period (16, 29, 75, 76, 80). Full term infants begin to show sustained hyperventilation in response to hypoxia after 1–2 weeks of age (76) and preterm infants after the first month of postnatal life (75, 76). That the preterm infant shows a progressively larger initial positive response (increase in V) with age has suggested to some investigators that the peripheral chemoreceptors mature postnatally (76). However, part of this increase in ventilation may result from maturational changes in respiratory mechanics, e.g. increase in lung compliance or decrease in airway resistance (19, 84).

Although many investigators have described the ventilatory response to hypoxia in newborn infants as biphasic, the term may be misleading. If "biphasic" implies a two-phase response, this is not unique to any age group. In fact, adults as well as infants show a biphasic response (35, 56, 75, 76, 80). There are two main differences, however, between the responses of infants and adults: (a) after the initial increase, ventilation starts to decline at a much earlier time in the young than in the adult; and (b) ventilation is usually reduced to levels that are below baseline in the newborn infant but rarely descend below baseline in the adult (56, 76). In addition, there is no consensus that the transient ventilatory response to hypoxia in the newborn infant is simply biphasic. Cotton & Grunstein (28), studying human infants (at high altitude), have shown that the infant response to hypoxia is made up of three phases. The immediate phase after the institution of hypoxia is actually a decrease (Phase 1) rather than an increase in V. This is followed by a transient increase (Phase 2) and then a sustained decrease in V (Phase 3). Whether this "triphasic" response in the newborn infant only occurs at high altitude or is a reflection of the high-resolution method of analysis used by these investigators (28) is not clear. However, since an initial transient decrease in V is often present in adult animals at sea level when they are exposed to hypoxia (28), the initial decrease in V that occurs in these newborns at high altitude may not be related to altitude or age.

The mechanisms responsible for the decrease in V (latter part of the biphasic response or Phase 3 of the triphasic response) are not well understood. However, recent human and animal studies suggest at least three possibilities. First, the fall in ventilation in early life may be related to a change in pulmonary mechanics induced by hypoxia (94, 95). Thus, newborn monkeys show a reduction in dynamic lung compliance during the decrease in V in the first week of life but not after three weeks of life, when an increase in V is sustained in response to hypoxia (94, 95). Second, hypoxia may lead to a depression of central respiratory output as measured by phrenic neurogram (E. E. Lawson, personal communication). The cause of this central respiratory depression is not known. Third, although chemoreceptors are active in the fetus and at birth, the "synaptic contacts" (58) of the carotid sinus nerve with the central nervous system (CNS) may not be fully mature, and the hypoxic depression of the CNS overwhelms any excitatory carotid afferent impulses. This third explanation is based on the fact that newborn infants respond to hypercapnea like the adult, but their response to hypoxia is different. This suggests that the central and efferent components of the control system are active but that the afferent (sensory) limb of the carotid chemoreceptor reflex, which is an important element of the response to hypoxia, may be at the basis of the decrease in ventilation in newborn infants acutely exposed to low O_2. It is also possible that this decrease in ventilation is related to all three mechanisms occurring simultaneously.

Henderson-Smart & Read (49) and Jeffery & Read (55) examined the ventilatory response to progressive hypoxia during sleep in puppies and calves in early life. These studies showed that, like in adults (73), the response in young animals to progressive hypoxia in REM (Rapid Eye Movement) sleep was not different from that in quiet sleep. Clearly, it is difficult to compare these studies using progressive hypoxia to those investigating the effect of steady levels of hypoxia on ventilatory function, because the changes in the inhaled gas concentrations in the former are so rapid that only a very few breaths characterize a given hypoxic level.

Studies examining the steady-state ventilatory response to hypoxia and controlling for state of consciousness or sleep state have been few in number (2, 42). Recent experiments from our laboratory have shown that, during a steady level of hypoxia and with no attempt to control $PaCO_2$, puppies increased their instantaneous minute ventilation [V_t/T_{tot} (tidal volume divided by total respiratory cycle time)] in REM sleep at every age studied [14, 19, 24, and 29 days] (Figure 1) (42). In contrast, there was a decrease in V_t/T_{tot} at 14 days of age in quiet sleep. This was followed by a period with little change in V_t/T_{tot} [19 and 24 days]. At 29 days of age, however, V_t/T_{tot} increased with hypoxia in quiet sleep (42). Therefore, as puppies matured, there was a progressively greater increase in V_t/T_{tot} with hypoxia in quiet sleep. No such maturational changes occurred in REM sleep (42). Baker & McGinty showed similar results by measuring respiratory frequency in maturing kittens exposed to 10% O_2 (2). Hypoxia induced episodes of decreased breathing in quiet sleep, but the onset of REM sleep always stimulated breathing (2). Interestingly, these results in kittens and puppies suggest that REM sleep, an ontogenetically older state than quiet sleep (2), may provide a more stable environment in the young under stress. Indeed, some investigators have speculated on the benefit to the young in spending a large percentage of time in REM than in quiet sleep or wakefulness (2). On the other hand, REM sleep is associated with other phenomena that would seem to represent a biologic disadvantage for the infant: (a) The frequency of respiratory pauses is increased in the young (as well as in the adult) (8, 82); (b) The inhibition of intercostal muscles may, especially in the newborn infant, render the chest wall less stable and lead to paradoxical

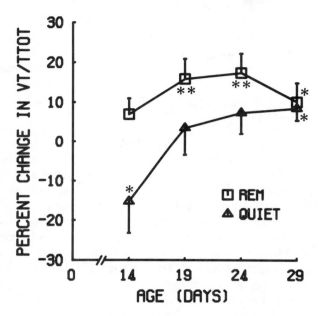

Figure 1   Instantaneous minute ventilation (V_t/T_{tot}) increased during hypoxia (percent change from baseline is plotted) in REM sleep at all ages. In quiet sleep, however, there was a decrease in V_t/T_{tot} at 14 days of age and a progressively larger increase in V_t/T_{tot} as puppies matured. Values are expressed as means ± SE. Comparisons were made between baseline measurements and those during hypoxia. Reproduced with permission from the Journal of Applied Physiology. *P<0.05.   **P<0.01.

breathing and increased work load (19, 20, 82); and (*c*) the FRC in the lungs decreases (48), thus reducing O_2 stores.

CHANGES IN METABOLIC RATE IN RESPONSE TO HYPOXIA

Another possible reason for the decrease in ventilation in response to hypoxia in the very young is a decrease in metabolic rate. Whether this is at the basis of the decrease in ventilation when the newborn is exposed to hypoxia (biphasic response) is not well understood. Indeed, there are very few studies on end-tidal CO_2, $PaCO_2$, or O_2 consumption during hypoxia at the time when ventilation is decreasing (28). At the moment, there is no clear and convincing evidence that this decrease in ventilation is a result of central respiratory depression (21), and the decrease in ventilation in response to hypoxia (latter part of the biphasic response) is not necessarily a sine qua non of hypoventilation.

When young animals are exposed to hypoxia for prolonged periods of time, however, recent longitudinal studies on puppies show that even though a decrease in ventilation occurs, $PaCO_2$ does not rise (42). On the contrary, the mean $PaCO_2$ decreases (42), suggesting a decrease in metabolic rate. Indeed, we have measured a decrease in metabolic rate in puppies in both REM and quiet sleep (17, 41). This decrease in metabolic rate during moderate hypoxia (mean $PaO_2=43$–48 mmHg) (42) in young animals contrasts with the lack of change in metabolic rate in adult animals exposed to the same hypoxic stimulus (83). A decrease in metabolic rate in adult animals does not occur until extremely low levels of PaO_2 are reached (83).

Environmental temperature has been recognized as an important variable that modulates metabolic rate in young awake animals (51, 52, 86). Experiments on awake young animals show that if the thermoneutral environment is not maintained, metabolic rate rises (51, 52, 86). During sleep, however, this may not be the case (38). When the environmental temperature falls to levels at which O_2 consumption rises during wakefulness (51, 52), metabolic rate does not change in REM sleep and increases only slightly in quiet sleep (38).

One question these studies (41, 42, 86) raise is why O_2 consumption drops in the young but not in the adult animal when exposed to moderate hypoxia. Recent results from our laboratory (unpublished observations) suggest that at a young age, animals do not increase and may even decrease their heart rate and cardiac output in response to mild to moderate hypoxia. Adult dogs, on the other hand, increase their heart rate and cardiac output when challenged with a similar level of hypoxia (44). That O_2 consumption falls in the puppy but not in the adult dog may be part of a strategy designed to protect the organism from hypoxia. To increase O_2 delivery to tissues, the adult dog increases cardiac output (44); to protect itself from hypoxia, the puppy, not being able to increase cardiac output to major organs, decreases its O_2 needs (41, 86). Whether redistribution of blood flow to major organs occurs during sleep under hypoxic conditions in the adult or in the human infant remains to be clarified.

HYPOXIA, DIAPHRAGMATIC MUSCLE FATIGUE, AND APNEA

Because of the very compliant chest wall in newborn infants, the diaphragm does not have a rigid support upon which to act. Hence, during tidal breathing and especially when large negative-pressure swings are generated, there is retraction of the rib cage (19, 20, 82). This is exaggerated in REM sleep, when there is inhibition of the intercostal muscles (19, 82). Hence, young infants generate more pressure and perform more work to move a given volume of air into the lungs than do older children and adults (20, 37). In fact, young infants have a PO.1 (mouth pressure 0.1 sec following mouth occlusion) that is similar to those of adults with chronic obstructive lung disease in acute exacerbation (37, 65, 66; J. Milic-Emili, personal communication). In addition, the time between the initiation of respiratory muscle contraction and the actual movement of air into the lungs, or the time needed to overcome the resistance and compliance of the respiratory system, is much larger as a proportion of the inspiratory duration in the newborn than in the older infant or adult (65, 66). Thus, respiratory or other disorders that shorten inspiratory duration would jeopardize ventilation and gas exchange much more in the very young than in the child or adult.

The young infant may also be at a mechanical disadvantage because of the biochemical and histologic composition of the diaphragm (57). Keens and coworkers (57) have shown that the proportion of fatiguing (fast twitch, glycolytic, type II) to fatigue-resistant (slow twitch, oxidative, type I) fibers is much higher in the young infant's diaphragm than that at a later age. While the diaphragm in the premature infant is made up of about 10% type I fibers (57), it is made up of about 55% of these fatigue-resistant fibers in the one year old, child, or adult. Very recently, however, Maxwell et al (63) have demonstrated that the premature baboon has a subtype of the type II fibers (IIc), a fatigue-resistant fiber, that develops with gestational and postnatal age into type I or type IIa fibers. This fatigue-resistant fiber type was not observed in the diaphragm of premature infants (57). It is likely that the differences between the studies of Keens et al (57) and those of Maxwell et al (63) are related to methodologic treatment of tissue samples, but difference in species may also be a factor. The latter studies (63) however, do not support the concept that the premature primate is more susceptible to diaphragmatic fatigue on the basis of muscle composition and biochemistry.

Although with considerable difficulty, diaphragmatic muscle fatigue can be induced experimentally in human volunteers (77, 78), in anesthetized animals in cardiogenic shock (1), and in unanesthetized animals (3) with inspiratory flow–resistive loads. Although type IIc fibers may exist in the diaphragm of premature infants (63), these infants may still be—although it is not proved— more susceptible to diaphragmatic muscle fatigue and respiratory failure than adult humans, on the basis of the mechanical disadvantages discussed above. It is not surprising, therefore, that at least some apneas in premature infants with lung disease (e.g. respiratory distress syndrome) have been attributed to an inability of the diaphragm to contract in the presence of central respiratory output (60, 69).

Muscle function can be further undermined if hypoxia is present (54). In adult humans, hypoxia shortens the endurance of the respiratory muscles to fatiguing-resistive loads (54). The causes for this are not fully understood, although lactic acidosis and a decreasing pH in the diaphragm are known to interfere with the ability of skeletal muscles to resynthesize or utilize ATP (32, 50, 90) and may be an important factor in shortening the endurance to loads. Although blood flow and energy sources are not believed to be limiting factors for the generation of diaphragmatic contractions under loaded conditions in the adult, stored energy fuels such as glycogen are more limited in the premature infant. This may significantly contribute to the development of muscle fatigue, especially during hypoxia.

SLEEP, HYPOXIA, AND AROUSAL RESPONSE

Although adult animals and humans respond to hypoxia during sleep by increasing ventilation (56) and cardiac output (44), presumably to preserve O_2 delivery to tissues, they also respond by arousing from sleep (5, 15, 70, 73). This is especially important for patients with parenchymal lung disease (e.g. chronic obstructive pulmonary disease) who, in contrast to the normal, exhibit a substantial fall in O_2 saturation during sleep (8, 34, 72). Arousal from sleep may also be of importance in the pathogenesis of the Sudden Infant Death Syndrome (SIDS). Infants believed to be at high risk for SIDS demonstrate (a) decreased waking episodes during the course of 24 hours (46) and (b) decreased arousal response to respiratory stimuli when compared with age-matched normal infants (53).

Hypoxic arousal response has recently been studied in adult animals and man (5, 15, 70, 73). Not surprising is the fact that the level of hypoxia at which arousal occurs varies with species and between subjects within a species (5, 15, 70, 73). These studies suggest that although the mechanisms for hypoxic arousal from sleep are complex, the carotid bodies play an important role in animals who are not sleep-deprived (15, 70, 73). Of clinical importance, however, is the recent observation that the majority of adult human subjects are not aroused by hypoxia even when O_2 saturation falls to 70–75% (5), a saturation level that can compromise cerebral structure and function. Thus hypoxic arousal may not be an effective arousal stimulus. Similar studies on animals or humans in early life are lacking.

The mechanisms by which central respiratory pauses with resulting hypoxia and hypercapnea leads to obstructive apnea and deterioration in blood gases and ultimately arousal have been recently elucidated by Cherniack and coworkers (27, 59, 92, 93). The studies of these investigators have shown that the muscles of the upper airways, and in particular the genioglossus muscle, play a key role in obstructive sleep apnea (27, 59, 92, 93). Of considerable significance in this regard is the fact that the threshold of electrical activation by chemostimulation of the genioglossus muscle is higher than that of the diaphragm (27, 59, 92, 93). Hence, in the presence of mild to moderate hypoxia and hypercapnea (gaseous alterations that may occur with central respiratory pauses), diaphragmatic contraction would be increased at a time when the electrical activity and tone of the genioglossus muscle has not changed (59, 93). With larger negative pressures thus generated by the diaphragm, the upper airways tend to collapse, leading to obstructive apnea and further deterioration of blood gases (27, 59, 93). It is not until more severe hypoxia and hypercapnea set in that the subject arouses, generating forceful contractions in the muscles of the upper airways and relieving the obstruction (27, 59, 93). Although we do not know whether differential activation of the diaphragm and muscles of the airways occurs in the infant, obstructive sleep apnea is a known phenomenon in the newborn and young infant (18, 62, 88), and the site of obstruction, which is usually at the level of the posterior pharyngeal wall in adults (74), appears to be the same in infants (18, 62, 88).

Arousal by bronchopulmonary stimulation during sleep has been studied in adult dogs (85). The results of these investigations indicate that arousal by such stimulation is depressed in REM sleep and that coughing and airway smooth muscle constriction—natural responses to bronchial stimulation during wakefulness—do not occur in the absence of arousal (85). No such systematic studies have been performed in early life, although the fetus and the premature infant have been known to lack the ability to cough when the tracheobronchial tree (e.g. carina) is mechanically stimulated.

NEUROTRANSMITTERS AND HYPOXIA

Whether hypoxia induces ventilatory and metabolic changes and an arousal response from sleep through a specific neurotransmitter or mediator substance is not known. However, the fact that the hypoxia-induced ventilatory changes depend on the severity of hypoxia itself in both newborn and adult subjects argues for the possible involvement of more than one neurotransmitter or mediator system. Additionally, because several chemosensitive areas participate in the ventilatory response to hypoxia, it is possible that different substances mediate the response in the different areas. The fact that the same mediator system may have different mediating actions, depending on the site of action, adds considerable complexity to this problem. For example, while both epinephrine and norepinephrine stimulate breathing by stimulation of the carotid chemoreceptors (30, 31, 61), they can induce a decrease in respiratory neuronal firing when in contact with central respiratory neurons (12, 22).

A decrease or an increase in V results from the net balance between inhibitory and facilatory influences on the central respiratory motor neuron pool. We believe that this net balance between excitation and inhibition in the presence of a hypoxic stimulus depends on the severity of the hypoxia, on the age of the subject and the degree of maturation of the peripheral and central chemoreceptors, and on factors that would influence the synthesis or metabolism of mediator substances. Severe hypoxia, for example, whether in adults or in infants, causes a decrease in V and induces periodic breathing (24–26, 40, 68). At least one substance has recently been suggested to mediate the ventilatory response to severe hypoxia (39). The decrease in V that occurs in rabbit pups when exposed to 5% O_2 is reversed by naloxone, an endorphin antagonist, suggesting that the decrease in V is secondary to the release of endorphins (39). Supporting this is the observation that β-endorphin levels increase in plasma of fetuses when they are subjected to severe hypoxia (91). Recent studies from our laboratory have also shown that the intracisternal injection of methionine- or leucine-enkephalins in unanesthetized chronically instrumented dogs produces striking periodic breathing, a breathing pattern similar to that present during severe hypoxia (Figure 2) (43). Studies on adult humans exposed to mild hypoxic stress, however, have shown that naloxone has little effect on V or on the pattern of breathing (56). To be noted in this regard is that these studies on adult subjects (56) did not show any decrease in V with the hypoxic stress prior to the administration of the opiate antagonist. Additionally, these studies were performed on adult rather than on young subjects and this may be an important consideration.

Although the studies of Grunstein et al (39) are the first to show that a relationship may exist between endorphins, hypoxia, and the regulation of breathing, further studies are required to prove this. Several questions have to be answered. For instance: (a) Are β-endorphins that are released near brain areas involved in the regulation of respiration during hypoxia? (b) Are methionine- or leucine-enkephalins, recently discovered naturally occurring opiate ligands believed to fulfill criteria of neurotransmitters (23, 36, 67, 81), released at synaptic clefts during hypoxia? (c) Can the effects of these ligands be blocked with small doses of naloxone? Large doses of this opiate antagonist may involve the action of other systems, like the GABA-ergic and dopaminergic systems (81). Finally, (d) Is the decrease in ventilation during severe hypoxia not reversible with inactive isomers of opiate antagonists?

Other neurotransmitters may also play a role in the mediation of the response to hypoxia (6, 7, 47, 64, 79, 87). For example, serotonin is decreased in concentration in brainstem nuclei involved in regulation of breathing following hypoxia (47). Since serotonin is believed to stimulate respiration centrally (64), the decrease of serotonin, which in this case is due to diminished synthesis, will lead to reduced ventilatory output. Several other mediators may also play a role, namely adenosine, GABA, epinephrine, norepinephrine, and dopamine (6, 7, 36, 47, 64, 79, 87). Clearly, however, this area needs further investigation.

DOG #4

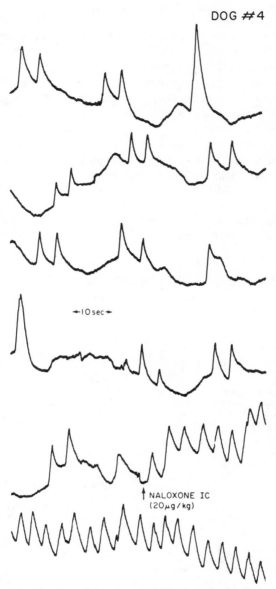

Figure 2 Respiratory waveform (using barometric plethysmography) is plotted against time. Note typical periodic breathing after intracisternal (IC) administration of D-Ala-Met-Enkephalinamide, a stable analog of Met-Enkephalin. IC injection of Naloxone reversed the pattern as well as the decrease in ventilation.

FUTURE DIRECTIONS

Research on the causes and consequences of hypoxia is of paramount importance for the very young in utero and in postnatal life. Although a considerable amount of knowledge has been generated in this area, we still do not fully understand the mechanisms responsible for the prolonged apneic spell or the upper airway obstruction during sleep in the premature infant. Investigations of factors that influence arousal and waking responses and those that regulate airway closure and patency during sleep should generate new and important data. Studies of respiratory-muscle function under conditions of respiratory loading, hypoxia, acidosis, and shock should provide insight into respiratory-muscle fatigue and into its contribution to respiratory failure in disease. Furthermore, studies elucidating the biochemical and neurophysiologic bases for the act of breathing, for the initiation of apnea and subsequent recovery, for hypoventilation, and for periodic breathing might provide opportunities for better modalities of therapy in the young as well as in the adult.

ACKNOWLEDGMENTS

This work was supported by NIH Grants HD-14565, HD-15736, HL-30028, and HL-07421 and by the Ritter Memorial Fund.

Literature Cited

1. Aubier, M., Trippenbach, T., Roussos, C. 1981. Respiratory muscle fatigue during cardiogenic shock. *J. Appl. Physiol.* 51:499–508
2. Baker, T. L., McGinty, D. J. 1977. Reversal of cardiopulmonary failure during active sleep in hypoxic kittens: implications for Sudden Infant Death. *Science* 199:419–21
3. Bazzy, A. R., Haddad, G. G., Gandhi, M. R., Mellins, R. B. 1983. Diaphragmatic muscle fatigue in the unanesthetized adult sheep. *Am. Rev. Respir. Dis.* In press
4. Belenky, D. A., Standaert, T. A., Woodrum, D. E. 1979. Maturation of hypoxic ventilatory response of the newborn lamb. *J. Appl. Physiol.* 47:927–30
5. Berthon-Jones, M., Sullivan, C. E. 1982. Ventilatory and arousal responses to hypoxia in sleeping humans. *Am. Rev. Respir. Dis.* 126:632–39
6. Bisgard, G. E., Mitchell, R. A., Herbert, D. A. 1979. Effects of dopamine, norepinephrine, and 5-hydroxytryptamine on the carotid body of the dog. *Respir. Physiol.* 37:61–80
7. Black, A. M. S., Comroe, J. S., Jacobs,

L. 1972. Species difference in carotid body response of cat and dog to dopamine and serotonin. *Am. J. Physiol.* 223: 1097–1102
8. Block, A. J., Boysen, P. G., Wynne, J. W., Hunt, L. A. 1979. Sleep apnea, hypopnea, and oxygen desaturation in normal subjects. *N. Engl. J. Med.* 300:513–17
9. Boddy, K., Dawes, G. S., Fisher, R., Pinter, S., Robinson, J. S. 1974. Foetal respiratory movements, electrocortical, and cardiovascular responses to hypoxemia and hypercapnea in sheep. *J. Physiol.* 243:599–618
10. Boddy, K., Dawes, G. S. 1975. Fetal breathing. *Br. Med. Bull.* 31:3–7
11. Boddy, K., Robinson, J. S. 1981. External method for detection of fetal breathing *in utero. Lancet* 2:1231–33
12. Bolme, P., Fuxe, K., 1973. Pharmacological studies on a possible role of central noradrenaline neurons in respiratory control. *J. Pharm. Pharmacol.* 25:351–52
13. Bowes, G., Adamson, T. M., Ritchie, B. C., Wilkinson, M. H., Maloney, J. E. 1981. Development of patterns of respiratory activity in unanesthetized fetal

sheep *in utero. J. Appl. Physiol.* 50:693–700

14. Bowes, G., Wilkinson, M. H., Dowling, M., Ritchie, B. C., Brodecky, V., Maloney, J. E. 1981. Hypercapnic stimulation of respiratory activity in unanesthetized fetal sheep *in utero. J. Appl. Physiol.* 50:701–8

15. Bowes, G., Townsend, E. R., Kozar, L. F., Bromley, S. M., Phillipson, E. A. 1981. Effect of carotid body denervation on arousal response to hypoxia in sleeping dogs. *J. Appl. Physiol.* 51:40–45

16. Brady, J. P., Ceruti, E. 1966. Chemoreceptor reflexes in the newborn infant: Effect of varying degrees of hypoxia on heart rate and ventilation in a warm environment. *J. Physiol.* 184:631–45

17. Brebbia, D. R., Altshuler, K. Z. 1965. Oxygen consumption rate and electroencephalographic stage of sleep. *Science* 150:1621–23

18. Brouillette, R. T., Thach, B. T. 1979. A neuromuscular mechanism maintaining extrathoracic airway patency. *J. Appl. Physiol.* 46:772–79

19. Bryan, A. C., Mansell, A. L., Levison, H. 1977. Development of the mechanical properties of the respiratory system. In *Development of the Lung*, ed. W. A. Hodson, pp. 445–68. New York: Dekker

20. Bryan, M. H., Bryan, A. C. 1979. Respiration during sleep in infants. In *Central Nervous Control Mechanisms in Breathing*, ed. C. von Euler, H. Lagercrantz, pp. 457–64. Oxford: Pergamon

21. Bureau, M. A., Begin, R. 1982. Diphasic ventilatory response to hypoxia in newborn lambs: evidence against the theory of central depression. *Am. Rev. Respir. Dis.* 125:186

22. Champagnat, J., Denavit-Saubie, M., Henry, J. L., Leviel, V. 1979. Catecholaminergic depressant effects on bulbar respiratory mechanisms. *Respir. Physiol.* 160:57–68

23. Chang, K. J., Cuatrecasas, P. 1981. Heterogeneity and properties of opiate receptors. *Fed. Proc.* 40:2729–34

24. Chernick, V., Heldrich, F., Avery, M. E. 1964. Periodic breathing of premature infants. *J. Pediatr.* 64:330–40

25. Cherniack, N. S., Edelman, N. H., Lahiri, S. 1971. Hypoxia and hypercapnia as respiratory stimulants and depressants. *Respir. Physiol.* 11:113–26

26. Cherniack, N. S., Longobordo, G. S. 1973. Cheyne-Stokes breathing. *N. Engl. J. Med.* 288:952–57

27. Cherniack, N. S., Longobardo, G. S., Gothe, B., Weiner, D. 1981. Interactive effects of central and obstructive apnea. In *Adv. Physiol. Sci. Respiration in CO₂ Storage in Tissues*, ed. I. Hutas, L. A. Debreczeni, pp. 553–60. New York: Pergamon

28. Cotton, E. K., Grunstein, M. M. 1980. Effects of hypoxia on respiratory control in neonates at high altitude. *J. Appl. Physiol.* 48:587–95

29. Cross, K. S., Oppe, T. W. 1952. The effect of inhalation of high and low concentrations of oxygen on the respiration of the premature infant. *J. Physiol.* 117:38–55

30. Cunningham, D. J. C., Hey, E. N., Lloyd, B. B. 1958. The effect of intravenous infusion of noradrenaline on the respiratory response to carbon dioxide. *Q. J. Exp. Physiol.* 43:394–99

31. Cunningham, D. J. C., Hey, E. N., Patrick, J. M., Lloyd, B. B. 1963. The effect of noradrenaline infusion on the relation between pulmonary ventilation and the alveolar PO_2 and PCO_2 in man. *Ann. NY Acad. Sci.* 109:756–71

32. Danforth, W. H. 1965. Activation of glycolytic pathway in muscle. In *Control of Energy Metabolism.* ed. B. Chance, R. W. Estabrook, New York: Academic

33. Dawes, G. S., Fox, H. E., Leduc, B. M., Liggins, G. C., Richards, R. T. 1972. Respiratory movements and rapid eye movement sleep in the foetal lamb. *J. Physiol.* 220:119–43

34. Douglas, N. J., Calverly, P. M. A., Leggett, R. G. E., Brash, H. M., Glenly, D. C., Brizinova, V. 1979. Transient hypoxemia during sleep in chronic bronchitis and emphysema. *Lancet* 1:1–4

35. Edelman, N. H., Cherniack, N. S., Lahiri, S., Fishman, A. P. 1966. Response of goats to acute, chronic, and life-long hypoxia. *Fed. Proc.* 28:1223–27

36. Eldridge, F. L., Millhorn, D. E. 1981. Central regulation of respiration by endogeneous neurotransmitters and neuromodulators. *Ann. Rev. Physiol.* 43:121–35

37. Gaultier, C., Perret, L., Boule, M., Buvry, A., Girard, F. 1981. Occlusion pressure and breathing pattern in healthy children. *Respir. Physiol.* 46:71–80

38. Glotzbach, S. F., Heller, H. C. 1976. Central nervous regulation of body temperature during sleep. *Science* 194:537–39

39. Grunstein, M. M., Hazinski, T. A., Schlueter, M. A. 1981. Respiratory control during hypoxia in newborn rabbits: implied action of endorphins. *J. Appl. Physiol.* 51:122–30

40. Guntheroth, W. G., Kawabori, I. 1975. Hypoxic apnea and gasping. *J. Clin. Invest.* 56:1371–77

41. Haddad, G. G., Gandhi, M. R., Mellins, R. B. 1981. O_2 consumption during hypoxia in sleeping puppies. *Am. Rev. Respir. Dis.* 123:183

42. Haddad, G. G., Gandhi, M. R., Mellins, R. B. 1982. Maturation of ventilatory response to hypoxia in puppies during sleep. *J. Appl. Physiol.* 52:309–14

43. Haddad, G. G., Gandhi, M. R., Hochwald, G. M., Lai, T. L. 1983. Enkephalin-induced changes in ventilation and ventilatory pattern in adult dogs. *J. Appl. Physiol.* In press

44. Hammill, S. C., Wagner, W. W., Latham, L. P., Frost, W. W., Weil, J. V. 1979. Autonomic cardiovascular control during hypoxia in the dog. *Circ. Res.* 44:569–75

45. Hanson, N., Okken, A. 1980. Transcutaneous oxygen tension of newborn infants in different behavioral states. *Pediatr. Res.* 14:911–15

46. Harper, R. M., Leake, B., Hoffman, H., Walter, D. O., Hoppenbrouwers, T., et al. 1981. Periodicity of sleep states is altered in infants at risk for the sudden infant death syndrome. *Science* 213: 1030–32

47. Hedner, T., Lundborg, P. 1980. Serotonin metabolism in neonatal rat brain during asphyxia and recovery. *Acta Physiol. Scand.* 109:163–68

48. Henderson-Smart, D. J., Read, D. J. C. 1979. Reduced lung volume during behavioral active sleep in the newborn. *J. Appl. Physiol.* 46:1081–85

49. Henderson-Smart, D. J., Read, D. J. C. 1979. Ventilatory response to hypoxaemia during sleep in the newborn. *J. Dev. Physiol.* 1:195–208

50. Hermansen, L. 1981. Effect of metabolic changes on force generation in skeletal muscle during maximal exercise. In *Human Muscle Fatigue: Physiological Mechanisms. Ciba Found. Symp.* 82:75–78. London: Pitman Medical

51. Hill, J. R. 1959. The oxygen consumption of new-born and adult mammals. Its dependence on the oxygen tension in the inspired air and on the environmental temperature. *J. Physiol.* 149:346–73

52. Hill, J. R., Rahimtulla, K. A. 1965. Heat balance and the metabolic rate of newborn babies in relation to environmental temperature; and the effect of age and of weight on basal metabolic rate. *J. Physiol.* 180:239–65

53. Hunt, C. E., McCulloch, K., Brouillette, R. T. 1981. Diminished hypoxic ventilatory responses in near-miss sudden infant death syndrome. *J. Appl. Physiol.* 50:1313–17

54. Jardim, J., Farkas, G., Prefaut, C., Thomas, D., Macklem, P. T., Roussos, C. 1981. The failing inspiratory muscles under normoxic and hypoxic conditions. *Am. Rev. Respir. Dis.* 124:274–79

55. Jeffrey, H. E., Read, D. J. C. 1980. Ventilatory responses of newborn calves to progressive hypoxia in quiet and active sleep. *J. Appl. Physiol.* 48:892–95

56. Kagawa, S., Stafford, M. J., Waggener, T. B., Severinghaus, J. W. 1982. No effect of naloxone on hypoxia-induced ventilatory depression in adults. *J. Appl. Physiol.* 52:1030–34

57. Keens, T. G., Ianuzzo, D. C. 1979. Development of fatigue-resistant muscle fibers in human ventilatory muscles. *Am. Rev. Respir. Dis.* 119:139–41

58. Lahiri, S., Brody, J. S., Motoyama, E. K., Velasquez, T. M. 1978. Regulation of breathing in newborns at high altitude. *J. Appl. Physiol.* 44:673–78

59. Longobardo, G. S., Gothe, B., Goldman, M. D., Cherniack, N. S. 1982. Sleep apnea considered as a control system instability. *Respir. Physiol.* 50:311–33

60. Lopes, J. M., Muller, N. L., Bryan, M. H., Bryan, A. C. 1981. Synergistic behavior of inspiratory muscles after diaphragmatic fatigue in the newborn. *J. Appl. Physiol.* 51:547–51

61. Lundholm, L., Svedmyr, N. 1966. Studies on the stimulating effects of adrenaline and noradrenaline on respiration in man. *Acta. Physiol. Scand.* 67:65–75

62. Mathew, O. P., Abu-Osba, Y. K., Thach, B. T. 1980. Response of airway maintaining respiratory muscles (genioglossus) to upper airway pressure changes. *Fed. Proc.* 39:1063

63. Maxwell, C. L., McCarter, R. J. M., Kuehl, T. J., Robotham, J. L. 1983. Development of histochemical and functional properties of baboon respiratory muscles. *J. Appl. Physiol.* 54:551–61

64. Milhorn, D. E., Eldridge, F. L., Waldrop, T. G. 1980. Prolonged stimulation of respiration by endogenous central serotonin. *Respir. Physiol.* 42:171–88

65. Milic-Emili, J. 1982. Recent advances in clinical assessment of control of breathing. *Lung* 160:1–17

66. Milic-Emili, J., Zin, A. W. 1983. Relationship between neuromuscular respiratory drive and ventilatory output. *Handbook of Physiology.* In press

67. Miller, R. J., Chang, K. J., Cuatrecasas, P., Wilkinson, S. 1977. The metabolic stability of the enkephalins. *Biochem. Biophys. Res. Commun.* 74:1311–17

68. Morrill, C. G., Meyer, J. R., Weil, J. V. 1975. Hypoxic ventilatory depression in dogs. *J. Appl. Physiol.* 38:143–46

69. Muller, N., Volgyesi, G., Eng, P., Bryan, H. M., Bryan, C. A. 1979. The consequences of diaphragmatic muscle fatigue in the newborn infant. *J. Pediatr.* 95:793–97

70. Neubauer, J. A., Santiago, T. V., Edelman, N. M. 1981. Hypoxic arousal in intact and carotid chemodenervated sleeping cats. *J. Appl. Physiol.* 51:1294–99

71. Patrick, J., Natale, R., Richardson, B. 1978. Patterns of human fetal breathing activity at 34–35 weeks gestational age. *Am. J. Obstet. Gynecol.* 132:507–13

72. Phillipson, E. A., Sullivan, C. E. 1978. Arousal: the forgotten response to respiratory stimuli. *Am. Rev. Respir. Dis.* 118:807–9

73. Phillipson, E. A., Sullivan, C. E., Read, D. J. C., Murphy, E., Kozar, L. F. 1978. Ventilatory and waking responses to hypoxia in sleeping dogs. *J. Appl. Physiol.* 44:512–20

74. Remmers, J. E., De Groot, W. T., Sauerland, E. K. et al. 1978. Pathogenesis of upper airway occlusion during sleep. *J. Appl. Physiol.* 44:931–38

75. Rigatto, H., Brady, J. P., Verduzco, R. T. 1975. Chemoreceptor reflexes in preterm infants: I. The effect of gestational and postnatal age on the ventilatory response to inhalation of 100% and 15% oxygen. *Pediatrics* 55:604–13

76. Rigatto, H. 1979. A critical analysis of the development of peripheral and central respiratory chemosensitivity during the neonatal period. In *Central Nervous Control Mechanisms in Breathing*, ed. C. von Euler, H. Lagercrantz, pp. 137–48. Oxford: Pergamon

77. Roussos, C., Macklem, P. T. 1977. Diaphragmatic fatigue in man. *J. Appl. Physiol.* 43:189–97

78. Roussos, C., Fixley, M., Gross, D., Macklem, P. T. 1979. Fatigue of inspiratory muscles and their synergic behavior. *J. Appl. Physiol.* 46:897–904

79. Sampson, S. S. R., Aminoff, M. F., Jaffe, R. A., Vidruk, E. H. 1976. Analysis of inhibitory effect of dopamine on carotid body chemoreceptors in cats. *Am. J. Physiol.* 230:1494–98

80. Sankaran, K., Wiebe, H., Seshia, M. M. K., Boychuk, R. B., Cates, D., Rigatto, H. 1979. Immediate and late ventilatory response to high and low O_2 in preterm infants and adult subjects. *Pediatr. Res.* 13:875–78

81. Sawynok, J. C., Pinsky, C., Labella, F. S. 1979. Minireview of the specificity of naloxone as an opiate antagonist. *Life Sci.* 25:1621–32

82. Schulte, F. J., Busse, C., Eichhorn, W. 1977. Rapid eye movements sleep, motoneurone inhibition, and apneic spells in preterm infants. *Pediatr. Res.* 11:709–13

83. Stainsby, W. N., Otis, A. B. 1964. Blood flow, blood oxygen tension, oxygen uptake, and oxygen transport in skeletal muscle. *Am. J. Physiol.* 206:858–66

84. Stockes, J., Godfrey, S. 1977. Specific airway conductance in relation to postconceptional age during infancy. *J. Appl. Physiol.* 43:144–54

85. Sullivan, C. E., Kozar, L. F., Murphy, E., Phillipson, E. A. 1979. Arousal, ventilatory, and airway responses to bronchopulmonary stimulation in sleeping dogs. *J. Appl. Physiol.* 47:17–25

86. Taylor, P. M. 1960. Oxygen consumption in new-born rats. *J. Physiol.* 154:153–68

87. Tenney, S. M., Ou, L. C. 1977. Hypoxic ventilatory response of cats at high altitude: an interpretation of blunting. *Respir. Physiol.* 30:185–99

88. Thach, B. T., Stark, A. R. 1979. Spontaneous neck flexion and airway obstruction during apneic spells in preterm infants. *J. Pediatr.* 94:275–81

89. Towell, M. E., Salvador, H. S. 1974. Intrauterine asphyxia and respiratory movements in the fetal goat. *Am. J. Obstet. Gynecol.* 118:1124–31

90. Ui, M. 1966. A role of phosphofructokinase in pH-dependent regulation of glycolysis. *Biochem. Biophys. Acta* 124:310–22

91. Wardlaw, S. L., Stark, R., Barc, L., Frantz, A. 1979. Plasma β-endorphin and β-lipotropin in human fetus at delivery. Correlation with arterial pH and PO_2. *Clin. Endocrinol. Metab.* 79:888–91

92. Weiner, D. J., Salamone, M. J., Nochomovitz, M., Cherniack, N. S. 1980. The effect of chemical drive on the electrical activity and force of contraction of the tongue and chest wall muscles. *Am. Rev. Respir. Dis.* 121S:418

93. Weiner, D. J., Salamone, M. J., Cherniack, N. S. 1982. Effect of chemical stimuli on nerves supplying upper airway muscles. *J. Appl. Physiol.* 52:530–36

94. Woodrum, D. E., Standaert, T. A., Parks, D., Belenky, D., Murphy, J., Hodson, W. A. 1977. Ventilatory response in the fetal lamb following peripheral chemodenervation. *J. Appl. Physiol.* 42:630–35

95. Woodrum, D. E., Standaert, T. A., Mayock, D. E., Guthrie, R. D. 1981. Hypoxic ventilatory response in the newborn monkey. *Pediatr. Res.* 15:367–70

Ann. Rev. Physiol. 1984. 46:645–59

FUNCTION OF THE LARYNX IN THE FETUS AND NEWBORN

R. Harding

Department of Physiology, Monash University, Melbourne, 3168, Australia

INTRODUCTION

Throughout postnatal life the larynx plays a part in many physiological functions, most importantly the defense of lower airways, the regulation of respiratory airflow, and vocalization. These functions are of special significance to the survival of the newborn, because the lower airways are at increased risk of invasion from ingesta or from refluxed gastric contents, and thoracic compliance is relatively high, leading to a tendency for the lungs to collapse during expiration.

The anatomical relationships of the upper airway change throughout gestation and early postnatal development, particularly in relation to the position of the larynx (8). In many species, including man, the neonatal larynx lies higher relative to the cervical vertebrae than in the adult, allowing the free portion of the epiglottis to lie behind the soft palate (45). This interlocking of the epiglottis and soft palate bestows on the infant the ability to breath while suckle feeding, and may also be responsible, in part, for the inability of the neonate to breath effectively via the mouth.

This review will deal principally with the sensory and motor aspects of laryngeal function, especially those related to respiration, in the late fetal and early postnatal periods. Much of the recently acquired knowledge on the function of the upper airway during infancy stems from an increasing interest in the etiology of sleep apnea and the Sudden Infant Death Syndrome.

645

0066-4278/84/0315-0645$02.00

LARYNGEAL FUNCTION IN THE FETUS

Laryngeal Activity in Relation to Fetal Breathing Movements

Throughout at least the latter half of gestation, fetal sheep and humans make intermittent, respiratory movements of the diaphragm. In the sheep, fetal breathing movements (FBMs) depress intrathoracic pressure and move small volumes (< 1 ml) of fluid to and fro within the trachea (16, 51). Two types of FBM exist in sheep and have been shown to have a close relationship to fetal sleep states. Rhythmical shallow FBM (< 5 mmHg) are associated with a state resembling REM sleep (16), during which the electrocorticogram is in a low-voltage condition, rapid eye movements (REM) are present, and postural muscles (such as the nuchal and intercostal muscles) lack sustained activity (29). The second type of FBMs have been referred to as "gasping" (16) or "deep inspiratory efforts" and are usually associated with the non-REM state (29). In order to define the function of the larynx in association with FBM, EMG recordings have been made from some of the major laryngeal muscles in fetal sheep (29).

The posterior cricoarytenoid (PCA) muscles are the principal muscles of laryngeal abduction. Postnatally, their function is to resist the tendency of the glottis to be narrowed due to falling airway pressure during inspiration. Their activity is thus closely linked to that of the diaphragm (64, 66). In sheep fetuses, PCA activity increases in phase with the diaphragm during rhythmical breathing movements (29). Visualization of the human fetus using ultrasound has confirmed the presence of respiratory movements of the larynx (17). Thus, even before birth, the central respiratory pattern generator drives laryngeal, as well as phrenic, motoneurones.

The close association between activation of the fetal diaphragm and PCA is not, however, immutable. During deep inspiratory efforts, activation of the diaphragm is not accompanied by that of PCA (29). The functional role of these infrequent inspiratory efforts is unknown, but in many ways they resemble regurgitative efforts in the ruminating animal. These involve a vigorous contraction of the diaphragm against a passively closed glottis, resulting in a sharp fall in intrathoracic pressure (29). It seems unlikely, however, that fetal sheep regurgitate in utero; EMG recordings from the esophagus do not show activity following deep inspiratory efforts (R. Harding, unpublished observations).

Regurgitative efforts of ruminating sheep and deep inspiratory efforts of fetal sheep are similar in some respects to hiccups: a rapid descent of the diaphragm, with a passive closure of the glottis (15). Although deep inspiratory efforts have not been described in the human fetus, it is known that they frequently engage in hiccuping (48, 58). It is a common observation that neonatal (and adult) hiccups usually follow soon after feeding; although their etiology is unknown, stimulation of the terminal esophagus or cardiac region of the stomach may be involved. Thus, hiccups in the human fetus and deep inspiratory efforts of the sheep fetus may be functionally analogous. This function remains a matter for speculation, however.

The thyroarytenoid muscles (TA) are the major adductor muscles of the larynx. EMG recordings from TA in fetal sheep indicate that, in the absence of FBM, these muscles are tonically active at a low level (29). At the onset of a bout of FBM, the muscles become essentially quiescent until there is another period of apnea. Their inactivity during the expiratory phase of FBM may be explained by the inhibitory influence of REM sleep, during which most FBM take place. Postnatally, these muscles are found to be active during expiration in quiet sleep. They are largely inactive throughout REM sleep (29), however, with the exception of episodes of central apnea. It is likely that the tonic discharges of TA during fetal apnea are a result of sustained activity in "expiratory" neurones of the medulla. Recordings from central respiratory neurones in exteriorized fetal sheep support this contention (12). These showed that expiratory neurones tonically discharged in the absence of rhythmical activation of inspiratory neurones. It is likely that changes in the level of activity of laryngeal adductor muscles influence the flow of fluid from the lungs (23a). In postnatal lambs, these muscles have a major effect on expiratory airflow and are influenced by volume information from the lungs (28). In the fetus, however, it has not proven possible to modify TA activity by manipulating lung volume (23a).

Recordings of TA activity have also yielded information on the ingestive behaviour of fetal sheep: a characteristic short, high-amplitude EMG burst occurs during each swallowing movement (29). In both fetal (29) and newborn lambs (30), swallowing (and sucking) occurs at a frequency of $1-4 \text{ sec}^{-1}$ and is highly coordinated with inspiratory muscle activity. During swallowing movements, which may occur at any stage in the respiratory cycle, the activity of the diaphragm (and PCA) is briefly inhibited (25, 30). Postnatally, this high degree of coordination between swallowing and inspiratory muscle activity is vital for successful suckle feeding and, in lambs, allows effective ventilation to be maintained while swallowing at a frequency of $4-5 \text{ sec}^{-1}$ (26).

The cricothyroid muscle (CT) is largely inactive in the apneic sheep fetus, but like PCA becomes increasingly active with each inspiratory effort during bouts of FBM (29). This is a similar pattern of activation to that seen in unanesthetized postnatal lambs, adult sheep (29), mature rats (66), and humans (43).

The Regulation of Fluid Flow in the Trachea

Throughout their development in utero the respiratory passages are filled with a fluid that originates within the lungs. Measurements of flow within the trachea have shown that there is a mean net efflux of 9 ml hr^{-1} in sheep fetuses of 100–130 days gestation (2), although the flow is quite irregular and at times reverses during fetal breathing movements (16, 51).

Although there is little evidence on the regulation of production of fetal lung liquid, it is now apparent that the rate of flow along the trachea is controlled, to some extent, by a resistance imposed in the upper respiratory tract. Measurement of pressure within the fetal sheep trachea reveals that it is normally slightly higher (2–5 mmHg) than pressure in the amniotic sac (1, 56, 76). It is now apparent that the existence of this pressure gradient may be necessary for normal lung development (3, 49). The site of the resistance between the trachea and the amniotic fluid is unknown, however. Early experiments involving intratracheal infusions of radio-opaque material in exteriorized fetal sheep suggested that the larynx is normally adducted, periodically opening to allow efflux of tracheal fluid (1). However, in these studies it is likely that the experimental conditions precluded respiratory movements, thus favoring tonic closure of the glottis (29). Studies in chronically monitored fetal sheep suggest that the resistance to flow is not actively maintained; it is not abolished by curare (49), indicating that more distal parts of the upper airway may be involved. This conclusion is supported by the observation that insertion of tubes into the nose and pharynx abolishes the pressure gradient between the trachea and amniotic sac (21).

These findings are, however, at variance with recent studies in which laryngeal and supralaryngeal resistances were measured in fetal sheep (23a). When fetal breathing movements were absent, resistance across the larynx increased, whereas the resistance of the remainder of the upper respiratory tract was unchanged. The elevated laryngeal resistance was closely correlated with tonic activity in the adductor muscles of the larynx (thyroarytenoid) and was abolished by the muscle relaxant Flaxedil. Furthermore, measurements of the efflux of fluid from the trachea have shown that it occurs predominantly when tonic activity in the laryngeal adductor muscles is absent and when fetal breathing movements are present (23a). These observations indicate that the flow of fluid from the fetal lungs is, at times, retarded by a laryngeal mechanism. Clearly, however, there is a need for further experimentation in this important area relating to prenatal development of the lungs.

THE RESPIRATORY FUNCTION OF THE LARYNX IN THE NEWBORN

There is now a considerable body of evidence to support the view that post-natally the larynx is involved in regulating airflow during both phases of the respiratory cycle. Much of this data has been obtained from adult experimental animals. It is now becoming apparent, however, that the larynx, through its action as a rapidly controllable resistance to airflow, plays an important regulatory role in respiration in the neonatal period. As a major source of airway resistance (69), the larynx has the potential of exerting a marked influence on the pattern of breathing. Respiratory air flow can be altered via activation of its two sets of opposing intrinsic muscles. For example, laryngeal resistance may be raised by increasing the activity of the muscles of adduction, or by reducing abductor activity, or by a combination of these. It is becoming apparent that there are species differences in the way in which changes in laryngeal resistance are accomplished.

The Regulation of Inspiratory Resistance

Laryngeal resistance to inspiratory airflow is regulated predominantly through the actions of the muscles of abduction (PCA). The adductor muscles (TA) are not active during the inspiratory phase (5, 29, 64). The abductor action of PCA is facilitated by the simultaneous activation of CT (41), which usually shows inspiratory activity (29, 43, 66). As discussed above, the simultaneous activation of PCA and the diaphragm is already well established in fetal life. There is, however, little direct evidence on the respiratory role of the abductor muscles in the neonate, although it is likely to be similar to that in the adult. The inaccessibility and small size of these muscles are, no doubt, largely responsible for this gap in our knowledge. However, as Farber (20) has shown, it is possible to obtain satisfactory EMG recordings, at least acutely, from young opossums.

Marked changes in inspiratory abduction of the larynx have been reported in relation to sleep states in mature animals. In the rat, for example, the inspiratory activity of PCA diminishes as the animal passes from quiet to REM sleep (66). Similarly, in mature cats glottic widening during inspiration is less pronounced in REM sleep than in quiet sleep (57). It is possible that these changes were related to respiratory frequency, but no comment was made on this by the authors.

The Regulation of Expiratory Resistance

The larynx is one of the major sites in the upper airway at which expiratory airflow may be retarded in a controlled manner, thus affecting the rate at which the lungs collapse towards functional residual capacity (FRC). In mature animals it has been shown that the larynx reflexly regulates both expiratory flow and expiratory time and that it may be assisted in this by postinspiratory activity in the diaphragm (22, 60).

In unanesthetized or lightly anesthetized lambs, retardation of expiratory airflow is brought about principally by the action of the adductor muscles (28). Except during REM sleep, there is little expiratory activity in the diaphragm or the abductor muscles (28) that could play a role in regulating expiratory airflow. Thus, there appear to be species (or maturational) differences in the relative involvement of abductor and adductor muscles of the larynx, and of the diaphragm, during expiration. The matter is confused, owing to the use of barbiturate anesthetic agents and tracheostomy in many studies. For example, there was no evidence of laryngeal adductor activity in phase with expiration in anesthetized suckling opossums (20) and mature cats (5). However, it has been demonstrated that adductor activity is preferentially depressed by barbiturate anesthesia (65). Thus it would appear that the use of anesthetic agents, particularly barbiturates, should be avoided wherever possible in studies involving the upper airway.

Laryngeal mechanisms affecting expiratory airflow are under the influence of volume information from the lungs. Pulmonary control can be effective at short latency, as has been demonstrated by Remmers & Bartlett (60) in anesthetized cats. Removal of the braking effects of the upper airway, by opening a tracheostomy during expiration, invokes a vagally mediated increase in diaphragmatic activity and a reduction in PCA activity; both of these responses would, in the intact animal, tend to retard pulmonary deflation. In lambs, opening a tracheostomy, or the application of negative end-expiratory pressure, lead to an increase in the expiratory activity of TA (23, 36). Conversely, increasing levels of end-expiratory pressure result in diminished TA activity (23). These responses are abolished by vagotomy and are probably controlled by pulmonary stretch receptors. Recordings from vagal fibers in lambs have demonstrated the existence of pulmonary stretch receptors with appreciable levels of expiratory activity even in the absence of a distending pressure (23). The activity of units such as these could account for changes in the activities of laryngeal muscles influencing expiratory airflow in response to small positive, or even negative, end-expiratory pressures.

Retardation of expiratory airflow appears to be particularly important in the period immediately following birth. A striking feature of the first breath of air taken by a newborn infant is the high degree of positive intrathoracic pressure during the expiratory phase (39, 54). Initially, expiratory esophageal pressures are as high as 92 cm H_2O (mean: 49 cm H_2O) but decline with subsequent breaths. These studies did not identify the site of the resistance to airflow, but EMG recordings obtained in animals would suggest that laryngeal adductor muscles may be involved (28). In newborn rabbits, positive expiratory airway pressures were not seen at birth (44), but tracheal cannulation would have negated any braking effect of the upper airway. Thus it would seem important in the study of normal respiratory function in the neonate for the airways to remain intact. It is likely that elevated expiratory airway pressures aid in maintaining pulmonary expansion during the onset of atmospheric breathing. The afferent signal for the increase in expiratory resistance may result from reduced pulmonary volume as a consequence of the loss of fluid from the airways and compression of the chest during birth. A similar mechanism seems to operate in infants with the Respiratory Distress Syndrome. A feature of this syndrome is expiratory grunting, due to partial closure of the glottis. Intubation of afflicted infants prevents both grunting and the development of elevated expiratory pressures within the airways, and leads to a deterioration in their condition (32), presumably due to a reduction in FRC. Expiratory grunting resulting from laryngeal adduction can be reflexly induced in lambs by applying a negative expiratory pressure to the lower airway (5cm H_2O) while passing a steady stream of air through the upper airway (37).

Retardation of expiratory airflow, like many other aspects of respiratory control, can be influenced by states of sleep. In lambs, for example, expiratory activity in laryngeal adductor muscles occurred principally during non-REM sleep (and quiet wakefulness), but was absent during REM sleep (29), even when TA activity was reflexly augmented by eliminating upper airway resistance (36). These findings are supported by observations in the human neonate showing retarded expiratory flow during quiet sleep, although in this case the site of the resistance has not been identified (59). The effects of retarded expiratory airflow include increased FRC (55). It has been confirmed that, in human neonates, FRC is greater during non-REM sleep than in REM sleep, although the REM-related loss of intercostal muscle activity may be a contributory factor (33).

REFLEXES ELICITED FROM THE LARYNX

The larynx has long been known to play a role in the protection of the lower airway, but it is only in the last two decades that the sensitivity of the laryngeal mucosa and the effects of its stimulation have been examined systematically. It is now known that laryngeal stimulation, particularly in the neonatal period, has a profound influence on ventilation, and may elicit swallowing, arousal, laryngeal adduction, and cardiovascular adjustments. While it is recognized that the larynx is sensitive to a wide range of stimuli, recent attention has been concentrated on the effects of liquids. The principal reason for this narrowing of interest is the possibility that entry of physiological liquids into the larynx may be involved in the etiology of the Sudden Infant Death Syndrome.

The Effect on Breathing

Interest in the effects of stimulation of the upper airway by liquids stemmed from experiments in newborn lambs in which immersion in water produced apnea which could be relieved by sectioning the superior laryngeal nerves (SLN) (31, 75). Although a similar response could be elicited in older animals (35, 75) a more prolonged, and sometimes fatal, inhibition of breathing occurred in the newborn. These observations have since been extended to piglets (18), kittens (27, 50), neonatal monkeys (27), and dog pups (7). In sheep, at least, the reflex is present before birth (12).

Electrical stimulation of the SLN, which is widely used to mimic the effects of laryngeal stimulation by liquids, has been shown to inhibit phrenic nerve discharges in adult cats (6), and central inspiratory neurones in the sheep fetus (12) and kitten (50). The inhibition of phrenic activity by single SLN stimuli occurs after a short latency (5–10 msec) and persists for 20–40 msec (6). The central neural mechanisms underlying this inhibition have not yet been fully elucidated, but they are probably distinct from those mediating the inhibitory effects of pulmonary afferents in the vagi (34, 46).

The Initiation of Swallowing

An important part of the response to stimulation of the laryngeal mucosa with liquids is vigorous swallowing (31, 35) that may lead to the removal of the stimulus. Coughing, although a feature of the response to laryngeal stimulation in adults (9), has not been described in the newborn. Reflex swallowing is also dependent upon the afferent fibers of the SLN, but may be eliminated by deep anesthesia (35). However, the production of apnea is not dependent on the presence of repeated swallowing. There is some evidence that swallowing is elicited by the recruitment of a population of SLN fibers distinct from those involved in the inhibition of respiration (53).

Cardiovascular Responses

Major cardiovascular responses are elicited by laryngeal mucosal stimulation with liquids or by SLN stimulation. In unanesthetized lambs, reflex apnea is accompanied by bradycardia and hypertension, both of which are rapidly reversed when the stimulus is removed and breathing reestablished (35). These findings were subsequently confirmed in anesthetized piglets (47). The bradycardia is vagally mediated (24) and is due, in part, to the cessation of rhythmical pulmonary afferent traffic secondary to respiratory arrest. Cardiac slowing, even to the point of arrest, may occur in response to combined stimulation of the SLN and carotid bodies (4). Carotid body stimulation occurs as a result of apnea which develops during laryngeal stimulation. However, the chemoreceptor stimulus to breathing appears to be overridden, especially in the neonate, by afferent inputs from the upper airway. The combined cardiac slowing effects of laryngeal and carotid body stimulation may be life threatening in some individuals, and may be of relevance to sudden death in infancy (14).

In newborn lambs (<24 hours old) laryngeal-induced apnea causes a major redistribution of blood flow; cardiac output falls while flow to the brain and head and heart increases (24). Elsewhere, blood flow is reduced, especially to the small intestines and kidneys. Similar changes in flow occur when hypoxemia is prevented, indicating that the response is not solely due to carotid body stimulation. However, the changes in heart rate and blood flow are no longer present when the lungs are rhythmically inflated throughout the period of laryngeal stimulation (24). These findings are suggestive of a role of pulmonary afferents in cardiac and circulatory reflexes (4).

Adduction of the Larynx

Adduction of the larynx, in response to stimulation of the laryngeal mucosa or SLN, has been interpreted as being part of its protective function. In an extreme form, reflex glottic closure is described as laryngospasm, a sustained, intense activation of the adductor muscles (74). EMG recordings from TA muscles in fetal and newborn lambs have shown that prolonged adductor discharges occur during stimulation of the laryngeal mucosa (25). However, only brief glottic closure was produced during SLN stimulation in anesthetized infant (and adult) monkeys, and was absent during the period of poststimulus apnea (73). In dog pups, there is evidence of a gradual postnatal development of the adductor response to single-shock SLN stimulation (62). At birth, no adductor response is elicited; furthermore, there is no evidence of glottic closure during swallowing. A period has been identified (50–70 days) during which the adductor reflex appears to be exaggerated; it is possible that during this period dog pups may be at increased risk of laryngospasm. These findings indicate that development of upper airway defense mechanisms are substantially delayed in the dog, a relatively immature species at birth. Developmental changes in the excitability of laryngeal reflexes have not yet been examined in other species. The lamb, a relatively mature animal at birth, not only has a well developed adductor response to SLN stimulation before birth, but adducts its larynx strongly during swallowing: as early as 0.7 of term (25). The human infant may resemble the dog pup in not having an obvious laryngeal adductor reflex (61). In adult man, however, the laryngeal adductor response to single SLN stimuli is well developed, and is similar to those in mature cats and dogs (62).

The Effect of Sleep States on Laryngeal Reflexes

Liquids entering the larynx of unanesthetized lambs often provoked a "startle" or "withdrawal" response (35). This may represent an important part of the overall defensive response to invasion of the upper airway during sleep. Because the majority of studies on the reflex effects of laryngeal stimulation have been performed under anesthesia, this arousing effect has received little attention, nor has the influence of sleep states on the other components of the response to laryngeal stimulation.

In adult dogs, the threshold for arousal from sleep by laryngeal stimulation was higher in REM sleep than in non-REM sleep and least during wakefulness

(72). The depression of the arousal response in REM sleep is in keeping with the effects of REM sleep on a range of afferent inputs (38). In contrast, however, the respiratory inhibition and bradycardia induced by subarousal stimuli was of greater duration and intensity during REM sleep than in non-REM sleep (72). A similar study in premature newborn lambs failed to establish a sleep-related difference in the incidence of arousal or in the degree of respiratory depression (52). However, inhibition of breathing was least marked when arousal occurred from sleep (and during wakefulness), establishing the survival value of the awake state. It is of interest that in this study on unanesthetized premature lambs, prolonged, potentially fatal apnea did not occur, in contrast to studies in which restraint (35) or anesthesia (18, 50) were employed.

Properties of Laryngeal Receptors

The characteristics of laryngeal receptors have been studied in two ways. First, the effects of laryngeal stimulation, principally on breathing, by a range of substances have been documented in a number of species. Second, recordings have been made from afferent fibers of the SLN. Using the first approach, Johnson (35) established that a wide range of solutions, when passed retrogradely through the larynx of fetal and newborn lambs, caused apnea and swallowing. Stimulants included water, HCl, sucrose and glucose solutions, cow's milk, and allantoic fluid. Isotonic saline, amniotic and tracheal fluids, and sheep's milk were without effect. The consistency of the relationship between the ability of a substance to suppress breathing and elicit swallowing has been confirmed in lightly anesthetized lambs (42).

Characteristics of laryngeal afferent fibers responding to liquids were defined initially in adult cats (9, 71) and rabbits (67). When studies have been performed in newborn animals (27, 50, 71), receptive properties have been found similar to those in the adult. Typically these units respond to liquids at short latency; many also respond to tactile stimulation (27, 70). Receptive fields of these units were concentrated over the laryngeal surface of the epiglottis, the arytenoid cartilages, and the vocal folds (27, 70).

Recordings from single SLN units have led to some insight into the ionic basis of receptor activation. The apparent excitatory effect of an absence of chloride ions (7, 9) supports earlier conclusions based on water sensitive endings in the lingual epithelium (13). In an analysis of laryngeal water receptors in the rabbit, Shingai (67) has postulated that the depression of the water response by chloride ions is due to permeation of the anions through the receptor membrane. The results of a more recent study (68) involving the use of anions that were not expected to permeate the receptor membrane indicated that the depression of the water response by anions such as Cl^- is caused by a hyperpolarization resulting from passage of anions through the receptor membrane.

Histological identification of laryngeal receptors responding to water and other liquids has not yet been accomplished. There are several lines of evidence, however, that indicate that taste buds, which are abundant in the epiglottal and laryngeal mucosa in the newborn sheep (35) and dog (40), are not the sensory element. In addition to taste buds, nerve fibers, apparently with simple free endings within the laryngeal mucosa, have been reported in the term dog fetus (40) and in neonatal lambs, kittens, and monkeys (27). On the basis of their responses to chemicals, it seems unlikely that water-sensitive units in the SLN arise from taste buds. Laryngeal "taste" units have quite different characteristics, which include a nonadapting discharge, excitation by NaCl or NH_4Cl, and suppression by water (71). These are also features of lingual taste units (11). By exclusion, therefore, it seems likely that water receptors are unspecialized nerve endings. Further evidence for the rejection of taste buds is that (a) water units are plentiful in the SLN of newborn kittens and monkeys, although taste buds are absent, and (b) water receptors have been located in older animals in regions of the larynx that are devoid of taste buds (27). The role of taste buds, which are abundant in newborn sheep on the laryngeal surface of the epiglottis (10), becomes a matter for speculation; their density and location, however, is suggestive of a role in the defense of the airway.

The Influence of Maturity on Laryngeal-Induced Apnea

Prolonged and potentially fatal apnea can be induced by liquids entering the larynx in lambs (35), kittens (50), piglets (47), and infant monkeys (73), whereas the same stimuli only briefly inhibit breathing in the mature animal. The reasons for the apparently greater vulnerability of the newborn are unknown and have not, as yet, been sought systematically in the absence of anesthesia. This is a very difficult area to study because it is likely that breathing is more readily depressed by anesthesia in the neonate than in the mature animal.

There is also a paucity of information on the influence of age of laryngeal receptor populations. Receptive properties were found to be unaffected by age in cats, sheep, and monkeys (27), although no evidence was obtained on the population size. In a nonquantitative examination of laryngeal innervation in fetal dogs at term, it was considered that there was a lower density of intraepithelial nerve terminals than in the adult (40). In sheep, epiglottal taste buds are abundant at birth and continue to increase in number, although their density does not alter (10). Thus, it is unlikely that the greater sensitivity of the neonate has its basis in the periphery.

The functional characteristics of central synaptic connections may change with age. Some support for this possibility is lent by observations in kittens (50), in which, compared to the adult cat (63), a greater proportion of respiratory neurones in the region of the solitary tract nucleus were inhibited by stimulation of the vagus or SLN; a smaller proportion were excited at short latency. However, the numbers of units were small and maturational differences in sensitivities of central neurones to anesthesia cannot be excluded as contributing to these observations.

It is possible that the functional development of the carotid bodies may be involved in the maturation of laryngeal reflexes. In the absence of direct evidence, Sutton et al (73) considered that a reduced hypoxic drive may account for their findings that infant, but not adult, anesthetized monkeys experienced longer periods of apnea following SLN stimulation. However, the duration of reflexly induced apnea in anesthetized piglets was not modified by carotid body denervation (19), confirming earlier observations in lambs (35). Thus it is unlikely that the greater apneic response of the young animal is due to reduced peripheral chemoreceptor function. Indeed, it appears that, on the basis of respiratory responses to 100% O_2, the carotid bodies are fully functional in the piglet within two weeks of birth (19).

The observation that respiratory arrest may persist beyond a period of laryngeal (but not vagal) stimulation, even when the subjects are ventilated and end-tidal PCO_2 is kept constant, suggests that afferent traffic from the larynx can invoke a central neural mechanism that inhibits the respiratory rhythm after the traffic ceases (46). However, it remains to be explained why this mechanism should only manifest itself in the neonate and not, apparently, in the adult.

SUMMARY

The muscles of the larynx function as a part of the respiratory system before birth, and like other respiratory muscles, have experienced considerable use by the moment of birth. In late fetal life the larynx appears to influence the outward flow of pulmonary liquid and thus may play a role in lung development. Immediately after birth and in cases of neonatal lung disease, elevated pressures within the airways during expiration, probably a result of laryngeal adduction, are involved in the maintenance of FRC. This mechanism is also present, to a lesser degree, in normal ovine (and probably human) neonates during quiet sleep. Whether it exists in other species remains to be established. Expiratory resistance of the larynx is under vagal control, and pulmonary stretch receptors are the likely sensors. Species differences apparently exist in the means by which expiratory airflow is retarded. These may be due in part, however, to the widespread use of anesthetic agents that selectively depress the activity of laryngeal adductor muscles. There is clearly a need for wider use of techniques involving chronic instrumentation, particularly in the neonatal period. Because the upper airway is involved in the regulation of tidal airflow, it also seems vital that the airway remains intact wherever possible.

In addition to controlling airflow, the larynx is an important sensory organ, protecting the lower airways from invasion by potentially harmful substances, e.g. during suckle feeding and regurgitation. In the neonate, laryngeal stimulation may result in prolonged respiratory arrest. Although there is some evidence that longer apnea can be elicited in the neonate than in the adult, the use of anesthesia, which may more strongly depress respiration in the young, complicates the issue. As yet, there are no firm grounds for explaining these findings, at either a peripheral or central level. Defensive mechanisms, including arousal, swallowing, and circulatory changes to cope with hypoxemia, are well established at birth. The healthy neonate would seem well equipped to survive entry of liquids into the larynx. However, it is not inconceivable that, under certain circumstances and in the absence of anesthesia, substances entering the larynx could trigger prolonged apnea or cardiac arrest.

Literature Cited

1. Adams, F. A., Desilets, D. T., Towers, B. 1967. Control of flow of fetal lung liquid at the laryngeal outlet. *Resp. Physiol.* 2:302–9
2. Adamson, T. M., Brodecky, V., Lambert, F. F., Maloney, J. E., Ritchie, B. C., Walker, A. M. 1975. Lung liquid production and composition in the "in utero" foetal lamb. *Aust. J. Exp. Biol. Med. Sci.* 53:65–75
3. Alcorn, D., Adamson, T. M., Lambert, T. F., Maloney, J. E., Ritchie, B. C., Robinson, P. M. 1977. Morphological effects of chronic tracheal ligation and drainage in fetal lamb. *J. Anat.* 123:649–60
4. Angell-James, J. E., Daly, M. de B. 1975. Some aspects of upper respiratory tract reflexes. *Acta Oto-Laryngol.* 79: 242–52
5. Bartlett, D., Remmers, J. E., Gautier, H. 1973. Laryngeal regulation of respiratory airflow. *Resp. Physiol.* 18:194–204
6. Biscoe, T. J., Sampson, S. R. 1970. An analysis of the inhibition of phrenic motoneurones that occurs on stimulation of some cranial nerve afferents. *J. Physiol.* 209:375–93
7. Boggs, D. F., Bartlett, D. 1982. Chemical specificity of a laryngeal apneic reflex in puppies. *J. Appl. Physiol.* 53:455–62
8. Bosma, J. F. 1975. Introduction to the Symposium. In *Development of Upper Respiratory Anatomy and Function*, ed. J. F. Bosma, J. Showacre, pp. 5–49. Washington: US Dept. Health, Educ. Welfare
9. Boushey, H. A., Richardson, P. S., Widdicombe, J. G., Wise, J. C. M. 1974. The response of laryngeal afferent fibres to mechanical and chemical stimuli. *J. Physiol.* 240:153–75
10. Bradley, R. M., Cheal, M. L., Kim, Y. H. 1980. Quantitative analysis of developing epiglottal taste buds in sheep. *J. Anat.* 130:25–32
11. Bradley, R. M., Mistretta, C. M. 1973. The gustatory sense in foetal sheep during the last third of gestation. *J. Physiol.* 231:271–82
12. Bystrzycka, E., Nail, B. S., Purves, M. J. 1975. Central and peripheral neural respiratory activity in the mature sheep foetus and newborn lamb. *Resp. Physiol.* 25:199–215
13. Cohen, M. J., Hagiwara, S., Zotterman, Y. 1955. The response spectrum of taste fibres in the cat: A single fibre analysis. *Acta Physiol. Scand.* 33:316–32
14. Daly, M. de B., Angell-James, J. E., Elsner, R. 1979. Role of carotid-body chemoreceptors and their reflex interactions in bradycardia and cardiac arrest. *Lancet* 1:764–67
15. Davis, J. N. 1970. An experimental study of hiccup. *Brain* 93:851–52
16. Dawes, G. S., Fox, H. E., Leduc, B. M., Liggins, G. C., Richards, R. T. 1972. Respiratory movements and rapid eye movement sleep in the foetal lamb. *J. Physiol.* 220:119–43
17. De Wolf, F., Vanderberghe, K. 1980. A study by ultrasound of the larynx in the human fetus. *Proc. 7th Int. Work. Fetal Breathing*, p. 32. Oxford
18. Downing, S. E., Lee, J. C. 1975. Laryngeal chemosensitivity: a possible mechanism for sudden infant death. *Pediatrics* 55:640–49
19. Fagenholz, S. A., Lee, J. C., Downing, S. E. 1979. Laryngeal reflex apnea in the chemodenervated newborn piglet. *Am. J. Physiol.* 237:R10–14
20. Farber, J. P. 1978. Laryngeal effects and

respiration in the suckling opossum. *Resp. Physiol.* 35:189–200

21. Fewell, J. E., Johnson, P. 1983. Upper airway dynamics during breathing and during apnoea in fetal lambs. *J. Physiol.* 339:495–504

22. Gautier, H., Remmers, J. E., Bartlett, D. 1973. Control of the duration of expiration. *Resp. Physiol.* 18:205–21

23. Harding, R. 1980. State related and developmental changes in laryngeal function. *Sleep* 3:307–22

23a. Harding, R. 1984. Perinatal development of laryngeal function. *J. Develop. Physiol.* In press

24. Harding, R., Johnson, P., Johnston, B. M., McClelland, M. E., Wilkinson, A. R. 1975. Cardiovascular changes in newborn lambs during apnea induced by stimulation of laryngeal receptors with water. *J. Physiol.* 256:35–36P

25. Harding, R., Johnson, P., McClelland, M. E., McLeod, C. N., Whyte, P. L. 1977. Laryngeal function during breathing and swallowing in fetal and newborn lambs. *J. Physiol.* 272:14–15P

26. Harding, R., Johnson, P., McClelland, M. E., McLeod, C. N., Whyte, P. L., Wilkinson, A. R. 1978. Respiratory and cardiovascular responses to feeding in lambs. *J. Physiol.* 275:40–41P

27. Harding, R., Johnson, P., McClelland, M. E., 1978. Liquid sensitive laryngeal receptors in the developing sheep, cat, and monkey. *J. Physiol.* 277:409–22

28. Harding, R., Johnson, P., McClelland, M. E. 1979. The expiratory role of the larynx during development and the influence of behavioural state. In *Central Nervous Control Mechanisms in Breathing,* ed. C. von Euler, H. Lagercrantz, pp. 353–59. Oxford: Pergamon

29. Harding, R., Johnson, P., McClelland, M. E. 1980. Respiratory function of the larynx in developing sheep and the influence of sleep state. *Resp. Physiol.* 40: 165–79

30. Harding, R., Titchen, D. A. 1981. Oesophageal and diaphragmatic activity during suckling in lambs. *J. Physiol.* 321:317–29

31. Harned, H. S., Myracle, J., Ferreiro, J. 1978. Respiratory suppression and swallowing from introduction of fluids into the laryngeal region of the lamb. *Pediatr. Res.* 12:1003–9

32. Harrison, V. C., Heese, H. de V., Klein, M. 1968. The significance of grunting in hyaline membrane disease. *Pediatrics* 41:549–59

33. Henderson-Smart, D. J., Read, D. J. C. 1979. Reduced lung volume during behavioural active sleep in the newborn. *J. Appl. Physiol.* 46:1081–85

34. Iscoe, S., Feldman, J. L., Cohen, M. I. 1979. Properties of inspiratory termination by superior laryngeal and vagal stimulation. *Resp. Physiol.* 36:353–66

35. Johnson, P. 1974. Laryngeal induced apnea. In *SIDS: Proceedings of the Francis E. Camps Symposium,* ed. R. R. Robinson, pp. 231–42. Toronto: Can. Found. Study of Infant Death

36. Johnson, P. 1979. Comparative aspects of control of breathing during development. In *Central Nervous Control Mechanisms in Breathing,* ed. C. von Euler, H. Lagercrantz, pp. 337–52. Oxford: Permagon

37. Johnson, P., Harding, R., McClelland, M. E., Whyte, P. 1977. Laryngeal influence on lung expansion and breathing in lambs. *Pediatr. Res.* 11:1025

38. Jouvet, M. 1967. Neurophysiology of sleep states. *Physiol. Rev.* 47:117–77

39. Karlberg, P., Cherry, R. B., Escardo, F. E., Koch, G. 1962. Respiratory studies in newborn infants. II. Pulmonary ventilation and mechanics of breathing in the first four minutes of life, including the onset of respiration. *Acta Pediatr. Scand.* 51:121–35

40. Koizumi, H., Mikami, S. 1953. On innervation of mucous membrane of larynx in canine fetus. *Tohoku J. Exp. Med.* 58:217–21

41. Konrad, H. R., Rattenborg, C. C. 1969. Combined action of laryngeal muscles. *Acta Oto–Laryngol.* 67:646–49

42. Kovar, I., Selstam, U., Catterton, W. Z., Stahlman, M. T., Sundell, H. W. 1979. Laryngeal chemoreflex in newborn lambs: Respiratory and swallowing response to salt, acids, and sugars. *Pediatr. Res.* 13:1144–49

43. Kurtz, D., Kreiger, J., Stierle, J. C. 1978. EMG activity of cricothyroid and chin muscles during wakefulness and sleeping in sleep apnea syndrome. *EEG & Clin. Neurophysiol.* 45:777–84

44. Lachmann, B., Grossmann, G., Nilsson, R., Robertson, B. 1979. Lung mechanics during spontaneous ventilation in premature and full term rabbit neonates. *Resp. Physiol.* 38:283–302

45. Laitman, J. T., Crelin, E. S., Conlogue, G. J. 1977. The function of the epiglottis in monkey and man. *Yale J. Biol. Med.* 50:43–48

46. Lawson, E. E. 1981. Prolonged central respiratory inhibition following reflex-induced apnea. *J. Appl. Physiol.* 50:874–79

47. Lee, J. C., Stoll, B. J., Downing, S. E. 1977. Properties of the laryngeal chemoreflex in neonatal piglets. *Am. J. Physiol.* 2:30–36

48. Lewis, P. J., Trudinger, B. 1977. Fetal hiccups. *Lancet* 2:355
49. Liggins, G. C., Kitterman, J. A. 1981. Development of the fetal lung. In *The Fetus and Independent Life, Ciba Found. Symp. 86*. pp. 308–30 London: Pitman
50. Lucier, G. E., Storey, A. T., Sessle, B. J. 1979. Effects of upper respiratory tract stimuli on neonatal respiration and single neuron analysis in the kitten. *Biol. Neonate* 38:82–89
51. Maloney, J. E., Adamson, T. M., Brodecky, V., Cranage, S., Lambert, T. F., Ritchie, B. C. 1975. Diaphragmatic activity and lung liquid flow in the unanaesthetized fetal sheep. *J. Appl. Physiol.* 39:423–28
52. Marchal, F., Corke, B. C., Sundell, H. 1982. Reflex apnea from laryngeal chemo-stimulation in the sleeping premature new-born lamb. *Pediatr. Res.* 16:621–27
53. Miller, A. J., Loizzi, R. F. 1974. Anatomical and functional differentiation of superior laryngeal nerve fibers affecting swallowing and respiration. *Exp. Neurol.* 42:369–87
54. Milner, A. D., Saunder, R. A. 1977. Pressure and volume changes during the first breath of human neonates. *Arch. Dis. Child.* 52:918–24
55. Moomjian, A. S., Schwartz, J. G., Wagaman, M. J., Shutack, J. G., Shaffer, T. H., Fox, W. W. 1980. The effect of external expiratory resistance on lung volume and pulmonary function in the neonate. *J. Pediatr.* 96:908–11
56. Muller-Tyl, E., Szalay, S., Losert, U., Salzer, H. 1981. Measuring intratracheal pressure in sheep fetuses *in utero*. *Z. Geburtshilfe Perinatol.* 185:354–59
57. Orem, J., Netick, A., Dement, W. C. 1977. Increased upper airway resistance to breathing during sleep in the cat. *EEG & Clin. Neurophysiol.* 43:14–22
58. Patrick, J., Fetherston, W., Vick, H., Voegelin, R. 1978. Human fetal breathing movements and gross fetal body movements at weeks 34 to 35 of gestation. *Am. J. Obstet. Gynecol.* 130:693–99
59. Radvanyi-Bouvet, M. F., Monset-Couchard, M., Morel-Kahn, F., Vicente G., Dreyfus-Brisac, C. 1981. Expiratory patterns during sleep in normal full-term and premature neonates. *Biol. Neonate* 41:74–84
60. Remmers, J. E., Bartlett, D. 1977. Reflex control of expiratory airflow and duration. *J. Appl. Physiol.* 42:80–87
61. Sasaki, C. T. 1979. Development of laryngeal function: etiologic significance in the sudden infant death syndrome. *Laryngoscope,* 89:1964–82
62. Sasaki, C. T., Suzuki, M. 1976. Laryngeal reflexes in cat, dog and man. *Arch. Otolaryngol.* 102:400–2
63. Sessle, B. J., Greenwood, L. F., Lund, J. P., Lucier, G. E. 1978. Effect of upper respiratory tract stimuli on respiration and single respiratory neurons in the adult cat. *Exp. Neurol.* 61:245–59
64. Sherrey, J. H., Megirian, D. 1974. Spontaneous and reflexly evoked laryngeal abductor and adductor muscle activity of cat. *Exp. Neurol.* 43:487–98
65. Sherrey, J. H., Megirian, D. 1975. Analysis of the respiratory role of intrinsic laryngeal motoneurones of cat. *Exp. Neurol.* 49:456–65
66. Sherrey, J. H., Megirian, D. 1980. Respiratory EMG activity of the posterior cricoarytenoid, cricothyroid, and diaphragm muscles during sleep. *Resp. Physiol.* 39:355–65
67. Shingai, T. 1977. Ionic mechanism of water receptors in the laryngeal mucosa of the rabbit. *Jpn. J. Physiol.* 27:27–42
68. Shingai, T. 1979. Physicochemical study of receptive mechanism of laryngeal water fibers in the rabbit. *Jpn. J. Physiol.* 29:459–570
69. Spann, R. W., Hyatt, R. E. 1971. Factors affecting upper airway resistance in conscious man. *J. Appl. Physiol.* 31:708–12
70. Storey, A. T. 1968. A functional analysis of sensory units innervating epiglottis and larynx. *Exp. Neurol.* 20:366–83
71. Storey, A. T., Johnson, P. 1975. Laryngeal water receptors initiating apnea in the lamb. *Exp. Neurol.* 47:42–55
72. Sullivan, C. E., Murphy, E., Kozar, L. F., Phillipson, E. A. 1978. Waking and ventilatory responses to laryngeal stimulation in sleeping dogs. *J. Appl. Physiol.* 45:681–89
73. Sutton, D., Taylor, E. M., Lindeman, R. C. 1978. Prolonged apnea in infant monkeys resulting from stimulation of superior laryngeal nerve. *Pediatrics* 61:519–21
74. Suzuki, M., Sasaki, C. 1977. Laryngeal spasm: a neurophysiological redefinition. *Ann. Otol. Rhinol. Laryngol.* 86:150–58
75. Tchobroutsky, C., Merlet, C., Rey, P. 1969. The diving reflex in rabbit, sheep, and newborn lambs and its afferent pathways. *Resp. Physiol.* 8:108–17
76. Vilos, G. A., Liggins, G. C. 1982. Intrathoracic pressures in fetal sheep. *J. Develop. Physiol.* 4:247–56

Ann. Rev. Physiol. 1984. 46:661–74

CONTROL OF VENTILATION IN THE NEWBORN

H. Rigatto

Department of Pediatrics, University of Manitoba, Winnipeg, Manitoba

INTRODUCTION

Neonates are unique in their control of ventilation. They differ in many respects from adults. In response to inhalation of low O_2, for example, they decrease rather than increase ventilation (9, 45). Furthermore, in response to inhaled CO_2 the increase in ventilation is greatest at highest-background O_2 concentration (47). This is the opposite of the response in the adult subject, in whom the response to CO_2 is greatest at lowest O_2 concentration. The reason for these peculiar responses in neonates is not known, but it is tempting to postulate that it reflects a transition in the development of the respiratory control system that, after birth, assumes the role of gas exchange—a job previously performed by the placenta in utero. This new job requires continuous breaths, as opposed to the intermittent process prevalent in utero. New levels of somatic and behavioral stimuli, such as O_2 tension, blood pressure, and feeding, represent a change in feedback input to which the respiratory system must adjust itself. This adjustment is not a simple task, and hence the respiratory control system tends towards instability. This instability may manifest itself in the form of periodic breathing, or by apnea. Because apnea may cause brain damage, understanding the factors controlling ventilation in the neonate is important. In this chapter, I review some of the new developments in this area.

METHODOLOGY APPLIED TO THE NEONATE

Newborn infants are small and do not cooperate. Measurements of the respiratory control system therefore require special facilities, equipment, and human resources. Infants must be studied in a quiet space, preferably adjacent to the nursery. Light, noise, and touch must be kept constant and minimal. Tempera-

661

0066-4278/84/0315-0661$02.00

ture should be rigorously controlled and provided by incubators with servo control. For measurements to be technically acceptable, equipment such as nosepieces, flowmeters, and nasal samplers must be adaptable to various sizes (44). Personnel requirements for study include one research nurse, one technician, and one physician. Because neonates sleep most of the time, sleep state must be monitored if we want to compare results with those in adults or in other species. Much of the earlier research done in this field inappropriately compared measurements in the sleeping infant with those in the awake adult. Because the compliant rib cage of neonates favors distortion of the chest wall, particularly during active sleep (7), it is imperative to monitor the presence of chest distortion while making measurements such as the ventilatory response to CO_2 or O_2 or the response to elastic loads.

In summary, the above factors have to be carefully controlled for results and comparisons to be meaningful.

FROM FETUS TO NEONATE

In order to understand better the control of breathing in neonates, it is useful to recall some aspects of respiratory control during fetal life. Dawes et al (11) and Merlet et al (30) settled a long-time debate by clearly demonstrating that the fetus indeed makes respiratory efforts in utero. Since this activity is not aimed at gas exchange and is present only during low-voltage electrocortical activity, it was thought by many to represent a sleep-state activity; that is, it would occur during rapid-eye-movement (REM) sleep as one of the manifestations of this sleep state, rather than as a reflection of a true development of respiratory activity. Some initial inability to assess effective chemical and vagal respiratory responses in the fetus helped nurture this view. With time, however, it became clear that the respiratory system of the fetus responds conventionally to increased CO_2 or vagotomy. It responds to low O_2 with abrupt cessation of respiratory efforts (6, 8). It also became clear that, although breathing does not occur during high-voltage electrocortical activity, the sleep state has little or nothing to do with the intermittent nature of fetal breathing. This statement is supported by the following observations. First, the appearance of intermittent breathing in utero precedes by 5–8 days the electrocortical differentiation (43). Second, after birth the newborn lamb breathes continuously, although the sleep-state cycling remains essentially unaltered from that of the fetus in late gestation. Sleep state seems therefore to modulate breathing in utero rather than providing a primary inducing role.

A discovery almost as thrilling as the one establishing fetal breathing was made recently, also by the Dawes group at Oxford (12). Continuous fetal breathing was induced in fetal lambs by brain section at mid-collicular level. These brain-sectioned fetuses responded to hypoxia with a sustained increase in ventilation. The results seem to indicate that the fetus does have the potential to breathe continuously and to respond to hypoxia with an increase in ventilation, but that it usually does not do so because of supra–mid-collicular inhibition. This inhibition is consistent with Barcroft's ideas of a respiratory system in utero inhibited during the second half of pregnancy (4). Perhaps this central inhibition persists during the newborn period and is responsible for the late (5 min) decrease in ventilation during hypoxia. This is certainly a tempting postulate.

THE CHEMICAL CONTROL OF BREATHING

The Response to Low O_2

The inability of preterm infants to sustain hyperventilation in response to hypoxia remains the most interesting chemical peculiarity of the respiratory control system in the neonatal period (9, 45). This type of response has also been shown in rabbits, kittens, and monkeys (51, 55). The exact mechanism involved is unknown, but some recent work performed in kittens produced some interesting results (5). In a manner similar to the human neonate, kittens responded "biphasically": with an initial increase in ventilation followed by a decrease when inspired oxygen concentrations were reduced from 20.9% to 6–12% (Figure 1). The initial increase in ventilation (1 min) was due to an increase in tidal volume and frequency, while the late (5–10 min) decrease in ventilation was due primarily to a decrease in frequency. That the peripheral chemoreceptors were active during hypoxia is reflected by a steady increase in carotid-body single-fiber firing. This increase in carotid-body activity contrasted with the simultaneous decrease in diaphragmatic activity towards the end of hypoxia (5 min) (Figure 2).

In experiments in which the phrenic nerve and the diaphragm were recorded simultaneously, there was an initial increase in activity to a peak level at about 1 min., followed by a decrease, usually in frequency, but at times in peak activity as well (Figure 3). There was no distinction between the phrenic and diaphragmatic electrical activity. These latter findings together with those showing an increase in carotid-nerve firing, which was maximum at the time respiratory efforts were about to stop, suggest that the late decrease in ventilation during hypoxia is due to inhibition at the central level. This line of thinking is consistent with the inhibition present in utero and released by mid-collicular section.

It has been recently suggested that the decrease in ventilation in response to hypoxia may be related to endogenous opiates. In the newborn rabbit, Grunstein et al were able to prevent the late decrease in ventilation by administration of naloxone, an endogenous opiate antagonist (17). Hazinski et al showed an

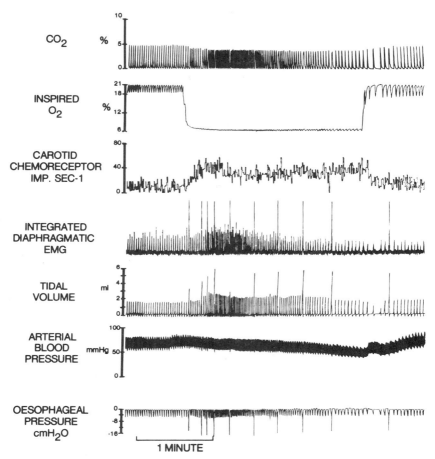

Figure 1 Pentobarbitone-anesthetized kitten, 17 days old. Effect on pattern of breathing of abruptly reducing inspired O_2 to 6% for 4.5 minutes. There are breaks in blood pressure when samples were taken. Note that, after an initial increase, frequency, tidal volume, and diaphragmatic EMG fall below control levels. For further discussion see text.

increase in ventilation of anesthetized rabbits in response to naloxone during the first four days of life (21). Preliminary observations in the newborn infant suggest that naloxone inhibits, at least in part, the late decrease in ventilation during hypoxia (13). Observations in the fetus are conflicting, with some studies showing a response and others no response to naloxone (32).

Sleep affects the response to low oxygen. The increase in ventilation in response to hypoxia was better sustained during quiet sleep than during active sleep or wakefulness (Figure 4) (48). Jeffery & Read (24) also found a more sustained increase in ventilation during quiet as compared to active sleep in

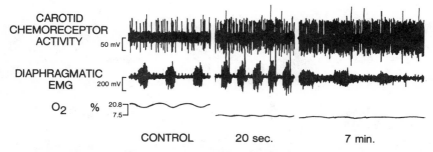

Figure 2 Effect of hypoxia on carotid chemoreceptor and diaphragmatic activity. At 20 sec of hypoxia both activities are increased. At 7 minutes of hypoxia, carotid-body nerve potentials are largely increased, whereas diaphragmatic EMG is much decreased.

calves. The increase in ventilation with hypoxia during quiet sleep in neonates, however, was not as well sustained as in adult subjects. The results imply that the "biphasic" response to hypoxia is altered, in part, by behavioral influences on breathing that are more pronounced during active sleep and wakefulness. This effect of sleep on the response to hypoxia, however, seems only modulatory, and the primary mechanism is likely to be central inhibition.

The Response to CO_2

The newborn infant responds to inhaled CO_2 with an increase in ventilation. Per body weight, the response of neonates is similar to that of adult subjects and is about 0.035 ml/min/Kg/mmHgPACO$_2$ (44). The position of the CO_2 response curve in neonates (i.e. minute ventilation vs inspired CO_2 concentration) is shifted to the left of that of adult subjects by about 4 mmHg. This has been traditionally explained on the basis of a lower bicarbonate level in neonates (2).

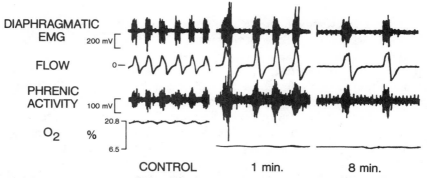

Figure 3 Electrical activity of the diaphragm and phrenic nerve during hypoxia. There is a simultaneous and transient increase in activity (1 min) followed by a decrease in frequency towards the end of hypoxia (8 min).

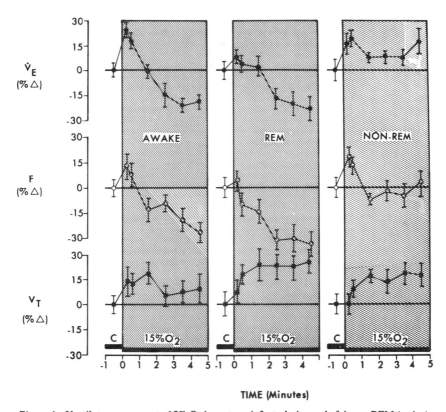

Figure 4 Ventilatory response to 15% O_2 in preterm infants during wakefulness, REM (active), and N-REM (quiet) sleep. With 15% O_2 there is an immediate increase, followed by a decrease in ventilation in wakefulness and REM sleep; in N-REM sleep hyperventilation is sustained.

Within the newborn population, preterm infants respond less to CO_2 than term infants (15, 27, 46). It is not clear whether the decreased response to CO_2 in preterm infants is due to less responsive central chemoreceptors, poor performance of the respiratory "pump," or both. To elucidate this we compared a group of preterm infants with a group of term infants using the rebreathing technique (31). Minute integrated diaphragmatic activity ($EMG_{di} \times f$), an index of central output, increased less in response to inhaled CO_2 in preterm than in term infants. However, indices of mechanical effectiveness, such as minute ventilation divided by mean inspiratory diaphragmatic activity ($\dot{V}_E$)/(EMG_{di}/T_i) were not different in preterm and term infants, suggesting that the respiratory "pump" effectively transforms the central output into negative intrapleural pressure or volume. These results indicate that the respiratory pump is not at fault in the decreased ventilatory response to CO_2 in preterm infants, and the decreased response is likely to be centrally mediated.

Using the steady-state method, we could not detect a difference in response to CO_2 in active vs quiet sleep (10). Our recent observations using the rebreathing technique, however, suggests that during the "phasic" part of active sleep the respiratory system is less responsive to CO_2. This agrees with studies in dogs in which the response to CO_2 was also less in phasic active sleep than in quiet sleep (36, 53).

Of interest has been the effect of chest distortion on the response to CO_2. The chest wall of preterm infants, because of its large compliance, distorts with great ease. This is accentuated in the phasic periods of active sleep. If the response to CO_2 in quiet and active sleep is standardized by fixing the duration of distorted and nondistorted breaths, the response to CO_2 becomes indistinguishable in both sleep states (29). These findings suggest that the decreased CO_2 response in active as compared to quiet sleep is not due to the possible mechanical disadvantage of chest distortion during active sleep. It is more likely that this decreased response to CO_2 relates to the basic mechanisms involved in the production of shorter and smaller breaths in active sleep. The combination of a high and variable frequency and small tidal volumes in active sleep may be less effective in generating an increase in ventilation during inhaled CO_2.

There has been controversy regarding the possibility that administration of low concentrations of CO_2 (less than 2%) may produce an increase in ventilation, mediated via chemoreceptors located in the airways (25). Such an increase in ventilation has been observed in the absence of an increase in arterial PCO_2. In our studies low concentrations of CO_2 did not alter ventilation unless there was a simultaneous increase in alveolar PCO_2 (26). Furthermore, the increased ventilatory response to low concentrations of CO_2 was due to an increase in breathing frequency during periodic breathing, and to an increase in tidal volume during regular breathing. This suggested to us that changes in respiratory pattern with low inhaled CO_2 are fundamentally dependent on whether the baseline respiration is periodic or regular.

Considerable interest has been generated by the notion that behavioral activity, for example phonation, can override, within limits, the chemical control of breathing. Phillipson et al (37) have shown that the response to inhaled CO_2 during speech mimics that seen in active sleep: it is quite scattered and decreased. We examined the effect of another behavioral activity, feeding, and found that the ventilatory response to CO_2 was reduced during sucking. The decreased response was related primarily to changes in "effective" respiratory timing, i.e. inspiratory time as a fraction of total respiratory cycle (T_i/T_{tot}), rather than in mean inspiratory flow (V_T/T_i) (14).

In recent experiments, Phillipson et al (34) have found that the afferent input provided by metabolic CO_2 load is vital to sustain respiratory rhythmicity (34, 52). In adult sheep, removal of venous CO_2 produced apnea that ceased only when CO_2 was loaded back into the venous blood (34). Similarly, the increase in ventilation during exercise was linearly related to the rate of CO_2 production (35). Surgical denervation of the carotid bodies was associated with hypoventilation and marked hypercapnia, suggesting that the peripheral chemoreceptors exert a major influence on the ventilatory response to changes in venous CO_2 load. These observations suggest that our notion of a "respiratory center" being a respiratory rhythm generator may need to be revised. The implication of these new concepts to the domain of neonatal respiratory control have not yet been fully evaluated.

In summary, in recent years it has become clear that the response of the neonate ventilation to CO_2 may be affected by sleep and by behavior. These factors may be important in the response to chemical stimuli, especially when the ability to arouse is impaired. The new concept of a "respiratory center" entirely dependent on afferent stimuli, particularly venous PCO_2, is provocative, and its significance to the respiratory control system in the newborn must be examined.

RESPIRATORY MECHANICS

The respiratory system develops such that total respiratory compliance (CL)/ lung volume ($CL = \Delta$ volume/ Δ transmural pressure) remains relatively unchanged with age (1, 3). The lung is stiff in the preterm infant, with an air/tissue ratio that is low in comparison to the adult person. The rib cage, on the other hand, is extremely cartilaginous. It is very compliant in the preterm infant, becoming less so with age. This compromise is disadvantageous to the preterm infant, whose rib cage is prone to collapse. Distortion in these infants is therefore common: the negative pressure created by the diaphragmatic contraction moves the rib cage inwards instead of displacing the lungs caudally.

We determined how much the effectiveness and efficiency of the respiratory apparatus are compromised by chest distortion. We studied preterm and term infants using breaths that were and were not associated with chest distortion with equal duration and similar chemical drive (29). A distorted breath produced the same instantaneous ventilation as a nondistorted breath. However, the work performed by the diaphragm was 40% more during distortion than during nondistortion (Figure 5) (29). The results suggested that chest distortion does not affect instantaneous ventilation but decreases the efficiency of the system due to excessive diaphragmatic work.

An implication of the peculiar coupling of diaphragm and chest wall in neonates relates to the postinspiratory activity of the diaphragm. This activity controls, in part, the duration of expiratory time (40, 41). In neonates we observed that this activity was more pronounced in the lateral than in the crural part of the diaphragm, longer in quiet than in active sleep, and more prolonged

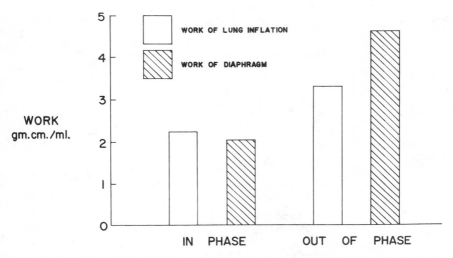

Figure 5   Work of lung inflation and of diaphragm when breathing is in-phase or out-of-phase. The work of lung inflation is not significantly different when the breath is in-phase or out-of-phase. However, the work of the diaphragm is approximately 40% greater when the breath is out-of-phase as opposed to in-phase.

in preterm than in term infants (Figure 6) (49). It correlated well with expiratory time when pulmonary resistance and tidal volume were kept constant (54). The length and variability of this activity in premature infants suggests that, due to their highly compliant chest wall, these infants use the postinspiratory diaphragmatic activity as a braking mechanism whose role in maintaining lung volume and controlling expiratory time is much more relevant than in older children or adult subjects.

Another implication of the lung and chest wall coupling in small infants is that regulation of upper airway resistance is of much greater relevance in determining expiratory time and preventing lung collapse at end expiration. Studies by Harding et al (20) in fetal and neonatal lambs suggest that the abductor muscles of the larynx— the posterior cricoarytenoid and cricothyroid—have inspiratory activities in parallel with that of the diaphragm, both during quiet and active sleep. On the contrary, the adductor muscles of the larynx—the thyroarytenoid, lateral cricoarytenoid, and intra-arytenoid—have a phasic expiratory activity during quiet sleep. This activity is lost during active sleep in the fetus and in the newborn lamb. Thus, these studies indicate that sleep state profoundly affects upper airway resistance. In conjunction with decreased intercostal tonus and decreased postinspiratory diaphragmatic activity during active sleep, a decrease in adductor activity of the larynx may be crucial for a decrease in lung volume observed during this sleep state (23). The

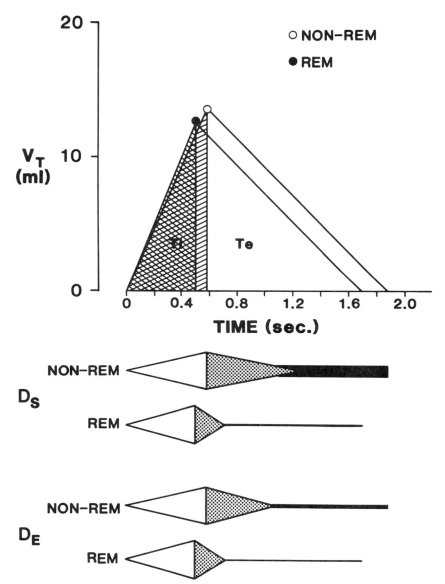

Figure 6   Diagramatic changes in tidal volume, "timing," and diaphragmatic EMG in non-REM (quiet) and REM (active) sleep. Note that total phasic activity diminishes from non-REM to REM sleep. Also, in both sleep states it is shorter in esophageal (D_E) than in surface EMG (D_S). Expiratory phasic activity as a proportion of total phasic activity decreases significantly from non-REM to REM sleep.

exact role of these muscles on the induction of obstructive apneas is not clear, as most apneas in the neonatal lambs are central in origin (20).

SLEEP

The effect of sleep on respiratory control has been a matter of considerable interest in recent years (10, 16, 18, 33, 38, 50). It may be relevant therefore, to examine the effect of sleep on respiration in the absence of stimulation.

First, various studies have suggested that sleep modifies the pattern of breathing (16, 19, 50). For instance, it accentuates periodic breathing and increases the length of the respiratory pause. Sleep is not, however, responsible for periodic breathing in small infants, because this respiratory pattern can be seen during wakefulness (48).

Second, the respiratory pattern differs between quiet sleep and active sleep. Breathing is more regular during quiet than during active sleep. However, it is a misconception derived from criteria used in adult subjects that infants in quiet sleep do not breathe periodically. They do, and both Prechtl and ourselves have documented this very clearly (38, 48). What happens is that periodic breathing is very "regular" during quiet sleep, with the length of breathing intervals and apneas being constant. During active sleep, periodic breathing is irregular, with breathing intervals and apneas that are variable in duration. Therefore, the breathing pattern in quiet sleep in preterm infants can be either regular or periodic.

Third, apneas are more common, longer, and more frequently associated with bradycardia during active than during quiet sleep (16, 42, 50). Apneas in quiet sleep may at times be associated with bradycardia, particularly when they are related to pulmonary or central nervous dysfunction. There is no evidence however, that apneas associated with bradycardia are obstructive rather than central, and a failure to arouse may be present in either type of apnea during sleep.

Fourth, sleep also affects the respiratory muscles. During the phasic part of active sleep, the intercostal muscles lose their tonus and the chest wall is more prone to collapse (19, 22, 28). Electromyographic evidence of intercostal inactivity during active sleep has been documented in newborn lambs (22) and in newborn infants (19, 28, 39). Henderson-Smart & Read (23) found a 30% decrease in functional residual capacity during active as opposed to quiet sleep in neonates. An increased frequency of chest distortions during active sleep has also been demonstrated (7).

In summary, in the newborn sleep seems to influence respiration via central and peripheral mechanisms. It modulates rather than determines the pattern of breathing. In most instances this role is of no consequence to the respiratory control system, but in situations where the controller system is disturbed by disease, sleep may be a crucial element in triggering irreversible apnea.

In conclusion, there are peculiarities affecting the respiratory control system during the neonatal period that are unique to this age period. The most fascinating of these is the inability to respond to hypoxia with sustained hyperventilation. It is tempting to consider this inability as a developmental phenomenom, by postulating that this inhibition is central and is the "tail" of the inhibition present in fetal life, a period when the response to hypoxia is a cessation of respiratory movements. It is also quite likely that sleep has a modulatory effect on breathing, which may be crucial in situations where this "congenital" inhibition of breathing is more pronounced. It may then impair the mechanism responsible for arousal.

Literature Cited

1. Agostoni, E. 1959. Volume-pressure relationships of the thorax and lung in the newborn. *J. Appl. Physiol.* 14:909–13
2. Avery, M. E., Chernick, V., Dutton, R. E., Permutt, S. 1963. Ventilatory response to inspired carbon dioxide in infants and adults. *J. Appl. Physiol.* 18:895–903
3. Avery, M. E., Cook, C. D. 1961. Volume-pressure relationships of lungs and thorax in fetal, newborn, and adult goats. *J. Appl. Physiol.* 16:1034–38
4. Barcroft, J. 1946. The onset of respiratory movement. In *Researches on Prenatal Life,* 1:260–72. Oxford: Blackwell Scientific
5. Blanco, C. E., Hanson, M. A., Johnson, P., Rigatto, H. 1981. The pattern of breathing of kittens during hypoxia. *Pediatr. Res.* 15:652
6. Boddy, K., Dawes, G. S., Fisher, R., Pinter, S., Robinson, J. S. 1974. Foetal respiratory movements, electrocortical and cardiovascular response to hypoxemia and hypercapnia in sheep. *J. Physiol.* 243:599–618
7. Bryan, A. C., Bryan, M. H. 1978. Control of respiration in the newborn. *Clin. Perinatol.* 5:269–81
8. Condorelli, S., Scarpelli, E. M. 1976. Fetal breathing: induction *in utero* and effects of vagotomy and barbiturates. *J. Pediatr.* 88:94–101
9. Cross, K. S., Oppe, T. W. 1952. The effect of inhalation of high and low concentrations of oxygen on the respiration of the premature infant. *J. Physiol.* 117:38–55
10. Davi, M., Sankaran, K., MacCallum, M., Cates, D., Rigatto, H. 1979. The effect of sleep state on chest distortion

and on the ventilatory response to CO_2 in neonates. *Pediatr. Res.* 13:982–86
11. Dawes, G. S., Fox, H. E., Leduc, B. M., Liggins, G. C., Richards, R. T. 1972. Respiratory movements and rapid eye movement in sleep in the fetal lamb. *J. Physiol.* 220:119–43
12. Dawes, G. S., Gardner, W. N., Johnston, B. M., Walker, D. W. 1980. Breathing patterns in lambs after midbrain transection. *J. Physiol.* 308:29P
13. DeBoeck, C., Van Reempts, P., Rigatto, H., Chernick, V. 1983. Endorphins and the ventilatory depression during hypoxia in newborn infants. *Pediatr. Res.* 17(4):374A
14. Durand, M., Leahy, F. N., MacCallum, M., Cates, D. B., Rigatto, H., Chernick, V. 1981. Effect of feeding on the chemical control of breathing in the newborn infant. *Pediatr. Res.* 15:1509–12
15. Frantz, I. D. III, Adler, S. M., Thach, B. T., Taeusch, H. W. Jr. 1976. Malnutritional effects on respiratory response to carbon dioxide in premature infants. *J. Appl. Physiol.* 41:41–45
16. Gabriel, M., Albani, M., Schulte, F. J. 1976. Apneic spells and sleep state in preterm infants. *Pediatrics* 57:142–47
17. Grunstein, M. M., Hazinski, T. A., Schlueter, M. A. 1981. Respiratory control during hypoxia in newborn rabbits: implied action of endorphins. *J. Appl. Physiol.* 51:122–30
18. Guilleminault, C., Ariagno, R., Korobkin, R., Nagel, L., Baldwin, R., et al. 1979. Mixed and obstructive sleep apnea and near miss for sudden infant death syndrome. 2. Comparison of near miss and normal control infants by age. *Pediatrics* 64:882–91

19. Hagan, R. A. C., Bryan, A. C., Bryan, M. H., Gulston, G. 1976. The effect of sleep state on intercostal muscle activity and rib cage motion. *Physiologist* 19:214

20. Harding, R., Johnson, P., McClelland, M. E. 1980. Respiratory function of the larynx in developing sheep and the influence of sleep state. *Resp. Physiol.* 40:165–79

21. Hazinski, T. A., Grunstein, M. M., Schlueter, M. A., Tooley, W. H. 1981. Effect of naloxone on ventilation in newborn rabbits. *J. Appl. Physiol.* 50:713–17

22. Henderson-Smart, D. J., Read, D. J. C. 1976. Depression of respiratory muscles and defective responses to nasal obstruction during active sleep in the newborn. *Aust. Paediatr. J.* 12:261–66

23. Henderson-Smart, D. J., Read, D. J. C. 1979. Reduced lung volume during behavioral active sleep in the newborn. *J. Appl. Physiol.* 46:1081–85

24. Jeffrey, H. E., Read, D. J. C. 1980. Ventilatory responses of newborn calves to progressive hypoxia in quiet and active sleep. *J. Appl. Physiol.* 48:892–95

25. Johnson, P. 1976. Evidence for lower airway chemoreceptors in newborn lambs. *Pediatr. Res.* 10:462

26. Kalapesi, Z., Durand, M., Leahy, F. N., Cates, D. B., MacCallum, M. et al. 1981. Effect of periodic or regular respiratory pattern on the ventilatory response to low inhaled CO_2 in preterm infants during sleep. *Am. Rev. Resp. Dis.* 11:123–28

27. Krauss, A. N., Klain, D. B., Waldman, S., Auld, P. A. M. 1975. Ventilatory response to carbon dioxide in newborn infants. *Pediatr. Res.* 9:46–50

28. Lopes, J., Muller, N. L., Bryan, M. H., Bryan, A. C. 1981. Importance of inspiratory muscle tone in maintenance of FRC in the newborn. *J. Appl. Physiol.* 51:830–34

29. Luz, J., Winter, A., Cates, D. B., Moore, M., Rigatto, H. 1982. Effect of chest breathing and abdomen uncoupling on ventilation and work of breathing in the newborn during sleep. *Pediatr. Res.* 16:296A

30. Merlet, C., Hoerter, J., Devilleneuve, O., Tchobroutsky, C. 1970. Mise en evidence de movements respiratoires chez le foetus d' agneau *in utero*. *J. Physiol. (Paris)* 62:416–17

31. Moriette, G., Van Reempts, P., Moore, M., Yorke, K., Rigatto, H. 1983. Does prematurity or chest distortion imply a mechanic disadvantage to neonates inhaling CO_2? *Pediatr. Res.* 17(4):328A

32. Moss, I. R., Scarpelli, E. M. 1979. Generation and regulation of breathing *in utero*: Fetal CO_2 response test. *J. Appl. Physiol.* 47:527–31

33. Phillipson, E. A. 1978. Control of breathing during sleep. *Am. Rev. Resp. Dis.* 118:909–39

34. Phillipson, E. A., Bowes, G., Townsend, E. R., Duffin, J., Cooper, J. D. 1981. Carotid chemoreceptors in ventilatory responses to changes in venous CO_2 load. *J. Appl. Physiol.* 51:1398–1403

35. Phillipson, E. A., Bowes, G., Townsend, E. R., Duffin, J., Cooper, J. D. 1981. Role of metabolic CO_2 production in ventilatory response to steady-state exercise. *J. Clin. Invest.* 68:768–74

36. Phillipson, E. A., Kozar, L. F., Rebuck, A. S., Murphy, E. 1977. Ventilatory and waking responses to CO_2 in sleeping dogs. *Am. Rev. Resp. Dis.* 115:251–59

37. Phillipson, E. A., McClean, P. A., Sullivan, C. E., Zamel, N. 1978. Interaction of metabolic and behavioral respiratory control during hypercapnia and speech. *Am. Rev. Resp. Dis.* 117:903–9

38. Prechtl, H. F. R. 1974. The behavioral states of the newborn infant. *Brain Res.* 76:185–212

39. Prechtl, H. F. R., VanEykern, L. A., O'Brien, M. J. 1977. Respiratory muscle EMG in newborns: a non-intrusive method. *Early Hum. Dev.* 1:265–83

40. Remmers, J. E., Bartlett, J. R. 1977. Reflex control of expiratory airflow and duration. *J. Appl. Physiol.* 42:80–87

41. Remmers, J. E., DeGroot, W. J., Sauerland, E. K., Anch, A. M. 1978. Pathogenesis of upper airway occlusion during sleep. *J. Appl. Physiol.* 44:931–38

42. Rigatto, H. 1982. Apnea. *Pediatr. Clin. North Am.* 29:1105–1116

43. Rigatto, H., Blanco, C. E., Walker, D. W. 1982. The response to stimulation of hind limb nerves in fetal sheep, *in utero*, during the different phases of electrocortical activity. *J. Dev. Physiol.* 4:175–85

44. Rigatto, H., Brady, J. P. 1972. Periodic breathing and apnea in preterm infants. I. Evidence of hypoventilation possibly due to central respiratory depression. *Pediatrics* 50:202–18

45. Rigatto, H., Brady, J. P. 1972. Periodic breathing and apnea in preterm infants. II. Hypoxia as a primary event. *Pediatrics* 50:219–28

46. Rigatto, H., Brady, J. P., de la Torre Verduzco, R. 1975. Chemoreceptor reflexes in preterm infants. 11. The effect of gestational and postnatal age on the ventilatory response to inhaled CO_2. *Pediatrics* 55:614–20

47. Rigatto, H., de la Torre Verduzco, R., Cates, D. 1975. Effects of O_2 on the

ventilatory responses to CO_2 in preterm infants. *J. Appl. Physiol.* 39:896–99

48. Rigatto, H., Kalapesi, Z., Leahy, F. N., Durand, M., MacCallum, M., et al. 1982. Ventilatory response to 100% and 15% O_2 during wakefulness and sleep in preterm infants. *Early Hum. Dev.* 7:1–16

49. Rigatto, H., Reis, F., Cates, D., Horvath, L. 1982. Effect of sleep on phasic and "tonic" diaphragmatic EMG in preterm infants. *Fed. Proc.* 41:1103

50. Schulte, F. J., Busse, C., Eichhorn, W. 1977. Rapid eye movement sleep, motoneurone inhibition, and apneic spells in preterm infants. *Ped. Res.* 11: 709–13

51. Schwieler, G. H. 1968. Respiratory regulation during postnatal development in cats and rabbits and some of its morphological substrate. *Acta. Physiol. Scan. (Suppl.)* 304:1–123

52. Sullivan, C. E., Kozar, L. F., Murphy, E., Phillipson, E. A. 1978. Primary role of respiratory afferents in sustaining breathing rhythm. *J. Appl. Physiol.* 45: 11–17

53. Sullivan, C. E., Murphy, E., Kozar, L. F., Phillipson, E. A. 1979. Ventilatory responses to CO_2 and lung inflation in tonic versus phasic REM sleep. *J. Appl. Physiol.* 47:1304–10

54. Van Reempts, P., Moriette, G., Cates, D., Yorke, K., Rigatto, H. 1983. The effect of post-inspiratory diaphragmatic activity (PI_{di}) on the control of expiration during sleep. *Pediatr. Res.* 17(4): 392A

55. Woodrum, D. E., Standaert, T. A., Mayock, D. E., Guthrie, R. D. 1981. Hypoxic ventilatory response in the newborn monkey. *Pediatr. Res.* 15: 367–70

Ann. Rev. Physiol. 1984. 46:675–85

REGULATION OF BREATHING IN THE NEWBORN DURING DIFFERENT BEHAVIORAL STATES

D. J. C. Read

Department of Physiology, University of Sydney, Sydney, N.S.W. 2006, Australia

D. J. Henderson-Smart

Perinatal Medicine, King George V Hospital, Camperdown, N.S.W. 2050, Australia

INTRODUCTION

In the newborn, reflexes that regulate breathing change remarkably in different states of sleep and wakefulness. The aim of this review is to introduce the reader to literature on this topic.

Behavioral states and respiratory reflexes have been studied for many years, but integration of these two disciplines is recent. Despite this, the literature already is extensive, especially in some clinical areas.

In this review, the bibliography emphasizes a comparison of sleep states and studies in healthy babies and newborn animals. For important concepts not yet tested in the newborn, some studies undertaken at older ages are cited.

Many valuable scientific contributions, including much pioneering research in the anesthetized state, had to be omitted due to space limitations. When appropriate, the text will state when authors have contributed important papers that can be found easily in recent publications. For more broadly based reviews, the reader should consult (27, 42, 46, 50).

675

0066-4278/84/0315-0675$02.00

DETERMINATION OF BEHAVIORAL STATES IN THE NEWBORN

In infants, several states usually are recognized: (*a*) active sleep (called rapid-eye-movement sleep, REM); (*b*) quiet sleep (called non-REM, NREM, or slow-wave sleep); (*c*) indeterminate sleep; and (*d*) waking (sometimes separated into crying, active, and quiet.) Usually, these states are defined by behavioral observations and polygraphic recordings of breathing, heart rate, eye movements, muscle tone, and electroencephalogram. For the mature human infant, standard criteria have been recommended (1). Use of behavioral criteria have been advocated to overcome the variability of physiological recordings in immature infants and animals (10, 11, 44).

BREATHING PATTERNS IN THE NEWBORN

The rate, depth, and regularity of breathing in newborn babies is closely related to their behavioral state. Many workers have contributed to this literature, as reviewed recently (6, 21). The various breathing patterns may reflect altered central-nervous-system activity, changes in the performance of the respiratory pump, as well as the different metabolic demand in each state (52).

In general, breathing is regular in quiet sleep and irregular in REM. Computer analysis reveals regular oscillations in the rate and depth of breathing, with a cycle length of 7–13 seconds in both states (20). In quiet sleep, the rate and depth cycles are out of phase, and the minute ventilation is stable. In active sleep, the rate and depth cycles are of larger amplitude and are in-phase, leading to marked swings in minute ventilation (4). It has been suggested that fluctuating chemoreceptor drives may be responsible for these oscillations.

Newborn babies have small oxygen stores in the lungs, in relation to metabolic oxygen consumption, and this is a factor producing instability of arterial oxygen tension. Further instability would be expected in active sleep, since lung volume is reduced (23) and metabolic rate is increased (56).

Fluctuation in the excitability of central neurones during active sleep probably is also important. In the fetus, arterial blood gases are more stable but similar periodicities of "breathing" have been recorded (14).

PROLONGED APNEA DURING SLEEP

Pauses in breathing of 2–10 sec are usual in preterm babies and often seen in term infants. These normal pauses are more common in active sleep, and their frequency decreases with advancing postnatal age. Many authors have contributed to this literature; for recent papers, with references to earlier work, see (13, 26).

Prolonged apneas of 20 sec or more are observed most commonly in preterm infants (see 47 and 51 for reviews). The relationship to sleep state is controversial, perhaps due to difficulties in sleep-state determination in preterm infants. One group emphasizes the occurence in active sleep, particularly during periods of maximal spinal inhibition (51); another claims it is more common in quiet sleep (29).

Prolonged apneas occur in the majority of babies under 30 weeks gestation, in about 50% of babies at 30–32 weeks, and in only 7% at 34–35 weeks gestation (21). Maturation of the brain-stem respiratory neurones may account for this relationship. Brain-stem immaturity has been inferred from a slow neuronal-conduction time, using auditory-evoked potentials. At a given post-conceptual age, babies with longer conduction times have more apnea (25). With maturation, apnea ceases as the conduction time shortens to values found in nonapneic babies at a similar age.

TYPES OF APNEA AND THEIR INCIDENCE

Polygraphic studies identify different types of apnea according to whether both nasal air flow and breathing efforts cease (central apnea), nasal air flow ceases but breathing efforts continue (obstructive apnea), or both of the above occur during an episode (mixed apnea).

Schulte (51) found the apneas of preterm infants to be mainly of the central type. To detect airway closure, Milner et al (36) recorded the loss of cardiac artifact on nasal air-flow recordings. Obstruction was detected during 50% of apneas of central onset. It was hypothesized that glottic closure occurred with cessation of breathing efforts, and that this obstruction persisted when breathing efforts resumed (mixed apnea).

Thach (60) used pharyngeal pressure to detect obstruction. He suggested that obstructive and mixed apneas were more common than central apneas, and that they were accentuated during spontaneous neck flexion.

A recent study showed that the role of airway obstruction was overestimated by misinterpretation of brief episodes of generalized body movements; these resembled arousal, and occurred at regular intervals during active sleep in normal preterm infants. During these episodes disorganized abdominal movements occurred, there was often vocalization, and air flow at the nose was reduced or absent. When these "apneas" were removed from analysis, 45% were central apneas, 43% were mixed apneas, with a predominant central component, and 12% were obstructive; the less common pure obstructive apneas occurred in neurologically abnormal babies (8).

GENERATION OF THE BREATHING RHYTHM

Recent studies indicate the importance of sensory systems in sustaining respiratory rhythm in quiet sleep, but not in REM sleep (58). In healthy dogs, afferent vagal blockade dramatically slowed breathing in quiet sleep; a single breath of

100% oxygen further delayed inspiration for 27 sec; addition of metabolic alkalosis increased this delay to 57 sec. In REM sleep, suppression of these sensory systems had little effect: the typical erratic breathing patterns persisted.

Similar results were obtained in experiments on newborn lambs (22). When lambs were artificially ventilated to maintain a normal CO_2 tension, breathing ceased in quiet sleep but returned in active sleep. These patterns were not altered by bilateral cervical vagotomy.

PHARYNGEAL REFLEXES AND AIRWAY OBSTRUCTION

The extensive literature on mechanisms preventing upper airway obstruction can be found in recent reviews, written by several outstanding contributors (33, 53, 60, 62). The papers of Sessle (53, 54) emphasize neurophysiological mechanisms.

To prevent obstruction, a correct balance is important between excitation of muscles that maintain the patency of the upper airway (such as genioglossus) and the muscles that generate airflow (such as diaphragm). In studies of awake humans, progressive excitation of the two components is balanced (38, 40). Anesthesia upsets this balance, depressing the genioglossus.

Activity of the genioglossus is particularly dependent on "nonspecific" excitatory influences. Such excitation increases on arousal from sleep, intermittently relieving obstruction in the sleep-apnea syndrome.

Genioglossus activity is controlled by negative feedback from mechanoreceptors. When subatmospheric pressures are applied to the airway, activity is increased (32). Subatmospheric pressure also prolongs inspiration and thus effectively reduces mean flow rate. Superficial mucosal mechanoreceptors seem responsible, because the effects are eliminated by mucosal anesthesia.

The influence of behavioral state on the upper airway muscles is important but poorly documented in the newborn. In healthy adults, during progression from quiet waking to NREM then REM, the EMG activity declined progressively in the genioglossus, tensor palati, and medial pterygoid (49).

An interesting theoretical analysis has been presented that clarifies the relationships between periodic breathing and obstructive and mixed apneas (30).

APNEIC REFLEXES EXCITED FROM LARYNX

Apnea induced by injection of water into the larynx has been studied in premature lambs, with recording of behavioral state (31, citing important early research). Apnea and bradycardia were induced in all states, but were pronounced when the injection of water into the larynx failed to produce arousal from sleep (in about two thirds of the tests). These responses were similar in quiet and in active sleep. Resuscitation often was required in younger animals in all states, but in older animals only during sleep.

In a study in premature infants, apnea and swallowing frequently occurred in response to hypopharyngeal instillation of 0.3 ml water, but not to saline (41). No observations on state were recorded. Water liquids with very low or very high pH, and especially liquids with low chloride concentration were most potent (3). A detailed analysis of anions depressing and facilitating water-receptor excitation was reported by Shingai (55).

The role of laryngeal reflexes in the control of airflow, respiratory rhythm, and lung volume is discussed later.

COUGHING AND AROUSAL

Some important concepts have developed from studies of laryngeal reflexes and behavioral state in adult dogs (59). The degree of laryngeal stimulation required to produce arousal and coughing was greater in REM sleep than slow-wave sleep. If the stimulus failed to produce arousal, coughing was not fully developed. Single expiratory efforts or brief apnea then occurred in slow-wave sleep, but often prolonged apnea and marked bradycardia occurred in REM sleep.

Sleep fragmentation impaired the arousal responses to laryngeal stimulation (5).

LUNG VOLUME AND PARADOXICAL MOTION OF THE RIB CAGE

Paradoxical deflation of the infant rib cage during inspiratory airflow has been studied by several research groups (6, 9, 21). A usual, but not invariable, link to REM sleep was shown (9). Electromyogram records revealed loss of both phasic and tonic intercostal activity in REM sleep in both babies and lambs. Esophageal-pressure recordings showed that the inspiratory deflation was not due to inspiratory obstruction (21). The inhibition of intercostal activity in REM sleep was shown to persist during nasal occlusion in the lamb.

In babies, the loss of intercostal activity in REM sleep is associated with a 30% reduction of end-expiratory lung volume (23). Maintenance of lung volume may be important for alveolar stability, but also for setting the level of oxygen stores.

The O_2 stores can be estimated from the volumes of the lung, venous, and arterial blood: in the infant, there is about 8 ml (16%) in the lungs and 43 ml (84%) in the blood; in the adult, about 250 ml (24%) in the lungs and 800 ml (76%) in the blood. However, the availability of these stores depends on oxygen tension, the gas in the lungs being the sole contributor in the early stages of hypoxia from apnea; later, when the fall of oxygen tension produces tensions corresponding to the steep part of the oxy-hemoglobin dissociation, the contribution from blood increases markedly.

Hypoxemia develops more rapidly during apnea in the infant (c.f. adult), since metabolic O_2 consumption is 2- to 3-fold greater in relation to the available O_2 store; representative values for infants and adults are 8 and 4 ml·min^{-1} per kg for O_2 consumption, and 0.5 and 0.27 ml·min^{-1} per ml O_2 store. In REM sleep, with reduction of the O_2 store in the lungs (23) and an increase in O_2 consumption (56), hypoxemia will be accelerated during apnea.

Systematic studies of the rates of oxygen desaturation in different states and with maturation have not been performed. However, rapid desaturation has been observed in term and preterm babies during even brief pauses in breathing (21).

The use of muscles to maintain lung volume has been inferred in infants from other observations. During apnea in the infant the lung deflates, presumably to the relaxation volume (6). The larynx may also play a role (19).

LARYNGEAL CONTROL OF AIRFLOW AND LUNG VOLUME

Several groups have studied behavioral influences on the larynx (19, 35, 39). In lambs, adductor muscle activity impedes expiratory airflow in quiet sleep but not in REM sleep. The activity in quiet sleep is increased by reduced lung volume. In rats during quiet sleep, hypercapnia opens the glottis widely during inspiration and expiration; hypoxia opens it widely during inspiration, but causes narrowing during expiration. These patterns of response may reflect the value of unimpeded airflow in hypercapnia and the importance of maintaining a high lung volume and O_2 store in hypoxia.

These responses do not occur in REM sleep, when the activities become irregular—possibly reflecting behavioral activity such as vocalization.

Observations of expiratory airflow suggest that similar mechanisms may operate in the full-term human newborn (45).

Details of these various reflexes have been examined only during anesthesia: these studies separate the roles of pulmonary stretch, irritant, and J-receptors (for references see 2).

REFLEXES EXCITED FROM THE RIB CAGE AND IRREGULAR BREATHING

Reflexes excited by paradoxical motion of the rib cage were investigated by several groups and postulated as the mechanism of breathing irregularity in

REM (for references see 6). Manual distortion of the lower rib cage shortened inspiratory time. During active sleep, inspiratory time was related to the rate of spontaneous rib-cage distortion.

Alternatively, irregular breathing has been related to irregular rhythm of brain-stem respiratory neurones in active sleep. This is favored by the observation of the typical irregular breathing pattern of active sleep in a baby with a lower cervical cord transection (61).

RESPIRATORY MUSCLE EFFICIENCY AND FATIGUE

For an introduction to this subject, the reader should consult a recent review on the respiratory muscles (48) and a monograph on muscle fatigue (43).

A claim has been made that fatigue in the diaphragm occurs in normal newborn infants during REM sleep, when the intercostal muscles are inhibited (37). Fatigue was inferred from a reduction of high-frequency and an increase of low-frequency power in the diaphragm electromyogram. If true, this physiology of the normal infant is surprising. However, there may be more than one mechanism for such spectral changes: synchronization of motor units, with altered loads, rather than true fatigue; slowing of action-potential propagation during fatigue.

Muller et al (37) argue that the literature on postnatal alternations of muscle enzymes supports their concept of immaturity and predisposition to fatigue at birth.

VENTILATORY AND AROUSAL RESPONSES TO HYPERCAPNIA

Several groups of investigators have examined the influence of sleep state on the ventilatory response to hypercapnia, arriving at different conclusions. In evaluating individual papers, the reader should be reminded of the technical complexity of measuring the CO_2 stimulus and the response (57).

Bryan et al (7) and Hagan & Gulston (18) found that the ventilatory response to CO_2 was reduced in REM sleep, compared with quiet sleep. In the study of Hagan & Gulston, although ventilation was depressed, the surface recordings of diaphragn EMG were not, suggesting that a mechanical limitation may exist. They suggested that the inspiratory rib-cage deflation in REM may have limited the ventilatory response.

In contrast, studies in preterm infants (47) and term infants during early infancy (12, 17) showed similar ventilatory responses to steady-state 2–5% CO_2 in NREM and REM.

The effects of sleep state and postnatal age on the "steady state" response to CO_2 have been examined in preterm and term newborn monkeys (15). In

NREM, the response lines relating ventilation per kg to CO_2 tension progressively increased in slope and shifted to the left between 2 and 21 days of age in both preterm and term monkeys. The sensitivity did not differ between REM and NREM in younger animals, but at 21 days of age the response was greater in NREM. The authors hypothesized that depression of CO_2 sensitivity in REM develops with advancing age.

Arousal occurred at higher CO_2 tension in REM compared with NREM when tested in adult dogs; sleep fragmentation increased the CO_2 tension required for arousal, in both states, without impairing the ventilatory responses (5).

VENTILATORY AND AROUSAL RESPONSES TO HYPOXIA

A perplexing range of responses to hypoxia have been reported. In the term infant, transient ventilatory depression during oxygen breathing, which is attributed to removal of a hypoxic stimulus, is similar in quiet and active sleep (4).

The preterm infant responds to 15% oxygen by sustained ventilatory increments in NREM, progressive ventilatory depression during REM, and an increment followed by depression in wakefulness (47).

In newborn lambs (24) and in calves (28) there is little or no ventilatory response to progressive hypoxia during active sleep; in quiet sleep, the response is progressive.

In puppies, the ventilatory response to progressive hypoxia is similar in quiet and active sleep (24). When steady-state hypoxia has been studied (16), comparable responses are found in quiet and active sleep, only in older animals. In the youngest puppies, respiratory rate and ventilation are depressed, rather than increased, during quiet sleep; in active sleep, the response is intact.

These apparent conflicts are not surprising in a multifactorial system. The factors include: opioid-mediated depression, only in the very young; effect of increased cerebral blood flow during REM or steady-state CO_2 testing, with consequent reduction of brain tissue CO_2 tension and of CO_2 stimulus; and species differences in the degree of paradoxical motion of the rib cage in REM. The baby, lamb, and calf exhibit rib-cage paradox; the puppy does not.

Arousal threshold is another important feature of the response to hypoxia. In calves and lambs (24, 28), arousal occurred at much lower arterial oxygen saturation in active compared with quiet sleep. This is consistent with observations in tracheostomized sleeping dogs, where the arousal was related by denervation experiments to carotid body chemoreceptors (42, 57). After sleep was fragmented by repeatedly waking dogs with auditory stimuli, a lower arterial O_2 saturation was required for arousal, in both states, but ventilatory responses were unimpaired.

CONCLUSIONS

In the last five years, much has been discovered about the profound influence of behavioral state on reflexes that regulate breathing. The studies in the newborn have revealed a number of effects peculiar to this age.

So far most studies have been concerned with overall reflex responses, with much less attention to underlying neurophysiological mechanisms. This is the challenge for the future. Pioneering studies of McGinty (34) show that it is possible to record activity of single neurones in the central nervous system without general anesthesia or restraint. Already his studies provide information on the changing activities of reticular and respiratory neurones in different behavioral states.

Another line of investigation, reviewed elsewhere (45a), concerns "humoral" factors in behavioral and respiratory regulation.

Much remains to be discovered.

ACKNOWLEDGMENTS

Supported by grants from the National Health and Medical Research Council of Australia and the Apex Sudden Infant Death Foundation.

We thank Mrs. Fabricatorian for help in the preparation of the manuscript.

Literature Cited

1. Anders, T., Emde, R., Parmelee, A. 1971. *A Manual of Standardized Terminology, Techniques, and Criteria for Scoring of States of Sleep and Wakefulness in Newborn Infants.* Los Angeles: UCLA Brain Inf. Serv./BRI Pub. Off. 40 pp.
2. Bartlett, D. Jr., Knuth, S. L., Knuth, K. V. 1981. Effects of pulmonary stretch receptor blockade on laryngeal responses to hypercapnia and hypoxia. *Resp. Physiol.* 45:67–77
3. Boggs, D. F., Bartlett, D. Jr. 1982. Chemical specificity of a laryngeal apneic reflex in puppies. *J. Appl. Physiol.* 53:455–62
4. Bolton, D. P. G., Herman, S. 1974. Ventilation and sleep state in the new-born. *J. Physiol.* 240:67–77
5. Bowes, G., Woolf, G. M., Sullivan, C. E., Phillipson, E. A. 1980. Effect of sleep fragmentation on ventilatory and arousal responses of sleeping dogs to respiratory stimuli. *Am. Rev. Respirat. Dis.* 122:899–908
6. Bryan, A. C., Bowes, G., Maloney, J. E. 1983. Control of breathing in the fetus and neonate. In *Handbook of Physiology, Respiration, Vol. 1. Control of Breathing,* ed. N. S. Cherniack, J. D. Widdi-

combe. Wash. DC: Am. Physiol. Soc. In press
7. Bryan, H. M., Hagan, R., Gulston, G., Bryan, A. C. 1976. CO_2 response and sleep state in infants. *Clin. Res.* 24:A689
8. Butcher-Puech, M., Holley, D., Henderson-Smart, D. J. 1983. Apnoea type, bradycardias, and neurological outcome in preterm infants. In *Perinatal Physiology and Behaviour,* Melbourne: IUPS Sat. Symp., Aust. Paed. J. 19(4): In press
9. Cruzi-Dascalova, L. 1978. Thoracic-abdominal respiratory correlations in infants: constancy and variability in different sleep states. *Early Human Devel.* 2/1:25–38
10. Dreyfus-Brisac, C. 1979. Ontogenesis of brain bioelectrical activity and sleep organisation in neonates and infants. In *Human Growth, Neurobiology and Nutrition,* ed. F. Falkner, J. M. Tanner, 3:157–82. London: Bailiere Tindall
11. Ellingson, R. J. 1972. Development of wakefulness-sleep cycles and associated EEG patterns in mammals. In *Sleep and the Maturing Nervous System,* ed. C. D. Clemente, D. P. Purpura, F. E. Meyer, pp. 166–74. New York: Academic
12. Fagenholz, S. A., O'Connell, K., Shannon, D. C. 1976. Chemoreceptor func-

tion and sleep state in apnea. *Pediatrics* 58:31–36

13. Flores-Guevara, R. 1982. Sleep apneas in normal neonates and infants during the first three months of life. *Neuropediatrics* 13:21–28

14. Gennser, G., Hathorn, M. 1979. Analysis of breathing movements in human fetus. *Lancet* 1:1298

15. Guthrie, R. D., Standaert, T. A., Hodson, W. A., Woodrum, D. E. 1981. Development of CO_2 sensitivity: effects of gestational age, postnatal age, and sleep state, *J. Appl. Physiol.* 50:956–61

16. Haddad, G. G., Gandhi, M. R., Mellins, R. B. 1982. Maturation of ventilatory response to hypoxia in puppies during sleep. *J. Appl. Physiol.* 52:309–14

17. Haddad, G. G., Leistner, H. L., Epstein, R. A., Epstein, M. A. F., Grodin, W. K., Mellins, R. B. 1980. CO_2-induced changes in ventilation and ventilatory pattern in normal sleeping infants. *J. Appl. Physiol.* 48:684–88

18. Hagan, R., Gulston, A. G. 1981. The newborn: respiratory electromyograms and breathing. *Aust. Paediatr. J.* 17:230–31

19. Harding, R., Johnson, P., McClelland, M. E. 1980. Respiratory function of the larynx in developing sheep and the influence of sleep state. *Respir. Physiol.* 40:165–79

20. Hathorn, M. K. S. 1978. Analysis of periodic changes in ventilation in newborn infants. *J. Physiol.* 285:85–99

21. Henderson-Smart, D. J. 1983. Regulation of breathing in the perinatal period. See Ref. 50, in press

22. Henderson-Smart, D. J., Johnson, P., McClelland, M. E. 1980. The abolition of spontaneous breathing during quiet sleep by eupnoeic positive pressure ventilation in lambs. *J. Physiol.* 308:48P–49P

23. Henderson-Smart, D. J., Read, D. J. C. 1979. Reduced lung volume during behavioral active sleep in the newborn. *J. Appl. Physiol.* 46:1081–85

24. Henderson-Smart, D. J., Read, D. J. C. 1979. Ventilatory responses to hypoxaemia during sleep in the newborn. *J. Develop. Physiol.* 1:195–208

25. Henderson-Smart, D. J., Pettigrew, A. G., Campbell, D. J. 1983. Clinical apnea and brain-stem neural function in preterm infants. *N. Engl. J. Med.* 308:353–57

26. Hodgman, J. E., Hoppenbrouwers, T. 1983. Cardio-respiratory behavior in infants at increased epidemiological risk for SIDS. In *Sudden Infant Death Syndrome*, ed. J. Tilden, L. M. Roeder, A. Steinschneider, pp. 669–79. New York: Academic

27. Hornbein, T. F., ed. 1982. *Regulation of Breathing. Lung Biology in Health and Disease,* vol. 17. New York: Dekker 1436 pp.

28. Jeffery, H. E., Read, D. J. C. 1980. Ventilatory responses of newborn calves to progressive hypoxia in quiet and active sleep. *J. Appl. Physiol.* 48:892–95

29. Krauss, A. N., Solomon, G. E., Auld, P. A. M. 1977. Sleep state, apnea, and bradycardia in preterm infants. *Devel. Med. Child. Neurol.* 19:160–68

30. Longobardo, G. S., Gothe, B., Goldman, M. D., Cherniak, N. S. 1982. Sleep apnea considered as a control system instability. *Respir. Physiol.* 50:311–33

31. Marchal, F., Corke, B. C., Sundell, H. 1982. Reflex apnea from laryngeal chemo-stimulation in the sleeping premature newborn lamb. *Pediatr. Res.* 16:621–27

32. Mathew, O. P., Abu-Osba, Y. K., Thach, B. T. 1982. Influence of upper airway pressure changes on genioglossus muscle respiratory activity. *J. Appl. Physiol.* 52:438–44

33. Mathew, O. P., Remmers, J. E. 1983. Respiratory function of the upper airway. See Ref. 50, in press

34. McGinty, D. J., Hoppenbrouwers, T. 1983. The reticular formation, breathing disorders during sleep, and SIDS. See Ref. 26, pp. 375–400

35. Megirian, D., Sherrey, J. H. 1980. Respiratory functions of the laryngeal muscles during sleep. *Sleep* 3:289–98

36. Milner, A. D., Boon, A. W., Saunders, R. A., Hopkin, I. E. 1980. Upper airways obstruction and apnoea in preterm babies. *Arch. Dis. Child.* 55:22–25

37. Muller, N., Gulston, G., Cade, D., Whitton, J., Froese, A. B., et al. 1979. Diaphragmatic muscle fatigue in the newborn. *J. Appl. Physiol.* 46:688–95

38. Onal, E., Lopata, M. 1982. Periodic breathing and the pathogenesis of occlusive sleep apneas. *Am. Rev. Respir. Dis.* 126:676–80

39. Orem, J. 1980. Neuronal mechanisms of respiration in REM sleep. *Sleep* 3:251–67

40. Patrick, G. B., Strohl, K. P., Rubin, S. B., Altose, M. D. 1982. Upper airway and diaphragm muscle responses to chemical stimulation and loading. *J. Appl. Physiol.* 53:1133–37

41. Perkett, E. A., Vaughan, R. L. 1982. Evidence for a laryngeal chemoreflex in some human preterm infants. *Acta Paediatr. Scand.* 71:969–72

42. Phillipson, E. A., Bowes, G. 1983. Control of breathing during sleep. See Ref. 6, in press

43. Porter, R., Whelan, J. 1981. *Human*

Muscle Fatigue: Physiological Mechanisms. Ciba Found. Symp. 82. London: Pitman Medical

44. Prechtl, H. F. R. 1974. The behavioural states of the newborn infant. *Brain Res.* 76:185–212

45. Radvanyi-Bouvet, M. F., Monset-Couchard, M., Morel-Kahn, F., Vicente, G., Dreyfus-Brisac, C. 1982. Expiratory patterns during sleep in normal full-term and premature neonates. *Biol. Neonate* 41:74–84

45a. Read, D. J. C., Jeffery, H. 1983. Some neurochemical influences on breathing. See Ref. 50, in press

46. Remmers, J. E. 1981. Control of breathing during sleep. See Ref. 27, pp. 1197–1249

47. Rigatto, H. 1982. Apnea. *Pediatr. Clin. North Am.* 29:1105–1116

48. Roussos, C., Macklem, P. T. 1982. The respiratory muscles. *N. Engl. J. Med.* 307:786–97

49. Sauerland, E. K., Orr, W. C., Hairston, L. E. 1981. EMG patterns of oropharyngeal muscles during respiration in wakefulness and sleep. *Electromyogr. Clin. Neurophysiol.* 21:307–16

50. Saunders, N. A., Sullivan, C. E., eds. 1983. *Sleep and Breathing, Lung Biology in Health and Disease,* Vol. 20. New York: Dekker. In press

51. Schulte, F. J. 1977. Apnea. *Clin. Perinatol.* 41:65–76

52. Schulze, K., Kairam, R., Stefanski, M., Sciacca, R., Bateman, D. 1981. Spontaneous variability in minute ventilation oxygen consumption and heart rate of low birth weight infants. *Pediatr. Res.* 15:1111–16

53. Sessie, B. J., Lucier, G. E. 1983. Functional aspects of the upper respiratory tract and larynx: a review. See Ref. 26, pp. 501–29

54. Sessle, B. J., Greenwood, L. F., Lund, J. P., Lucier, G. E. 1978. Effects of upper respiratory tract stimuli on respiration and single respiratory neurons in the adult cat. *Exp. Neurol.* 61:245–59

55. Shingai, T. 1977. Ionic mechanisms of water receptors in the laryngeal mucosa of the rabbit. *Jpn. J. Physiol.* 27:27–42

56. Stothers, J. K., Warner, R. M. 1978. Oxygen consumption and neonatal sleep states. *J. Physiol.* 278:435–40

57. Sullivan, C. E. 1980. Breathing in sleep. In *Physiology in Sleep,* ed. J. Orem, C. D. Barnes, pp. 213–72. New York: Academic

58. Sullivan, C. E., Kozar, L. F., Murphy, E., Phillipson, E. A. 1978. Primary role of respiratory afferents in sustaining breathing rhythm. *J. Appl. Physiol.* 4:11–17

59. Sullivan, C. E., Murphy, E., Kozar, L. F., Phillipson, E. A. 1978. Waking and ventilatory responses to laryngeal stimulation in sleeping dogs. *J. Appl. Physiol.* 45:681–89

60. Thach, B. T. 1983. The role of pharyngeal airway obstruction in prolonging infantile apneic spells. See Ref. 26, pp. 279–92

61. Thach, B. T., Abroms, I. F., Frantz, I. D. III, Sotrel, A., Bruce, E. N., Goldman, M. D. 1980. Intercostal muscle reflexes and sleep breathing patterns in the human infant. *J. Appl. Physiol.* 48:139–146

62. Tonkin, S. 1983. Pharyngeal airway obstruction—physical signs and factors in its production. See Ref 26, pp. 453–65

Ann. Rev. Physiol. 1984. 46:687–703
Copyright © 1984 by Annual Reviews Inc. All rights reserved

PERIPHERAL AND CENTRAL CHEMORECEPTORS IN THE FETUS AND NEWBORN

David W. Walker

Department of Physiology, Monash University, Clayton, Victoria, Australia, 3168

INTRODUCTION

This review concentrates on recent evidence that amplifies understanding of the chemoreceptor control of circulation and breathing in the fetus and newborn. Emphasis is given to studies with unanesthetized animals, because these generally allow ready comparison with clinical studies of human infants. As will be seen, a great deal of information has accumulated showing how fetal and newborn animals differ in their response to alteration of blood gases and pH, and the role that peripheral and central chemoreceptor mechanisms may play in the onset and maintenance of gaseous ventilation after birth. It will also become clear that the preoccupation to work with unanesthetized subjects after minimal surgical interference raises many questions that will only be resolved by more deductive and mechanistic experimental methods.

FETUS

Peripheral Chemoreceptors

AORTIC   Experiments with anesthetized fetal lambs showed that the aortic chemoreceptors were readily excited by injection of cyanide or nicotine (30) or by alteration of PaO_2[1] and $PaCO_2$ over the physiological range (2, 29), causing

---

[1]Abbreviations used: $PaCO_2$, arterial PCO_2; PaO_2, arterial PO_2; $F_I O_2$, fraction of O_2 in inspired gas; NREM, nonrapid-eye-movement sleep; REM, rapid-eye-movement sleep; T_E, expiratory time; T_I, inspiratory time; V_T, tidal volume.

0066-4278/84/0315-0687$02.00

bradycardia, increased arterial pressure, and sympathetic constriction of the femoral and renal circulations. This established that the fetal cardiac output was redistributed away from peripheral regions to maintain blood flow to the heart, brain, and placenta during hypoxia or asphyxia. Microsphere studies in unanesthetized fetal lambs confirmed that blood flows to the carcass, gut, and kidneys were decreased after a 1 hour exposure to hypoxemia ($P_aO_2 \sim 12$ mmHg), while flow to the brain and heart were increased (23). The changes were greater when acidemia occurred during the hypoxemia. The aortic chemoreceptors were thus regarded as tonically active in the normal range of PaO_2 and $PaCO_2$, influencing the distribution of cardiac output to the various vascular beds. However, a careful study with microspheres showed that whereas blood flow to the heart, brain, and adrenals increased, and pulmonary flow decreased, as a continuous function of O_2 content between 6 and 1 mM (69), blood flow to the kidneys, gut, and carcass either remained constant or increased slightly over the range 6–2 mM, but below this level decreased sharply. These results suggest that, in utero, reflex vasoconstriction of the abdominal organs and carcass does not occur until arterial O_2 levels are reduced considerably. They also suggest that there is a wide range around the physiologically normal at which organ blood flow is regulated by local mechanisms.

A disadvantage with microsphere studies is that the injections of microspheres are made many minutes after the induction of hypoxia, when a steady state is presumed to have been established. Vasoactive hormones accumulate in the fetal circulation during hypoxia (54, 80), and therefore blood flow changes are not due to reflex vasoconstriction alone. It is not known if the adrenal release of catecholamines during hypoxia is produced just by reflex splanchnic activity, or by direct action of low O_2 upon the medullary cells. Also, after a time hypoxia is accompanied by a fall of arterial pH that may potentiate the effects of low O_2 on the arterial chemoreceptors. Release of vasopressin, which is greatest when the vagi are intact (80), and of catecholamines (54) is augmented during hypoxia with acidosis, perhaps explaining the greater increase of peripheral resistance in this circumstance. Acidemia alone may not be sufficient to stimulate the aortic chemoreceptors because infusion of acid into fetal lambs did not produce blood-pressure or heart-rate changes like those seen during hypoxia (46, 62).

The bradycardia produced by hypoxia in unanesthetized fetal lambs after 120 days gestation is abolished by atropine (22, 87); it is certainly reflex because it does not occur after combined aortic and carotid body deafferentation (48). Before 120 days gestation bradycardia does not occur because of simultaneous and approximately equal increase of both sympathetic and parasympathetic cardiac effects (87). Thus the ability of the chemoreceptors to alter activity in the vasomotor neurone pools is altered during development in sheep.

Chemoreceptor activity has been recorded in single- or few-fiber preparations of the vagus nerve of anesthetised fetal lambs (10, 71). Changes of PaO_2 between 10 and 30 mmHg caused only modest changes in firing rate (71). More detailed studies on the stimulus-response characteristics of chemoreceptors in the fetus and newborn are required because, as discussed below for the carotid chemoreceptors, there must be a resetting of the operating range of the receptor if activity is present at the P_aO_2 prevailing in both the fetus and the neonate.

CAROTID   Whereas the activity and reflex effects of the aortic chemoreceptors in the fetus are indisputable, the evidence that the carotid chemoreceptors are active before birth is less certain. They produce no important respiratory effects unless stimulated with large quantities of cyanide, lobeline, and nicotine (29), and the pattern of breathing movements in utero is not obviously altered after denervation of the carotid bifurcation (49). Acute hypoxia never stimulates breathing movements of intact fetuses in utero (14, 31).

Carotid bodies excised from fetal lambs and superfused exhibited readily identifiable chemoreceptor activity and unequivocal responses to changes of O_2 and CO_2 (51). The relative inactivity of these chemoreceptors in vivo might therefore be due to unique biochemical or metabolic conditions restricted to fetal life, although precisely what they might be is unclear. It has been suggested that increase of the catecholamine content of the glomus cells immediately before term is responsible for the increased sensitivity of the carotid chemoreceptors (72), but details have not been published. Certainly, long-term loss of catecholamines from glomus cells in adult rats after freezing of the carotid body in situ is associated with loss of chemosensitivity (86).

A recent study in which chemoreceptor activity was readily identified in 6 fetal lambs anesthetized with halothane suggested that the carotid body was more active prenatally than previously thought (10). Random activity at $\sim$ 5Hz occurred at a P_aO_2 of 25 mm Hg and was increased by retrograde injection of CO_2-saturated saline, but not fetal blood, into the lingual artery. When background activity was increased by occlusion of the umbilical cord, injection of hyperoxic maternal blood decreased activity. Chemoreceptor activity was readily identified in fetal lambs and in lambs more than 3 days old, but none was observed in 8 lambs on the first postnatal day. It was concluded that in the hours and days after birth when the P_aO_2 increases from about 20 to 60 mmHg, the carotid chemoreceptors become inactive until such time that their activity is reset into the adult range. However, some aspect of technique seems to be important here, because others (51, 72) using almost identical procedures observed vigorous chemoreceptor discharge in lambs <1 day old. They reported the firing rates and stimulus-response relationship for O_2 and CO_2 to be similar to those for the adult cat.

Whatever the level of activity really is in utero, the carotid chemoreceptors have no important effects upon breathing movements. If the carotid chemoreceptors are active in utero and respond appropriately to changes in O_2 and CO_2, an explanation must be found for their inability to produce reflex alteration of breathing movements. Possibly there is a high threshold for chemoreceptor traffic within the brainstem. Deep, regular breathing movements were produced by injections of pilocarpine into intact but not carotid-denervated fetal lambs (17). It was suggested that the principal action of this drug was upon the reticular formation, producing arousal, so that the normally low chemoreceptor output was then effective in eliciting respiratory activity. This proposal must be viewed with some reservation, because no evidence of central nervous system arousal was given, and the experiments upon the denervated fetal lambs, which were anesthetized, are not strictly comparable with those in the intact fetuses. Doxapram also produced bouts of vigorous breathing (70), and although this effect was explained in terms of the accepted analeptic effect of the drug upon the CNS, this substance has been shown to powerfully excite the peripheral chemoreceptors in adult cats (67). This might be the cause of the effect of the drug in fetal lambs. Possibly, high sustained levels of discharge from the carotid chemoreceptors into the brainstem is required to produce respiratory effects.

In the adult, stimulation of the carotid chemoreceptors during apnea causes profound bradycardia, often with decrease of cardiac output (see 33 for summary). Since the fetus is apneic for substantial periods of time, insensitivity of the carotid chemoreceptors in utero may be an adaptation to prevent reflex vagal inhibition of the heart.

The distribution of blood flow through the carotid body of the fetal lamb is probably different from that of the newborn and adult, since no systematic differences of tissue PO_2 were observed as a microelectrode was moved through the carotid body of fetal lambs (1). The gradient between blood and interstitium was increased after occlusion of the umbilical cord; this persisted when the lambs were resuscitated, even if the P_aO_2 was then reduced to near fetal levels. It was suggested that the increase of P_aO_2 at the onset of air breathing might act to constrict the blood vessels within the carotid body irreversibly (1, 72), as it does within the ductus arteriosus and umbilical vessels. Sympathetic efferent discharge to the carotid body increased the excitability of the carotid chemosensors in both fetal lambs (7) and adult cats (6), and the fall of carotid-body blood flow at the instant of cord clamping is mediated by sympathetic nerves (51). But sympathetic denervation of the carotid bifurcation of fetal lambs did not abolish the increase in chemoreceptor activity that followed cord clamping, and had little effect upon single-fiber activity over the P_aO_2 range of 30–60 mm Hg (51). Thus, the increase of chemoreceptor activity following ligation of the umbilical cord is probably not caused by sympathetic efferent discharge or local redistribution of blood flow (1, 51, 72).

Central Chemoreceptors

CARBON DIOXIDE AND H$^+$ Breathing movements increase when the P_aCO_2 is raised in fetal lambs (14, 20). Ventriculo-cisternal perfusion with mock cerebro-spinal fluid containing various concentrations of HCO_3^- increased the depth and incidence of breathing movements as CSF [H$^+$] increased from 45 to 73 nEq. L^{-1} (9). Also, intravenous infusion of NH_4Cl or HCl caused long bouts of vigorous breathing movements, although after a delay of some hours (46, 52). The lag is attributed to slow penetration of H$^+$ into the interstitium of the brain. Together, these results show the chemosensitivity of the brainstem in fetal lambs, and this presumably resides within the classical chemosensitive areas near the ventrolateral surface of the medulla. The delayed response to acid also shows that rapid decrease of arterial pH does not stimulate breathing via the peripheral chemoreceptors.

The principal effect of hypercapnia is to increase the depth and regularity of the breathing movements (20, 31). There is little effect on T_I, and T_E is either unchanged or shortened only slightly (31). A change in the mean rate of breathing is not a consistent finding. Breath amplitude measured from tracheal pressure increased progressively over the P_aCO_2 range 37–87 mm Hg (31). In some fetuses inspiratory intercostal activity was initiated and showed graded increases as the P_aCO_2 was raised. The change of tracheal pressure amplitude correlated well with the increase of P_aCO_2, whereas the amplitude and inspiratory slope of the diaphragm electromyogram increased only over the lower part of the CO_2 range (31). The increase of tracheal pressure amplitude throughout the CO_2 range suggests that the accessory respiratory muscles, including the intercostals, contribute to an increasing degree to the response to CO_2. More rigorous attention to the placement of electrodes in the diaphragm is warranted, because activity may vary from site to site (44). However, tracheal pressure amplitude can be regarded as the best measure of "central respiratory drive" since it is an integration of the actions of all the respiratory muscles on the thorax. The sensitivity of phrenic and intercostal motorneurones to CO_2 may well differ, because the intercostal muscles become less active towards term (21, 31). There is no evidence that the sensitivity to CO_2 changes with gestational age.

Hypercapnia also has effects on the electrocorticogram, slightly increasing the amount of low-voltage activity and the number of transitions between high and low voltage (14). The episodic pattern of breathing is maintained, but a greater proportion of the low-voltage period is occupied by breathing (14, 50). Although CO_2-response curves have been determined (31, 63), they are not readily compared to postnatal breathing, because the changes in thoracic volume and work of breathing are then quite different. Such comparison would also be valid for REM sleep only. From experiments with partially exteriorized fetuses it was suggested that CO_2 produced a more aroused CNS state and that this influenced the level of respiratory response that followed (63). However, in unanesthetized lambs in utero there is no evidence of CNS arousal (31), and the excitability of hind-limb polysynaptic reflexes was not increased by hypercapnia (12), which might have been expected if arousal and wakefulness were present.

In humans, fetal breathing movements are altered by changes in maternal blood gases. Breathing movements were increased after the maternal inhalation of 5% CO_2 (79), or when the mother performed work on a bicycle ergometer sufficient to raise her capillary PCO_2 by a small amount (60). Breathing movements decreased during maternal hypocapnia caused by overbreathing. Breathing of 50% O_2 was associated with a small fall in the incidence of breathing movements in one study (60), which might be interpreted as due to unloading of the peripheral chemoreceptors, but this finding was not confirmed by others (78). In pregnancies complicated by pre-eclampsia or fetal growth retardation, hyperoxia caused a paradoxical increase of breathing movements (78). This also occurs in the human newborn (81); it has been attributed to central accumulation of CO_2 following cerebral constriction by high O_2 (59). Excess of CO_2 and H^+ in the brain, derived from glucose utilization, has also been proposed to explain the increase of breathing movements in human fetuses after meals (68) or after bolus infusions of glucose to the mother (66). Although CO_2 normally increases cerebral blood flow and would not be expected to accumulate, a fall of cerebral blood flow does occur in human neonates after a meal (73).

HYPOXIA   Acute reduction of the PO_2 in pregnant sheep (14) and monkeys (61) caused reduction and eventual cessation of fetal breathing movements. Limb movements and muscle activity also decrease (12, 21, 65). The effect in humans is not known. Hypoxia also decreases the effect of CO_2 on breathing movements (31) and has been noted to overide the stimulatory effects of doxapram, caffeine (70), strychnine, and bicuculline (D. Walker & R. Harding, unpublished observations). The effect of hypoxia is of rapid onset and lasts for at least 2 hours (65); the result of more prolonged exposure has not been established. When the resting PaO_2 and $PaCO_2$ were correlated with the number of breathing movements, most fetuses with low PaO_2 without raised $PaCO_2$ were apneic (8). Breathing movements were present at lower PaO_2s when the $PaCO_2$ was higher than normal; this may be due to central effects of CO_2 on cerebral blood flow or CSF HCO_3^- concentration. That compensation to low PaO_2 can occur is suggested by the observation that chronically hypoxic, growth-retarded fetal lambs show relatively normal breathing patterns (J. S. Robinson, personal communication).

Several lines of evidence point to the effects of hypoxia being mediated through specific neural pathways. Whereas hind-limb polysynaptic reflexes are depressed by hypoxia, reflex activation of the digastric and thyro-arytenoid muscles is not, these having cranial and not spinal pathways (88). Hypoxia did not alter hind-limb spinal reflexes in fetal lambs with chronic transection of the spinal cord at $T_{12}-L_1$ (12), suggesting that this effect was mediated through descending inhibitory pathways. The phrenic motoneurones may also be inhibited by this mechanism. Hypoxia appears to activate pathways within the brainstem situated below the hypothalamus but above the pons (32). Whether such networks can be classified as O_2 chemoreceptors is uncertain, but the response of the fetal brain to low O_2 is clearly an important aspect of the adaptation to acute decrease of PaO_2. This response may persist into early postnatal life and contribute to the apparent decrease of ventilation during hypoxia in some species (see below).

NEWBORN

Peripheral Chemoreceptors

THORACIC   The cardiovascular effects of hypoxia and hypercapnia in the newborn have been summarized recently (37). There is a bewildering array of responses, due no doubt to differences in species, anesthesia, postnatal age, the persistence or only partial closure of the fetal cardiac shunts, and to the degree of hypoxia, hypercapnia, or asphyxia used. The circulatory and respiratory adjustments that must be achieved at birth and during the first week of life provide a shifting baseline upon which reflex adaptation necessarily is imposed. Sympathetically mediated reflex adjustments of the circulation are probably of less importance and are perhaps subordinated to hormonal mechanisms directed toward the maintenance of blood pressure and blood volume (64). Arterial hypoxia may be followed by hypotension and increased peripheral blood flow in newborn lambs (35) and by hypotension—in spite of peripheral vasoconstriction—in the human infant (15). Nor do chemoreceptor (or baroreceptor) responses have the primary role in the defense of blood pressure during hemorrhage in newborn rabbits and kittens (64). Since good aortic chemoreflexes and afferent chemoreceptor traffic are present in fetal life at a lower PaO_2 than in postnatal life, the relatively small responses to induced hypoxia after birth probably relate not to immaturity of chemoreceptor mechanisms (37) but to the changes and adaptation of the circulation at this time. The interaction of circulatory and respiratory reflexes (see 33) would be expected to obscure the primary circulatory responses to stimulation of the chemoreceptors, particularly by alterations of blood gases, but this has not received direct attention in the newborn. During spontaneous arrest of breathing in premature infants, there was bradycardia and peripheral vasoconstriction that increased gradually and often reached a maximum after the resumption of breathing (85). It is reasonable to suppose that this is the chemoreceptor response to mild asphyxia, as shown by fetal lambs (14, 29), but the contribution of aortic and carotid chemoreceptors is uncertain. In adults, stimulation of the carotid chemoreceptors during apnea likewise causes bradycardia and vasoconstriction, and these responses are inhibited or even reversed in the presence of respiratory activity (33). Hypoxia produced tachycardia in freely ventilating infants (15) and newborn lambs (87).

The observation that fine vessels supply the glomus tissue of the aortico-pulmonary region in the human fetus suggested that these receptors might be sensitive to changes in the composition of venous blood. But the pulmonary contribution to the aortic bodies regresses after birth in the human and cat, and the aortic chemoreceptors of kittens are sensitive to changes in the composition of systemic and not pulmonary blood (25). However, in anesthetized puppies 1–10 weeks old, alteration of mixed venous PO_2 and PCO_2 by veno-venous bypass caused changes in respiration, with an additive interaction between O_2 and CO_2 (55). These experiments, which deserve to be confirmed and extended, provide evidence for an active chemoreceptor in the prepulmonary or venous circulation. The course of the afferent fibers was not identified.

CAROTID CHEMORECEPTORS AND THE VENTILATORY RESPONSE TO LOW AND HIGH O_2:   The carotid chemoreceptors are active at eupnea soon after birth in several species, because inhalation of 50% or 100% O_2 is associated with a prompt decrease of ventilation (18, 36, 81). As in the adult, this response is attributed to cessation of carotid chemoreceptor firing, when the PaO_2 exceeds the upper level of chemosensitivity (i.e. "functional denervation"). But maintenance of hyperoxia eventually increased ventilation in both infants and adult man (81). This was attributed to cerebral vasoconstriction and retention of metabolic CO_2. Using jugular venous occlusion to estimate cerebral blood flow by cranial plethysmography in preterm infants, it was found that inhalation of 100% O_2 for approximately 6 mins was associated with a 15% decrease of flow (59).

A decrease of inspired O_2 causes an increase of ventilation in all species studied, but this is only transient in some. In the kitten (13, 81), monkey (59, 90), rabbit (38, 82), and human infant (15, 16, 74), a *sudden* decrease of inspired O_2 is associated with a transient increase of ventilation which, after 30–90 sec, falls back to or even below the control level of ventilation. This "biphasic" response occurs in infants from at least 33 weeks gestational age (74). It occurs whether the alveolar PCO_2 is allowed to fall, is maintained, or increased during the hypoxia (16). This response pattern persists for about 1 week in term infants and up to 3 weeks in those born prematurely (74). The duration of hypoxia in the human is usually limited to 3–5 mins, and most animal studies have followed suit. It is not known how long the hypoventilatory phase lasts or if an eventual accommodation to hypoxia takes place. Ventilation of newborn rabbits was reduced 50% after 20 mins of breathing 5% O_2 (38). The animal studies have generally used a lower F_{I,O_2} [5–14%] than that employed with infants [13–18%]. The biphasic response does not occur in lambs or puppies.

Breath-by-breath analysis of the response of infants to inhalation of 13% O_2 for 2 mins revealed a more complex change of ventilation (27). The transient hyperventilation was itself preceded by a small fall in ventilation, and this initial fall was greater in those infants who subsequently showed the greater secondary fall of ventilation. Although these infants were conceived and born at high altitude (3100m), the authors suggest this might also be characteristic of the response at sea level. They suggested that stimulation of pulmonary or venous chemoreceptors could mediate the initial brief decrease of ventilation.

Progressive isocapnic hypoxia is associated with progressive increase of ventilation in lambs (45), calves (52), and puppies (45). It is not known if neonates that show a biphasic response to a sudden decrease of inspired O_2 also show a progressive increase of ventilation during isocapnic rebreathing. The increase of ventilation during hypoxia, whether transient or sustained, has been attributed to periperal chemoreceptor stimulation. Carotid chemoreceptor discharge increased with decrease of PaO_2 in newborn lambs $<$ 1 day old (51). Newborn lambs with denervation of the carotid bifurcation showed little or no increase of breathing during hypoxia (11); at rest they hypoventilated and had a lower PaO_2 and higher $PaCO_2$ compared to intact lambs.

Other evidence suggests that there is a postnatal increase in the magnitude of the peripheral chemoreceptor effect on ventilation. The response to progressive isocapnic hypoxia was less in 2-day-old lambs compared to lambs of 10 days and older (18). Transient hyperoxia decreased ventilation by 30% at 2 days of age and by 37–67% in the older lambs, and the excitatory effect of intra-arterial cyanide was also greater in the older group. A sudden reduction of inspired O_2 produced a response with greater delay at 1 than at 9 days of age (5.7 vs 1.8 secs) in lambs (4). Greater desaturation occurred in the younger lambs before the onset of hyperventilation. Carotid denervation increased the delay and degree of desaturation in both age groups and reduced the proportion of tests giving a clear response (4). Hence, carotid chemoreceptor input becomes brisker and causes greater changes of ventilation as lambs mature postnatally. This occurs despite improvement of arterial blood gases from levels that are mildly asphyxic compared to the adult. It is not clear whether the change occurs peripherally at the chemosensor or centrally at loci associated with the integration of the chemoreceptor input. The observation that the carotid chemoreceptors of lambs were relatively inactive up to 3 days of age (10) indicates that the peripheral receptor undergoes an adaptation and resetting in postnatal life, although some activity must occur to account for the responses described in other studies (4, 18, 45).

Failure to maintain increased ventilation has been attributed to the central effects of hypoxemia, either because of a depressant effect of low PO_2 itself on medullary neurones, or to alkalinization of CSF due to increased cerebral blood flow and washout of CO_2, or to decreased metabolic rate and production of CO_2 (see 15, 16, 38, 74, 90). It should be noted that $PaCO_2$ generally remains below normal even though ventilation may subside from a maximum. Tidal volume and "effective respiratory drive" (V_T/T_I) are decreased, suggesting effects upon central neuronal output (27, 38, 90), although this has not been observed in premature infants (75). In infant monkeys the pressure generated during an occluded breath (also regarded as a measure of central respiratory drive) was found to remain elevated throughout hypoxia, and the decrease of tidal volume was attributed to mechanical changes within the thorax (56). But interpretation of occlusion pressures in these circumstances is difficult, especially where the contributions of the chest wall, diaphragm, and abdomen are likely to change (45). However, if the hypoventilatory phase is due to a decrease of respiratory motor output, this may not depend critically upon the hypoxemia. Continuous stimulation of the carotid sinus nerve of anesthetized piglets produced only a transient increase in respiratory output (58). Piglets reportedly show a biphasic ventilatory response; lambs do not and stimulation of the sinus nerve in this species produced an increase of ventilation that was sustained. Thus, low O_2 may not be an obligatory part of the biphasic response, and the inability to maintain respiratory output in some species may be a general feature of their response to sustained peripheral stimulation. The carotid chemoreceptors are active throughout hypoxia in kittens (13, 82), and in infants a further fall of ventilation on inhalation of 100% O_2 demonstrate that peripheral chemoreceptor drive was present throughout (27, 74).

Sleep has an influence on the respiratory response to low O_2. In newborn lambs and calves, progressive isocapnic hypoxia produced smaller ventilatory responses in rapid eye movement sleep (REM) compared to nonrapid eye movement (NREM), quiet sleep (45, 52). In REM sleep the ventilatory response was often erratic and the arterial desaturation greater before arousal occurred. In puppies the response to progressive hypoxia was similar in the two sleep stages, although arousal occurred at lower O_2 saturations in REM sleep (45). Because puppies do not show paradoxical rib cage collapse in REM sleep, the different response to O_2 in REM and NREM in the lamb could be due simply to changes in chest wall mechanics (45). The difference of the O_2 saturation at arousal is difficult to interpret, because cerebral blood flow is usually higher in REM sleep in the newborn, and therefore O_2 delivery to the brain may be similar in the two sleep states. When steady-state hypoxia ($F_I,O_2 = 0.15$) was employed, ventilation decreased in NREM but increased in

REM sleep in 14-day-old puppies (40). By 19 days of age, ventilation increased in both sleep states. Kittens exposed to 10% O_2 for 8 hr/day for 8 days showed decreased respiratory rate and increased heart rate variability during NREM sleep and waking but not during REM sleep (3), leading to the hypothesis that active (REM) sleep protects against cardiorespiratory abnormalities induced by chronic hypoxia. This is consistent with the view that the regulation of breathing during REM sleep is largely independent of chemical and peripheral reflex control.

There is less agreement on the effect of sleep on the ventilatory response to low O_2 in the primate. Most studies of the biphasic response to hypoxia have not been able to distinguish between sleep states. The response occurs during NREM sleep in infant monkeys (90) but possibly not in human infants (77). A difficulty arises with the classification of sleep state in infants when observations are restricted to the regularity of breathing or presence of body movements.

Infants diagnosed to be at risk for fatal apnea on the basis of at least one apneic episode requiring intervention had a smaller response to hypoxia than control infants, and they showed a lower incidence of arousal (47). Abnormalities of carotid body ultrastructure in victims of sudden infant death syndrome, in which glomus cell size, number, and dense cytoplasmic granules were reduced (24), suggested that these infants possess defective carotid chemoreceptor function and that they may have suffered from recurrent hypoxic episodes without appropriate respiratory compensation.

Central Chemoreceptors and the Response to CO_2 and H^+

Newborn animals and premature and mature infants increase ventilation when breathing low concentrations of CO_2 (39, 41, 75, 76). The magnitude of response is approximately the same in REM and NREM sleep. Tidal volume is increased with little or no effect on breath timing, so that the calculated "central inspiratory drive" (V_T/V_I) is increased. Infant monkeys studied serially using 2–5% CO_2 showed an increase of slope of the CO_2 response curve between 2 and 21 days of age (39). This was attributed to change of sensitivity of central chemoreceptor mechanisms, although an increased contribution from the peripheral chemoreceptors, paralleling that to O_2 (see above), should not be ruled out. But other studies, in which measurement of occlusion pressure was used to estimate central respiratory drive, found no difference in the relationship between occlusion pressure and alveolar PCO_2 in premature and mature infants (84), normal and "respiratory distressed" infants (84), and neonates 7–15 days old compared with older children and adults (26). However, most studies show a leftward shift of the CO_2-response curve with age, reflecting the decrease of the $PaCO_2$ at rest from about 40 to 30 mmHg (39); i.e. there is a change of the set-point of the CO_2-response curve.

Steady inhalation of very low concentrations of CO_2 (0.3–1.2%) in infants was shown to make periodic and irregular breathing more regular; breath frequency increased and tidal volume fell (76). Because spontaneous changes from an irregular to regular pattern were similarly brought about by a reciprocal change of frequency and tidal volume, it was suggested that this might be mediated by endogenous CO_2. When breathing was regular, CO_2 tended to increase tidal volume with little change of breath timing (54a). This shows that there is significant interaction between the central effects of CO_2 and the neural mechanisms that determine the ongoing respiratory pattern. Higher concentrations of CO_2 also stabilize breathing pattern and increase tidal volume with little change of frequency.

A difference in resting ventilation and in the response to CO_2 when REM and NREM sleep episodes were compared was not apparent in newborn monkeys before 3 weeks of age (39), nor in premature infants (54a, 76) or term infants until about 3 months (41). A small increase of ventilation during sleep was noted in 11-week-old infants in one study (36). But the definitive sleep pattern is laid down gradually over several months, and there must be some difficulty in distinguishing each sleep state clearly in the very young infant. Oxygen consumption and the thermoregulatory response to cooling were also similar in both sleep states in premature infants (28); this differs from the adult, where O_2 consumption is higher and the fall of body temperature greater during cooling in REM sleep. Thus, sleep-related mechanisms that modulate breathing, metabolism, thermoregulation, and the response to CO_2 do not operate fully in the newborn primate.

Infants who had had an unexplained bout of apnea requiring resuscitation or revival had a greater ventilatory response to inhaling 2% CO_2 than age-matched controls (42). These infants also had higher resting heart rates and shortened QT intervals; it was suggested that increased sympatho-adrenal activity caused the raised CO_2 response, since infusion of catecholamines in the adult is known to increase the slope of the CO_2 response curve. Plasma catecholamines were not measured in these infants. Others have not observed altered CO_2 sensitivity when infants showing prolonged (>20 secs) spontaneous apnea were compared to those with regular breathing (36). Infants with persistent hypoventilation during sleep had a very low sensitivity to CO_2, an effect attributed to impairment of central CO_2 sensitivity, because peripheral chemoreceptor responses appeared to be normal (57, 83, 89).

Of equal importance is the acid-base regulation of CSF. During metabolic acidosis in newborn lambs, produced by intravenous infusion of HCl, there was an increase of ventilation, but this did not increase progressively as the arterial and CSF pH fell (19). The lambs did not develop "paradoxical" alkalinization of CSF, which occurs in the adult due to rapid loss of CO_2 from CSF to plasma. The fall of arterial [HCO_3^-] was followed immediately by a fall of CSF

[HCO_3^-], presumably due to relatively fast movement of HCO_3^- across the blood-brain barrier. Greater transfer of HCO_3^- into the brain from blood occurred in 1-week-old rats in which the permeability of the blood-brain barrier to inulin was 3 times greater than in adults (53). Thus CSF pH appears to be less well regulated in the newborn. Although relatively large changes of arterial and CSF pH were noted to cause an unexpectedly small change of ventilation, the accompanying increase of arterial and CSF PO_2 may have ameliorated the central response to acidemia (5, 19). Acidemia also caused a shift to the right of the O_2-dissociation curve, which would favor the unloading of O_2 at the tissues (5).

CONCLUDING REMARKS

It is clear that the overall effect of hypoxia in the fetal lamb is inhibitory (11, 12, 14), whereas after birth ventilation is increased and behavioral arousal is prompt (11, 12, 45, 52). Likewise, hypercapnia will cause arousal from sleep in the newborn but not before birth, when the response is limited to an increase of breathing during REM sleep. Without intact carotid chemoreceptors, hypoxia after birth is associated with delayed arousal and the appearance of synchronized EEG activity characteristic of quiet sleep. The ventilatory response in such animals may be preceded by apnea, hypotension, bradycardia, loss of muscle tone, and active inhibition of some limb reflexes (11). These observations point to a critical role of the carotid chemoreceptors after birth in providing an excitatory input to the reticular formation, and in activating reticulo-cortical pathways (34) in order to inhibit or competitively reduce the descending spinal inhibition that is present during hypoxia in the fetal state (12) and which may persist after birth (11). The absence of excitatory responses in utero can be seen to be appropriate, because increased O_2 consumption is thereby avoided. However, if the carotid chemoreceptors are indeed active in utero (10), this afferent activity must be gated within the brainstem by mechanisms not yet described. Such mechanisms may also be active during the hypoventilatory phase of the biphasic response in some neonates, because the carotid chemoreceptors continue to fire even though ventilation falls (13, 82). The observation that naloxone reverses the hypoventilation and fall in body temperature during hypoxia in newborn rabbits (38) suggests that opioid compounds are released by hypoxia, and one of their actions may be to raise the threshold for the central actions of chemoreceptor afferents upon the respiratory networks. The gradual increase in magnitude of the ventilatory response to both hypoxia and hypercapnia after birth may be due to the gradual diminution of endogenous opioid activity. Naloxone increased resting ventilation in rabbit pups less than 4 days old but had little effect after this (43). The presence of an endogenous inhibiting substance may also explain the relatively poor ventilatory response to metabolic acidosis in newborn lambs (19).

Alteration of activity at central synapses may, therefore, explain the increase in magnitude and sensitivity of chemoreflexes in the transition from fetus to newborn and within the newborn period. But the changes that must occur at the peripheral chemoreceptors have not been adequately described. The stimulus-response relationship for aortic and carotid chemoreceptors is yet to be determined for a fetus and newborn over a comparable range of PO_2 values, taking into account PCO_2, pH, and O_2 content of the blood. Likewise, a significant and increasing part of the response of the intact newborn animal to inspired CO_2 may be mediated by the peripheral receptors and not by central chemoreceptors alone.

There is a preoccupation with study of the effects of a sudden reduction of inspired O_2 on the ventilatory response of the newborn. While this is an ideal method for identifying short-term reflex adaptation, it is clear that some infants may have to acclimatize to hypoxia or mild asphyxia of long standing, due to ventilatory inefficiency or to sleep-related hypoventilation. Indeed, it is often held that infants who die during sleep may have succumbed to a final episode of previously recurring hypoxia. With perhaps one exception (3), this problem of short-term and long-term adaptation to mild hypoxia (or asphyxia) in the newborn has not been addressed experimentally.

Literature Cited

1. Acker, H., Lubbers, D. W., Purves, M. J., Tan, E. D. 1980. Measurements of the partial pressure of oxygen in the carotid body of fetal sheep and newborn lambs. *J. Developmental Physiol.* 2:323–38

2. Baillie, P., Dawes, G. S., Merlet, C. L., Richards, R. 1971. Maternal hyperventilation and foetal hypocapnia in sheep. *J. Physiol.* 218:635–50

3. Baker, T. L., McGinty, D. J. 1977. Reversal of cardiopulmonary failure during active sleep in hypoxic kittens: implications for sudden infant death. *Science* 198:419–21

4. Belenkey, D. A., Standeart, T. A., Woodrum, D. E. 1979. Maturation of the hypoxic ventilatory response of the newborn lamb. *J. Appl. Physiol.* 47:927–30

5. Berthiaume, Y., Bureau, M. A., Begin, R. 1981. The adaptation of neonatal blood to metabolic acidosis and its effect on cisternal oxygen tension. *Pediatr. Res.* 15:809–10

6. Biscoe, T. J., Purves, M. J. 1967. Observations on carotid body chemoreceptor activity and cervical sympathetic discharge in the cat. *J. Physiol.* 190:413–24

7. Biscoe, T. J., Purves, M. J., Sampson, S. R. 1969. Types of nervous activity

which may be recorded from the carotid sinus nerve in the sheep fetus. *J. Physiol.* 202:1–23

8. Bissonnette, J. M., Hohimer, A. R., Cronan, J. Z., Paul, M. S. 1980. Effect of oxygen and of carbon dioxide tension on the incidence of apnea in fetal lambs. *Am. J. Obstet. Gynecol.* 137:575–78

9. Bissonnette, J. M., Hohimer, A. R., Richardson, B. S. 1980. Role of CSF [H^+] in the control of fetal breathing movements. *Physiologist* 23:141

10. Blanco, C. E., Dawes, G. S., Hanson, M. A., McCooke, H. B. 1982. The arterial chemoreceptors in fetal sheep and newborn lambs. *J. Physiol.* 330:38P

11. Blanco, C. E., Dawes, G. S., Walker, D. W. 1982. Effects of hypoxia in conscious newborn lambs before and after denervation of the carotid bifurcation. *J. Physiol.* 339:467–74

12. Blanco, C. E., Dawes, G. S., Walker, D. W. 1983. Effect of hypoxia on polysynaptic hindlimb reflexes of unanaesthetized fetal and newborn lambs. *J. Physiol.* 339:453–66

13. Blanco, C., Hanson, M., Johnson, P., Rigatto, H. 1981. The pattern of breathing of kittens during hypoxia. *J. Physiol.* 316:28P

14. Boddy, K., Dawes, G. S., Fisher, R. L., Pinter, J., Robinson, J. S. 1974. Foetal respiratory movements, electrocortical, and cardiovascular responses to hypoxaemia and hypercapnia in sheep. *J. Physiol.* 243:599–618

15. Brady, J. P., Ceruti, E. 1966. Chemoreflexes in the newborn infant: effects of varying degrees of hypoxia on heart rate and ventilation in a warm environment. *J. Physiol.* 184:631–45

16. Brady, J. P., Dunn, P. M. 1970. Chemoreceptor reflexes in the newborn infant: effect of CO_2 on the ventilatory response to hypoxia. *Pediatrics* 45:206–15

17. Brown, E. R., Lawson, E. E., Jansen, A., Chernick, V., Taeusch, H. W. 1981. Regular fetal breathing induced by pilocarpine infusion in the near term fetal lamb. *J. Appl. Physiol.* 50:1348–52

18. Bureau, M. A., Begin, R. 1982. Postnatal maturation of the respiratory response to O_2 in awake newborn lambs. *J. Appl. Physiol.* 52:428–33

19. Bureau, M. A., Begin, R., Berthiaume, Y. 1979. Central chemical regulation of respiration in term newborn. *J. Appl. Physiol.* 47:1212–7

20. Chapman, R. L. K., Dawes, G. S., Rurak, D. W., Wilds, P. L. 1980. Breathing movements in fetal lambs and the effect of hypercapnia. *J. Physiol.* 302:19–29

21. Clewlow, F., Dawes, G. S., Johnston, B. M., Walker, D. W. 1983. Changes in breathing, electrocortical, and muscle activity in unanaesthetized fetal lambs with age. *J. Physiol.* In press

22. Cohn, H. E., Piasecki, G. J., Jackson, B. T. 1980. The effect of fetal heart rate on cardiovascular function during hypoxemia. *Am. J. Obstet. Gynecol.* 138:1190–99

23. Cohn, E. H., Sacks, E. J., Heymann, M. A., Rudolph, A. M. 1974. Cardiovascular responses to hypoxemia and acidemia in fetal lambs. *Am. J. Obstet. Gynecol.* 120:817–24

24. Cole, S., Lindenberg, L. B., Galioto, F. M., Howe, P. E., DeGraff, A. C., Davis, J. M., Lubka, R., Gross, E. M. 1979. Ultrastructural abnormalities of the carotid body in sudden infant death syndrome. *Pediatrics* 63:13–17

25. Coleridge, H. M., Coleridge, J. C. G., Howe, A. 1967. A search for pulmonary arterial chemoreceptors in the cat with comparison of the blood supply of the aortic bodies in the newborn and adult animals. *J. Physiol.* 191:353–74

26. Cosgrove, J. F., Neunburger, N., Bryan, M. H., Bryan, A. C., Levinson, H. 1975. A new method of evaluating the

chemosensitivity of the respiratory center in children. *Pediatrics* 56:972–80

27. Cotton, E. K., Grunstein, M. M. 1980. Effects of hypoxia on respiratory control in neonates at high altitude. *J. Appl. Physiol.* 48:487–95

28. Darnall, R. A., Ariagno, R. L. 1982. The effect of sleep state on active thermoregulation in the premature infant. *Pediatr. Res.* 16:512–14

29. Dawes, G. S., Duncan, S. L., Lewis, B. V., Merlet, C. L., Owen-Thomas, J. B., Reeves, J. T. 1969. Hypoxaemia and aortic chemoreceptor function in foetal lambs. *J. Physiol.* 201:105–16

30. Dawes, G. S., Duncan, S. L., Lewis, B. V., Merlet, C. L., Owen-Thomas, J. B., Reeves, J. T. 1969. Cyanide stimulation of the systemic arterial chemoreceptors in foetal lambs. *J. Physiol.* 201:117–28

31. Dawes, G. S., Gardner, W. N., Johnston, B. M., Walker, D. W. 1982. Effects of hypercapnia on tracheal pressure, diaphragm, and intercostal electromyograms in unanaesthetized fetal lambs. *J. Physiol.* 326:461–74

32. Dawes, G. S., Gardner, W. N., Johnston, B. M., Walker, D. W. 1983. Breathing in fetal lambs: the effects of brain stem and mid-brain transection. *J. Physiol.* 335:535–53

33. De Burgh Daly, M., Angell-James, J. E., Elsner, R. 1979. Role of carotid body chemoreceptors and their reflex interactions in bradycardia and cardiac arrest. *Lancet* 1:764–67

34. Dell, P., Hugelin, A., Bonvallet, M. 1961. Effects of hypoxia on the reticular and cortical diffuse systems. In *Cerebral Anoxia and the EEG*, ed. H. Gastaut, J. J. Meyers, pp. 46–58. Springfield, Ill: Thomas

35. Downing, S. E., Rocamora, J. N. 1968. Cardiovascular responses to hypoxemia and acidemia in the intact anesthetized lambs. *Yale J. Biol. Med.* 40:296–313

36. Fagenholz, S. A., O'Connell, K., Shannon, D. C. 1976. Chemoreceptor function and sleep state in apnea. *Pediatrics* 58:31–36

37. Gootman, P. M., Buckley, N. M., Gottman, N. 1979. Postnatal maturation of neural control of the circulation. In *Reviews in Perinatal Medicine*, ed. E. M. Scarpelli, E. V. Cosmi, pp. 1–72. New York: Raven

38. Grunstein, M. M., Hazinski, T. A., Schleuter, M. A. 1981. Respiratory control during hypoxia in newborn rabbits: implied action of endorphines. *J. Appl. Physiol.* 51:122–30

39. Guthrie, R. D., Standaert, T. A., Hodson, W. A., Woodrum, D. E. 1980.

Sleep and maturation of eucapnic ventilation and CO_2 sensitivity in the premature primate. *J. Appl. Physiol.* 48:347–54

40. Haddad, G. G., Gandhi, M. R., Mellins, R. B. 1982. Maturation of the ventilatory response to hypoxia in puppies during sleep. *J. Appl. Physiol.* 52:309–14

41. Haddad, G. G., Leistner, H. L., Epstein, R. A., Epstein, M. A. F., Grodin, W. K., Mellins, R. B. 1980. CO_2-induced changes in ventilation and ventilatory pattern in normal sleeping infants. *J. Appl. Physiol.* 48:684–88

42. Haddad, G. G., Leistner, H. L., Lai, T. L., Mellins, R. 1981. Ventilation and ventilatory pattern during sleep in aborted sudden infant death syndrome. *Pediatr. Res.* 15:879–83

43. Hazinski, T. A., Grunstein, M. M., Schlueter, M. H., Tooley, W. H. 1981. Effect of naloxone on ventilation in newborn rabbits. *J. Appl. Physiol.* 50:713–17

44. Henderson-Smart, D. J., Johnson, P., McClelland, M. E. 1979. Asynchronous activity of the diaphragm during breathing in lambs. *J. Physiol.* 296:22–23P

45. Henderson-Smart, D. J., Read, D. J. C. 1979. Ventilatory response to hypoxaemia during active sleep in the newborn. *J. Devel. Physiol.* 1:195–208

46. Hohimer, A. R., Bissonnette, J. M. 1981. Effect of metabolic acidosis on fetal breathing movements *in utero. Resp. Physiol.* 43:99–106

47. Hunt, C. E., McCulloch, K., Brouillette, R. T. 1981. Diminished hypoxic ventilatory responses in near-miss sudden infant death syndrome. *J. Appl. Physiol.* 50: 1313–17

48. Itskovitz, J., Rudolph, A. M. 1982. Denervation of the arterial chemoreceptors and baroreceptors in fetal lambs *in utero. Am. J. Physiol.* 242:H916–20

49. Jansen, A. H., Ioffe, S., Russell, B. J., Chernick, V. 1981. Effect of carotid chemoreceptor denervation on breathing *in utero* before and after birth. *J. Appl. Physiol.* 51:630–33

50. Jansen, A. H., Ioffe, S., Russell, B. J., Chernick, V. 1982. Influence of sleep state on the response to hypercapnia of fetal lambs. *Resp. Physiol.* 48:125–42

51. Jansen, A. H., Purves, M. J., Tan, E. D. 1980. The role of sympathetic nerves in the activation of the carotid body chemoreceptors at birth in the sheep. *J. Devel. Physiol.* 2:305–21

52. Jeffrey, H. E., Read, D. J. C. 1980. Ventilatory responses of newborn calves to progressive hypoxia in quiet and active sleep. *J. Appl. Physiol.* 48:892–95

53. Johanson, C. E., Woodbury, D. M., Withrow, C. D. 1976. Distribution of bicarbonate between blood and cerebrospinal fluid in the neonatal rat in metabolic acidosis and alkalosis. *Life Sci.* 19:691–700

54. Jones, C. T., Robinson, R. O. 1975. Plasma catecholamines in foetal and adult sheep. *J. Physiol.* 248:15–33

54a. Kalapesi, Z., Durand, M., Leahy, F. N., Cates, D. B., MacCallum, M., Rigatto, H. 1981. Effect of periodic or regular respiratory pattern on the ventilatory response to low inhaled CO_2 in preterm infants during sleep. *Am. Rev. Respir. Dis.* 123:8–11

55. Kollmeyer, K., Kleinman, L. 1975. A respiratory venous chemoreceptor in the young puppy. *J. Appl. Physiol.* 38:819–26

56. LaFramboise, W. A., Standeart, T. A., Woodrum, D. E., Guthrie, R. D. 1981. Occlusion pressures during the ventilatory response to hypoxemia in the newborn monkey. *J. Appl. Physiol.* 51:1169–74

57. Lagercrantz, H., Broberger, U., Milerad, J., von Euler, C. 1980. Ventilatory studies in two older infants with prolonged apnea. *Acta Paediatr. Scand.* 69:545–48

58. Lawson, E. E., Long, W. A. 1980. Carotid sinus nerve and respiratory drive in newborns. *Physiologist* 23:140

59. Leahy, F. A. N., Cates, D., MacCallum, M., Rigatto, H. 1980. Effect of CO_2 and 100% O_2 on cerebral blood flow in preterm infants. *J. Appl. Physiol.* 48: 468–72

60. Marsal, K., Gennser, G., Lofgren, O. 1979. Effects on fetal breathing movements of maternal challenges. *Acta Obstet. Gynecol. Scand.* 58:335–42

61. Martin, C. B., Murato, Y., Ikenoue, T. 1975. Effects of pO_2 and pCO_2 on fetal breathing movements in rhesus monkeys. *Gynecol. Invest.* 6:74

62. Molteni, R. A., Melmed, M. H., Sheldon, R. E., Jones, M. D., Meschia, G. 1980. Induction of fetal breathing by metabolic acidemia and its effect on blood flow to the respiratory muscles. *Am. J. Obstet. Gynecol.* 136:609–20

63. Moss, I., Scarpelli, E. 1979. Generation and regulation of breathing *in utero:* fetal CO_2 response test. *J. Appl. Physiol.* 47:527–31

64. Mott, J. C. 1971. Baro- and chemoreceptor mechanisms in hemorrhage. In *Neurohumoral and Metabolic Aspects of Injury,* ed. A. G. B. Korach, H. B. Stoner, J. J. Spitzer, pp. 445–61. New York: Plenum

65. Natale, R., Clewlow, G., Dawes, G. S. 1981. Measurement of fetal forelimb

movements in the lamb *in utero*. *Am. J. Obstet. Gynecol.* 140:545–51

66. Natale, R., Richardson, B., Patrick, J. 1981. Effect of intravenous glucose infusion on human fetal breathing activity. *Obstet. Gynecol.* 59:320–24

67. Nishino, T., Mokashi, A., Lahiri, S. 1982. Stimulation of the carotid chemoreceptors and ventilation by doxapram in the cat. *J. Appl. Physiol.* 52:1261–65

68. Patrick, J., Natale, R., Richardson, B. 1978. Patterns of human fetal breathing activity at 34 to 35 weeks gestational age. *Am. J. Obstet. Gynecol.* 132:507–12

69. Peeters, L. L. H., Sheldon, R. E., Jones, M. D., Makowski, E. L., Meschia, G. 1979. Blood flow to fetal organs as a function of arterial oxygen content. *Am. J. Obstet. Gynecol.* 135:637–46

70. Piercy, W. N., Day, M. A., Neims, A. H., Williams, R. L. 1977. Alteration of ovine fetal respiratory-like activity by diazepam, caffeine, and doxapram. *Am. J. Obstet. Gynecol.* 127:43–49

71. Ponte, J., Purves, M. J. 1973. Types of afferent nervous activity which may be measured in the vagus nerve of the sheep foetus. *J. Physiol.* 229:51–76

72. Purves, M. J. 1981. Chemoreceptors and their reflexes with special reference to the fetus and newborn. *J. Devel. Physiol.* 3:21–57

73. Rahilly, P. M. 1980. Effect of sleep state and feeding on cranial blood flow in the human neonate. *Arch. Dis. Child.* 55:265–70

74. Rigatto, H. 1977. Ventilatory response to hypoxia. *Semin. Perinatology* 1:357–62

75. Rigatto, H., Desai, U., Leahy, F., Kalapesi, Z., Cates, D. 1981. The effect of 2% CO_2, 100% O_2, theophylline, and 15% O_2 on "inspiratory drive" and "effective" timing in preterm infants. *Early Human Develop.* 5:63–70

76. Rigatto, H., Kalapesi, Z., Leahy, F. N., Durand, M., MacCallum, M., Cates, D. 1980. Chemical control of respiratory frequency and tidal volume during sleep in preterm infants. *Respir. Physiol.* 41:117–25

77. Rigatto, H., Kalapesi, Z., Leahy, F., MacCallum, M., Cates, D. 1979. Ventilatory response to 100% and 15% O_2 during wakefulness and sleep. *Pediatr. Res.* 13:504

78. Ritchie, J. W. K., Lakhani, L. 1980. Fetal breathing movements and maternal hyperoxia. *Br. J. Obstet. Gynaecol.* 87:1084–88

79. Ritchie, J. W. K., Lakhani, L. 1980. Fetal breathing movements in response to maternal inhalation of 5% carbon dioxide. *Am. J. Obstet. Gynecol.* 136:386–88

80. Rurak, D. W. 1978. Plasma vasopressin levels during hypoxaemia and the cardiovascular effects of exogenous vasopressin in foetal and adult sheep. *J. Physiol.* 277:341–57

81. Sankaran, K., Wiebe, H., Seschia, M. M. K., Boychuk, R. D., Cates, D., Rigatto, H. 1979. Immediate and late ventilatory response to high and low O_2 in preterm infants and adults. *Pediatr. Res.* 13:875–78

82. Schweiler, G. H. 1968. Respiratory regulation during postnatal development in cats and rabbits and some of its morphological substrate. *Acta Physiol. Scand. Suppl.* 304:49–63

83. Shannon, D. C., Marsland, D. W., Gould, J. B., Callahan, B., Todres, I. D., Dennis, J. 1976. Central hypoventilation during quiet sleep in two infants. *Pediatrics* 57:342–46

84. Simbruner, G., Popov, C. 1982. Untersuchungen zur Atemmechanik und Atemregulation bei gesunden und respiratisch erkrankten Neugeborenen verschiedenen Gestationsalters. *Paediatr. Paedol.* 17:535–48

85. Storrs, C. N. 1977. Cardiovascular effects of apnea in preterm infants. *Arch. Dis. Child.* 52:534–40

86. Verna, A., Ronmy, M., Leitner, L. M. 1980. Role of the carotid body cells: long-term consequences of their cryodestruction. *Neurosci. Lett.* 16:281–85

87. Walker, A. M., Cannata, J. P., Dowling, M. H., Kitchie, B. C., Maloney, J. E. 1979. Age-dependent pattern of autonomic heart rate control during hypoxia in fetal and newborn lambs. *Biol. Neonate* 35:198–208

88. Walker, D., Harding, R. 1983. Effect of hypoxemia on the excitability of two cranial reflexes in unanaesthetized fetal lambs. *Proc. Aust. Perinat. Soc., Exc. Med. Asia Pac. Congr. Ser.* 4:28

89. Wells, H. H., Kattwinkel, J., Morrow, J. D. 1980. Control of ventilation in Ondine's curse. *J. Pediat.* 96:865–67

90. Woodrum, D. E., Standaert, T. A., Maycock, D. E., Guthrie, R. D. 1981. Hypoxic ventilatory response in the newborn monkey. *Pediatr. Res.* 15:367–70

SUBJECT INDEX

A

Acetazolamide
  bicarbonate secretion and, 436
  chloride absorption and, 436
Acetylcholine
  endplate channel currents and,
    459–61
  pancreatic acinar cell depolar-
    ization and, 465
  pancreatic cellular differentia-
    tion and, 371
  parietal cell stimulation and,
    382
  potassium ion channel activa-
    tion and, 462–63
Acetylcholine receptor
  myasthenia gravis and, 526
Acetylstrophanthidin
  ventricular fibrillation and,
    168
Aconitine
  sodium ion channels and, 519
Acoustic chiasm, 276–80
Acoustic clicks
  cochlear hair cells and, 249
ACTH secretion
  angiotensin II and, 24, 26
Actin
  actomyosin solution dis-
    aggregation and, 2–3
Action potentials
  nerve birefringence and, 11
Activation
  steroid receptors and, 84
Actomyosin solution
  disaggregation into myosin
    and actin, 2–3
Adaptation
  cochlear hair cells and, 249–
    50
Adenohypophysis
  brain renin in, 21
Adenosine
  hypoxia and, 638
Adenosine triphosphate
  see ATP
Adenylate cyclase system
  steroid hormones and, 120–21
Adrenal glands
  renin-angiotensin system in,
    17
Adrenalectomy
  beta-adrenergic receptors and,
    126–27
  renin substrate concentrations
    and, 17–18

Adrenergic blocking agents
  plasma renin activity and,
    297
Adrenergic hyperreactivity
  hypertension and, 145–47
Adrenergic receptors
  renal baroreceptors and, 299–
    302
  see also specific type
Adrenergic signal
  renin release and, 297
Affinity labeling
  steroid receptor structure and,
    94–96
After-depolarizations
  heart and, 477–78
Airflow
  laryngeal control of, 680
Airway obstruction
  pharyngeal reflexes and, 678
Alamethicin
  lipid bilayer endplate channel
    currents and, 460
Alanine transport
  transepithelial, 428–31
Aldosterone
  colonic sodium pump activity
    and, 446
  renal kallikrein synthesis and,
    317
  sodium absorption and, 435,
    439, 441
  sodium ion transport and,
    509–10
Aldosteronism
  urinary kallikrein excretion
    and, 316
Alpha-adrenergic agonists
  renin release and, 305
Alpha-adrenergic blockade
  coronary vascular resistance
    and, 191
Alpha-adrenergic receptors
  stress-induced arrhythmias
    and, 161–62
Alveoli
  postnatal development of,
    624–26
Amiloride
  apical sodium ion transport
    and, 502–3
  mucosal sodium ion uptake
    and, 499
  renal kallikrein synthesis and,
    317
  sodium absorption and, 435
Amino acid transport, 420–24

basolateral membranes and,
  423
  brush-border membranes and,
    420–22
Aminoglycosides
  cochlear damage and, 221
Aminopyrine
  parietal cell accumulation of,
    380–81
Amygdaloid nuclei
  brain renin in, 21
Androgen receptors
  androgen action regulation
    and, 109–12
  antiandrogens and, 112–14
  characteristics of, 108
  chromatin and, 107
  molybdate and, 69–70
Androgens
  electroreceptor tuning and,
    562–63
Angiotensin
  pituitary gland and, 25–26
Angiotensin I
  blood-brain barrier and, 18
  conversion to angiotensin II
    kininase II and, 313
  CSF, 21
Angiotensin II
  binding sites in brain, 19
  blood-brain barrier and, 18
  brain tissue, 22
  circumventricular organs and,
    24–25
  CSF, 21–22
  pituitary gland and, 25–26
  renin release and, 303,
    305
Angiotensin III
  CSF, 21–22
Angiotensinase
  CSF, 19
Angiotensinogen
  CSF, 19
Angiotensin receptors
  brain, 19
Angiotensins
  circumventricular organs and,
    18
  renal prostaglandin production
    and, 332
Antiandrogens
  androgen receptors and, 112–
    14
Antibody R6
  relaxin and, 44–45
Antidiuretic hormone

epithelial sodium ion channels and, 510
urinary kallikrein excretion and, 318
Antihypertensive agents
catecholamines and, 180
Aortic chemoreceptors
fetal, 687–89
Apical membrane
sodium absorption and, 436–44
Apnea
cardiovascular responses to, 652–53
hypoxia and, 634–36
laryngeal-induced
maturity and, 655–56
prolonged during sleep, 676–77
types and incidence of, 677
Apneic reflexes
larynx and, 678–79
Aprotinin
sodium reabsorption and, 317
Apteronotus
electric organ discharges of, 562
Arachidonic acid metabolism
see Renal arachidonate metabolism
Area postrema
renin substrate in, 19
Arousal response
hypercapnia and, 681–82
hypoxia and, 636–37, 682
laryngeal reflexes and, 679
Arrhythmias
after-depolarizations and, 477–78
behavioral stress and, 155–71
coronary vasoconstriction and, 162–64
see also specific type
Arrhythmogenicity
neural pathways in, 155
steroid hormones and, 119–20
Asthma
steroid hormones and, 120, 124
ATP
actomyosin solution disaggregation and, 2–3
discovery in muscle, 4
parietal cell metabolism and, 387–89
Atrial natriuretic factor, 343
Atropine
conditioned tachycardia and, 189
pepsinogen secretion and, 395
Auditory cortex
sound localization and, 283–84

Auditory hair cells
electroreceptors and, 563–64
Auditory nerve fibers
crossed olivocochlear bundle and, 241
two-tone suppression in, 241
Auditory pathways
neural response properties of
development of, 219–21
Auditory system
ontogeny of, 213–23
influences on, 221–23
see also specific components
Aversive conditioning
cardiovascular neurobiology and, 203
Azide
parietal cell aminopyrine accumulation and, 380

B

Barium chloride
ventricular arrhythmias and, 155
Baroreflex
cardiac component of, 137–38
cardiovascular activity and, 203
emotional stress and, 138–39
exercise and, 134–38
modulation of
mechanisms of, 133–34
Bartter's syndrome
renal kinin-prostaglandin interactions and, 320
urinary kallikrein excretion and, 316
Basilar membrane
compressive nonlinear motion of, 252
frequency selectivity and, 253–54
Mossbauer effect and, 232–33
nonlinear vibration in, 234
place principle and, 217–19
tuning of, 234–35
lability of, 235–36
Basolateral membranes
amino acid transport and, 423
glucose transport and, 428
potassium ion permeability of, 498
sodium absorption and, 445–46
Bat sonar, 599–613
see also Echolocation
Batrachotoxin
liposomal sodium ion channels and, 554–55
sodium ion channels and, 519
Behavioral stress
arrhythmias and, 155–71

blood pressure and, 143–45
coronary vasoconstriction and, 162–64
experimental hypertension via, 149–50
renal hyperreactivity to, 146–47
ventricular vulnerability and, 158–59
Benzimidazoles
parietal cell aminopyrine accumulation and, 380
Benzimidazolyl-guanidine
epithelial sodium channel self-inhibition and, 501
Beta-adrenergic agonists
pepsinogen secretion and, 395
Beta-adrenergic blockade
conditioned tachycardia and, 189
ventricular arrhythmias and, 161
Beta-adrenergic receptors
renin release and, 303–4
steroidal regulation of
biochemical manifestations of, 123–27
mechanisms of, 120–23
physiologic manifestations of, 119–20
Beta-endorphins
hypoxia and, 638
see also Endorphins
Bicarbonate secretion
acetazolamide and, 436
Bicuculline
hypoxia and, 692
Birds
directional sensitivity of, 588–89
location sensitivity of, 589–90
magnetic material in, 594
Birefringence
actomyosin solution disaggregation and, 2–3
contracting muscle and, 4
nerve
action potentials and, 11
Blood-brain barrier
renin-angiotensin system and, 17–18
Blood pressure
angiotensin II and, 24, 25
baroreflex and, 133–40
behavioral stress and, 143–45
isometric exercise and, 177–78
renal function and, 143–45
sympathetic arousal and, 143–45
see also Hypertension
Blood pressure regulation
salt intake and, 147–49

Blood vessels
 renin-angiotensin system in,
 17
Bombesin
 digestive enzyme secretion
 and, 370
 pancreatic amylase release
 and, 366–68
BOMT
 androgen receptor function
 and, 113
Bradycardia
 conditioned, 189
 laryngeal-induced apnea and,
 652
Bradykinin
 proximal tubule sodium reabsorption and, 315–16
Brain amines
 angiotensin II and, 25
Brain capillary permeability
 angiotensin II and, 26
Brain renin
 distribution of, 21
Brain renin-angiotensin system,
 17–27
 brain tissue and, 19–23
 circulatory system and, 17–18
 functions of, 24–26
Brain stem
 angiotensin II in, 22
 brain renin in, 21
Brain tissue
 angiotensin II in, 22
 angiotensin-generating activity
 in, 20–21
 angiotensin-like immunoreactivity in, 22–23
 converting enzyme in, 20
 renin substrate in, 19–20
Breathing
 see Ventilation
Bromocriptine
 hypertension and, 180
 ventricular fibrillation and,
 168
Brush-border membranes
 amino acid transport and,
 420–22
 glucose transport and, 424–27

C

Caerulein
 pepsinogen secretion and,
 395–96
Caffeine
 after-depolarizations and, 478
 hypoxia and, 692
Calcium
 exocytosis in gastric chief
 cells and, 400

pepsinogen secretion and,
 398–99
 potassium ion channel activation and, 490–92
 see also Intracellular calcium
Calcium ion
 epithelial sodium channel regulation and, 500–3
Calcium ion channels
 bursting behavior and, 460
 cardiac cell membrane, 475–
 77
 small cell, 468
 voltage-activated
 current flow through, 462
Calcium ionophore A23187
 pepsinogen secretion and, 396
Calmodulin
 renin release and, 305
Carbachol
 gastric gland cyclic AMP content and, 398–99
Carbohydrate metabolism
 human growth hormone and,
 39–40
Cardiac arrest
 laryngeal-induced apnea and,
 652
Cardiac arrhythmias
 see Arrhythmias
Cardiac cell membranes
 ion channels in, 473–81
Cardiac glycosides
 after-depolarizations and, 478
Cardiac sympathetic drive
 tryptophan and, 168–69
Cardiac vagal tone
 ventricular fibrillation and,
 165
Cardiovascular conditioning,
 187–95
 neural control in, 192–95
 operant, 199–208
Cardiovascular function
 physiologic mechanisms
 affecting, 179–81
Cardiovascular system
 laryngeal-induced apnea and,
 652–53
Carotid bodies
 hypoxic arousal response and,
 636
Carotid chemoreceptors
 fetal, 689–91
 ventilatory response to O_2
 and, 694–97
Carotid sinus
 plasma renin activity and,
 300–2
Catecholamine agonists
 beta-adrenergic receptors and,
 124
Catecholamines

antihypertensive agents and,
 180
 desensitization and, 124
 pancreatic cellular differentiation and, 371
 plasma renin activity and, 297
 tachyphylaxis and, 120
Catecholamine turnover
 angiotensin II and, 25
Cell suspensions
 hydrogen secretion in
 measurement of, 379
Central nervous system
 see CNS
Cerebellum
 angiotensin II binding sites in,
 19
 brain renin in, 21
Cerebral cortex
 angiotensin II binding sites in,
 19
 angiotensin II in, 22
 neuron electrical activity in
 angiotensin II and, 26
Cerebrospinal fluid
 see CSF
Cervix
 relaxin and, 49
Chemoreceptors
 fetal, 687–93
 neonatal, 693–99
 see also specific type
Chloride absorption
 acetazolamide and, 436
Chloride ion
 gastric acid secretion and,
 386–87
Chloride ion channels
 Torpedo electroplax, 555–56
 transmitter-gated, 463
Chloroquine
 chylomicron remnant hydrolysis and, 410
Chlorpromazine
 pepsinogen secretion and, 399
Cholecystokinin
 digestive enzyme secretion
 and, 370
 pancreatic acinar cell depolarization and, 465
 pancreatic cellular differentiation and, 371
 pancreatic hypertrophy/hyper-
 plasia and, 364
Cholecystokinin-octapeptide
 pepsinogen secretion and,
 395–96
Cholera toxin
 pepsinogen secretion and, 396
Cholinergic agents
 pepsinogen secretion and, 395
Cholinergic hyperreactivity
 hypertension and, 145–47

Choroid plexus
  brain renin in, 21
Chromaffin cells
  single calcium ion channels
    in, 462
Chromatin
  androgen receptors and, 107
Chronic obstructive pulmonary
  disease
  arousal response and, 636
Chronotropism
  control of, 189–90
  steroid hormones and, 119–20
Chylomicron remnants
  lipoprotein synthesis and, 410
Chymotrypsin
  meroreceptor production and,
    89
Cimetidine
  pepsinogen secretion and, 395
Circulatory system
  renin-angiotensin system in,
    17–18
Circumventricular organs
  angiotensin II and, 24–25
  angiotensins and, 18
Cirrhosis
  natriuresis and, 350
Citrate synthase
  synthesis of
    aldosterone and, 509–10
Clonidine
  ventricular fibrillation and,
    168
CNS
  baroreflex and, 133–34
  cardiovascular activity and,
    203–4
  catecholamine turnover in
    angiotensin II and, 25
Cochlea
  basilar membrane tuning and,
    236
  efferents to, 241
  emissions and echoes of, 240
  maturation of, 216
  stereocilia structure and, 216
  structure of, 231–32
Cochlear hair cells
  adaptation and, 249–50
  receptor potentials of, 248–49
Cochlear mechanics, 231–43
Cochlear nerve fibers
  spike rates of, 250–51
Cochlear neurons
  frequency selectivity and,
    253–55
  temporal synchronization and,
    252–53
Cochlear tuning
  nonmammalian, 236
Colchicine
  chylomicron remnant hydroly-
    sis and, 410

Colon
  sodium absorption by, 435–48
Consonants
  discrimination of, 266–67
Converting enzyme
  blood-brain barrier and, 18
  brain tissue, 20
Corollary discharge
  effects of, 570–71
  electric organ pacemaker,
    565–71
Coronary vascular beds
  control of, 191–92
Coronary vasoconstriction
  arrhythmias during behavioral
    stress and, 162–64
Cortisone acetate
  beta-adrenergic receptors and,
    123
Coughing
  laryngeal reflexes and, 679
Creatine phosphate
  discovery in muscle, 4
Crossed olivocochlear bundle
  acoustic attenuation and, 266
  auditory nerve fibers and, 241
CSF
  angiotensin I in, 21
  angiotensinogen in, 19
  angiotensins II and III in, 21–
    22
  renin substrate in, 17, 19
Cyanate
  parietal cell aminopyrine accu-
    mulation and, 380
cyclic AMP
  pepsinogen secretion and,
    396, 397–98
  relaxin secretion and, 46
  renin release and, 303–5
cyclic GMP
  pepsinogen secretion and,
    395–96
Cyclic nucleotides
  pepsinogen secretion and, 396
Cyclooxygenase
  renal synthesis of eicosanoids
    and, 327–28
Cyproterone acetate
  androgen receptor function
    and, 113
Cytochrome p-450 monooxyge-
    nase
  renal synthesis of eicosanoids
    and, 327–28
Cytosol
  steroid binding and, 68–69

D

Deoxycorticosterone acetate
  colonic sodium pump activity
    and, 446

Dephosphorylation
  Mullerian inhibiting substance
    and, 57–63
  steroid binding and, 69
  steroid receptor transformation
    and, 84
Desamethasone
  renin substrate concentrations
    and, 17–18
Diacylglycerol acyltransferase
  triglyceride synthesis and, 408
Diaphragmatic muscle fatigue
  hypoxia and, 634–36
Diazepam
  ventricular arrhythmias and,
    161
Dihydrotestosterone
  electroreceptor tuning and,
    562–63
Dihydroxycholecalciferol recep-
    tors
  molybdate and, 69–70
Diisopropylflurophosphate
  tissue kallikrein and, 309
Diltiazem
  calcium ion channels and, 476
Diphytanoylphosphatidylcholine
  membranes
  gramicidin channels in, 536
Direction sensitivity, 587–89
Dithiothreitol
  steroid binding and, 69–70
Dopamine
  hypoxia and, 638
  renal baroreceptors and, 299–
    300
Dorsal root ganglion cells
  single calcium ion channels
    in, 462
Doxapram
  hypoxia and, 692
  respiratory activity and, 690
Dromotropism
  control of, 190

E

Echolocation
  signal processing in, 601–13
EGF
  Mullerian duct regression and,
    55–58
Eicosanoids
  renal synthesis of
    enzymatic pathways in,
      327–28
Eigenmannia
  electric organ discharges of,
    562
  jamming avoidance response
    in, 575
Electric fish, 561–80
  see also Electroreceptors
Electric organ pacemaker

electroreceptor inputs and, 565–71
Electrolytes
parietal cell, 386–87
Electrophilic affinity labeling
steroid receptor structure and, 94–95
Electrophorus electricus
tetrodotoxin receptor of, 520–21
Electroreceptors
electric organ pacemaker and, 565–71
frequency tuning of, 561–65
phase sensitivity of, 564–65
Emotional stress
baroreflex and, 138–39
Endogenous opiates
ventilatory response to hypoxia and, 663–64
Endorphins
hypoxia and, 638
Enkephalins
hypoxia and, 638
Enterocytes
transport pathways in, 418–20
Enzyme-linked immunoadsorbent assay
steroid receptors and, 97–98
Epidermal growth factor
pancreatic secretory function and, 364
Epinephrine
gastric gland cyclic AMP content and, 398–99
hypoxia and, 637–38
relaxin secretion and, 46
renal baroreceptors and, 299
renin secretion and, 297
salivary gland hypertrophy/hyperplasia and, 364
ventricular arrhythmias and, 155
Epithelia
sodium ion channels in, 497–511
structure of, 498–99
Eptesicus fuscus
echolocation and, 600
sonar echoes and, 603
sonar emissions of, 602
Estradiol
electroreceptor tuning and, 562–63
progesterone receptor synthesis and, 110
relaxin secretion and, 46
Estrogen receptors
complexes of, 85–86
molybdate and, 69–70
pancreatic, 364
steroid-binding subunits of, 88
translocation inhibitors and, 77

Estrogens
androgen receptor function and, 112–14
biologic action of
nuclear receptors and, 110
electroreceptor tuning and, 562–63
hepatic very low density lipoproteins and, 409
Ethmozin
ventricular fibrillation and, 168
Exercise
baroreflex and, 134–38
cardiovascular and renal responses to, 177–79
cardiovascular concomitants of, 202–3
tachycardia of, 206–7
Expiratory airflow
laryngeal regulation of, 649–51
External ear
development of, 214
Extracellular fluid volume
renal sodium excretion and, 343
Extrasystoles
after-depolarizations and, 477–78

F

Fatigue
respiratory muscle efficiency and, 681
Feline sarcoma virus
tyrosine phosphorylation and, 57
Fetal breathing movements
laryngeal function and, 646–47
Fish
directional sensitivity of, 589
magnetic material in, 594
Flouride
Mullerian duct regression and, 55
Flutamide
androgen receptor function and, 112–14
Formant frequencies
of speech sound, 263
Forskolin
pepsinogen secretion and, 396, 397–98
Frequency selectivity
cochlear neurons and, 253–55
Fujinama sarcoma virus
tyrosine phosphorylation and, 57
Functional residual capacity
REM sleep and, 651

Furosemide
colonic sodium fluxes and, 318

G

GABA
hypoxia and, 638
spinal cord chloride ion channels and, 466
Gastric chief cells
exocytosis in
calcium and, 400
isolation of, 394
Gastrin
parietal cell stimulation and, 382–83
pepsinogen secretion and, 396
Gland suspensions
hydrogen secretion in
measurement of, 379
Glucagon
lipogenesis in hepatocyte cultures and, 408–9
Glucocorticocoid binding
sulfyhydryl moieties and, 69
Glucocorticoid receptors
antibodies against, 96
complexes of, 85–86
malignancy and, 92–93
pancreatic, 364
photoaffinity labeling and, 95–96
pyridoxal phosphate and, 75
steroid-binding subunits of, 88
Glucocorticoids
beta-adrenergic receptors and, 123–24
colonic sodium pump activity and, 446
Glucose intolerance
human growth hormone and, 39
Glucose metabolism
low-frequency sound localization and, 279
Glucose transport
basolateral membranes and, 428
brush-border membranes and, 424–27
mechanism of, 426–27
transepithelial, 428–31
Glucose uptake
relaxin and, 49
steroid hormones and, 120
Glucuronidase
activity of
testosterone and, 110–12
Glycosylation
lipoprotein transport and, 404
Gramicidin A
crystallization of, 532–33
Gramicidin channels, 531–42

chemical modification of,
540–41
equilibrium ion binding and,
539–40
gating characteristics of, 533
molecular dynamic simulation
of, 541–42
permeability characteristics of,
533–38
lipid modulation and, 538–
39
Gramicidins
structure of, 531–33
Grayanotoxin
sodium ion channels and, 519
Growth hormone
see Human growth hormone
Growth hormone secretion
angiotensin II and, 26
Guanfacine
hypertension and, 180
Gymnotiform fish
laminated electrosensory structures of, 571–80
Gymnotoids
electric organ discharges of,
563

H

Hartnup's disease
transport defects in, 423–24
Heart cell cultures
single calcium ion channels
in, 462
Heart cells
cationic channels in, 465
Heart rate
psychologic stimuli and, 178
Helix neurons
single calcium ion channels
in, 462
Hepatic glucose production
steroid hormones and, 120
Hepatic lipid metabolism
high density lipoproteins and,
411–12
Hepatocyte monolayers, 403–12
lipoprotein catabolism and,
409–12
lipoprotein metabolism and,
403–12
High density lipoproteins
hepatic lipid metabolism and,
411–12
synthesis and secretion of,
407
Hippocampus
angiotensin II binding sites in,
19
angiotensin II in, 22
ion channels in, 465
neuron electrical activity in

angiotensin II and, 26
Histamine
parietal cell stimulation and,
382
Histamine uptake
parietal cell, 384
Honey bees
directional sensitivity of, 587–
88
time sense of, 590–91
Human growth hormone
20,000-dalton variant of, 34–
35
alkaline forms of, 35
carbohydrate metabolism and,
39–40
disulfide dimer of, 36–37
hyperglycemia and, 39
insulin-potentiating activity of,
38
noncovalently linked two-
chain forms of, 37–38
as prohormone, 39–40
proteolytically cleaved forms
of, 37
Human ovarian carcinoma
Mullerian inhibiting substance
and, 63
Human placental lactogen
relaxin secretion and, 46
Hydrocortisone
beta-adrenergic receptors and,
123
neutrophil beta-adrenergic receptors and, 125–26
tachyphylaxis and, 120
Hydroperoxyeicosatetraenoic
acids
prostacyclin synthetase inhibition and, 327–28
Hydroxydopamine hydrobromide
conditioned bradycardia and,
190
Hypercapnia
breathing movements and,
691–92
cardiovascular effects of, 693–
94
ventilatory and arousal responses to, 681–82
Hyperdibasicaminoaciduria
transport defects in, 424
Hyperglycemia
human growth hormone and,
39
Hypertension
adrenergic hyperreactivity
and, 145–47
cholinergic hyperreactivity
and, 145–47
drugs affecting, 180
exercise and, 177–78
experimental

induction of, 149–50
genetic factors in, 181–83
laryngeal-induced apnea and,
652
natriuretic hormone and, 350–
55
psychological factors and, 183
renal function and, 178–79
see also Blood pressure
Hyperventilation
neonatal, 631
Hypothalamus
angiotensin II binding sites in,
19
brain renin in, 21
converting enzyme in, 20
renin substrate in, 19–20
Hypothyroidism
beta-adrenergic receptor coupling and, 123
Hypoxemia
neonatal, 680
Hypoxia
apnea and, 634–36
arousal response and, 636–37
breathing movements and, 692
cardiovascular effects of, 693–
94
diaphragmatic muscle fatigue
and, 634–36
metabolic rate changes and,
633–34
neonatal ventilatory response
to, 630–33
neural mediation of, 693
neurotransmitters and, 637–38
ventilatory and arousal responses to, 682
ventilatory response to
endogenous opiates and,
663–64

I

Immunoreactivity
angiotensin-like in brain, 22–
23
Indomethacin
renin release and, 303–4
Induction
magnetic field detection and,
592
Inferior colliculus
sound localization and, 282
Inferior vena caval constriction
plasma renin activity and, 303
Inner ear
differentiation of, 215–16
Inotropism
steroid hormones and, 119–20
Inspiratory airflow
laryngeal resistance to
regulation of, 649

Insulin
  human growth hormone and, 38
  lipogenesis in hepatocyte cultures and, 408–9
  relaxin and, 43, 49
  tyrosine phosphorylation and, 57
Interpubic ligament
  relaxin and, 48
Intracellular calcium
  ion channel activation and, 464–65
  renin release and, 303–5
Intracellular compartment
  sodium absorption and, 444–45
Invertebrates
  magnetic material in, 594
Iodo-acetic acid
  muscle glycolysis and, 4
Ion channels
  cardiac cell membrane, 473–81
  hormone-regulated, 465–66
  inward-rectifying, 480
  liposomal, 549–56
  outward, 480–81
  voltage-activated
    bursting behavior and, 460
  see also specific type
Ion currents
  small cell, 467
Isometric exercise
  cardiovascular and renal responses to, 177–78
Isoproterenol
  calcium ion channels and, 477
  neutrophil beta-adrenergic receptors and, 125–26
  pepsinogen secretion and, 395, 397–98
  plasma renin activity and, 304

J

Jamming avoidance response
  electric fish, 575–78

K

Kallikrein
  see specific type
Kallikrein-kinin system
  see Renal kallikrein-kinin system
Kanamycin
  ototoxicity of, 237–38
Kininase II
  angiotension conversion and, 313
Kinins
  colonic sodium fluxes and, 318

prostaglandins and, 332–33
prostaglandin synthesis and, 319

L

Lamina terminalis
  renin substrate in, 19
Lanthanum
  renin release and, 305
Laryngeal abduction
  posterior cricoarytenoid muscles and, 646
Laryngeal adduction, 653
  thyroarytenoid muscles and, 647
Laryngeal function
  fetal, 646–48
  neonatal, 648–51
Laryngeal receptors
  properties of, 654–55
Laryngeal reflexes
  coughing and arousal and, 679
  sleep and, 653–54
Laryngospasm, 653
Larynx
  airflow and lung volume and, 680
  apneic reflexes excited from, 678–79
  expiratory airflow regulation and, 649–51
  inspiratory airflow regulation and, 649
  reflexes elicited from, 651–56
Leukemia
  altered steroid receptors and, 93
Lidocaine
  cardiac cell membrane ionic channels and, 475
Lipid bilayers
  endplate channel currents in, 460
  gramicidin channel permeability and, 538–39
Lipoprotein catabolism
  hepatocyte monolayers and, 409–12
Lipoprotein metabolism
  hepatic monolayers and, 403–12
Lipoproteins
  synthesis and secretion of, 404–7
    physiologic factors affecting, 407–9
Liposomes
  ion channels in, 549–56
Lipoxygenase
  renal synthesis of eicosanoids and, 327–28
Location sensitivity, 589–90

Locus ceruleus
  converting enzyme in, 20
Low density lipoproteins
  intracellular processing of, 410–11
  synthesis and secretion of, 405–7
Lung compliance
  neonatal, 631
Lung development, 617–27
  embryonic, 618–19
  fetal, 620–24
  postnatal, 624–26
Lung parenchyma
  postnatal development of, 621
Lung volume
  laryngeal control of, 680
  paradoxical rib cage motion and, 679–80
Luteinizing hormone
  relaxin secretion and, 45
Luteinizing hormone secretion
  angiotensin II and, 24–25
Lymphocytes
  steroid hormones and, 126
Lysophosphatidylcholine
  micelles
    gramicidin A channels and, 540
Lysosomal extracts
  meroreceptor production and, 89

M

Magnetic sensitivity, 585–95
  behavioral evidence for, 587–91
  receptors and, 592–95
Malignancy
  altered steroid receptors and, 91–94
Mammalian steroid receptors, 83–99
  affinity labeling of, 94–96
  aggregated
    RNA and, 91
  antibodies against, 96–97
  dimeric, 87
  immunologic probes and, 97–99
  malignancy and, 91–94
  molybdate-stabilized, 86–87
  monomeric, 88–91
  subunits, 88
Mammals
  directional sensitivity of, 589
  magnetic material in, 595
Mammary gland
  relaxin and, 49
Mannitol
  pepsinogen secretion and, 396
Meclofenamate

renin release and, 303–4
Median eminence
  angiotensin II in, 22
  renin substrate in, 19–20
Melanocyte-stimulating hormone
  natriuresis and, 348–49
Mellitin
  membrane-bound kallikrein
    and, 310
Membrane potentials
  amino acid uptake and, 421
Membrane vesicles
  transport properties of, 418
Meroreceptors, 89
Metabolic rate
  neonatal
    hypoxia and, 633–34
Methylprednisolone
  colonic sodium pump activity
    and, 446
  tachyphylaxis and, 120
Methylprogesterone
  androgen receptor function
    and, 114
Metoprolol
  conditioned tachycardia and,
    189
Mevalonolactone
  chylomicron remnant uptake
    and, 410
Microorganisms
  directional sensitivity of, 587
  magnetotactic, 593–94
Middle ear
  development of, 214–15
Mineralocorticoid receptors
  molybdate and, 69–70
Mineralocorticoids
  beta-adrenergic receptors and,
    127
  colonic sodium pump activity
    and, 446
Molybdate
  steroid receptor aggregates
    and, 91
  steroid receptors and, 69–75,
    86–87
Monoclonal antibodies
  electroplax protein and, 526
  steroid receptors and, 97
Mormyrids
  electric organ discharges of,
    563
  sympatric species of, 566
Morphine sulfate
  ventricular fibrillation and,
    168
Mossbauer effect
  basilar membrane and, 232–33
Mullerian duct regression
  phorphorylation and, 53–57
Mullerian inhibiting substance
  dephosphorylation and, 57–61

phosphorylation and, 53–57
Murine leukemia virus
  tyrosine phosphorylation and,
    57
Muscle glycolysis
  iodo-acetic acid and, 4
Myasthenia gravis
  acetylcholine receptor and,
    526
Myelinated nerve fiber
  saltatory conduction in, 10
Myocardial ischemia
  ventricular fibrillation and,
    159
Myometrium
  relaxin and, 48–49
Myosin
  actomyosin solution dis-
    aggregation and, 2–3
Myotis grisescens
  sonar echoes and, 603
Myotis lucifugus
  echolocation and, 599–600

N

Naloxone
  hypoxia and, 638
  ventilatory response to hypox-
    ia and, 663–64
Natriuretic hormone, 343–55
  biochemical nature of, 347–50
  characterization of, 344–47
  hypertension and, 350–55
  volume regulation and, 350
Neprectomy
  renin substrate concentrations
    and, 17–18
Nerve growth factor
  angiotensin-generacting activ-
    ity and, 21
Neuroblastoma cells
  calcium-activated, nonselec-
    tive channels in, 479
  cationic channels in, 465
Neurohypophysis
  brain renin in, 21
Neurotoxins
  sodium ion channels and,
    518–19
Neurotransmitter precursors
  ventricular vulnerability and,
    168–70
Neurotransmitters
  hypoxia and, 637–38
  pepsinogen secretion and, 395
Neutrophils
  steroid hormones and, 125–26
Nicotine
  ventricular arrhythmias and,
    155
Nicotinic acetylcholine receptor,
  551–54

Nifedipine
  calcium ion channels and, 476
Nimodipine
  calcium ion channels and, 477
Nisoldipine
  calcium ion channels and, 476
Nitrendipine
  calcium ion channels and,
    476–77
Noise analysis
  apical sodium ion transport
    and, 503–10
Noise exposure
  cochlear damage and, 221
Norepinephrine
  hypothalamic levels of
    salt intake and, 148
  hypoxia and, 637–38
  plasma renin activity and,
    294–95
  renin secretion and, 297
Norepinephrine release
  angiotensin II and, 25

O

Oleic acid
  very low density lipoprotein
    secretion and, 408
Oligomycin
  parietal cell aminopyrine accu-
    mulation and, 380
Operant conditioning
  cardiovascular, 199–208
Ornithine decarboxylase
  activity of
    testosterone and, 110–12
Ototoxic agents
  frequency threshold curves
    and, 237–38
Ouabain
  natriuresis and, 347
  renin release and, 305
  ventricular fibrillation and,
    168
Ovarian carcinoma
  Mullerian inhibiting substance
    and, 63
Oxidative metabolism
  parietal cell histamine uptake
    and, 384
Oxytocin
  natriuresis and, 348
  relaxin and, 49

P

Pacemaker current
  activation of, 479–80
Pancreatic acinar cells
  calcium-activated, nonselec-
    tive channels in, 479
  cationic channels in, 465

depolarization and, 465
Pancreatic function
  regulation of, 364–72
Papain
  meroreceptor production and,
    89
Parachloromercury-phenyl-
  sulfonate
  epithelial sodium channel self-
    inhibition and, 501
Paramagnetism
  magnetic field detection and,
    592–93
Parenchymal lung disease
  arousal response and, 636
Parietal cell, 377–90
  activity of
    measurement of, 378–80
  electrolytes of, 386–87
  histamine uptake and, 384
  metabolism of, 387–89
  oxygen consumption in, 379
  somatostatin binding and, 385
  weak base accumulation site
    in, 380–82
Passive diffusion
  amino acid transport and, 420,
    423
Patch clamp techniques, 455–68
  cell-attached configuration,
    458–63
  inside-out patch and, 463–66
  outside-out patch and, 466
  variants of, 455–58
  whole-cell configuration, 466–
    68
Pepsinogen secretion, 393–401
  calcium and, 398–99
  cellular models of, 394–95
  cyclic AMP and, 397–98
  mechanism of, 399–400
  secretagogues and, 395–96
Peptide hormones
  pepsinogen secretion and,
    395–96
Permanent magnetism
  magnetic field detection and,
    593–95
Pharyngeal reflexes
  airway obstruction and, 678
Phentolamine
  conditioned tachycardia and,
    189
  coronary vascular resistance
    and, 191
Phenylalanine
  uptake pathways of, 421–22
Phloretin
  parietal cell metabolism and,
    389
Phosphate moieties
  steroid receptor regulation
    and, 68–69

Phospholipase A_2
  membrane-bound kallikrein
    and, 310
Phospholipids
  gramicidin A crystallization
    and, 532
Phosphorylation
  Mullerian inhibiting substance
    and, 53–57
  steroid binding and, 69
Phosphotyrosyl protein phospha-
  tase
  Mullerian duct regression and,
    55–56, 55
Photoaffinity labeling
  steroid receptor structure and,
    95–96
Physalaemin
  pancreatic amylase release
    and, 366–68
Physiologic stress
  cardiovascular and renal re-
    sponses to, 177–79
Picrotoxin
  ventricular arrhythmias and,
    162
Pilocarpine
  respiratory activity and, 690
Pimozide
  serum prolactin levels and,
    181
Pineal gland
  brain renin in, 21
  renin-angiotensin system in,
    17
Pitch
  discrimination of, 270–71
Pitch frequency
  of speech sound, 261
Pituitary gland
  brain renin-angiotensin system
    and, 25–26
  ion channels in, 465
  renin-angiotensin system in,
    17
Place principle
  development of, 217–19
Plasma membranes
  amino acid transport and,
    418
Plasma renin activity
  dietary sodium intake and,
    295–97
  norepinephrine and, 294–95
Plasminogen activator secretion
  relaxin and, 45–46
Polyclonal antisera
  steroid receptors and, 96
Posterior cricoarytenoid muscles
  laryngeal abduction and, 646
Potassium ion
  gastric acid secretion and,
    386–87

membrane permeability for
  optical signals and, 11
Potassium ion channels, 485–92
  acetylcholine-activated, 462–
    63
  basolateral membrane, 498
  bursting behavior and, 460
  calcium-activated, 490–92
  delayed rectifiers, 486–88
  inward rectifiers, 488–90
  inward-rectifying, 462
  voltage-regulated, 459
PRC II virus
  tyrosine phosphorylation and,
    57
Prednisolone
  neutrophil beta-adrenergic re-
    ceptors and, 126
Prednisone
  beta-adrenergic receptors and,
    123
Pregnancy
  relaxin and, 47–49
Progesterone
  relaxin and, 48
Progesterone receptors
  synthesis of
    estradiol and, 110
  translocation inhibitors and,
    77
Progestin receptors
  antibodies against, 96
  complexes of, 85–86
  molybdate and, 69–70
  steroid-binding subunits of,
    88
Progestins
  androgen receptor function
    and, 112–14
  biologic action of
    nuclear receptors and, 110
Prokallikrein
  activation of, 310
Prolactin
  cardiovascular function and,
    180
  disulfide dimer of, 37–37
  forms of, 36
  as prohormone, 39–40
  proteolytically cleaved forms
    of, 37
  serum
    psychological factors and,
      181
Prolactin secretion
  angiotensin II and, 24–25
Prolinuria
  transport defects in, 424
Propranolol
  conditioned tachycardia and,
    189
  pepsinogen secretion and, 395
  renin release and, 303–4

ventricular fibrillation and, 160
Prostacyclin
  kinins and, 319
Prostacyclin synthetase
  inhibitors of, 327–28
Prostaglandins
  kinins and, 332–33
  relaxin and, 49
  renin-angiotensin system and, 332
  renin release and, 303–5
  vasopressin and, 333–34
Prostaglandin synthesis
  kinins and, 319
  see also Renal prostaglandin synthesis
Protein kinases
  pancreatic and salivary, 371
Proteolysis
  steroid receptor transformation and, 84
Psychological stimuli
  renal responses to, 178–79
Psychological stress
  cardiovascular and renal responses to, 177–79
  ventricular fibrillation and, 157
Psychological testing
  cardiovascular and renal responses to, 178
Pulmonary surfactant
  respiratory distress syndrome and, 617
Pyridoxal phosphate
  glucocorticoid receptors and, 75

Q

Quinidine
  cardiac cell membrane ion channels and, 475

R

Radioimmunoassay
  relaxin and, 44
Reflexes
  see specific type
Relaxin
  assay methods for, 44–45
  males and, 50
  nonpregnant state and, 45–46
  pregnancy and, 47–49
  species specificity of, 45
  structure of, 43–44
REM sleep
  functional residual capacity and, 651
  hypercapnia and, 681–82
  hypoxia and, 682

laryngeal reflexes and, 653–54
neonatal breathing patterns and, 676
paradoxical rib cage motion and, 680–81
ventilatory response to hypoxia during, 632
ventilatory response to O_2 and, 696–97
see also Sleep
Renal arachidonate metabolism, 327–28
  renal pathophysiology and, 334–36
Renal baroreceptors
  adrenergic receptors and, 299–302
  sodium signal and, 298–99
Renal electrolyte and water excretion, 315–18
Renal function
  blood pressure and, 143–45
Renal hemodynamics, 313–15
Renal kallikrein
  endogenous inhibitors of, 311
  kinin formation and release and, 312
  localization of, 310–11
Renal kallikrein-kinin system, 309–21
  hormones and intrarenal biochemicals and, 319–21
  renal electrolyte and water excretion and, 315–18
  renal hemodynamics and, 313–15
Renal perfusion pressure signal
  renin release and, 294–95
Renal prostaglandin synthesis, 327–36
  cellular sites of, 328–31
Renal vascular beds
  control of, 191–92
Renin
  pituitary gland and, 25–26
Renin-angiotensin system
  prostaglandins and, 332
Renin release, 291–305
  adrenergic signal and, 297
  cellular mechanism influencing, 303–5
  renal perfusion pressure signal and, 294–95
  sodium signal and, 295–97
  stimuli influencing interaction of, 297–303
Renin substrate
  brain tissue, 19–20
  concentration in CSF, 19
Reptiles
  magnetic material in, 594
Respiratory control

fetal, 662–63
  sleep and, 671–72
Respiratory control system
  immaturity at birth, 629–30
Respiratory distress syndrome
  expiratory grunting and, 651
  pulmonary surfactant and, 617
Respiratory muscle efficiency
  fatigue and, 681
Rhinolophus ferrumeguinum
  sonar echoes and, 603
Rib cage motion
  paradoxical
    lung volume and, 679–80
    reflexes excited from, 680–81
Ribonucleases
  steroid receptor aggregates and, 91
RNA
  steroid receptor aggregates and, 91
RNA polymerase II
  androgenic regulation of, 112
Rous sarcoma virus
  tyrosine phosphorylation and, 56
RU 2956
  androgen receptor function and, 113

S

Salivary function
  regulation of, 364–72
Salivary glands
  renin-angiotensin system in, 17
Salt intake
  blood pressure regulation and, 147–49
Salt metabolism
  angiotensin II and, 25
Sarcoma virus
  tyrosine phosphorylation and, 56–57
Saxitoxin
  sodium ion channels and, 519
Saxitoxin receptor
  sarcolemmal, 521
    peptide composition of, 523
  synaptosomal, 521–22
    peptide composition of, 523
Second messengers
  hormone-regulated ion channels and, 465–66
Secretagogues
  pepsinogen secretion and, 395–96
Secretin
  digestive enzyme secretion and, 370
  pepsinogen secretion and, 396

Serotonin
  hypoxia and, 638
  sympathetic neural activity
    and, 168
Serotonin synthesis
  angiotensin II and, 25
Shock
  ventricular arrhythmias and,
    161
Sleep
  hypoxia and, 636–37
  laryngeal reflexes and, 653–54
  neonatal breathing patterns
    and, 676
  prolonged apnea during, 676–
    77
  ventilation and, 671–72
  ventilatory response to CO_2
    and, 667
  ventilatory response to hypox-
    ia during, 632
  ventilatory response to O_2
    and, 664–65, 696–97
  ventricular arrhythmias and,
    166–68
  see also REM sleep
Small intestine
  amino acid and glucose
    absorption and, 417–18
Smooth muscle cells
  ion channels in, 465
Sodium
  amino acid transport and,
    420–21, 423
  glucose transport and, 425–26
  plasma renin activity and,
    295–97
Sodium absorption, 435–48
  absorptive cell and, 446–48
  apical membrane and, 436–44
  basolateral membrane and,
    445–46
  intracellular compartment and,
    444–45
Sodium/calcium exchange
    system
  basolateral membrane, 498
Sodium ion
  epithelial sodium channel reg-
    ulation and, 500–3
  gastric acid secretion and,
    386–87
  membrane permeability for
    optical signals and, 11
  parietal cell histamine uptake
    and, 384
Sodium ion channels
  cardiac cell membrane, 474–
    75
  epithelial, 497–511
    ionic regulation of, 500–3
    functional design of, 517–18
    hormonal effects on, 509–10

  neurotoxins and, 518–19
  ontogenesis and, 509–10
  voltage-regulated, 517–26
Sodium pump
  basolateral membrane,
    498
Sodium signal
  renal baroreceptors and, 298
  renin release and, 295–97
Somatostatin
  parietal cell binding of, 385
Sound direction
  neural representation of, 280–
    84
Sound localization, 275–84
Speech
  neural coding of, 261–72
  pitch frequency of, 261
Spinal cord
  brain renin in, 21
  ion channels in, 465
  neuron electrical activity in
    angiotensin II and, 26
Spinal cord neurons
  transmitter-gated chloride ion
    channels in, 466
Spironolactone
  androgen receptor function
    and, 113
  renal kallikrein synthesis and,
    317
Stereociliary tufts
  micromechanical resonances
    of, 254
Sternopygus
  electric organ discharges of,
    562
Steroid hormones
  beta-adrenergic receptor reg-
    ulation by, 119–28
  electroreceptor tuning and,
    562–63
  urinary kinin excretion and,
    320
Steroid receptors, 67–77
  endogenous inhibitor of, 75–
    76
  endogenous translocation in-
    hibitors of, 76–77
  molybdate and, 69–75
  regulation by phosphate and
    sulfydryl moieties, 68–69
  see also Mammalian steroid
    receptors
Stress
  cardiovascular response to,
    177–83
  see also specific type
Striatum
  angiotensin II binding sites in,
    19
Strychnine
  hypoxia and, 692

Substantia nigra
  converting enzyme in, 20
Sudden infant death syndrome
  arousal response and, 636
  carotid chemoreceptor func-
    tion and, 697
Sulfydryl moieties
  steroid receptor regulation
    and, 68–69
Superior colliculus
  sound localization and, 282–
    83
Superparamagnetism
  magnetic field detection and,
    595
Supraoptic nucleus
  neuron electrical activity in
    angiotensin II and, 26
Swallowing
  laryngeal stimulation and, 652
Sympathetic arousal
  blood pressure and, 143–45
Sympathetic neural activity
  serotonin and, 168
Sympathetic neurons
  ionic channels in, 465

T

Tachycardia
  conditioned, 189
  exercise, 206–7
Tachyphylaxis
  catecholamines and, 120
Temporal synchronization
  cochlear neurons and, 252–53
Terbutaline
  lymphocyte beta-adrenergic
    receptors and, 126
Testosterone
  electroreceptor tuning and,
    562–63
  enzyme activity and, 110–12
  nuclear receptor residence
    time and, 110
Tetrodotoxin
  cardiac cell membrane ion
    channels and, 475
  sodium ion channels and, 519
Tetrodotoxin receptor
  electroplax, 520–21
  peptide composition of, 522–
    23
Thalamus
  angiotensin II binding sites in,
    19
  renin substrate in, 19–20
Thiocyanate
  parietal cell aminopyrine accu-
    mulation and, 380
Thoracic chemoreceptors
  neonatal, 693–94
Thromboxane A_2

kinins and, 319
Thyroarytenoid muscles
  laryngeal adduction and, 647
Time sensitivity, 590–91
Tissue kallikrein
  classification of, 309
  structural analyses of, 310
Tolamolol
  ventricular arrhythmias and,
    161
Torpedo electroplax
  chloride ion channel of, 555–
    56
Trachea
  fluid flow in
    fetal regulation of, 647–48
Transformation
  steroid receptor and, 83
Translocation inhibitors
  steroid receptors and, 76–77
Triamcinolone acetonide
  photoaffinity labeling and,
    95–96
Trifluoperazine
  renin release and, 305
Triglyceride synthesis
  diacylglycerol acyltransferase
    and, 408
Trypsin
  meroreceptor production and,
    89
Tryptophan
  cardiac sympathetic drive and,
    168–69
Tumor cells
  single calcium ion channels
    in, 462
Tungstate
  steroid receptors and, 70
Tunicamycin
  glycosylation and, 404
Tyrosine
  phosphorylation of, 56–57

U

Uterus
  relaxin and, 48
  renin-angiotensin system in,
    17

V

Vagus nerve activity
  ventricular fibrillation and,
    166
Vanadate
  steroid receptors and, 70
Vasoactive intestinal peptide
  digestive enzyme secretion
    and, 370
  pepsinogen secretion and, 396
Vasopressin
  natriuresis and, 348
  prostaglandin synthesis and,
    330
  prostaglandins and, 333–34
  renin release and, 305
Vasopressin secretion
  angiotensin II and, 24
  angiotensins and, 18
Ventilation
  chemical control of, 663–68
  mechanics of, 668–71
  neonatal control of, 661–72
    behavioral states and, 675–
      83
    sleep and, 671–72
Ventilatory rhythm
  generation of, 677–78
Ventricular arrhythmias
  behavioral stress and, 158–59
  induction of, 155
  neural mechanisms in, 160
  sleep and, 166–68
Ventricular fibrillation
  cardiac vagal tone and, 165

myocardial ischemia and, 159
  pharmacologic agents and,
    168
  psychological stress and, 157
  vagus nerve activity and, 166
Ventricular inotropism
  control of, 191
Ventricular vulnerability
  adrenergic mechanisms in,
    160
  cholinergic influences on, 164
  neurotransmitter precursors
    and, 168–70
  sympathetic-parasympathetic
    interactions and, 164–65
Verapamil
  calcium ion channels and, 476
  colonic sodium fluxes and,
    318
  renin release and, 305
Veratridine
  liposomal sodium ion channels
    and, 555
  sodium ion channels and, 519
Very low density lipoproteins
  synthesis and secretion of,
    404–5
Vowels
  discrimination of, 263–64

W

Water intake
  angiotensin II and, 24
Water metabolism
  angiotensin II and, 25

Y

Y73 virus
  tyrosine phosphorylation and,
    57
Yohimbine
  sodium ion channels and, 519

CUMULATIVE INDEXES

CONTRIBUTING AUTHORS, VOLUMES 42–46

A

Agnew, W. S., 46:517–30
Agus, Z. S., 43:583–95
Akera, T., 44:375–88
Andersen, O. S., 46:531–48
Anderson, D. E., 46:143–53
Armstrong, D. T., 42:71–82
Aukland, K., 42:543–55
Aurback, G. D., 44:653–66

B

Baer, P. G., 42:589–601
Baker, M. A., 44:85–96
Bárány, K., 42:275–92
Bárány, M., 42:275–92
Barde, Y.-A., 45:601–12
Bardin, C. W., 43:189–98
Bardin, C. W., 46:107–18
Barger, A. C., 46:291–308
Bastian, J., 46:561–83
Beaugé, L., 45:313–24
Becker, R., 43:189–98
Beeuwkes, R. III, 42:531–42
Bell, P. D., 42:557–71
Berglindh, T., 46:377–92
Bergofsky, E. H., 42:221–33
Berry, C., 44:181–201
Biagi, B. A., 45:497–517
Bisgaier, C., 45:625–36
Blantz, R. C., 42:573–88
Bliss, C., 45:651–77
Blomqvist, C. G., 45:169–89
Bloom, F. E., 44:571–82
Bollenbacher, W. E., 42:493–510
Boron, W., 45:483–96
Bowers, C. W., 43:673–87
Boyd, A., 44:501–17
Brengelmann, G. L., 45:191–212
Brody, M. J., 42:441–53
Brody, T. M., 44:375–88
Brownstein, M. J., 45:129–35
Buckalew, V. M., 46:343–58
Budzik, G. P., 46:53–65
Bulger, R., 44:147–79
Bundgaard, M., 42:325–36
Burg, M., 45:533–47
Burri, P. H., 46:617–28
Butler, J., 42:187–98
Bye, P. T. P., 45:439–51

C

Calder, W. A. III, 43:301–22
Campbell, E. J. M., 45:465–79
Carey, M., 45:651–77
Castellini, M. A., 43:343–56
Chabardès, D., 43:569–81
Chafouleas, J. G., 44:667–82
Chan, L., 45:615–23
Chatterjee, B., 45:37–50
Cheng, S.-L., 43:189–98
Chiarandini, D. J., 44:357–72
Chou, C. C., 44:29–42
Christensen, N. J., 45:139–53
Cohen, D. H., 46:187–97
Cohen, M. L., 43:91–104
Cokelet, G. R., 42:311–24
Coleridge, H. M., 42:413–27
Coleridge, J. C. G., 42:413–27
Conger, J., 42:603–14
Coronado, R., 46:485–95
Crawshaw, L. I., 42:473–91
Culver, B. H., 42:187–98
Currie, M. G., 46:327–41

D

Dahmer, M. K., 46:67–81
Davies, A., 46:119–30
Davis, R. W., 43:343–56
Dedman, J. R., 42:59–70
DeLuca, H. F., 43:199–209
DeVries, A. L., 45:245–60
DiPolo, R., 45:313–24
Dizon, A. E., 44:121–31
Dobyan, D., 44:147–79
Docherty, K., 44:625–38
Donahoe, P. K., 46:53–65
Donald, D. E., 42:429–39
Downing, S. E., 42:199–210
Duling, B. R., 42:373–82
Duman, J., 45:261–70
Dzau, V. J., 46:291–308

E

Edgar, D., 45:601–12
Eisenberg, E., 42:293–309
Eldrige, F., 43:121–35
Engle, B. T., 46:199–210

F

Fallat, M. E., 46:53–65
Fambrough, D., 44:319–35

Fanestil, D. D., 43:637–49
Fantone, J., 44:283–93
Farhi, E. R., 46:291–308
Farkas, G. A., 45:439–51
Farner, D. S., 42:457–72
Fevold, H. R., 45:19–36
Fisher, K. A., 42:261–73
Fishman, A. P., 42:211–20
Fishman, J., 45:61–72
Flaim, S., 43:455–76
Flenley, D. C., 45:415–26
Forte, J. G., 42:111–26
Forte, T. M., 46:403–15
Frawley, L. S., 45:109–27
Friesen, H. G., 42:83–96
Frohman, L. A., 45:95–107
Fullmer, C. S., 45:375–90

G

Galbo, H., 45:139–53
Ganong, W. F., 46:17–31
Gerisch, G., 44:535–52
Gibbons, G. H., 46:291–308
Gibert, A. J., 46:393–402
Giebisch, G., 45:497–517
Gil, J., 42:177–86
Gilbert, L. I., 42:493–510
Gillis, C. N., 44:269–81
Gilula, N. B., 43:479–91
Glickman, R., 45:625–36
Glitsch, H. G., 44:389–400
Goldfarb, S., 43:583–95
Good, D., 45:533–47
Gore, R. W., 42:337–57
Gospodarowicz, D., 43:251–63
Gould, J. L., 46:585–98
Granger, N. A., 42:493–510; 43:409–18
Greenberg, M. J., 45:271–88
Greene, L. E., 42:293–309
Griffith, L., 45:427–37
Gruber, K. A., 46:343–58
Grumbach, M., 44:595–613
Gunn, R. B., 42:249–59
Gunsalus, G., 43:189–98
Gustafsson, J. A., 45:51–60
Guth, P. H., 44:3–12

H

Habener, J., 43:211–23
Haddad, G. G., 46:629–43
Hall, V. E., 43:1–5

Handler, J., 43:611–24
Harding, R., 46:645–59
Harris, W., 43:689–710
Hartshorne, D. J., 43:519–30
Hasselbach, W., 45:325–39
Haywood, J. R., 42:441–53
Heath, J. E., 44:133–43
Heath, M. S. 44:133–43
Heglund, N., 44:97–107
Heiligenberg, W., 46:561–83
Heindel, J. J., 42:37–57
Henderson-Smart, D. J.,
    46:675–86
Herd, A. H., 46:177–85
Hersey, S., 46:393–402
Hertzberg, E. L., 43:479–91
Heymann, M. A., 43:371–83
Hilton, S. M., 42:399–411
Hodgkin, A. L., 45:1–16
Hoffman, B., 44:475–84
Holmes, K. C., 43:553–65
Horwath, K., 45:261–70
Housley, P. R., 46:67–81
Hutson, J. M., 46:53–65
Hsueh, A. J. W., 45:83–94

I

Ikemoto, N., 44:297–317
Imbert-Teboul, M., 43:569–81
Imura, H., 43:265–78
Imig, T. J., 46:275–87
Ingram, R. H. Jr., 45:453–63
Insel, P., 43:625–36
Iwamoto, G. A., 45:229–42

J

Jacobson, E. D., 44:71–81
Jaffe, R. B., 43:141–62
Jänne, O. A., 46:107–18
Johansson, B., 43:359–70
Jolesz, F., 43:531–52
Jones, N. L., 45:427–37
Jones, P. B. C., 45:83–94

K

Kalia, M. P., 43:105–20
Kamagata, S., 46:53–65
Kane, J. P., 45:637–50
Kaufman, M. P., 45:229–42
Kaunitz, J. D., 46:417–33
Katz, A., 44:401–23
Katzenellenbogen, B. S., 42:17–
    35
Kick, S. A., 46:599–614
Killian, K. J., 45:465–79
Klitzman, B., 42:373–82
Knobil, E., 44:583–93
Koeppen, B. M., 45:497–517
Koob, G. F., 44:571–82
Kontos, H. A., 43:397–407
Kooyman, G. L., 43:343–56

Kotite, N., 43:189–98
Kream, B. E., 43:225–38
Kregenow, F., 43:493–505
Kung, C., 44:519–34
Kunkel, S., 44:283–93
Kupfermann, I., 42:629–41
Kvietys, P. R., 43:409–18

L

Landis, S., 45:567–80
Langer, G. A., 44:435–49
Larrea, F., 43:189–98
LaTorre, R., 46:485–95
Lawrence, T. S., 43:479–91
Lazdunski, M., 44:463–73
Le Douarin, N. M., 43:653–71
Lee, J. C., 42:199–210
Lefkowitz, R., 44:475–84
Lefkowitz, R. J., 46:119–30
Le Lièvre, C. S., 43:653–71
Leong, D. A., 45:109–27
Leung, P. C. K., 42:71–82
Levy, M. N., 43:443–53
Lewis, U. J., 46:33–42
Lictman, J., 45:553–65
Liedtke, A. J., 43:455–76
Lindemann, B., 46:497–515
Lown, B., 46:155–76
Ludbrook, J., 45:155–68

M

MacDonald, P. C., 43:163–88
Machen, T. E., 42:111–26
Mailman, D., 44:43–55
Malik, K. U., 43:597–609
Margolius, H. S., 46:309–26
Martin, P. J., 43:443–53
Martonosi, A., 44:337–55
Masterton, R. B., 46:275–87
McDonagh, P. F., 42:337–57
McDonald, T., 44:425–34
McEwen, B. S., 42:97–110
McFadden, E. R., 45:453–63
McGiff, J. G., 42:589–601
Means, A. R., 42:59–70;
    44:667–82
Mellins, R. B., 46:629–43
Miller, C., 46:549–58
Millhorn, D. E., 43:121–35
Mitchell, J. H., 45:229–42
Mode, A., 45:51–60
Moore, E. N., 44:485–97
Morel, F., 43:569–81
Murphy, D. J., 45:289–99
Musto, N., 43:189–98

N

Nakai, Y., 43:265–78
Nasjletti, A., 43:597–609
Navar, L. G., 42:557–71

Needleman, P., 46:327–41
Neely, J., 43:419–30
Neher, E., 46:455–72
Neill, J. D., 45:109–27
Nellis, S., 43:455–76
Nelson, D. O., 43:281–300
Niall, H. D., 44:615–24
Norris, S. H., 46:393–402
Norstedt, G., 45:51–60

O

Öbrink, K. J., 42:111–26
Oetliker, H., 45:325–39
Olsson, R. A., 43:385–95
Orloff, J., 43:611–24

P

Pack, A. I., 43:73–90
Page, E., 43:431–41
Pardridge, W. M., 45:73–82
Park, C. S., 43:637–49
Passow, H., 45:359–74
Pastan, I., 43:239–50
Peck, E. J. Jr., 42:615–27
Pitt, B. R., 44:269–81
Ploth, D. W., 42:557–71
Pohl, C. R., 44:583–93
Pratt, W. B., 46:67–81
Price, H. M., 45:271–88
Prosser, C. L., 43:281–300
Pugh, C. E., 45:427–37
Pumplin, D., 44:319–35
Purves, D., 45:553–65

R

Randall, D. C., 46:187–97
Raisz, L. G., 43:225–38
Rayner, J. M. V., 44:109–19
Read, D. J. C., 46:675–86
Reibel, D. K., 43:419–30
Reiter, E. O., 44:595–613
Renaud, J. F., 44:463–73
Reuter, H., 46:473–84
Rhode, W. S., 46:231–46
Richardson, P., 44:57–69
Riddiford, L. M., 42:511–28
Rigatto, H., 46:661–74
Robison, G. A., 42:37–57
Rogart, R., 43:711–25
Rose, R. C., 42:157–71
Rosell, S., 42:259–71
Roth, J., 44:639–51
Roussos, Ch., 45:439–51
Roy, A. K., 45:37–50
Rubel, E. W, 46:213–29
Rudolph, A. M., 43:371–83
Ryan, J. W., 44:241–55
Ryan, U. S., 44:223–39

S

Sachs, M. B., 46:261–73
Sackin, H., 45:483–96
Said, S. I., 44:257–68
Saimi, Y., 44:519–34
Sakmann, B., 46:455–72
Salen, G., 45:679–85
Saltin, B., 45:169–89
Sanborn, B. M., 42:37–57
Sanes, J., 45:581–600
Saz, H. J., 43:323–41
Schatzmann, H. J., 45:303–12
Schiffmann, E., 44:553–68
Schneider, M. E., 43:507–17
Schneiderman, N., 46:199–210
Schrier, R. W., 42:603–14
Schultz, S. G., 46:435–51
Schulz, I., 42:127–56
Schwarz, W., 45:359–74
Serón-Ferré, M., 43:141–62
Shefer, S., 45:679–85
Shepherd, A. P., 44:13–27
Shepherd, J. T., 42:429–39
Sherman, M. R., 46:83–105
Shibata, Y., 43:431–41
Shiu, R. P. C., 42:83–96
Siemankowski, R. F., 43:519–30
Simmons, J. A., 46:599–614
Simon, M., 44:501–17
Simpson, E. R., 43:163–88
Skett, P., 45:51–60
Small, D., 45:651–77
Smith, J., 43:653–71
Snavely, M. D., 43:625–36
Sonnenschein, R. R., 43:1–5

Spear, J. F., 44:485–97
Spyer, K. M., 42:399–41
Sreter, F. A., 43:531–52
Stefani, E., 44:357–72
Steiner, D., 44:625–38
Stephenson, R. B., 46:133–42
Stevens, B. R., 46:417–33
Stevens, C. F., 42:643–52
Stevens, E. D., 44:121–31
Stevens, J., 46:83–105
Stolze, H. H., 42:127–56
Stone, H. L., 45:213–27
Stuesse, S. L., 43:443–53
Sutton, J. R., 45:427–37
Szurszewski, J. H., 43:53–68

T

Tada, M., 44:401–23
Tash, J. S., 42:59–70
Taylor, A., 45:519–32
Taylor, C. R., 44:97–107
Taylor, S., 44:639–51
Tepperman, B., 44:71–82
Thoenen, H., 45:601–12
Tindall, D. J., 42:59–70
Touw, K. B., 42:441–54
Tsien, R. W., 45:341–58

U

Ussing, H. H., 42:1–16

V

Valtin, H., 44:203–19
van Sickle, M., 42:59–70

Vary, T. C., 43:419–30
Vergara, C., 46:485–95
Verrier, R. L., 46:155–76
von Muralt, A., 46:1–13

W

Wagner, P. D., 42:235–47
Walker, D., 46:687–703
Walker, L., 44:203–19
Ward, P., 44:283–93
Warren, P. M., 45:415–26
Wasserman, R. H., 45:375–90
Wasserstein, A., 43:583–95
Weems, W., 43:9–19
Weisbrodt, N., 43:21–31
Weiss, G., 46:43–52
Weiss, T. F., 46:247–59
Welsh, M. J., 42:59–70
Westfall, T. C., 42:383–97
Whipp, B. J., 45:393–413
Williams, J. A., 46:361–75
Willingham, M., 43:239–50
Windhager, E., 45:519–32
Winegrad, S., 44:451–62
Wingfield, J. C., 42:457–72
Withrington, P., 44:57–69
Wolfe, L. S., 41:669–84
Wood, J. D., 43:33–51
Wray, J. S., 43:553–65
Wright, E. M., 46:417–33

Z

Zelis, R., 43:455–76
Zigmond, R., 43:673–87

CHAPTER TITLES, VOLUMES 42–46

CARDIOVASCULAR PHYSIOLOGY

Rheology and Hemodynamics	G. R. Cokelet	42:311–24
Transport Pathways in Capillaries—In Search of Pores	M. Bundgaard	42:325–36
Fluid Exchange Across Single Capillaries	R. W. Gore, P. F. McDonagh	42:337–57
Neuronal Control of Microvessels	S. Rosell	42:359–71
Local Control of Microvascular Function: Role in Tissue Oxygen Supply	B. R. Duling, B. Klitzman	42:373–82
Neuroeffector Mechanisms	T. C. Westfall	42:383–97
Central Nervous Regulation of Vascular Resistance	S. M. Hilton, K. M. Spyer	42:399–411
Cardiovascular Afferents Involved in Regulation of Peripheral Vessels	H. M. Coleridge, J. C. G. Coleridge	42:413–27
Autonomic Regulation of the Peripheral Circulation	D. E. Donald, J. T. Shepherd	42:429–39
Neural Mechanisms in Hypertension	M. J. Brody, J. R. Haywood, K. B. Touw	42:441–53
Vascular Smooth Muscle Reactivity	B. Johansson	43:359–70
Factors Affecting Changes in the Neonatal Systemic Circulation	M. A. Heymann, H. S. Iwamoto, A. M. Rudolph	43:371–83
Local Factors Regulating Cardiac and Skeletal Muscle Blood Flow	R. A. Olsson	43:385–95
Regulation of the Cerebral Circulation	H. A. Kontos	43:397–407
The Splanchnic Circulation: Intrinsic Regulation	D. N. Granger, P. R. Kvietys	43:409–18
Control of Energy Metabolism of Heart Muscle	T. C. Vary, D. K. Reibel, J. R. Neely	43:419–30
Permeable Junctions Between Cardiac Cells	E. Page and Y. Shibata	43:431–41
Neural Regulation of the Heart Beat	M. N. Levy, P. J. Martin, S. L. Stuesse	43:443–53
Cardiocirculatory Dynamics in the Normal and Failing Heart	R. Zelis, S. F. Flaim, A. J. Liedtke, S. H. Nellis	43:455–76
Myocardial Membranes: Regulation and Function of the Sodium Pump	T. Akera, T. M. Brody	44:375–88
Electrogenic Na Pumping in the Heart	H. G. Glitsch	44:389–400
Phosphorylation of the Sarcoplasmic Reticulum and Sarcolemma	M. Tada, A. M. Katz	44:401–23
The Slow Inward Calcium Current in the Heart	T. F. McDonald	44:425–34
Sodium-Calcium Exchange in the Heart	G. A. Langer	44:435–49
Calcium Release from Cardiac Sarcoplasmic Reticulum	S. Winegrad	44:451–62
The Action of Cardiotoxins on Cardiac Plasma Membranes	M. Lazdunski, J. F. Renaud	44:463–73
Adrenergic Receptors in the Heart	B. B. Hoffman, R. J. Lefkowitz	44:475–84
Mechanisms of Cardiac Arrhythmias	J. F. Spear, E. N. Moore	44:485–97
Sympathetic Nervous Activity During Exercise	N. J. Christensen and H. Galbo	45:139–53
Reflex Control of Blood Pressure During Exercise	J. Ludbrook	45:155–68

720

Cardiovascular Adaptations to Physical
  Training   C. Gunnar Blomqvist and Bengt
                                                Saltin   45:169–89
Circulatory Adjustments to Exercise and
  Heat Stress   G. L. Brengelmann   45:191–212
Control of the Coronary Circulation During
  Exercise   H. Lowell Stone   45:213–27
The Exercise Pressor Reflex: Its
  Cardiovascular Effects, Afferent
  Mechanisms, and Control Pathways   Jere H. Mitchell, Marc P. Kaufman,
                                                and Gary A. Iwamoto   45:229–42
Modification of Reflex Regulation of Blood
  Pressure by Behavior   R. B. Stephenson   46:133–42
Interactions of Stress, Salt, and Blood
  Pressure   D. E. Anderson   46:143–53
Behavioral Stress and Cardiac Arrhythmias   R. L. Verrier, B. Lown   46:155–76
Cardiovascular Response to Stress in Man   J. A. Herd   46:177–85
Classical Conditioning of Cardiovascular
  Responses   D. H. Cohen, D. C. Randall   46:187–97
Operant Conditioning and the Modulation of
  Cardiovascular Function   B. T. Engel, N. Schneiderman   46:199–210

CELL AND MEMBRANE PHYSIOLOGY
Co- and Counter-Transport Mechanisms in
  Cell Membranes   R. B. Gunn   42:249–59
Split Membrane Analysis   K. A. Fisher   42:261–73
Phosphorylation of the Myofibrillar Proteins M. Barany, K. Barany   42:275–92
The Relation of Muscle Biochemistry to
  Muscle Physiology   E. Eisenberg, L. E. Greene   42:293–309
Gap Junctional Communication   E. L. Hertzberg, T. S. Lawrence, N.
                                                B. Gilula   43:479–91
Osmoregulatory Salt Transporting
  Mechanisms: Control of Cell Volume in
  Anisotonic Media   F. M. Kregenow   43:493–505
Membrane Charge Movement and
  Depolarization-Contraction Coupling   M. F. Schneider   43:507–17
Regulation of Smooth Muscle Actomyosin   D. J. Hartshorne and R. F.
                                                Siemankowski   43:519–30
Development, Innervation, and
  Activity-Pattern Induced Changes in
  Skeletal Muscle   F. Jolesz, F. A. Sreter   43:531–52
X-Ray Diffraction Studies of Muscle   J. S. Wray, K. C. Holmes   43:553–65
Structure and Function of the Calcium Pump
  Protein of Sarcoplasmic Reticulum   N. Ikemoto   44:297–317
Turnover of Acetylcholine Receptors in
  Skeletal Muscle   D. W. Pumplin, D. M. Fambrough   44:319–35
The Development of Sarcoplasmic
  Reticulum Membranes   A. Martonosi   44:337–55
Ionic Channels in Skeletal Muscle   E. Stefani, D. J. Chiarandini   44:357–72
The Red Cell Calcium Pump   H. J. Schatzmann   45:303–12
The Calcium Pump and Sodium-Calcium
  Exchange in Squid Axons   R. DiPolo and L. Beaugé   45:313–24
Energetics and Electrogenicity of the
  Sarcoplasmic Reticulum Calcium Pump   W. Hasselbach and H. Oetliker   45:325–39
Calcium Channels in Excitable Cell
  Membranes   R. W. Tsien   45:341–58
Ca^{2+}-Activated K^+ Channels in Erythrocytes
  and Excitable Cells   Wolfgang Schwartz and Hermann
                                                Passow   45:359–74
Calcium Transport Proteins, Calcium
  Absorption and Vitamin D   R. H. Wasserman and C. S. Fullmer   45:375–90
Patch Clamp Techniques for Studying Ionic
  Channels in Excitable Membranes   B. Sakmann, E. Neher   46:455–72

Ion Channels in Cardiac Cell Membranes   H. Reuter   46:473–84
K⁺Channels Gated by Voltage and Ions   R. Latorre, R. Coronado, C.
                                          Vergara   46:485–95
Fluctuation Analysis of Sodium Channels in
  Epithelia   B. Lindemann   46:497–515
Voltage-Regulated Sodium Channel
  Molecules   W. S. Agnew   46:517–30
Gramacidin Channels   O. S. Andersen   46:531–48
Ion Channels in Liposomes   C. Miller   46:549–58

CELLULAR NEUROBIOLOGY
Receptors for Amino Acids   E. J. Peck Jr.   42:615–27
Role of Cyclic Nucleotides in Excitable
  Cells   I. Kupfermann   42:629–41
Biophysical Analyses of the Function of
  Receptors   C. F. Stevens   42:643–52

CHEMOTAXIS
Bacterial Chemotaxis   A. Boyd, M. Simon   44:501–17
The Physiological Basis of Taxes in
  Paramecium   Ching Kung, Y. Saimi   44:519–34
Chemotaxis in Dictyostelium   G. Gerisch   44:535–52
Leukocyte Chemotaxis   E. Shiffmann   44:553–68

CNS
From the Neural Crest to the Ganglia of the
  Peripheral Nervous System   N. M. Le Douarin, J. Smith, C. S.
                                          Le Lièvre   43:653–71
Influence of Nerve Activity on the
  Macromolecular Content of Neurons and
  Their Effector Organs   R. E. Zigmond and C. W. Bowers   43:673–87
Neural Activity and Development   W. A. Harris   43:689–710
Sodium Channels in Nerve and Muscle
  Membrane   R. Rogart   43:711–25
Specific Connections Between Nerve Cells D. Purves and J. W. Lichtman   45:553–65
Neuronal Growth Cones   S. C. Landis   45:567–80
Roles of Extracellular Matrix in Neural
  Development   Joshua R. Sanes   45:581–600
New Neurotrophic Factors   Y.-A. Barde, D. Edgar and H.
                                          Thoenen   45:601–12

COMPARATIVE PHYSIOLOGY

BODY TEMPERATURE
Temperature Regulation in Vertebrates   L. I. Crawshaw   42:473–91
The Role of Nervous Systems in the
  Temperature Adaptation of Poikilotherms C. L. Prosser, D. O. Nelson   43:281–300
Brain Cooling in Endotherms in Heat and
  Exercise   M. A. Baker   44:85–96
Antifreeze Peptides and Glycopeptides in
  Cold-Water Fishes   A. L. DeVries   45:245–60
The Role of Hemolymph Proteins in the
  Cold Tolerance of Insects   J. Duman and K. Horwath   45:261–70
Invertebrate Neuropeptides: Native and
  Naturalized   M. J. Greenberg and D. A. Price   45:271–88
Freezing Resistance in Intertidal
  Invertebrates   D. J. Murphy   45:289–99

ENERGETICS
Energetics and Mechanics of Terrestrial
  Locomotion   C. R. Taylor, N. C. Heglund   44:97–107
Avian Flight Energetics   J. M. V. Rayner   44:109–19
Energetics of Locomotion in Warm-Bodied
  Fish   E. D. Stevens, A. E. Dizon   44:121–31
Energetics of Locomotion in Endothermic
  Insects   J. E. Heath, M. S. Heath   44:133–43

Insect Endocrinology: Action of Hormones
at the Cellular Level   L. M. Riddiford   42:511

ENVIRONMENTAL SENSING
The Electric Sense of Weakly Electric Fish   W. Heiligenberg, J. Bastian   46:561–83
Magnetic Field Sensitivity in Animals   J. L. Gould   46:585–98
Physiological Mechanisms for Spatial
Filtering and Image Enhancement in the
Sonar of Bats   J. A. Simmons, S. A. Kick   46:599–614

RESPIRATION AND METABOLISM
Scaling of Physiological Processes in
Homeothermic Animals   W. A. Calder III   43:301–22
Energy Metabolisms of Parasitic Helminths:
Adaptations to Parasitism   H. J. Saz   43:323–41
Physiology of Diving in Marine Mammals   G. L. Kooyman, M. A. Castellini,
                                                     R. W. Davis   43:343–56

REPRODUCTION
Reproductive Endocrinology of Birds   D. S. Farner, J. C. Wingfield   42:457–72

ENDOCRINOLOGY
Dynamics of Steroid Hormone Receptor
Action   B. S. Katzenellenbogen   42:17–35
The Role of Cyclic Nucleotides in
Reproductive Processes   B. M. Sanborn, J. J. Heindel, A. G.
                                                     Robison   42:37–57

Regulation of the Testis Sertoli Cell by
Follicle Stimulating Hormone   A. R. Means, J. R. Dedman, J. S.
                                                     Tash, D. J. Tindall, M. van
                                                     Sickle, M. J. Welsh   42:59–70

Interactions of Steroids and Gonadotropins
in the Control of Steroidogenesis in the
Ovarian Follicle   P. C. K. Leung, D. T. Armstrong   42:71–82
Mechanism of Action of Prolactin in the
Control of Mammary Gland Function   R. P. C. Shiu, H. G. Friesen   42:83–96
Binding and Metabolism of Sex Steroids by
the Hypothalamic-Pituitary Unit:
Physiological Implications   B. S. McEwen   42:97–110
The Fetal Adrenal Gland   M. Serón-Ferré, R. Jaffe   43:141–62
Endocrine Physiology of the Placenta   E. R. Simpson, P. C. MacDonald   43:163–88
Extracellular Androgen Binding Proteins   C. W. Bardin, N. Musto, G.
                                                     Gunsalus, N. Kotite, S.-L. Cheng,
                                                     F. Larrea, R. Becker   43:189–98

Recent Advances in the Metabolism of
Vitamin D   H. F. DeLuca   43:199–209
Regulation of Parathyroid Hormone
Secretion and Biosynthesis   J. F. Habener   43:211–23
Hormonal Control of Skeletal Growth   L. G. Raisz and B. E. Kream   43:225–38
Receptor-Mediated Endocytosis of
Hormones in Cultured Cells   Ira M. Pastan, M. C. Willingham   43:239–50
Epidermal and Nerve Growth Factors in
Mammalian Development   D. Gospodarowicz   43:251–63
"Endorphins" in Pituitary and Other Tissues   H. Imura, Y. Nakai   43:265–78
Behavioral Effects of Neuropeptides:
Endorphins and Vasopressin   G. F. Koob, F. E. Bloom   44:571–82
The Role of the Central Nervous System in
the Control of Ovarian Function in Higher
Primates   C. R. Pohl, E. Knobil   44:583–93
Neuroendocrine Control Mechanisms and the
Onset of Puberty   E. O. Reiter, M. M. Grumbach   44:595–613
The Evolution of Peptide Hormones   H. D. Niall   44:615–24
Post-Translational Proteolysis in Polypeptide
Hormone Biosynthesis   K. Docherty, D. F. Steiner   44:625–38

Receptors for Peptide Hormones: Alterations
in Diseases of Humans — J. Roth, S. I. Taylor — 44:639–51
Polypeptide and Amine Hormone Regulation
of Adenylate Cyclase — G. D. Aurbach — 44:653–66
Calmodulin in Endocrine Cells — A. R. Means, J. G. Chafouleas — 44:667–82
Regulation of the Adrenal and Gonadal
Microsomal Mixed Function Oxygenases
of Steroid Hormone Biosynthesis — H. R. Fevold — 45:19–36
Sexual Dimorphism in the Liver — A. K. Roy and B. Chatterjee — 45:37–50
Sex Steroid Induced Changes in Hepatic
Enzymes — J.-A. Gustafsson, A. Mode, G. Norstedt, and P. Skett — 45:51–60
Aromatic Hydroxylation of Estrogens — Jack Fishman — 45:61–72
Neuropeptides and the Blood-Brain Barrier — William M. Pardridge — 45:73–82
Gonadotropin Releasing Hormone:
Extrapituitary Actions and Paracrine
Control Mechanisms — Aaron J. W. Hsueh and Phillip B. C. Jones — 45:83–94
CNS Peptides and Glucoregulation — Lawrence A. Frohman — 45:95–107
Neuroendocrine Control of Prolactin
Secretion — Denis A. Leong, L. Stephen Frawley, and Jimmy D. Neill — 45:109–27
Biosynthesis of Vasopressin and Oxytocin — Michael J. Brownstein — 45:129–35
Insect Endocrinology: Regulation of
Endocrine Glands, Hormone Titer, and
Hormone Metabolism — L. I. Gilbert, W. E. Bollenbacher, N. A. Granger — 42:493–510
The Brain Renin-Angiotensin System — W. F. Ganong — 46:17–31
Variants of Growth Hormone and Prolactin
and Their Posttranslational Modifications — U. J. Lewis — 46:33–42
Relaxin — G. Weiss — 46:43–52
Mechanism of Action of Mullerian
Inhibiting Substance — P. K. Donahoe, J. M. Hutson, M. E. Fallat, S. Kamagata, G. P. Budzik — 46:53–65
Effects of Molybdate and Endogenous
Inhibitors on Steroid-Receptor
Inactivation, Transformation, and
Translocation — M. K. Dahmer, P. R. Housley, W. B. Pratt — 46:67–81
Structure of Mammalian Steroid Receptors:
Evolving Concepts and Methodological
Developments — M. R. Sherman, J. Stevens — 46:83–105
Androgen and Antiandrogen Receptor
Binding — O. A. Jänne, C. W. Bardin — 46:107–18
Regulation of Beta-Adrenergic Receptors by
Steroid Hormones — A. O. Davies, R. J. Lefkowitz — 46:119–30

GASTROINTESTINAL PHYSIOLOGY

Mechanisms of Gastric H^+ and Cl^-
Transport — J. G. Forte, T. E. Machen, K. J. Öbrink — 42:111–26
The Exocrine Pancreas: The Role of
Secretagogues, Cyclic Nucleotides, and
Calcium in Enzyme Secretion — I. Schulz, H. H. Stolze — 42:127–56
Water-Soluble Vitamin Absorption in
Intestine — R. C. Rose — 42:157–71
The Intestine as a Fluid Propelling System — W. A. Weems — 43:9–19
Patterns of Intestinal Motility — N. W. Weisbrodt — 43:21–31
Intrinsic Neural Control of Intestinal
Motility — J. D. Wood — 43:33–51
Physiology of Mammalian Prevertebral
Ganglia — J. H. Szurszewski — 43:53–68

Stomach Blood Flow and Acid Secretion   P. H. Guth   44:3–12
Local Control of Intestinal Oxygenation and
    Blood Flow   A. P. Shepherd   44:13–27
Relationship Between Intestinal Blood Flow
    and Motility   C. C. Chou   44:29–42
Relationships Between Intestinal Absorption
    and Hemodynamics   D. Mailman   44:43–55
Physiological Regulation of the Hepatic   P. D. I. Richardson, P. G.
    Circulation   Withrington   44:57–69
Measurement of Gastrointestinal Blood Flow   B. L. Tepperman, E. D. Jacobson   44:71–82
Hormonal Control of Apolipoprotein
    Synthesis   L. Chan   45:615–23
Intestinal Synthesis, Secretion, and
    Transport of Lipoproteins   C. Bisgaier and R. M. Glickman   45:625–36
Apolipoprotein B: Structural and Metabolic
    Heterogeneity   J. P. Kane   45:637–50
Lipid Digestion and Absorption   M. C. Carey, D. M. Small and C.
                                                     M. Bliss   45:651–77
Bile Acid Synthesis   G. Salen and S. Shefer   45:679–85
Regulatory Mechanisms in Pancreas and
    Salivary Acini   J. A. Williams   46:361–75
The Mammalian Gastric Parietal Cell in
    Vitro   T. Berglindh   46:377–92
Cellular Control of Pepsinogen Secretion   S. J. Hersey, S. H. Norris, A. J.
                                                     Gibert   46:393–402
Primary Hepatocytes in Monolayer Culture:
    A Model for Studies on Lipoprotein
    Metabolism   T. M. Forte   46:403–15
Intestinal Transport of Amino Acids and
    Sugars: Advances Using Membrane   B. R. Stevens, J. D. Kaunitz, E. M.
    Vesicles   Wright   46:417–33
A Cellular Model for Active Sodium
    Absorption by Mammalian Colon   S. G. Schultz   46:435–51

HEARING
    Ontogeny of Auditory System Function   E. W Rubel   46:213–29
    Cochlear Mechanics   W. S. Rhode   46:231–46
    Relation of Receptor Potentials of Cochlear
        Hair Cells to Spike Discharges of
        Cochlear Neurons   T. F. Weiss   46:247–59
    Neural Coding of Complex Sounds: Speech   M. B. Sachs   46:261–73
    Neural Mechanisms for Sound Localization   R. B. Masterton, T. J. Imig   46:275–87

PREFATORY CHAPTERS
    Life With Tracers   H. H. Ussing   42:1–16
    The Annual Review of Physiology: Past and
        Present   V. E. Hall, R. R. Sonnenschein   43:1–5
    Beginning: Some Reminiscences of My
        Early Life (1914–1947)   A. L. Hodgkin   45:1–17
    A Life with Several Facets   A. von Muralt   46:1–13

RENAL & ELECTROLYTE PHYSIOLOGY
    The Vascular Organization of the Kidney   R. Beeuwkes III   42:531–42
    Methods for Measuring Renal Blood Flow:
        Total Flow and Regional Distribution   K. Aukland   42:543–55
    Distal Tubular Feedback Control of Renal   L. G. Navar, D. W. Ploth, P. D.
        Hemodynamics and Autoregulation   Bell   42:557–71
    Segmental Renal Vascular Resistance: Single
        Nephron   R. C. Blantz   42:573–88
    Hormonal Systems and Renal
        Hemodynamics   P. G. Bauer, J. C. McGiff   42:589–601

Renal Hemodynamics in Acute Renal
  Failure | R. W. Schreier, J. Conger | 42:603–14
Distribution of Hormone-Dependent
  Adenylate Cyclase in the Nephron and Its
  Physiological Significance | F. Morel, M. Imbert-Teboul, D.
  Chabardès | 43:569–81
PTH, Calcitonin, Cyclic Nucleotides and the
  Kidney | Z. S. Agus, A. Wasserstein, S.
  Goldfarb | 43:583–95
The Renal Kallikrein-Kinin and
  Prostaglandin Systems Interaction | A. Nasjletti, K. U. Malik | 43:597–609
Antidiuretic Hormone | J. S. Handler, J. Orloff | 43:611–24
Catecholamines and the Kidney: Receptors
  and Renal Function | P. A. Insel, M. D. Snavely | 43:625–36
Steroid Hormones and the Kidney | D. D. Fanestil, C. S. Park | 43:637–49
Recent Advances in Renal Morphology | R. E. Bulger, D. C. Dobyan | 44:147–79
Heterogeneity of Tubular Transport
  Processes in the Nephron | C. A. Berry | 44:181–201
Biological Importance of Nephron
  Heterogeneity | L. A. Walker, H. Valtin | 44:203–19
Measurement of Intracellular Ionic
  Composition and Activities in Renal
  Tubules | W. F. Boron and H. Sackin | 45:483–96
Electrophysiology of Mammalian Renal
  Tubules: Inferences from Intracellular
  Microelectrode Studies | B. M. Koeppen, B. A. Biagi, and
  G. Giebisch | 45:497–517
Regulatory Role of Intracellular Calcium
  Ions in Epithelial Na Transport | E. E. Windhager and A. Taylor | 45:519–32
Sodium Chloride Coupled Transport in
  Mammalian Nephrons | M. Burg and D. Good | 45:533–47
Interaction of Signals Influencing Renin
  Release | G. H. Gibbons, V. J. Dzau, E. R.
  Farhi, A. C. Barger | 46:291–308
The Kallikrein-Kinin System and the Kidney | H. S. Margolius | 46:309–26
Renal Arachidonic Acid Metabolism | M. G. Currie, P. Needleman | 46:327–41
Natriuretic Hormone | V. M. Buckalew, Jr., K. A. Gruber | 46:343–58

RESPIRATORY PHYSIOLOGY
Organization of Microcirculation in the
  Lung | J. Gil | 42:177–86
Mechanical Influences on the Pulmonary
  Microcirculation | B. H. Culver, J. Butler | 42:187–98
Nervous Control of the Pulmonary
  Circulation | S. E. Downing, J. C. Lee | 42:199–210
Vasomotor Regulation of the Pulmonary
  Circulation | A. P. Fishman | 42:211–20
Humoral Control of the Pulmonary
  Circulation | E. H. Bergofsky | 42:221–33
Ventilation-Perfusion Relationships | P. D. Wagner | 42:235–47
Sensory Inputs to the Medulla | A. I. Pack | 43:73–90
Central Determinants of Respiratory Rhythm | M. I. Cohen | 43:91–104
Anatomical Organizations of Central
  Respiratory Neurons | M. P. Kalia | 43:105–20
Central Regulation of Respiration by
  Endogenous Neurotransmitters and
  Neuromodulators | F. L. Eldridge, D. E. Millhorn | 43:121–35
Structural Bases for Metabolic Activity | U. S. Ryan | 44:223–39
Processing of Endogenous Polypeptides by
  the Lungs | J. W. Ryan | 44:241–55
Pulmonary Metabolism of Prostaglandins
  and Vasoactive Peptides | S. I. Said | 44:257–68
The Fate of Circulating Amines within the
  Pulmonary Circulation | C. N. Gillis, B. R. Pitt | 44:269–81

Chemotactic Mediators in
  Neutrophil-Dependent Lung Injury   J. C. Fantone, S. L. Kunkel, P. A.
                                         Ward   44:283–93
Ventilatory Control During Exercise in
  Humans   B. J. Whipp   45:393–413
Ventilatory Responses to O_2 and CO_2
  During Exercise   D. C. Flenley and P. M. Warren   45:415–26
Exercise at Altitude   J. R. Sutton, L. Griffith, C. E.
                                        Pugh, N. L. Jones   45:427–37
Respiratory Factors Limiting Exercise P. T. P. Bye, G. A. Farkas, C.
                                        Roussos   45:439–51
Exercise-Induced Airway Obstruction   E. R. McFadden, Jr., R. H. Ingram,
                                        Jr.   45:453–63
Dyspnea and Exercise   K. J. Killian, E. J. M. Campbell   45:465–79
Fetal and Postnatal Development of the
  Lung   P. H. Burri   46:617–28
Hypoxia and Respiratory Control in Early
  Life   G. G. Haddad, R. B. Mellins   46:629–43
Function of the Larynx in the Fetus and
  Newborn   R. Harding   46:645–59
Control of Ventilation in the Newborn H. Rigatto   46:661–74
Regulation of Breathing in the Newborn
  During Different Behavioral States D. J. C. Read, D. J.
                                        Henderson-Smart   46:675–86
Peripheral and Central Chemoreceptors in
  the Fetus and Newborn   D. Walker   46:687–703

NEW BOOKS
FROM
ANNUAL REVIEWS INC.

NOW YOU CAN
CHARGE THEM
TO

VISA   MasterCard

ORDER FORM

A NONPROFIT SCIENTIFIC PUBLISHER

Annual Reviews Inc.

4139 EL CAMINO WAY • PALO ALTO, CA 94306 USA • (415) 493-4400

Please list the volumes you wish to order by volume number. If you wish a standing order (the latest volume sent to you automatically each year), indicate volume number to begin order. Volumes not yet published will be shipped in month and year indicated. All prices subject to change without notice. Prepayment required from individuals. Telephone orders charged to VISA, MasterCard, American Express, welcomed.

ANNUAL REVIEW SERIES

		Prices Postpaid per volume USA/elsewhere	Regular Order Please send: Vol. number	Standing Order Begin with: Vol. number
Annual Review of ANTHROPOLOGY				
Vols. 1-10	(1972-1981) .... $20.00/$21.00			
Vol. 11	(1982) .... $22.00/$25.00			
Vol. 12	(1983) .... $27.00/$30.00			
Vol. 13	(avail. Oct. 1984) .... $27.00/$30.00		Vol(s). _____	Vol. _____
Annual Review of ASTRONOMY AND ASTROPHYSICS				
Vols. 1-19	(1963-1981) .... $20.00/$21.00			
Vol. 20	(1982) .... $22.00/$25.00			
Vol. 21	(1983) .... $44.00/$47.00			
Vol. 22	(avail. Sept. 1984) .... $44.00/$47.00		Vol(s). _____	Vol. _____
Annual Review of BIOCHEMISTRY				
Vols. 29-50	(1960-1981) .... $21.00/$22.00			
Vol. 51	(1982) .... $23.00/$26.00			
Vol. 52	(1983) .... $29.00/$32.00			
Vol. 53	(avail. July 1984) .... $29.00/$32.00		Vol(s). _____	Vol. _____
Annual Review of BIOPHYSICS AND BIOENGINEERING				
Vols. 1-10	(1972-1981) .... $20.00/$21.00			
Vol. 11	(1982) .... $22.00/$25.00			
Vol. 12	(1983) .... $47.00/$50.00			
Vol. 13	(avail. June 1984) .... $47.00/$50.00		Vol(s). _____	Vol. _____
Annual Review of EARTH AND PLANETARY SCIENCES				
Vols. 1-9	(1973-1981) .... $20.00/$21.00			
Vol. 10	(1982) .... $22.00/$25.00			
Vol. 11	(1983) .... $44.00/$47.00			
Vol. 12	(avail. May 1984) .... $44.00/$47.00		Vol(s). _____	Vol. _____
Annual Review of ECOLOGY AND SYSTEMATICS				
Vols. 1-12	(1970-1981) .... $20.00/$21.00			
Vol. 13	(1982) .... $22.00/$25.00			
Vol. 14	(1983) .... $27.00/$30.00			
Vol. 15	(avail. Nov. 1984) .... $27.00/$30.00		Vol(s). _____	Vol. _____

1

		Prices Postpaid per volume USA/elsewhere	Regular Order Please send:	Standing Order Begin with:
Annual Review of **ENERGY**			Vol. number	Vol. number
Vols. 1-6	(1976-1981)	$20.00/$21.00		
Vol. 7	(1982)	$22.00/$25.00		
Vol. 8	(1983)	$56.00/$59.00		
Vol. 9	(avail. Oct. 1984)	$56.00/$59.00	Vol(s). _____	Vol. _____

Annual Review of **ENTOMOLOGY**				
Vols. 7-16, 18-26	(1962-1971; 1973-1981)	$20.00/$21.00		
Vol. 27	(1982)	$22.00/$25.00		
Vol. 28	(1983)	$27.00/$30.00		
Vol. 29	(avail. Jan. 1984)	$27.00/$30.00	Vol(s). _____	Vol. _____

Annual Review of **FLUID MECHANICS**				
Vols. 1-13	(1969-1981)	$20.00/$21.00		
Vol. 14	(1982)	$22.00/$25.00		
Vol. 15	(1983)	$28.00/$31.00		
Vol. 16	(avail. Jan. 1984)	$28.00/$31.00	Vol(s). _____	Vol. _____

Annual Review of **GENETICS**				
Vols. 1-15	(1967-1981)	$20.00/$21.00		
Vol. 16	(1982)	$22.00/$25.00		
Vol. 17	(1983)	$27.00/$30.00		
Vol. 18	(avail. Dec. 1984)	$27.00/$30.00	Vol(s). _____	Vol. _____

Annual Review of **IMMUNOLOGY**				
Vol. 1	(1983)	$27.00/$30.00		
Vol. 2	(avail. April 1984)	$27.00/$30.00	Vol(s). _____	Vol. _____

Annual Review of **MATERIALS SCIENCE**				
Vols. 1-11	(1971-1981)	$20.00/$21.00		
Vol. 12	(1982)	$22.00/$25.00		
Vol. 13	(1983)	$64.00/$67.00		
Vol. 14	(avail. Aug. 1984)	$64.00/$67.00	Vol(s). _____	Vol. _____

Annual Review of **MEDICINE: Selected Topics in the Clinical Sciences**				
Vols. 1-3, 5-15	(1950-1952; 1954-1964)	$20.00/$21.00		
Vols. 17-32	(1966-1981)	$20.00/$21.00		
Vol. 33	(1982)	$22.00/$25.00		
Vol. 34	(1983)	$27.00/$30.00		
Vol. 35	(avail. April 1984)	$27.00/$30.00	Vol(s). _____	Vol. _____

Annual Review of **MICROBIOLOGY**				
Vols. 17-35	(1963-1981)	$20.00/$21.00		
Vol. 36	(1982)	$22.00/$25.00		
Vol. 37	(1983)	$27.00/$30.00		
Vol. 38	(avail. Oct. 1984)	$27.00/$30.00	Vol(s). _____	Vol. _____

Annual Review of **NEUROSCIENCE**				
Vols. 1-4	(1978-1981)	$20.00/$21.00		
Vol. 5	(1982)	$22.00/$25.00		
Vol. 6	(1983)	$27.00/$30.00		
Vol. 7	(avail. March 1984)	$27.00/$30.00	Vol(s). _____	Vol. _____

Annual Review of **NUCLEAR AND PARTICLE SCIENCE**				
Vols. 12-31	(1962-1981)	$22.50/$23.50		
Vol. 32	(1982)	$25.00/$28.00		
Vol. 33	(1983)	$30.00/$33.00		
Vol. 34	(avail. Dec. 1984)	$30.00/$33.00	Vol(s). _____	Vol. _____

2